area A **width** w **base** b
perimeter P **surface area** S **circumference** C
length l **altitude (height)** h **radius** r

Rectangle

$A = lw \quad P = 2l + 2w$

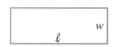

Triangle

$A = \dfrac{1}{2}bh$

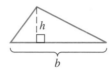

Square

$A = s^2 \quad P = 4s$

Parallelogram

$A = bh$

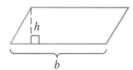

Trapezoid

$A = \dfrac{1}{2}h(b_1 + b_2)$

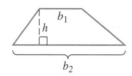

Circle

$A = \pi r^2 \quad C = 2\pi r$

30°–60° Right Triangle

Right Triangle

$a^2 + b^2 = c^2$

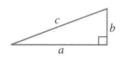

Isosceles Right Triangle

Right Circular Cylinder

$V = \pi r^2 h \quad S = 2\pi r^2 + 2\pi rh$

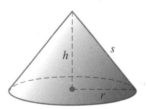

Sphere

$S = 4\pi r^2 \quad V = \dfrac{4}{3}\pi r^3$

Right Circular Cone

$V = \dfrac{1}{3}\pi r^2 h \quad S = \pi r^2 + \pi rs$

Pyramid

$V = \dfrac{1}{3}Bh$

Prism

$V = Bh$

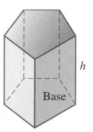

Intermediate Algebra and College Algebra

Jerome E. Kaufmann | Karen L. Schwitters

CENGAGE
Learning·

Australia • Brazil • Japan • Korea • Mexico • Singapore • Spain • United Kingdom • United States

CENGAGE
Learning·

Intermediate Algebra and College Algebra:

Jerome E. Kaufmann | Karen L. Schwitters

Executive Editors:
Maureen Staudt
Michael Stranz

Senior Project Development Manager:
Linda deStefano

Marketing Specialist:
Courtney Sheldon

Senior Production/Manufacturing Manager:
Donna M. Brown

PreMedia Manager:
Joel Brennecke

Sr. Rights Acquisition Account Manager:
Todd Osborne

Cover Image:
Getty Images*

*Unless otherwise noted, all cover images used by Custom
Solutions, a part of Cengage Learning, have been supplied
courtesy of Getty Images with the exception of the Earthview
cover image, which has been supplied by the National
Aeronautics and Space Administration (NASA).

Algebra for College Students, 9e
Jerome E. Kaufmann | Karen L. Schwitters

© 2011, 2007 Cengage Learning. All rights reserved.

For product information and technology assistance, contact us at
Cengage Learning Customer & Sales Support, 1-800-354-9706

For permission to use material from this text or product,
submit all requests online at **cengage.com/permissions**
Further permissions questions can be emailed to
permissionrequest@cengage.com

This book contains select works from existing Cengage Learning resources and
was produced by Cengage Learning Custom Solutions for collegiate use. As such,
those adopting and/or contributing to this work are responsible for editorial
content accuracy, continuity and completeness.

Compilation © 2012 Cengage Learning

ISBN-13: 978-1-133-88731-7

ISBN-10: 1-133-88731-7

Cengage Learning
5191 Natorp Boulevard
Mason, Ohio 45040
USA
Cengage Learning is a leading provider of customized learning solutions with
office locations around the globe, including Singapore, the United Kingdom,
Australia, Mexico, Brazil, and Japan. Locate your local office at:
international.cengage.com/region.

Cengage Learning products are represented in Canada by Nelson Education, Ltd.
For your lifelong learning solutions, visit **www.cengage.com/custom.**
Visit our corporate website at **www.cengage.com.**

Printed in the United States of America

WebAssign Student Quick Start Guide

You can use WebAssign to access your homework, quizzes, and tests — whatever your instructor chooses — at any time of day or night, from any computer with a connection to the Internet and a Web browser. Your instructor creates your assignments, schedules them, and decides how many submissions you get. Your instructor also determines if you can have an extension, if you can save your work without submitting it at the time, and how much feedback you get after you submit an assignment.

The WebAssign support staff cannot change your username or password, give extensions, change your score, give you extra submissions, or help you with the content of your assignments.

Logging In

You can log in to WebAssign using any Web browser connected to the Internet. There are two different ways to log in to WebAssign. Each requires information from your teacher. If you are unsure about how to log in, please check with your teacher or another student in your class.

Go to the login page at http://webassign.net/login.html or the web address provided by your teacher. The way you log in depends on how your instructor set up the class:

- If your teacher created a WebAssign account for you, they will provide you with a **Username**, an **Institution** code and a **Password**. Simply enter this information in the boxes provided and click the **Log In** button.

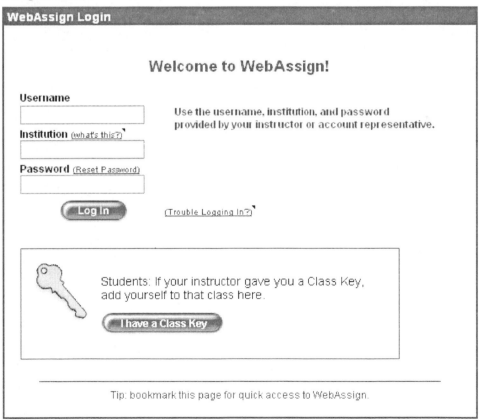

Web**Assign**.

- If your teacher wants you to **Self-Enroll** in the WebAssign course they will provide you with a **Class Key**. You will create your own username and password. It is important that you remember this information so you can log in for the remainder of the class. In this case, just click the **I have a Class Key** button. You don't need to enter any other information on this page.

  Then, enter the **Class Key** your instructor provided and click **Submit**. Verify you are enrolling in the correct class on the next page.

Class Key

Enter the Class Key that you received from your instructor. You will only need to complete this once. After you have created your account, you can log in on the main page.

Class Key

[_____] [_____] [_____]

Class Keys generally start with an institution code, followed by two sets of four digits.

[Submit]

- Enter your preferred Login and Student information.

- Click the **Create My Account** button to complete the enrollment process.

- A review screen will display, showing your username, institution code, and password. **Retain a copy of this information.** You will need it to log into WebAssign.

Log In Information

Required fields are marked with an asterisk (*).

Preferred Username	* [_____]	Check Availability
	Your username may contain letters, numbers, and the following characters: underscore (_), hyphen (-), period (.)	
Institution Code	**webassign**	
Password	* [_____]	
Re-Enter Password	* [_____]	
	Passwords are case-sensitive.	

Student Information

Required fields are marked with an asterisk (*).

First Name	* [_____]
Last Name	* [_____]
Email Address	* [_____]
Student ID Number	[_____]

[Create My Account]

Access Codes

Once you log in, you may see a WebAssign Notice about entering an access code for your class. You can get an Access Code from any of the following places if you need to use one:

- A new textbook you purchased for the class.
- Your bookstore, which may sell Access Code cards.
- Online, where you can purchase an access code with a credit card.

You have a 14 day grace period to use WebAssign, starting with the WebAssign class start date. During this time you can work on and view your WebAssign assignments without registering a code.

After the grace period is over you will only see the code registration message until you submit or purchase a code.

There are two types of WebAssign access code cards. The small card requires you to scratch off the silver surface in order to reveal the complete access code.

WebAssign.

The larger security envelope card requires you to open the card to reveal the access code number.

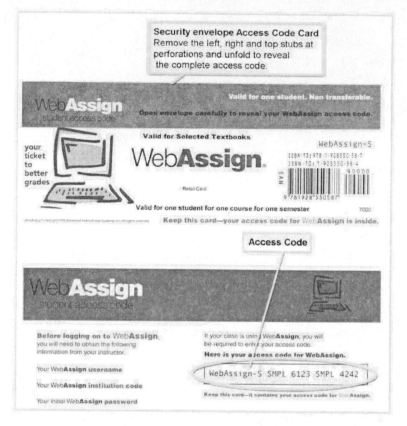

If you would like to purchase an access code directly from WebAssign online, you may do so with a credit card. Your code will be automatically registered to your WebAssign account as soon as the transaction is complete. You will receive an email confirmation. Please keep a copy for your records.

WebAssign.

Your WebAssign Home Page

Once you have successfully logged in you will see your WebAssign homepage. If you are taking more than one WebAssign class, you will need to select which class you wish to view first.

The upper right corner features links to a complete Student **Guide**, as well as a link to WebAssign Technical Support under **Help**. If you want to change your password or add or update your email address, simply click **My Options** in the upper right hand corner.

You will see your assignments and due dates listed, as well as any Communications, Grades, and Announcements posted by your teacher.

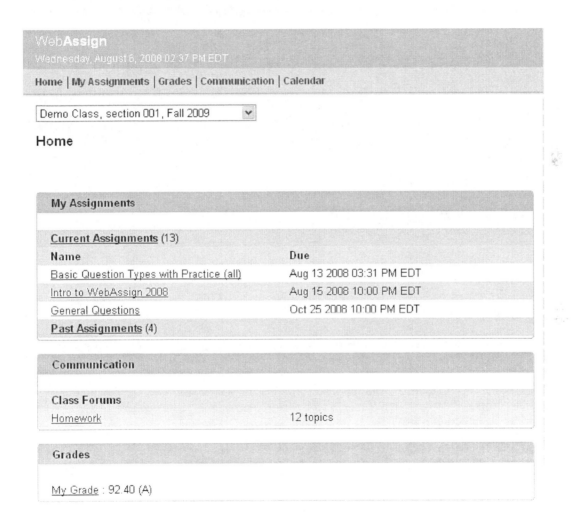

Web**Assign**
Wednesday, August 6, 2008 02:37 PM EDT

Home | My Assignments | Grades | Communication | Calendar

Demo Class, section 001, Fall 2009

Home

My Assignments

Current Assignments (13)

Name	Due
Basic Question Types with Practice (all)	Aug 13 2008 03:31 PM EDT
Intro to WebAssign 2008	Aug 15 2008 10:00 PM EDT
General Questions	Oct 25 2008 10:00 PM EDT

Past Assignments (4)

Communication

Class Forums

Homework	12 topics

Grades

My Grade : 92.40 (A)

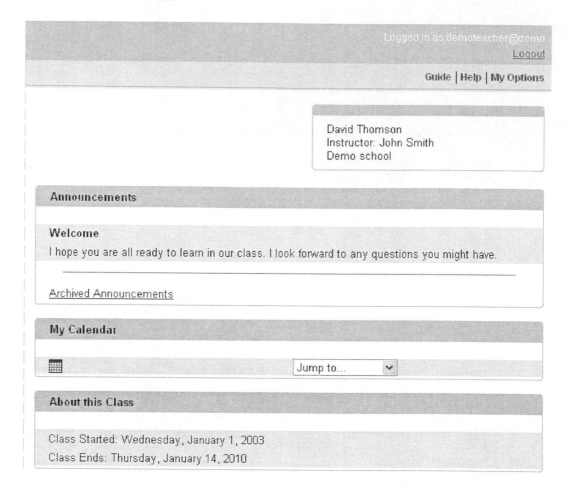

David Thomson
Instructor: John Smith
Demo school

Announcements

Welcome

I hope you are all ready to learn in our class. I look forward to any questions you might have.

Archived Announcements

My Calendar

Jump to...

About this Class

Class Started: Wednesday, January 1, 2003
Class Ends: Thursday, January 14, 2010

Answering Questions

WebAssign has a variety of different question types, ranging from multiple choice to fill-in-the-blank to symbolic questions. Here are some things to keep in mind as you work through your assignments:

- Some questions may include numbers or words that appear in red. This signifies that the number or word has been randomized, so that you receive a different version of the same basic question from your classmates.

- Some WebAssign questions check the number of significant figures in your answer. If you enter the correct value with the wrong number of significant figures, you will not receive credit, but you will receive a hint that your number does not have the correct number of significant figures.

- Some questions require entering symbolic notation. Answer symbolic questions by using calculator notation. You must use the exact variables specified in the questions. The order is not important as long as it is mathematically correct. Clicking on the eye button previews the expression you enter in proper mathematical notation. Clicking on the symbolic formatting help button provides tips for using the correct keystrokes.

WebAssign

- When you click on some WebAssign chemistry or math questions an input palette will open. These palettes, called chemPad and mathPad, will help you enter your answer in proper notation.

- Some questions may require the use of an Active Figure simulation. Active Figures require the free Macromedia Flash Player plug-in, downloadable from www.macromedia.com.

- If your instructor allows it, you can save your work without grading by selecting the Save Work button at the end of the question. After you save your work, it will be available to you the next time you click the assignment.

- Please note that WebAssign will **not** automatically submit your answers for scoring if you only **Save** your work. Your teacher will not be able to see your submissions. Please be sure to **Submit** prior to the due date and time.

- If your instructor allows it, you can submit answers by question part or for the entire assignment. To submit an individual question answer for grading, click the **Submit New Answers to Question __** button at the bottom of each question. To submit the entire assignment for grading, click the **Submit All New Answers** button at the end of the assignment.

Technical Support

If you are having difficulty logging in, please be sure to check with your teacher and verify whether an account has been created for you or whether you need to self-enroll. In either case your teacher needs to provide the appropriate information (username, institution code and password OR Class Key).

To email WebAssign Support go to http://www.webassign.net/info/support/report.html. This page also lists answers to **Common Problems**, and provides links to the **Student Guide**.

August 7, 2008

CONTENTS

1   Basic Concepts and Properties   1

1.1   Sets, Real Numbers, and Numerical Expressions   2

1.2   Operations with Real Numbers   10

1.3   Properties of Real Numbers and the Use of Exponents   20

1.4   Algebraic Expressions   27

Chapter 1 Summary   36

Chapter 1 Review Problem Set   38

Chapter 1 Test   40

2   Equations, Inequalities, and Problem Solving   41

2.1   Solving First-Degree Equations   42

2.2   Equations Involving Fractional Forms   49

2.3   Equations Involving Decimals and Problem Solving   57

2.4   Formulas   64

2.5   Inequalities   74

2.6   More on Inequalities and Problem Solving   81

2.7   Equations and Inequalities Involving Absolute Value   90

Chapter 2 Summary   97

Chapter 2 Review Problem Set   101

Chapter 2 Test   104

Chapters 1–2 Cumulative Review Problem Set   105

3   Polynomials   107

3.1   Polynomials: Sums and Differences   108

3.2   Products and Quotients of Monomials   114

3.3   Multiplying Polynomials   119

3.4   Factoring: Greatest Common Factor and Common Binomial Factor   127

3.5   Factoring: Difference of Two Squares and Sum or Difference of Two Cubes   135

3.6   Factoring Trinomials   141

3.7   Equations and Problem Solving   149

Chapter 3 Summary   155

Chapter 3 Review Problem Set   158

Chapter 3 Test   161

4   Rational Expressions   163

4.1 Simplifying Rational Expressions   164

4.2 Multiplying and Dividing Rational Expressions   169

4.3 Adding and Subtracting Rational Expressions   175

4.4 More on Rational Expressions and Complex Fractions   182

4.5 Dividing Polynomials   190

4.6 Fractional Equations   196

4.7 More Fractional Equations and Applications   202

Chapter 4 Summary   211

Chapter 4 Review Problem Set   216

Chapter 4 Test   218

Chapters 1–4 Cumulative Review Problem Set   219

5   Exponents and Radicals   221

5.1 Using Integers as Exponents   222

5.2 Roots and Radicals   229

5.3 Combining Radicals and Simplifying Radicals That Contain Variables   238

5.4 Products and Quotients Involving Radicals   243

5.5 Equations Involving Radicals   249

5.6 Merging Exponents and Roots   254

5.7 Scientific Notation   259

Chapter 5 Summary   265

Chapter 5 Review Problem Set   269

Chapter 5 Test   271

6   Quadratic Equations and Inequalities   273

6.1 Complex Numbers   274

6.2 Quadratic Equations   281

6.3 Completing the Square   289

6.4 Quadratic Formula   293

6.5 More Quadratic Equations and Applications   300

6.6 Quadratic and Other Nonlinear Inequalities   308

Chapter 6 Summary   314

Chapter 6 Review Problem Set   318

Chapter 6 Test   320

Chapters 1–6 Cumulative Review Problem Set   321

7   Linear Equations and Inequalities in Two Variables   323

7.1 Rectangular Coordinate System and Linear Equations   324

7.2 Linear Inequalities in Two Variables   337

7.3 Distance and Slope 342

7.4 Determining the Equation of a Line 353

7.5 Graphing Nonlinear Equations 363

Chapter 7 Summary 371

Chapter 7 Review Problem Set 376

Chapter 7 Test 379

8 Functions 381

8.1 Concept of a Function 382

8.2 Linear Functions and Applications 391

8.3 Quadratic Functions 398

8.4 More Quadratic Functions and Applications 407

8.5 Transformations of Some Basic Curves 416

8.6 Combining Functions 425

8.7 Direct and Inverse Variation 432

Chapter 8 Summary 440

Chapter 8 Review Problem Set 447

Chapter 8 Test 449

Chapters 1–8 Cumulative Review Problem Set 450

9 Polynomial and Rational Functions 453

9.1 Synthetic Division 454

9.2 Remainder and Factor Theorems 458

9.3 Polynomial Equations 463

9.4 Graphing Polynomial Functions 473

9.5 Graphing Rational Functions 483

9.6 More on Graphing Rational Functions 492

Chapter 9 Summary 499

Chapter 9 Review Problem Set 503

Chapter 9 Test 504

10 Exponential and Logarithmic Functions 505

10.1 Exponents and Exponential Functions 506

10.2 Applications of Exponential Functions 513

10.3 Inverse Functions 524

10.4 Logarithms 534

10.5 Logarithmic Functions 542

10.6 Exponential Equations, Logarithmic Equations, and Problem Solving 549

Chapter 10 Summary 559

Chapter 10 Review Problem Set 565

Chapter 10 Test 567

Chapters 1–10 Cumulative Review Problem Set 568

11 Systems of Equations 571

11.1 Systems of Two Linear Equations in Two Variables 572
11.2 Systems of Three Linear Equations in Three Variables 582
11.3 Matrix Approach to Solving Linear Systems 589
11.4 Determinants 598
11.5 Cramer's Rule 607
11.6 Partial Fractions (Optional) 613
Chapter 11 Summary 619
Chapter 11 Review Problem Set 623
Chapter 11 Test 625

12 Algebra of Matrices 627

12.1 Algebra of 2×2 Matrices 628
12.2 Multiplicative Inverses 634
12.3 $m \times n$ Matrices 640
12.4 Systems of Linear Inequalities: Linear Programming 649
Chapter 12 Summary 658
Chapter 12 Review Problem Set 662
Chapter 12 Test 664
Chapters 1 – 12 Cumulative Review Problem Set 665

13 Conic Sections 669

13.1 Circles 670
13.2 Parabolas 676
13.3 Ellipses 684
13.4 Hyperbolas 693
13.5 Systems Involving Nonlinear Equations 702
Chapter 13 Summary 709
Chapter 13 Review Problem Set 714
Chapter 13 Test 715

14 Sequences and Mathematical Induction 717

14.1 Arithmetic Sequences 718
14.2 Geometric Sequences 725
14.3 Another Look at Problem Solving 733
14.4 Mathematical Induction 738
Chapter 14 Summary 744
Chapter 14 Review Problem Set 746
Chapter 14 Test 748

Appendix A   Prime Numbers and Operations with Fractions 749
Appendix B   Binomial Theorem 757
Answers to Odd-Numbered Problems and All Chapter Review, Chapter Test, Cumulative Review, and Appendix A Problems 761

Index I-1

When preparing *Algebra for College Students, Ninth Edition*, we wanted to preserve the features that made the previous editions successful, and at the same time incorporate the improvements suggested by reviewers.

This text covers topics that are usually associated with intermediate algebra and college algebra. It can be used in a one-semester course, but it contains ample material for a two-semester sequence.

In this book we present the basic concepts of algebra in a simple, straightforward way. Algebraic ideas are developed in a logical sequence and in an easy-to-read manner without excessive formalism. Concepts are developed through examples, reinforced through additional examples, and then applied in a variety of problem-solving situations.

There is a common thread that runs throughout the book:

1. **Learn a skill,**

2. **Practice the skill** to help solve equations, and

3. **Apply the skill** to solve application problems.

This thread influenced some of the decisions we made in preparing the text.

- In the appropriate sections, problem sets contain an ample number of word problems. Approximately 450 word problems are scattered throughout the text. These problems deal with a variety of applications that show the connection between mathematics and its use in the real world.

- Many problem-solving suggestions are offered throughout the text, and there are special discussions on problem solving in several sections. Whenever appropriate, different methods for solving the same problem are shown for both word problems and other skill problems.

- Newly acquired skills are used as soon as possible to solve equations and inequalities, which are, in turn, used to solve word problems. The concept of solving equations and inequalities is introduced early and reinforced throughout the text. The concepts of factoring, solving equations, and solving word problems are tied together in Chapter 3.

In approximately 600 worked-out examples, we demonstrate a wide variety of situations, but we leave some things for students to think about in the problem sets. We also use examples to guide students in organizing their work and to help them decide when they may try a shortcut. The progression from showing all the steps to offering some suggested shortcuts is a gradual one.

As recommended by the American Mathematical Association of Two-Year Colleges, many basic geometry concepts are integrated into a problem-solving setting. This book contains worked-out examples and problems that connect algebra, geometry, and real world applications. The specific discussions of geometric concepts are contained in the following sections:

Section 2.2 Complementary and supplementary angles: the sum of the measurements of the angles of a triangle equals 180°

Section 2.4 Area and volume formulas

Section 3.4 The Pythagorean theorem

Section 6.2 More on the Pythagorean theorem, including work with isosceles right triangles and 30°–60° right triangles

New Features

Design

The new design creates a spacious format that allows for continuous and easy reading, as color and form guide students through the concepts presented in the text. Page size has been slightly enlarged, enhancing the design to be visually intuitive without increasing the length of the book.

OBJECTIVES	
1	Solve first-degree equations by simplifying both sides and then applying properties of equality
2	Solve first-degree equations that are contradictions
3	Solve first-degree equations that are identities
4	Solve word problems that represent several quantities in terms of the same variable
5	Solve word problems involving geometric relationships

◀Learning Objectives

Found at the beginning of each section, Learning Objectives are mapped to Problem Sets and to the Chapter Summary.

▶Classroom Examples

To provide the instructor with more resources, a Classroom Example is written for every example. Instructors can use these to present in class or for student practice exercises. These classroom examples appear in the margin, to the left of the corresponding example, in both the Annotated Instructor's Edition and in the Student Edition. Answers to the Classroom Examples appear only in the Annotated Instructor's Edition, however.

Classroom Example
Find the measures of the three angles of a triangle if the second angle is twice the first angle, and the third angle is half the second angle.

$45°, 90°, 45°$

EXAMPLE 9

Find the measures of the three angles of a triangle if the second is three times the first and the third is twice the second.

Solution

If we let a represent the measure of the smallest angle, then $3a$ and $2(3a)$ represent the measures of the other two angles. Therefore, we can set up and solve the following equation:

$$a + 3a + 2(3a) = 180$$
$$a + 3a + 6a = 180$$
$$10a = 180$$
$$\frac{10a}{10} = \frac{180}{10}$$
$$a = 18$$

If $a = 18$, then $3a = 54$ and $2(3a) = 108$. So the angles have measures of $18°$, $54°$, and $108°$.

◀Concept Quiz

Every section has a Concept Quiz that immediately precedes the problem set. The questions are predominantly true/false questions that allow students to check their understanding of the mathematical concepts and definitions introduced in the section before moving on to their homework. Answers to the Concept Quiz are located at the end of the Problem Set.

Concept Quiz 3.1

For Problems 1–10, answer true or false.

1. Equivalent equations have the same solution set.
2. $x^2 = 9$ is a first-degree equation.
3. The set of all solutions is called a solution set.
4. If the solution set is the null set, then the equation has at least one solution.
5. Solving an equation refers to obtaining any other equivalent equation.
6. If 5 is a solution, then a true numerical statement is formed when 5 is substituted for the variable in the equation.
7. Any number can be subtracted from both sides of an equation, and the result is an equivalent equation.
8. Any number can divide both sides of an equation to obtain an equivalent equation.
9. By the reflexive property, if $y = 2$ then $2 = y$.
10. By the transitive property, if $x = y$ and $y = 4$, then $x = 4$.

▶**Chapter Summary**

The new grid format of the Chapter Summary allows students to review material quickly and easily. Each row of the Chapter Summary includes a learning objective, a summary of that objective, and a worked-out example for that objective.

Chapter 2 **Summary**		
OBJECTIVE	SUMMARY	EXAMPLE
Classify numbers in the real number system. (Section 2.3/Objective 1)	Any number that has a terminating or repeating decimal representation is a rational number. Any number that has a non-terminating or non-repeating decimal representation is an irrational number. The rational numbers together with the irrational numbers form the set of real numbers.	Classify -1, $\sqrt{7}$, and $\frac{3}{4}$. **Solution** -1 is a real number, a rational number, an integer, and negative. $\sqrt{7}$ is a real number, an irrational number, and positive. $\frac{3}{4}$ is a real number, a rational number, noninteger, and positive.
Reduce rational numbers to lowest terms. (Section 2.1/Objective 1)	The property $\frac{a \cdot k}{b \cdot k} = \frac{a}{b}$ is used to express fractions in reduced form.	Reduce $\frac{6xy}{14x}$. **Solution** $\frac{6xy}{14x} = \frac{2 \cdot 3 \cdot x \cdot y}{2 \cdot 7 \cdot x}$ $= \frac{2 \cdot 3 \cdot \cancel{x} \cdot y}{2 \cdot 7 \cdot \cancel{x}}$ $= \frac{3y}{7}$

Continuing Features

Explanations
Annotations in the examples and text provide further explanations of the material.

Examples
More than 600 worked-out Examples show students how to use and apply mathematical concepts. Every example has a corresponding Classroom Example for the teacher to use.

Thoughts Into Words
Every problem set includes Thoughts Into Words problems, which give students an opportunity to express in written form their thoughts about various mathematical ideas.

Further Investigations
Many problem sets include Further Investigations, which allow students to pursue more complicated ideas. Many of these investigations lend themselves to small group work.

Graphing Calculator Activities
Certain problem sets contain a group of problems called Graphing Calculator Activities. In this text, the use of a graphing calculator is optional.

Problem Sets
Problems Sets contain a wide variety of skill-development exercises.

Chapter Review Problem Sets and Chapter Tests
Chapter Review Problem Sets and Chapter Tests appear at the end of every chapter.

Cumulative Review Problem Sets
Cumulative Review Problem Sets help students retain skills introduced earlier in the text.

Answers
The answer section at the back of the text provides answers to the odd-numbered exercises in the problem sets and to all exercises in the Chapter Review Problem Sets, Chapter Tests, and Cumulative Review Problem Sets.

Content Changes

- Chapter 7 has been reorganized so that Sections 7.1–7.4 cover only linear equations in two variables. Then, in Section 7.5, the emphasis is on graphing nonlinear equations and using graphs to motivate tests for x-axis, y-axis, and origin symmetry. These symmetry tests are used in Chapters 8, 9, 10, and 13, and will also be used in subsequent mathematics courses as students' graphing skills are enhanced.

- A focal point of every revision is the problem sets. Some users of the previous edition have suggested that the "very good" problem sets could be made even better by adding some new problems in different places. For example, in Problem Set 3.4 more problems on factoring out a binomial factor and more problems on factoring by grouping were added in this edition.

- Students often make errors when simplifying the rational expressions that result from using the quadratic formula; hence they obtain incorrect solutions for quadratic equations. Section 6.4 now includes an example and exercises to help students with this issue.

- Because retaining skills is so important in the study of mathematics, we have added Cumulative Review Problem Sets at the end of every other chapter. These cumulative review problem sets contain problems from Chapter 1 through the current chapter. In other words, Chapter 4 ends with Chapters 1–4 Cumulative Review Problem Set.

Additional Comments about Some of the Other Chapters

- Chapter 1 was written so that it can be covered quickly, or on an individual basis if necessary, by those who need a brief review of some basic arithmetic and algebraic concepts.

- Chapter 2 presents an early introduction to the heart of an algebra course. Problem solving and the solving of equations and inequalities are introduced early so they can be used as unifying themes throughout the text.

- Chapter 6 is organized to give students the opportunity to learn, on a day-by-day basis, different factoring techniques for solving quadratic equations. The process of completing the square is treated as a viable equation-solving tool for certain types of quadratic equations. The emphasis on completing the square in this setting pays off in Chapter 13 when we graph parabolas, circles, ellipses, and hyperbolas. Section 6.5 offers some guidance as to when to use a particular technique for solving a quadratic equation.

- Chapter 8 is devoted entirely to functions; our treatment of the topic does not jump back and forth between functions and relations that are not functions. This chapter includes some work with the composition of functions and the use of linear and quadratic functions in problem-solving situations. Linear and quadratic functions are covered extensively and used in a variety of problem-solving situations.

- Chapter 14 has been written in a way that lends itself to individual or small-group work. Sequences are introduced and then used to solve problems.

Ancillaries for the Instructor

Print Ancillaries

Annotated Instructor's Edition

This special version of the complete student text contains the answers to every problem in the problem sets and every new classroom example; the answers are printed next to all respective elements. Graphs, tables, and other answers appear in a special answer section at the back of the text.

Complete Solutions Manual

The Complete Solutions Manual provides worked-out solutions to all of the problems in the text.

Instructor's Resource Binder

New! Each section of the main text is discussed in uniquely designed Teaching Guides, which contain instruction tips, examples, activities, worksheets, overheads, assessments, and solutions to all worksheets and activities.

These cumulative review problem sets contain problems from Chapter 1 through the current chapter. For example, Chapter 4 ends with Chapters 1–4 Cumulative Review Problem Set.

Electronic Ancillaries

Solution Builder

This online solutions manual allows instructors to create customizable solutions that they can print out to distribute or post as needed. This is a convenient and expedient way to deliver solutions to specific homework sets. Visit www.cengage.com/solutionbuilder.

Enhanced WebAssign

Enhanced WebAssign, used by over one million students at more than 1100 institutions, allows you to assign, collect, grade, and record homework assignments via the web. This proven and reliable homework system includes thousands of algorithmically generated homework problems, an eBook, links to relevant textbook sections, video examples, problem-specific tutorials, and more.

Note that the WebAssign problems for this text are highlighted by a ▶.

PowerLecture with ExamView®

This CD-ROM provides the instructor with dynamic media tools for teaching. Create, deliver, and customize tests (both print and online) in minutes with *ExamView® Computerized Testing Featuring Algorithmic Equations*. Easily build solution sets for homework or exams using *Solution Builder's* online solutions manual. Microsoft® PowerPoint® lecture slides and figures from the book are also included on this CD-ROM.

Text Specific DVDs

These 10- to 20-minute problem-solving lessons, created by Rena Petrello of Moorpark College, cover nearly all the learning objectives from every section of each chapter in the text. Recipient of the "Mark Dever Award for Excellence in Teaching," Rena Petrello presents each lesson using her experience teaching online mathematics courses. It was through this online teaching experience that Rena discovered the lack of suitable content for online instructors, which inspired her to develop her own video lessons—and ultimately create this video project. These videos have won two Telly Awards, one Communicator Award, and one Aurora Award (an international honor). Students will love the additional guidance and support if they have missed a class or when they are preparing for an upcoming quiz or exam. The videos are available for purchase as a set of DVDs or online via www.ichapters.com.

Ancillaries for the Student

Print Ancillaries

Student Solutions Manual

The Student Solutions Manual provides worked-out solutions to the odd-numbered problems in the problem sets as well as to all problems in the Chapter Review, Chapter Test, and Cumulative Review sections.

Student Workbook

NEW! Get a head-start: The Student Workbook contains all of the Assessments, Activities, and Worksheets from the Instructor's Resource Binder for classroom discussions, in-class activities, and group work.

Electronic Ancillaries

Enhanced WebAssign

Enhanced WebAssign, used by over one million students at more than 1100 institutions, allows you to do homework assignments and get extra help and practice via the web. This proven and reliable homework system includes thousands of algorithmically generated homework problems, an eBook, links to relevant textbook sections, video examples, problem-specific tutorials, and more.

Text-Specific DVDs

These 10- to 20-minute problem-solving lessons, created by Rena Petrello of Moorpark College, cover nearly all the learning objectives from every section of each chapter in the text. Recipient of the "Mark Dever Award for Excellence in Teaching," Rena Petrello presents each lesson using her experience teaching online mathematics courses. It was through this online teaching experience that Rena discovered the lack of suitable content for online instructors, which inspired her to develop her own video lessons—and ultimately create this video project. These videos have won two Telly Awards, one Communicator Award, and one Aurora Award (an international honor). Students will love the additional guidance and support if they have missed a class or when they are preparing for an upcoming quiz or exam. The videos are available for purchase as a set of DVDs or online via www.ichapters.com.

Additional Resources

Mastering Mathematics: How to Be a Great Math Student, 3e (0-534-34947-1)

Richard Manning Smith, Ph.D., *Bryant College*

Providing solid tips for every stage of study, *Mastering Mathematics* stresses the importance of a positive attitude and gives students the tools to succeed in their math course. This practical guide will help students avoid mental blocks during math exams, identify and improve areas of weakness, get the most out of class time, study more effectively, overcome a perceived "low math ability," be successful on math tests, get back on track when feeling lost, and much more!

Conquering Math Anxiety (with CD-ROM), Third Edition (0-495-82940-4)

Cynthia A. Arem, Ph.D., *Pima Community College*

Written by Cynthia Arem (Pima Community College), this comprehensive workbook provides a variety of exercises and worksheets along with detailed explanations of methods to help "math-anxious" students deal with and overcome math fears.

Math Study Skills Workbook, Third Edition (0-618-83746-9)

Paul D. Nolting, Ph.D., *Learning Specialist*

This best-selling workbook helps students identify their strengths, weaknesses, and personal learning styles in math. Nolting offers proven study tips, test-taking strategies, a homework system, and recommendations for reducing anxiety and improving grades.

Acknowledgments

We would like to take this opportunity to thank the following people who served as reviewers for the ninth editions of the Kaufmann-Schwitters algebra series:

Yusuf Abdi
Rutgers, the State University of New Jersey

Radha Sankaran
Passaic County Community College

Kim Gwydir
University of Miami;
Florida International University

Joan Smeltzer
Penn State University, York Campus

Janet Hansen
Dixie Junior College

Brandon Smith
Wallace Community College, Hanceville

M. Randall Holmes
Boise State University

Kathy Spradlin
Liberty University

Carolyn Horseman
Polk Community College, Winter Haven

Hien Van Eaton
Liberty University

Jeffrey Osikiewicz
Kent State University

James Wood
Tarleton State University

Tammy Ott
Penn State University

Rebecca Wulf
Ivy Tech Community College, Lafayette

We would like to express our sincere gratitude to the staff of Cengage Learning, especially to Marc Bove, for his continuous cooperation and assistance throughout this project; and to Susan Graham and Tanya Nigh, who carry out the many details of production. Finally, very special thanks are due to Arlene Kaufmann, who spends numerous hours reading page proofs.

Jerome E. Kaufmann
Karen L. Schwitters

1

Basic Concepts and Properties

1.1 Sets, Real Numbers, and Numerical Expressions

1.2 Operations with Real Numbers

1.3 Properties of Real Numbers and the Use of Exponents

1.4 Algebraic Expressions

Numbers from the set of integers are used to express temperatures that are below 0°F.

© Photostio

The temperature at 6 P.M. was −3°F. By 11 P.M. the temperature had dropped another 5°F. We can use the *numerical expression* −3 − 5 to determine the temperature at 11 P.M.

Justin has *p* pennies, *n* nickels, and *d* dimes in his pocket. The *algebraic expression* $p + 5n + 10d$ represents that amount of money in cents.

Algebra is often described as a *generalized arithmetic*. That description may not tell the whole story, but it does convey an important idea: A good understanding of arithmetic provides a sound basis for the study of algebra. In this chapter we use the concepts of *numerical expression* and *algebraic expression* to review some ideas from arithmetic and to begin the transition to algebra. Be sure that you thoroughly understand the basic concepts we review in this first chapter.

Video tutorials based on section learning objectives are available in a variety of delivery modes.

1.1	Sets, Real Numbers, and Numerical Expressions

OBJECTIVES

1. Identify certain sets of numbers
2. Apply the properties of equality
3. Simplify numerical expressions

In arithmetic, we use symbols such as 6, $\frac{2}{3}$, 0.27, and π to represent numbers. The symbols $+$, $-$, $\cdot$, and $\div$ commonly indicate the basic operations of addition, subtraction, multiplication, and division, respectively. Thus we can form specific **numerical expressions**. For example, we can write the indicated sum of six and eight as $6 + 8$.

In algebra, the concept of a variable provides the basis for generalizing arithmetic ideas. For example, by using x and y to represent any numbers, we can use the expression $x + y$ to represent the indicated sum of any two numbers. The x and y in such an expression are called **variables**, and the phrase $x + y$ is called an **algebraic expression**.

We can extend to algebra many of the notational agreements we make in arithmetic, with a few modifications. The following chart summarizes the notational agreements that pertain to the four basic operations.

Operation	Arithmetic	Algebra	Vocabulary
Addition	$4 + 6$	$x + y$	The *sum* of x and y
Subtraction	$14 - 10$	$a - b$	The *difference* of a and b
Multiplication	$7 \cdot 5$ or 7×5	$a \cdot b$, $a(b)$, $(a)b$, $(a)(b)$, or ab	The *product* of a and b
Division	$8 \div 4$, $\frac{8}{4}$, or $4\overline{)8}$	$x \div y$, $\frac{x}{y}$, or $y\overline{)x}$	The *quotient* of x and y

Note the different ways to indicate a product, including the use of parentheses. The ab form is the simplest and probably the most widely used form. Expressions such as abc, $6xy$, and $14xyz$ all indicate multiplication. We also call your attention to the various forms that indicate division; in algebra, we usually use the fractional form $\frac{x}{y}$ although the other forms do serve a purpose at times.

Use of Sets

We can use some of the basic vocabulary and symbolism associated with the concept of sets in the study of algebra. A **set** is a collection of objects, and the objects are called **elements** or **members** of the set. In arithmetic and algebra the elements of a set are usually numbers.

The use of set braces, { }, to enclose the elements (or a description of the elements) and the use of capital letters to name sets provide a convenient way to communicate about sets. For example, we can represent a set A, which consists of the vowels of the alphabet, in any of the following ways:

$A = \{$vowels of the alphabet$\}$ Word description

$A = \{a, e, i, o, u\}$ List or roster description

$A = \{x | x$ is a vowel$\}$ Set builder notation

We can modify the listing approach if the number of elements is quite large. For example, all of the letters of the alphabet can be listed as

$$\{a, b, c, \ldots, z\}$$

We simply begin by writing enough elements to establish a pattern; then the three dots indicate that the set continues in that pattern. The final entry indicates the last element of the pattern. If we write

$$\{1, 2, 3, \ldots\}$$

the set begins with the counting numbers 1, 2, and 3. The three dots indicate that it continues in a like manner forever; there is no last element. A set that consists of no elements is called the **null set** (written $\varnothing$).

Set builder notation combines the use of braces and the concept of a variable. For example, $\{x | x$ is a vowel$\}$ is read "the set of all x such that x is a vowel." Note that the vertical line is read "such that." We can use set builder notation to describe the set $\{1, 2, 3, \ldots\}$ as $\{x | x > 0$ and x is a whole number$\}$.

We use the symbol $\in$ to denote set membership. Thus if $A = \{a, e, i, o, u\}$, we can write $e \in A$, which we read as "e is an element of A." The slash symbol, $/$, is commonly used in mathematics as a negation symbol. For example, $m \notin A$ is read as "m is not an element of A."

Two sets are said to be *equal* if they contain exactly the same elements. For example,

$$\{1, 2, 3\} = \{2, 1, 3\}$$

because both sets contain the same elements; the order in which the elements are written doesn't matter. The slash mark through the equality symbol denotes "is not equal to." Thus if $A = \{1, 2, 3\}$ and $B = \{1, 2, 3, 4\}$, we can write $A \neq B$, which we read as "set A is not equal to set B."

Real Numbers

We refer to most of the algebra that we will study in this text as the **algebra of real numbers**. This simply means that the variables represent real numbers. Therefore, it is necessary for us to be familiar with the various terms that are used to classify different types of real numbers.

$\{1, 2, 3, 4, \ldots\}$	Natural numbers, counting numbers, positive integers
$\{0, 1, 2, 3, \ldots\}$	Whole numbers, nonnegative integers
$\{\ldots -3, -2, -1\}$	Negative integers
$\{\ldots -3, -2, -1, 0\}$	Nonpositive integers
$\{\ldots -3, -2, -1, 0, 1, 2, 3, \ldots\}$	Integers

We define a **rational number** as follows:

Definition 1.1 Rational Numbers

A rational number is any number that can be written in the form $\dfrac{a}{b}$, where a and b are integers, and b does not equal zero.

We can easily recognize that each of the following numbers fits the definition of a rational number.

$$\frac{-3}{4} \qquad \frac{2}{3} \qquad \frac{15}{4} \qquad \text{and} \qquad \frac{1}{-5}$$

However, numbers such as -4, 0, 0.3, and $6\frac{1}{2}$ are also rational numbers. All of these numbers could be written in the form $\frac{a}{b}$ as follows.

-4 can be written as $\dfrac{-4}{1}$ or $\dfrac{4}{-1}$

0 can be written as $\dfrac{0}{1} = \dfrac{0}{2} = \dfrac{0}{3} = \ldots$

0.3 can be written as $\dfrac{3}{10}$

$6\frac{1}{2}$ can be written as $\dfrac{13}{2}$

We can also define a rational number in terms of decimal representation. We classify decimals as terminating, repeating, or nonrepeating.

Type	Definition	Examples	Rational numbers
Terminating	A terminating decimal ends.	0.3, 0.46, 0.6234, 1.25	Yes
Repeating	A repeating decimal has a block of digits that repeats indefinitely.	0.66666 . . . 0.141414 . . . 0.694694694 . . . 0.23171717 . . .	Yes
Nonrepeating	A nonrepeating decimal does not have a block of digits that repeats indefinitely and does not terminate.	3.1415926535 . . . 1.414213562 . . . 0.276314583 . . .	No

A repeating decimal has a block of digits that can be any number of digits and may or may not begin immediately after the decimal point. A small horizontal bar (overbar) is commonly used to indicate the repeat block. Thus 0.6666 . . . is written as $0.\overline{6}$, and 0.2317171717 . . . is written as $0.23\overline{17}$.

In terms of decimals, we define a rational number as a number that has a terminating or a repeating decimal representation. The following examples illustrate some rational numbers written in $\frac{a}{b}$ form and in decimal form.

$$\frac{3}{4} = 0.75 \qquad \frac{3}{11} = 0.\overline{27} \qquad \frac{1}{8} = 0.125 \qquad \frac{1}{7} = 0.\overline{142857} \qquad \frac{1}{3} = 0.\overline{3}$$

We define an **irrational number** as a number that *cannot* be expressed in $\frac{a}{b}$ form, where a and b are integers, and b is not zero. Furthermore, an irrational number has a nonrepeating and nonterminating decimal representation. Some examples of irrational numbers and a partial decimal representation for each follow.

$$\sqrt{2} = 1.414213562373095 \ldots \qquad \sqrt{3} = 1.73205080756887 \ldots$$
$$\pi = 3.14159265358979 \ldots$$

The set of **real numbers** is composed of the rational numbers along with the irrational numbers. Every real number is either a rational number or an irrational number. The following tree diagram summarizes the various classifications of the real number system.

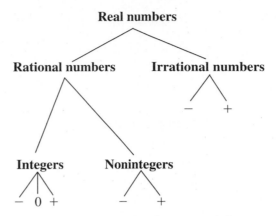

We can trace any real number down through the diagram as follows:

7 is real, rational, an integer, and positive

$-\dfrac{2}{3}$ is real, rational, noninteger, and negative

$\sqrt{7}$ is real, irrational, and positive

0.38 is real, rational, noninteger, and positive

Remark: We usually refer to the set of nonnegative integers, $\{0, 1, 2, 3, \ldots\}$, as the set of **whole numbers**, and we refer to the set of positive integers, $\{1, 2, 3, \ldots\}$, as the set of **natural numbers**. The set of whole numbers differs from the set of natural numbers by the inclusion of the number zero.

The concept of subset is convenient to discuss at this time. A set A is a **subset** of a set B if and only if every element of A is also an element of B. This is written as $A \subseteq B$ and read as "A is a subset of B." For example, if $A = \{1, 2, 3\}$ and $B = \{1, 2, 3, 5, 9\}$, then $A \subseteq B$ because every element of A is also an element of B. The slash mark denotes negation, so if $A = \{1, 2, 5\}$ and $B = \{2, 4, 7\}$, we can say that A is not a subset of B by writing $A \nsubseteq B$. Figure 1.1 represents the subset relationships for the set of real numbers. Refer to Figure 1.1 as you study the following statements, which use subset vocabulary and subset symbolism.

1. The set of whole numbers is a subset of the set of integers.

$$\{0, 1, 2, 3, \ldots\} \subseteq \{\ldots, -2, -1, 0, 1, 2, \ldots\}$$

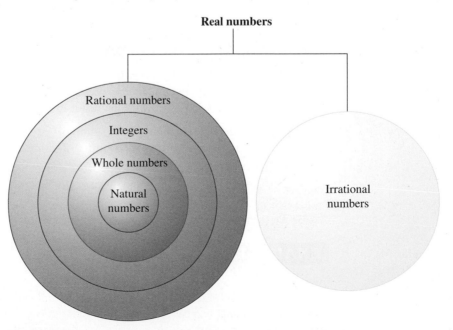

Figure 1.1

2. The set of integers is a subset of the set of rational numbers.

$$\{\ldots, -2, -1, 0, 1, 2, \ldots\} \subseteq \{x | x \text{ is a rational number}\}$$

3. The set of rational numbers is a subset of the set of real numbers.

$$\{x | x \text{ is a rational number}\} \subseteq \{y | y \text{ is a real number}\}$$

Properties of Equality

The relation *equality* plays an important role in mathematics—especially when we are manipulating real numbers and algebraic expressions that represent real numbers. An **equality** is a statement in which two symbols, or groups of symbols, are names for the same number. The symbol $=$ is used to express an equality. Thus we can write

$$6 + 1 = 7 \qquad 18 - 2 = 16 \qquad 36 \div 4 = 9$$

(The symbol $\neq$ denotes *is not equal to*.) The following four basic properties of equality are self-evident, but we do need to keep them in mind. (We will expand this list in Chapter 2 when we work with solutions of equations.)

Properties of equality	Definition: For real numbers a, b, and c	Examples
Reflexive property	$a = a$	$14 = 14$, $x = x$, $a + b = a + b$
Symmetric property	If $a = b$, then $b = a$.	If $3 + 1 = 4$, then $4 = 3 + 1$. If $x = 10$, then $10 = x$.
Transitive property	If $a = b$ and $b = c$, then $a = c$.	If $x = 7$ and $7 = y$, then $x = y$. If $x + 5 = y$ and $y = 8$, then $x + 5 = 8$.
Substitution property	If $a = b$, then a may be replaced by b, or b may be replaced by a, without changing the meaning of the statement.	If $x + y = 4$ and $x = 2$, then we can replace x in the first equation with the value 2, which will yield $2 + y = 4$.

Simplifying Numerical Expressions

Let's conclude this section by *simplifying some numerical expressions* that involve whole numbers. When simplifying numerical expressions, we perform the operations in the following order. Be sure that you agree with the result in each example.

1. Perform the operations inside the symbols of inclusion (parentheses, brackets, and braces) and above and below each fraction bar. Start with the innermost inclusion symbol.

2. Perform all multiplications and divisions in the order in which they appear from left to right.

3. Perform all additions and subtractions in the order in which they appear from left to right.

Classroom Example
Simplify $25 + 55 \div 11 \cdot 4$.

EXAMPLE 1   Simplify $20 + 60 \div 10 \cdot 2$.

Solution

First do the division.

$$20 + 60 \div 10 \cdot 2 = 20 + 6 \cdot 2$$

Next do the multiplication.

$$20 + 6 \cdot 2 = 20 + 12$$

Then do the addition.

$$20 + 12 = 32$$

Thus $20 + 60 \div 10 \cdot 2$ simplifies to 32.

Classroom Example
Simplify $4 \cdot 9 \div 3 \cdot 6 \div 8$.

EXAMPLE 2   Simplify $7 \cdot 4 \div 2 \cdot 3 \cdot 2 \div 4$.

Solution

The multiplications and divisions are to be done from left to right in the order in which they appear.

$$
\begin{aligned}
7 \cdot 4 \div 2 \cdot 3 \cdot 2 \div 4 &= 28 \div 2 \cdot 3 \cdot 2 \div 4 \\
&= 14 \cdot 3 \cdot 2 \div 4 \\
&= 42 \cdot 2 \div 4 \\
&= 84 \div 4 \\
&= 21
\end{aligned}
$$

Thus $7 \cdot 4 \div 2 \cdot 3 \cdot 2 \div 4$ simplifies to 21.

Classroom Example
Simplify $3 \cdot 7 + 16 \div 4 - 3 \cdot 8 + 6 \div 2$.

EXAMPLE 3   Simplify $5 \cdot 3 + 4 \div 2 - 2 \cdot 6 - 28 \div 7$.

Solution

First we do the multiplications and divisions in the order in which they appear. Then we do the additions and subtractions in the order in which they appear. Our work may take on the following format.

$$5 \cdot 3 + 4 \div 2 - 2 \cdot 6 - 28 \div 7 = 15 + 2 - 12 - 4 = 1$$

Classroom Example
Simplify $(7 + 2)(3 + 8)$.

EXAMPLE 4   Simplify $(4 + 6)(7 + 8)$.

Solution

We use the parentheses to indicate the *product* of the quantities $4 + 6$ and $7 + 8$. We perform the additions inside the parentheses first and then multiply.

$$(4 + 6)(7 + 8) = (10)(15) = 150$$

Classroom Example
Simplify $(2 \cdot 5 + 3 \cdot 6) \cdot (7 \cdot 4 - 8 \cdot 3)$.

EXAMPLE 5   Simplify $(3 \cdot 2 + 4 \cdot 5)(6 \cdot 8 - 5 \cdot 7)$.

Solution

First we do the multiplications inside the parentheses.

$$(3 \cdot 2 + 4 \cdot 5)(6 \cdot 8 - 5 \cdot 7) = (6 + 20)(48 - 35)$$

Then we do the addition and subtraction inside the parentheses.

$$(6 + 20)(48 - 35) = (26)(13)$$

Then we find the final product.

$$(26)(13) = 338$$

Classroom Example
Simplify $3 + 9[2(5 + 4)]$.

EXAMPLE 6   Simplify $6 + 7[3(4 + 6)]$.

Solution

We use brackets for the same purposes as parentheses. In such a problem we need to simplify *from the inside out*; that is, we perform the operations in the innermost parentheses first. We thus obtain

$$6 + 7[3(4 + 6)] = 6 + 7[3(10)]$$
$$= 6 + 7[30]$$
$$= 6 + 210$$
$$= 216$$

Classroom Example
Simplify $\dfrac{7 \cdot 6 - 3 \cdot 3}{2 \cdot 6 \div 3 - 1}$.

EXAMPLE 7   Simplify $\dfrac{6 \cdot 8 \div 4 - 2}{5 \cdot 4 - 9 \cdot 2}$.

Solution

First we perform the operations above and below the fraction bar. Then we find the final quotient.

$$\frac{6 \cdot 8 \div 4 - 2}{5 \cdot 4 - 9 \cdot 2} = \frac{48 \div 4 - 2}{20 - 18} = \frac{12 - 2}{2} = \frac{10}{2} = 5$$

Remark: With parentheses we could write the problem in Example 7 as $(6 \cdot 8 \div 4 - 2) \div (5 \cdot 4 - 9 \cdot 2)$.

Concept Quiz 1.1

For Problems 1–10, answer true or false.

1. The expression ab indicates the sum of a and b.
2. The set $\{1, 2, 3 \ldots\}$ contains infinitely many elements.
3. The sets $A = \{1, 2, 4, 6\}$ and $B = \{6, 4, 1, 2\}$ are equal sets.
4. Every irrational number is also classified as a real number.
5. To evaluate $24 \div 6 \cdot 2$, the first operation to be performed is to multiply 6 times 2.
6. To evaluate $6 + 8 \cdot 3$, the first operation to be performed is to multiply 8 times 3.
7. The number 0.15 is real, irrational, and positive.
8. If $4 = x + 3$, then $x + 3 = 4$ is an example of the symmetric property of equality.
9. The numerical expression $6 \cdot 2 + 3 \cdot 5 - 6$ simplifies to 21.
10. The number represented by $0.\overline{12}$ is a rational number.

Problem Set 1.1

For Problems 1–10, identify each statement as true or false.
(Objective 1)

1. Every irrational number is a real number.
2. Every rational number is a real number.
3. If a number is real, then it is irrational.
4. Every real number is a rational number.
5. All integers are rational numbers.
6. Some irrational numbers are also rational numbers.
7. Zero is a positive integer.

8. Zero is a rational number.

9. All whole numbers are integers.

10. Zero is a negative integer.

For Problems 11–18, from the list 0, 14, $\frac{2}{3}$, π, $\sqrt{7}$, $-\frac{11}{14}$, 2.34, -19, $\frac{55}{8}$, $-\sqrt{17}$, $3.2\overline{1}$, and -2.6, identify each of the following. (Objective 1)

11. The whole numbers

12. The natural numbers

13. The rational numbers

14. The integers

15. The nonnegative integers

16. The irrational numbers

17. The real numbers

18. The nonpositive integers

For Problems 19–28, use the following set designations.

$N = \{x|x \text{ is a natural number}\}$

$Q = \{x|x \text{ is a rational number}\}$

$W = \{x|x \text{ is a whole number}\}$

$H = \{x|x \text{ is an irrational number}\}$

$I = \{x|x \text{ is an integer}\}$

$R = \{x|x \text{ is a real number}\}$

Place $\subseteq$ or $\not\subseteq$ in each blank to make a true statement. (Objective 1)

19. R _____ N

20. N _____ R

21. I _____ Q

22. N _____ I

23. Q _____ H

24. H _____ Q

25. N _____ W

26. W _____ I

27. I _____ N

28. I _____ W

For Problems 29–32, classify the real number by tracing through the diagram in the text (see page 5). (Objective 1)

29. -8

30. 0.9

31. $-\sqrt{2}$

32. $\frac{5}{6}$

For Problems 33–42, list the elements of each set. For example, the elements of $\{x|x \text{ is a natural number less than 4}\}$ can be listed as $\{1, 2, 3\}$. (Objective 1)

33. $\{x|x \text{ is a natural number less than 3}\}$

34. $\{x|x \text{ is a natural number greater than 3}\}$

35. $\{n|n \text{ is a whole number less than 6}\}$

36. $\{y|y \text{ is an integer greater than } -4\}$

37. $\{y|y \text{ is an integer less than 3}\}$

38. $\{n|n \text{ is a positive integer greater than } -7\}$

39. $\{x|x \text{ is a whole number less than 0}\}$

40. $\{x|x \text{ is a negative integer greater than } -3\}$

41. $\{n|n \text{ is a nonnegative integer less than 5}\}$

42. $\{n|n \text{ is a nonpositive integer greater than 3}\}$

For Problems 43–50, replace each question mark to make the given statement an application of the indicated property of equality. For example, $16 = ?$ becomes $16 = 16$ because of the reflexive property of equality. (Objective 2)

43. If $y = x$ and $x = -6$, then $y = ?$ (Transitive property of equality)

44. $5x + 7 = ?$ (Reflexive property of equality)

45. If $n = 2$ and $3n + 4 = 10$, then $3(?) + 4 = 10$ (Substitution property of equality)

46. If $y = x$ and $x = z + 2$, then $y = ?$ (Transitive property of equality)

47. If $4 = 3x + 1$, then $? = 4$ (Symmetric property of equality)

48. If $t = 4$ and $s + t = 9$, then $s + ? = 9$ (Substitution property of equality)

49. $5x = ?$ (Reflexive property of equality)

50. If $5 = n + 3$, then $n + 3 = ?$ (Symmetric property of equality)

For Problems 51–74, simplify each of the numerical expressions. (Objective 3)

51. $16 + 9 - 4 - 2 + 8 - 1$

52. $18 + 17 - 9 - 2 + 14 - 11$

53. $9 \div 3 \cdot 4 \div 2 \cdot 14$

54. $21 \div 7 \cdot 5 \cdot 2 \div 6$

55. $7 + 8 \cdot 2$

56. $21 - 4 \cdot 3 + 2$

57. $9 \cdot 7 - 4 \cdot 5 - 3 \cdot 2 + 4 \cdot 7$

58. $6 \cdot 3 + 5 \cdot 4 - 2 \cdot 8 + 3 \cdot 2$

59. $(17 - 12)(13 - 9)(7 - 4)$

60. $(14 - 12)(13 - 8)(9 - 6)$

61. $13 + (7 - 2)(5 - 1)$

62. $48 - (14 - 11)(10 - 6)$

63. $(5 \cdot 9 - 3 \cdot 4)(6 \cdot 9 - 2 \cdot 7)$

64. $(3 \cdot 4 + 2 \cdot 1)(5 \cdot 2 + 6 \cdot 7)$

65. $7[3(6 - 2)] - 64$

66. $12 + 5[3(7 - 4)]$

67. $[3 + 2(4 \cdot 1 - 2)][18 - (2 \cdot 4 - 7 \cdot 1)]$

68. $3[4(6 + 7)] + 2[3(4 - 2)]$

69. $14 + 4\left(\dfrac{8 - 2}{12 - 9}\right) - 2\left(\dfrac{9 - 1}{19 - 15}\right)$

70. $12 + 2\left(\dfrac{12 - 2}{7 - 2}\right) - 3\left(\dfrac{12 - 9}{17 - 14}\right)$

71. $[7 + 2 \cdot 3 \cdot 5 - 5] \div 8$

72. $[27 - (4 \cdot 2 + 5 \cdot 2)][(5 \cdot 6 - 4) - 20]$

73. $\dfrac{3 \cdot 8 - 4 \cdot 3}{5 \cdot 7 - 34} + 19$

74. $\dfrac{4 \cdot 9 - 3 \cdot 5 - 3}{18 - 12}$

75. You must of course be able to do calculations like those in Problems 51–74 both with and without a calculator. Furthermore, different types of calculators handle the priority-of-operations issue in different ways. Be sure you can do Problems 51–74 with *your* calculator.

Thoughts Into Words

76. Explain in your own words the difference between the reflexive property of equality and the symmetric property of equality.

77. Your friend keeps getting an answer of 30 when simplifying $7 + 8(2)$. What mistake is he making and how would you help him?

78. Do you think $3\sqrt{2}$ is a rational or an irrational number? Defend your answer.

79. Explain why every integer is a rational number but not every rational number is an integer.

80. Explain the difference between $1.\overline{3}$ and 1.3.

Answers to the Concept Quiz

1. False   **2.** True   **3.** True   **4.** True   **5.** False   **6.** True   **7.** False   **8.** True   **9.** True   **10.** True

---

1.2   Operations with Real Numbers

OBJECTIVES

1. Review the real number line
2. Find the absolute value of a number
3. Add real numbers
4. Subtract real numbers
5. Multiply real numbers
6. Divide real numbers
7. Simplify numerical expressions
8. Use real numbers to represent problems

Before we review the four basic operations with real numbers, let's briefly discuss some concepts and terminology we commonly use with this material. It is often helpful to have a geometric representation of the set of real numbers as indicated in Figure 1.2. Such a representation, called the **real number line**, indicates a one-to-one correspondence between the set of real numbers and the points on a line. In other words, to each real number there corresponds one and only one point on the line, and to each point on the line there corresponds one and only one real number. The number associated with each point on the line is called the **coordinate** of the point.

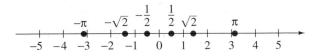

Figure 1.2

Many operations, relations, properties, and concepts pertaining to real numbers can be given a geometric interpretation on the real number line. For example, the addition problem $(-1) + (-2)$ can be depicted on the number line as in Figure 1.3.

Figure 1.3

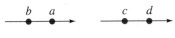

Figure 1.4

The inequality relations also have a geometric interpretation. The statement $a > b$ (which is read "a is greater than b") means that a is to the right of b, and the statement $c < d$ (which is read "c is less than d") means that c is to the left of d as shown in Figure 1.4. The symbol $\leq$ means *is less than or equal to*, and the symbol $\geq$ means *is greater than or equal to*.

The property $-(-x) = x$ can be represented on the number line by following the sequence of steps shown in Figure 1.5.

1. Choose a point that has a coordinate of x.
2. Locate its opposite, written as $-x$, on the other side of zero.
3. Locate the opposite of $-x$, written as $-(-x)$, on the other side of zero.

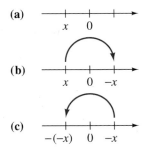

Figure 1.5

Therefore, we conclude that *the opposite of the opposite of any real number is the number itself*, and we symbolically express this by $-(-x) = x$.

Remark: The symbol -1 can be read "negative one," "the negative of one," "the opposite of one," or "the additive inverse of one." The opposite-of and additive-inverse-of terminology is especially meaningful when working with variables. For example, the symbol $-x$, which is read "the opposite of x" or "the additive inverse of x," emphasizes an important issue. Because x can be any real number, $-x$ (the opposite of x) can be zero, positive, or negative. If x is positive, then $-x$ is negative. If x is negative, then $-x$ is positive. If x is zero, then $-x$ is zero.

Absolute Value

We can use the concept of *absolute value* to describe precisely how to operate with positive and negative numbers. Geometrically, the **absolute value** of any number is the distance between the number and zero on the number line. For example, the absolute value of 2 is 2. The absolute value of -3 is 3. The absolute value of 0 is 0 (see Figure 1.6).

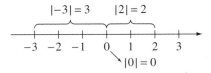

Figure 1.6

Symbolically, absolute value is denoted with vertical bars. Thus we write

$$|2| = 2 \qquad |-3| = 3 \qquad |0| = 0$$

More formally, we define the concept of absolute value as follows:

Definition 1.2

For all real numbers a,

1. If $a \geq 0$, then $|a| = a$.
2. If $a < 0$, then $|a| = -a$.

According to Definition 1.2, we obtain

$|6| = 6$	By applying part 1 of Definition 1.2
$|0| = 0$	By applying part 1 of Definition 1.2
$|-7| = -(-7) = 7$	By applying part 2 of Definition 1.2

Note that the absolute value of a positive number is the number itself, but the absolute value of a negative number is its opposite. Thus the absolute value of any number except zero is positive, and the absolute value of zero is zero. Together these facts indicate that the absolute value of any real number is equal to the absolute value of its opposite. We summarize these ideas in the following properties.

Properties of Absolute Value

The variables a and b represent any real number.

1. $|a| \geq 0$
2. $|a| = |-a|$
3. $|a - b| = |b - a|$ $a - b$ and $b - a$ are opposites of each other

---

Adding Real Numbers

We can use various physical models to describe the addition of real numbers. For example, profits and losses pertaining to investments: A loss of \$25.75 (written as -25.75) on one investment, along with a profit of \$22.20 (written as 22.20) on a second investment, produces an overall loss of \$3.55. Thus $(-25.75) + 22.20 = -3.55$. Think in terms of profits and losses for each of the following examples.

$$50 + 75 = 125 \qquad\qquad 20 + (-30) = -10$$

$$-4.3 + (-6.2) = -10.5 \qquad -27 + 43 = 16$$

$$\frac{7}{8} + \left(-\frac{1}{4}\right) = \frac{5}{8} \qquad\qquad -3\frac{1}{2} + \left(-3\frac{1}{2}\right) = -7$$

Though all problems that involve addition of real numbers could be solved using the profit-loss interpretation, it is sometimes convenient to have a more precise description of the addition process. For this purpose we use the concept of absolute value.

Addition of Real Numbers

Two Positive Numbers The sum of two positive real numbers is the sum of their absolute values.

Two Negative Numbers The sum of two negative real numbers is the opposite of the sum of their absolute values.

One Positive and One Negative Number   The sum of a positive real number and a negative real number can be found by subtracting the smaller absolute value from the larger absolute value and giving the result the sign of the original number that has the larger absolute value. If the two numbers have the same absolute value, then their sum is 0.

Zero and Another Number   The sum of 0 and any real number is the real number itself.

Now consider the following examples in terms of the previous description of addition. These examples include operations with rational numbers in common fraction form. If you need a review on operations with fractions, see Appendix A.

Classroom Example
Find the sum:
(a) $-4.5 + 6$
(b) $4\frac{2}{3} + \left(-1\frac{1}{4}\right)$
(c) $21 + (-57)$
(d) $-36.2 + 36.2$

EXAMPLE 1   Find the sum of the two numbers:

(a) $(-6) + (-8)$ **(b)** $6\frac{3}{4} + \left(-2\frac{1}{2}\right)$ **(c)** $14 + (-21)$ **(d)** $-72.4 + 72.4$

Solution

(a) $(-6) + (-8) = -(|-6| + |-8|) = -(6 + 8) = -14$

(b) $6\frac{3}{4} + \left(-2\frac{1}{2}\right) = \left(\left|6\frac{3}{4}\right| - \left|-2\frac{1}{2}\right|\right) = \left(6\frac{3}{4} - 2\frac{1}{2}\right) = \left(6\frac{3}{4} - 2\frac{2}{4}\right) = 4\frac{1}{4}$

(c) $14 + (-21) = -(|-21| - |14|) = -(21 - 14) = -7$

(d) $-72.4 + 72.4 = 0$

Subtracting Real Numbers

We can describe the subtraction of real numbers in terms of addition.

Subtraction of Real Numbers

If a and b are real numbers, then

$$a - b = a + (-b)$$

It may be helpful for you to read $a - b = a + (-b)$ as "a minus b is equal to a plus the opposite of b." In other words, every subtraction problem can be changed to an equivalent addition problem. Consider the following example.

Classroom Example
Find the difference:
(a) $6 - 10$
(b) $-3 - (-15)$
(c) $11.3 - (-8.7)$
(d) $-\frac{5}{9} - \left(-\frac{2}{3}\right)$

EXAMPLE 2   Find the difference between the two numbers:

(a) $7 - 9$ **(b)** $-5 - (-13)$ **(c)** $6.1 - (-14.2)$ **(d)** $-\frac{7}{8} - \left(-\frac{1}{4}\right)$

Solution

(a) $7 - 9 = 7 + (-9) = -2$

(b) $-5 - (-13) = -5 + 13 = 8$

(c) $6.1 - (-14.2) = 6.1 + 14.2 = 20.3$

(d) $-\frac{7}{8} - \left(-\frac{1}{4}\right) = -\frac{7}{8} + \frac{1}{4} = -\frac{7}{8} + \frac{2}{8} = -\frac{5}{8}$

It should be apparent that addition is a key operation. To simplify numerical expressions that involve addition and subtraction, we can first change all subtractions to additions and then perform the additions.

Classroom Example
Simplify $3 - 19 - 2 + 16 - 4 + 5$.

EXAMPLE 3 Simplify $7 - 9 - 14 + 12 - 6 + 4$.

Solution

$$7 - 9 - 14 + 12 - 6 + 4 = 7 + (-9) + (-14) + 12 + (-6) + 4$$
$$= -6$$

Classroom Example
Simplify $-3\dfrac{2}{3} + \dfrac{7}{12} - \left(-\dfrac{1}{4}\right) + \dfrac{1}{12}$.

EXAMPLE 4 Simplify $-2\dfrac{1}{8} + \dfrac{3}{4} - \left(-\dfrac{3}{8}\right) - \dfrac{1}{2}$.

Solution

$$-2\frac{1}{8} + \frac{3}{4} - \left(-\frac{3}{8}\right) - \frac{1}{2} = -2\frac{1}{8} + \frac{3}{4} + \frac{3}{8} + \left(-\frac{1}{2}\right)$$

$$= -\frac{17}{8} + \frac{6}{8} + \frac{3}{8} + \left(-\frac{4}{8}\right) \qquad \text{Change to equivalent fractions with a common denominator}$$

$$= -\frac{12}{8} = -\frac{3}{2}$$

It is often helpful to convert subtractions to additions *mentally*. In the next two examples, the work shown in the dashed boxes could be done in your head.

Classroom Example
Simplify $6 - 13 - 7 + 9 - 1$.

EXAMPLE 5 Simplify $4 - 9 - 18 + 13 - 10$.

Solution

$$4 - 9 - 18 + 13 - 10 = \boxed{4 + (-9) + (-18) + 13 + (-10)}$$
$$= -20$$

Classroom Example
Simplify $\left(\dfrac{3}{8} - \dfrac{1}{3}\right) - \left(\dfrac{3}{4} - \dfrac{11}{12}\right)$.

EXAMPLE 6 Simplify $\left(\dfrac{2}{3} - \dfrac{1}{5}\right) - \left(\dfrac{1}{2} - \dfrac{7}{10}\right)$.

Solution

$$\left(\frac{2}{3} - \frac{1}{5}\right) - \left(\frac{1}{2} - \frac{7}{10}\right) = \boxed{\left[\frac{2}{3} + \left(-\frac{1}{5}\right)\right] - \left[\frac{1}{2} + \left(-\frac{7}{10}\right)\right]}$$

$$= \left[\frac{10}{15} + \left(-\frac{3}{15}\right)\right] - \left[\frac{5}{10} + \left(-\frac{7}{10}\right)\right] \qquad \begin{array}{l}\text{Within the brackets,} \\ \text{change to equivalent} \\ \text{fractions with a} \\ \text{common denominator}\end{array}$$

$$= \left(\frac{7}{15}\right) - \left(-\frac{2}{10}\right)$$

$$= \boxed{\left(\frac{7}{15}\right) + \left(+\frac{2}{10}\right)}$$

$$= \frac{14}{30} + \left(+\frac{6}{30}\right) \qquad \begin{array}{l}\text{Change to equivalent} \\ \text{fractions with a} \\ \text{common denominator}\end{array}$$

$$= \frac{20}{30} = \frac{2}{3}$$

Multiplying Real Numbers

To determine the product of a positive number and a negative number, we can consider the multiplication of whole numbers as repeated addition. For example, $4 \cdot 2$ means four 2s; thus $4 \cdot 2 = 2 + 2 + 2 + 2 = 8$. Applying this concept to the product of 4 and -2 we get the following,

$$4(-2) = -2 + (-2) + (-2) + (-2) = -8$$

Because the order in which we multiply two numbers does not change the product, we know the following

$$4(-2) = -2(4) = -8$$

Therefore, the product of a positive real number and a negative real number is a negative number.

Finally, let's consider the product of two negative integers. The following pattern using integers helps with the reasoning.

$$4(-2) = -8 \qquad 3(-2) = -6 \qquad 2(-2) = -4$$
$$1(-2) = -2 \qquad 0(-2) = 0 \qquad (-1)(-2) = ?$$

To continue this pattern, the product of -1 and -2 has to be 2. In general, this type of reasoning helps us realize that the product of any two negative real numbers is a positive real number. Using the concept of absolute value, we can describe the *multiplication of real numbers* as follows:

Multiplication of Real Numbers

1. The product of two positive or two negative real numbers is the product of their absolute values.

2. The product of a positive real number and a negative real number (either order) is the opposite of the product of their absolute values.

3. The product of zero and any real number is zero.

The following example illustrates this description of multiplication. Again, the steps shown in the dashed boxes can be performed mentally.

Classroom Example
Find the product for each of the following:
(a) $(-3)(-8)$
(b) $(7)(-11)$
(c) $\left(-\dfrac{5}{6}\right)\left(\dfrac{2}{5}\right)$

EXAMPLE 7   Find the product for each of the following:

(a) $(-6)(-7)$ (b) $(8)(-9)$ (c) $\left(-\dfrac{3}{4}\right)\left(\dfrac{1}{3}\right)$

Solution

(a) $(-6)(-7) = |-6| \cdot |-7| = 6 \cdot 7 = 42$

(b) $(8)(-9) = -(|8| \cdot |-9|) = -(8 \cdot 9) = -72$

(c) $\left(-\dfrac{3}{4}\right)\left(\dfrac{1}{3}\right) = -\left(\left|-\dfrac{3}{4}\right| \cdot \left|\dfrac{1}{3}\right|\right) = -\left(\dfrac{3}{4} \cdot \dfrac{1}{3}\right) = -\dfrac{1}{4}$

Example 7 illustrates a step-by-step process for multiplying real numbers. In practice, however, the key is to remember that the product of two positive or two negative numbers is positive, and the product of a positive number and a negative number (either order) is negative.

Dividing Real Numbers

The relationship between multiplication and division provides the basis for dividing real numbers. For example, we know that $8 \div 2 = 4$ because $2 \cdot 4 = 8$. In other words, the quotient of two numbers can be found by looking at a related multiplication problem. In the following examples, we used this same reasoning to determine some quotients that involve integers.

$$\frac{6}{-2} = -3 \quad \text{because } (-2)(-3) = 6$$

$$\frac{-12}{3} = -4 \quad \text{because } (3)(-4) = -12$$

$$\frac{-18}{-2} = 9 \quad \text{because } (-2)(9) = -18$$

$$\frac{0}{-5} = 0 \quad \text{because } (-5)(0) = 0$$

$$\frac{-8}{0} \text{ is undefined} \qquad \text{Remember that division by zero is undefined!}$$

A precise description for *division of real numbers* follows.

Division of Real Numbers

1. The quotient of two positive or two negative real numbers is the quotient of their absolute values.
2. The quotient of a positive real number and a negative real number or of a negative real number and a positive real number is the opposite of the quotient of their absolute values.
3. The quotient of zero and any nonzero real number is zero.
4. The quotient of any nonzero real number and zero is undefined.

The following example illustrates this description of division. Again, for practical purposes, the key is to remember whether the quotient is positive or negative.

Classroom Example
Find the quotient for each of the following:

(a) $\dfrac{-18}{-9}$

(b) $\dfrac{36}{-4}$

(c) $\dfrac{-5.2}{4}$

(d) $\dfrac{0}{\frac{5}{9}}$

EXAMPLE 8   Find the quotient for each of the following:

(a) $\dfrac{-16}{-4}$ (b) $\dfrac{28}{-7}$ (c) $\dfrac{-3.6}{4}$ (d) $\dfrac{0}{\frac{7}{8}}$

Solution

(a) $\dfrac{-16}{-4} = \dfrac{|-16|}{|-4|} = \dfrac{16}{4} = 4$

(b) $\dfrac{28}{-7} = -\left(\dfrac{|28|}{|-7|}\right) = -\left(\dfrac{28}{7}\right) = -4$

(c) $\dfrac{-3.6}{4} = -\left(\dfrac{|-3.6|}{|4|}\right) = -\left(\dfrac{3.6}{4}\right) = -0.9$

(d) $\dfrac{0}{\frac{7}{8}} = 0$

Now let's simplify some numerical expressions that involve the four basic operations with real numbers. Remember that multiplications and divisions are done first, from left to right, before additions and subtractions are performed.

Classroom Example
Simplify:

$$-4\frac{1}{2} - 3\left(\frac{1}{6}\right) - (-2)\left(-\frac{3}{4}\right)$$

EXAMPLE 9   Simplify $-2\frac{1}{3} + 4\left(-\frac{2}{3}\right) - (-5)\left(-\frac{1}{3}\right)$.

Solution

$$-2\frac{1}{3} + 4\left(-\frac{2}{3}\right) - (-5)\left(-\frac{1}{3}\right) = -2\frac{1}{3} + \left(-\frac{8}{3}\right) + \left(-\frac{5}{3}\right)$$

$$= -\frac{7}{3} + \left(-\frac{8}{3}\right) + \left(-\frac{5}{3}\right) \qquad \text{Change to an improper fraction}$$

$$= -\frac{20}{3}$$

Classroom Example
Simplify $21 \div (-3) + 7(-2)$.

EXAMPLE 10   Simplify $-24 \div 4 + 8(-5) - (-5)(3)$.

Solution

$$-24 \div 4 + 8(-5) - (-5)(3) = -6 + (-40) - (-15)$$

$$= -6 + (-40) + 15$$

$$= -31$$

Classroom Example
Simplify $-3.8 - 4[-2.7(1 - (-4))]$.

EXAMPLE 11   Simplify $-7.3 - 2[-4.6(6 - 7)]$.

Solution

$$-7.3 - 2[-4.6(6 - 7)] = -7.3 - 2[-4.6(-1)] = -7.3 - 2[4.6]$$

$$= -7.3 - 9.2$$

$$= -7.3 + (-9.2)$$

$$= -16.5$$

Classroom Example
Simplify:

$$[5(-2) - 6(4)][4(-2) + 7(1)]$$

EXAMPLE 12   Simplify $[3(-7) - 2(9)][5(-7) + 3(9)]$.

Solution

$$[3(-7) - 2(9)][5(-7) + 3(9)] = [-21 - 18][-35 + 27]$$

$$= [-39][-8]$$

$$= 312$$

EXAMPLE 13

On a flight from Orlando to Washington, D.C., the airline sold 52 economy seats, 25 business-class seats, 12 first-class seats, and there were 20 empty seats. The airline has determined that it makes a profit of $550 per first-class seat and $100 profit per business-class seat. However, the airline incurs a loss of $20 per economy seat and a loss of $75 per empty seat. Determine the profit (or loss) for the flight.

Classroom Example
On a flight from Chicago to San Francisco, an airline sold 65 economy seats, 32 business-class seats, 15 first-class seats, and there were 8 empty seats. The airline has determined that it makes a profit of $475 per first-class seat and $120 profit per business-class seat. However, the airline incurs a loss of $25 per economy seat and a loss of $80 per empty seat. Determine the profit (or loss) for the flight.

Solution

Let the profit be represented by positive numbers and the loss be represented by negative numbers. Then the following expression would represent the profit or loss for this flight.

$$52(-20) + 25(100) + 12(550) + 20(-75)$$

Simplify this expression as follows:

$$52(-20) + 25(100) + 12(550) + 20(-75)$$
$$= -1040 + 2500 + 6600 - 1500 = 6560$$

Therefore, the flight had a profit of $6560.

Concept Quiz 1.2

For Problems 1–10, answer true or false.

1. The product of two negative real numbers is a positive real number.
2. The quotient of two negative integers is a negative integer.
3. The quotient of any nonzero real number and zero is zero.
4. If x represents any real number, then $-x$ represents a negative real number.
5. The product of three negative real numbers is a negative real number.
6. The statement $|6 - 4| = |4 - 6|$ is a true statement.
7. The absolute value of every real number is a positive real number.
8. The absolute value of zero does not exist.
9. The sum of a positive number plus a negative number is always a negative number.
10. Every subtraction problem can be changed to an equivalent addition problem.

Problem Set 1.2

1. Graph the following points and their opposites on the real number line: 1, −2, and 4.
2. Graph the following points and their opposites on the real number line: −3, −1, and 5.
3. Find the following absolute values: **(a)** $|-7|$ **(b)** $|0|$ **(c)** $|15|$
4. Find the following absolute values: **(a)** $|2|$ **(b)** $|-1|$ **(c)** $|-10|$

For Problems 5–54, perform the following operations with real numbers. (Objectives 3–6)

5. $8 + (-15)$
6. $9 + (-18)$
7. $(-12) + (-7)$
8. $(-7) + (-14)$
9. $-8 - 14$
10. $-17 - 9$
11. $9 - 16$
12. $8 - 22$
13. $(-9)(-12)$
14. $(-6)(-13)$
15. $(5)(-14)$
16. $(-17)(4)$
17. $(-56) \div (-4)$
18. $(-81) \div (-3)$
19. $\dfrac{-112}{16}$
20. $\dfrac{-75}{5}$
21. $-2\dfrac{3}{8} + 5\dfrac{7}{8}$
22. $-1\dfrac{1}{5} + 3\dfrac{4}{5}$
23. $4\dfrac{1}{3} - \left(-1\dfrac{1}{6}\right)$
24. $1\dfrac{1}{12} - \left(-5\dfrac{3}{4}\right)$
25. $\left(-\dfrac{1}{3}\right)\left(\dfrac{2}{5}\right)$
26. $(-8)\left(\dfrac{1}{3}\right)$
27. $\dfrac{1}{2} \div \left(-\dfrac{1}{8}\right)$
28. $\dfrac{2}{3} \div \left(-\dfrac{1}{6}\right)$
29. $0 \div (-14)$
30. $(-19) \div 0$
31. $(-21) \div 0$
32. $0 \div (-11)$
33. $-21 - 39$
34. $-23 - 38$
35. $-17.3 + 12.5$
36. $-16.3 + 19.6$
37. $21.42 - 7.29$
38. $2.73 - 8.14$
39. $-21.4 - (-14.9)$
40. $-32.6 - (-9.8)$
41. $(5.4)(-7.2)$
42. $(-8.5)(-3.3)$
43. $\dfrac{-1.2}{-6}$
44. $\dfrac{-6.3}{0.7}$
45. $\left(-\dfrac{1}{3}\right) + \left(-\dfrac{3}{4}\right)$
46. $-\dfrac{5}{6} + \dfrac{3}{8}$
47. $-\dfrac{3}{2} - \left(-\dfrac{3}{4}\right)$
48. $\dfrac{5}{8} - \dfrac{11}{12}$
49. $-\dfrac{2}{3} - \dfrac{7}{9}$
50. $\dfrac{5}{6} - \left(-\dfrac{2}{9}\right)$

51. $\left(-\dfrac{3}{4}\right)\left(\dfrac{4}{5}\right)$ **52.** $\left(\dfrac{1}{2}\right)\left(-\dfrac{4}{5}\right)$

53. $\dfrac{3}{4} \div \left(-\dfrac{1}{2}\right)$ **54.** $\left(-\dfrac{5}{6}\right) \div \left(-\dfrac{7}{8}\right)$

For Problems 55–94, simplify each numerical expression. (Objective 7)

55. $9 - 12 - 8 + 5 - 6$

56. $6 - 9 + 11 - 8 - 7 + 14$

57. $-21 + (-17) - 11 + 15 - (-10)$

58. $-16 - (-14) + 16 + 17 - 19$

59. $7\dfrac{1}{8} - \left(2\dfrac{1}{4} - 3\dfrac{7}{8}\right)$

60. $-4\dfrac{3}{5} - \left(1\dfrac{1}{5} - 2\dfrac{3}{10}\right)$

61. $16 - 18 + 19 - [14 - 22 - (31 - 41)]$

62. $-19 - [15 - 13 - (-12 + 8)]$

63. $[14 - (16 - 18)] - [32 - (8 - 9)]$

64. $[-17 - (14 - 18)] - [21 - (-6 - 5)]$

65. $4\dfrac{1}{12} - \dfrac{1}{2}\left(\dfrac{1}{3}\right)$ **66.** $-\dfrac{4}{5} - \dfrac{1}{2}\left(-\dfrac{3}{5}\right)$

67. $-5 + (-2)(7) - (-3)(8)$

68. $-9 - 4(-2) + (-7)(6)$

69. $\dfrac{2}{5}\left(-\dfrac{3}{4}\right) - \left(-\dfrac{1}{2}\right)\left(\dfrac{3}{5}\right)$

70. $-\dfrac{2}{3}\left(\dfrac{1}{4}\right) + \left(-\dfrac{1}{3}\right)\left(\dfrac{5}{4}\right)$

71. $(-6)(-9) + (-7)(4)$

72. $(-7)(-7) - (-6)(4)$

73. $3(5 - 9) - 3(-6)$

74. $7(8 - 9) + (-6)(4)$

75. $(6 - 11)(4 - 9)$

76. $(7 - 12)(-3 - 2)$

77. $-6(-3 - 9 - 1)$

78. $-8(-3 - 4 - 6)$

79. $56 \div (-8) - (-6) \div (-2)$

80. $-65 \div 5 - (-13)(-2) + (-36) \div 12$

81. $-3[5 - (-2)] - 2(-4 - 9)$

82. $-2(-7 + 13) + 6(-3 - 2)$

83. $\dfrac{-6 + 24}{-3} + \dfrac{-7}{-6 - 1}$

84. $\dfrac{-12 + 20}{-4} + \dfrac{-7 - 11}{-9}$

85. $14.1 - (17.2 - 13.6)$

86. $-9.3 - (10.4 + 12.8)$

87. $3(2.1) - 4(3.2) - 2(-1.6)$

88. $5(-1.6) - 3(2.7) + 5(6.6)$

89. $7(6.2 - 7.1) - 6(-1.4 - 2.9)$

90. $-3(2.2 - 4.5) - 2(1.9 + 4.5)$

91. $\dfrac{2}{3} - \left(\dfrac{3}{4} - \dfrac{5}{6}\right)$

92. $-\dfrac{1}{2} - \left(\dfrac{3}{8} + \dfrac{1}{4}\right)$

93. $3\left(\dfrac{1}{2}\right) + 4\left(\dfrac{2}{3}\right) - 2\left(\dfrac{5}{6}\right)$

94. $2\left(\dfrac{3}{8}\right) - 5\left(\dfrac{1}{2}\right) + 6\left(\dfrac{3}{4}\right)$

95. Use a calculator to check your answers for Problems 55–94.

For Problems 96–104, write a numerical statement to represent the problem. Then simplify the numerical expression to answer the question. (Objective 8)

96. A scuba diver was 32 feet below sea level when he noticed that his partner had his extra knife. He ascended 13 feet to meet his partner, get the knife, and then dove down 50 feet. How far below sea level is the diver?

97. Jeff played 18 holes of golf on Saturday. On each of 6 holes he was 1 under par, on each of 4 holes he was 2 over par, on 1 hole he was 3 over par, on each of 2 holes he shot par, and on each of 5 holes he was 1 over par. How did he finish relative to par?

98. After dieting for 30 days, Ignacio has lost 18 pounds. What number describes his average weight change per day?

99. Michael bet $5 on each of the 9 races at the racetrack. His only winnings were $28.50 on one race. How much did he win (or lose) for the day?

100. Max bought a piece of trim molding that measured $11\dfrac{3}{8}$ feet in length. Because of defects in the wood, he had to trim $1\dfrac{5}{8}$ feet off one end, and he also had to remove $\dfrac{3}{4}$ of a foot off the other end. How long was the piece of molding after he trimmed the ends?

101. Natasha recorded the daily gains or losses for her company stock for a week. On Monday it gained 1.25 dollars; on Tuesday it gained 0.88 dollar; on Wednesday it lost 0.50 dollar; on Thursday it lost 1.13 dollars; on Friday it gained 0.38 dollar. What was the net gain (or loss) for the week?

102. On a summer day in Florida, the afternoon temperature was 96°F. After a thunderstorm, the temperature dropped 8°F. What would be the temperature if the sun came back out and the temperature rose 5°F?

103. In an attempt to lighten a dragster, the racing team exchanged two rear wheels for wheels that each weighed 15.6 pounds less. They also exchanged the crankshaft for one that weighed 4.8 pounds less. They changed the rear axle for one that weighed 23.7 pounds less but had to add an additional roll bar that weighed 10.6 pounds. If they wanted to lighten the dragster by 50 pounds, did they meet their goal?

104. A large corporation has five divisions. Two of the divisions had earnings of $2,300,000 each. The other three divisions had a loss of $1,450,000, a loss of $640,000, and a gain of $1,850,000, respectively. What was the net gain (or loss) of the corporation for the year?

Thoughts Into Words

105. Explain why $\dfrac{0}{8} = 0$, but $\dfrac{8}{0}$ is undefined.

106. The following simplification problem is incorrect. The answer should be -11. Find and correct the error.
$$8 \div (-4)(2) - 3(4) \div 2 + (-1) = (-2)(2) - 12 \div 1$$
$$= -4 - 12$$
$$= -16$$

Answers to the Concept Quiz

1. True **2.** False **3.** False **4.** False **5.** True **6.** True **7.** False **8.** False **9.** False **10.** True

---

1.3 Properties of Real Numbers and the Use of Exponents

OBJECTIVES

1 Review the properties of the real numbers

2 Apply properties to simplify expressions

3 Evaluate the exponential expressions

At the beginning of this section we will list and briefly discuss some of the basic properties of real numbers. Be sure that you understand these properties, for they not only facilitate manipulations with real numbers but also serve as the basis for many algebraic computations.

Closure Property for Addition

If a and b are real numbers, then $a + b$ is a unique real number.

Closure Property for Multiplication

If a and b are real numbers, then ab is a unique real number.

We say that the set of real numbers is *closed* with respect to addition and also with respect to multiplication. That is, the sum of two real numbers is a unique real number, and the product of two real numbers is a unique real number. We use the word "unique" to indicate "exactly one."

Commutative Property of Addition

If a and b are real numbers, then

$$a + b = b + a$$

Commutative Property of Multiplication

If a and b are real numbers, then

$$ab = ba$$

We say that addition and multiplication are commutative operations. This means that the order in which we add or multiply two numbers does not affect the result. For example, $6 + (-8) = (-8) + 6$ and $(-4)(-3) = (-3)(-4)$. It is important to realize that subtraction and division are *not* commutative operations; order *does* make a difference. For example, $3 - 4 = -1$ but $4 - 3 = 1$. Likewise, $2 \div 1 = 2$ but $1 \div 2 = \dfrac{1}{2}$.

Associative Property of Addition

If a, b, and c are real numbers, then

$$(a + b) + c = a + (b + c)$$

Associative Property of Multiplication

If a, b, and c are real numbers, then

$$(ab)c = a(bc)$$

Addition and multiplication are **binary operations**. That is, we add (or multiply) two numbers at a time. The associative properties apply if more than two numbers are to be added or multiplied; they are grouping properties. For example, $(-8 + 9) + 6 = -8 + (9 + 6)$; changing the grouping of the numbers does not affect the final sum. This is also true for multiplication, which is illustrated by $[(-4)(-3)](2) = (-4)[(-3)(2)]$. Subtraction and division are *not* associative operations. For example, $(8 - 6) - 10 = -8$, but $8 - (6 - 10) = 12$. An example showing that division is not associative is $(8 \div 4) \div 2 = 1$, but $8 \div (4 \div 2) = 4$.

Identity Property of Addition

If a is any real number, then

$$a + 0 = 0 + a = a$$

Zero is called the identity element for addition. This means that the sum of any real number and zero is the same real number. For example, $-87 + 0 = 0 + (-87) = -87$.

Identity Property of Multiplication

If a is any real number, then

$$a(1) = 1(a) = a$$

We call 1 the identity element for multiplication. The product of any real number and 1 is the same real number. For example, $(-119)(1) = (1)(-119) = -119$.

Additive Inverse Property

For every real number a, there exists a unique real number $-a$ such that

$$a + (-a) = -a + a = 0$$

The real number $-a$ is called the *additive inverse of a* or the *opposite of a*. For example, 16 and -16 are additive inverses, and their sum is 0. The additive inverse of 0 is 0.

Multiplication Property of Zero

If a is any real number, then

$$(a)(0) = (0)(a) = 0$$

The product of any real number and zero is zero. For example, $(-17)(0) = 0(-17) = 0$.

Multiplication Property of Negative One

If a is any real number, then

$$(a)(-1) = (-1)(a) = -a$$

The product of any real number and -1 is the opposite of the real number. For example, $(-1)(52) = (52)(-1) = -52$.

Multiplicative Inverse Property

For every nonzero real number a, there exists a unique real number $\dfrac{1}{a}$ such that

$$a\left(\frac{1}{a}\right) = \frac{1}{a}(a) = 1$$

The number $\dfrac{1}{a}$ is called the *multiplicative inverse of a* or the *reciprocal of a*. For example, the reciprocal of 2 is $\dfrac{1}{2}$ and $2\left(\dfrac{1}{2}\right) = \dfrac{1}{2}(2) = 1$. Likewise, the reciprocal of $\dfrac{1}{2}$ is $\dfrac{1}{\frac{1}{2}} = 2$. Therefore, 2 and $\dfrac{1}{2}$ are said to be reciprocals (or multiplicative inverses) of each other. Because division by zero is undefined, zero does not have a reciprocal.

> ## Distributive Property
>
> If a, b, and c are real numbers, then
>
> $$a(b + c) = ab + ac$$

The distributive property ties together the operations of addition and multiplication. We say that *multiplication distributes over addition*. For example, $7(3 + 8) = 7(3) + 7(8)$. Because $b - c = b + (-c)$, it follows that *multiplication also distributes over subtraction*. This can be expressed symbolically as $a(b - c) = ab - ac$. For example, $6(8 - 10) = 6(8) - 6(10)$.

The following examples illustrate the use of the properties of real numbers to facilitate certain types of manipulations.

Classroom Example
Simplify $[57 + (-14)] + 14$.

EXAMPLE 1   Simplify $[74 + (-36)] + 36$.

Solution

In such a problem, it is much more advantageous to group -36 and 36.

$$[74 + (-36)] + 36 = 74 + [(-36) + 36]$$
$$= 74 + 0 = 74$$

By using the associative property of addition

Classroom Example
Simplify $5[(-20)(18)]$.

EXAMPLE 2   Simplify $[(-19)(25)](-4)$.

Solution

It is much easier to group 25 and -4. Thus

$$[(-19)(25)](-4) = (-19)[(25)(-4)]$$
$$= (-19)(-100)$$
$$= 1900$$

By using the associative property of multiplication

Classroom Example
Simplify $(-21) + 13 + 26 + (-14) + 30 + (-42) + (-8)$.

EXAMPLE 3   Simplify $17 + (-14) + (-18) + 13 + (-21) + 15 + (-33)$.

Solution

We could add in the order in which the numbers appear. However, because addition is commutative and associative, we could change the order and group in any convenient way. For example, we could add all of the positive integers and add all of the negative integers, and then find the sum of these two results. It might be convenient to use the vertical format as follows:

$$
\begin{array}{rrr}
 & -14 & \\
17 & -18 & \\
13 & -21 & -86 \\
15 & -33 & 45 \\
\hline
45 & -86 & -41
\end{array}
$$

Classroom Example
Simplify $-12(-3 + 20)$.

EXAMPLE 4   Simplify $-25(-2 + 100)$.

Solution

For this problem, it might be easiest to apply the distributive property first and then simplify.

$$-25(-2 + 100) = (-25)(-2) + (-25)(100)$$
$$= 50 + (-2500)$$
$$= -2450$$ ∎

Classroom Example
Simplify $(-21)(-32 + 28)$.

EXAMPLE 5   Simplify $(-87)(-26 + 25)$.

Solution

For this problem, it would be better not to apply the distributive property but instead to add the numbers inside the parentheses first and then find the indicated product.

$$(-87)(-26 + 25) = (-87)(-1)$$
$$= 87$$ ∎

Classroom Example
Simplify $4.9(20) + 4.9(-30)$.

EXAMPLE 6   Simplify $3.7(104) + 3.7(-4)$.

Solution

Remember that the distributive property allows us to change from the form $a(b + c)$ to $ab + ac$ or from the form $ab + ac$ to $a(b + c)$. In this problem, we want to use the latter conversion. Thus

$$3.7(104) + 3.7(-4) = 3.7[104 + (-4)]$$
$$= 3.7(100)$$
$$= 370$$ ∎

Examples 4, 5, and 6 illustrate an important issue. Sometimes the form $a(b + c)$ is more convenient, but at other times the form $ab + ac$ is better. In these cases, as well as in the cases of other properties, you should *think first* and decide whether or not the properties can be used to make the manipulations easier.

Exponents

Exponents are used to indicate repeated multiplication. For example, we can write $4 \cdot 4 \cdot 4$ as 4^3, where the "raised 3" indicates that 4 is to be used as a factor 3 times. The following general definition is helpful.

> **Definition 1.3**
>
> If n is a positive integer and b is any real number, then
>
> $$b^n = \underbrace{bbb \cdots b}_{n \text{ factors of } b}$$

We refer to the b as the **base** and to n as the **exponent**. The expression b^n can be read "b to the nth power." We commonly associate the terms *squared* and *cubed* with exponents of 2 and 3, respectively. For example, b^2 is read "b squared" and b^3 as "b cubed." An exponent of 1 is usually not written, so b^1 is written as b. The following examples illustrate Definition 1.3.

$$2^3 = 2 \cdot 2 \cdot 2 = 8 \qquad \left(\frac{1}{2}\right)^5 = \frac{1}{2} \cdot \frac{1}{2} \cdot \frac{1}{2} \cdot \frac{1}{2} \cdot \frac{1}{2} = \frac{1}{32}$$

$$3^4 = 3 \cdot 3 \cdot 3 \cdot 3 = 81 \qquad (0.7)^2 = (0.7)(0.7) = 0.49$$

$$-5^2 = -(5 \cdot 5) = -25 \qquad (-5)^2 = (-5)(-5) = 25$$

Please take special note of the last two examples. Note that $(-5)^2$ means that -5 is the base and is to be used as a factor twice. However, -5^2 means that 5 is the base and that after it is squared, we take the opposite of that result.

Simplifying numerical expressions that contain exponents creates no trouble if we keep in mind that exponents are used to indicate repeated multiplication. Let's consider some examples.

EXAMPLE 7   Simplify $3(-4)^2 + 5(-3)^2$.

Solution

$$\begin{aligned}
3(-4)^2 + 5(-3)^2 &= 3(16) + 5(9) \qquad \text{Find the powers} \\
&= 48 + 45 \\
&= 93
\end{aligned}$$

EXAMPLE 8   Simplify $(2 + 3)^2$.

Solution

$$\begin{aligned}
(2 + 3)^2 &= (5)^2 \qquad \text{Add inside the parentheses before applying the exponent} \\
&= 25 \qquad\quad \text{Square the 5}
\end{aligned}$$

EXAMPLE 9   Simplify $[3(-1) - 2(1)]^3$.

Solution

$$\begin{aligned}
[3(-1) - 2(1)]^3 &= [-3 - 2]^3 \\
&= [-5]^3 \\
&= -125
\end{aligned}$$

EXAMPLE 10   Simplify $4\left(\frac{1}{2}\right)^3 - 3\left(\frac{1}{2}\right)^2 + 6\left(\frac{1}{2}\right) + 2$.

Solution

$$\begin{aligned}
4\left(\frac{1}{2}\right)^3 - 3\left(\frac{1}{2}\right)^2 + 6\left(\frac{1}{2}\right) + 2 &= 4\left(\frac{1}{8}\right) - 3\left(\frac{1}{4}\right) + 6\left(\frac{1}{2}\right) + 2 \\
&= \frac{1}{2} - \frac{3}{4} + 3 + 2 \\
&= \frac{19}{4}
\end{aligned}$$

Concept Quiz 1.3

For Problems 1–10, answer true or false.

1. Addition is a commutative operation.
2. Subtraction is a commutative operation.
3. Zero is the identity element for addition.
4. The multiplicative inverse of 0 is 0.
5. The numerical expression $(-25)(-16)(-4)$ simplifies to -1600.
6. The numerical expression $82(8) + 82(2)$ simplifies to 820.
7. Exponents are used to indicate repeated additions.
8. The numerical expression $65(7^2) + 35(7^2)$ simplifies to 4900.
9. In the expression $(-4)^3$, the base is 4.
10. In the expression -4^3, the base is 4.

Problem Set 1.3

For Problems 1–14, state the property that justifies each of the statements. For example, $3 + (-4) = (-4) + 3$ because of the commutative property of addition. (Objective 1)

1. $[6 + (-2)] + 4 = 6 + [(-2) + 4]$
2. $x(3) = 3(x)$
3. $42 + (-17) = -17 + 42$
4. $1(x) = x$
5. $-114 + 114 = 0$
6. $(-1)(48) = -48$
7. $-1(x + y) = -(x + y)$
8. $-3(2 + 4) = -3(2) + (-3)(4)$
9. $12yx = 12xy$
10. $[(-7)(4)](-25) = (-7)[4(-25)]$
11. $7(4) + 9(4) = (7 + 9)4$
12. $(x + 3) + (-3) = x + [3 + (-3)]$
13. $[(-14)(8)](25) = (-14)[8(25)]$
14. $\left(\dfrac{3}{4}\right)\left(\dfrac{4}{3}\right) = 1$

For Problems 15–26, simplify each numerical expression. Be sure to take advantage of the properties whenever they can be used to make the computations easier. (Objective 2)

15. $36 + (-14) + (-12) + 21 + (-9) - 4$
16. $-37 + 42 + 18 + 37 + (-42) - 6$
17. $[83 + (-99)] + 18$
18. $[63 + (-87)] + (-64)$
19. $(25)(-13)(4)$
20. $(14)(25)(-13)(4)$
21. $17(97) + 17(3)$
22. $-86[49 + (-48)]$
23. $14 - 12 - 21 - 14 + 17 - 18 + 19 - 32$
24. $16 - 14 - 13 - 18 + 19 + 14 - 17 + 21$
25. $(-50)(15)(-2) - (-4)(17)(25)$
26. $(2)(17)(-5) - (4)(13)(-25)$

For Problems 27–54, simplify each of the numerical expressions. (Objective 2)

27. $2^3 - 3^3$
28. $3^2 - 2^4$
29. $-5^2 - 4^2$
30. $-7^2 + 5^2$
31. $(-2)^3 - 3^2$
32. $(-3)^3 + 3^2$
33. $3(-1)^3 - 4(3)^2$
34. $4(-2)^3 - 3(-1)^4$
35. $7(2)^3 + 4(-2)^3$
36. $-4(-1)^2 - 3(2)^3$
37. $-3(-2)^3 + 4(-1)^5$
38. $5(-1)^3 - (-3)^3$
39. $(-3)^2 - 3(-2)(5) + 4^2$
40. $(-2)^2 - 3(-2)(6) - (-5)^2$
41. $2^3 + 3(-1)^3(-2)^2 - 5(-1)(2)^2$
42. $-2(3)^2 - 2(-2)^3 - 6(-1)^5$
43. $(3 + 4)^2$
44. $(4 - 9)^2$
45. $[3(-2)^2 - 2(-3)^2]^3$
46. $[-3(-1)^3 - 4(-2)^2]^2$
47. $2(-1)^3 - 3(-1)^2 + 4(-1) - 5$
48. $(-2)^3 + 2(-2)^2 - 3(-2) - 1$

49. $2^4 - 2(2)^3 - 3(2)^2 + 7(2) - 10$

50. $3(-3)^3 + 4(-3)^2 - 5(-3) + 7$

51. $3\left(\dfrac{1}{2}\right)^4 - 2\left(\dfrac{1}{2}\right)^3 + 5\left(\dfrac{1}{2}\right)^2 - 4\left(\dfrac{1}{2}\right) + 1$

52. $4(0.1)^2 - 6(0.1) + 0.7$

53. $-\left(\dfrac{2}{3}\right)^2 + 5\left(\dfrac{2}{3}\right) - 4$

54. $4\left(\dfrac{1}{3}\right)^3 + 3\left(\dfrac{1}{3}\right)^2 + 2\left(\dfrac{1}{3}\right) + 6$

55. Use your calculator to check your answers for Problems 27–52.

For Problems 56–64, use your calculator to evaluate each numerical expression. (Objective 3)

56. 2^{10}　　　　　**57.** 3^7

58. $(-2)^8$　　　　**59.** $(-2)^{11}$

60. -4^9　　　　　**61.** -5^6

62. $(3.14)^3$　　　**63.** $(1.41)^4$

64. $(1.73)^5$

Thoughts Into Words

65. State, in your own words, the multiplication property of negative one.

66. Explain how the associative and commutative properties can help simplify $[(25)(97)](-4)$.

67. Your friend keeps getting an answer of 64 when simplifying -2^6. What mistake is he making, and how would you help him?

68. Write a sentence explaining, in your own words, how to evaluate the expression $(-8)^2$. Also write a sentence explaining how to evaluate -8^2.

69. For what natural numbers n does $(-1)^n = -1$? For what natural numbers n does $(-1)^n = 1$? Explain your answers.

70. Is the set $\{0, 1\}$ closed with respect to addition? Is the set $\{0, 1\}$ closed with respect to multiplication? Explain your answers.

Answers to the Concept Quiz
1. True　　**2.** False　　**3.** True　　**4.** False　　**5.** True　　**6.** True　　**7.** False　　**8.** True　　**9.** False　　**10.** True

---

1.4　Algebraic Expressions

OBJECTIVES
1. Simplify algebraic expressions
2. Evaluate algebraic expressions
3. Translate from English to algebra

Algebraic expressions such as

$$2x, \qquad 8xy, \qquad 3xy^2, \qquad -4a^2b^3c, \qquad \text{and} \qquad z$$

are called *terms*. A **term** is an indicated product that may have any number of factors. The variables involved in a term are called **literal factors**, and the numerical factor is called the **numerical coefficient**. Thus in $8xy$, the x and y are literal factors, and 8 is the numerical coefficient. The numerical coefficient of the term $-4a^2bc$ is -4. Because $1(z) = z$, the numerical coefficient of the term z is understood to be 1. Terms that have the same literal factors are called **similar terms** or **like terms**. Some examples of similar terms are

$$3x \quad \text{and} \quad 14x \qquad\qquad 5x^2 \quad \text{and} \quad 18x^2$$
$$7xy \quad \text{and} \quad -9xy \qquad\qquad 9x^2y \quad \text{and} \quad -14x^2y$$
$$2x^3y^2, \quad 3x^3y^2, \quad \text{and} \quad -7x^3y^2$$

By the symmetric property of equality, we can write the distributive property as

$$ab + ac = a(b + c)$$

Then the commutative property of multiplication can be applied to change the form to

$$ba + ca = (b + c)a$$

This latter form provides the basis for simplifying algebraic expressions by *combining similar terms*. Consider the following examples.

$$3x + 5x = (3 + 5)x = 8x \qquad\qquad -6xy + 4xy = (-6 + 4)xy = -2xy$$
$$5x^2 + 7x^2 + 9x^2 = (5 + 7 + 9)x^2 = 21x^2 \quad 4x - x = 4x - 1x = (4 - 1)x = 3x$$

More complicated expressions might require that we first rearrange the terms by applying the commutative property for addition.

$$7x + 2y + 9x + 6y = 7x + 9x + 2y + 6y$$
$$= (7 + 9)x + (2 + 6)y \qquad \text{Distributive property}$$
$$= 16x + 8y$$

$$6a - 5 - 11a + 9 = 6a + (-5) + (-11a) + 9$$
$$= 6a + (-11a) + (-5) + 9 \quad \text{Commutative property}$$
$$= [6 + (-11)]a + 4 \qquad \text{Distributive property}$$
$$= -5a + 4$$

As soon as you thoroughly understand the various simplifying steps, you may want to do the steps mentally. Then you could go directly from the given expression to the simplified form, as follows:

$$14x + 13y - 9x + 2y = 5x + 15y$$
$$3x^2y - 2y + 5x^2y + 8y = 8x^2y + 6y$$
$$-4x^2 + 5y^2 - x^2 - 7y^2 = -5x^2 - 2y^2$$

Applying the distributive property to remove parentheses, and then to combine similar terms, sometimes simplifies an algebraic expression (as Example 1 illustrates).

EXAMPLE 1　　Simplify the following:

(a) $4(x + 2) + 3(x + 6)$　　**(b)** $-5(y + 3) - 2(y - 8)$　　**(c)** $5(x - y) - (x + y)$

Solution

(a) $4(x + 2) + 3(x + 6) = 4(x) + 4(2) + 3(x) + 3(6)$
$$= 4x + 8 + 3x + 18$$
$$= 4x + 3x + 8 + 18$$
$$= (4 + 3)x + 26$$
$$= 7x + 26$$

(b) $-5(y + 3) - 2(y - 8) = -5(y) - 5(3) - 2(y) - 2(-8)$
$$= -5y - 15 - 2y + 16$$
$$= -5y - 2y - 15 + 16$$
$$= -7y + 1$$

(c) $5(x - y) - (x + y) = 5(x - y) - 1(x + y)$　　　Remember, $-a = -1(a)$
$$= 5(x) - 5(y) - 1(x) - 1(y)$$
$$= 5x - 5y - 1x - 1y$$
$$= 4x - 6y$$

When we are multiplying two terms such as 3 and $2x$, the associative property for multiplication provides the basis for simplifying the product.

$$3(2x) = (3 \cdot 2)x = 6x$$

This idea is put to use in Example 2.

Classroom Example
Simplify $2(6m - 7n) - 5(3m - 4n)$.

EXAMPLE 2   Simplify $3(2x + 5y) + 4(3x + 2y)$.

Solution

$$
\begin{aligned}
3(2x + 5y) + 4(3x + 2y) &= 3(2x) + 3(5y) + 4(3x) + 4(2y) \\
&= 6x + 15y + 12x + 8y \\
&= 6x + 12x + 15y + 8y \\
&= 18x + 23y
\end{aligned}
$$

After you are sure of each step, a more simplified format may be used, as the following examples illustrate.

$$5(a + 4) - 7(a + 3) = 5a + 20 - 7a - 21 \qquad \text{Be careful with this sign}$$
$$= -2a - 1$$
$$3(x^2 + 2) + 4(x^2 - 6) = 3x^2 + 6 + 4x^2 - 24$$
$$= 7x^2 - 18$$
$$2(3x - 4y) - 5(2x - 6y) = 6x - 8y - 10x + 30y$$
$$= -4x + 22y$$

Evaluating Algebraic Expressions

An algebraic expression takes on a numerical value whenever each variable in the expression is replaced by a real number. For example, if x is replaced by 5 and y by 9, the algebraic expression $x + y$ becomes the numerical expression $5 + 9$, which simplifies to 14. We say that $x + y$ has a value of 14 when x equals 5 and y equals 9. If $x = -3$ and $y = 7$, then $x + y$ has a value of $-3 + 7 = 4$. The following examples illustrate the process of finding a value of an algebraic expression; we commonly refer to the process as **evaluating algebraic expressions**.

Classroom Example
Find the value of $5a - 9b$ when $a = 4$ and $b = -2$.

EXAMPLE 3   Find the value of $3x - 4y$ when $x = 2$ and $y = -3$.

Solution

$$
\begin{aligned}
3x - 4y &= 3(2) - 4(-3) \quad \text{when } x = 2 \text{ and } y = -3 \\
&= 6 + 12 \\
&= 18
\end{aligned}
$$

Classroom Example
Evaluate $s^2 - 4st + t^2$ for $s = -6$ and $t = 2$.

EXAMPLE 4   Evaluate $x^2 - 2xy + y^2$ for $x = -2$ and $y = -5$.

Solution

$$
\begin{aligned}
x^2 - 2xy + y^2 &= (-2)^2 - 2(-2)(-5) + (-5)^2 \quad \text{when } x = -2 \text{ and } y = -5 \\
&= 4 - 20 + 25 \\
&= 9
\end{aligned}
$$

Classroom Example
Evaluate $(x - y)^3$ for $x = -5$ and $y = -7$.

EXAMPLE 5   Evaluate $(a + b)^2$ for $a = 6$ and $b = -2$.

Solution

$$(a + b)^2 = [6 + (-2)]^2 \quad \text{when } a = 6 \text{ and } b = -2$$
$$= (4)^2$$
$$= 16$$

Classroom Example
Evaluate $(5m + 3n)(2m - 7n)$ for $m = -2$ and $n = 3$.

EXAMPLE 6   Evaluate $(3x + 2y)(2x - y)$ for $x = 4$ and $y = -1$.

Solution

$$(3x + 2y)(2x - y) = [3(4) + 2(-1)][2(4) - (-1)] \quad \text{when } x = 4 \text{ and } y = -1$$
$$= (12 - 2)(8 + 1)$$
$$= (10)(9)$$
$$= 90$$

Classroom Example
Evaluate $-3x + 4y + 8x - 7y$
for $x = \dfrac{3}{5}$ and $y = -\dfrac{1}{9}$.

EXAMPLE 7   Evaluate $7x - 2y + 4x - 3y$ for $x = -\dfrac{1}{2}$ and $y = \dfrac{2}{3}$.

Solution

Let's first simplify the given expression.

$$7x - 2y + 4x - 3y = 11x - 5y$$

Now we can substitute $-\dfrac{1}{2}$ for x and $\dfrac{2}{3}$ for y.

$$11x - 5y = 11\left(-\frac{1}{2}\right) - 5\left(\frac{2}{3}\right)$$
$$= -\frac{11}{2} - \frac{10}{3}$$
$$= -\frac{33}{6} - \frac{20}{6} \quad \text{Change to equivalent fractions with a common denominator}$$
$$= -\frac{53}{6}$$

Classroom Example
Evaluate $-2(8x - 7) + 6(3x + 5)$
for $x = -9.1$.

EXAMPLE 8   Evaluate $2(3x + 1) - 3(4x - 3)$ for $x = -6.2$.

Solution

Let's first simplify the given expression.

$$2(3x + 1) - 3(4x - 3) = 6x + 2 - 12x + 9$$
$$= -6x + 11$$

Now we can substitute -6.2 for x.

$$-6x + 11 = -6(-6.2) + 11$$
$$= 37.2 + 11$$
$$= 48.2$$

Classroom Example
Evaluate $5(x^3 - 1) - 8(x^3 + 2) - (x^3 + 3)$ for $x = -3$.

EXAMPLE 9 Evaluate $2(a^2 + 1) - 3(a^2 + 5) + 4(a^2 - 1)$ for $a = 10$.

Solution

Let's first simplify the given expression.

$$2(a^2 + 1) - 3(a^2 + 5) + 4(a^2 - 1) = 2a^2 + 2 - 3a^2 - 15 + 4a^2 - 4$$
$$= 3a^2 - 17$$

Substituting $a = 10$, we obtain
$$3a^2 - 17 = 3(10)^2 - 17$$
$$= 3(100) - 17$$
$$= 300 - 17$$
$$= 283$$

Translating from English to Algebra

To use the tools of algebra to solve problems, we must be able to translate from English to algebra. This translation process requires that we recognize key phrases in the English language that translate into algebraic expressions (which involve the operations of addition, subtraction, multiplication, and division). Some of these key phrases and their algebraic counterparts are listed in the following table. The variable n represents the number being referred to in each phrase. When translating, remember that the commutative property holds only for the operations of addition and multiplication. Therefore, order will be crucial to algebraic expressions that involve subtraction and division.

English phrase	Algebraic expression
Addition	
The sum of a number and 4	$n + 4$
7 more than a number	$n + 7$
A number plus 10	$n + 10$
A number increased by 6	$n + 6$
8 added to a number	$n + 8$
Subtraction	
14 minus a number	$14 - n$
12 less than a number	$n - 12$
A number decreased by 10	$n - 10$
The difference between a number and 2	$n - 2$
5 subtracted from a number	$n - 5$
Multiplication	
14 times a number	$14n$
The product of 4 and a number	$4n$
$\frac{3}{4}$ of a number	$\frac{3}{4}n$
Twice a number	$2n$
Multiply a number by 12	$12n$

(continued)

English phrase	Algebraic expression
Division	
The quotient of 6 and a number	$\dfrac{6}{n}$
The quotient of a number and 6	$\dfrac{n}{6}$
A number divided by 9	$\dfrac{n}{9}$
The ratio of a number and 4	$\dfrac{n}{4}$
Combination of operations	
4 more than three times a number	$3n + 4$
5 less than twice a number	$2n - 5$
3 times the sum of a number and 2	$3(n + 2)$
2 more than the quotient of a number and 12	$\dfrac{n}{12} + 2$
7 times the difference of 6 and a number	$7(6 - n)$

An English statement may not always contain a key word such as *sum, difference, product*, or *quotient*. Instead, the statement may describe a physical situation, and from this description we must deduce the operations involved. Some suggestions for handling such situations are given in the following examples.

Classroom Example
Caitlin can read 550 words per minute. How many words will she read in *n* minutes?

EXAMPLE 10

Sonya can keyboard 65 words per minute. How many words will she keyboard in *m* minutes?

Solution

The total number of words keyboarded equals the product of the rate per minute and the number of minutes. Therefore, Sonya should be able to keyboard $65m$ words in *m* minutes. ∎

Classroom Example
Greg has *n* nickels and *q* quarters. Express this amount of money in cents.

EXAMPLE 11

Russ has *n* nickels and *d* dimes. Express this amount of money in cents.

Solution

Each nickel is worth 5 cents and each dime is worth 10 cents. We represent the amount in cents by $5n + 10d$. ∎

Classroom Example
The cost of a 20-pound bag of unpopped popcorn is *d* dollars. What is the cost per pound for the popcorn?

EXAMPLE 12

The cost of a 50-pound sack of fertilizer is *d* dollars. What is the cost per pound for the fertilizer?

Solution

We calculate the cost per pound by dividing the total cost by the number of pounds. We represent the cost per pound by $\dfrac{d}{50}$. ∎

The English statement we want to translate into algebra may contain some geometric ideas. Tables 1.1 and 1.2 contain some of the basic relationships that pertain to linear measurement in the English and metric systems, respectively.

Table 1.1   English System
12 inches = 1 foot
3 feet = 1 yard
1760 yards = 1 mile
5280 feet = 1 mile

Table 1.2 Metric System	
1 kilometer =	1000 meters
1 hectometer =	100 meters
1 dekameter =	10 meters
1 decimeter =	0.1 meter
1 centimeter =	0.01 meter
1 millimeter =	0.001 meter

Classroom Example
The distance between two buildings is f feet. Express this distance in yards.

EXAMPLE 13

The distance between two cities is k kilometers. Express this distance in meters.

Solution

Because 1 kilometer equals 1000 meters, the distance in meters is represented by $1000k$.

Classroom Example
The length of the outdoor mall is k kilometers and h hectometers. Express this length in meters.

EXAMPLE 14

The length of a rope is y yards and f feet. Express this length in inches.

Solution

Because 1 foot equals 12 inches, and 1 yard equals 36 inches, the length of the rope in inches can be represented by $36y + 12f$.

Classroom Example
The length of a rectangle is l yards, and the width is w yards. Express the perimeter in feet.

EXAMPLE 15

The length of a rectangle is l centimeters, and the width is w centimeters. Express the perimeter of the rectangle in meters.

Solution

A sketch of the rectangle may be helpful (Figure 1.7).

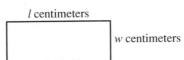

l centimeters

w centimeters

Figure 1.7

The perimeter of a rectangle is the sum of the lengths of the four sides. Thus the perimeter in centimeters is $l + w + l + w$, which simplifies to $2l + 2w$. Now because 1 centimeter equals 0.01 meter, the perimeter, in meters, is $0.01(2l + 2w)$. This could also be written as
$$\frac{2l + 2w}{100} = \frac{2(l + w)}{100} = \frac{l + w}{50}.$$

Concept Quiz 1.4

For Problems 1–10, answer true or false.

1. The numerical coefficient of the term xy is 1.
2. The terms $5x^2y$ and $6xy^2$ are similar terms.
3. The algebraic expression $(3x - 4y) - (3x - 4y)$ simplifies to 0.
4. The algebraic expression $(x - y) - (x - y)$ simplifies to $2x - 2y$.
5. The value of $x^2 - y^2$ is 29 when $x = 5$ and $y = -2$.
6. The English phrase "4 less than twice the number n" translates into the algebraic expression $2n - 4$.

7. The algebraic expression for the English phrase "2 less than y" can be written as $y - 2$ or $2 - y$.

8. In the metric system, 1 centimeter = 10 millimeters.

9. If the length of a rectangle is l inches and its width is w inches, then the perimeter, in feet, can be represented by $24(l + w)$.

10. The value, in dollars, of x five-dollar bills and y ten-dollar bills can be represented by $5x + 10y$.

Problem Set 1.4

Simplify the algebraic expressions in Problems 1–14 by combining similar terms. (Objective 1)

1. $-7x + 11x$

2. $5x - 8x + x$

3. $5a^2 - 6a^2$

4. $12b^3 - 17b^3$

5. $4n - 9n - n$

6. $6n + 13n - 15n$

7. $4x - 9x + 2y$

8. $7x - 9y - 10x - 13y$

9. $-3a^2 + 7b^2 + 9a^2 - 2b^2$

10. $-xy + z - 8xy - 7z$

11. $15x - 4 + 6x - 9$

12. $5x - 2 - 7x + 4 - x - 1$

13. $5a^2b - ab^2 - 7a^2b$

14. $8xy^2 - 5x^2y + 2xy^2 + 7x^2y$

Simplify the algebraic expressions in Problems 15–34 by removing parentheses and combining similar terms. (Objective 1)

15. $3(x + 2) + 5(x + 3)$

16. $5(x - 1) + 7(x + 4)$

17. $-2(a - 4) - 3(a + 2)$

18. $-7(a + 1) - 9(a + 4)$

19. $3(n^2 + 1) - 8(n^2 - 1)$

20. $4(n^2 + 3) + (n^2 - 7)$

21. $-6(x^2 - 5) - (x^2 - 2)$

22. $3(x + y) - 2(x - y)$

23. $5(2x + 1) + 4(3x - 2)$

24. $5(3x - 1) + 6(2x + 3)$

25. $3(2x - 5) - 4(5x - 2)$

26. $3(2x - 3) - 7(3x - 1)$

27. $-2(n^2 - 4) - 4(2n^2 + 1)$

28. $-4(n^2 + 3) - (2n^2 - 7)$

29. $3(2x - 4y) - 2(x + 9y)$

30. $-7(2x - 3y) + 9(3x + y)$

31. $3(2x - 1) - 4(x + 2) - 5(3x + 4)$

32. $-2(x - 1) - 5(2x + 1) + 4(2x - 7)$

33. $-(3x - 1) - 2(5x - 1) + 4(-2x - 3)$

34. $4(-x - 1) + 3(-2x - 5) - 2(x + 1)$

Evaluate the algebraic expressions in Problems 35–57 for the given values of the variables. (Objective 2)

35. $3x + 7y$, $x = -1$ and $y = -2$

36. $5x - 9y$, $x = -2$ and $y = 5$

37. $4x^2 - y^2$, $x = 2$ and $y = -2$

38. $3a^2 + 2b^2$, $a = 2$ and $b = 5$

39. $2a^2 - ab + b^2$, $a = -1$ and $b = -2$

40. $-x^2 + 2xy + 3y^2$, $x = -3$ and $y = 3$

41. $2x^2 - 4xy - 3y^2$, $x = 1$ and $y = -1$

42. $4x^2 + xy - y^2$, $x = 3$ and $y = -2$

43. $3xy - x^2y^2 + 2y^2$, $x = 5$ and $y = -1$

44. $x^2y^3 - 2xy + x^2y^2$, $x = -1$ and $y = -3$

45. $7a - 2b - 9a + 3b$, $a = 4$ and $b = -6$

46. $-4x + 9y - 3x - y$, $x = -4$ and $y = 7$

47. $(x - y)^2$, $x = 5$ and $y = -3$

48. $2(a + b)^2$, $a = 6$ and $b = -1$

49. $-2a - 3a + 7b - b$, $a = -10$ and $b = 9$

50. $3(x - 2) - 4(x + 3)$, $x = -2$

51. $-2(x + 4) - (2x - 1)$, $x = -3$

52. $-4(2x - 1) + 7(3x + 4)$, $x = 4$

53. $2(x - 1) - (x + 2) - 3(2x - 1)$, $x = -1$

54. $-3(x + 1) + 4(-x - 2) - 3(-x + 4)$, $x = -\dfrac{1}{2}$

55. $3(x^2 - 1) - 4(x^2 + 1) - (2x^2 - 1)$, $x = \dfrac{2}{3}$

56. $2(n^2 + 1) - 3(n^2 - 3) + 3(5n^2 - 2)$, $n = \dfrac{1}{4}$

57. $5(x - 2y) - 3(2x + y) - 2(x - y)$, $x = \dfrac{1}{3}$ and $y = -\dfrac{3}{4}$

For Problems 58–63, use your calculator and evaluate each of the algebraic expressions for the indicated values. Express the final answers to the nearest tenth. (Objective 2)

58. πr^2, $\pi = 3.14$ and $r = 2.1$

59. πr^2, $\pi = 3.14$ and $r = 8.4$

60. πr^2h, $\pi = 3.14$, $r = 1.6$, and $h = 11.2$

61. πr^2h, $\pi = 3.14$, $r = 4.8$, and $h = 15.1$

62. $2\pi r^2 + 2\pi rh$, $\pi = 3.14$, $r = 3.9$, and $h = 17.6$

63. $2\pi r^2 + 2\pi rh$, $\pi = 3.14$, $r = 7.8$, and $h = 21.2$

For Problems 64–78, translate each English phrase into an algebraic expression and use *n* to represent the unknown number. (Objective 3)

64. The sum of a number and 4

65. A number increased by 12

66. A number decreased by 7

67. Five less than a number

68. A number subtracted from 75

69. The product of a number and 50

70. One-third of a number

71. Four less than one-half of a number

72. Seven more than three times a number

73. The quotient of a number and 8

74. The quotient of 50 and a number

75. Nine less than twice a number

76. Six more than one-third of a number

77. Ten times the difference of a number and 6

78. Twelve times the sum of a number and 7

For Problems 79–99, answer the question with an algebraic expression. (Objective 3)

79. Brian is *n* years old. How old will he be in 20 years?

80. Crystal is *n* years old. How old was she 5 years ago?

81. Pam is *t* years old, and her mother is 3 less than twice as old as Pam. What is the age of Pam's mother?

82. The sum of two numbers is 65, and one of the numbers is *x*. What is the other number?

83. The difference of two numbers is 47, and the smaller number is *n*. What is the other number?

84. The product of two numbers is 98, and one of the numbers is *n*. What is the other number?

85. The quotient of two numbers is 8, and the smaller number is *y*. What is the other number?

86. The perimeter of a square is *c* centimeters. How long is each side of the square?

87. The perimeter of a square is *m* meters. How long, in centimeters, is each side of the square?

88. Jesse has *n* nickels, *d* dimes, and *q* quarters in his bank. How much money, in cents, does he have in his bank?

89. Tina has *c* cents, which is all in quarters. How many quarters does she have?

90. If *n* represents a whole number, what represents the next larger whole number?

91. If *n* represents an odd integer, what represents the next larger odd integer?

92. If *n* represents an even integer, what represents the next larger even integer?

93. The cost of a 5-pound box of candy is *c* cents. What is the price per pound?

94. Larry's annual salary is *d* dollars. What is his monthly salary?

95. Mila's monthly salary is *d* dollars. What is her annual salary?

96. The perimeter of a square is *i* inches. What is the perimeter expressed in feet?

97. The perimeter of a rectangle is *y* yards and *f* feet. What is the perimeter expressed in feet?

98. The length of a line segment is *d* decimeters. How long is the line segment expressed in meters?

99. The distance between two cities is *m* miles. How far is this, expressed in feet?

100. Use your calculator to check your answers for Problems 35–54.

Thoughts Into Words

101. Explain the difference between simplifying a numerical expression and evaluating an algebraic expression.

102. How would you help someone who is having difficulty expressing *n* nickels and *d* dimes in terms of cents?

103. When asked to write an algebraic expression for "8 more than a number," you wrote $x + 8$ and another student wrote $8 + x$. Are both expressions correct? Explain your answer.

104. When asked to write an algebraic expression for "6 less than a number," you wrote $x - 6$, and another student wrote $6 - x$. Are both expressions correct? Explain your answer.

Answers to the Concept Quiz

1. True   **2.** False   **3.** True   **4.** False   **5.** False   **6.** True   **7.** False   **8.** True   **9.** False   **10.** True

Chapter 1 Summary

OBJECTIVE	SUMMARY	EXAMPLE
Identify certain sets of numbers. (Section 1.1/Objective 1)	A set is a collection of objects. The objects are called elements or members of the set. The sets of natural numbers, whole numbers, integers, rational numbers, and irrational numbers are all subsets of the set of real numbers.	From the list $-4, \dfrac{7}{5}, 0.35, \sqrt{2}$, and 0, identify the integers. **Solution** The integers are -4 and 0.
Apply the properties of equality and the properties of real numbers. (Section 1.1/Objective 2)	The properties of real numbers help with numerical manipulations and serve as a basis for algebraic computation. The properties of equality are listed on page 6, and the properties of real numbers are listed on pages 20–23.	State the property that justifies the statement, "If $x = y$ and $y = 7$, then $x = 7$." **Solution** The statement, "If $x = y$ and $y = 7$, *then* $x = 7$," is justified by the transitive property of equality.
Find the absolute value of a number. (Section 1.2/Objective 2)	Geometrically, the absolute value of any number is the distance between the number and zero on the number line. More formally, the absolute value of a real number a is defined as follows: **1.** If $a \geq 0$, then $|a| = a$. **2.** If $a < 0$, then $|a| = -a$.	Find the absolute value of the following: **(a)** $\|-2\|$ **(b)** $\left\|\dfrac{15}{4}\right\|$ **(c)** $\|-\sqrt{3}\|$ **Solution** **(a)** $\|-2\| = -(-2) = 2$ **(b)** $\left\|\dfrac{15}{4}\right\| = \dfrac{15}{4}$ **(c)** $\|-\sqrt{3}\| = -(-\sqrt{3}) = \sqrt{3}$
Addition of real numbers (Section 1.2/Objective 3) Subtraction of real numbers (Section 1.2/Objective 4) Multiplication and Division of real numbers (Section 1.2/Objectives 5 and 6)	The rules for addition of real numbers are on pages 12 and 13. Applying the principle $a - b = a + (-b)$ changes every subtraction problem, to an equivalent addition problem. **1.** The product (or quotient) of two positive numbers or two negative numbers is the product (or quotient) of their absolute values. **2.** The product (or quotient) of one positive and one negative number is the opposite of the product (or quotient) of their absolute values.	Simplify: **(a)** $-20 + 15 + (-4)$ **(b)** $40 - (-8)$ **(c)** $-3(-4)(-5)$ **Solution** **(a)** $-20 + 15 + (-4) = -5 + (-4)$ $= -9$ **(b)** $40 - (-8) = 40 + (+8) = 48$ **(c)** $-3(-4)(-5) = 12(-5)$ $= -60$
Evaluate exponential expressions. (Section 1.3/Objective 3)	Exponents are used to indicate repeated multiplications. The expression b^n can be read "b to the nth power". We refer to b as the base and n as the exponent.	Simplify $2(-5)^3 + 3(-2)^2$. **Solution** $2(-5)^3 + 3(-2)^2$ $= 2(-125) + 3(4)$ $= -250 + 12$ $= -238$

OBJECTIVE	SUMMARY	EXAMPLE
Simplify numerical expressions. (Section 1.1/Objective 3; Section 1.2/Objective 7)	We can evaluate *numerical expressions* by performing the operations in the following order. **1.** Perform the operations inside the parentheses and above and below the fraction bars. **2.** Evaluate all numbers raised to an exponent. **3.** Perform all multiplications and divisions in the order they appear from left to right. **4.** Perform all additions and subtractions in the order they appear from left to right.	Simplify $60 \div 2 \cdot 3 - (1 - 5)^2$. **Solution** $60 \div 2 \cdot 3 - (1 - 5)^2$ $= 60 \div 2 \cdot 3 - (-4)^2$ $= 60 \div 2 \cdot 3 - 16$ $= 30 \cdot 3 - 16$ $= 90 - 16$ $= 74$
Simplify algebraic expressions. (Section 1.3/Objective 2; Section 1.4/Objective 1)	Algebraic expressions such as $2x$, $3xy^2$, and $-4a^2b^3c$ are called *terms*. We call the variables in a term the literal factors, and we call the numerical factor the numerical coefficient. Terms that have the same literal factors are called similar or like terms. The distributive property in the form $ba + ca = (b + c)a$ serves as a basis for combining like terms.	Simplify $5x^2 + 3x - 2x^2 - 7x$. **Solution** $5x^2 + 3x - 2x^2 - 7x$ $= 5x^2 - 2x^2 + 3x - 7x$ $= (5 - 2)x^2 + (3 - 7)x$ $= 3x^2 + (-4)x$ $= 3x^2 - 4x$
Evaluate algebraic expressions. (Section 1.3/Objective 3; Section 1.4/Objective 2)	An algebraic expression takes on a numerical value whenever each variable in the expression is replaced by a real number. The process of finding a value of an algebraic expression is referred to as *evaluating algebraic expressions*.	Evaluate $x^2 - 2xy + y^2$ when $x = 3$ and $y = -4$. **Solution** $x^2 - 2xy + y^2 =$ $\quad (3)^2 - 2(3)(-4) + (-4)^2$ when $x = 3$ and $y = -4$. $(3)^2 - 2(3)(-4) + (-4)^2 =$ $9 + 24 + 16 = 49$
Translate from English to algebra. (Section 1.4/Objective 3)	To translate English phrases into algebraic expressions you must be familiar with key phrases that signal whether we are to find a sum, difference, product, or quotient.	Translate the English phrase *six less than twice a number* into an algebraic expression. **Solution** Let n represent the number. "Six less than" means that 6 will be subtracted from twice the number. "Twice the number" means that the number will be multiplied by 2. The phrase *six less than twice a number* translates into $2n - 6$.
Use real numbers to represent problems. (Section 1.2/Objective 8)	Real numbers can be used to represent many situations in the real world.	A patient in the hospital had a body temperature of $106.7°$. Over the next three hours his temperature fell $1.2°$ per hour. What was his temperature after the three hours? **Solution** $106.7 - 3(1.2)$ $= 106.7 - 3.6 = 103.1$ His temperature was $103.1°$.

Chapter 1   Review Problem Set

1. From the list $0, \sqrt{2}, \dfrac{3}{4}, -\dfrac{5}{6}, \dfrac{25}{3}, -\sqrt{3}, -8, 0.34, 0.2\overline{3},$

   $67,$ and $\dfrac{9}{7}$, identify each of the following.

(a) The natural numbers

(b) The integers

(c) The nonnegative integers

(d) The rational numbers

(e) The irrational numbers

For Problems 2–10, state the property of equality or the property of real numbers that justifies each of the statements. For example, $6(-7) = -7(6)$ because of the commutative property of multiplication; and if $2 = x + 3$, then $x + 3 = 2$ is true because of the symmetric property of equality.

2. $7 + [3 + (-8)] = (7 + 3) + (-8)$

3. If $x = 2$ and $x + y = 9$, then $2 + y = 9$.

4. $-1(x + 2) = -(x + 2)$

5. $3(x + 4) = 3(x) + 3(4)$

6. $[(17)(4)](25) = (17)[(4)(25)]$

7. $x + 3 = 3 + x$

8. $3(98) + 3(2) = 3(98 + 2)$

9. $\left(\dfrac{3}{4}\right)\left(\dfrac{4}{3}\right) = 1$

10. If $4 = 3x - 1$, then $3x - 1 = 4$.

For Problems 11–14, find the absolute value.

11. $|-6.2|$

12. $\left|\dfrac{7}{3}\right|$

13. $|-\sqrt{15}|$

14. $|-8|$

For Problems 15–26, simplify each of the numerical expressions.

15. $-8\dfrac{1}{4} + \left(-4\dfrac{5}{8}\right) - \left(-6\dfrac{3}{8}\right)$

16. $9\dfrac{1}{3} - 12\dfrac{1}{2} + \left(-4\dfrac{1}{6}\right) - \left(-1\dfrac{1}{6}\right)$

17. $-8(2) - 16 \div (-4) + (-2)(-2)$

18. $4(-3) - 12 \div (-4) + (-2)(-1) - 8$

19. $-3(2 - 4) - 4(7 - 9) + 6$

20. $[48 + (-73)] + 74$

21. $[5(-2) - 3(-1)][-2(-1) + 3(2)]$

22. $3 - [-2(3 - 4)] + 7$

23. $-4^2 - 2^3$

24. $(-2)^4 + (-1)^3 - 3^2$

25. $2(-1)^2 - 3(-1)(2) - 2^2$

26. $[4(-1) - 2(3)]^2$

For Problems 27–36, simplify each of the algebraic expressions by combining similar terms.

27. $3a^2 - 2b^2 - 7a^2 - 3b^2$

28. $4x - 6 - 2x - 8 + x + 12$

29. $\dfrac{1}{5}ab^2 - \dfrac{3}{10}ab^2 + \dfrac{2}{5}ab^2 + \dfrac{7}{10}ab^2$

30. $-\dfrac{2}{3}x^2y - \left(-\dfrac{3}{4}x^2y\right) - \dfrac{5}{12}x^2y - 2x^2y$

31. $3(2n^2 + 1) + 4(n^2 - 5)$

32. $-2(3a - 1) + 4(2a + 3) - 5(3a + 2)$

33. $-(n - 1) - (n + 2) + 3$

34. $3(2x - 3y) - 4(3x + 5y) - x$

35. $4(a - 6) - (3a - 1) - 2(4a - 7)$

36. $-5(x^2 - 4) - 2(3x^2 + 6) + (2x^2 - 1)$

For Problems 37–46, evaluate each of the algebraic expressions for the given values of the variables.

37. $-5x + 4y$ for $x = \dfrac{1}{2}$ and $y = -1$

38. $3x^2 - 2y^2$ for $x = \dfrac{1}{4}$ and $y = -\dfrac{1}{2}$

39. $-5(2x - 3y)$ for $x = 1$ and $y = -3$

40. $(3a - 2b)^2$ for $a = -2$ and $b = 3$

41. $a^2 + 3ab - 2b^2$ for $a = 2$ and $b = -2$

42. $3n^2 - 4 - 4n^2 + 9$ for $n = 7$

43. $3(2x - 1) + 2(3x + 4)$ for $x = 1.2$

44. $-4(3x - 1) - 5(2x - 1)$ for $x = -2.3$

45. $2(n^2 + 3) - 3(n^2 + 1) + 4(n^2 - 6)$ for $n = -\dfrac{2}{3}$

46. $5(3n - 1) - 7(-2n + 1) + 4(3n - 1)$ for $n = \dfrac{1}{2}$

For Problems 47–54, translate each English phrase into an algebraic expression, and use n to represent the unknown number.

47. Four increased by twice a number

48. Fifty subtracted from three times a number

49. Six less than two-thirds of a number

50. Ten times the difference of a number and 14

51. Eight subtracted from five times a number

52. The quotient of a number and three less than the number

53. Three less than five times the sum of a number and 2

54. Three-fourths of the sum of a number and 12

For Problems 55–64, answer the question with an algebraic expression.

55. The sum of two numbers is 37, and one of the numbers is n. What is the other number?

56. Yuriko can type w words in an hour. What is her typing rate per minute?

57. Harry is y years old. His brother is 7 years less than twice as old as Harry. How old is Harry's brother?

58. If n represents a multiple of 3, what represents the next largest multiple of 3?

59. Celia has p pennies, n nickels, and q quarters. How much, in cents, does Celia have?

60. The perimeter of a square is i inches. How long, in feet, is each side of the square?

61. The length of a rectangle is y yards, and the width is f feet. What is the perimeter of the rectangle expressed in inches?

62. The length of a piece of wire is d decimeters. What is the length expressed in centimeters?

63. Joan is f feet and i inches tall. How tall is she in inches?

64. The perimeter of a rectangle is 50 centimeters. If the rectangle is c centimeters long, how wide is it?

65. Kalya has the capacity to record 4 minutes of video on her cellular phone. She currently has $3\frac{1}{2}$ minutes of video clips. How much recording capacity will she have left if she deletes $2\frac{1}{4}$ minutes of clips and adds $1\frac{3}{4}$ minutes of recording?

66. During the week, the price of a stock recorded the following gains and losses: Monday lost $1.25, Tuesday lost $0.45, Wednesday gained $0.67, Thursday gained $1.10, and Friday lost $0.22. What is the average daily gain or loss for the week?

67. A crime-scene investigator has 3.4 ounces of a sample. He needs to conduct four tests that each require 0.6 ounces of the sample, and one test that requires 0.8 ounces of the sample. How much of the sample remains after he uses it for the five tests?

68. For week 1 of a weight loss competition, Team A had three members lose 8 pounds each, two members lose 5 pounds each, one member loses 4 pounds, and two members gain 3 pounds. What was the total weight loss for Team A in the first week of the competition?

Chapter 1 Test

1. State the property of equality that justifies writing $x + 4 = 6$ for $6 = x + 4$.

2. State the property of real numbers that justifies writing $5(10 + 2)$ as $5(10) + 5(2)$.

For Problems 3–11, simplify each numerical expression.

3. $-4 - (-3) + (-5) - 7 + 10$

4. $7 - 8 - 3 + 4 - 9 - 4 + 2 - 12$

5. $5\left(-\dfrac{1}{3}\right) - 3\left(-\dfrac{1}{2}\right) + 7\left(-\dfrac{2}{3}\right) + 1$

6. $(-6) \cdot 3 \div (-2) - 8 \div (-4)$

7. $-\dfrac{1}{2}(3 - 7) - \dfrac{2}{5}(2 - 17)$

8. $[48 + (-93)] + (-49)$

9. $3(-2)^3 + 4(-2)^2 - 9(-2) - 14$

10. $[2(-6) + 5(-4)][-3(-4) - 7(6)]$

11. $[-2(-3) - 4(2)]^5$

12. Simplify $6x^2 - 3x - 7x^2 - 5x - 2$ by combining similar terms.

13. Simplify $3(3n - 1) - 4(2n + 3) + 5(-4n - 1)$ by removing parentheses and combining similar terms.

For Problems 14–20, evaluate each algebraic expression for the given values of the variables.

14. $-7x - 3y$ for $x = -6$ and $y = 5$

15. $3a^2 - 4b^2$ for $a = -\dfrac{3}{4}$ and $b = \dfrac{1}{2}$

16. $6x - 9y - 8x + 4y$ for $x = \dfrac{1}{2}$ and $y = -\dfrac{1}{3}$

17. $-5n^2 - 6n + 7n^2 + 5n - 1$ for $n = -6$

18. $-7(x - 2) + 6(x - 1) - 4(x + 3)$ for $x = 3.7$

19. $-2xy - x + 4y$ for $x = -3$ and $y = 9$

20. $4(n^2 + 1) - (2n^2 + 3) - 2(n^2 + 3)$ for $n = -4$

For Problems 21 and 22, translate the English phrase into an algebraic expression using n to represent the unknown number.

21. Thirty subtracted from six times a number

22. Four more than three times the sum of a number and 8

For Problems 23–25, answer each question with an algebraic expression.

23. The product of two numbers is 72, and one of the numbers is n. What is the other number?

24. Tao has n nickels, d dimes, and q quarters. How much money, in cents, does she have?

25. The length of a rectangle is x yards and the width is y feet. What is the perimeter of the rectangle expressed in feet?

2 Equations, Inequalities, and Problem Solving

2.1 Solving First-Degree Equations

2.2 Equations Involving Fractional Forms

2.3 Equations Involving Decimals and Problem Solving

2.4 Formulas

2.5 Inequalities

2.6 More on Inequalities and Problem Solving

2.7 Equations and Inequalities Involving Absolute Value

Most shoppers take advantage of the discounts offered by retailers. When making decisions about purchases, it is beneficial to be able to compute the sale prices.

A retailer of sporting goods bought a putter for $18. He wants to price the putter to make a profit of 40% of the selling price. What price should he mark on the putter? The equation $s = 18 + 0.4s$ can be used to determine that the putter should be sold for $30.

Throughout this text, we develop algebraic skills, use these skills to help solve equations and inequalities, and then use equations and inequalities to solve applied problems. In this chapter, we review and expand concepts that are important to the development of problem-solving skills.

Video tutorials based on section learning objectives are available in a variety of delivery modes.

2.1	Solving First-Degree Equations

O B J E C T I V E S

1 Solve first-degree equations

2 Use equations to solve word problems

In Section 1.1, we stated that an equality (equation) is a statement in which two symbols, or groups of symbols, are names for the same number. It should be further stated that an equation may be true or false. For example, the equation $3 + (-8) = -5$ is true, but the equation $-7 + 4 = 2$ is false.

Algebraic equations contain one or more variables. The following are examples of algebraic equations.

$$3x + 5 = 8 \qquad 4y - 6 = -7y + 9 \qquad x^2 - 5x - 8 = 0$$

$$3x + 5y = 4 \qquad x^3 + 6x^2 - 7x - 2 = 0$$

An algebraic equation such as $3x + 5 = 8$ is neither true nor false as it stands, and we often refer to it as an "open sentence." Each time that a number is substituted for x, the algebraic equation $3x + 5 = 8$ becomes a numerical statement that is true or false. For example, if $x = 0$, then $3x + 5 = 8$ becomes $3(0) + 5 = 8$, which is a false statement. If $x = 1$, then $3x + 5 = 8$ becomes $3(1) + 5 = 8$, which is a true statement. **Solving an equation** refers to the process of finding the number (or numbers) that make(s) an algebraic equation a true numerical statement. We call such numbers the **solutions** or **roots** of the equation, and we say that they *satisfy* the equation. We call the set of all solutions of an equation its **solution set**. Thus {1} is the solution set of $3x + 5 = 8$.

In this chapter, we will consider techniques for solving **first-degree equations in one variable**. This means that the equations contain only one variable and that this variable has an exponent of 1. The following are examples of first-degree equations in one variable.

$$3x + 5 = 8 \qquad \frac{2}{3}y + 7 = 9$$

$$7a - 6 = 3a + 4 \qquad \frac{x - 2}{4} = \frac{x - 3}{5}$$

Equivalent equations are equations that have the same solution set. For example,

1. $3x + 5 = 8$
2. $3x = 3$
3. $x = 1$

are all equivalent equations because {1} is the solution set of each.

The general procedure for solving an equation is to continue replacing the given equation with equivalent but simpler equations until we obtain an equation of the form *variable = constant* or *constant = variable*. Thus in the example above, $3x + 5 = 8$ was simplified to $3x = 3$, which was further simplified to $x = 1$, from which the solution set {1} is obvious.

To solve equations we need to use the various properties of equality. In addition to the reflexive, symmetric, transitive, and substitution properties we listed in Section 1.1, the following properties of equality are important for problem solving.

Addition Property of Equality

For all real numbers a, b, and c,

$$a = b \quad \text{if and only if} \quad a + c = b + c$$

> **Multiplication Property of Equality**
>
> For all real numbers a, b, and c, where $c \neq 0$,
>
> $$a = b \quad \text{if and only if} \quad ac = bc$$

The addition property of equality states that when the same number is added to both sides of an equation, an equivalent equation is produced. The multiplication property of equality states that we obtain an equivalent equation whenever we multiply both sides of an equation by the same *nonzero* real number. The following examples demonstrate the use of these properties to solve equations.

Classroom Example
Solve $3x - 5 = 16$.

EXAMPLE 1   Solve $2x - 1 = 13$.

Solution

$$2x - 1 = 13$$
$$2x - 1 + 1 = 13 + 1 \qquad \text{Add 1 to both sides}$$
$$2x = 14$$
$$\frac{1}{2}(2x) = \frac{1}{2}(14) \qquad \text{Multiply both sides by } \frac{1}{2}$$
$$x = 7$$

The solution set is $\{7\}$.

To check an apparent solution, we can substitute it into the original equation and see if we obtain a true numerical statement.

✔ **Check**

$$2x - 1 = 13$$
$$2(7) - 1 \overset{?}{=} 13$$
$$14 - 1 \overset{?}{=} 13$$
$$13 = 13$$

Now we know that $\{7\}$ is the solution set of $2x - 1 = 13$. We will not show our checks for every example in this text, but do remember that checking is a way to detect arithmetic errors.

Classroom Example
Solve $-5 = -4a + 8$.

EXAMPLE 2   Solve $-7 = -5a + 9$.

Solution

$$-7 = -5a + 9$$
$$-7 + (-9) = 5a + 9 + (-9) \qquad \text{Add } -9 \text{ to both sides}$$
$$-16 = -5a$$
$$-\frac{1}{5}(-16) = -\frac{1}{5}(-5a) \qquad \text{Multiply both sides by } -\frac{1}{5}$$
$$\frac{16}{5} = a$$

The solution set is $\left\{\dfrac{16}{5}\right\}$.

Note that in Example 2 the final equation is $\frac{16}{5} = a$ instead of $a = \frac{16}{5}$. Technically, the symmetric property of equality (if $a = b$, then $b = a$) would permit us to change from $\frac{16}{5} = a$ to $a = \frac{16}{5}$, but such a change is not necessary to determine that the solution is $\frac{16}{5}$. Note that we could use the symmetric property at the very beginning to change $-7 = -5a + 9$ to $-5a + 9 = -7$; some people prefer having the variable on the left side of the equation.

Let's clarify another point. We stated the properties of equality in terms of only two operations, addition and multiplication. We could also include the operations of subtraction and division in the statements of the properties. That is, we could think in terms of subtracting the same number from both sides of an equation and also in terms of dividing both sides of an equation by the same nonzero number. For example, in the solution of Example 2, we could subtract 9 from both sides rather than adding -9 to both sides. Likewise, we could divide both sides by -5 instead of multiplying both sides by $-\frac{1}{5}$.

Classroom Example
Solve $8m - 7 = 5m + 8$.

EXAMPLE 3   Solve $7x - 3 = 5x + 9$.

Solution

$$7x - 3 = 5x + 9$$
$$7x - 3 + (-5x) = 5x + 9 + (-5x) \qquad \text{Add } -5x \text{ to both sides}$$
$$2x - 3 = 9$$
$$2x - 3 + 3 = 9 + 3 \qquad \text{Add 3 to both sides}$$
$$2x = 12$$
$$\frac{1}{2}(2x) = \frac{1}{2}(12) \qquad \text{Multiply both sides by } \frac{1}{2}$$
$$x = 6$$

The solution set is $\{6\}$.

Classroom Example
Solve $2(x + 3) + 6(x - 4) = 5(x - 9)$.

EXAMPLE 4   Solve $4(y - 1) + 5(y + 2) = 3(y - 8)$.

Solution

$$4(y - 1) + 5(y + 2) = 3(y - 8)$$
$$4y - 4 + 5y + 10 = 3y - 24 \qquad \text{Remove parentheses by applying the distributive property}$$
$$9y + 6 = 3y - 24 \qquad \text{Simplify the left side by combining similar terms}$$
$$9y + 6 + (-3y) = 3y - 24 + (-3y) \qquad \text{Add } -3y \text{ to both sides}$$
$$6y + 6 = -24$$
$$6y + 6 + (-6) = -24 + (-6) \qquad \text{Add } -6 \text{ to both sides}$$
$$6y = -30$$
$$\frac{1}{6}(6y) = \frac{1}{6}(-30) \qquad \text{Multiply both sides by } \frac{1}{6}$$
$$y = -5$$

The solution set is $\{-5\}$.

We can summarize the process of solving first-degree equations in one variable as follows:

Step 1 Simplify both sides of the equation as much as possible.

Step 2 Use the addition property of equality to isolate a term that contains the variable on one side of the equation and a constant on the other side.

Step 3 Use the multiplication property of equality to make the coefficient of the variable 1; that is, multiply both sides of the equation by the reciprocal of the numerical coefficient of the variable. The solution set should now be obvious.

Step 4 Check each solution by substituting it in the original equation and verifying that the resulting numerical statement is true.

Using Equations to Solve Problems

To use the tools of algebra to solve problems, we must be able to translate back and forth between the English language and the language of algebra. More specifically, we need to translate English sentences into algebraic equations. Such translations allow us to use our knowledge of equation solving to solve word problems. Let's consider an example.

Classroom Example
If we subtract 19 from two times a certain number, the result is 3. Find the number.

EXAMPLE 5

If we subtract 27 from three times a certain number, the result is 18. Find the number.

Solution

Let n represent the number to be found. The sentence "If we subtract 27 from three times a certain number, the result is 18" translates into the equation $3n - 27 = 18$. Solving this equation, we obtain

$$3n - 27 = 18$$
$$3n = 45 \qquad \text{Add 27 to both sides}$$
$$n = 15 \qquad \text{Multiply both sides by } \frac{1}{3}$$

The number to be found is 15.

We often refer to the statement "Let n represent the number to be found" as **declaring the variable**. We need to choose a letter to use as a variable and indicate what it represents for a specific problem. This may seem like an insignificant exercise, but as the problems become more complex, the process of declaring the variable becomes even more important. Furthermore, it is true that you could probably solve a problem such as Example 5 without setting up an algebraic equation. However, as problems increase in difficulty, the translation from English to algebra becomes a key issue. Therefore, even with these relatively easy problems, we suggest that you concentrate on the translation process.

The next example involves the use of integers. Remember that the set of integers consists of $\{\ldots -2, -1, 0, 1, 2, \ldots\}$. Furthermore, the integers can be classified as even, $\{\ldots -4, -2, 0, 2, 4, \ldots\}$, or odd, $\{\ldots -3, -1, 1, 3, \ldots\}$.

Classroom Example
The sum of three consecutive odd integers is six less than two times the largest of the three odd integers. Find the integers.

EXAMPLE 6

The sum of three consecutive integers is 13 greater than twice the smallest of the three integers. Find the integers.

Solution

Because consecutive integers differ by 1, we will represent them as follows: Let n represent the smallest of the three consecutive integers; then $n + 1$ represents the second largest, and $n + 2$ represents the largest.

The sum of the three
consecutive integers   13 greater than twice the smallest

$$n + (n + 1) + (n + 2) = 2n + 13$$
$$3n + 3 = 2n + 13$$
$$n = 10$$

The three consecutive integers are 10, 11, and 12.

To check our answers for Example 6, we must determine whether or not they satisfy the conditions stated in the original problem. Because 10, 11, and 12 are consecutive integers whose sum is 33, and because twice the smallest plus 13 is also 33 (2(10) + 13 = 33), we know that our answers are correct. (Remember, in checking a result for a word problem, it is *not* sufficient to check the result in the equation set up to solve the problem; the equation itself may be in error!)

In the two previous examples, the equation formed was almost a direct translation of a sentence in the statement of the problem. Now let's consider a situation where we need to think in terms of a guideline not explicitly stated in the problem.

Classroom Example
Erik received a car repair bill for $389. This included $159 for parts, $43 per hour for each hour of labor, and $15 for taxes. Find the number of hours of labor.

EXAMPLE 7

Khoa received a car repair bill for $412. This included $175 for parts, $60 per hour for each hour of labor, and $27 for taxes. Find the number of hours of labor.

Solution

See Figure 2.1. Let h represent the number of hours of labor. Then $60h$ represents the total charge for labor.

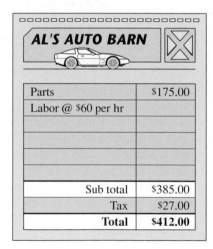

AL'S AUTO BARN

Parts	$175.00
Labor @ $60 per hr	
Sub total	$385.00
Tax	$27.00
Total	**$412.00**

Figure 2.1

We can use this guideline: *charge for parts plus charge for labor plus tax equals the total bill* to set up the following equation.

Parts   Labor   Tax   Total bill

$$175 + 60h + 27 = 412$$

Solving this equation, we obtain

$$60h + 202 = 412$$
$$60h = 210$$
$$h = 3\frac{1}{2}$$

Khoa was charged for $3\frac{1}{2}$ hours of labor.

_____ ▪

Concept Quiz 2.1

For Problems 1–10, answer true or false.

1. Equivalent equations have the same solution set.
2. $x^2 = 9$ is a first-degree equation.
3. The set of all solutions is called a solution set.
4. If the solution set is the null set, then the equation has at least one solution.
5. Solving an equation refers to obtaining any other equivalent equation.
6. If 5 is a solution, then a true numerical statement is formed when 5 is substituted for the variable in the equation.
7. Any number can be subtracted from both sides of an equation, and the result is an equivalent equation.
8. Any number can divide both sides of an equation to obtain an equivalent equation.
9. The equation $2x + 7 = 3y$ is a first-degree equation in one variable.
10. The multiplication property of equality states that an equivalent equation is obtained whenever both sides of an equation are multiplied by a nonzero number.

Problem Set 2.1

For Problems 1–50, solve each equation. (Objective 1)

1. $3x + 4 = 16$
2. $4x + 2 = 22$
3. $5x + 1 = -14$
4. $7x + 4 = -31$
5. $-x - 6 = 8$
6. $8 - x = -2$
7. $4y - 3 = 21$
8. $6y - 7 = 41$
9. $3x - 4 = 15$
10. $5x + 1 = 12$
11. $-4 = 2x - 6$
12. $-14 = 3a - 2$
13. $-6y - 4 = 16$
14. $-8y - 2 = 18$
15. $4x - 1 = 2x + 7$
16. $9x - 3 = 6x + 18$
17. $5y + 2 = 2y - 11$
18. $9y + 3 = 4y - 10$
19. $3x + 4 = 5x - 2$
20. $2x - 1 = 6x + 15$
21. $-7a + 6 = -8a + 14$
22. $-6a - 4 = -7a + 11$
23. $5x + 3 - 2x = x - 15$
24. $4x - 2 - x = 5x + 10$
25. $6y + 18 + y = 2y + 3$
26. $5y + 14 + y = 3y - 7$
27. $4x - 3 + 2x = 8x - 3 - x$
28. $x - 4 - 4x = 6x + 9 - 8x$
29. $6n - 4 - 3n = 3n + 10 + 4n$
30. $2n - 1 - 3n = 5n - 7 - 3n$
31. $4(x - 3) = -20$
32. $3(x + 2) = -15$
33. $-3(x - 2) = 11$
34. $-5(x - 1) = 12$
35. $5(2x + 1) = 4(3x - 7)$
36. $3(2x - 1) = 2(4x + 7)$
37. $5x - 4(x - 6) = -11$
38. $3x - 5(2x + 1) = 13$
39. $-2(3x - 1) - 3 = -4$
40. $-6(x - 4) - 10 = -12$
41. $-2(3x + 5) = -3(4x + 3)$
42. $-(2x - 1) = -5(2x + 9)$

43. $3(x - 4) - 7(x + 2) = -2(x + 18)$

44. $4(x - 2) - 3(x - 1) = 2(x + 6)$

45. $-2(3n - 1) + 3(n + 5) = -4(n - 4)$

46. $-3(4n + 2) + 2(n - 6) = -2(n + 1)$

47. $3(2a - 1) - 2(5a + 1) = 4(3a + 4)$

48. $4(2a + 3) - 3(4a - 2) = 5(4a - 7)$

49. $-2(n - 4) - (3n - 1) = -2 + (2n - 1)$

50. $-(2n - 1) + 6(n + 3) = -4 - (7n - 11)$

For Problems 51–66, use an algebraic approach to solve each problem. (Objective 2)

51. If 15 is subtracted from three times a certain number, the result is 27. Find the number.

52. If one is subtracted from seven times a certain number, the result is the same as if 31 is added to three times the number. Find the number.

53. Find three consecutive integers whose sum is 42.

54. Find four consecutive integers whose sum is −118.

55. Find three consecutive odd integers such that three times the second minus the third is 11 more than the first.

56. Find three consecutive even integers such that four times the first minus the third is six more than twice the second.

57. The difference of two numbers is 67. The larger number is three less than six times the smaller number. Find the numbers.

58. The sum of two numbers is 103. The larger number is one more than five times the smaller number. Find the numbers.

59. Angelo is paid double time for each hour he works over 40 hours in a week. Last week he worked 46 hours and earned $572. What is his normal hourly rate?

60. Suppose that a plumbing repair bill, not including tax, was $130. This included $25 for parts and an amount for 2 hours of labor. Find the hourly rate that was charged for labor.

61. Suppose that Maria has 150 coins consisting of pennies, nickels, and dimes. The number of nickels she has is 10 less than twice the number of pennies; the number of dimes she has is 20 less than three times the number of pennies. How many coins of each kind does she have?

62. Hector has a collection of nickels, dimes, and quarters totaling 122 coins. The number of dimes he has is 3 more than four times the number of nickels, and the number of quarters he has is 19 less than the number of dimes. How many coins of each kind does he have?

63. The selling price of a ring is $750. This represents $150 less than three times the cost of the ring. Find the cost of the ring.

64. In a class of 62 students, the number of females is one less than twice the number of males. How many females and how many males are there in the class?

65. An apartment complex contains 230 apartments, each having one, two, or three bedrooms. The number of two-bedroom apartments is 10 more than three times the number of three-bedroom apartments. The number of one-bedroom apartments is twice the number of two-bedroom apartments. How many apartments of each kind are in the complex?

66. Barry sells bicycles on a salary-plus-commission basis. He receives a weekly salary of $300 and a commission of $15 for each bicycle that he sells. How many bicycles must he sell in a week to have a total weekly income of $750?

Thoughts Into Words

67. Explain the difference between a numerical statement and an algebraic equation.

68. Are the equations $7 = 9x - 4$ and $9x - 4 = 7$ equivalent equations? Defend your answer.

69. Suppose that your friend shows you the following solution to an equation.

$$17 = 4 - 2x$$
$$17 + 2x = 4 - 2x + 2x$$
$$17 + 2x = 4$$
$$17 + 2x - 17 = 4 - 17$$
$$2x = -13$$
$$x = \frac{-13}{2}$$

Is this a correct solution? What suggestions would you have in terms of the method used to solve the equation?

70. Explain in your own words what it means to declare a variable when solving a word problem.

71. Make up an equation whose solution set is the null set and explain why this is the solution set.

72. Make up an equation whose solution set is the set of all real numbers and explain why this is the solution set.

Further Investigations

73. Solve each of the following equations.
  (a) $5x + 7 = 5x - 4$
  (b) $4(x - 1) = 4x - 4$
  (c) $3(x - 4) = 2(x - 6)$
  (d) $7x - 2 = -7x + 4$
  (e) $2(x - 1) + 3(x + 2) = 5(x - 7)$
  (f) $-4(x - 7) = -2(2x + 1)$

74. Verify that for any three consecutive integers, the sum of the smallest and largest is equal to twice the middle integer. [*Hint*: Use n, $n + 1$, and $n + 2$ to represent the three consecutive integers.]

Answers to the Concept Quiz

1. True   **2.** False   **3.** True   **4.** False   **5.** False   **6.** True   **7.** True   **8.** False   **9.** False   **10.** True

2.2   Equations Involving Fractional Forms

OBJECTIVES
  1 Solve equations involving fractions
  2 Solve word problems

To solve equations that involve fractions, it is usually easiest to begin by *clearing the equation of all fractions*. This can be accomplished by multiplying both sides of the equation by the least common multiple of all the denominators in the equation. Remember that the least common multiple of a set of whole numbers is the smallest nonzero whole number that is divisible by each of the numbers. For example, the least common multiple of 2, 3, and 6 is 12. When working with fractions, we refer to the least common multiple of a set of denominators as the **least common denominator** (LCD). Let's consider some equations involving fractions.

Classroom Example
Solve $\dfrac{3}{8}x + \dfrac{1}{3} = \dfrac{7}{12}$.

EXAMPLE 1   Solve $\dfrac{1}{2}x + \dfrac{2}{3} = \dfrac{3}{4}$.

Solution

$$\frac{1}{2}x + \frac{2}{3} = \frac{3}{4}$$

$$12\left(\frac{1}{2}x + \frac{2}{3}\right) = 12\left(\frac{3}{4}\right) \qquad \text{Multiply both sides by 12, which is the LCM of 2, 3, and 4}$$

$$12\left(\frac{1}{2}x\right) + 12\left(\frac{2}{3}\right) = 12\left(\frac{3}{4}\right) \qquad \text{Apply the distributive property to the left side}$$

$$6x + 8 = 9$$

$$6x = 1$$

$$x = \frac{1}{6}$$

The solution set is $\left\{\dfrac{1}{6}\right\}$.

✔ **Check**

$$\frac{1}{2}x + \frac{2}{3} = \frac{3}{4}$$

$$\frac{1}{2}\left(\frac{1}{6}\right) + \frac{2}{3} \overset{?}{=} \frac{3}{4}$$

$$\frac{1}{12} + \frac{2}{3} \overset{?}{=} \frac{3}{4}$$

$$\frac{1}{12} + \frac{8}{12} \overset{?}{=} \frac{3}{4}$$

$$\frac{9}{12} \overset{?}{=} \frac{3}{4}$$

$$\frac{3}{4} = \frac{3}{4}$$

Classroom Example

Solve $\dfrac{m}{3} - \dfrac{m}{5} = 2$.

EXAMPLE 2 Solve $\dfrac{x}{2} + \dfrac{x}{3} = 10$.

Solution

$$\frac{x}{2} + \frac{x}{3} = 10 \qquad \text{Recall that } \frac{x}{2} = \frac{1}{2}x$$

$$6\left(\frac{x}{2} + \frac{x}{3}\right) = 6(10) \qquad \text{Multiply both sides by the LCD}$$

$$6\left(\frac{x}{2}\right) + 6\left(\frac{x}{3}\right) = 6(10) \qquad \text{Apply the distributive property to the left side}$$

$$3x + 2x = 60$$

$$5x = 60$$

$$x = 12$$

The solution set is $\{12\}$.

As you study the examples in this section, pay special attention to the steps shown in the solutions. There are no hard and fast rules as to which steps should be performed mentally; this is an individual decision. When you solve problems, show enough steps to allow the flow of the process to be understood and to minimize the chances of making careless computational errors.

Classroom Example

Solve $\dfrac{a - 3}{2} - \dfrac{a + 4}{9} = \dfrac{7}{6}$.

EXAMPLE 3 Solve $\dfrac{x - 2}{3} + \dfrac{x + 1}{8} = \dfrac{5}{6}$.

Solution

$$\frac{x - 2}{3} + \frac{x + 1}{8} = \frac{5}{6}$$

$$24\left(\frac{x-2}{3} + \frac{x+1}{8}\right) = 24\left(\frac{5}{6}\right)$$ Multiply both sides by the LCD

$$24\left(\frac{x-2}{3}\right) + 24\left(\frac{x+1}{8}\right) = 24\left(\frac{5}{6}\right)$$ Apply the distributive property to the left side

$$8(x-2) + 3(x+1) = 20$$

$$8x - 16 + 3x + 3 = 20$$

$$11x - 13 = 20$$

$$11x = 33$$

$$x = 3$$

The solution set is {3}.

Classroom Example

Solve $\dfrac{4x+7}{3} - \dfrac{x+3}{2} = 1$.

EXAMPLE 4   Solve $\dfrac{3t-1}{5} - \dfrac{t-4}{3} = 1$.

Solution

$$\frac{3t-1}{5} - \frac{t-4}{3} = 1$$

$$15\left(\frac{3t-1}{5} - \frac{t-4}{3}\right) = 15(1)$$ Multiply both sides by the LCD

$$15\left(\frac{3t-1}{5}\right) - 15\left(\frac{t-4}{3}\right) = 15(1)$$ Apply the distributive property to the left side

$$3(3t-1) - 5(t-4) = 15$$

$$9t - 3 - 5t + 20 = 15$$ Be careful with this sign!

$$4t + 17 = 15$$

$$4t = -2$$

$$t = -\frac{2}{4} = -\frac{1}{2}$$ Reduce!

The solution set is $\left\{-\dfrac{1}{2}\right\}$.

Solving Word Problems

As we expand our skills for solving equations, we also expand our capabilities for solving word problems. There is no one definite procedure that will ensure success at solving word problems, but the following suggestions should be helpful.

Suggestions for Solving Word Problems

1. Read the problem carefully and make certain that you understand the meanings of all of the words. Be especially alert for any technical terms used in the statement of the problem.
2. Read the problem a second time (perhaps even a third time) to get an overview of the situation being described. Determine the known facts as well as what is to be found.
3. Sketch any figure, diagram, or chart that might be helpful in analyzing the problem.
4. Choose a meaningful variable to represent an unknown quantity in the problem (perhaps t, if time is an unknown quantity) and represent any other unknowns in terms of that variable.

5. Look for a guideline that you can use to set up an equation. A guideline might be a formula, such as *distance equals rate times time*, or a statement of a relationship, such as "The sum of the two numbers is 28."

6. Form an equation that contains the variable and that translates the conditions of the guideline from English to algebra.

7. Solve the equation, and use the solution to determine all facts requested in the problem.

8. Check all answers back into the **original statement of the problem**.

Keep these suggestions in mind as we continue to solve problems. We will elaborate on some of these suggestions at different times throughout the text. Now let's consider some examples.

Classroom Example
Find a number such that five-sixths of the number minus two-thirds of it is one less than one-fourth of the number.

EXAMPLE 5

Find a number such that three-eighths of the number minus one-half of it is 14 less than three-fourths of the number.

Solution

Let *n* represent the number to be found.

$$\frac{3}{8}n - \frac{1}{2}n = \frac{3}{4}n - 14$$

$$8\left(\frac{3}{8}n - \frac{1}{2}n\right) = 8\left(\frac{3}{4}n - 14\right)$$

$$8\left(\frac{3}{8}n\right) - 8\left(\frac{1}{2}n\right) = 8\left(\frac{3}{4}n\right) - 8(14)$$

$$3n - 4n = 6n - 112$$

$$-n = 6n - 112$$

$$-7n = -112$$

$$n = 16$$

The number is 16. Check it!

Classroom Example
The width of a rectangular parking lot is 4 meters less than two-thirds of the length. The perimeter of the lot is 192 meters. Find the length and width of the lot.

EXAMPLE 6

The width of a rectangular parking lot is 8 feet less than three-fifths of the length. The perimeter of the lot is 400 feet. Find the length and width of the lot.

Solution

Let *l* represent the length of the lot. Then $\frac{3}{5}l - 8$ represents the width (Figure 2.2).

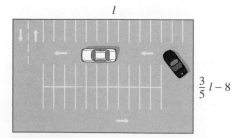

l

$\frac{3}{5}l - 8$

Figure 2.2

A guideline for this problem is the formula, *the perimeter of a rectangle equals twice the length plus twice the width* ($P = 2l + 2w$). Use this formula to form the following equation.

$$P = 2l + 2w$$

$$400 = 2l + 2\left(\frac{3}{5}l - 8\right)$$

Solving this equation, we obtain

$$400 = 2l + \frac{6l}{5} - 16$$

$$5(400) = 5\left(2l + \frac{6l}{5} - 16\right)$$

$$2000 = 10l + 6l - 80$$

$$2000 = 16l - 80$$

$$2080 = 16l$$

$$130 = l$$

The length of the lot is 130 feet, and the width is $\frac{3}{5}(130) - 8 = 70$ feet.

In Examples 5 and 6, note the use of different letters as variables. It is helpful to choose a variable that has significance for the problem you are working on. For example, in Example 6, the choice of l to represent the length seems natural and meaningful. (Certainly this is another matter of personal preference, but you might consider it.)

In Example 6 a geometric relationship, ($P = 2l + 2w$), serves as a guideline for setting up the equation. The following geometric relationships pertaining to angle measure may also serve as guidelines.

1. Complementary angles are two angles that together measure 90°.
2. Supplementary angles are two angles that together measure 180°.
3. The sum of the measures of the three angles of a triangle is 180°.

Classroom Example
One of two supplementary angles is 15° larger than one-fourth of the other angle. Find the measure of each of the angles.

EXAMPLE 7

One of two complementary angles is 6° larger than one-half of the other angle. Find the measure of each of the angles.

Solution

Let a represent the measure of one of the angles. Then $\frac{1}{2}a + 6$ represents the measure of the other angle. Because they are complementary angles, the sum of their measures is 90°.

$$a + \left(\frac{1}{2}a + 6\right) = 90$$

$$2a + a + 12 = 180$$

$$3a + 12 = 180$$

$$3a = 168$$

$$a = 56$$

If $a = 56$, then $\frac{1}{2}a + 6$ becomes $\frac{1}{2}(56) + 6 = 34$. The angles have measures of 34° and 56°.

EXAMPLE 8

Dominic's present age is 10 years more than Michele's present age. In 5 years Michele's age will be three-fifths of Dominic's age. What are their present ages?

Solution

Let x represent Michele's present age. Then Dominic's age will be represented by $x + 10$. In 5 years, everyone's age is increased by 5 years, so we need to add 5 to Michele's present age and 5 to Dominic's present age to represent their ages in 5 years. Therefore, in 5 years Michele's age will be represented by $x + 5$, and Dominic's age will be represented by $x + 15$. Thus we can set up the equation reflecting the fact that in 5 years, Michele's age will be three-fifths of Dominic's age.

$$x + 5 = \frac{3}{5}(x + 15)$$
$$5(x + 5) = 5\left[\frac{3}{5}(x + 15)\right]$$
$$5x + 25 = 3(x + 15)$$
$$5x + 25 = 3x + 45$$
$$2x + 25 = 45$$
$$2x = 20$$
$$x = 10$$

Because x represents Michele's present age, we know her age is 10. Dominic's present age is represented by $x + 10$, so his age is 20.

◼

Keep in mind that the problem-solving suggestions offered in this section simply outline a general algebraic approach to solving problems. You will add to this list throughout this course and in any subsequent mathematics courses that you take. Furthermore, you will be able to pick up additional problem-solving ideas from your instructor and from fellow classmates as you discuss problems in class. Always be on the alert for any ideas that might help you become a better problem solver.

Concept Quiz 2.2

For Problems 1–10, answer true or false.

1. When solving an equation that involves fractions, the equation can be cleared of all the fractions by multiplying both sides of the equation by the least common multiple of all the denominators in the problem.

2. The least common multiple of a set of denominators is referred to as the lowest common denominator.

3. The least common multiple of 4, 6, and 9 is 36.

4. The least common multiple of 3, 9, and 18 is 36.

5. Answers for word problems need to be checked back into the original statement of the problem.

6. In a right triangle, the two acute angles are complementary angles.

7. A triangle can have two supplementary angles.

8. The sum of the measures of the three angles in a triangle is 100°.

9. If x represents Eric's present age, then $5x$ represents his age in 5 years.

10. If x represents Joni's present age, then $x - 4$ represents her age in 4 years.

Problem Set 2.2

For Problems 1–40, solve each equation. (Objective 1)

1. $\dfrac{3}{4}x = 9$

2. $\dfrac{2}{3}x = -14$

3. $\dfrac{-2x}{3} = \dfrac{2}{5}$

4. $\dfrac{-5x}{4} = \dfrac{7}{2}$

5. $\dfrac{n}{2} - \dfrac{2}{3} = \dfrac{5}{6}$

6. $\dfrac{n}{4} - \dfrac{5}{6} = \dfrac{5}{12}$

7. $\dfrac{5n}{6} - \dfrac{n}{8} = \dfrac{-17}{12}$

8. $\dfrac{2n}{5} - \dfrac{n}{6} = \dfrac{-7}{10}$

9. $\dfrac{a}{4} - 1 = \dfrac{a}{3} + 2$

10. $\dfrac{3a}{7} - 1 = \dfrac{a}{3}$

11. $\dfrac{h}{4} + \dfrac{h}{5} = 1$

12. $\dfrac{h}{6} + \dfrac{3h}{8} = 1$

13. $\dfrac{h}{2} - \dfrac{h}{3} + \dfrac{h}{6} = 1$

14. $\dfrac{3h}{4} + \dfrac{2h}{5} = 1$

15. $\dfrac{x - 2}{3} + \dfrac{x + 3}{4} = \dfrac{11}{6}$

16. $\dfrac{x + 4}{5} + \dfrac{x - 1}{4} = \dfrac{37}{10}$

17. $\dfrac{x + 2}{2} - \dfrac{x - 1}{5} = \dfrac{3}{5}$

18. $\dfrac{2x + 1}{3} - \dfrac{x + 1}{7} = -\dfrac{1}{3}$

19. $\dfrac{n + 2}{4} - \dfrac{2n - 1}{3} = \dfrac{1}{6}$

20. $\dfrac{n - 1}{9} - \dfrac{n + 2}{6} = \dfrac{3}{4}$

21. $\dfrac{y}{3} + \dfrac{y - 5}{10} = \dfrac{4y + 3}{5}$

22. $\dfrac{y}{3} + \dfrac{y - 2}{8} = \dfrac{6y - 1}{12}$

23. $\dfrac{4x - 1}{10} - \dfrac{5x + 2}{4} = -3$

24. $\dfrac{2x - 1}{2} - \dfrac{3x + 1}{4} = \dfrac{3}{10}$

25. $\dfrac{2x - 1}{8} - 1 = \dfrac{x + 5}{7}$

26. $\dfrac{3x + 1}{9} + 2 = \dfrac{x - 1}{4}$

27. $\dfrac{2a - 3}{6} + \dfrac{3a - 2}{4} + \dfrac{5a + 6}{12} = 4$

28. $\dfrac{3a - 1}{4} + \dfrac{a - 2}{3} - \dfrac{a - 1}{5} = \dfrac{21}{20}$

29. $x + \dfrac{3x - 1}{9} - 4 = \dfrac{3x + 1}{3}$

30. $\dfrac{2x + 7}{8} + x - 2 - \dfrac{x - 1}{2}$

31. $\dfrac{x + 3}{2} + \dfrac{x + 4}{5} = \dfrac{3}{10}$

32. $\dfrac{x - 2}{5} - \dfrac{x - 3}{4} = -\dfrac{1}{20}$

33. $n + \dfrac{2n - 3}{9} - 2 = \dfrac{2n + 1}{3}$

34. $n - \dfrac{3n + 1}{6} - 1 = \dfrac{2n + 4}{12}$

35. $\dfrac{3}{4}(t - 2) - \dfrac{2}{5}(2t - 3) = \dfrac{1}{5}$

36. $\dfrac{2}{3}(2t + 1) - \dfrac{1}{2}(3t - 2) = 2$

37. $\dfrac{1}{2}(2x - 1) - \dfrac{1}{3}(5x + 2) = 3$

38. $\dfrac{2}{5}(4x - 1) + \dfrac{1}{4}(5x + 2) = -1$

39. $3x - 1 + \dfrac{2}{7}(7x - 2) = -\dfrac{11}{7}$

40. $2x + 5 + \dfrac{1}{2}(6x - 1) = -\dfrac{1}{2}$

For Problems 41–58, use an algebraic approach to solve each problem. (Objective 2)

41. Find a number such that one-half of the number is 3 less than two-thirds of the number.

42. One-half of a number plus three-fourths of the number is 2 more than four-thirds of the number. Find the number.

43. Suppose that the width of a certain rectangle is 1 inch more than one-fourth of its length. The perimeter of the rectangle is 42 inches. Find the length and width of the rectangle.

44. Suppose that the width of a rectangle is 3 centimeters less than two-thirds of its length. The perimeter of the rectangle is 114 centimeters. Find the length and width of the rectangle.

45. Find three consecutive integers such that the sum of the first plus one-third of the second plus three-eighths of the third is 25.

46. Lou is paid $1\frac{1}{2}$ times his normal hourly rate for each hour he works over 40 hours in a week. Last week he worked 44 hours and earned $483. What is his normal hourly rate?

47. A coaxial cable 20 feet long is cut into two pieces such that the length of one piece is two-thirds of the length of the other piece. Find the length of the shorter piece of cable.

48. Jody has a collection of 116 coins consisting of dimes, quarters, and silver dollars. The number of quarters is 5 less than three-fourths the number of dimes. The number of silver dollars is 7 more than five-eighths the number of dimes. How many coins of each kind are in her collection?

49. The sum of the present ages of Angie and her mother is 64 years. In eight years Angie will be three-fifths as old as her mother at that time. Find the present ages of Angie and her mother.

50. Annilee's present age is two-thirds of Jessie's present age. In 12 years the sum of their ages will be 54 years. Find their present ages.

51. Sydney's present age is one-half of Marcus's present age. In 12 years, Sydney's age will be five-eighths of Marcus's age. Find their present ages.

52. The sum of the present ages of Ian and his brother is 45. In 5 years, Ian's age will be five-sixths of his brother's age. Find their present ages.

53. Aura took three biology exams and has an average score of 88. Her second exam score was 10 points better than her first, and her third exam score was 4 points better than her second exam. What were her three exam scores?

54. The average of the salaries of Tim, Maida, and Aaron is $34,000 per year. Maida earns $10,000 more than Tim, and Aaron's salary is $8000 less than twice Tim's salary. Find the salary of each person.

55. One of two supplementary angles is 4° more than one-third of the other angle. Find the measure of each of the angles.

56. If one-half of the complement of an angle plus three-fourths of the supplement of the angle equals 110°, find the measure of the angle.

57. If the complement of an angle is 5° less than one-sixth of its supplement, find the measure of the angle.

58. In $\triangle ABC$, angle B is 8° less than one-half of angle A, and angle C is 28° larger than angle A. Find the measures of the three angles of the triangle.

Thoughts Into Words

59. Explain why the solution set of the equation $x + 3 = x + 4$ is the null set.

60. Explain why the solution set of the equation $\frac{x}{3} + \frac{x}{2} = \frac{5x}{6}$ is the entire set of real numbers.

61. Why must potential answers to word problems be checked back into the original statement of the problem?

62. Suppose your friend solved the problem, *find two consecutive odd integers whose sum is 28* like this:

$$x + x + 1 = 28$$
$$2x = 27$$
$$x = \frac{27}{2} = 13\frac{1}{2}$$

She claims that $13\frac{1}{2}$ will check in the equation. Where has she gone wrong and how would you help her?

2.3 Equations Involving Decimals and Problem Solving

OBJECTIVES
1. Solve equations involving decimals
2. Solve word problems including those involving discount and selling price

In solving equations that involve fractions, usually the procedure is to clear the equation of all fractions. To solve equations that involve decimals, there are two commonly used procedures. One procedure is to keep the numbers in decimal form and solve the equation by applying the properties. Another procedure is to multiply both sides of the equation by an appropriate power of 10 to clear the equation of all decimals. Which technique to use depends on your personal preference and on the complexity of the equation. The following examples demonstrate both techniques.

Classroom Example
Solve $0.3t - 0.17 = 0.08t + 1.15$.

EXAMPLE 1   Solve $0.2x + 0.24 = 0.08x + 0.72$.

Solution

Let's clear the decimals by multiplying both sides of the equation by 100.

$$0.2x + 0.24 = 0.08x + 0.72$$
$$100(0.2x + 0.24) = 100(0.08x + 0.72)$$
$$100(0.2x) + 100(0.24) = 100(0.08x) + 100(0.72)$$
$$20x + 24 = 8x + 72$$
$$12x + 24 = 72$$
$$12x = 48$$
$$x = 4$$

✔ **Check**

$$0.2x + 0.24 = 0.08x + 0.72$$
$$0.2(4) + 0.24 \overset{?}{=} 0.08(4) + 0.72$$
$$0.8 + 0.24 \overset{?}{=} 0.32 + 0.72$$
$$1.04 = 1.04$$

The solution set is $\{4\}$.

Classroom Example
Solve $0.04m + 0.08m = 4.8$.

EXAMPLE 2   Solve $0.07x + 0.11x = 3.6$.

Solution

Let's keep this problem in decimal form.

$$0.07x + 0.11x = 3.6$$
$$0.18x = 3.6$$
$$x = \frac{3.6}{0.18}$$
$$x = 20$$

✔ **Check**

$$0.07x + 0.11x = 3.6$$
$$0.07(20) + 0.11(20) \overset{?}{=} 3.6$$
$$1.4 + 2.2 \overset{?}{=} 3.6$$
$$3.6 = 3.6$$

The solution set is $\{20\}$.

Classroom Example
Solve $y = 2.16 + 0.73y$.

EXAMPLE 3   Solve $s = 1.95 + 0.35s$.

Solution

Let's keep this problem in decimal form.

$$s = 1.95 + 0.35s$$
$$s + (-0.35s) = 1.95 + 0.35s + (-0.35s)$$
$$0.65s = 1.95 \qquad \text{Remember, } s = 1.00s$$
$$s = \frac{1.95}{0.65}$$
$$s = 3$$

The solution set is $\{3\}$. Check it!

Classroom Example
Solve $0.16n + 0.21(6000 - n) = 1050$.

EXAMPLE 4   Solve $0.12x + 0.11(7000 - x) = 790$.

Solution

Let's clear the decimals by multiplying both sides of the equation by 100.

$$0.12x + 0.11(7000 - x) = 790$$
$$100[0.12x + 0.11(7000 - x)] = 100(790) \qquad \text{Multiply both sides by 100}$$
$$100(0.12x) + 100[0.11(7000 - x)] = 100(790)$$
$$12x + 11(7000 - x) = 79,000$$
$$12x + 77,000 - 11x = 79,000$$
$$x + 77,000 = 79,000$$
$$x = 2000$$

The solution set is $\{2000\}$.

Solving Word Problems, Including Discount and Selling Price Problems

We can solve many consumer problems with an algebraic approach. For example, let's consider some discount sale problems involving the relationship, *original selling price minus discount equals discount sale price*.

Original selling price − Discount = Discount sale price

Classroom Example
Karyn bought a coat at a 25% discount sale for $97.50. What was the original price of the coat?

EXAMPLE 5

Karyl bought a dress at a 35% discount sale for $32.50. What was the original price of the dress?

Solution

Let p represent the original price of the dress. Using the discount sale relationship as a guideline, we find that the problem translates into an equation as follows:

Original selling price	Minus	Discount	Equals	Discount sale price
p	−	$(35\%)(p)$	=	$\$32.50$

Switching this equation to decimal form and solving the equation, we obtain

$$p - (35\%)(p) = 32.50$$
$$(65\%)(p) = 32.50$$

$$0.65p = 32.50$$
$$p = 50$$

The original price of the dress was $50.

───────────────── ■

EXAMPLE 6

Jason received a private mailing coupon from an electronic store that offered 12% off any item. If he uses the coupon, how much will he have to pay for a laptop computer that is priced at $980?

Solution

Let s represent the discount sale price.

Original price	Minus	Discount	Equals	Sale price
$980	−	(12%)($980)	=	s

Solving this equation we obtain

$$980 - (12\%)(980) = s$$
$$980 - (0.12)(980) = s$$
$$980 - 117.60 = s$$
$$862.40 = s$$

With the coupon, Jason will pay $862.40 for the laptop computer.

───────────────── ■

Remark: Keep in mind that if an item is on sale for 35% off, then the purchaser will pay $100\% - 35\% = 65\%$ of the original price. Thus in Example 5 you could begin with the equation $0.65p = 32.50$. Likewise in Example 6 you could start with the equation $s = 0.88(980)$.

Another basic relationship that pertains to consumer problems is *selling price equals cost plus profit*. We can state profit (also called markup, markon, and margin of profit) in different ways. Profit may be stated as a percent of the selling price, as a percent of the cost, or simply in terms of dollars and cents. We shall consider some problems for which the profit is calculated either as a percent of the cost or as a percent of the selling price.

Selling price = Cost + Profit

EXAMPLE 7

Heather bought some artwork at an online auction for $400. She wants to resell the artwork on line and make a profit of 40% of the cost. What price should Heather list on line to make her profit?

Solution

Let s represent the selling price. Use the relationship *selling price equals cost plus profit* as a guideline.

Selling price	Equals	Cost	Plus	Profit
s	=	$400	+	(40%)($400)

Solving this equation yields

$$s = 400 + (40\%)(400)$$
$$s = 400 + (0.4)(400)$$
$$s = 400 + 160$$
$$s = 560$$

The selling price should be $560.

───────────────── ■

Remark: A profit of 40% of the cost means that the selling price is 100% of the cost plus 40% of the cost, or 140% of the cost. Thus in Example 7 we could solve the equation $s = 1.4(400)$.

EXAMPLE 8

A college bookstore purchased math textbooks for $54 each. At what price should the bookstore sell the books if the bookstore wants to make a profit of 60% of the selling price?

Solution

Let s represent the selling price.

Selling price	Equals	Cost	Plus	Profit
↓		↓		↓
s	$=$	54	$+$	$(60\%)(s)$

Solving this equation yields

$$s = 54 + (60\%)(s)$$
$$s = 54 + 0.6s$$
$$0.4s = 54$$
$$s = 135$$

The selling price should be $135.

EXAMPLE 9

If a maple tree costs a landscaper $55.00, and he sells it for $80.00, what is his rate of profit based on the cost? Round the rate to the nearest tenth of a percent.

Solution

Let r represent the rate of profit, and use the following guideline.

Selling price	Equals	Cost	Plus	Profit
↓		↓		↓
80.00	$=$	55.00	$+$	$r(55.00)$
25.00	$=$	$r(55.00)$		
$\dfrac{25.00}{55.00}$	$=$	r		
0.455	$\approx$	r		

To change the answer to a percent, multiply 0.455 by 100. Thus his rate of profit is 45.5%.

We can solve certain types of investment and money problems by using an algebraic approach. Consider the following examples.

EXAMPLE 10

Erick has 40 coins, consisting only of dimes and nickels, worth $3.35. How many dimes and how many nickels does he have?

Solution

Let x represent the number of dimes. Then the number of nickels can be represented by the total number of coins minus the number of dimes. Hence $40 - x$ represents the number of nickels. Because we know the amount of money Erick has, we need to multiply the number of each coin by its value. Use the following guideline.

Money from the dimes	Plus	Money from the nickels	Equals	Total money	
↓		↓		↓	
$0.10x$	$+$	$0.05(40 - x)$	$=$	3.35	
$10x$	$+$	$5(40 - x)$	$=$	335	Multiply both
$10x$	$+$	$200 - 5x$	$=$	335	sides by 100
		$5x + 200$	$=$	335	
		$5x$	$=$	135	
		x	$=$	27	

The number of dimes is 27, and the number of nickels is $40 - x = 13$. So, Erick has 27 dimes and 13 nickels.

EXAMPLE 11

Classroom Example
A woman invests $12,000, part of it at 2% and the remainder at 3%. Her total yearly interest from the two investments is $304. How much did she invest at each rate?

A man invests $8000, part of it at 6% and the remainder at 8%. His total yearly interest from the two investments is $580. How much did he invest at each rate?

Solution

Let x represent the amount he invested at 6%. Then $8000 - x$ represents the amount he invested at 8%. Use the following guideline.

Interest earned from 6% investment	$+$	Interest earned from 8% investment	$=$	Total amount of interest earned
↓		↓		↓
$(6\%)(x)$	$+$	$(8\%)(8000 - x)$	$=$	$\$580$

Solving this equation yields

$$(6\%)(x) + (8\%)(8000 - x) = 580$$
$$0.06x + 0.08(8000 - x) = 580$$
$$6x + 8(8000 - x) = 58,000 \qquad \text{Multiply both sides by 100}$$
$$6x + 64,000 - 8x = 58,000$$
$$-2x + 64,000 = 58,000$$
$$-2x = -6000$$
$$x = 3000$$

Therefore, $3000 was invested at 6%, and $8000 - \$3000 = \$5000$ was invested at 8%.

Don't forget to check word problems; determine whether the answers satisfy the conditions stated in the *original* problem. A check for Example 11 follows.

✔ Check

We claim that $3000 is invested at 6% and $5000 at 8%, and this satisfies the condition that $8000 is invested. The $3000 at 6% produces $180 of interest, and the $5000 at 8% produces $400. Therefore, the interest from the investments is $580. The conditions of the problem are satisfied, and our answers are correct.

As you tackle word problems throughout this text, keep in mind that our primary objective is to expand your repertoire of problem-solving techniques. We have chosen problems that provide you with the opportunity to use a variety of approaches to solving problems. Don't fall into the trap of thinking "I will never be faced with this kind of problem." That is not the issue; the goal is to develop problem-solving techniques. In the examples we are sharing some of our ideas for solving problems, but don't hesitate to use your own ingenuity. Furthermore, don't become discouraged—all of us have difficulty with some problems. Give each your best shot!

Concept Quiz 2.3

For Problems 1–10, answer true or false.

1. To solve an equation involving decimals, you must first multiply both sides of the equation by a power of 10.

2. When using the formula "selling price = cost + profit" the profit is always a percentage of the cost.

3. If Kim bought a putter for $50 and then sold it to a friend for $60, her rate of profit based on the cost was 10%.

4. To determine the selling price when the profit is a percent of the selling price, you can subtract the percent of profit from 100% and then divide the cost by that result.

5. If an item is bought for $30, then it should be sold for $37.50 in order to obtain a profit of 20% based on the selling price.

6. A discount of 10% followed by a discount of 20% is the same as a discount of 30%.

7. If an item is bought for $25, then it should be sold for $30 in order to obtain a profit of 20% based on the cost.

8. To solve the equation $0.4x + 0.15 = 0.06x + 0.71$, you can start by multiplying both sides of the equation by 100.

9. A 10% discount followed by a 40% discount is the same as a 40% discount followed by a 10% discount.

10. Multiplying both sides of the equation $0.4(x - 1.2) = 0.6$ by 10 produces the equivalent equation $4(x - 12) = 6$.

Problem Set 2.3

For Problems 1–28, solve each equation. (Objective 1)

1. $0.14x = 2.8$

2. $1.6x = 8$

3. $0.09y = 4.5$

4. $0.07y = 0.42$

5. $n + 0.4n = 56$

6. $n - 0.5n = 12$

7. $s = 9 + 0.25s$

8. $s = 15 + 0.4s$

9. $s = 3.3 + 0.45s$

10. $s = 2.1 + 0.6s$

11. $0.11x + 0.12(900 - x) = 104$

12. $0.09x + 0.11(500 - x) = 51$

13. $0.08(x + 200) = 0.07x + 20$

14. $0.07x = 152 - 0.08(2000 - x)$

15. $0.12t - 2.1 = 0.07t - 0.2$

16. $0.13t - 3.4 = 0.08t - 0.4$

17. $0.92 + 0.9(x - 0.3) = 2x - 5.95$

18. $0.3(2n - 5) = 11 - 0.65n$

19. $0.1d + 0.11(d + 1500) = 795$

20. $0.8x + 0.9(850 - x) = 715$

21. $0.12x + 0.1(5000 - x) = 560$

22. $0.10t + 0.12(t + 1000) = 560$

23. $0.09(x + 200) = 0.08x + 22$

24. $0.09x = 1650 - 0.12(x + 5000)$

25. $0.3(2t + 0.1) = 8.43$

26. $0.5(3t + 0.7) = 20.6$

27. $0.1(x - 0.1) - 0.4(x + 2) = -5.31$

28. $0.2(x + 0.2) + 0.5(x - 0.4) = 5.44$

For Problems 29–50, use an algebraic approach to solve each problem. (Objective 2)

29. Judy bought a coat at a 20% discount sale for $72. What was the original price of the coat?

30. Jim bought a pair of jeans at a 25% discount sale for $45. What was the original price of the jeans?

31. Find the discount sale price of a $64 item that is on sale for 15% off.

32. Find the discount sale price of a $72 item that is on sale for 35% off.

33. A retailer has some skirts that cost $30 each. She wants to sell them at a profit of 60% of the cost. What price should she charge for the skirts?

34. The owner of a pizza parlor wants to make a profit of 70% of the cost for each pizza sold. If it costs $7.50 to make a pizza, at what price should each pizza be sold?

35. If a ring costs a jeweler $1200, at what price should it be sold to yield a profit of 50% on the selling price?

36. If a head of lettuce costs a retailer $0.68, at what price should it be sold to yield a profit of 60% on the selling price?

37. If a pair of shoes costs a retailer $24, and he sells them for $39.60, what is his rate of profit based on the cost?

38. A retailer has some jackets that cost her $45 each. If she sells them for $83.25 per jacket, find her rate of profit based on the cost.

39. If a computer costs an electronics dealer $300, and she sells them for $800, what is her rate of profit based on the selling price?

40. A textbook costs a bookstore $45, and the store sells it for $60. Find the rate of profit based on the selling price.

41. Mitsuko's salary for next year is $44,940. This represents a 7% increase over this year's salary. Find Mitsuko's present salary.

42. Don bought a used car for $15,794, with 6% tax included. What was the price of the car without the tax?

43. Eva invested a certain amount of money at 4% interest and $1500 more than that amount at 6%. Her total yearly interest was $390. How much did she invest at each rate?

44. A total of $4000 was invested, part of it at 5% interest and the remainder at 6%. If the total yearly interest amounted to $230, how much was invested at each rate?

45. A sum of $95,000 is split between two investments, one paying 3% and the other 5%. If the total yearly interest amounted to $3910, how much was invested at 5%?

46. If $1500 is invested at 2% interest, how much money must be invested at 4% so that the total return for both investments is $100?

47. Suppose that Javier has a handful of coins, consisting of pennies, nickels, and dimes, worth $2.63. The number of nickels is 1 less than twice the number of pennies, and the number of dimes is 3 more than the number of nickels. How many coins of each kind does he have?

48. Sarah has a collection of nickels, dimes, and quarters worth $15.75. She has 10 more dimes than nickels and twice as many quarters as dimes. How many coins of each kind does she have?

49. A collection of 70 coins consisting of dimes, quarters, and half-dollars has a value of $17.75. There are three times as many quarters as dimes. Find the number of each kind of coin.

50. Abby has 37 coins, consisting only of dimes and quarters, worth $7.45. How many dimes and how many quarters does she have?

Thoughts Into Words

51. Go to Problem 39 and calculate the rate of profit based on cost. Compare the rate of profit based on cost to the rate of profit based on selling price. From a consumer's viewpoint, would you prefer that a retailer figure his profit on the basis of the cost of an item or on the basis of its selling price? Explain your answer.

52. Is a 10% discount followed by a 30% discount the same as a 30% discount followed by a 10% discount? Justify your answer.

53. What is wrong with the following solution and how should it be done?

$$1.2x + 2 = 3.8$$
$$10(1.2x) + 2 = 10(3.8)$$
$$12x + 2 = 38$$
$$12x = 36$$
$$x = 3$$

Further Investigations

For Problems 54–63, solve each equation and express the solutions in decimal form. Be sure to check your solutions. Use your calculator whenever it seems helpful.

54. $1.2x + 3.4 = 5.2$

55. $0.12x - 0.24 = 0.66$

56. $0.12x + 0.14(550 - x) = 72.5$

57. $0.14t + 0.13(890 - t) = 67.95$

58. $0.7n + 1.4 = 3.92$

59. $0.14n - 0.26 = 0.958$

60. $0.3(d + 1.8) = 4.86$

61. $0.6(d - 4.8) = 7.38$

62. $0.8(2x - 1.4) = 19.52$

63. $0.5(3x + 0.7) = 20.6$

64. The following formula can be used to determine the selling price of an item when the profit is based on a percent of the selling price.

$$\text{Selling price} = \frac{\text{Cost}}{100\% - \text{Percent of profit}}$$

Show how this formula is developed.

65. A retailer buys an item for $90, resells it for $100, and claims that she is making only a 10% profit. Is this claim correct?

66. Is a 10% discount followed by a 20% discount equal to a 30% discount? Defend your answer.

Answers to the Concept Quiz

1. False   **2.** False   **3.** False   **4.** True   **5.** True   **6.** False   **7.** True   **8.** True   **9.** True   **10.** False

---

2.4   Formulas

OBJECTIVES

1 Evaluate formulas for given values

2 Solve formulas for a specified variable

3 Use formulas to solve problems

To find the distance traveled in 4 hours at a rate of 55 miles per hour, we multiply the rate times the time; thus the distance is $55(4) = 220$ miles. We can state the rule *distance equals rate times time* as a formula, $d = rt$. **Formulas** are rules we state in symbolic form, usually as equations.

Formulas are typically used in two different ways. At times a formula is solved for a specific variable when we are given the numerical values for the other variables. This is much like evaluating an algebraic expression. At other times we need to change the form of an equation by solving for one variable in terms of the other variables. Throughout our work on formulas, we will use the properties of equality and the techniques we have previously learned for solving equations. Let's consider some examples.

Classroom Example
If we invest P dollars at r percent for t years, the amount of simple interest i is given by the formula $i = Prt$. Find the amount of interest earned by $400 at 3% for 3 years.

EXAMPLE 1

If we invest P dollars at r percent for t years, the amount of simple interest i is given by the formula $i = Prt$. Find the amount of interest earned by $5000 invested at 4% for 2 years.

Solution

By substituting $5000 for P, 4% for r, and 2 for t, we obtain

$$i = Prt$$
$$i = (5000)(4\%)(2)$$
$$i = (5000)(0.04)(2)$$
$$i = 400$$

Thus we earn $400 in interest.

EXAMPLE 2

If we invest P dollars at a simple rate of r percent, then the amount A accumulated after t years is given by the formula $A = P + Prt$. If we invest $5000 at 5%, how many years will it take to accumulate $6000?

Solution

Substituting $5000 for P, 5% for r, and $6000 for A, we obtain

$$A = P + Prt$$
$$6000 = 5000 + 5000(5\%)(t)$$

Solving this equation for t yields

$$6000 = 5000 + 5000(0.05)(t)$$
$$6000 = 5000 + 250t$$
$$1000 = 250t$$
$$4 = t$$

It will take 4 years to accumulate $6000. ▬

Solving Formulas for a Specified Variable

When we are using a formula, it is sometimes necessary to change its form. If we wanted to use a calculator or a spreadsheet to complete the following chart, we would have to solve the perimeter formula for a rectangle $(P = 2l + 2w)$ for w.

Perimeter (P)	32	24	36	18	56	80	
Length (l)	10	7	14	5	15	22	All in centimeters
Width (w)	?	?	?	?	?	?	

To perform the computational work or enter the formula into a spreadsheet, we would first solve the formula for w.

$$P = 2l + 2w$$

$$P - 2l = 2w \qquad \text{Add } -2l \text{ to both sides}$$

$$\frac{P - 2l}{2} = w \qquad \text{Multiply both sides by } \frac{1}{2}$$

$$w = \frac{P - 2l}{2} \qquad \text{Apply the symmetric property of equality}$$

Now for each value for P and l, we can easily determine the corresponding value for w. Be sure you agree with the following values for w: 6, 5, 4, 4, 13, and 18. Likewise we can also solve the formula $P = 2l + 2w$ for l in terms of P and w. The result would be $l = \dfrac{P - 2w}{2}$.

Let's consider some other often-used formulas and see how we can use the properties of equality to alter their forms. Here we will be solving a formula for a specified variable in terms of the other variables. The key is to isolate the term that contains the variable being solved for. Then, by appropriately applying the multiplication property of equality, we will solve the formula for the specified variable. Throughout this section, we will identify formulas when we first use them. (Some geometric formulas are also given on the endsheets.)

Classroom Example
Solve $V = \frac{1}{3}Bh$ for B (volume of a pyramid).

EXAMPLE 3   Solve $A = \frac{1}{2}bh$ for h (area of a triangle).

Solution

$$A = \frac{1}{2}bh$$

$$2A = bh \qquad \text{Multiply both sides by 2}$$

$$\frac{2A}{b} = h \qquad \text{Multiply both sides by } \frac{1}{b}$$

$$h = \frac{2A}{b} \qquad \text{Apply the symmetric property of equality}$$

Classroom Example
Solve $P = S - Sdt$ for d.

EXAMPLE 4   Solve $A = P + Prt$ for t.

Solution

$$A = P + Prt$$

$$A - P = Prt \qquad \text{Add } -P \text{ to both sides}$$

$$\frac{A - P}{Pr} = t \qquad \text{Multiply both sides by } \frac{1}{Pr}$$

$$t = \frac{A - P}{Pr} \qquad \text{Apply the symmetric property of equality}$$

Classroom Example
Solve $P = S - Sdt$ for S.

EXAMPLE 5   Solve $A = P + Prt$ for P.

Solution

$$A = P + Prt$$

$$A = P(1 + rt) \qquad \text{Apply the distributive property to the right side}$$

$$\frac{A}{1 + rt} = P \qquad \text{Multiply both sides by } \frac{1}{1 + rt}$$

$$P = \frac{A}{1 + rt} \qquad \text{Apply the symmetric property of equality}$$

Classroom Example
Solve $A = \frac{1}{2}h(b_1 + b_2)$ for b_2.

EXAMPLE 6   Solve $A = \frac{1}{2}h(b_1 + b_2)$ for b_1 (area of a trapezoid).

Solution

$$A = \frac{1}{2}h(b_1 + b_2)$$

$$2A = h(b_1 + b_2) \qquad \text{Multiply both sides by 2}$$

$$2A = hb_1 + hb_2 \qquad \text{Apply the distributive property to right side}$$

$$2A - hb_2 = hb_1 \qquad \text{Add } -hb_2 \text{ to both sides}$$

$$\frac{2A - hb_2}{h} = b_1 \qquad \text{Multiply both sides by } \frac{1}{h}$$

$$b_1 = \frac{2A - hb_2}{h} \qquad \text{Apply the symmetric property of equality}$$

In order to isolate the term containing the variable being solved for, we will apply the distributive property in different ways. In Example 5 you *must* use the distributive property to change from the form $P + Prt$ to $P(1 + rt)$. However, in Example 6 we used the distributive property to change $h(b_1 + b_2)$ to $hb_1 + hb_2$. In both problems the key is to isolate the term that contains the variable being solved for, so that an appropriate application of the multiplication property of equality will produce the desired result. Also note the use of subscripts to identify the two bases of a trapezoid. Subscripts enable us to use the same letter b to identify the bases, but b_1 represents one base and b_2 the other.

Sometimes we are faced with equations such as $ax + b = c$, where x is the variable and a, b, and c are referred to as *arbitrary constants*. Again we can use the properties of equality to solve the equation for x as follows:

$$ax + b = c$$
$$ax = c - b \qquad \text{Add } -b \text{ to both sides}$$
$$x = \frac{c - b}{a} \qquad \text{Multiply both sides by } \frac{1}{a}$$

In Chapter 7, we will be working with equations such as $2x - 5y = 7$, which are called equations of two variables in x and y. Often we need to change the form of such equations by solving for one variable in terms of the other variable. The properties of equality provide the basis for doing this.

Classroom Example
Solve $2x - 5y = 7$ for y in terms of x.

EXAMPLE 7   Solve $2x - 5y = 7$ for y in terms of x.

Solution

$$2x - 5y = 7$$
$$-5y = 7 - 2x \qquad \text{Add } -2x \text{ to both sides}$$
$$y = \frac{7 - 2x}{-5} \qquad \text{Multiply both sides by } -\frac{1}{5}$$
$$y = \frac{2x - 7}{5} \qquad \begin{array}{l}\text{Multiply the numerator and denominator of the fraction on the right}\\ \text{by } -1 \text{ (This final step is not absolutely necessary, but usually we}\\ \text{prefer to have a positive number as a denominator)}\end{array}$$

Equations of two variables may also contain arbitrary constants. For example, the equation $\frac{x}{a} + \frac{y}{b} = 1$ contains the variables x and y and the arbitrary constants a and b.

Classroom Example
Solve the equation $\frac{x}{a} - \frac{y}{b} = 1$ for y.

EXAMPLE 8   Solve the equation $\frac{x}{a} + \frac{y}{b} = 1$ for x.

Solution

$$\frac{x}{a} + \frac{y}{b} = 1$$
$$ab\left(\frac{x}{a} + \frac{y}{b}\right) = ab(1) \qquad \text{Multiply both sides by } ab$$
$$bx + ay = ab$$
$$bx = ab - ay \qquad \text{Add } -ay \text{ to both sides}$$
$$x = \frac{ab - ay}{b} \qquad \text{Multiply both sides by } \frac{1}{b}$$

Remark: Traditionally, equations that contain more than one variable, such as those in Examples 3–8, are called **literal equations**. As illustrated, it is sometimes necessary to solve a literal equation for one variable in terms of the other variable(s).

Using Formulas to Solve Problems

We often use formulas as guidelines for setting up an appropriate algebraic equation when solving a word problem. Let's consider an example to illustrate this point.

Classroom Example
How long will it take $400 to double itself if we invest it at 4% simple interest?

EXAMPLE 9

How long will it take $1000 to double itself if we invest it at 5% simple interest?

Solution

For $1000 to grow into $2000 (double itself), it must earn $1000 in interest. Thus we let t represent the number of years it will take $1000 to earn $1000 in interest. Now we can use the formula $i = Prt$ as a guideline.

$$i = Prt$$

$$1000 = 1000(5\%)(t)$$

Solving this equation, we obtain

$$1000 = 1000(0.05)(t)$$

$$1 = 0.05t \qquad \text{Divided both sides by 1000}$$

$$100 = 5t \qquad \text{Multiplied both sides by 100}$$

$$20 = t$$

It will take 20 years.

Sometimes we use formulas in the analysis of a problem but not as the main guideline for setting up the equation. For example, although uniform motion problems involve the formula $d = rt$, the main guideline for setting up an equation for such problems is usually a statement about times, rates, or distances. Let's consider an example to demonstrate.

Classroom Example
Latesha starts jogging at 3 miles per hour. Twenty minutes later, Sean starts jogging on the same route at 5 miles per hour. How long will it take Sean to catch Latesha?

EXAMPLE 10

Mercedes starts jogging at 5 miles per hour. One-half hour later, Karen starts jogging on the same route at 7 miles per hour. How long will it take Karen to catch Mercedes?

Solution

First, let's sketch a diagram and record some information (Figure 2.3).

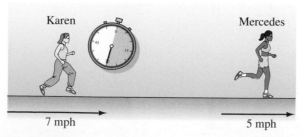

Figure 2.3

If we let t represent Karen's time, then $t + \dfrac{1}{2}$ represents Mercedes' time. We can use the statement *Karen's distance equals Mercedes' distance* as a guideline.

Karen's distance   Mercedes' distance

$$7t \quad = \quad 5\left(t + \dfrac{1}{2}\right)$$

Solving this equation, we obtain

$$7t = 5t + \dfrac{5}{2}$$

$$2t = \dfrac{5}{2}$$

$$t = \dfrac{5}{4}$$

Karen should catch Mercedes in $1\dfrac{1}{4}$ hours.

Remark: An important tool for problem solving is sketching a meaningful figure that can be used to record the given information and help in the analysis of the problem. Our sketches were done by professional artists for aesthetic purposes. Your sketches can be very roughly drawn as long as they depict the situation in a way that helps you analyze the problem.

Note that in the solution of Example 10 we used a figure and a simple arrow diagram to record and organize the information pertinent to the problem. Some people find it helpful to use a chart for that purpose. We shall use a chart in Example 11. Keep in mind that we are not trying to dictate a particular approach; you decide what works best for you.

EXAMPLE 11

Two trains leave a city at the same time, one traveling east and the other traveling west. At the end of $9\dfrac{1}{2}$ hours, they are 1292 miles apart. If the rate of the train traveling east is 8 miles per hour faster than the rate of the other train, find their rates.

Solution

If we let r represent the rate of the westbound train, then $r + 8$ represents the rate of the eastbound train. Now we can record the times and rates in a chart and then use the distance formula ($d = rt$) to represent the distances.

	Rate	Time	Distance ($d = rt$)
Westbound train	r	$9\dfrac{1}{2}$	$\dfrac{19}{2}r$
Eastbound train	$r + 8$	$9\dfrac{1}{2}$	$\dfrac{19}{2}(r + 8)$

Because the distance that the westbound train travels plus the distance that the eastbound train travels equals 1292 miles, we can set up and solve the following equation.

$$\underset{\text{distance}}{\text{Eastbound}} + \underset{\text{distance}}{\text{Westbound}} = \underset{\text{apart}}{\text{Miles}}$$

$$\frac{19r}{2} + \frac{19(r + 8)}{2} = 1292$$

$$19r + 19(r + 8) = 2584$$

$$19r + 19r + 152 = 2584$$

$$38r = 2432$$

$$r = 64$$

The westbound train travels at a rate of 64 miles per hour, and the eastbound train travels at a rate of $64 + 8 = 72$ miles per hour.

Now let's consider a problem that is often referred to as a mixture problem. There is no basic formula that applies to all of these problems, but we suggest that you think in terms of a pure substance, which is often helpful in setting up a guideline. Also keep in mind that the phrase "a 40% solution of some substance" means that the solution contains 40% of that particular substance and 60% of something else mixed with it. For example, a 40% salt solution contains 40% salt, and the other 60% is something else, probably water. Now let's illustrate what we mean by suggesting that you think in terms of a pure substance.

Classroom Example
Larson's Nursery stocks a 10% solution of herbicide and a 22% solution of herbicide. How many liters of each should be mixed to produce 20 liters of an 18% solution of herbicide?

EXAMPLE 12

Bryan's Pest Control stocks a 7% solution of insecticide for lawns and also a 15% solution. How many gallons of each should be mixed to produce 40 gallons that is 12% insecticide?

Solution

The key idea in solving such a problem is to recognize the following guideline.

$$\left(\begin{array}{c}\text{Amount of insecticide} \\ \text{in the 7\% solution}\end{array}\right) + \left(\begin{array}{c}\text{Amount of insecticide} \\ \text{in the 15\% solution}\end{array}\right) = \left(\begin{array}{c}\text{Amount of insecticide in} \\ \text{40 gallons of 12\% solution}\end{array}\right)$$

Let x represent the gallons of 7% solution. Then $40 - x$ represents the gallons of 15% solution. The guideline translates into the following equation.

$$(7\%)(x) + (15\%)(40 - x) = 12\%(40)$$

Solving this equation yields

$$0.07x + 0.15(40 - x) = 0.12(40)$$

$$0.07x + 6 - 0.15x = 4.8$$

$$-0.08x + 6 = 4.8$$

$$-0.08x = -1.2$$

$$x = 15$$

Thus 15 gallons of 7% solution and $40 - x = 25$ gallons of 15% solution need to be mixed to obtain 40 gallons of 12% solution.

Classroom Example
How many gallons of pure antifreeze must be added to 12 gallons of a 30% solution to obtain a 70% solution?

EXAMPLE 13

How many liters of pure alcohol must we add to 20 liters of a 40% solution to obtain a 60% solution?

Solution

The key idea in solving such a problem is to recognize the following guideline.

$$\left(\begin{array}{c}\text{Amount of pure} \\ \text{alcohol in the} \\ \text{original solution}\end{array}\right) + \left(\begin{array}{c}\text{Amount of} \\ \text{pure alcohol} \\ \text{to be added}\end{array}\right) = \left(\begin{array}{c}\text{Amount of pure} \\ \text{alcohol in the} \\ \text{final solution}\end{array}\right)$$

Let l represent the number of liters of pure alcohol to be added, and the guideline translates into the following equation.

$$(40\%)(20) + l = 60\%(20 + l)$$

Solving this equation yields

$$0.4(20) + l = 0.6(20 + l)$$
$$8 + l = 12 + 0.6l$$
$$0.4l = 4$$
$$l = 10$$

We need to add 10 liters of pure alcohol. (Remember to check this answer back into the original statement of the problem.)

■

Concept Quiz 2.4

For Problems 1–10, answer true or false.

1. Formulas are rules stated in symbolic form, usually as algebraic expressions.
2. The properties of equality that apply to solving equations also apply to solving formulas.
3. The formula $A = P + Prt$ can be solved for r or t but not for P.
4. The formula $i = Prt$ is equivalent to $P = \dfrac{i}{rt}$.
5. The equation $y = mx + b$ is equivalent to $x = \dfrac{y - b}{m}$.
6. The formula $F = \dfrac{9}{5}C + 32$ is equivalent to $C = \dfrac{5}{9}(F - 32)$.
7. Using the formula $F = \dfrac{9}{5}C + 32$, a temperature of 30° Celsius is equal to 86° Fahrenheit.
8. Using the formula $C = \dfrac{5}{9}(F - 32)$, a temperature of 32° Fahrenheit is equal to 0° Celsius.
9. The amount of pure acid in 30 ounces of a 20% acid solution is 10 ounces.
10. For an equation such as $ax + b = c$, where x is the variable, a, b, and c are referred to as arbitrary constants.

Problem Set 2.4

For Problems 1–16, use the formula to solve for the given variable. (Objective 1)

1. Solve $i = Prt$ for i, given that $P = \$3000$, $r = 4\%$, and $t = 5$ years.

2. Solve $i = Prt$ for i, given that $P = \$5000$, $r = 6\%$, and $t = 3\dfrac{1}{2}$ years.

3. Solve $i = Prt$ for t, given that $P = \$4000$, $r = 5\%$, and $i = \$600$.

4. Solve $i = Prt$ for t, given that $P = \$1250$, $r = 3\%$, and $i = \$150$.

5. Solve $i = Prt$ for r, given that $P = \$600$, $t = 2\dfrac{1}{2}$ years, and $i = \$90$. Express r as a percent.

6. Solve $i = Prt$ for r, given that $P = \$700$, $t = 2$ years, and $i = \$84$. Express r as a percent.

7. Solve $i = Prt$ for P, given that $r = 9\%$, $t = 3$ years, and $i = \$216$.

8. Solve $i = Prt$ for P, given that $r = 8\dfrac{1}{2}\%$, $t = 2$ years, and $i = \$204$.

9. Solve $A = P + Prt$ for A, given that $P = \$1000$, $r = 7\%$, and $t = 5$ years.

10. Solve $A = P + Prt$ for A, given that $P = \$850$, $r = 4\dfrac{1}{2}\%$, and $t = 10$ years.

11. Solve $A = P + Prt$ for r, given that $A = \$1372$, $P = \$700$, and $t = 12$ years. Express r as a percent.

12. Solve $A = P + Prt$ for r, given that $A = \$516$, $P = \$300$, and $t = 8$ years. Express r as a percent.

13. Solve $A = P + Prt$ for P, given that $A = \$326$, $r = 7\%$, and $t = 9$ years.

14. Solve $A = P + Prt$ for P, given that $A = \$720$, $r = 8\%$, and $t = 10$ years.

15. Solve the formula $A = \dfrac{1}{2}h(b_1 + b_2)$ for b_2 and complete the following chart.

A	98	104	49	162	$16\frac{1}{2}$	$38\frac{1}{2}$	square feet
h	14	8	7	9	3	11	feet
b_1	8	12	4	16	4	5	feet
b_2	?	?	?	?	?	?	feet

A = area, h = height, b_1 = one base, b_2 = other base

16. Solve the formula $P = 2l + 2w$ for l and complete the following chart.

P	28	18	12	34	68	centimeters
w	6	3	2	7	14	centimeters
l	?	?	?	?	?	centimeters

P = perimeter, w = width, l = length

For Problems 17–26, solve each of the following for the indicated variable. (**Objective 2**)

17. $V = Bh$ for h (Volume of a prism)

18. $A = lw$ for l (Area of a rectangle)

19. $V = \pi r^2 h$ for h (Volume of a circular cylinder)

20. $V = \dfrac{1}{3}Bh$ for B (Volume of a pyramid)

21. $C = 2\pi r$ for r (Circumference of a circle)

22. $A = 2\pi r^2 + 2\pi rh$ for h (Surface area of a circular cylinder)

23. $I = \dfrac{100M}{C}$ for C (Intelligence quotient)

24. $A = \dfrac{1}{2}h(b_1 + b_2)$ for h (Area of a trapezoid)

25. $F = \dfrac{9}{5}C + 32$ for C (Celsius to Fahrenheit)

26. $C = \dfrac{5}{9}(F - 32)$ for F (Fahrenheit to Celsius)

For Problems 27–36, solve each equation for x. (**Objective 2**)

27. $y = mx + b$

28. $\dfrac{x}{a} + \dfrac{y}{b} = 1$

29. $y - y_1 = m(x - x_1)$

30. $a(x + b) = c$

31. $a(x + b) = b(x - c)$

32. $x(a - b) = m(x - c)$

33. $\dfrac{x - a}{b} = c$

34. $\dfrac{x}{a} - 1 = b$

35. $\dfrac{1}{3}x + a = \dfrac{1}{2}b$

36. $\dfrac{2}{3}x - \dfrac{1}{4}a = b$

For Problems 37–46, solve each equation for the indicated variable. (**Objective 2**)

37. $2x - 5y = 7$ for x

38. $5x - 6y = 12$ for x

39. $-7x - y = 4$ for y

40. $3x - 2y = -1$ for y

41. $3(x - 2y) = 4$ for x

42. $7(2x + 5y) = 6$ for y

43. $\dfrac{y - a}{b} = \dfrac{x + b}{c}$ for x

44. $\dfrac{x - a}{b} = \dfrac{y - a}{c}$ for y

45. $(y + 1)(a - 3) = x - 2$ for y

46. $(y - 2)(a + 1) = x$ for y

Solve each of Problems 47–62 by setting up and solving an appropriate algebraic equation. (**Objective 3**)

47. Suppose that the length of a certain rectangle is 2 meters less than four times its width. The perimeter of the rectangle is 56 meters. Find the length and width of the rectangle.

48. The perimeter of a triangle is 42 inches. The second side is 1 inch more than twice the first side, and the third side is 1 inch less than three times the first side. Find the lengths of the three sides of the triangle.

49. How long will it take $500 to double itself at 6% simple interest?

50. How long will it take $700 to triple itself at 5% simple interest?

51. How long will it take P dollars to double itself at 6% simple interest?

52. How long will it take P dollars to triple itself at 5% simple interest?

53. Two airplanes leave Chicago at the same time and fly in opposite directions. If one travels at 450 miles per hour and the other at 550 miles per hour, how long will it take for them to be 4000 miles apart?

54. Look at Figure 2.4. Tyrone leaves city A on a moped traveling toward city B at 18 miles per hour. At the same time, Tina leaves city B on a bicycle traveling toward city A at 14 miles per hour. The distance between the two cities is 112 miles. How long will it take before Tyrone and Tina meet?

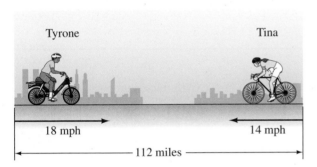

Tyrone   Tina

18 mph   14 mph

— 112 miles —

Figure 2.4

55. Juan starts walking at 4 miles per hour. An hour and a half later, Cathy starts jogging along the same route at 6 miles per hour. How long will it take Cathy to catch up with Juan?

56. A car leaves a town at 60 kilometers per hour. How long will it take a second car, traveling at 75 kilometers per hour, to catch the first car if it leaves 1 hour later?

57. Bret started on a 70-mile bicycle ride at 20 miles per hour. After a time he became a little tired and slowed down to 12 miles per hour for the rest of the trip. The entire trip of 70 miles took $4\frac{1}{2}$ hours. How far had Bret ridden when he reduced his speed to 12 miles per hour?

58. How many gallons of a 12%-salt solution must be mixed with 6 gallons of a 20%-salt solution to obtain a 15%-salt solution?

59. A pharmacist has a 6% solution of cough syrup and a 14% solution of the same cough syrup. How many ounces of each must be mixed to make 16 ounces of a 10% solution of cough syrup?

60. Suppose that you have a supply of a 30% solution of alcohol and a 70% solution of alcohol. How many quarts of each should be mixed to produce 20 quarts that is 40% alcohol?

61. How many milliliters of pure acid must be added to 150 milliliters of a 30% solution of acid to obtain a 40% solution?

62. How many cups of grapefruit juice must be added to 40 cups of punch that is 5% grapefruit juice to obtain a punch that is 10% grapefruit juice?

Thoughts Into Words

63. Some people subtract 32 and then divide by 2 to estimate the change from a Fahrenheit reading to a Celsius reading. Why does this give an estimate, and how good is the estimate?

64. One of your classmates analyzes Problem 56 as follows: "The first car has traveled 60 kilometers before the second car starts. Because the second car travels 15 kilometers per hour faster, it will take $\frac{60}{15} = 4$ hours for the second car to overtake the first car." How would you react to this analysis of the problem?

65. Summarize the new ideas that you have learned thus far in this course that relate to problem solving.

Further Investigations

For Problems 66–73, use your calculator to help solve each formula for the indicated variable.

66. Solve $i = Prt$ for i, given that $P = \$875$, $r = 3\frac{1}{2}\%$, and $t = 4$ years.

67. Solve $i = Prt$ for i, given that $P = \$1125$, $r = 6\frac{1}{4}\%$, and $t = 4$ years.

68. Solve $i = Prt$ for t, given that $i = \$129.50$, $P = \$925$, and $r = 4\%$.

69. Solve $i = Prt$ for t, given that $i = \$56.25$, $P = \$1250$, and $r = 3\%$.

70. Solve $i = Prt$ for r, given that $i = \$232.50$, $P = \$1550$, and $t = 2$ years. Express r as a percent.

71. Solve $i = Prt$ for r, given that $i = \$88.00$, $P = \$2200$, and $t = 0.5$ of a year. Express r as a percent.

72. Solve $A = P + Prt$ for P, given that $A = \$1358.50$, $r = 4\frac{1}{2}\%$, and $t = 1$ year.

73. Solve $A = P + Prt$ for P, given that $A = \$2173.75$, $r = 8\frac{3}{4}\%$, and $t = 2$ years.

74. If you have access to computer software that includes spreadsheets, go to Problems 15 and 16. You should be able to enter the given information in rows. Then, when you enter a formula in a cell below the information and drag that formula across the columns, the software should produce all the answers.

Answers to the Concept Quiz

1. False   **2.** True   **3.** False   **4.** True   **5.** True   **6.** True   **7.** True   **8.** True   **9.** False   **10.** True

---

2.5   Inequalities

OBJECTIVES   **1** Write solution sets in interval notation

2 Solve inequalities

We listed the basic inequality symbols in Section 1.2. With these symbols we can make various **statements of inequality**:

$a < b$ means a is less than b

$a \leq b$ means a is less than or equal to b

$a > b$ means a is greater than b

$a \geq b$ means a is greater than or equal to b

Here are some examples of **numerical statements of inequality**:

$$7 + 8 > 10 \qquad\qquad -4 + (-6) \geq -10$$
$$-4 > -6 \qquad\qquad 7 - 9 \leq -2$$
$$7 - 1 < 20 \qquad\qquad 3 + 4 > 12$$
$$8(-3) < 5(-3) \qquad 7 - 1 < 0$$

Note that only $3 + 4 > 12$ and $7 - 1 < 0$ are *false*; the other six are *true* numerical statements.

Algebraic inequalities contain one or more variables. The following are examples of algebraic inequalities.

$$x + 4 > 8 \qquad\qquad 3x + 2y \leq 4$$
$$3x - 1 < 15 \qquad\qquad x^2 + y^2 + z^2 \geq 7$$
$$y^2 + 2y - 4 \geq 0$$

An algebraic inequality such as $x + 4 > 8$ is neither true nor false as it stands, and we call it an **open sentence**. For each numerical value we substitute for x, the algebraic inequality $x + 4 > 8$ becomes a numerical statement of inequality that is true or false. For example, if $x = -3$, then $x + 4 > 8$ becomes $-3 + 4 > 8$, which is false. If $x = 5$, then $x + 4 > 8$ becomes $5 + 4 > 8$, which is true. **Solving an inequality** is the process of finding the numbers that make an algebraic inequality a true numerical statement. We call such numbers the *solutions* of the inequality; the solutions *satisfy* the inequality.

There are various ways to display the solution set of an inequality. The three most common ways to show the solution set are set builder notation, a line graph of the solution, or interval notation. The examples in Figure 2.5 contain some simple algebraic inequalities, their solution sets, graphs of the solution sets, and the solution sets written in interval notation. Look them over carefully to be sure you understand the symbols.

Algebraic inequality	Solution set	Graph of solution set	Interval notation
$x < 2$	$\{x \mid x < 2\}$	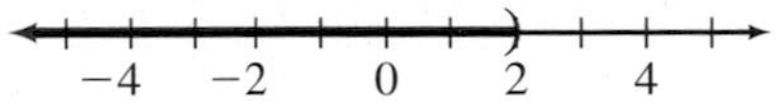	$(-\infty, 2)$
$x > -1$	$\{x \mid x > -1\}$	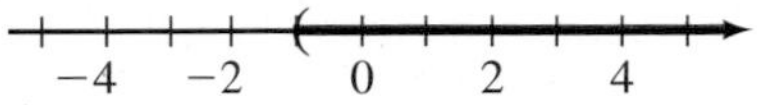	$(-1, \infty)$
$3 < x$	$\{x \mid x > 3\}$	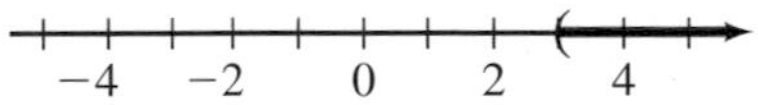	$(3, \infty)$
$x \geq 1$ ($\geq$ is read "greater than or equal to")	$\{x \mid x \geq 1\}$	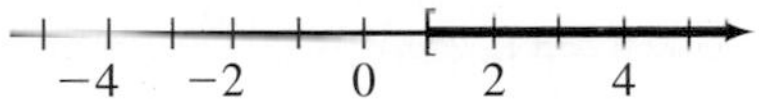	$[1, \infty)$
$x \leq 2$ ($\leq$ is read "less than or equal to")	$\{x \mid x \leq 2\}$	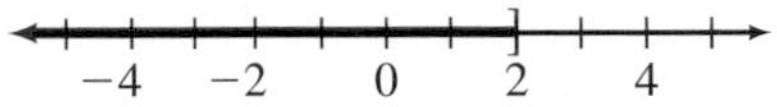	$(-\infty, 2]$
$1 \geq x$	$\{x \mid x \leq 1\}$	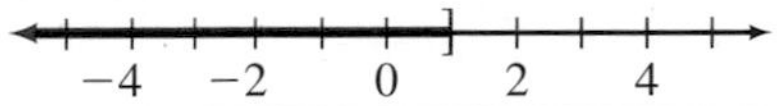	$(-\infty, 1]$

Figure 2.5

Classroom Example
Express the given inequalities in interval notation and graph the interval on a number line:

(a) $x > -1$

(b) $x \leq -2$

(c) $x < 2$

(d) $x \geq 1$

EXAMPLE 1

Express the given inequalities in interval notation and graph the interval on a number line:

(a) $x > -2$ (b) $x \leq -1$ (c) $x < 3$ (d) $x \geq 2$

Solution

(a) For the solution set of the inequality $x > -2$, we want all the numbers greater than -2 but not including -2. In interval notation, the solution set is written as $(-2, \infty)$; the parentheses are used to indicate exclusion of the endpoint. The use of a parenthesis carries over to the graph of the solution set. In Figure 2.6, the left-hand parenthesis at -2 indicates that -2 is *not* a solution, and the red part of the line to the right of -2 indicates that all real numbers greater than -2 are solutions. We refer to the red portion of the number line as the *graph* of the solution set.

Inequality   Interval notation   Graph

$x > -2$ $(-2, \infty)$

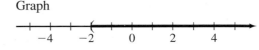

Figure 2.6

(b) For the solution set of the inequality $x \leq -1$, we want all the numbers less than or equal to -1. In interval notation, the solution set is written as $(-\infty, -1]$, where a square bracket is used to indicate inclusion of the endpoint. The use of a square bracket carries over to the graph of the solution set. In Figure 2.7, the right-hand square bracket at -1 indicates that -1 is part of the solution, and the red part of the line to the left of -1 indicates that all real numbers less than -1 are solutions.

Inequality   Interval notation   Graph

$x \leq -1$ $(-\infty, -1]$

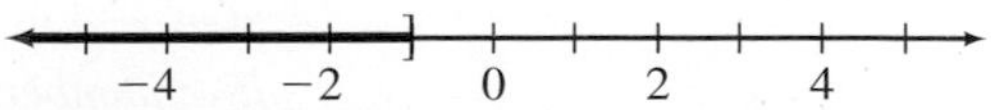

Figure 2.7

(c) For the solution set of the inequality $x < 3$, we want all the numbers less than 3 but not including 3. In interval notation, the solution set is written as $(-\infty, 3)$; see Figure 2.8.

Inequality	Interval notation	Graph
$x < 3$	$(-\infty, 3)$	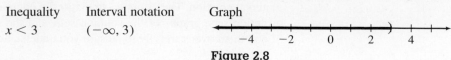

Figure 2.8

(d) For the solution set of the inequality $x \geq 2$, we want all the numbers greater than or equal to 2. In interval notation, the solution set is written as $[2, \infty)$; see Figure 2.9.

Inequality	Interval notation	Graph
$x \geq 2$	$[2, \infty)$	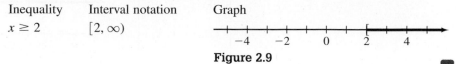

Figure 2.9

Remark: Note that the infinity symbol always has a parenthesis next to it because no actual endpoint could be included.

Solving Inequalities

The general process for solving inequalities closely parallels the process for solving equations. We continue to replace the given inequality with equivalent, but simpler, inequalities. For example,

$$3x + 4 > 10 \qquad (1)$$

$$3x > 6 \qquad (2)$$

$$x > 2 \qquad (3)$$

are all equivalent inequalities; that is, they all have the same solutions. By inspection we see that the solutions for (3) are all numbers greater than 2. Thus (1) has the same solutions.

The exact procedure for simplifying inequalities so that we can determine the solutions is based primarily on two properties. The first of these is the addition property of inequality.

Addition Property of Inequality

For all real numbers a, b, and c,

$$a > b \quad \text{if and only if} \quad a + c > b + c$$

The addition property of inequality states that we can add any number to both sides of an inequality to produce an equivalent inequality. We have stated the property in terms of $>$, but analogous properties exist for $<$, $\geq$, and $\leq$.

Before we state the multiplication property of inequality, let's look at some numerical examples.

$2 < 5$	Multiply both sides by 4	$8 < 20$
$-3 > -7$	Multiply both sides by 2	$-6 > -14$
$-4 < 6$	Multiply both sides by 10	$-40 < 60$
$4 < 8$	Multiply both sides by -3	$-12 > -24$
$3 > -2$	Multiply both sides by -4	$-12 < 8$
$-4 < -1$	Multiply both sides by -2	$8 > 2$

Notice in the first three examples that when we multiply both sides of an inequality by a *positive number*, we get an inequality of the *same sense*. That means that if the original inequality is *less than*, then the new inequality is *less than*; and if the original inequality is *greater than*, then the new inequality is *greater than*. The last three examples illustrate that when we multiply both sides of an inequality by a *negative number* we get an inequality of the *opposite sense*.

We can state the multiplication property of inequality as follows.

Multiplication Property of Inequality

(a) For all real numbers a, b, and c, with $c > 0$,

$$a > b \quad \text{if and only if} \quad ac > bc$$

(b) For all real numbers a, b, and c, with $c < 0$,

$$a > b \quad \text{if and only if} \quad ac < bc$$

Similar properties hold if we reverse each inequality or if we replace $>$ with $\geq$ and $<$ with $\leq$. For example, if $a \leq b$ and $c < 0$, then $ac > bc$.

Now let's use the addition and multiplication properties of inequality to help solve some inequalities.

Classroom Example
Solve $2x + 5 > -1$, and graph the solutions.

EXAMPLE 2   Solve $3x - 4 > 8$ and graph the solutions.

Solution

$$3x - 4 > 8$$
$$3x - 4 + 4 > 8 + 4 \qquad \text{Add 4 to both sides}$$
$$3x > 12$$
$$\frac{1}{3}(3x) > \frac{1}{3}(12) \qquad \text{Multiply both sides by } \frac{1}{3}$$
$$x > 4$$

The solution set is $(4, \infty)$. Figure 2.10 shows the graph of the solution set.

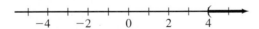

Figure 2.10

Classroom Example
Solve $-5x + 4 > 9$, and graph the solutions.

EXAMPLE 3   Solve $-2x + 1 > 5$ and graph the solutions.

Solution

$$-2x + 1 > 5$$
$$-2x + 1 + (-1) > 5 + (-1) \qquad \text{Add } -1 \text{ to both sides}$$
$$-2x > 4$$
$$-\frac{1}{2}(-2x) < -\frac{1}{2}(4) \qquad \text{Multiply both sides by } -\frac{1}{2}$$

Note that the sense of the
$$x < -2 \qquad \text{inequality has been reversed}$$

The solution set is $(-\infty, -2)$, which can be illustrated on a number line as in Figure 2.11.

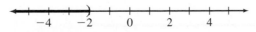

Figure 2.11

Checking solutions for an inequality presents a problem. Obviously, we cannot check all of the infinitely many solutions for a particular inequality. However, by checking at least one solution, especially when the multiplication property has been used, we might catch the common mistake of forgetting to change the sense of an inequality. In Example 3 we are claiming that all numbers less than -2 will satisfy the original inequality. Let's check one such number, say -4.

$$-2x + 1 > 5$$

$$-2(-4) + 1 \overset{?}{>} 5 \quad \text{when } x = -4$$

$$8 + 1 \overset{?}{>} 5$$

$$9 > 5$$

Thus -4 satisfies the original inequality. Had we forgotten to switch the sense of the inequality when both sides were multiplied by $-\dfrac{1}{2}$, our answer would have been $x > -2$, and we would have detected such an error by the check.

Many of the same techniques used to solve equations, such as removing parentheses and combining similar terms, may be used to solve inequalities. However, we must be extremely careful when using the multiplication property of inequality. Study each of the following examples very carefully. The format we used highlights the major steps of a solution.

Classroom Example
Solve $-4x + 7x + 3 \le 5x - 4 - x$.

EXAMPLE 4   Solve $-3x + 5x - 2 \ge 8x - 7 - 9x$.

Solution

$$-3x + 5x - 2 \ge 8x - 7 - 9x$$

$2x - 2 \ge -x - 7$	Combine similar terms on both sides
$3x - 2 \ge -7$	Add x to both sides
$3x \ge -5$	Add 2 to both sides
$\dfrac{1}{3}(3x) \ge \dfrac{1}{3}(-5)$	Multiply both sides by $\dfrac{1}{3}$
$x \ge -\dfrac{5}{3}$	

The solution set is $\left[-\dfrac{5}{3}, \infty \right)$.

Classroom Example
Solve $-2(x + 3) \ge 4$, and graph the solutions.

EXAMPLE 5   Solve $-5(x - 1) \le 10$ and graph the solutions.

Solution

$-5(x - 1) \le 10$	
$-5x + 5 \le 10$	Apply the distributive property on the left
$-5x \le 5$	Add -5 to both sides
$-\dfrac{1}{5}(-5x) \ge -\dfrac{1}{5}(5)$	Multiply both sides by $-\dfrac{1}{5}$, which reverses the inequality
$x \ge -1$	

The solution set is $[-1, \infty)$, and it can be graphed as in Figure 2.12.

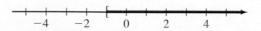

Figure 2.12

Classroom Example
Solve $3(x + 1) < 5(x - 2)$.

EXAMPLE 6   Solve $4(x - 3) > 9(x + 1)$.

Solution

$$4(x - 3) > 9(x + 1)$$
$$4x - 12 > 9x + 9 \qquad \text{Apply the distributive property}$$
$$-5x - 12 > 9 \qquad \text{Add } -9x \text{ to both sides}$$
$$-5x > 21 \qquad \text{Add 12 to both sides}$$
$$-\frac{1}{5}(-5x) < -\frac{1}{5}(21) \qquad \text{Multiply both sides by } -\frac{1}{5}, \text{ which reverses the inequality}$$
$$x < -\frac{21}{5}$$

The solution set is $\left(-\infty, -\frac{21}{5}\right)$.

The next example will solve the inequality without indicating the justification for each step. Be sure that you can supply the reasons for the steps.

Classroom Example
Solve $4(3x - 5) + 7(2x + 3) > 5(7x + 3)$.

EXAMPLE 7   Solve $3(2x + 1) - 2(2x + 5) < 5(3x - 2)$.

Solution

$$3(2x + 1) - 2(2x + 5) < 5(3x - 2)$$
$$6x + 3 - 4x - 10 < 15x - 10$$
$$2x - 7 < 15x - 10$$
$$-13x - 7 < -10$$
$$-13x < -3$$
$$-\frac{1}{13}(-13x) > -\frac{1}{13}(-3)$$
$$x > \frac{3}{13}$$

The solution set is $\left(\frac{3}{13}, \infty\right)$.

Concept Quiz 2.5

For Problems 1–10, answer true or false.

1. Numerical statements of inequality are always true.
2. The algebraic statement $x + 4 > 6$ is called an open sentence.
3. The algebraic inequality $2x > 10$ has one solution.
4. The algebraic inequality $x < 3$ has an infinite number of solutions.
5. The solution set for the inequality $-3x - 1 > 2$ is $(-1, \infty)$.
6. When graphing the solution set of an inequality, a square bracket is used to include the endpoint.
7. The solution set of the inequality $x \geq 4$ is written $(4, \infty)$.
8. The solution set of the inequality $x < -5$ is written $(-\infty, -5)$.
9. When multiplying both sides of an inequality by a negative number, the sense of the inequality stays the same.
10. When adding a negative number to both sides of an inequality, the sense of the inequality stays the same.

Problem Set 2.5

For Problems 1–8, express the given inequality in interval notation and sketch a graph of the interval. **(Objective 1)**

1. $x > 1$

2. $x > -2$

3. $x \geq -1$

4. $x \geq 3$

5. $x < -2$

6. $x < 1$

7. $x \leq 2$

8. $x \leq 0$

For Problems 9–16, express each interval as an inequality using the variable x. For example, we can express the interval $[5, \infty)$ as $x \geq 5$. **(Objective 1)**

9. $(-\infty, 4)$

10. $(-\infty, -2)$

11. $(-\infty, -7]$

12. $(-\infty, 9]$

13. $(8, \infty)$

14. $(-5, \infty)$

15. $[-7, \infty)$

16. $[10, \infty)$

For Problems 17–40, solve each of the inequalities and graph the solution set on a number line. **(Objective 2)**

17. $x - 3 > -2$

18. $x + 2 < 1$

19. $-2x \geq 8$

20. $-3x \leq -9$

21. $5x \leq -10$

22. $4x \geq -4$

23. $2x + 1 < 5$

24. $2x + 2 > 4$

25. $3x - 2 > -5$

26. $5x - 3 < -3$

27. $-7x - 3 \leq 4$

28. $-3x - 1 \geq 8$

29. $2 + 6x > -10$

30. $1 + 6x > -17$

31. $5 - 3x < 11$

32. $4 - 2x < 12$

33. $15 < 1 - 7x$

34. $12 < 2 - 5x$

35. $-10 \leq 2 + 4x$

36. $-9 \leq 1 + 2x$

37. $3(x + 2) > 6$

38. $2(x - 1) < -4$

39. $5x + 2 \geq 4x + 6$

40. $6x - 4 \leq 5x - 4$

For Problems 41–70, solve each inequality and express the solution set using interval notation. **(Objective 2)**

41. $2x - 1 > 6$

42. $3x - 2 < 12$

43. $-5x - 2 < -14$

44. $5 - 4x > -2$

45. $-3(2x + 1) \geq 12$

46. $-2(3x + 2) \leq 18$

47. $4(3x - 2) \geq -3$

48. $3(4x - 3) \leq -11$

49. $6x - 2 > 4x - 14$

50. $9x + 5 < 6x - 10$

51. $2x - 7 < 6x + 13$

52. $2x - 3 > 7x + 22$

53. $4(x - 3) \leq -2(x + 1)$

54. $3(x - 1) \geq -(x + 4)$

55. $5(x - 4) - 6(x + 2) < 4$

56. $3(x + 2) - 4(x - 1) < 6$

57. $-3(3x + 2) - 2(4x + 1) \geq 0$

58. $-4(2x - 1) - 3(x + 2) \geq 0$

59. $-(x - 3) + 2(x - 1) < 3(x + 4)$

60. $3(x - 1) - (x - 2) > -2(x + 4)$

61. $7(x + 1) - 8(x - 2) < 0$

62. $5(x - 6) - 6(x + 2) < 0$

63. $-5(x - 1) + 3 > 3x - 4 - 4x$

64. $3(x + 2) + 4 < -2x + 14 + x$

65. $3(x - 2) - 5(2x - 1) \geq 0$

66. $4(2x - 1) - 3(3x + 4) \geq 0$

67. $-5(3x + 4) < -2(7x - 1)$

68. $-3(2x + 1) > -2(x + 4)$

69. $-3(x + 2) > 2(x - 6)$

70. $-2(x - 4) < 5(x - 1)$

Thoughts Into Words

71. Do the *less than* and *greater than* relations possess a symmetric property similar to the symmetric property of equality? Defend your answer.

72. Give a step-by-step description of how you would solve the inequality $-3 > 5 - 2x$.

73. How would you explain to someone why it is necessary to reverse the inequality symbol when multiplying both sides of an inequality by a negative number?

Further Investigations

74. Solve each of the following inequalities.

(a) $5x - 2 > 5x + 3$

(b) $3x - 4 < 3x + 7$

(c) $4(x + 1) < 2(2x + 5)$

(d) $-2(x - 1) > 2(x + 7)$

(e) $3(x - 2) < -3(x + 1)$

(f) $2(x + 1) + 3(x + 2) < 5(x - 3)$

Answers to the Concept Quiz

1. False   **2.** True   **3.** False   **4.** True   **5.** False   **6.** True   **7.** False   **8.** True   **9.** False   **10.** True

---

2.6   More on Inequalities and Problem Solving

OBJECTIVES

1. Solve inequalities involving fractions or decimals

2. Solve inequalities that are compound statements

3. Use inequalities to solve word problems

When we discussed solving equations that involve fractions, we found that *clearing the equation of all fractions* is frequently an effective technique. To accomplish this, we multiply both sides of the equation by the least common denominator (LCD) of all the denominators in the equation. This same basic approach also works very well with inequalities that involve fractions, as the next examples demonstrate.

Classroom Example
Solve $\dfrac{1}{2}m + \dfrac{3}{4}m < \dfrac{3}{8}$.

EXAMPLE 1   Solve $\dfrac{2}{3}x - \dfrac{1}{2}x > \dfrac{3}{4}$.

Solution

$$\frac{2}{3}x - \frac{1}{2}x > \frac{3}{4}$$

$$12\left(\frac{2}{3}x - \frac{1}{2}x\right) > 12\left(\frac{3}{4}\right) \quad \text{Multiply both sides by 12, which is the LCD of 3, 2, and 4}$$

$$12\left(\frac{2}{3}x\right) - 12\left(\frac{1}{2}x\right) > 12\left(\frac{3}{4}\right) \quad \text{Apply the distributive property}$$

$$8x - 6x > 9$$

$$2x > 9$$

$$x > \frac{9}{2}$$

The solution set is $\left(\dfrac{9}{2}, \infty\right)$.

Classroom Example
Solve $\dfrac{t+5}{3} + \dfrac{t-2}{9} > 3$.

EXAMPLE 2 Solve $\dfrac{x+2}{4} + \dfrac{x-3}{8} < 1$.

Solution

$$\frac{x+2}{4} + \frac{x-3}{8} < 1$$

$$8\left(\frac{x+2}{4} + \frac{x-3}{8}\right) < 8(1) \quad \text{Multiply both sides by 8, which is the LCD of 4 and 8}$$

$$8\left(\frac{x+2}{4}\right) + 8\left(\frac{x-3}{8}\right) < 8(1)$$

$$2(x+2) + (x-3) < 8$$

$$2x + 4 + x - 3 < 8$$

$$3x + 1 < 8$$

$$3x < 7$$

$$x < \frac{7}{3}$$

The solution set is $\left(-\infty, \dfrac{7}{3}\right)$.

Classroom Example
Solve $\dfrac{d}{3} - \dfrac{d+3}{7} \le \dfrac{d-3}{21} - 1$.

EXAMPLE 3 Solve $\dfrac{x}{2} - \dfrac{x-1}{5} \ge \dfrac{x+2}{10} - 4$.

Solution

$$\frac{x}{2} - \frac{x-1}{5} \ge \frac{x+2}{10} - 4$$

$$10\left(\frac{x}{2} - \frac{x-1}{5}\right) \ge 10\left(\frac{x+2}{10} - 4\right)$$

$$10\left(\frac{x}{2}\right) - 10\left(\frac{x-1}{5}\right) \ge 10\left(\frac{x+2}{10}\right) - 10(4)$$

$$5x - 2(x-1) \ge x + 2 - 40$$

$$5x - 2x + 2 \ge x - 38$$

$$3x + 2 \ge x - 38$$

$$2x + 2 \ge -38$$

$$2x \ge -40$$

$$x \ge -20$$

The solution set is $[-20, \infty)$.

The idea of *clearing all decimals* also works with inequalities in much the same way as it does with equations. We can multiply both sides of an inequality by an appropriate power of 10 and then proceed in the usual way. The next two examples illustrate this procedure.

Classroom Example
Solve $m \le 3.2 + 0.6m$.

EXAMPLE 4 Solve $x \ge 1.6 + 0.2x$.

Solution

$$x \ge 1.6 + 0.2x$$

$$10(x) \ge 10(1.6 + 0.2x) \quad \text{Multiply both sides by 10}$$

$$10x \ge 16 + 2x$$

$$8x \ge 16$$

$$x \ge 2$$

The solution set is $[2, \infty)$.

Classroom Example
Solve $0.03n + 0.05(n + 20) \leq 43$.

EXAMPLE 5   Solve $0.08x + 0.09(x + 100) \geq 43$.

Solution

$$0.08x + 0.09(x + 100) \geq 43$$
$$100(0.08)x + 0.09(x + 100)) \geq 100(43) \qquad \text{Multiply both sides by 100}$$
$$8x + 9(x + 100) \geq 4300$$
$$8x + 9x + 900 \geq 4300$$
$$17x + 900 \geq 4300$$
$$17x \geq 3400$$
$$x \geq 200$$

The solution set is $[200, \infty)$.

Solving Inequalities That Are Compound Statements

We use the words "and" and "or" in mathematics to form **compound statements**. The following are examples of compound numerical statements that use "and." We call such statements **conjunctions**. We agree to call a conjunction true only if all of its component parts are true. Statements 1 and 2 below are true, but statements 3, 4, and 5 are false.

1. $3 + 4 = 7$	and	$-4 < -3$		True
2. $-3 < -2$	and	$-6 > -10$		True
3. $6 > 5$	and	$-4 < -8$		False
4. $4 < 2$	and	$0 < 10$		False
5. $-3 + 2 = 1$	and	$5 + 4 = 8$		False

We call compound statements that use "or" **disjunctions**. The following are examples of disjunctions that involve numerical statements.

6. $0.14 > 0.13$	or	$0.235 < 0.237$		True
7. $\dfrac{3}{4} > \dfrac{1}{2}$	or	$-4 + (-3) = 10$		True
8. $-\dfrac{2}{3} > \dfrac{1}{3}$	or	$(0.4)(0.3) = 0.12$		True
9. $\dfrac{2}{5} < -\dfrac{2}{5}$	or	$7 + (-9) = 16$		False

A disjunction is true if at least one of its component parts is true. In other words, disjunctions are false only if all of the component parts are false. Thus statements 6, 7, and 8 are true, but statement 9 is false.

Now let's consider finding solutions for some compound statements that involve algebraic inequalities. Keep in mind that our previous agreements for labeling conjunctions and disjunctions true or false form the basis for our reasoning.

Classroom Example
Graph the solution set for the conjunction $x > -2$ and $x < 1$.

EXAMPLE 6   Graph the solution set for the conjunction $x > -1$ and $x < 3$.

Solution

The key word is "and," so we need to satisfy both inequalities. Thus all numbers between -1 and 3 are solutions, and we can indicate this on a number line as in Figure 2.13.

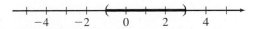

Figure 2.13

Using interval notation, we can represent the interval enclosed in parentheses in Figure 2.13 by $(-1, 3)$. Using set builder notation we can express the same interval as $\{x \mid -1 < x < 3\}$. The statement $-1 < x < 3$ can be read "Negative one is less than x, and x is less than three." In other words, x is between -1 and 3.

Example 6 represents another concept that pertains to sets. The set of all elements common to two sets is called the *intersection* of the two sets. Thus in Example 6, we found the intersection of the two sets $\{x \mid x > -1\}$ and $\{x \mid x < 3\}$ to be the set $\{x \mid -1 < x < 3\}$. In general, we define the intersection of two sets as follows:

> **Definition 2.1**
>
> The **intersection** of two sets A and B (written $A \cap B$) is the set of all elements that are in both A and in B. Using set builder notation, we can write
>
> $$A \cap B = \{x \mid x \in A \text{ and } x \in B\}$$

EXAMPLE 7

Solve the conjunction $3x + 1 > -5$ *and* $2x + 5 > 7$, and graph its solution set on a number line.

Solution

First, let's simplify both inequalities.

$$
\begin{aligned}
3x + 1 &> -5 & \text{and} & & 2x + 5 &> 7 \\
3x &> -6 & \text{and} & & 2x &> 2 \\
x &> -2 & \text{and} & & x &> 1
\end{aligned}
$$

Because this is a conjunction, we must satisfy both inequalities. Thus all numbers greater than 1 are solutions, and the solution set is $(1, \infty)$. We show the graph of the solution set in Figure 2.14.

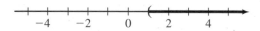

Figure 2.14

We can solve a conjunction such as $3x + 1 > -3$ and $3x + 1 < 7$, in which the same algebraic expression (in this case $3x + 1$) is contained in both inequalities, by using the *compact form* $-3 < 3x + 1 < 7$ as follows:

$$
\begin{aligned}
-3 &< 3x + 1 < 7 & \\
-4 &< 3x < 6 & \text{Add } -1 \text{ to the left side, middle, and right side} \\
-\frac{4}{3} &< x < 2 & \text{Multiply through by } \frac{1}{3}
\end{aligned}
$$

The solution set is $\left(-\dfrac{4}{3}, 2\right)$.

The word *and* ties the concept of a conjunction to the set concept of intersection. In a like manner, the word *or* links the idea of a disjunction to the set concept of *union*. We define the union of two sets as follows:

Definition 2.2

The **union** of two sets A and B (written $A \cup B$) is the set of all elements that are in A or in B, or in both. Using set builder notation, we can write

$$A \cup B = \{x | x \in A \text{ or } x \in B\}$$

Classroom Example
Graph the solution set for the disjunction $x < 0$ or $x > 3$, and express it using interval notation.

EXAMPLE 8

Graph the solution set for the disjunction $x < -1$ *or* $x > 2$, and express it using interval notation.

Solution

The key word is "or," so all numbers that satisfy either inequality (or both) are solutions. Thus all numbers less than -1, along with all numbers greater than 2, are the solutions. The graph of the solution set is shown in Figure 2.15.

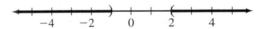

Figure 2.15

Using interval notation and the set concept of union, we can express the solution set as $(-\infty, -1) \cup (2, \infty)$.

Example 8 illustrates that in terms of set vocabulary, the solution set of a disjunction is the union of the solution sets of the component parts of the disjunction. Note that there is no compact form for writing $x < -1$ or $x > 2$ or for any disjunction.

Classroom Example
Solve the disjunction $3x + 2 \leq -1$ or $6x - 5 > 7$, and graph its solution set on a number line.

EXAMPLE 9

Solve the disjunction $2x - 5 < -11$ or $5x + 1 \geq 6$, and graph its solution set on a number line.

Solution

First, let's simplify both inequalities.

$$2x - 5 < -11 \quad \text{or} \quad 5x + 1 \geq 6$$
$$2x < -6 \quad \text{or} \quad 5x \geq 5$$
$$x < -3 \quad \text{or} \quad x \geq 1$$

This is a disjunction, and all numbers less than -3, along with all numbers greater than or equal to 1, will satisfy it. Thus the solution set is $(-\infty, -3) \cup [1, \infty)$. Its graph is shown in Figure 2.16.

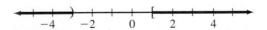

Figure 2.16

In summary, to solve a compound sentence involving an inequality, proceed as follows:

1. Solve separately each inequality in the compound sentence.
2. If it is a conjunction, the solution set is the intersection of the solution sets of each inequality.
3. If it is a disjunction, the solution set is the union of the solution sets of each inequality.

The following agreements on the use of interval notation (Figure 2.17) should be added to the list in Figure 2.5.

Set	Graph	Interval notation
$\{x \mid a < x < b\}$		(a, b)
$\{x \mid a \le x < b\}$		$[a, b)$
$\{x \mid a < x \le b\}$		$(a, b]$
$\{x \mid a \le x \le b\}$		$[a, b]$

Figure 2.17

Using Inequalities to Solve Word Problems

We will conclude this section with some word problems that contain inequality statements.

Classroom Example
Rebekah had scores of 92, 96, and 89 on her first three quizzes of the quarter. What score must she obtain on the fourth quiz to have an average of 93 or better for the four quizzes?

EXAMPLE 10

Sari had scores of 94, 84, 86, and 88 on her first four exams of the semester. What score must she obtain on the fifth exam to have an average of 90 or better for the five exams?

Solution

Let s represent the score Sari needs on the fifth exam. Because the average is computed by adding all scores and dividing by the number of scores, we have the following inequality to solve.

$$\frac{94 + 84 + 86 + 88 + s}{5} \ge 90$$

Solving this inequality, we obtain

$$\frac{352 + s}{5} \ge 90$$

$$5\left(\frac{352 + s}{5}\right) \ge 5(90) \quad \text{Multiply both sides by 5}$$

$$352 + s \ge 450$$

$$s \ge 98$$

Sari must receive a score of 98 or better.

Classroom Example
An investor has $2500 to invest. Suppose he invests $1500 at 5% interest. At what rate must he invest the rest so that the two investments together yield more than $109 of yearly interest?

EXAMPLE 11

An investor has $1000 to invest. Suppose she invests $500 at 8% interest. At what rate must she invest the other $500 so that the two investments together yield more than $100 of yearly interest?

Solution

Let r represent the unknown rate of interest. We can use the following guideline to set up an inequality.

$$\begin{array}{ccccc} \text{Interest from} & + & \text{Interest from } r & > & \$100 \\ \text{8\% investment} & & \text{percent investment} & & \end{array}$$

$$\begin{array}{ccccc} (8\%)(\$500) & + & r(\$500) & > & \$100 \end{array}$$

Solving this inequality yields

$$40 + 500r > 100$$
$$500r > 60$$
$$r > \frac{60}{500}$$
$$r > 0.12 \qquad \text{Change to a decimal}$$

She must invest the other $500 at a rate greater than 12%.

Classroom Example
If the temperature for a 24-hour period ranged between 41°F and 59°F, inclusive, what was the range in Celsius degrees?

EXAMPLE 12

A nursery advertises that a particular plant only thrives when the temperature is between 50°F and 86°F, inclusive. The nursery wants to display this information in both Fahrenheit and Celsius scales on an international Web site. What temperature range in Celsius should the nursery display for this particular plant?

Solution

Use the formula $F = \frac{9}{5}C + 32$ to solve the following compound inequality.

$$50 \le \frac{9}{5}C + 32 \le 86$$

Solving this yields

$$18 \le \frac{9}{5}C \le 54 \qquad \text{Add } -32$$

$$\frac{5}{9}(18) \le \frac{5}{9}\left(\frac{9}{5}C\right) \le \frac{5}{9}(54) \qquad \text{Multiply by } \frac{5}{9}$$

$$10 \le C \le 30$$

The range is between 10°C and 30°C, inclusive.

Concept Quiz 2.6

For Problems 1–5, answer true or false.

1. The solution set of a compound inequality formed by the word "and" is an intersection of the solution sets of the two inequalities.

2. The solution set of any compound inequality is the union of the solution sets of the two inequalities.

3. The intersection of two sets contains the elements that are common to both sets.

4. The union of two sets contains an the elements in both sets.

5. The intersection of set A and set B is denoted by $A \cap B$.

For Problems 6–10, match the compound statement with the graph of its solution set.

6. $x > 4$ or $x < -1$

7. $x > 4$ and $x > -1$

8. $x > 4$ or $x > -1$

9. $x \leq 4$ and $x \geq -1$

10. $x > 4$ or $x \geq -1$

A.

B.

C.

D.

E.

Problem Set 2.6

For Problems 1–18, solve each of the inequalities and express the solution sets in interval notation. **(Objective 1)**

1. $\dfrac{2}{5}x + \dfrac{1}{3}x > \dfrac{44}{15}$

2. $\dfrac{1}{4}x - \dfrac{4}{3}x < -13$

3. $x - \dfrac{5}{6} < \dfrac{x}{2} + 3$

4. $x + \dfrac{2}{7} > \dfrac{x}{2} - 5$

5. $\dfrac{x-2}{3} + \dfrac{x+1}{4} \geq \dfrac{5}{2}$

6. $\dfrac{x-1}{3} + \dfrac{x+2}{5} \leq \dfrac{3}{5}$

7. $\dfrac{3-x}{6} + \dfrac{x+2}{7} \leq 1$

8. $\dfrac{4-x}{5} + \dfrac{x+1}{6} \geq 2$

9. $\dfrac{x+3}{8} - \dfrac{x+5}{5} \geq \dfrac{3}{10}$

10. $\dfrac{x-4}{6} - \dfrac{x-2}{9} \leq \dfrac{5}{18}$

11. $\dfrac{4x-3}{6} - \dfrac{2x-1}{12} < -2$

12. $\dfrac{3x+2}{9} - \dfrac{2x+1}{3} > -1$

13. $0.06x + 0.08(250 - x) \geq 19$

14. $0.08x + 0.09(2x) \geq 130$

15. $0.09x + 0.1(x + 200) > 77$

16. $0.07x + 0.08(x + 100) > 38$

17. $x \geq 3.4 + 0.15x$

18. $x \geq 2.1 + 0.3x$

For Problems 19–34, graph the solution set for each compound incquality, and express the solution sets in interval notation. **(Objective 2)**

19. $x > -1$ and $x < 2$

20. $x > 1$ and $x < 4$

21. $x \leq 2$ and $x > -1$

22. $x \leq 4$ and $x \geq -2$

23. $x > 2$ or $x < -1$

24. $x > 1$ or $x < -4$

25. $x \leq 1$ or $x > 3$

26. $x < -2$ or $x \geq 1$

27. $x > 0$ and $x > -1$

28. $x > -2$ and $x > 2$

29. $x < 0$ and $x > 4$

30. $x > 1$ or $x < 2$

31. $x > -2$ or $x < 3$

32. $x > 3$ and $x < -1$

33. $x > -1$ or $x > 2$

34. $x < -2$ or $x < 1$

For Problems 35–44, solve each compound inequality and graph the solution sets. Express the solution sets in interval notation. **(Objective 2)**

35. $x - 2 > -1$ and $x - 2 < 1$

36. $x + 3 > -2$ and $x + 3 < 2$

37. $x + 2 < -3$ or $x + 2 > 3$

38. $x - 4 < -2$ or $x - 4 > 2$

39. $2x - 1 \geq 5$ and $x > 0$

40. $3x + 2 > 17$ and $x \geq 0$

41. $5x - 2 < 0$ and $3x - 1 > 0$

42. $x + 1 > 0$ and $3x - 4 < 0$

43. $3x + 2 < -1$ or $3x + 2 > 1$

44. $5x - 2 < -2$ or $5x - 2 > 2$

For Problems 45–56, solve each compound inequality using the compact form. Express the solution sets in interval notation. **(Objective 2)**

45. $-3 < 2x + 1 < 5$

46. $-7 < 3x - 1 < 8$

47. $-17 \leq 3x - 2 \leq 10$

48. $-25 \leq 4x + 3 \leq 19$

49. $1 < 4x + 3 < 9$

50. $0 < 2x + 5 < 12$

51. $-6 < 4x - 5 < 6$

52. $-2 < 3x + 4 < 2$

53. $-4 \leq \dfrac{x-1}{3} \leq 4$

54. $-1 \leq \dfrac{x+2}{4} \leq 1$

55. $-3 < 2 - x < 3$

56. $-4 < 3 - x < 4$

For Problems 57–67, solve each problem by setting up and solving an appropriate inequality. **(Objective 3)**

57. Suppose that Lance has $5000 to invest. If he invests $3000 at 5% interest, at what rate must he invest the remaining $2000 so that the two investments yield more than $300 in yearly interest?

58. Mona invests $1000 at 8% yearly interest. How much does she have to invest at 6% so that the total yearly interest from the two investments exceeds $170?

59. The average height of the two forwards and the center of a basketball team is 6 feet and 8 inches. What must the average height of the two guards be so that the team average is at least 6 feet and 4 inches?

60. Thanh has scores of 52, 84, 65, and 74 on his first four math exams. What score must he make on the fifth exam to have an average of 70 or better for the five exams?

61. Marsha bowled 142 and 170 in her first two games. What must she bowl in the third game to have an average of at least 160 for the three games?

62. Candace had scores of 95, 82, 93, and 84 on her first four exams of the semester. What score must she obtain on the fifth exam to have an average of 90 or better for the five exams?

63. Suppose that Derwin shot rounds of 82, 84, 78, and 79 on the first four days of a golf tournament. What must he shoot on the fifth day of the tournament to average 80 or less for the five days?

64. The temperatures for a 24-hour period ranged between $-4°F$ and $23°F$, inclusive. What was the range in Celsius degrees? $\left(\text{Use } F = \dfrac{9}{5}C + 32. \right)$

65. Oven temperatures for baking various foods usually range between $325°F$ and $425°F$, inclusive. Express this range in Celsius degrees. (Round answers to the nearest degree.)

66. A person's intelligence quotient (I) is found by dividing mental age (M), as indicated by standard tests, by chronological age (C) and then multiplying this ratio by 100. The formula $I = \dfrac{100M}{C}$ can be used. If the I range of a group of 11-year-olds is given by $80 \leq I \leq 140$, find the range of the mental age of this group.

67. Repeat Problem 66 for an I range of 70 to 125, inclusive, for a group of 9-year-olds.

Thoughts Into Words

68. Explain the difference between a conjunction and a disjunction. Give an example of each (outside the field of mathematics).

69. How do you know by inspection that the solution set of the inequality $x + 3 > x + 2$ is the entire set of real numbers?

70. Find the solution set for each of the following compound statements, and in each case explain your reasoning.
   (a) $x < 3$ and $5 > 2$
   (b) $x < 3$ or $5 > 2$
   (c) $x < 3$ and $6 < 4$
   (d) $x < 3$ or $6 < 4$

Equations and Inequalities Involving Absolute Value

OBJECTIVES   **1** Solve equations that involve absolute value

2 Solve inequalities that involve absolute value

In Section 1.2, we defined the absolute value of a real number by

$$|a| = \begin{cases} a, & \text{if } a \geq 0 \\ -a, & \text{if } a < 0 \end{cases}$$

We also interpreted the absolute value of any real number to be the distance between the number and zero on a number line. For example, $|6| = 6$ translates to 6 units between 6 and 0. Likewise, $|-8| = 8$ translates to 8 units between -8 and 0.

The interpretation of absolute value as distance on a number line provides a straightforward approach to solving a variety of equations and inequalities involving absolute value. First, let's consider some equations.

Classroom Example
Solve $|x| = 6$.

EXAMPLE 1   Solve $|x| = 2$.

Solution

Think in terms of distance between the number and zero, and you will see that x must be 2 or -2. That is, the equation $|x| = 2$ is equivalent to

$$x = -2 \quad \text{or} \quad x = 2$$

The solution set is $\{-2, 2\}$.

Classroom Example
Solve $|m - 3| = 4$.

EXAMPLE 2   Solve $|x + 2| = 5$.

Solution

The number, $x + 2$, must be -5 or 5. Thus $|x + 2| = 5$ is equivalent to

$$x + 2 = -5 \quad \text{or} \quad x + 2 = 5$$

Solving each equation of the disjunction yields

$$x + 2 = -5 \quad \text{or} \quad x + 2 = 5$$
$$x = -7 \quad \text{or} \quad x = 3$$

✔ **Check**

When $x = -7$	**When $x = 3$**
$\|x + 2\| = 5$	$\|x + 2\| = 5$
$\|-7 + 2\| \stackrel{?}{=} 5$	$\|3 + 2\| \stackrel{?}{=} 5$
$\|-5\| \stackrel{?}{=} 5$	$\|5\| \stackrel{?}{=} 5$
$5 = 5$	$5 = 5$

The solution set is $\{-7, 3\}$.

The following general property should seem reasonable from the distance interpretation of absolute value.

Property 2.1

$|x| = k$ is equivalent to $x = -k$ or $x = k$, where k is a positive number.

Example 3 demonstrates our format for solving equations of the form $|x| = k$.

Classroom Example
Solve $|2w - 5| = 4$.

EXAMPLE 3   Solve $|5x + 3| = 7$.

Solution

$$|5x + 3| = 7$$

$$5x + 3 = -7 \quad \text{or} \quad 5x + 3 = 7$$

$$5x = -10 \quad \text{or} \quad 5x = 4$$

$$x = -2 \quad \text{or} \quad x = \frac{4}{5}$$

The solution set is $\left\{-2, \dfrac{4}{5}\right\}$. Check these solutions!

Classroom Example
Solve $|3x - 4| + 2 = 9$.

EXAMPLE 4   Solve $|2x + 5| - 3 = 8$.

Solution

First isolate the absolute value expression by adding 3 to both sides of the equation.

$$|2x + 5| - 3 = 8$$

$$|2x + 5| - 3 + 3 = 8 + 3$$

$$|2x + 5| = 11$$

$$2x + 5 = 11 \quad \text{or} \quad 2x + 5 = -11$$

$$2x = 6 \quad \text{or} \quad 2x = -16$$

$$x = 3 \quad \text{or} \quad x = -8$$

The solution set is $\{-8, 3\}$. Check these solutions.

Solving Inequalities That Involve Absolute Value

The distance interpretation for absolute value also provides a good basis for solving some inequalities that involve absolute value. Consider the following examples.

Classroom Example
Solve $|m| < 4$ and graph the
solution set.

EXAMPLE 5   Solve $|x| < 2$ and graph the solution set.

Solution

The number, x, must be less than two units away from zero. Thus $|x| < 2$ is equivalent to

$$x > -2 \quad \text{and} \quad x < 2$$

The solution set is $(-2, 2)$, and its graph is shown in Figure 2.18.

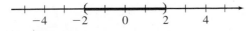

Figure 2.18

EXAMPLE 6   Solve $|x + 3| < 1$ and graph the solutions.

Solution

Let's continue to think in terms of distance on a number line. The number, $x + 3$, must be less than one unit away from zero. Thus $|x + 3| < 1$ is equivalent to

$$x + 3 > -1 \quad \text{and} \quad x + 3 < 1$$

Solving this conjunction yields

$$x + 3 > -1 \quad \text{and} \quad x + 3 < 1$$
$$x > -4 \quad \text{and} \quad x < -2$$

The solution set is $(-4, -2)$, and its graph is shown in Figure 2.19.

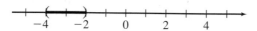

Figure 2.19

Take another look at Examples 5 and 6. The following general property should seem reasonable.

> **Property 2.2**
>
> $|x| < k$ is equivalent to $x > -k$ and $x < k$, where k is a positive number.

Remember that we can write a conjunction such as $x > -k$ and $x < k$ in the compact form $-k < x < k$. The compact form provides a very convenient format for solving inequalities such as $|3x - 1| < 8$, as Example 7 illustrates.

EXAMPLE 7   Solve $|3x - 1| < 8$ and graph the solutions.

Solution

$$|3x - 1| < 8$$
$$-8 < 3x - 1 < 8$$
$$-7 < 3x < 9 \qquad \text{Add 1 to left side, middle, and right side}$$
$$\frac{1}{3}(-7) < \frac{1}{3}(3x) < \frac{1}{3}(9) \qquad \text{Multiply through by } \frac{1}{3}$$
$$-\frac{7}{3} < x < 3$$

The solution set is $\left(-\frac{7}{3}, 3\right)$, and its graph is shown in Figure 2.20.

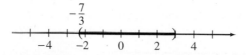

Figure 2.20

The distance interpretation also clarifies a property that pertains to *greater than* situations involving absolute value. Consider the following examples.

Classroom Example
Solve $|x| \geq \frac{3}{2}$ and graph the solutions.

EXAMPLE 8 Solve $|x| > 1$ and graph the solutions.

Solution

The number, x, must be more than one unit away from zero. Thus $|x| > 1$ is equivalent to

$$x < -1 \quad \text{or} \quad x > 1$$

The solution set is $(-\infty, -1) \cup (1, \infty)$, and its graph is shown in Figure 2.21.

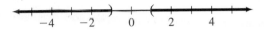

Figure 2.21

Classroom Example
Solve $|x + 2| \geq 4$ and graph the solutions.

EXAMPLE 9 Solve $|x - 1| > 3$ and graph the solutions.

Solution

The number, $x - 1$, must be more than three units away from zero. Thus $|x - 1| > 3$ is equivalent to

$$x - 1 < -3 \quad \text{or} \quad x - 1 > 3$$

Solving this disjunction yields

$$x - 1 < -3 \quad \text{or} \quad x - 1 > 3$$
$$x < -2 \quad \text{or} \quad x > 4$$

The solution set is $(-\infty, -2) \cup (4, \infty)$, and its graph is shown in Figure 2.22.

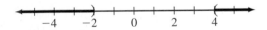

Figure 2.22

Examples 8 and 9 illustrate the following general property.

> **Property 2.3**
> $|x| > k$ is equivalent to $x < -k$ or $x > k$, where k is a positive number.

Therefore, solving inequalities of the form $|x| > k$ can take the format shown in Example 10.

Classroom Example
Solve $|5x - 1| > 4$ and graph the solutions.

EXAMPLE 10 Solve $|3x - 1| + 4 > 6$ and graph the solution.

Solution

First isolate the absolute value expression by subtracting 4 from both sides of the equation.

$$|3x - 1| + 4 > 6$$

$$|3x - 1| + 4 - 4 > 6 - 4 \quad \text{Subtract 4 from both sides}$$

$$|3x - 1| > 2$$

$$3x - 1 < -2 \quad \text{or} \quad 3x - 1 > 2$$

$$3x < -1 \quad \text{or} \quad 3x > 3$$

$$x < -\frac{1}{3} \quad \text{or} \quad x > 1$$

The solution set is $\left(-\infty, -\dfrac{1}{3}\right) \cup (1, \infty)$, and its graph is shown in Figure 2.23.

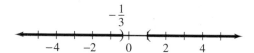

Figure 2.23

Properties 2.1, 2.2, and 2.3 provide the basis for solving a variety of equations and inequalities that involve absolute value. However, if at any time you become doubtful about what property applies, don't forget the distance interpretation. Furthermore, note that in each of the properties, k is a positive number. If k is a nonpositive number, we can determine the solution sets by inspection, as indicated by the following examples.

$|x + 3| = 0$ has a solution of $x = -3$, because the number $x + 3$ has to be 0. The solution set of $|x + 3| = 0$ is $\{-3\}$.

$|2x - 5| = -3$ has no solutions, because the absolute value (distance) cannot be negative. The solution set is $\emptyset$, the null set.

$|x - 7| < -4$ has no solutions, because we cannot obtain an absolute value less than -4. The solution set is $\emptyset$.

$|2x - 1| > -1$ is satisfied by all real numbers because the absolute value of $(2x - 1)$, regardless of what number is substituted for x, will always be greater than -1. The solution set is the set of all real numbers, which we can express in interval notation as $(-\infty, \infty)$.

Concept Quiz 2.7

For Problems 1–10, answer true or false.

1. The absolute value of a negative number is the opposite of the number.
2. The absolute value of a number is always positive or zero.
3. The absolute value of a number is equal to the absolute value of its opposite.
4. The compound statement $x < 1$ or $x > 3$ can be written in compact form $3 < x < 1$.
5. The solution set for the equation $|x + 5| = 0$ is the null set, $\emptyset$.
6. The solution set for $|x - 2| \geq -6$ is all real numbers.
7. The solution set for $|x + 1| < -3$ is all real numbers.
8. The solution set for $|x - 4| \leq 0$ is $\{4\}$.

9. If a solution set in interval notation is $(-4, -2)$, then it can be expressed as $\{x|-4 < x < -2\}$ in set builder notation.

10. If a solution set in interval notation is $(-\infty, -2) \cup (4, \infty)$, then it can be expressed as $\{x|x < -2 \text{ or } x > 4\}$ in set builder notation.

Problem Set 2.7

For Problems 1–16, solve each equation. **(Objective 1)**

1. $|x - 1| = 8$

2. $|x + 2| = 9$

3. $|2x - 4| = 6$

4. $|3x - 4| - 14$

5. $|3x + 4| = 11$

6. $|5x - 7| = 14$

7. $|4 - 2x| = 6$

8. $|3 - 4x| = 8$

9. $\left|x - \dfrac{3}{4}\right| = \dfrac{2}{3}$

10. $\left|x + \dfrac{1}{2}\right| = \dfrac{3}{5}$

11. $|2x - 3| + 2 = 5$

12. $|3x - 1| - 1 = 9$

13. $|x + 2| - 6 = -2$

14. $|x - 3| - 4 = -1$

15. $|4x - 3| + 2 = 2$

16. $|5x + 1| + 4 = 4$

For Problems 17–30, solve each inequality and graph the solution. **(Objective 2)**

17. $|x| < 5$

18. $|x| < 1$

19. $|x| \leq 2$

20. $|x| \leq 4$

21. $|x| > 2$

22. $|x| > 3$

23. $|x - 1| < 2$

24. $|x - 2| < 4$

25. $|x + 2| \leq 4$

26. $|x + 1| \leq 1$

27. $|x + 2| > 1$

28. $|x + 1| > 3$

29. $|x - 3| \geq 2$

30. $|x - 2| \geq 1$

For Problems 31–54, solve each inequality. **(Objective 2)**

31. $|x - 2| > 6$

32. $|x - 3| > 9$

33. $|x + 3| < 5$

34. $|x + 1| < 8$

35. $|2x - 1| \leq 9$

36. $|3x + 1| \leq 13$

37. $|4x + 2| \geq 12$

38. $|5x - 2| \geq 10$

39. $|2 \quad x| > 4$

40. $|4 - x| > 3$

41. $|1 - 2x| < 2$

42. $|2 - 3x| < 5$

43. $|5x + 9| \leq 16$

44. $|7x - 6| \geq 22$

45. $|-2x + 7| \leq 13$

46. $|-3x - 4| \leq 15$

47. $\left|\dfrac{x - 3}{4}\right| < 2$

48. $\left|\dfrac{x + 2}{3}\right| < 1$

49. $\left|\dfrac{2x + 1}{2}\right| > 1$

50. $\left|\dfrac{3x - 1}{4}\right| > 3$

51. $|x + 7| - 3 \geq 4$

52. $|x - 2| + 4 \geq 10$

53. $|2x - 1| + 1 \leq 6$

54. $|4x + 3| - 2 \leq 5$

For Problems 55–64, solve each equation and inequality *by inspection*. **(Objectives 1 and 2)**

55. $|2x + 1| = -4$

56. $|5x - 1| = -2$

57. $|3x - 1| > -2$

58. $|4x + 3| < -4$

59. $|5x - 2| = 0$

60. $|3x - 1| = 0$

61. $|4x - 6| < -1$

62. $|x + 9| > -6$

63. $|x + 4| < 0$

64. $|x + 6| > 0$

Thoughts Into Words

65. Explain how you would solve the inequality $|2x + 5| > -3$.

66. Why is 2 the only solution for $|x - 2| \leq 0$?

67. Explain how you would solve the equation $|2x - 3| = 0$.

Further Investigations

Consider the equation $|x| = |y|$. This equation will be a true statement if x is equal to y or if x is equal to the opposite of y. Use the following format, $x = y$ or $x = -y$, to solve the equations in Problems 68–73.

For Problems 68–73, solve each equation.

68. $|3x + 1| = |2x + 3|$

69. $|-2x - 3| = |x + 1|$

70. $|2x - 1| = |x - 3|$

71. $|x - 2| = |x + 6|$

72. $|x + 1| = |x - 4|$

73. $|x + 1| = |x - 1|$

74. Use the definition of absolute value to help prove Property 2.1.

75. Use the definition of absolute value to help prove Property 2.2.

76. Use the definition of absolute value to help prove Property 2.3.

Answers to the Concept Quiz

1. True   **2.** True   **3.** True   **4.** False   **5.** False   **6.** True   **7.** False   **8.** True   **9.** True   **10.** True

Chapter 2 Summary

OBJECTIVE	SUMMARY	EXAMPLE
Solve first-degree equations. (Section 2.1/Objective 1)	Solving an algebraic equation refers to the process of finding the number (or numbers) that make(s) the algebraic equation a true numerical statement. We call such numbers the **solutions** or **roots** of the equation that satisfy the equation. We call the set of all solutions of an equation the **solution set**. The general procedure for solving an equation is to continue replacing the given equation with equivalent but simpler equations until we arrive at one that can be solved by inspection. Two properties of equality play an important role in solving equations. **Addition Property of Equality** $a = b$ if and only if $a + c = b + c$. **Multiplication Property of Equality** For $c \neq 0$, $a = b$ if and only if $ac = bc$.	Solve $3(2x - 1) = 2x + 6 - 5x$. **Solution** $$3(2x - 1) = 2x + 6 - 5x$$ $$6x - 3 = -3x + 6$$ $$9x - 3 = 6$$ $$9x = 9$$ $$x = 1$$ The solution set is $\{1\}$.
Solve equations involving fractions. (Section 2.2/Objective 1)	To solve an equation involving fractions, it is usually easiest to begin by multiplying both sides of the equation by the least common multiple of all the denominators in the equation. This process clears the equation of fractions.	Solve $\dfrac{x}{2} - \dfrac{x}{5} = \dfrac{7}{10}$. **Solution** $$\frac{x}{2} - \frac{x}{5} = \frac{7}{10}$$ $$10\left(\frac{x}{2} - \frac{x}{5}\right) = 10\left(\frac{7}{10}\right)$$ $$10\left(\frac{x}{2}\right) - 10\left(\frac{x}{5}\right) = 7$$ $$5x - 2x = 7$$ $$3x = 7$$ $$x = \frac{7}{3}$$ The solution set is $\left\{\dfrac{7}{3}\right\}$.
Solve equations involving decimals. (Section 2.3/Objective 1)	To solve equations that contain decimals, you can clear the equation of the decimals by multiplying both sides by an appropriate power of 10 or you can keep the problem in decimal form and perform the calculations with decimals.	Solve $0.04x + 0.07(2x) = 90$. **Solution** $$0.04x + 0.07(2x) = 90$$ $$100[0.04x + 0.07(2x)] = 100(90)$$ $$4x + 7(2x) = 9000$$ $$4x + 14x = 9000$$ $$18x = 9000$$ $$x = 500$$ The solution set is $\{500\}$.

(continued)

OBJECTIVE	SUMMARY	EXAMPLE
Use equations to solve word problems. (Section 2.1/Objective 2; Section 2.2/Objective 2)	Keep the following suggestions in mind as you solve word problems. 1. Read the problem carefully. 2. Sketch any figure, diagram, or chart that might be helpful. 3. Choose a meaningful variable. 4. Look for a guideline. 5. Form an equation. 6. Solve the equation. 7. Check your answers.	The length of a rectangle is 4 feet less than twice the width. The perimeter of the rectangle is 34 feet. Find the length and the width. **Solution** Let w represent the width; then $2w - 4$ represents the length. Use the formula $P = 2w + 2l$. $34 = 2w + 2(2w - 4)$ $34 = 2w + 4w - 8$ $42 = 6w$ $7 = w$ So the width is 7 feet, and the length is $2(7) - 4 = 10$ feet.
Solve word problems involving discount and selling price. (Section 2.3/Objective 2)	Discount sale problems involve the relationship *original selling price minus discount equals sale price*. Another basic relationship is *selling price equals cost plus profit*. Profit may be stated as a percent of the selling price, as a percent of the cost, or as an amount.	A car repair shop has some brake pads that cost $30 each. The owner wants to sell them at a profit of 70% of the cost. What selling price will be charged to the customer? **Solution** Selling price = Cost + Profit $s = 30 + (60\%)(30)$ $s = 30 + (0.60)(30)$ $s = 30 + 18$ $= 48$ The selling price would be $48.00.
Evaluate formulas for given values. (Section 2.4/Objective 1)	A formula can be solved for a specific variable when we are given the numerical values for the other variables.	Solve $i = Prt$ for r, given that $P = \$1200$, $t = 4$ years, and $i = \$360$. **Solution** $i = Prt$ $360 = (1200)(r)(4)$ $360 = 4800r$ $r = \dfrac{360}{4800}$ $= 0.075$ The rate, r, would be 0.075 or 7.5%.

OBJECTIVE	SUMMARY	EXAMPLE
Solve formulas for a specified variable. (Section 2.4/Objective 2)	We can change the form of an equation by solving for one variable in terms of the other variables.	Solve $A = \frac{1}{2}bh$ for b. **Solution** $$A = \frac{1}{2}bh$$ $$2A = 2\left(\frac{1}{2}bh\right)$$ $$2A = bh$$ $$\frac{2A}{h} = b$$
Use formulas to solve problems. (Section 2.4/Objective 3)	Formulas are often used as guidelines for setting up an algebraic equation when solving a word problem. Sometimes formulas are used in the analysis of a problem but not as the main guideline. For example, uniform motion problems use the formula $d = rt$, but the guideline is usually a statement about times, rates, or distances.	How long will it take $400 to triple if it is invested at 8% simple interest? **Solution** Use the formula $i = Prt$. For $400 to triple (to be worth $1200), it must earn $800 in interest. $800 = 400(8\%)(t)$ $800 = 400(0.08)(t)$ $\quad 2 = 0.08t \qquad$ Divided by 400 $$t = \frac{2}{0.08} = 25$$ It will take 25 years to triple.
Write solution sets in interval notation. (Section 2.5/Objective 1)	The solution set for an algebraic inequality can be written in interval notation. See the table below for examples of various algebraic inequalities and how their solution sets would be written in interval notation.	Express the solution set for $x \le 4$ in interval notation. **Solution** For the solution set we want all numbers less than or equal to 4. In interval notation, the solution set is written $(-\infty, 4]$.

Solution set	Graph	Interval notation
$\{x \mid x > 1\}$		$(1, \infty)$
$\{x \mid x \ge 2\}$		$[2, \infty)$
$\{x \mid x < 0\}$		$(-\infty, 0)$
$\{x \mid x \le -1\}$		$(-\infty, -1]$
$\{x \mid -2 < x \le 2\}$		$(-2, 2]$
$\{x \mid x \le -1 \text{ or } x > 1\}$		$(-\infty, -1] \cup (1, \infty)$

(continued)

OBJECTIVE	SUMMARY	EXAMPLE
Solve inequalities. (Section 2.5/Objective 2)	The addition property of equality states that any number can be added to each side of an inequality to produce an equivalent inequality. The multiplication property of equality states that both sides of an inequality can be multiplied by a positive number to produce an equivalent inequality. If both sides of an inequality are multiplied by a negative number, then an inequality of the *opposite sense* is produced. When multiplying or dividing both sides of an inequality by a negative number, be sure to reverse the inequality symbol.	Solve $-8x + 2(x - 7) < 40$. **Solution** $$-8x + 2(x - 7) < 40$$ $$-8x + 2x - 14 < 40$$ $$-6x - 14 < 40$$ $$-6x < 54$$ $$\frac{-6x}{-6} > \frac{54}{-6}$$ $$x > -9$$ The solution set is $(-9, \infty)$.
Solve inequalities involving fractions or decimals. (Section 2.6/Objective 1)	When solving inequalities that involve fractions, multiply the inequality by the least common multiple of all the denominators to clear the equation of fractions. The same technique can be used for inequalities involving decimals.	Solve $\dfrac{x + 5}{3} - \dfrac{x + 1}{2} < \dfrac{5}{6}$. **Solution** Multiply both sides of the inequality by 6. $$6\left(\frac{x + 5}{3} - \frac{x + 1}{2}\right) < 6\left(\frac{5}{6}\right)$$ $$2(x + 5) - 3(x + 1) < 5$$ $$2x + 10 - 3x - 3 < 5$$ $$-x + 7 < 5$$ $$-x < -2$$ $$-1(-x) > -1(-2)$$ $$x > 2$$ The solution set is $(2, \infty)$.
Solve inequalities that are compound statements. (Section 2.6/Objective 2)	Inequalities connected with the words "and" form a compound statement called a conjunction. A conjunction is true only if all of its component parts are true. The solution set of a conjunction is the *intersection* of the solution sets of each inequality. Inequalities connected with the words "or" form a compound statement called a disjunction. A disjunction is true if at least one of its component parts is true. The solution set of a disjunction is the *union* of the solution sets of each inequality. We define the intersection and union of two sets as follows. **Intersection** $A \cap B = \{x \mid x \in A \text{ and } x \in B\}$ **Union** $A \cup B = \{x \mid x \in A \text{ or } x \in B\}$	Solve the compound statement $x + 4 \leq -10$ or $x - 2 \geq 1$. **Solution** Simplify each inequality. $$x + 4 \leq -10 \quad \text{or} \quad x - 2 \geq 1$$ $$x \leq -14 \quad \text{or} \quad x \geq 3$$ The solution set is $(-\infty, -14] \cup [3, \infty)$.

OBJECTIVE	SUMMARY	EXAMPLE
Use inequalities to solve word problems. (Section 2.6/Objective 3)	To solve word problems involving inequalities, use the same suggestions given for solving word problems; however, the guideline will translate into an inequality rather than an equation.	Cheryl bowled 156 and 180 in her first two games. What must she bowl in the third game to have an average of at least 170 for the three games? **Solution** Let s represent the score in the third game. $$\frac{156 + 180 + s}{3} \geq 170$$ $$156 + 180 + s \geq 510$$ $$336 + s \geq 510$$ $$s \geq 174$$ She must bowl 174 or greater.
Solve absolute value equations. (Section 2.7/Objective 1)	Property 2.1 states that $|x| = k$ is equivalent to $x = k$ or $x = -k$, where k is a positive number. This property is applied to solve absolute value equations.	Solve $|2x - 5| = 9$. **Solution** $$|2x - 5| = 9$$ $$2x - 5 = 9 \quad \text{or} \quad 2x - 5 = -9$$ $$2x = 14 \quad \text{or} \quad 2x = -4$$ $$x = 7 \quad \text{or} \quad x = -2$$ The solution set is $\{-2, 7\}$.
Solve absolute value inequalities (Section 2.7/Objective 2)	Property 2.2 states that $|x| < k$ is equivalent to $x > -k$ and $x < k$, where k is a positive number. This conjunction can be written in compact form as $-k < x < k$. For example, $|x + 3| < 7$ can be written as $-7 < x + 3 < 7$ to begin the process of solving the inequality. Property 2.3 states that $|x| > k$ is equivalent to $x < -k$ or $x > k$, where k is a positive number. This disjunction cannot be written in a compact form.	Solve $|x + 5| > 8$. **Solution** $$|x + 5| > 8$$ $$x + 5 < -8 \quad \text{or} \quad x + 5 > 8$$ $$x < -13 \quad \text{or} \quad x > 3$$ The solution set is $(-\infty, -13) \cup (3, \infty)$.

Chapter 2   Review Problem Set

For Problems 1–14, solve each of the equations.

1. $5(x - 6) = 3(x + 2)$

2. $2(2x + 1) - (x - 4) = 4(x + 5)$

3. $-(2n - 1) + 3(n + 2) = 7$

4. $2(3n - 4) + 3(2n - 3) = -2(n + 5)$

5. $\dfrac{3t - 2}{4} = \dfrac{2t + 1}{3}$

6. $\dfrac{x + 6}{5} + \dfrac{x - 1}{4} = 2$

7. $1 - \dfrac{2x - 1}{6} = \dfrac{3x}{8}$

8. $\dfrac{2x + 1}{3} + \dfrac{3x - 1}{5} = \dfrac{1}{10}$

9. $\dfrac{3n - 1}{2} - \dfrac{2n + 3}{7} = 1$

10. $\dfrac{5x + 6}{2} - \dfrac{x - 4}{3} = \dfrac{5}{6}$

11. $0.06x + 0.08 \, (x + 100) = 15$

12. $0.4(t - 6) = 0.3(2t + 5)$

13. $0.1(n + 300) = 0.09n + 32$

14. $0.2(x - 0.5) - 0.3(x + 1) = 0.4$

Solve each of Problems 15–24 by setting up and solving an appropriate equation.

15. The width of a rectangle is 2 meters more than one-third of the length. The perimeter of the rectangle is 44 meters. Find the length and width of the rectangle.

16. Find three consecutive integers such that the sum of one-half of the smallest and one-third of the largest is one less than the other integer.

17. Pat is paid time-and-a-half for each hour he works over 36 hours in a week. Last week he worked 42 hours for a total of $472.50. What is his normal hourly rate?

18. Marcela has a collection of nickels, dimes, and quarters worth $24.75. The number of dimes is 10 more than twice the number of nickels, and the number of quarters is 25 more than the numbers of dimes. How many coins of each kind does she have?

19. If the complement of an angle is one-tenth of the supplement of the angle, find the measure of the angle.

20. A total of $500 was invested, part of it at 7% interest and the remainder at 8%. If the total yearly interest from both investments amounted to $38, how much was invested at each rate?

21. A retailer has some sweaters that cost her $38 each. She wants to sell them at a profit of 20% of her cost. What price should she charge for each sweater?

22. If a necklace cost a jeweler $60, at what price should it be sold to yield a profit 80% based on the selling price?

23. If a DVD player costs a retailer $40 and it sells for $100, what is the rate of profit on the selling price?

24. Yuri bought a pair of running shoes at a 25% discount sale for $48. What was the original price of the running shoes?

25. Solve $i = Prt$ for P, given that $r = 6\%$, $t = 3$ years, and $i = \$1440$.

26. Solve $A = P + Prt$ for r, given that $A = \$3706$, $P = \$3400$, and $t = 2$ years. Express r as a percent.

27. Solve $P = 2w + 2l$ for w, given that $P = 86$ meters and $l = 32$ meters.

28. Solve $C = \dfrac{5}{9}(F - 32)$ for C, given that $F = -4°$.

For Problems 29–33, solve each equation for x.

29. $ax - b = b + 2$

30. $ax = bx + c$

31. $m(x + a) = p(x + b)$

32. $5x - 7y = 11$

33. $\dfrac{x - a}{b} = \dfrac{y + 1}{c}$

For Problems 34–38, solve each of the formulas for the indicated variable.

34. $A = \pi r^2 + \pi rs$ for s

35. $A = \dfrac{1}{2}h(b_1 + b_2)$ for b_2

36. $S_n = \dfrac{n(a_1 + a_2)}{2}$ for n

37. $\dfrac{1}{R} = \dfrac{1}{R_1} + \dfrac{1}{R_2}$ for R

38. $ax + by = c$ for y

39. How many pints of a 1% hydrogen peroxide solution should be mixed with a 4% hydrogen peroxide solution to obtain 10 pints of a 2% hydrogen peroxide solution?

40. Gladys leaves a town driving at a rate of 40 miles per hour. Two hours later, Reena leaves from the same place traveling the same route. She catches Gladys in 5 hours and 20 minutes. How fast was Reena traveling?

41. In $1\dfrac{1}{4}$ hours more time, Rita, riding her bicycle at 12 miles per hour, rode 2 miles farther than Sonya, who was riding her bicycle at 16 miles per hour. How long did each girl ride?

42. How many cups of orange juice must be added to 50 cups of a punch that is 10% orange juice to obtain a punch that is 20% orange juice?

For Problems 43–46, express the given inequality in interval notation.

43. $x \geq -2$

44. $x > 6$

45. $x < -1$

46. $x \leq 0$

For Problems 47–56, solve each of the inequalities.

47. $5x - 2 \geq 4x - 7$

48. $3 - 2x < -5$

49. $2(3x - 1) - 3(x - 3) > 0$

50. $3(x + 4) \leq 5(x - 1)$

51. $-3(2t - 1) - (t + 2) > -6(t - 3)$

52. $\dfrac{5}{6}n - \dfrac{1}{3}n < \dfrac{1}{6}$

53. $\dfrac{n - 4}{5} + \dfrac{n - 3}{6} > \dfrac{7}{15}$

54. $\dfrac{2}{3}(x - 1) + \dfrac{1}{4}(2x + 1) < \dfrac{5}{6}(x - 2)$

55. $s \geq 4.5 + 0.25s$

56. $0.07x + 0.09(500 - x) \geq 43$

For Problems 57–64, graph the solutions of each compound inequality.

57. $x > -1$ and $x < 1$

58. $x > 2$ or $x \leq -3$

59. $x > 2$ and $x > 3$

60. $x < 2$ or $x > -1$

61. $2x + 1 > 3$ or $2x + 1 < -3$

62. $2 < x + 4 < 5$

63. $-1 < 4x - 3 \leq 9$

64. $x + 1 > 3$ and $x - 3 < -5$

65. Susan's average score for her first three psychology exams is 84. What must she get on the fourth exam so that her average for the four exams is 85 or better?

66. Marci invests $3000 at 6% yearly interest. How much does she have to invest at 8% so that the yearly interest from the two investments exceeds $500?

For Problems 67–70, solve each of the equations.

67. $|3x - 1| = 11$

68. $|2n + 3| = 4$

69. $|3x + 1| - 8 = 2$

70. $\left|\dfrac{1}{2}x + 3\right| - 1 = 5$

For Problems 71–74, solve each of the inequalities.

71. $|2x - 1| < 11$

72. $|3x + 1| > 10$

73. $|5x - 4| \geq 8$

74. $\left|\dfrac{1}{4}x + 1\right| \leq 6$

Chapter 2 Test

For Problems 1–10, solve each equation.

1. $5x - 2 = 2x - 11$

2. $6(n - 2) - 4(n + 3) = -14$

3. $-3(x + 4) = 3(x - 5)$

4. $3(2x - 1) - 2(x + 5) = -(x - 3)$

5. $\dfrac{3t - 2}{4} = \dfrac{5t + 1}{5}$

6. $\dfrac{5x + 2}{3} - \dfrac{2x + 4}{6} = -\dfrac{4}{3}$

7. $|4x - 3| = 9$

8. $\dfrac{1 - 3x}{4} + \dfrac{2x + 3}{3} = 1$

9. $2 - \dfrac{3x - 1}{5} = -4$

10. $0.05x + 0.06(1500 - x) = 83.5$

11. Solve $\dfrac{2}{3}x - \dfrac{3}{4}y = 2$ for y

12. Solve $S = 2\pi r(r + h)$ for h

For Problems 13–20, solve each inequality and express the solution set using interval notation.

13. $7x - 4 > 5x - 8$

14. $-3x - 4 \leq x + 12$

15. $2(x - 1) - 3(3x + 1) \geq -6(x - 5)$

16. $\dfrac{3}{5}x - \dfrac{1}{2}x < 1$

17. $\dfrac{x - 2}{6} - \dfrac{x + 3}{9} > -\dfrac{1}{2}$

18. $0.05x + 0.07(800 - x) \geq 52$

19. $|6x - 4| < 10$

20. $|4x + 5| \geq 6$

For Problems 21–25, solve each problem by setting up and solving an appropriate equation or inequality.

21. Dela bought a dress at a 20% discount sale for $57.60. Find the original price of the dress.

22. The length of a rectangle is one centimeter more than three times its width. If the perimeter of the rectangle is 50 centimeters, find the length of the rectangle.

23. How many cups of grapefruit juice must be added to 30 cups of a punch that is 8% grapefruit juice to obtain a punch that is 10% grapefruit juice?

24. Rex has scores of 85, 92, 87, 88, and 91 on the first five exams. What score must he get on the sixth exam to have an average of 90 or better for all six exams?

25. If the complement of an angle is $\dfrac{2}{11}$ of the supplement of the angle, find the measure of the angle.

1. Place a check mark in the table to identify all the sets that the identified number belongs to.

Identified numbers	Natural numbers	Whole numbers	Integers	Rational numbers	Irrational numbers	Real numbers
9						
$-\dfrac{1}{2}$						
$-\sqrt{7}$						
$0.\overline{3}$						
$\dfrac{8}{3}$						
-2						
0						

2. State the property of equality or the property of real numbers that justifies the statements.

    a. $c(x) = x(c)$

    b. $4(23 + 2) = 4(23) + 4(2)$

    c. If $10 = a + 3$, then $a + 3 = 10$.

For Problems 3–9, simplify each numerical expression.

3. $20 \div 10 \cdot 2 - 6 \div 1 + 5$

4. $15 + 9\left(\dfrac{8 - 2}{4 - 1}\right) - 18 \div 2$

5. $(30 - 18)(16 \div 2 - 4 \div 4)$

6. $\left(\dfrac{30 - 3 \cdot 8 + 12 \div 2}{20 - 4 \cdot 4}\right) - 16 \div 8$

7. $4\left(-\dfrac{2}{3}\right) - 2\left(\dfrac{3}{5}\right) + 3\left(-\dfrac{1}{5}\right)$

8. $(-2)^2 - (-1)^3 - 5^2$

9. $\dfrac{4}{5}(10 - 15) - \dfrac{1}{3}(12 - 18)$

For Problems 10–12, simplify each algebraic expression by combining similar terms.

10. $3c^2 - 7 - 10c^2 + 8 + c^2$

11. $11(2a - 1) + 6(a + 3) - (3a - 2)$

12. $-\dfrac{1}{4}cd^2 + \dfrac{5}{6}cd^2 + \dfrac{11}{12}cd^2 - \dfrac{2}{3}cd^2$

For Problems 13–15, evaluate each algebraic expression for the given values of the variables.

13. $3x - 7y$ for $x = -5$ and $y = -2$

14. $5(x - 7) - 2(x - 18) - (x + 4)$ for $x = 5.2$

15. $6a^2 - b^2$ for $a = \dfrac{1}{2}$ and $b = -\dfrac{2}{3}$

16. Translate the following sentence into an algebraic expression. Use x to represent the unknown number: The quotient of twice the number and the quantity two less than three times the number.

For Problems 17–23, solve each equation for x.

17. $4(x - 7) - (x + 5) = -7 - 8(x - 3)$

18. $\dfrac{2x - 1}{6} - 3 = \dfrac{6x + 13}{3}$

19. $0.05x + 0.04(x - 400) = 92$

20. $\dfrac{2}{3}x - \dfrac{1}{2}y = z$

21. $|3x - 4| - 7 = 22$

22. $|4x - 1| = -5$

23. $|9x - 6| = 0$

For Problems 24–28, solve each inequality, expressing the solution set in interval notation, and graph the solution set.

24. $7(2x - 4) \geq 2(6x - 11) - 10$

25. $\dfrac{x}{5} - \dfrac{x - 6}{2} > \dfrac{x + 5}{5}$

26. $|3x - 4| \leq 5$

27. $|5 - 2x| > 5$

28. $|10x - 1| < -4$

Solve each of Problems 29–36 by setting up and solving an appropriate equation.

29. Last week Kari worked 52 hours and earned $1044. When she works more than 40 hours per week, she is paid time and a half for overtime hours. What is Kari's hourly rate?

30. Becky sells dog leashes and collars at agility shows every weekend. One weekend she sold a total of 34 items. The number of leashes she sold was two less than three times the number of collars. How many of each did Becky sell?

31. Carolyn has 19 bills consisting of ten-dollar bills, twenty-dollar bills, and fifty-dollar bills. The number of twenties is three times the number of tens, and the number of fifties is one less than the number of tens. How many of each bill does Carolyn have? How much money does she have?

32. A Florida beach house rents at a 30% discount during the month of January. If the usual weekly rental amount is $3750, what would be the rent for one week in January?

33. Twice the complement of an angle plus one half the supplement of the angle equals 60°. Find the angle.

34. Uta is driving from Florida to Tennessee for a family reunion. Her brother, Sven, is driving the same route, but he is leaving one-half hour later. Uta drives at an average speed of 65 miles per hour, and her brother drives at an average speed of 70 miles per hour. How many hours will Sven drive before he catches up to Uta?

35. Glenn invests $4000 at 5% annual interest. How much more must he invest at that rate if he wants to earn $500 in annual interest?

36. An automobile dealership is advertising their hybrid vehicle for $24,900. If the county sales tax is 6.5%, what will the vehicle actually cost with the tax included?

3 Polynomials

3.1 Polynomials: Sums and Differences

3.2 Products and Quotients of Monomials

3.3 Multiplying Polynomials

3.4 Factoring: Greatest Common Factor and Common Binomial Factor

3.5 Factoring: Difference of Two Squares and Sum or Difference of Two Cubes

3.6 Factoring Trinomials

3.7 Equations and Problem Solving

A quadratic equation can be solved to determine the width of a uniform strip cropped from both sides and ends of a photograph to obtain a specified area for the image.

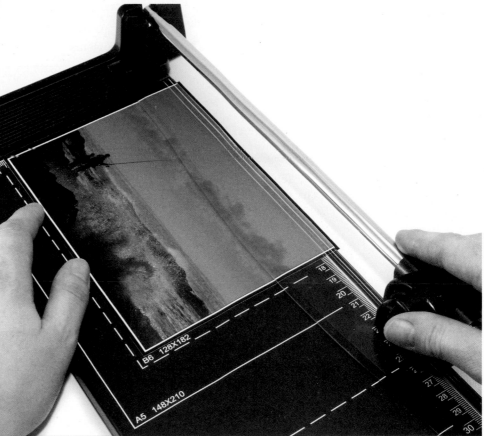

© Shane White

A uniform amount needs to be cropped from both ends and both sides of a photograph originally 5 inches by 7 inches so that the final area is 15 square inches. Find the width of the amount to be cropped. With the equation $(7 - 2x)(5 - 2x) = 15$, you can determine that the amount to be cropped from all four sides is 1 inch.

The main object of this text is to help you develop algebraic skills, use these skills to solve equations and inequalities, and use equations and inequalities to solve word problems. The work in this chapter will focus on a class of algebraic expressions called **polynomials.**

Video tutorials based on section learning objectives are available in a variety of delivery modes.

3.1   Polynomials: Sums and Differences

OBJECTIVES

1 Find the degree of a polynomial

2 Add and subtract polynomials

3 Simplify polynomial expressions

4 Use polynomials in geometry problems

Recall that algebraic expressions such as $5x$, $-6y^2$, $7xy$, $14a^2b$, and $-17ab^2c^3$ are called terms. A **term** is an indicated product and may contain any number of factors. The variables in a term are called **literal factors**, and the numerical factor is called the **numerical coefficient**. Thus for $7xy$, the x and y are literal factors, 7 is the numerical coefficient, and the term is in two variables (x and y).

Terms that contain variables with only whole numbers as exponents are called **monomials**. The terms previously listed, $5x$, $-6y^2$, $7xy$, $14a^2b$, and $-17ab^2c^3$, are all monomials. (We shall work later with some algebraic expressions, such as $7x^{-1}y^{-1}$ and $6a^{-2}b^{-3}$, which are not monomials.)

The **degree** of a monomial is the sum of the exponents of the literal factors.

$7xy$ is of degree 2

$14a^2b$ is of degree 3

$-17ab^2c^3$ is of degree 6

$5x$ is of degree 1

$-6y^2$ is of degree 2

If the monomial contains only one variable, then the exponent of the variable is the degree of the monomial. The last two examples illustrate this point. We say that any nonzero constant term is of degree zero.

A **polynomial** is a monomial or a finite sum (or difference) of monomials. Thus

$$4x^2, \qquad 3x^2 - 2x - 4, \qquad 7x^4 - 6x^3 + 4x^2 + x - 1,$$

$$3x^2y - 2xy^2, \qquad \frac{1}{5}a^2 - \frac{2}{3}b^2, \qquad \text{and} \qquad 14$$

are examples of polynomials. In addition to calling a polynomial with one term a **monomial**, we also classify polynomials with two terms as **binomials**, and those with three terms as **trinomials**.

The **degree of a polynomial** is the degree of the term with the highest degree in the polynomial. The following examples illustrate some of this terminology.

The polynomial $4x^3y^4$ is a monomial in two variables of degree 7.

The polynomial $4x^2y - 2xy$ is a binomial in two variables of degree 3.

The polynomial $9x^2 - 7x + 1$ is a trinomial in one variable of degree 2.

Adding and Subtracting Polynomials

Remember that *similar terms,* or *like terms,* are terms that have the same literal factors. In the preceding chapters, we have frequently simplified algebraic expressions by combining similar terms, as the next examples illustrate.

$$2x + 3y + 7x + 8y = \boxed{2x + 7x + 3y + 8y}$$
$$= \boxed{(2 + 7)x + (3 + 8)y}$$
$$= 9x + 11y$$

⟶ Steps in dashed boxes are usually done mentally

$$4a - 7 - 9a + 10 = \boxed{4a + (-7) + (-9a) + 10}$$
$$= \boxed{4a + (-9a) + (-7) + 10} \longrightarrow \text{Steps in dashed boxes}$$
$$= \boxed{(4 + (-9))a + (-7) + 10} \quad \text{are usually done mentally}$$
$$= -5a + 3$$

Both addition and subtraction of polynomials rely on basically the same ideas. The commutative, associative, and distributive properties provide the basis for rearranging, regrouping, and combining similar terms. Let's consider some examples.

Classroom Example
Add $3x^2 - 4x + 1$ and
$5x^2 + 3x - 6$.

EXAMPLE 1   Add $4x^2 + 5x + 1$ and $7x^2 - 9x + 4$.

Solution

We generally use the horizontal format for such work. Thus

$$(4x^2 + 5x + 1) + (7x^2 - 9x + 4) = (4x^2 + 7x^2) + (5x - 9x) + (1 + 4)$$
$$= 11x^2 - 4x + 5$$

Classroom Example
Add $2m + 9, 5m - 2,$ and $10m - 6$.

EXAMPLE 2   Add $5x - 3, 3x + 2,$ and $8x + 6$.

Solution

$$(5x - 3) + (3x + 2) + (8x + 6) = (5x + 3x + 8x) + (-3 + 2 + 6)$$
$$= 16x + 5$$

Classroom Example
Find the indicated sum:

$(3a^2b - 2ab^2) + (-6a^2b + 9ab^2)$
$+ (7a^2b - 5ab^2).$

EXAMPLE 3

Find the indicated sum: $(-4x^2y + xy^2) + (7x^2y - 9xy^2) + (5x^2y - 4xy^2)$.

Solution

$$(-4x^2y + xy^2) + (7x^2y - 9xy^2) + (5x^2y - 4xy^2)$$
$$= (-4x^2y + 7x^2y + 5x^2y) + (xy^2 - 9xy^2 - 4xy^2)$$
$$= 8x^2y - 12xy^2$$

The concept of subtraction as adding the opposite extends to polynomials in general. Hence the expression $a - b$ is equivalent to $a + (-b)$. We can form the opposite of a polynomial by taking the opposite of each term. For example, the opposite of $3x^2 - 7x + 1$ is $-3x^2 + 7x - 1$. We express this in symbols as

$$-(3x^2 - 7x + 1) = -3x^2 + 7x - 1$$

Now consider the following subtraction problems.

Classroom Example
Subtract $2x^2 - 5x + 4$ from
$6x^2 + 7x - 3$.

EXAMPLE 4   Subtract $3x^2 + 7x - 1$ from $7x^2 - 2x - 4$.

Solution

Use the horizontal format to obtain

$$(7x^2 - 2x - 4) - (3x^2 + 7x - 1) = (7x^2 - 2x - 4) + (-3x^2 - 7x + 1)$$
$$= (7x^2 - 3x^2) + (-2x - 7x) + (-4 + 1)$$
$$= 4x^2 - 9x - 3$$

Classroom Example
Subtract $4m^2 - 9m - 7$ from $10m^2 + 3$.

EXAMPLE 5   Subtract $-3y^2 + y - 2$ from $4y^2 + 7$.

Solution

Because subtraction is not a commutative operation, be sure to perform the subtraction in the correct order.

$$(4y^2 + 7) - (-3y^2 + y - 2) = (4y^2 + 7) + (3y^2 - y + 2)$$
$$= (4y^2 + 3y^2) + (-y) + (7 + 2)$$
$$= 7y^2 - y + 9$$

The next example demonstrates the use of the vertical format for this work.

Classroom Example
Subtract $5a^2 - 4ab + 11$ from $2a^2 + 3ab + 7$.

EXAMPLE 6   Subtract $4x^2 - 7xy + 5y^2$ from $3x^2 - 2xy + y^2$.

Solution

$$\begin{array}{l} 3x^2 - 2xy + y^2 \\ \underline{4x^2 - 7xy + 5y^2} \end{array}$$ Note which polynomial goes on the bottom and how the similar terms are aligned

Now we can mentally form the opposite of the bottom polynomial and add.

$$\begin{array}{l} 3x^2 - 2xy + y^2 \\ \underline{4x^2 - 7xy + 5y^2} \\ -x^2 + 5xy - 4y^2 \end{array}$$ The opposite of $4x^2 - 7xy + 5y^2$ is $-4x^2 + 7xy - 5y^2$

We can also use the distributive property and the properties $a = 1(a)$ and $-a = -1(a)$ when adding and subtracting polynomials. The next examples illustrate this approach.

Classroom Example
Perform the indicated operations:

$(12t + 3) - (4t - 5) + (7t + 1)$

EXAMPLE 7   Perform the indicated operations: $(5x - 2) + (2x - 1) - (3x + 4)$.

Solution

$$(5x - 2) + (2x - 1) - (3x + 4) = 1(5x - 2) + 1(2x - 1) - 1(3x + 4)$$
$$= 1(5x) - 1(2) + 1(2x) - 1(1) - 1(3x) - 1(4)$$
$$= 5x - 2 + 2x - 1 - 3x - 4$$
$$= 5x + 2x - 3x - 2 - 1 - 4$$
$$= 4x - 7$$

We can do some of the steps mentally and simplify our format, as shown in the next two examples.

Classroom Example
Perform the indicated operations:

$(9x^2 - 4y) - (2x^2 - 3)$
$+ (-3y + 6)$

EXAMPLE 8

Perform the indicated operations: $(5a^2 - 2b) - (2a^2 + 4) + (-7b - 3)$.

Solution

$$(5a^2 - 2b) - (2a^2 + 4) + (-7b - 3) = 5a^2 - 2b - 2a^2 - 4 - 7b - 3$$
$$= 3a^2 - 9b - 7$$

Classroom Example
Simplify $(8x^2 + 3x - 7)$
$- (3x^2 - x - 2)$.

EXAMPLE 9   Simplify $(4t^2 - 7t - 1) - (t^2 + 2t - 6)$.

Solution

$$(4t^2 - 7t - 1) - (t^2 + 2t - 6) = 4t^2 - 7t - 1 - t^2 - 2t + 6$$
$$= 3t^2 - 9t + 5$$

Remember that a polynomial in parentheses preceded by a negative sign can be written without the parentheses by replacing each term with its opposite. Thus in Example 9, $-(t^2 + 2t - 6) = -t^2 - 2t + 6$. Finally, let's consider a simplification problem that contains grouping symbols within grouping symbols.

Classroom Example
Simplify $12m + [5m - (m - 6)]$.

EXAMPLE 10   Simplify $7x + [3x - (2x + 7)]$.

Solution

$$7x + [3x - (2x + 7)] = 7x + [3x - 2x - 7] \qquad \text{Remove the innermost}$$
$$= 7x + [x - 7] \qquad\qquad \text{parentheses first}$$
$$= 7x + x - 7$$
$$= 8x - 7$$

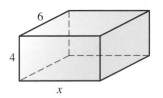

Figure 3.1

Sometimes we encounter polynomials in a geometric setting. For example, we can find a polynomial that represents the total surface area of the rectangular solid in Figure 3.1 as follows:

$4x$	+	$4x$	+	$6x$	+	$6x$	+	24	+	24
Area of front		Area of back		Area of top		Area of bottom		Area of left side		Area of right side

Simplifying $4x + 4x + 6x + 6x + 24 + 24$, we obtain the polynomial $20x + 48$, which represents the total surface area of the rectangular solid. Furthermore, by evaluating the polynomial $20x + 48$ for different positive values of x, we can determine the total surface area of any rectangular solid for which two dimensions are 4 and 6. The following chart contains some specific rectangular solids.

x	4 by 6 by x Rectangular solid	Total surface area $(20x + 48)$
2	4 by 6 by 2	$20(2) + 48 = 88$
4	4 by 6 by 4	$20(4) + 48 = 128$
5	4 by 6 by 5	$20(5) + 48 = 148$
7	4 by 6 by 7	$20(7) + 48 = 188$
12	4 by 6 by 12	$20(12) + 48 = 288$

Concept Quiz 3.1

For Problems 1–10, answer true or false.

1. The degree of the monomial $4x^2y$ is 3.

2. The degree of the polynomial $2x^4 - 5x^3 + 7x^2 - 4x + 6$ is 10.

3. A three-term polynomial is called a binomial.

4. A polynomial is a monomial or a finite sum of monomials.

5. Monomial terms must have whole number exponents for each variable.

6. The sum of $-2x - 1$, $-x + 4$, and $5x - 7$ is $8x - 4$.

7. If $3x - 4$ is subtracted from $-7x + 2$, the result is $-10x + 6$.

8. Polynomials must be of the same degree if they are to be added.

9. If $-x - 1$ is subtracted from the sum of $2x - 1$ and $-4x - 6$, the result is $-x - 6$.

10. We can form the opposite of a polynomial by taking the opposite of each term.

Problem Set 3.1

For Problems 1–10, determine the degree of the given polynomials. (Objective 1)

1. $7xy + 6y$

2. $-5x^2y^2 - 6xy^2 + x$

3. $-x^2y + 2xy^2 - xy$

4. $5x^3y^2 - 6x^3y^3$

5. $5x^2 - 7x - 2$

6. $7x^3 - 2x + 4$

7. $8x^6 + 9$

8. $5y^6 + y^4 - 2y^2 - 8$

9. -12

10. $7x - 2y$

For Problems 11–20, add the given polynomials. (Objective 2)

11. $3x - 7$ and $7x + 4$

12. $9x + 6$ and $5x - 3$

13. $-5t - 4$ and $-6t + 9$

14. $-7t + 14$ and $-3t - 6$

15. $3x^2 - 5x - 1$ and $-4x^2 + 7x - 1$

16. $6x^2 + 8x + 4$ and $-7x^2 - 7x - 10$

17. $12a^2b^2 - 9ab$ and $5a^2b^2 + 4ab$

18. $15a^2b^2 - ab$ and $-20a^2b^2 - 6ab$

19. $2x - 4$, $-7x + 2$, and $-4x + 9$

20. $-x^2 - x - 4$, $2x^2 - 7x + 9$, and $-3x^2 + 6x - 10$

For Problems 21–30, subtract the polynomials using the horizontal format. (Objective 2)

21. $5x - 2$ from $3x + 4$

22. $7x + 5$ from $2x - 1$

23. $-4a - 5$ from $6a + 2$

24. $5a + 7$ from $-a - 4$

25. $3x^2 - x + 2$ from $7x^2 + 9x + 8$

26. $5x^2 + 4x - 7$ from $3x^2 + 2x - 9$

27. $2a^2 - 6a - 4$ from $-4a^2 + 6a + 10$

28. $-3a^2 - 6a + 3$ from $3a^2 + 6a - 11$

29. $2x^3 + x^2 - 7x - 2$ from $5x^3 + 2x^2 + 6x - 13$

30. $6x^3 + x^2 + 4$ from $9x^3 - x - 2$

For Problems 31–40, subtract the polynomials using the vertical format. (Objective 2)

31. $5x - 2$ from $12x + 6$

32. $3x - 7$ from $2x + 1$

33. $-4x + 7$ from $-7x - 9$

34. $-6x - 2$ from $5x + 6$

35. $2x^2 + x + 6$ from $4x^2 - x - 2$

36. $4x^2 - 3x - 7$ from $-x^2 - 6x + 9$

37. $x^3 + x^2 - x - 1$ from $-2x^3 + 6x^2 - 3x + 8$

38. $2x^3 - x + 6$ from $x^3 + 4x^2 + 1$

39. $-5x^2 + 6x - 12$ from $2x - 1$

40. $2x^2 - 7x - 10$ from $-x^3 - 12$

For Problems 41–46, perform the operations as described. (Objective 2)

41. Subtract $2x^2 - 7x - 1$ from the sum of $x^2 + 9x - 4$ and $-5x^2 - 7x + 10$.

42. Subtract $4x^2 + 6x + 9$ from the sum of $-3x^2 - 9x + 6$ and $-2x^2 + 6x - 4$.

43. Subtract $-x^2 - 7x - 1$ from the sum of $4x^2 + 3$ and $-7x^2 + 2x$.

44. Subtract $-4x^2 + 6x - 3$ from the sum of $-3x + 4$ and $9x^2 - 6$.

45. Subtract the sum of $5n^2 - 3n - 2$ and $-7n^2 + n + 2$ from $-12n^2 - n + 9$.

46. Subtract the sum of $-6n^2 + 2n - 4$ and $4n^2 - 2n + 4$ from $-n^2 - n + 1$.

For Problems 47–56, perform the indicated operations. (Objective 2)

47. $(5x + 2) + (7x - 1) + (-4x - 3)$

48. $(-3x + 1) + (6x - 2) + (9x - 4)$

49. $(12x - 9) - (-3x + 4) - (7x + 1)$

50. $(6x + 4) - (4x - 2) - (-x - 1)$

51. $(2x^2 - 7x - 1) + (-4x^2 - x + 6) + (-7x^2 - 4x - 1)$

52. $(5x^2 + x + 4) + (-x^2 + 2x + 4) + (-14x^2 - x + 6)$

53. $(7x^2 - x - 4) - (9x^2 - 10x + 8) + (12x^2 + 4x - 6)$

54. $(-6x^2 + 2x + 5) - (4x^2 + 4x - 1) + (7x^2 + 4)$

55. $(n^2 - 7n - 9) - (-3n + 4) - (2n^2 - 9)$

56. $(6n^2 - 4) - (5n^2 + 9) - (6n + 4)$

For Problems 57–70, simplify by removing the inner parentheses first and working outward. (Objective 3)

57. $3x - [5x - (x + 6)]$

58. $7x - [2x - (-x - 4)]$

59. $2x^2 - [-3x^2 - (x^2 - 4)]$

60. $4x^2 - [-x^2 - (5x^2 - 6)]$

61. $-2n^2 - [n^2 - (-4n^2 + n + 6)]$

62. $-7n^2 - [3n^2 - (-n^2 - n + 4)]$

63. $[4t^2 - (2t + 1) + 3] - [3t^2 + (2t - 1) - 5]$

64. $-(3n^2 - 2n + 4) - [2n^2 - (n^2 + n + 3)]$

65. $[2n^2 - (2n^2 - n + 5)] + [3n^2 + (n^2 - 2n - 7)]$

66. $3x^2 - [4x^2 - 2x - (x^2 - 2x + 6)]$

67. $[7xy - (2x - 3xy + y)] - [3x - (x - 10xy - y)]$

68. $[9xy - (4x + xy - y)] - [4y - (2x - xy + 6y)]$

69. $[4x^3 - (2x^2 - x - 1)] - [5x^3 - (x^2 + 2x - 1)]$

70. $[x^3 - (x^2 - x + 1)] - [-x^3 + (7x^2 - x + 10)]$

For Problems 71–73, use geometry to solve the problems. (Objective 4)

71. Find a polynomial that represents the perimeter of each of the following figures (Figures 3.2, 3.3, and 3.4).

(a)
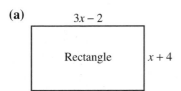
Figure 3.2

(b)
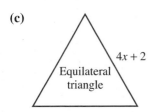
Figure 3.3

(c)
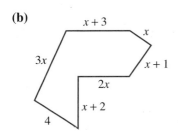
Figure 3.4

72. Find a polynomial that represents the total surface area of the rectangular solid in Figure 3.5.

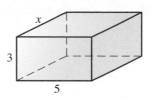
Figure 3.5

Now use that polynomial to determine the total surface area of each of the following rectangular solids.

(a) 3 by 5 by $\underline{4}$ **(b)** 3 by 5 by $\underline{7}$

(c) 3 by 5 by $\underline{11}$ **(d)** 3 by 5 by $\underline{13}$

73. Find a polynomial that represents the total surface area of the right circular cylinder in Figure 3.6. Now use that polynomial to determine the total surface area of each of the following right circular cylinders that have a base with a radius of 4. Use 3.14 for π, and express the answers to the nearest tenth.

(a) $h = 5$ **(b)** $h = 7$

(c) $h = 14$ **(d)** $h = 18$

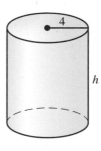
Figure 3.6

Thoughts Into Words

74. Explain how to subtract the polynomial $-3x^2 + 2x - 4$ from $4x^2 + 6$.

75. Is the sum of two binomials always another binomial? Defend your answer.

76. Explain how to simplify the expression
$7x - [3x - (2x - 4) + 2] - x$

Answers to the Concept Quiz
1. True   **2.** False   **3.** False   **4.** True   **5.** True   **6.** False   **7.** True   **8.** False   **9.** True   **10.** True

3.2   Products and Quotients of Monomials

OBJECTIVES   **1** Multiply monomials

2 Raise a monomial to an exponent

3 Divide monomials

4 Use polynomials in geometry problems

Suppose that we want to find the product of two monomials such as $3x^2y$ and $4x^3y^2$. To proceed, use the properties of real numbers, and keep in mind that exponents indicate repeated multiplication.

$$(3x^2y)(4x^3y^2) = (3 \cdot x \cdot x \cdot y)(4 \cdot x \cdot x \cdot x \cdot y \cdot y)$$
$$= 3 \cdot 4 \cdot x \cdot x \cdot x \cdot x \cdot x \cdot y \cdot y \cdot y$$
$$= 12x^5y^3$$

You can use such an approach to find the product of any two monomials. However, there are some basic properties of exponents that make the process of multiplying monomials a much easier task. Let's consider each of these properties and illustrate its use when multiplying monomials. The following examples demonstrate the first property.

$$x^2 \cdot x^3 = (x \cdot x)(x \cdot x \cdot x) = x^5$$
$$a^4 \cdot a^2 = (a \cdot a \cdot a \cdot a)(a \cdot a) = a^6$$
$$b^3 \cdot b^4 = (b \cdot b \cdot b)(b \cdot b \cdot b \cdot b) = b^7$$

In general,

$$b^n \cdot b^m = \underbrace{(b \cdot b \cdot b \cdot \ldots b)}_{\substack{n \text{ factors} \\ \text{of } b}}\underbrace{(b \cdot b \cdot b \cdot \ldots b)}_{\substack{m \text{ factors} \\ \text{of } b}}$$
$$= \underbrace{b \cdot b \cdot b \cdot \ldots b}_{(n+m) \text{ factors of } b}$$
$$= b^{n+m}$$

We can state the first property as follows:

Property 3.1   Product of the Same Base with Integer Exponents

If b is any real number, and n and m are positive integers, then

$$b^n \cdot b^m = b^{n+m}$$

Property 3.1 says that to find the product of two positive integral powers of the same base, we add the exponents and use this sum as the exponent of the common base.

$$x^7 \cdot x^8 = x^{7+8} = x^{15} \qquad\qquad y^6 \cdot y^4 = y^{6+4} = y^{10}$$
$$2^3 \cdot 2^8 = 2^{3+8} = 2^{11} \qquad\qquad (-3)^4 \cdot (-3)^5 = (-3)^{4+5} = (-3)^9$$
$$\left(\frac{2}{3}\right)^7 \cdot \left(\frac{2}{3}\right)^5 = \left(\frac{2}{3}\right)^{5+7} = \left(\frac{2}{3}\right)^{12}$$

The following examples illustrate the use of Property 3.1, along with the commutative and associative properties of multiplication, to form the basis for multiplying monomials. The steps enclosed in the dashed boxes could be performed mentally.

Classroom Example
$(2x^3y^4)(5xy^2)$

EXAMPLE 1

$$
\begin{aligned}
(3x^2y)(4x^3y^2) &= 3 \cdot 4 \cdot x^2 \cdot x^3 \cdot y \cdot y^2 \\
&= 12x^{2+3}y^{1+2} \\
&= 12x^5y^3
\end{aligned}
$$

Classroom Example
$(3m^2n^5)(-7m^2n^2)$

EXAMPLE 2

$$
\begin{aligned}
(-5a^3b^4)(7a^2b^5) &= -5 \cdot 7 \cdot a^3 \cdot a^2 \cdot b^4 \cdot b^5 \\
&= -35a^{3+2}b^{4+5} \\
&= -35a^5b^9
\end{aligned}
$$

Classroom Example
$\left(\frac{1}{3}x^5y^4\right)\left(\frac{3}{8}x^2y^3\right)$

EXAMPLE 3

$$
\begin{aligned}
\left(\frac{3}{4}xy\right)\left(\frac{1}{2}x^5y^6\right) &= \frac{3}{4} \cdot \frac{1}{2} \cdot x \cdot x^5 \cdot y \cdot y^6 \\
&= \frac{3}{8}x^{1+5}y^{1+6} \\
&= \frac{3}{8}x^6y^7
\end{aligned}
$$

Classroom Example
$(-4m^3n^2)(-m^2n)$

EXAMPLE 4

$$
\begin{aligned}
(-ab^2)(-5a^2b) &= (-1)(-5)(a)(a^2)(b^2)(b) \\
&= 5a^{1+2}b^{2+1} \\
&= 5a^3b^3
\end{aligned}
$$

Classroom Example
$(6xy^4)(2x^4)(3x^3y^2)$

EXAMPLE 5

$$
\begin{aligned}
(2x^2y^2)(3x^2y)(4y^3) &= 2 \cdot 3 \cdot 4 \cdot x^2 \cdot x^2 \cdot y^2 \cdot y \cdot y^3 \\
&= 24x^{2+2}y^{2+1+3} \\
&= 24x^4y^6
\end{aligned}
$$

The following examples demonstrate another useful property of exponents.

$$
(x^2)^3 = x^2 \cdot x^2 \cdot x^2 = x^{2+2+2} = x^6
$$
$$
(a^3)^2 = a^3 \cdot a^3 = a^{3+3} = a^6
$$
$$
(b^4)^3 = b^4 \cdot b^4 \cdot b^4 = b^{4+4+4} = b^{12}
$$

In general,

$$
(b^n)^m = \underbrace{b^n \cdot b^n \cdot b^n \cdot \ldots b^n}_{m \text{ factors of } b^n}
$$

$$
= b^{\overbrace{n+n+n+\cdots+n}^{\text{adding } m \text{ of these}}}
$$

$$
= b^{mn}
$$

We can state this property as follows:

Property 3.2 Power Raised to a Power

If b is any real number, and m and n are positive integers, then

$$
(b^n)^m = b^{mn}
$$

The following examples show how Property 3.2 is used to find "the power of a power."

$$
(x^4)^5 = x^{5(4)} = x^{20} \qquad (y^6)^3 = y^{3(6)} = y^{18}
$$
$$
(2^3)^7 = 2^{7(3)} = 2^{21}
$$

A third property of exponents pertains to raising a monomial to a power. Consider the following examples, which we use to introduce the property.

$$(3x)^2 = (3x)(3x) = 3 \cdot 3 \cdot x \cdot x = 3^2 \cdot x^2$$

$$(4y^2)^3 = (4y^2)(4y^2)(4y^2) = 4 \cdot 4 \cdot 4 \cdot y^2 \cdot y^2 \cdot y^2 = (4)^3(y^2)^3$$

$$(-2a^3b^4)^2 = (-2a^3b^4)(-2a^3b^4) = (-2)(-2)(a^3)(a^3)(b^4)(b^4)$$
$$= (-2)^2(a^3)^2(b^4)^2$$

In general,

$$(ab)^n = \underbrace{(ab)(ab)(ab) \cdot \ldots (ab)}_{n \text{ factors of } ab}$$

$$= \underbrace{(a \cdot a \cdot a \cdot a \cdot \ldots a)}_{n \text{ factors of } a}\underbrace{(b \cdot b \cdot b \cdot \ldots b)}_{n \text{ factors of } b}$$

$$= a^n b^n$$

We can formally state Property 3.3 as follows:

Property 3.3 Power of a Product

If a and b are real numbers, and n is a positive integer, then

$$(ab)^n = a^n b^n$$

Properties 3.2 and 3.3 form the basis for raising a monomial to a power, as in the next examples.

Classroom Example
$(m^4n^2)^7$

EXAMPLE 6

$$(x^2y^3)^4 = (x^2)^4(y^3)^4 \qquad \text{Use } (ab)^n = a^n b^n$$
$$= x^8y^{12} \qquad \text{Use } (b^n)^m = b^{mn}$$

Classroom Example
$(2r^3)^4$

EXAMPLE 7

$$(3a^5)^3 = (3)^3(a^5)^3$$
$$= 27a^{15}$$

Classroom Example
$(-3m^5n)^3$

EXAMPLE 8

$$(-2xy^4)^5 = (-2)^5(x)^5(y^4)^5$$
$$= -32x^5y^{20}$$

Dividing Monomials

To develop an effective process for dividing by a monomial, we need yet another property of exponents. This property is a direct consequence of the definition of an exponent. Study the following examples.

$$\frac{x^4}{x^3} = \frac{x \cdot x \cdot x \cdot x}{x \cdot x \cdot x} = x \qquad\qquad \frac{x^3}{x^3} = \frac{x \cdot x \cdot x}{x \cdot x \cdot x} = 1$$

$$\frac{a^5}{a^2} = \frac{a \cdot a \cdot a \cdot a \cdot a}{a \cdot a} = a^3 \qquad\qquad \frac{y^5}{y^5} = \frac{y \cdot y \cdot y \cdot y \cdot y}{y \cdot y \cdot y \cdot y \cdot y} = 1$$

$$\frac{y^8}{y^4} = \frac{y \cdot y \cdot y \cdot y \cdot y \cdot y \cdot y \cdot y}{y \cdot y \cdot y \cdot y} = y^4$$

We can state the general property as follows:

> **Property 3.4   Quotient of Same Base with Integer Exponents**
>
> If b is any nonzero real number, and m and n are positive integers, then
>
> **1.** $\dfrac{b^n}{b^m} = b^{n-m}$ when $n > m$ **2.** $\dfrac{b^n}{b^m} = 1$ when $n = m$

Applying Property 3.4 to the previous examples yields

$$\frac{x^4}{x^3} = x^{4-3} = x^1 = x \qquad\qquad \frac{x^3}{x^3} = 1$$

$$\frac{a^5}{a^2} = a^{5-2} = a^3 \qquad\qquad \frac{y^5}{y^5} = 1$$

$$\frac{y^8}{y^4} = y^{8-4} = y^4$$

(We will discuss the situation when $n < m$ in a later chapter.)

Property 3.4, along with our knowledge of dividing integers, provides the basis for dividing monomials. The following example demonstrates the process.

Classroom Example

Simplify the following:

(a) $\dfrac{32y^6}{4y^3}$ (b) $\dfrac{-42m^{11}}{-14m^6}$

(c) $\dfrac{-48t^7}{6t^2}$ (d) $\dfrac{54a^4}{6a^4}$

(e) $\dfrac{56y^6}{-14y}$ (f) $\dfrac{16x^6y^9}{4x^2y^5}$

EXAMPLE 9   Simplify the following:

(a) $\dfrac{24x^5}{3x^2}$ (b) $\dfrac{-36a^{13}}{-12a^5}$ (c) $\dfrac{-56x^9}{7x^4}$ (d) $\dfrac{72b^5}{8b^5}$ (e) $\dfrac{48y^7}{-12y}$ (f) $\dfrac{12x^4y^7}{2x^2y^4}$

Solution

(a) $\dfrac{24x^5}{3x^2} = 8x^{5-2} = 8x^3$

(b) $\dfrac{-36a^{13}}{-12a^5} = 3a^{13-5} = 3a^8$

(c) $\dfrac{-56x^9}{7x^4} = -8x^{9-4} = -8x^5$

(d) $\dfrac{72b^5}{8b^5} = 9 \qquad \dfrac{b^5}{b^5} = 1$

(e) $\dfrac{48y^7}{-12y} = -4y^{7-1} = -4y^6$

(f) $\dfrac{12x^4y^7}{2x^2y^4} = 6x^{4-2}y^{7-4} = 6x^2y^3$

Concept Quiz 3.2

For Problems 1–10, answer true or false.

1. When multiplying factors with the same base, add the exponents.

2. $3^2 \cdot 3^2 = 9^4$

3. $2x^2 \cdot 3x^3 = 6x^6$

4. $(x^2)^3 = x^5$

5. $(-4x^3)^2 = -4x^6$

6. To simplify $(3x^2y)(2x^3y^2)^4$ according to the order of operations, first raise $2x^3y^2$ to the fourth power and then multiply the monomials.

7. $\dfrac{-8x^6}{2x^2} = -4x^3$

8. $\dfrac{24x^3y^2}{-xy} = -24x^2y$

9. $\dfrac{-14xy^3}{-7xy^3} = 2$

10. $\dfrac{36a^2b^3c}{-18ab^2} = -2abc$

Problem Set 3.2

For Problems 1–36, find each product. (Objective 1)

1. $(4x^3)(9x)$
2. $(6x^3)(7x^2)$
3. $(-2x^2)(6x^3)$
4. $(2xy)(-4x^2y)$
5. $(-a^2b)(-4ab^3)$
6. $(-8a^2b^2)(-3ab^3)$
7. $(x^2yz^2)(-3xyz^4)$
8. $(-2xy^2z^2)(-x^2y^3z)$
9. $(5xy)(-6y^3)$
10. $(-7xy)(4x^4)$
11. $(3a^2b)(9a^2b^4)$
12. $(-8a^2b^2)(-12ab^5)$
13. $(m^2n)(-mn^2)$
14. $(-x^3y^2)(xy^3)$
15. $\left(\dfrac{2}{5}xy^2\right)\left(\dfrac{3}{4}x^2y^4\right)$
16. $\left(\dfrac{1}{2}x^2y^6\right)\left(\dfrac{2}{3}xy\right)$
17. $\left(-\dfrac{3}{4}ab\right)\left(\dfrac{1}{5}a^2b^3\right)$
18. $\left(-\dfrac{2}{7}a^2\right)\left(\dfrac{3}{5}ab^3\right)$
19. $\left(-\dfrac{1}{2}xy\right)\left(\dfrac{1}{3}x^2y^3\right)$
20. $\left(\dfrac{3}{4}x^4y^5\right)(-x^2y)$
21. $(3x)(-2x^2)(-5x^3)$
22. $(-2x)(-6x^3)(x^2)$
23. $(-6x^2)(3x^3)(x^4)$
24. $(-7x^2)(3x)(4x^3)$
25. $(x^2y)(-3xy^2)(x^3y^3)$
26. $(xy^2)(-5xy)(x^2y^4)$
27. $(-3y^2)(-2y^2)(-4y^5)$
28. $(-y^3)(-6y)(-8y^4)$
29. $(4ab)(-2a^2b)(7a)$
30. $(3b)(-2ab^2)(7a)$
31. $(-ab)(-3ab)(-6ab)$
32. $(-3a^2b)(-ab^2)(-7a)$
33. $\left(\dfrac{2}{3}xy\right)(-3x^2y)(5x^4y^5)$
34. $\left(\dfrac{3}{4}x\right)(-4x^2y^2)(9y^3)$
35. $(12y)(-5x)\left(-\dfrac{5}{6}x^4y\right)$
36. $(-12x)(3y)\left(-\dfrac{3}{4}xy^6\right)$

For Problems 37–58, raise each monomial to the indicated power. (Objective 2)

37. $(3xy^2)^3$
38. $(4x^2y^3)^3$
39. $(-2x^2y)^5$
40. $(-3xy^4)^3$
41. $(-x^4y^5)^4$
42. $(-x^5y^2)^4$
43. $(ab^2c^3)^6$
44. $(a^2b^3c^5)^5$
45. $(2a^2b^3)^6$
46. $(2a^3b^2)^6$
47. $(9xy^4)^2$
48. $(8x^2y^5)^2$
49. $(-3ab^3)^4$
50. $(-2a^2b^4)^4$
51. $-(2ab)^4$
52. $-(3ab)^4$
53. $-(xy^2z^3)^6$
54. $-(xy^2z^3)^8$
55. $(-5a^2b^2c)^3$
56. $(-4abc^4)^3$
57. $(-xy^4z^2)^7$
58. $(-x^2y^4z^5)^5$

For Problems 59–74, find each quotient. (Objective 3)

59. $\dfrac{9x^4y^5}{3xy^2}$
60. $\dfrac{12x^2y^7}{6x^2y^3}$
61. $\dfrac{25x^5y^6}{-5x^2y^4}$
62. $\dfrac{56x^6y^4}{-7x^2y^3}$
63. $\dfrac{-54ab^2c^3}{-6abc}$
64. $\dfrac{-48a^3bc^5}{-6a^2c^4}$
65. $\dfrac{-18x^2y^2z^6}{xyz^2}$
66. $\dfrac{-32x^4y^5z^8}{x^2yz^3}$
67. $\dfrac{a^3b^4c^7}{-abc^5}$
68. $\dfrac{-a^4b^5c}{a^2b^4c}$
69. $\dfrac{-72x^2y^4}{-8x^2y^4}$
70. $\dfrac{-96x^4y^5}{12x^4y^4}$
71. $\dfrac{14ab^3}{-14ab}$
72. $\dfrac{-12abc^2}{12bc}$
73. $\dfrac{-36x^3y^5}{2y^5}$
74. $\dfrac{-48xyz^2}{2xz}$

For Problems 75–90, find each product. Assume that the variables in the exponents represent positive integers. (Objective 1) For example, $(x^{2n})(x^{3n}) = x^{2n+3n} = x^{5n}$.

75. $(2x^n)(3x^{2n})$
76. $(3x^{2n})(x^{3n-1})$
77. $(a^{2n-1})(a^{3n+4})$
78. $(a^{5n-1})(a^{5n+1})$
79. $(x^{3n-2})(x^{n+2})$
80. $(x^{n-1})(x^{4n+3})$
81. $(a^{5n-2})(a^3)$
82. $(x^{3n-4})(x^4)$
83. $(2x^n)(-5x^n)$
84. $(4x^{2n-1})(-3x^{n+1})$
85. $(-3a^2)(-4a^{n+2})$
86. $(-5x^{n-1})(-6x^{2n+4})$
87. $(x^n)(2x^{2n})(3x^2)$
88. $(2x^n)(3x^{3n-1})(-4x^{2n+5})$
89. $(3x^{n-1})(x^{n+1})(4x^{2-n})$
90. $(-5x^{n+2})(x^{n-2})(4x^{3-2n})$

For Problems 91–93, use geometry to solve the problems.
(Objective 4)

91. Find a polynomial that represents the total surface area of the rectangular solid in Figure 3.7. Also find a polynomial that represents the volume.

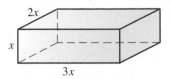

Figure 3.7

92. Find a polynomial that represents the total surface area of the rectangular solid in Figure 3.8. Also find a polynomial that represents the volume.

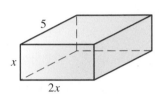

Figure 3.8

93. Find a polynomial that represents the area of the shaded region in Figure 3.9. The length of a radius of the larger circle is r units, and the length of a radius of the smaller circle is 6 units.

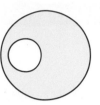

Figure 3.9

Thoughts Into Words

94. How would you convince someone that $\dfrac{x^6}{x^2}$ is x^4 and not x^3?

95. Your friend simplifies $2^3 \cdot 2^2$ as follows:
$$2^3 \cdot 2^2 = 4^{3+2} = 4^5 = 1024$$

What has she done incorrectly and how would you help her?

Answers to the Concept Quiz

1. True   **2.** False   **3.** False   **4.** False   **5.** False   **6.** True   **7.** False   **8.** True   **9.** True   **10.** True

---

3.3	Multiplying Polynomials

OBJECTIVES
1. Multiply polynomials
2. Multiply two binomials
3. Use a pattern to find the square of a binomial
4. Find the cube of a binomial
5. Use polynomials in geometry problems

We usually state the distributive property as $a(b + c) = ab + ac$; however, we can extend it as follows:
$$a(b + c + d) = ab + ac + ad$$
$$a(b + c + d + e) = ab + ac + ad + ae, \quad \text{etc.}$$

We apply the commutative and associative properties, the properties of exponents, and the distributive property together to find the product of a monomial and a polynomial. The following examples illustrate this idea.

Classroom Example
$4n^3(3n^2 + 2n - 3)$

EXAMPLE 1

$$3x^2(2x^2 + 5x + 3) = 3x^2(2x^2) + 3x^2(5x) + 3x^2(3)$$
$$= 6x^4 + 15x^3 + 9x^2$$ ▪

Classroom Example
$-5mn(2m^3 + 6m^2n - 4mn^2 - 3n^3)$

EXAMPLE 2

$$-2xy(3x^3 - 4x^2y - 5xy^2 + y^3)$$
$$= -2xy(3x^3) - (-2xy)(4x^2y) - (-2xy)(5xy^2) + (-2xy)(y^3)$$
$$= -6x^4y + 8x^3y^2 + 10x^2y^3 - 2xy^4$$ ▪

Now let's consider the product of two polynomials, neither of which is a monomial. Consider the following examples.

Classroom Example
$(x + 4)(y + 8)$

EXAMPLE 3

$$(x + 2)(y + 5) = x(y + 5) + 2(y + 5)$$
$$= x(y) + x(5) + 2(y) + 2(5)$$
$$= xy + 5x + 2y + 10$$ ▪

Note that each term of the first polynomial is multiplied by each term of the second polynomial.

Classroom Example
$(r - 5)(s - t + 4)$

EXAMPLE 4

$$(x - 3)(y + z + 3) = x(y + z + 3) - 3(y + z + 3)$$
$$= xy + xz + 3x - 3y - 3z - 9$$ ▪

Multiplying polynomials often produces similar terms that can be combined to simplify the resulting polynomial.

Classroom Example
$(x + 3)(x + 9)$

EXAMPLE 5

$$(x + 5)(x + 7) = x(x + 7) + 5(x + 7)$$
$$= x^2 + 7x + 5x + 35$$
$$= x^2 + 12x + 35$$ ▪

Classroom Example
$(x - 3)(x^2 + 2x - 7)$

EXAMPLE 6

$$(x - 2)(x^2 - 3x + 4) = x(x^2 - 3x + 4) - 2(x^2 - 3x + 4)$$
$$= x^3 - 3x^2 + 4x - 2x^2 + 6x - 8$$
$$= x^3 - 5x^2 + 10x - 8$$ ▪

In Example 6, we are claiming that

$$(x - 2)(x^2 - 3x + 4) = x^3 - 5x^2 + 10x - 8$$

for all real numbers. In addition to going back over our work, how can we verify such a claim? Obviously, we cannot try all real numbers, but trying at least one number gives us a partial check. Let's try the number 4.

$$(x - 2)(x^2 - 3x + 4) = (4 - 2)(4^2 - 3(4) + 4) \qquad \text{When } x = 4$$
$$= 2(16 - 12 + 4)$$
$$= 2(8)$$
$$= 16$$
$$x^3 - 5x^2 + 10x - 8 = 4^3 - 5(4)^2 + 10(4) - 8 \qquad \text{When } x = 4$$
$$= 64 - 80 + 40 - 8$$
$$= 16$$

Classroom Example
$(5m - 3n)(m^2 - 3mn + n^2)$

EXAMPLE 7

$$(3x - 2y)(x^2 + xy - y^2)$$
$$= 3x(x^2 + xy - y^2) - 2y(x^2 + xy - y^2)$$
$$= 3x^3 + 3x^2y - 3xy^2 - 2x^2y - 2xy^2 + 2y^3$$
$$= 3x^3 + x^2y - 5xy^2 + 2y^3$$

It helps to be able to find the product of two binomials without showing all of the intermediate steps. This is quite easy to do with the *three-step shortcut pattern* demonstrated by Figures 3.10 and 3.11 in the following examples.

Classroom Example
$(x + 2)(x + 7)$

EXAMPLE 8   Multiply $(x + 3)(x + 8)$.

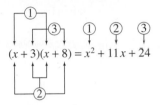

Figure 3.10

Step 1 Multiply $x \cdot x$.

Step 2 Multiply $3 \cdot x$ and $8 \cdot x$ and combine.

Step 3 Multiply $3 \cdot 8$.

Classroom Example
$(4d + 1)(3d - 2)$

EXAMPLE 9   Multiply $(3x + 2)(2x - 1)$.

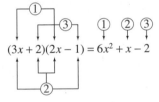

Figure 3.11

The mnemonic device FOIL is often used to remember the pattern for multiplying binomials. The letters in FOIL represent, First, Outside, Inside, and Last. If you look back at Examples 8 and 9, step 1 is to find the product of the first terms in the binomial; step 2 is to find the sum of the product of the outside terms and the product of the inside terms; and step 3 is to find the product of the last terms in each binomial.

Now see if you can use the pattern to find the following products.

$$(x + 2)(x + 6) = ?$$
$$(x - 3)(x + 5) = ?$$
$$(2x + 5)(3x + 7) = ?$$
$$(3x - 1)(4x - 3) = ?$$

Your answers should be $x^2 + 8x + 12$, $x^2 + 2x - 15$, $6x^2 + 29x + 35$, and $12x^2 - 13x + 3$. Keep in mind that this shortcut pattern applies only to finding the product of two binomials.

We can use exponents to indicate repeated multiplication of polynomials. For example, $(x + 3)^2$ means $(x + 3)(x + 3)$, and $(x + 4)^3$ means $(x + 4)(x + 4)(x + 4)$. To square a binomial, we simply write it as the product of two equal binomials and apply the shortcut pattern. Thus

$$(x + 3)^2 = (x + 3)(x + 3) = x^2 + 6x + 9$$
$$(x - 6)^2 = (x - 6)(x - 6) = x^2 - 12x + 36 \quad \text{and}$$
$$(3x - 4)^2 = (3x - 4)(3x - 4) = 9x^2 - 24x + 16$$

When squaring binomials, be careful not to forget the middle term. That is to say, $(x + 3)^2 \neq x^2 + 3^2$; instead, $(x + 3)^2 = x^2 + 6x + 9$.

When multiplying binomials, there are some special patterns that you should recognize. We can use these patterns to find products, and later we will use some of them when factoring polynomials.

Pattern 1 $(a + b)^2 = (a + b)(a + b) = a^2 \quad + \quad 2ab \quad + \quad b^2$

Square of   Twice the   Square of
first term   +   product of   +   second term
of binomial   the two terms   of binomial
                     of binomial

Classroom Example
(a) $(x + 6)^2$
(b) $(3x + y)^2$
(c) $(4x + 5y)^2$

EXAMPLE 10   Expand the following squares of binomials:

(a) $(x + 4)^2$ (b) $(2x + 3y)^2$ (c) $(5a + 7b)^2$

Solution

Square of   Twice the   Square of
the first term +   product of   +   second term
of binomial   the terms   of binomial
                     of binomial

(a) $(x + 4)^2 = x^2 + 8x + 16$

(b) $(2x + 3y)^2 = 4x^2 + 12xy + 9y^2$

(c) $(5a + 7b)^2 = 25a^2 + 70ab + 49b^2$

Pattern 2 $(a - b)^2 = (a - b)(a - b) = a^2 \quad - \quad 2ab \quad + \quad b^2$

Square of   Twice the   Square of
first term   −   product of   +   second term
of binomial   the two terms   of binomial
                     of binomial

Classroom Example
(a) $(m - 4)^2$
(b) $(2x - 5y)^2$
(c) $(3x - 7y)^2$

EXAMPLE 11   Expand the following squares of binomials:

(a) $(x - 8)^2$ (b) $(3x - 4y)^2$ (c) $(4a - 9b)^2$

Solution

Square of   Twice the   Square of
the first term −   product of   +   second term
of binomial   the terms   of binomial
                     of binomial

(a) $(x - 8)^2 = x^2 - 16x + 64$

(b) $(3x - 4y)^2 = 9x^2 - 24xy + 16y^2$

(c) $(4a - 9b)^2 = 16a^2 - 72ab + 81b^2$

Pattern 3 $(a + b)(a - b) = a^2 - b^2$

Square of
first term $-$
of binomials

Square of
second term
of binomials

Classroom Example
(a) $(x + 8)(x - 8)$
(b) $(x - 4y)(x + 4y)$
(c) $(6x + 5y)(6x - 5y)$

EXAMPLE 12   Find the product for the following:

(a) $(x + 7)(x - 7)$ **(b)** $(2x + y)(2x - y)$ **(c)** $(3a - 2b)(3a + 2b)$

Solution

Square of
the first term $-$
of binomial

Square of
second term
of binomial

(a) $(x + 7)(x - 7) = x^2 - 49$

(b) $(2x + y)(2x - y) = 4x^2 - y^2$

(c) $(3a - 2b)(3a + 2b) = 9a^2 - 4b^2$

Now suppose that we want to cube a binomial. One approach is as follows:

$$(x + 4)^3 = (x + 4)(x + 4)(x + 4)$$
$$= (x + 4)(x^2 + 8x + 16)$$
$$= x(x^2 + 8x + 16) + 4(x^2 + 8x + 16)$$
$$= x^3 + 8x^2 + 16x + 4x^2 + 32x + 64$$
$$= x^3 + 12x^2 + 48x + 64$$

Another approach is to cube a general binomial and then use the resulting pattern.

Pattern 4 $(a + b)^3 = (a + b)(a + b)(a + b)$
$$= (a + b)(a^2 + 2ab + b^2)$$
$$= a(a^2 + 2ab + b^2) + b(a^2 + 2ab + b^2)$$
$$= a^3 + 2a^2b + ab^2 + a^2b + 2ab^2 + b^3$$
$$= a^3 + 3a^2b + 3ab^2 + b^3$$

Classroom Example
$(x + 5)^3$

EXAMPLE 13   Expand $(x + 4)^3$.

Solution

Let's use the pattern $(a + b)^3 = a^3 + 3a^2b + 3ab^2 + b^3$ to cube the binomial $x + 4$.

$$(x + 4)^3 = x^3 + 3x^2(4) + 3x(4)^2 + 4^3$$
$$= x^3 + 12x^2 + 48x + 64$$

Because $a - b = a + (-b)$, we can easily develop a pattern for cubing $a - b$.

Pattern 5 $(a - b)^3 = [a + (-b)]^3$
$$= a^3 + 3a^2(-b) + 3a(-b)^2 + (-b)^3$$
$$= a^3 - 3a^2b + 3ab^2 - b^3$$

EXAMPLE 14   Expand $(3x - 2y)^3$.

Solution

Now let's use the pattern $(a - b)^3 = a^3 - 3a^2b + 3ab^2 - b^3$ to cube the binomial $3x - 2y$.

$$(3x - 2y)^3 = (3x)^3 - 3(3x)^2(2y) + 3(3x)(2y)^2 - (2y)^3$$
$$= 27x^3 - 54x^2y + 36xy^2 - 8y^3$$

Finally, we need to realize that if the patterns are forgotten or do not apply, then we can revert to applying the distributive property.

$$(2x - 1)(x^2 - 4x + 6) = 2x(x^2 - 4x + 6) - 1(x^2 - 4x + 6)$$
$$= 2x^3 - 8x^2 + 12x - x^2 + 4x - 6$$
$$= 2x^3 - 9x^2 + 16x - 6$$

Back to the Geometry Connection

As you might expect, there are geometric interpretations for many of the algebraic concepts we present in this section. We will give you the opportunity to make some of these connections between algebra and geometry in the next problem set. Let's conclude this section with a problem that allows us to use some algebra and geometry.

EXAMPLE 15

A rectangular piece of tin is 16 inches long and 12 inches wide as shown in Figure 3.12. From each corner a square piece x inches on a side is cut out. The flaps are then turned up to form an open box. Find polynomials that represent the volume and outside surface area of the box.

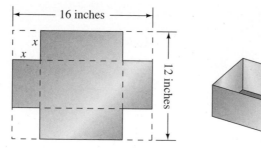

Figure 3.12

Solution

The length of the box will be $16 - 2x$, the width $12 - 2x$, and the height x. With the volume formula $V = lwh$, the polynomial $(16 - 2x)(12 - 2x)(x)$, which simplifies to $4x^3 - 56x^2 + 192x$, represents the volume.

The outside surface area of the box is the area of the original piece of tin, minus the four corners that were cut off. Therefore, the polynomial $16(12) - 4x^2$, or $192 - 4x^2$, represents the outside surface area of the box.

Remark: Recall that in Section 3.1 we found the total surface area of a rectangular solid by adding the areas of the sides, top, and bottom. Use this approach for the open box in Example 15 to check our answer of $192 - 4x^2$. Keep in mind that the box has no top.

Concept Quiz 3.3

For Problems 1–10, answer true or false.

1. The algebraic expression $(x + y)^2$ is called the square of a binomials.
2. The algebraic expression $(x + y)(x + 2xy + y)$ is called the product of two binomials.
3. The mnemonic device FOIL stands for first, outside, inside, and last.
4. Although the distributive property is usually stated as $a(b + c) = ab + ac$, it can be extended, as in $a(b + c + d + e) = ab + ac + ad + ae$, when multiplying polynomials.
5. Multiplying polynomials often produces similar terms that can be combined to simplify the resulting product.
6. The pattern for $(a + b)^2$ is $a^2 + b^2$.
7. The pattern for $(a - b)^2$ is $a^2 - 2ab - b^2$.
8. The pattern for $(a + b)(a - b)$ is $a^2 - b^2$.
9. The pattern for $(a + b)^3$ is $a^3 + 3ab + b^3$.
10. The pattern for $(a - b)^3$ is $a^3 + 3a^2b - 3ab^2 - b^3$.

Problem Set 3.3

For Problems 1–74, find each indicated product. Remember the shortcut for multiplying binomials and the other special patterns we discussed in this section. (Objectives 1–4)

1. $2xy(5xy^2 + 3x^2y^3)$
2. $3x^2y(6y^2 - 5x^2y^4)$
3. $-3a^2b(4ab^2 - 5a^3)$
4. $-7ab^2(2b^3 - 3a^2)$
5. $8a^3b^4(3ab - 2ab^2 + 4a^2b^2)$
6. $9a^3b(2a - 3b + 7ab)$
7. $-x^2y(6xy^2 + 3x^2y^3 - x^3y)$
8. $-ab^2(5a + 3b - 6a^2b^3)$
9. $(a + 2b)(x + y)$
10. $(t - s)(x + y)$
11. $(a - 3b)(c + 4d)$
12. $(a - 4b)(c - d)$
13. $(x + 6)(x + 10)$
14. $(x + 2)(x + 10)$
15. $(y - 5)(y + 11)$
16. $(y - 3)(y + 9)$
17. $(n + 2)(n - 7)$
18. $(n + 3)(n - 12)$
19. $(x + 6)(x - 6)$
20. $(t + 8)(t - 8)$
21. $(x - 6)^2$
22. $(x - 2)^2$
23. $(x - 6)(x - 8)$
24. $(x - 3)(x - 13)$
25. $(x + 1)(x - 2)(x - 3)$
26. $(x - 1)(x + 4)(x - 6)$
27. $(x - 3)(x + 3)(x - 1)$
28. $(x - 5)(x + 5)(x - 8)$
29. $(t + 9)^2$
30. $(t + 13)^2$
31. $(y - 7)^2$
32. $(y - 4)^2$
33. $(4x + 5)(x + 7)$
34. $(6x + 5)(x + 3)$
35. $(3y - 1)(3y + 1)$
36. $(5y - 2)(5y + 2)$

37. $(7x - 2)(2x + 1)$
38. $(6x - 1)(3x + 2)$
39. $(1 + t)(5 - 2t)$
40. $(3 - t)(2 + 4t)$
41. $(3t + 7)^2$
42. $(4t + 6)^2$
43. $(2 - 5x)(2 + 5x)$
44. $(6 - 3x)(6 + 3x)$
45. $(7x - 4)^2$
46. $(5x - 7)^2$
47. $(6x + 7)(3x - 10)$
48. $(4x - 7)(7x + 4)$
49. $(2x - 5y)(x + 3y)$
50. $(x - 4y)(3x + 7y)$
51. $(5x - 2a)(5x + 2a)$
52. $(9x - 2y)(9x + 2y)$
53. $(t + 3)(t^2 - 3t - 5)$
54. $(t - 2)(t^2 + 7t + 2)$
55. $(x - 4)(x^2 + 5x - 4)$
56. $(x + 6)(2x^2 - x - 7)$
57. $(2x - 3)(x^2 + 6x + 10)$
58. $(3x + 4)(2x^2 - 2x - 6)$
59. $(4x - 1)(3x^2 - x + 6)$
60. $(5x - 2)(6x^2 + 2x - 1)$
61. $(x^2 + 2x + 1)(x^2 + 3x + 4)$
62. $(x^2 - x + 6)(x^2 - 5x - 8)$
63. $(2x^2 + 3x - 4)(x^2 - 2x - 1)$
64. $(3x^2 - 2x + 1)(2x^2 + x - 2)$
65. $(x + 2)^3$
66. $(x + 1)^3$
67. $(x - 4)^3$
68. $(x - 5)^3$
69. $(2x + 3)^3$
70. $(3x + 1)^3$
71. $(4x - 1)^3$
72. $(3x - 2)^3$
73. $(5x + 2)^3$
74. $(4x - 5)^3$

For Problems 75–84, find the indicated products. Assume all variables that appear as exponents represent positive integers. (Objectives 2 and 3)

75. $(x^n - 4)(x^n + 4)$

76. $(x^{3a} - 1)(x^{3a} + 1)$

77. $(x^a + 6)(x^a - 2)$

78. $(x^a + 4)(x^a - 9)$

79. $(2x^n + 5)(3x^n - 7)$

80. $(3x^n + 5)(4x^n - 9)$

81. $(x^{2a} - 7)(x^{2a} - 3)$

82. $(x^{2a} + 6)(x^{2a} - 4)$

83. $(2x^n + 5)^2$

84. $(3x^n - 7)^2$

For Problems 85–89, use geometry to solve the problems. (Objective 5)

85. Explain how Figure 3.13 can be used to demonstrate geometrically that $(x + 2)(x + 6) = x^2 + 8x + 12$.

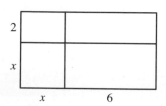

Figure 3.13

86. Find a polynomial that represents the sum of the areas of the two rectangles shown in Figure 3.14.

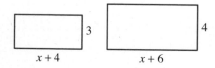

Figure 3.14

87. Find a polynomial that represents the area of the shaded region in Figure 3.15.

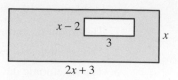

Figure 3.15

88. Explain how Figure 3.16 can be used to demonstrate geometrically that $(x + 7)(x - 3) = x^2 + 4x - 21$.

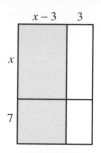

Figure 3.16

89. A square piece of cardboard is 16 inches on a side. A square piece x inches on a side is cut out from each corner. The flaps are then turned up to form an open box. Find polynomials that represent the volume and outside surface area of the box.

Thoughts Into Words

90. How would you simplify $(2^3 + 2^2)^2$? Explain your reasoning.

91. Describe the process of multiplying two polynomials.

92. Determine the number of terms in the product of $(x + y)$ and $(a + b + c + d)$ without doing the multiplication. Explain how you arrived at your answer.

Further Investigations

93. We have used the following two multiplication patterns.

$$(a + b)^2 = a^2 + 2ab + b^2$$

$$(a + b)^3 = a^3 + 3a^2b + 3ab^2 + b^3$$

By multiplying, we can extend these patterns as follows:

$$(a + b)^4 = a^4 + 4a^3b + 6a^2b^2 + 4ab^3 + b^4$$

$$(a + b)^5 = a^5 + 5a^4b + 10a^3b^2 + 10a^2b^3 + 5ab^4 + b^5$$

On the basis of these results, see if you can determine a pattern that will enable you to complete each of the following without using the long-multiplication process.

(a) $(a + b)^6$

(b) $(a + b)^7$

(c) $(a + b)^8$

(d) $(a + b)^9$

94. Find each of the following indicated products. These patterns will be used again in Section 3.5.

(a) $(x - 1)(x^2 + x + 1)$

(b) $(x + 1)(x^2 - x + 1)$

(c) $(x + 3)(x^2 - 3x + 9)$

(d) $(x - 4)(x^2 + 4x + 16)$

(e) $(2x - 3)(4x^2 + 6x + 9)$

(f) $(3x + 5)(9x^2 - 15x + 25)$

95. Some of the product patterns can be used to do arithmetic computations mentally. For example, let's use the pattern $(a + b)^2 = a^2 + 2ab + b^2$ to compute 31^2 mentally. Your thought process should be "$31^2 = (30 + 1)^2 = 30^2 + 2(30)(1) + 1^2 = 961$." Compute each of the following numbers mentally, and then check your answers.

(a) 21^2 **(b)** 41^2 **(c)** 71^2

(d) 32^2 **(e)** 52^2 **(f)** 82^2

96. Use the pattern $(a - b)^2 = a^2 - 2ab + b^2$ to compute each of the following numbers mentally, and then check your answers.

(a) 19^2 **(b)** 29^2 **(c)** 49^2

(d) 79^2 **(e)** 38^2 **(f)** 58^2

97. Every whole number with a units digit of 5 can be represented by the expression $10x + 5$, where x is a whole number. For example, $35 = 10(3) + 5$ and $145 = 10(14) + 5$. Now let's observe the following pattern when squaring such a number.

$$(10x + 5)^2 = 100x^2 + 100x + 25$$
$$= \boxed{100x(x + 1) + 25}$$

The pattern inside the dashed box can be stated as "add 25 to the product of x, $x + 1$, and 100." Thus, to compute 35^2 mentally, we can figure "$35^2 = 3(4)(100) + 25 = 1225$." Compute each of the following numbers mentally, and then check your answers.

(a) 15^2 **(b)** 25^2 **(c)** 45^2

(d) 55^2 **(e)** 65^2 **(f)** 75^2

(g) 85^2 **(h)** 95^2 **(i)** 105^2

Answers to the Concept Quiz

1. True   **2.** False   **3.** True   **4.** True   **5.** True   **6.** False   **7.** False   **8.** True   **9.** False   **10.** False

---

3.4   Factoring: Greatest Common Factor and Common Binomial Factor

OBJECTIVES

1 Classify numbers as prime or composite

2 Factor composite numbers into a product of prime numbers

3 Understand the rules about completely factored form

4 Factor out the highest common monomial factor

5 Factor out a common binomial factor

6 Factor by grouping

7 Use factoring to solve equations

8 Solve word problems that involve factoring

Recall that 2 and 3 are said to be *factors* of 6 because the product of 2 and 3 is 6. Likewise, in an indicated product such as $7ab$, the 7, a, and b are called factors of the product. If a positive integer greater than 1 has no factors that are positive integers other than itself and 1, then it is called a **prime number**. Thus the prime numbers less than 20 are 2, 3, 5, 7, 11, 13, 17, and 19. A positive integer greater than 1 that is not a prime number is called a **composite number**. The composite numbers less than 20 are 4, 6, 8, 9, 10, 12, 14, 15, 16, and 18. Every composite number is the product of prime numbers. Consider the following examples.

$$4 = 2 \cdot 2 \qquad\qquad 63 = 3 \cdot 3 \cdot 7$$
$$12 = 2 \cdot 2 \cdot 3 \qquad 121 = 11 \cdot 11$$
$$35 = 5 \cdot 7$$

The indicated product form that contains only prime factors is called the **prime factorization form** of a number. Thus the prime factorization form of 63 is $3 \cdot 3 \cdot 7$. We also say that the number has been *completely factored* when it is in the prime factorization form.

In general, factoring is the reverse of multiplication. Previously, we have used the distributive property to find the product of a monomial and a polynomial, as in the Table 3.1.

Table 3.1 Use the Distributive Property to Find a Product

Expression	Apply the distributive property	Product
$3(x + 2)$	$3(x) + 3(2)$	$3x + 6$
$5(2x - 1)$	$5(2x) + 5(-1)$	$10x - 5$
$x(x^2 + 6x - 4)$	$x(x^2) + x(6x) + x(-4)$	$x^3 + 6x^2 - 4x$

We shall also use the distributive property [in the form $ab + ac = a(b + c)$] to reverse the process—that is, to factor a given polynomial. Consider the examples in Table 3.2.

Table 3.2 Use the Distributive Property to Factor

Expression	Rewrite the expression	Factored form when the distributive property is applied
$3x + 6$	$3(x) + 3(2)$	$3(x + 2)$
$10x - 5$	$5(2x) + 5(-1)$	$5(2x - 1)$
$x^3 + 6x^2 - 4x$	$x(x^2) + x(6x) + x(-4)$	$x(x^2 + 6x - 4)$

Note that in each example a given polynomial has been factored into the product of a monomial and a polynomial. Obviously, polynomials could be factored in a variety of ways. Consider some factorizations of $3x^2 + 12x$.

$$3x^2 + 12x = 3x(x + 4) \quad \text{or} \quad 3x^2 + 12x = 3(x^2 + 4x) \quad \text{or}$$

$$3x^2 + 12x = x(3x + 12) \quad \text{or} \quad 3x^2 + 12x = \frac{1}{2}(6x^2 + 24x)$$

We are, however, primarily interested in the first of the previous factorization forms, which we refer to as the **completely factored form**. A polynomial with integral coefficients is in completely factored form if

1. It is expressed as a product of polynomials with *integral coefficients*, and
2. No polynomial, other than a monomial, within the factored form can be further factored into polynomials with integral coefficients.

Do you see why only the first of the above factored forms of $3x^2 + 12x$ is said to be in completely factored form? In each of the other three forms, the polynomial inside the parentheses can be factored further. Moreover, in the last form, $\frac{1}{2}(6x^2 + 24x)$, the condition of using only integral coefficients is violated.

EXAMPLE 1

For each of the following, determine if the factorization is in completely factored form. If it is not in completely factored form, state which rule has been violated.

(a) $4m^3 + 8m^4n = 4m^2(m + 2m^2n)$ **(b)** $32p^2q^4 + 8pq = 8pq(4pq^3 + 1)$

(c) $8x^2y^5 + 4x^3y^2 = 8x^2y^2(y^3 + 0.5x)$ **(d)** $10ab^3 + 20a^4b = 2ab(5b^2 + 10a^3)$

(a) $5x^6 + 15x^7y = 5x^5(x + 3x^2y)$

(b) $12m^2n^3 + 4mn^2 = 4mn^2(3mn + 1)$

(c) $12p^7q^3 + 3p^3q^4 = 12p^3q^3(p^4 + 0.25q)$

(d) $24a^4b + 12ab^3 = 3ab(8a^3 + 4b^2)$

Solution

(a) No, it is not completely factored. The polynomial inside the parentheses can be factored further.

(b) Yes, it is completely factored.

(c) No, it is not completely factored. The coefficient of 0.5 is not an integer.

(d) No, it is not completely factored. The polynomial inside the parentheses can be factored further.

▬

Factoring out the Highest Common Monomial Factor

The factoring process that we discuss in this section, $ab + ac = a(b + c)$, is often referred to as **factoring out the highest common monomial factor**. The key idea in this process is to recognize the monomial factor that is common to all terms. For example, we observe that each term of the polynomial $2x^3 + 4x^2 + 6x$ has a factor of $2x$. Thus we write

$$2x^3 + 4x^2 + 6x = 2x(\qquad)$$

and insert within the parentheses the appropriate polynomial factor. We determine the terms of this polynomial factor by dividing each term of the original polynomial by the factor of $2x$. The final, completely factored form is

$$2x^3 + 4x^2 + 6x = 2x(x^2 + 2x + 3)$$

The following examples further demonstrate this process of factoring out the highest common monomial factor.

$$12x^3 + 16x^2 = 4x^2(3x + 4) \qquad 6x^2y^3 + 27xy^4 = 3xy^3(2x + 9y)$$

$$8ab - 18b = 2b(4a - 9) \qquad 8y^3 + 4y^2 = 4y^2(2y + 1)$$

$$30x^3 + 42x^4 - 24x^5 = 6x^3(5 + 7x - 4x^2)$$

Note that in each example, the common monomial factor itself is not in a completely factored form. For example, $4x^2(3x + 4)$ is not written as $2 \cdot 2 \cdot x \cdot x \cdot (3x + 4)$.

EXAMPLE 2   Factor out the highest common factor for each of the following:

(a) $3x^4 + 15x^3 - 21x^2$ **(b)** $8x^3y^2 - 2x^4y - 12xy^2$

Solution

(a) Each term of the polynomial has a common factor of $3x^2$.

$$3x^4 + 15x^3 - 21x^2 = 3x^2(x^2 + 5x - 7)$$

(b) Each term of the polynomial has a common factor of $2xy$.

$$8x^3y^2 - 2x^4y - 12xy^2 = 2xy(4x^2y - x^3 - 6y)$$ ▬

Factoring out a Common Binomial Factor

Sometimes there may be a common binomial factor rather than a common monomial factor. For example, each of the two terms of the expression $x(y + 2) + z(y + 2)$ has a binomial factor of $(y + 2)$. Thus we can factor $(y + 2)$ from each term, and our result is

$$x(y + 2) + z(y + 2) = (y + 2)(x + z)$$

Consider an example that involves a common binomial factor.

EXAMPLE 3   For each of the following, factor out the common binomial factor:

(a) $a^2(b + 1) + 2(b + 1)$ **(b)** $x(2y - 1) - y(2y - 1)$ **(c)** $x(x + 2) + 3(x + 2)$

(a) $n^3(m + 2) + 4(m + 2)$

(b) $a(3b + 4) - b(3b + 4)$

(c) $y(y - 3) + 5(y - 3)$

Solution

(a) $a^2(b + 1) + 2(b + 1) = (b + 1)(a^2 + 2)$

(b) $x(2y - 1) - y(2y - 1) = (2y - 1)(x - y)$

(c) $x(x + 2) + 3(x + 2) = (x + 2)(x + 3)$

Factoring by Grouping

It may be that the original polynomial exhibits no apparent common monomial or binomial factor, which is the case with $ab + 3a + bc + 3c$. However, by factoring a from the first two terms and c from the last two terms, we get

$$ab + 3a + bc + 3c = a(b + 3) + c(b + 3)$$

Now a common binomial factor of $(b + 3)$ is obvious, and we can proceed as before.

$$a(b + 3) + c(b + 3) = (b + 3)(a + c)$$

We refer to this factoring process as **factoring by grouping**. Let's consider a few examples of this type.

Classroom Example
Factor the following using factoring by grouping:

(a) $x^2y + 4x^2 - 3y^2 - 12y$

(b) $x^2 - 5x + 2x - 10$

(c) $m^2 - 2m + 4m - 8$

EXAMPLE 4   Factor the following using factoring by grouping:

(a) $ab^2 - 4b^2 + 3a - 12$ **(b)** $x^2 - x + 5x - 5$ **(c)** $x^2 + 2x - 3x - 6$

Solution

(a) $ab^2 - 4b^2 + 3a - 12 = b^2(a - 4) + 3(a - 4)$ Factor b^2 from the first two terms and 3 from the last two terms

$\qquad\qquad\qquad\qquad\quad = (a - 4)(b^2 + 3)$ Factor common binomial from both terms

(b) $x^2 - x + 5x - 5 = x(x - 1) + 5(x - 1)$ Factor x from the first two terms and 5 from the last two terms

$\qquad\qquad\qquad\quad = (x - 1)(x + 5)$ Factor common binomial from both terms

(c) $x^2 + 2x - 3x - 6 = x(x + 2) - 3(x + 2)$ Factor x from the first two terms and -3 from the last two terms

$\qquad\qquad\qquad\quad = (x + 2)(x - 3)$ Factor common binomial factor from both terms

It may be necessary to rearrange some terms before applying the distributive property. Terms that contain common factors need to be grouped together, and this may be done in more than one way. The next example shows two different methods.

Method 1 $4a^2 - bc^2 - a^2b + 4c^2 = 4a^2 - a^2b + 4c^2 - bc^2$

$\qquad\qquad\qquad\qquad\qquad\qquad = a^2(4 - b) + c^2(4 - b)$

$\qquad\qquad\qquad\qquad\qquad\qquad = (4 - b)(a^2 + c^2)$ or

Method 2 $4a^2 - bc^2 - a^2b + 4c^2 = 4a^2 + 4c^2 - bc^2 - a^2b$

$\qquad\qquad\qquad\qquad\qquad\qquad = 4(a^2 + c^2) - b(c^2 + a^2)$

$\qquad\qquad\qquad\qquad\qquad\qquad = 4(a^2 + c^2) - b(a^2 + c^2)$

$\qquad\qquad\qquad\qquad\qquad\qquad = (a^2 + c^2)(4 - b)$

Using Factoring to Solve Equations

One reason that factoring is an important algebraic skill is that it extends our techniques for solving equations. Each time we examine a factoring technique, we will then use it to help solve certain types of equations.

We need another property of equality before we consider some equations for which the highest-common-factor technique is useful. Suppose that the product of two numbers is zero. Can we conclude that at least one of these numbers must itself be zero? Yes. Let's state a property that formalizes this idea. Property 3.5, along with the highest-common-factor pattern, provides us with another technique for solving equations.

> **Property 3.5**
>
> Let a and b be real numbers. Then
>
> $$ab = 0 \quad \text{if and only if} \quad a = 0 \text{ or } b = 0$$

Classroom Example
Solve $a^2 + 7a = 0$.

EXAMPLE 5   Solve $x^2 + 6x = 0$.

Solution

$$x^2 + 6x = 0$$
$$x(x + 6) = 0 \qquad \text{Factor the left side}$$

$$x = 0 \quad \text{or} \quad x + 6 = 0 \qquad ab = 0 \text{ if and only if } a = 0 \text{ or } b = 0$$
$$x = 0 \quad \text{or} \quad x = -6$$

Thus both 0 and -6 will satisfy the original equation, and the solution set is $\{-6, 0\}$. ∎

Classroom Example
Solve $x^2 = 10x$.

EXAMPLE 6   Solve $a^2 = 11a$.

Solution

$$a^2 = 11a$$
$$a^2 - 11a = 0 \qquad \text{Add } -11a \text{ to both sides}$$
$$a(a - 11) = 0 \qquad \text{Factor the left side}$$

$$a = 0 \quad \text{or} \quad a - 11 = 0 \qquad ab = 0 \text{ if and only if } a = 0 \text{ or } b = 0$$
$$a = 0 \quad \text{or} \quad a = 11$$

The solution set is $\{0, 11\}$. ∎

Remark: Note that in Example 6 we did *not* divide both sides of the equation by a. This would cause us to lose the solution of 0.

Classroom Example
Solve $7n^2 - 8n = 0$.

EXAMPLE 7   Solve $3n^2 - 5n = 0$.

Solution

$$3n^2 - 5n = 0$$
$$n(3n - 5) = 0$$

$$n = 0 \quad \text{or} \quad 3n - 5 = 0$$
$$n = 0 \quad \text{or} \quad 3n = 5$$
$$n = 0 \quad \text{or} \quad n = \frac{5}{3}$$

The solution set is $\left\{0, \dfrac{5}{3}\right\}$. ∎

EXAMPLE 8   Solve $3ax^2 + bx = 0$ for x.

Solution

$$3ax^2 + bx = 0$$
$$x(3ax + b) = 0$$

$x = 0$	or	$3ax + b = 0$
$x = 0$	or	$3ax = -b$
$x = 0$	or	$x = -\dfrac{b}{3a}$

The solution set is $\left\{ 0, -\dfrac{b}{3a} \right\}$.

Solving Word Problems That Involve Factoring

Many of the problems that we solve in the next few sections have a geometric setting. Some basic geometric figures, along with appropriate formulas, are listed in the inside front cover of this text. You may need to refer to them to refresh your memory.

EXAMPLE 9

The area of a square is three times its perimeter. Find the length of a side of the square.

Solution

Let s represent the length of a side of the square (Figure 3.17). The area is represented by s^2 and the perimeter by $4s$. Thus

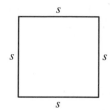

$$s^2 = 3(4s) \qquad \text{The area is to be three}$$
$$s^2 = 12s \qquad \text{times the perimeter}$$
$$s^2 - 12s = 0$$
$$s(s - 12) = 0$$

$s = 0$	or	$s = 12$

Figure 3.17

Because 0 is not a reasonable solution, it must be a 12-by-12 square. (Be sure to check this answer in the original statement of the problem!)

EXAMPLE 10

Suppose that the volume of a right circular cylinder is numerically equal to the total surface area of the cylinder. If the height of the cylinder is equal to the length of a radius of the base, find the height.

Solution

Because $r = h$, the formula for volume $V = \pi r^2 h$ becomes $V = \pi r^3$, and the formula for the total surface area $S = 2\pi r^2 + 2\pi rh$ becomes $S = 2\pi r^2 + 2\pi r^2$, or $S = 4\pi r^2$. Therefore, we can set up and solve the following equation.

$$\pi r^3 = 4\pi r^2 \qquad \text{Volume is to be equal to the surface area}$$
$$\pi r^3 - 4\pi r^2 = 0$$
$$\pi r^2(r - 4) = 0$$

$\pi r^2 = 0$	or	$r - 4 = 0$
$r = 0$	or	$r = 4$

Zero is not a reasonable answer, therefore the height must be 4 units.

Concept Quiz 3.4

For Problems 1–10, answer true or false.

1. Factoring is the reverse of multiplication.
2. The distributive property in the form $ab + ac = a(b + c)$ is applied to factor polynomials.
3. A polynomial could have many factored forms but only one completely factored form.
4. The greatest common factor of $6x^2y^3 - 12x^3y^2 + 18x^4y$ is $2x^2y$.
5. If the factored form of a polynomial can be factored further, then it has not met the conditions to be considered "factored completely."
6. Common factors are always monomials.
7. If the product of x and y is zero, then x is zero or y is zero.
8. The factored form, $3a(2a^2 + 4)$, is factored completely.
9. The solutions for the equation $x(x + 2) = 7$ are 7 and 5.
10. The solution set for $x^2 = 7x$ is $\{7\}$.

Problem Set 3.4

For Problems 1–10, classify each number as prime or composite. (Objective 1)

1. 63
2. 81
3. 59
4. 83
5. 51
6. 69
7. 91
8. 119
9. 71
10. 101

For Problems 11–20, factor each of the composite numbers into the product of prime numbers. For example, $30 = 2 \cdot 3 \cdot 5$. (Objective 2)

11. 28
12. 39
13. 44
14. 49
15. 56
16. 64
17. 72
18. 84
19. 87
20. 91

For Problems 21–24, state if the polynomial is factored completely. (Objective 3)

21. $6x^2y + 12xy^2 = 2xy(3x + 6y)$

22. $2a^3b^2 + 4a^2b^2 = 4a^2b^2\left(\dfrac{1}{2}a + 1\right)$

23. $10m^2n^3 + 15m^4n^2 = 5m^2n(2n^2 + 3m^2n)$

24. $24ab + 12bc - 18bd = 6b(4a + 2c - 3d)$

For Problems 25–50, factor completely. (Objectives 3 and 4)

25. $6x + 3y$
26. $12x + 8y$
27. $6x^2 + 14x$
28. $15x^2 + 6x$
29. $28y^2 - 4y$
30. $42y^2 - 6y$
31. $20xy - 15x$
32. $27xy - 36y$
33. $7x^3 + 10x^2$
34. $12x^3 - 10x^2$
35. $18a^2b + 27ab^2$
36. $24a^3b^2 + 36a^2b$
37. $12x^3y^4 - 39x^4y^3$
38. $15x^4y^2 - 45x^5y^4$
39. $8x^4 + 12x^3 - 24x^2$
40. $6x^5 - 18x^3 + 24x$
41. $5x + 7x^2 + 9x^4$
42. $9x^2 - 17x^4 + 21x^5$
43. $15x^2y^3 + 20xy^2 + 35x^3y^4$
44. $8x^5y^3 - 6x^4y^5 + 12x^2y^3$
45. $x(y + 2) + 3(y + 2)$
46. $x(y - 1) + 5(y - 1)$
47. $3x(2a + b) - 2y(2a + b)$
48. $5x(a - b) + y(a - b)$
49. $x(x + 2) + 5(x + 2)$
50. $x(x - 1) - 3(x - 1)$

For Problems 51–68, factor by grouping. (Objective 6)

51. $ax + 4x + ay + 4y$
52. $ax - 2x + ay - 2y$
53. $ax - 2bx + ay - 2by$
54. $2ax - bx + 2ay - by$
55. $3ax - 3bx - ay + by$
56. $5ax - 5bx - 2ay + 2by$
57. $2ax + 2x + ay + y$
58. $3bx + 3x + by + y$
59. $ax^2 - x^2 + 2a - 2$
60. $ax^2 - 2x^2 + 3a - 6$
61. $2ac + 3bd + 2bc + 3ad$
62. $2bx + cy + cx + 2by$

63. $ax - by + bx - ay$ **64.** $2a^2 - 3bc - 2ab + 3ac$

65. $x^2 + 9x + 6x + 54$ **66.** $x^2 - 2x + 5x - 10$

67. $2x^2 + 8x + x + 4$ **68.** $3x^2 + 18x - 2x - 12$

For Problems 69–84, solve each of the equations. (Objective 7)

69. $x^2 + 7x = 0$ **70.** $x^2 + 9x = 0$

71. $x^2 - x = 0$ **72.** $x^2 - 14x = 0$

73. $a^2 = 5a$ **74.** $b^2 = -7b$

75. $-2y = 4y^2$ **76.** $-6x = 2x^2$

77. $3x^2 + 7x = 0$ **78.** $-4x^2 + 9x = 0$

79. $4x^2 = 5x$ **80.** $3x = 11x^2$

81. $x - 4x^2 = 0$ **82.** $x - 6x^2 = 0$

83. $12a = -a^2$ **84.** $-5a = -a^2$

For Problems 85–90, solve each equation for the indicated variable. (Objective 7)

85. $5bx^2 - 3ax = 0$ for x **86.** $ax^2 + bx = 0$ for x

87. $2by^2 = -3ay$ for y **88.** $3ay^2 = by$ for y

89. $y^2 - ay + 2by - 2ab = 0$ for y

90. $x^2 + ax + bx + ab = 0$ for x

For Problems 91–100, set up an equation and solve each of the following problems. (Objective 8)

91. The square of a number equals seven times the number. Find the number.

92. Suppose that the area of a square is six times its perimeter. Find the length of a side of the square.

93. The area of a circular region is numerically equal to three times the circumference of the circle. Find the length of a radius of the circle.

94. Find the length of a radius of a circle such that the circumference of the circle is numerically equal to the area of the circle.

95. Suppose that the area of a circle is numerically equal to the perimeter of a square and that the length of a radius of the circle is equal to the length of a side of the square. Find the length of a side of the square. Express your answer in terms of π.

96. Find the length of a radius of a sphere such that the surface area of the sphere is numerically equal to the volume of the sphere.

97. Suppose that the area of a square lot is twice the area of an adjoining rectangular plot of ground. If the rectangular plot is 50 feet wide, and its length is the same as the length of a side of the square lot, find the dimensions of both the square and the rectangle.

98. The area of a square is one-fourth as large as the area of a triangle. One side of the triangle is 16 inches long, and the altitude to that side is the same length as a side of the square. Find the length of a side of the square.

99. Suppose that the volume of a sphere is numerically equal to twice the surface area of the sphere. Find the length of a radius of the sphere.

100. Suppose that a radius of a sphere is equal in length to a radius of a circle. If the volume of the sphere is numerically equal to four times the area of the circle, find the length of a radius for both the sphere and the circle.

Thoughts Into Words

101. Is $2 \cdot 3 \cdot 5 \cdot 7 \cdot 11 + 7$ a prime or a composite number? Defend your answer.

102. Suppose that your friend factors $36x^2y + 48xy^2$ as follows:

$$36x^2y + 48xy^2 = (4xy)(9x + 12y)$$
$$= (4xy)(3)(3x + 4y)$$
$$= 12xy(3x + 4y)$$

Is this a correct approach? Would you have any suggestion to offer your friend?

103. Your classmate solves the equation $3ax + bx = 0$ for x as follows:

$$3ax + bx = 0$$
$$3ax = -bx$$
$$x = \frac{-bx}{3a}$$

How should he know that the solution is incorrect? How would you help him obtain the correct solution?

Further Investigations

104. The total surface area of a right circular cylinder is given by the formula $A = 2\pi r^2 + 2\pi rh$, where r represents the radius of a base, and h represents the height of the cylinder. For computational purposes, it may be more convenient to change the form of the right side of the formula by factoring it.

$$A = 2\pi r^2 + 2\pi rh$$
$$= 2\pi r(r + h)$$

Use $A = 2\pi r(r + h)$ to find the total surface area of each of the following cylinders. Also, use $\dfrac{22}{7}$ as an approximation for π.

(a) $r = 7$ centimeters and $h = 12$ centimeters

(b) $r = 14$ meters and $h = 20$ meters

(c) $r = 3$ feet and $h = 4$ feet

(d) $r = 5$ yards and $h = 9$ yards

For Problems 105–110, factor each expression. Assume that all variables that appear as exponents represent positive integers.

105. $2x^{2a} - 3x^a$

106. $6x^{2a} + 8x^a$

107. $y^{3m} + 5y^{2m}$

108. $3y^{5m} - y^{4m} - y^{3m}$

109. $2x^{6a} - 3x^{5a} + 7x^{4a}$

110. $6x^{3a} - 10x^{2a}$

Answers to the Concept Quiz

1. True   **2.** True   **3.** True   **4.** False   **5.** True   **6.** False   **7.** True   **8.** False   **9.** False   **10.** False

---

| 3.5 | Factoring: Difference of Two Squares and Sum or Difference of Two Cubes |

OBJECTIVES

1 Factor the difference of two squares

2 Factor the sum or difference of two cubes

3 Use factoring to solve equations

4 Solve word problems that involve factoring

In Section 3.3, we examined some special multiplication patterns. One of these patterns was

$$(a + b)(a - b) = a^2 - b^2$$

This same pattern, viewed as a factoring pattern, is referred to as the difference of two squares.

> **Difference of Two Squares**
> $$a^2 - b^2 = (a + b)(a - b)$$

Applying the pattern is fairly simple, as the next example demonstrates.

Classroom Example
Factor each of the following:

(a) $x^2 - 49$
(b) $9x^2 - 16$
(c) $25x^2 - 4y^2$
(d) $1 - y^2$

EXAMPLE 1   Factor each of the following:

(a) $x^2 - 16$ **(b)** $4x^2 - 25$
(c) $16x^2 - 9y^2$ **(d)** $1 - a^2$

Solution

(a) $x^2 - 16 = (x)^2 - (4)^2 = (x + 4)(x - 4)$

(b) $4x^2 - 25 = (2x)^2 - (5)^2 = (2x + 5)(2x - 5)$

(c) $16x^2 - 9y^2 = (4x)^2 - (3y)^2 = (4x + 3y)(4x - 3y)$

(d) $1 - a^2 = (1)^2 - (a)^2 = (1 + a)(1 - a)$ ◼

Multiplication is commutative, so the order of writing the factors is not important. For example, $(x + 4)(x - 4)$ can also be written as $(x - 4)(x + 4)$.

You must be careful not to assume an analogous factoring pattern for the *sum* of two squares; *it does not exist*. For example, $x^2 + 4 \neq (x + 2)(x + 2)$ because $(x + 2)(x + 2) = x^2 + 4x + 4$. We say that a polynomial such as $x^2 + 4$ is a **prime polynomial** or that it is not factorable using integers.

Sometimes the difference-of-two-squares pattern can be applied more than once, as the next example illustrates.

EXAMPLE 2   Completely factor each of the following:

(a) $x^4 - y^4$ (b) $16x^4 - 81y^4$

Solution

(a) $x^4 - y^4 = (x^2 + y^2)(x^2 - y^2) = (x^2 + y^2)(x + y)(x - y)$

(b) $16x^4 - 81y^4 = (4x^2 + 9y^2)(4x^2 - 9y^2) = (4x^2 + 9y^2)(2x + 3y)(2x - 3y)$ ◼

It may also be that the squares are other than simple monomial squares, as in the next example.

EXAMPLE 3   Completely factor each of the following:

(a) $(x + 3)^2 - y^2$ (b) $4x^2 - (2y + 1)^2$ (c) $(x - 1)^2 - (x + 4)^2$

Solution

(a) $(x + 3)^2 - y^2 = ((x + 3) + y)((x + 3) - y) = (x + 3 + y)(x + 3 - y)$

(b) $4x^2 - (2y + 1)^2 = (2x + (2y + 1))(2x - (2y + 1))$
$$= (2x + 2y + 1)(2x - 2y - 1)$$

(c) $(x - 1)^2 - (x + 4)^2 = ((x - 1) + (x + 4))((x - 1) - (x + 4))$
$$= (x - 1 + x + 4)(x - 1 - x - 4)$$
$$= (2x + 3)(-5)$$ ◼

It is possible to apply both the technique of factoring out a common monomial factor and the pattern of the difference of two squares to the same problem. In general, it is best to look first for a common monomial factor. Consider the following example.

EXAMPLE 4   Completely factor each of the following:

(a) $2x^2 - 50$ (b) $9x^2 - 36$ (c) $48y^3 - 27y$

Solution

(a) $2x^2 - 50 = 2(x^2 - 25) = 2(x + 5)(x - 5)$

(b) $9x^2 - 36 = 9(x^2 - 4) = 9(x + 2)(x - 2)$

(c) $48y^3 - 27y = 3y(16y^2 - 9) = 3y(4y + 3)(4y - 3)$ ◼

Word of Caution The polynomial $9x^2 - 36$ can be factored as follows:

$$9x^2 - 36 = (3x + 6)(3x - 6)$$
$$= 3(x + 2)(3)(x - 2)$$
$$= 9(x + 2)(x - 2)$$

However, when one takes this approach, there seems to be a tendency to stop at the step $(3x + 6)(3x - 6)$. Therefore, remember the suggestion to *look first for a common monomial factor*.

The following examples should help you summarize all of the factoring techniques we have considered thus far.

$7x^2 + 28 = 7(x^2 + 4)$

$4x^2y - 14xy^2 = 2xy(2x - 7y)$

$x^2 - 4 = (x + 2)(x - 2)$

$18 - 2x^2 = 2(9 - x^2) = 2(3 + x)(3 - x)$

$y^2 + 9$ is not factorable using integers

$5x + 13y$ is not factorable using integers

$x^4 - 16 = (x^2 + 4)(x^2 - 4) = (x^2 + 4)(x + 2)(x - 2)$

Factoring the Sum and Difference of Two Cubes

As we pointed out before, there exists no sum-of-squares pattern analogous to the difference-of-squares factoring pattern. That is, a polynomial such as $x^2 + 9$ is not factorable using integers. However, patterns do exist for both the sum and the difference of two cubes. These patterns are as follows:

Sum and Difference of Two Cubes

$$a^3 + b^3 = (a + b)(a^2 - ab + b^2)$$
$$a^3 - b^3 = (a - b)(a^2 + ab + b^2)$$

Note how we apply these patterns in the next example.

Classroom Example
Factor each of the following:
(a) $x^3 + 64$
(b) $27m^3 + 1000n^3$
(c) $1 - y^3$
(d) $8x^3 - 27y^3$

> **EXAMPLE 5**   Factor each of the following:
>
> **(a)** $x^3 + 27$ **(b)** $8a^3 + 125b^3$ **(c)** $x^3 - 1$ **(d)** $27y^3 - 64x^3$

Solution

(a) $x^3 + 27 = (x)^3 + (3)^3 = (x + 3)(x^2 - 3x + 9)$

(b) $8a^3 + 125b^3 = (2a)^3 + (5b)^3 = (2a + 5b)(4a^2 - 10ab + 25b^2)$

(c) $x^3 - 1 = (x)^3 - (1)^3 = (x - 1)(x^2 + x + 1)$

(d) $27y^3 - 64x^3 = (3y)^3 - (4x)^3 = (3y - 4x)(9y^2 + 12xy + 16x^2)$

Using Factoring to Solve Equations

Remember that each time we pick up a new factoring technique we also develop more power for solving equations. Let's consider how we can use the difference-of-two-squares factoring pattern to help solve certain types of equations.

Classroom Example
Solve $n^2 = 49$.

EXAMPLE 6   Solve $x^2 = 16$.

Solution

$$x^2 = 16$$
$$x^2 - 16 = 0$$
$$(x + 4)(x - 4) = 0$$
$$x + 4 = 0 \quad \text{or} \quad x - 4 = 0$$
$$x = -4 \quad \text{or} \quad x = 4$$

The solution set is $\{-4, 4\}$. (Be sure to check these solutions in the original equation!) ■

Classroom Example
Solve $16m^2 = 81$.

EXAMPLE 7   Solve $9x^2 = 64$.

Solution

$$9x^2 = 64$$
$$9x^2 - 64 = 0$$
$$(3x + 8)(3x - 8) = 0$$
$$3x + 8 = 0 \quad \text{or} \quad 3x - 8 = 0$$
$$3x = -8 \quad \text{or} \quad 3x = 8$$
$$x = -\frac{8}{3} \quad \text{or} \quad x = \frac{8}{3}$$

The solution set is $\left\{-\dfrac{8}{3}, \dfrac{8}{3}\right\}$. ■

Classroom Example
Solve $3x^2 - 12 = 0$.

EXAMPLE 8   Solve $7x^2 - 7 = 0$.

Solution

$$7x^2 - 7 = 0$$
$$7(x^2 - 1) = 0$$
$$x^2 - 1 = 0 \quad \text{Multiply both sides by } \frac{1}{7}$$
$$(x + 1)(x - 1) = 0$$
$$x + 1 = 0 \quad \text{or} \quad x - 1 = 0$$
$$x = -1 \quad \text{or} \quad x = 1$$

The solution set is $\{-1, 1\}$. ■

In the previous examples we have been using the property $ab = 0$ if and only if $a = 0$ or $b = 0$. This property can be extended to any number of factors whose product is zero. Thus for three factors, the property could be stated $abc = 0$ if and only if $a = 0$ or $b = 0$ or $c = 0$. The next two examples illustrate this idea.

Classroom Example
Solve $a^4 - 81 = 0$.

EXAMPLE 9   Solve $x^4 - 16 = 0$.

Solution

$$x^4 - 16 = 0$$
$$(x^2 + 4)(x^2 - 4) = 0$$
$$(x^2 + 4)(x + 2)(x - 2) = 0$$

$$x^2 + 4 = 0 \quad \text{or} \quad x + 2 = 0 \quad \text{or} \quad x - 2 = 0$$
$$x^2 = -4 \quad \text{or} \quad x = -2 \quad \text{or} \quad x = 2$$

The solution set is $\{-2, 2\}$. (Because no real numbers, when squared, will produce -4, the equation $x^2 = -4$ yields no additional real number solutions.) ▬

Classroom Example
Solve $t^3 - 25t = 0$.

| EXAMPLE 10 | Solve $x^3 - 49x = 0$.

Solution

$$x^3 - 49x = 0$$
$$x(x^2 - 49) = 0$$
$$x(x + 7)(x - 7) = 0$$
$$x - 0 \quad \text{or} \quad x + 7 = 0 \quad \text{or} \quad x - 7 = 0$$
$$x = 0 \quad \text{or} \quad x = -7 \quad \text{or} \quad x = 7$$

The solution set is $\{-7, 0, 7\}$. ▬

Solving Word Problems That Involve Factoring

The more we know about solving equations, the more resources we have for solving word problems.

Classroom Example
The combined area of two squares is 2600 square inches. Each side of one square is five times as long as a side of the other square. Find the dimensions of each of the squares.

| EXAMPLE 11 |

The combined area of two squares is 40 square centimeters. Each side of one square is three times as long as a side of the other square. Find the dimensions of each of the squares.

Solution

Let s represent the length of a side of the smaller square. Then $3s$ represents the length of a side of the larger square (Figure 3.18).

$$s^2 + (3s)^2 = 40$$
$$s^2 + 9s^2 = 40$$
$$10s^2 = 40$$
$$s^2 = 4$$
$$s^2 - 4 = 0$$
$$(s + 2)(s - 2) = 0$$
$$s + 2 = 0 \quad \text{or} \quad s - 2 = 0$$
$$s = -2 \quad \text{or} \quad s = 2$$

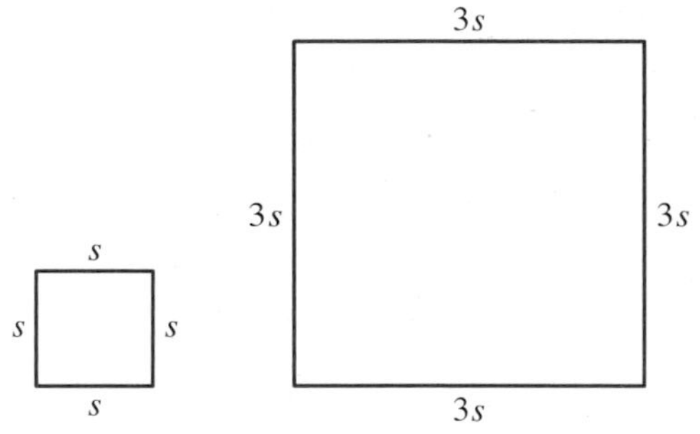

Figure 3.18

Because s represents the length of a side of a square, the solution -2 has to be disregarded. Thus the length of a side of the small square is 2 centimeters, and the large square has sides of length $3(2) = 6$ centimeters. ▬

Concept Quiz 3.5

For Problems 1–10, answer true or false.

1. A binomial that has two perfect square terms that are subtracted is called the difference of two squares.

2. The sum of two squares is factorable using integers.

3. The sum of two cubes is factorable using integers.

4. The difference of two squares is factorable using integers.

5. The difference of two cubes is factorable using integers.

6. When factoring it is usually best to look for a common factor first.

7. The polynomial $4x^2 + y^2$ factors into $(2x + y)(2x + y)$.

8. The completely factored form of $y^4 - 81$ is $(y^2 + 9)(y^2 - 9)$.

9. The equation $x^2 = -9$ does not have any real number solutions.

10. The equation $abc = 0$ if and only if $a = 0$.

Problem Set 3.5

For Problems 1–20, use the difference-of-squares pattern to factor each of the following. **(Objective 1)**

1. $x^2 - 1$
2. $x^2 - 9$
3. $16x^2 - 25$
4. $4x^2 - 49$
5. $9x^2 - 25y^2$
6. $x^2 - 64y^2$
7. $25x^2y^2 - 36$
8. $x^2y^2 - a^2b^2$
9. $4x^2 - y^4$
10. $x^6 - 9y^2$
11. $1 - 144n^2$
12. $25 - 49n^2$
13. $(x + 2)^2 - y^2$
14. $(3x + 5)^2 - y^2$
15. $4x^2 - (y + 1)^2$
16. $x^2 - (y - 5)^2$
17. $9a^2 - (2b + 3)^2$
18. $16s^2 - (3t + 1)^2$
19. $(x + 2)^2 - (x + 7)^2$
20. $(x - 1)^2 - (x - 8)^2$

For Problems 21–44, factor each of the following polynomials completely. Indicate any that are not factorable using integers. Don't forget to look first for a common monomial factor. **(Objective 1)**

21. $9x^2 - 36$
22. $8x^2 - 72$
23. $5x^2 + 5$
24. $7x^2 + 28$
25. $8y^2 - 32$
26. $5y^2 - 80$
27. $a^3b - 9ab$
28. $x^3y^2 - xy^2$
29. $16x^2 + 25$
30. $x^4 - 16$
31. $n^4 - 81$
32. $4x^2 + 9$
33. $3x^3 + 27x$
34. $20x^3 + 45x$
35. $4x^3y - 64xy^3$
36. $12x^3 - 27xy^2$
37. $6x - 6x^3$
38. $1 - 16x^4$
39. $1 - x^4y^4$
40. $20x - 5x^3$
41. $4x^2 - 64y^2$
42. $9x^2 - 81y^2$
43. $3x^4 - 48$
44. $2x^5 - 162x$

For Problems 45–56, use the sum-of-two-cubes or the difference-of-two-cubes pattern to factor each of the following. **(Objective 2)**

45. $a^3 - 64$
46. $a^3 - 27$
47. $x^3 + 1$
48. $x^3 + 8$
49. $27x^3 + 64y^3$
50. $8x^3 + 27y^3$
51. $1 - 27a^3$
52. $1 - 8x^3$
53. $x^3y^3 - 1$
54. $125x^3 + 27y^3$
55. $x^6 - y^6$
56. $x^6 + y^6$

For Problems 57–70, find all real number solutions for each equation. **(Objective 3)**

57. $x^2 - 25 = 0$
58. $x^2 - 1 = 0$
59. $9x^2 - 49 = 0$
60. $4y^2 = 25$
61. $8x^2 - 32 = 0$
62. $3x^2 - 108 = 0$
63. $3x^3 = 3x$
64. $4x^3 = 64x$
65. $20 - 5x^2 = 0$
66. $54 - 6x^2 = 0$
67. $x^4 - 81 = 0$
68. $x^5 - x = 0$
69. $6x^3 + 24x = 0$
70. $4x^3 + 12x = 0$

For Problems 71–80, set up an equation and solve each of the following problems. **(Objective 4)**

71. The cube of a number equals nine times the same number. Find the number.

72. The cube of a number equals the square of the same number. Find the number.

73. The combined area of two circles is 80π square centimeters. The length of a radius of one circle is twice the length of a radius of the other circle. Find the length of the radius of each circle.

74. The combined area of two squares is 26 square meters. The sides of the larger square are five times as long as the sides of the smaller square. Find the dimensions of each of the squares.

75. A rectangle is twice as long as it is wide, and its area is 50 square meters. Find the length and the width of the rectangle.

76. Suppose that the length of a rectangle is one and one-third times as long as its width. The area of the rectangle is 48 square centimeters. Find the length and width of the rectangle.

77. The total surface area of a right circular cylinder is 54π square inches. If the altitude of the cylinder is twice the length of a radius, find the altitude of the cylinder.

78. The total surface area of a right circular cone is 108π square feet. If the slant height of the cone is twice the length of a radius of the base, find the length of a radius.

79. The sum, in square yards, of the areas of a circle and a square is $(16\pi + 64)$. If a side of the square is twice the length of a radius of the circle, find the length of a side of the square.

80. The length of an altitude of a triangle is one-third the length of the side to which it is drawn. If the area of the triangle is 6 square centimeters, find the length of that altitude.

Thoughts Into Words

81. Explain how you would solve the equation $4x^3 = 64x$.

82. What is wrong with the following factoring process?

$$25x^2 - 100 = (5x + 10)(5x - 10)$$

How would you correct the error?

83. Consider the following solution:

$$6x^2 - 24 = 0$$
$$6(x^2 - 4) = 0$$
$$6(x + 2)(x - 2) = 0$$

$6 = 0$ or $x + 2 = 0$ or $x - 2 = 0$

$6 = 0$ or $x = -2$ or $x = 2$

The solution set is $\{-2, 2\}$.

Is this a correct solution? Would you have any suggestion to offer the person who used this approach?

Answers to the Concept Quiz

1. True   **2.** False   **3.** True   **4.** True   **5.** True   **6.** True   **7.** False   **8.** False   **9.** True   **10.** False

3.6   Factoring Trinomials

OBJECTIVES
1. Factor trinomials of the form $x^2 + bx + c$
2. Factor trinomials of the form $ax^2 + bx + c$
3. Factor perfect-square trinomials
4. Summary of factoring techniques

One of the most common types of factoring used in algebra is the expression of a trinomial as the product of two binomials. To develop a factoring technique, we first look at some multiplication ideas. Let's consider the product $(x + a)(x + b)$ and use the distributive property to show how each term of the resulting trinomial is formed.

$$(x + a)(x + b) = x(x + b) + a(x + b)$$
$$= x(x) + x(b) + a(x) + a(b)$$
$$= x^2 + (a + b)x + ab$$

Note that the coefficient of the middle term is the sum of a and b and that the last term is the product of a and b. These two relationships can be used to factor trinomials. Let's consider some examples.

Classroom Example
Factor $x^2 + 13x + 40$.

EXAMPLE 1   Factor $x^2 + 8x + 12$.

Solution

We need to complete the following with two integers whose sum is 8 and whose product is 12.

$$x^2 + 8x + 12 = (x + \underline{})(x + \underline{})$$

The possible pairs of factors of 12 are 1(12), 2(6), and 3(4). Because $6 + 2 = 8$, we can complete the factoring as follows:

$$x^2 + 8x + 12 = (x + 6)(x + 2)$$

To check our answer, we find the product of $(x + 6)$ and $(x + 2)$.   ■

Classroom Example
Factor $m^2 - 8m + 15$.

EXAMPLE 2   Factor $x^2 - 10x + 24$.

Solution

We need two integers whose product is 24 and whose sum is -10. Let's use a small table to organize our thinking.

Factors	Product of the factors	Sum of the factors
$(-1)(-24)$	24	-25
$(-2)(-12)$	24	-14
$(-3)(-8)$	24	-11
$(-4)(-6)$	24	-10

The bottom line contains the numbers that we need. Thus

$$x^2 - 10x + 24 = (x - 4)(x - 6)$$ ■

Classroom Example
Factor $a^2 + 7a - 44$.

EXAMPLE 3   Factor $x^2 + 7x - 30$.

Solution

We need two integers whose product is -30 and whose sum is 7.

Factors	Product of the factors	Sum of the factors
$(-1)(30)$	-30	29
$(1)(-30)$	-30	-29
$(2)(-15)$	-30	-13
$(-2)(15)$	-30	13
$(-3)(10)$	-30	7

No need to search any further

The numbers that we need are -3 and 10, and we can complete the factoring.

$$x^2 + 7x - 30 = (x + 10)(x - 3)$$ ■

Classroom Example
Factor $y^2 + 5y + 12$.

EXAMPLE 4   Factor $x^2 + 7x + 16$.

Solution

We need two integers whose product is 16 and whose sum is 7.

Factors	Product of the factors	Sum of the factors
(1)(16)	16	17
(2)(8)	16	10
(4)(4)	16	8

We have exhausted all possible pairs of factors of 16 and no two factors have a sum of 7, so we conclude that $x^2 + 7x + 16$ *is not factorable using integers.*

The tables in Examples 2, 3, and 4 were used to illustrate one way of organizing your thoughts for such problems. Normally you would probably factor such problems mentally without taking the time to formulate a table. Note, however, that in Example 4 the table helped us to be absolutely sure that we tried all the possibilities. Whether or not you use the table, keep in mind that the key ideas are the product and sum relationships.

Classroom Example
Factor $x^2 - x - 12$.

EXAMPLE 5   Factor $n^2 - n - 72$.

Solution

Note that the coefficient of the middle term is -1. Hence we are looking for two integers whose product is -72, and because their sum is -1, the absolute value of the negative number must be 1 larger than the positive number. The numbers are -9 and 8, and we can complete the factoring.

$$n^2 - n - 72 = (n - 9)(n + 8)$$

Classroom Example
Factor $m^2 + 4m - 117$.

EXAMPLE 6   Factor $t^2 + 2t - 168$.

Solution

We need two integers whose product is -168 and whose sum is 2. Because the absolute value of the constant term is rather large, it might help to look at it in prime factored form.

$$168 = 2 \cdot 2 \cdot 2 \cdot 3 \cdot 7$$

Now we can mentally form two numbers by using all of these factors in different combinations. Using two 2s and a 3 in one number and the other 2 and the 7 in the second number produces $2 \cdot 2 \cdot 3 = 12$ and $2 \cdot 7 = 14$. The coefficient of the middle term of the trinomial is 2, so we know that we must use 14 and -12. Thus we obtain

$$t^2 + 2t - 168 = (t + 14)(t - 12)$$

Factoring Trinomials of the Form $ax^2 + bx + c$

We have been factoring trinomials of the form $x^2 + bx + c$; that is, trinomials where the coefficient of the squared term is 1. Now let's consider factoring trinomials where the coefficient of the squared term is not 1. First, let's illustrate an informal trial-and-error technique that works quite well for certain types of trinomials. This technique is based on our knowledge of multiplication of binomials.

Classroom Example
Factor $3x^2 + 11x + 6$.

EXAMPLE 7   Factor $2x^2 + 11x + 5$.

Solution

By looking at the first term, $2x^2$, and the positive signs of the other two terms, we know that the binomials are of the form

$$(x + \underline{\quad})(2x + \underline{\quad})$$

Because the factors of the last term, 5, are 1 and 5, we have only the following two possibilities to try.

$$(x + 1)(2x + 5) \quad \text{or} \quad (x + 5)(2x + 1)$$

By checking the middle term formed in each of these products, we find that the second possibility yields the correct middle term of $11x$. Therefore,

$$2x^2 + 11x + 5 = (x + 5)(2x + 1)$$

Classroom Example
Factor $15x^2 - 17x - 4$.

EXAMPLE 8   Factor $10x^2 - 17x + 3$.

Solution

First, observe that $10x^2$ can be written as $x \cdot 10x$ or $2x \cdot 5x$. Second, because the middle term of the trinomial is negative, and the last term is positive, we know that the binomials are of the form

$$(x - \underline{\quad})(10x - \underline{\quad}) \quad \text{or} \quad (2x - \underline{\quad})(5x - \underline{\quad})$$

The factors of the last term, 3, are 1 and 3, so the following possibilities exist.

$$(x - 1)(10x - 3) \qquad (2x - 1)(5x - 3)$$
$$(x - 3)(10x - 1) \qquad (2x - 3)(5x - 1)$$

By checking the middle term formed in each of these products, we find that the product $(2x - 3)(5x - 1)$ yields the desired middle term of $-17x$. Therefore,

$$10x^2 - 17x + 3 = (2x - 3)(5x - 1)$$

Classroom Example
Factor $9x^2 + 14x + 16$.

EXAMPLE 9   Factor $4x^2 + 6x + 9$.

Solution

The first term, $4x^2$, and the positive signs of the middle and last terms indicate that the binomials are of the form

$$(x + \underline{\quad})(4x + \underline{\quad}) \quad \text{or} \quad (2x + \underline{\quad})(2x + \underline{\quad}).$$

Because the factors of 9 are 1 and 9 or 3 and 3, we have the following five possibilities to try.

$$(x + 1)(4x + 9) \qquad (2x + 1)(2x + 9)$$
$$(x + 9)(4x + 1) \qquad (2x + 3)(2x + 3)$$
$$(x + 3)(4x + 3)$$

When we try all of these possibilities we find that none of them yields a middle term of $6x$. Therefore, $4x^2 + 6x + 9$ is not factorable using integers.

Another Method of Factoring the Form $ax^2 + bx + c$

By now it is obvious that factoring trinomials of the form $ax^2 + bx + c$ can be tedious. The key idea is to organize your work so that you consider all possibilities. We suggested one possible format in the previous three examples. As you practice such problems, you may come across a format of your own. Whatever works best for you is the right approach.

There is another, more systematic technique that you may wish to use with some trinomials. It is an extension of the technique we used at the beginning of this section. To see the basis of this technique, let's look at the following product.

$$(px + r)(qx + s) = px(qx) + px(s) + r(qx) + r(s)$$
$$= (pq)x^2 + (ps + rq)x + rs$$

Note that the product of the coefficient of the x^2 term and the constant term is $pqrs$. Likewise, the product of the two coefficients of x, ps and rq, is also $pqrs$. Therefore, when we are factoring the trinomial $(pq)x^2 + (ps + rq)x + rs$, the two coefficients of x must have a sum of $(ps) + (rq)$ and a product of $pqrs$. Let's see how this works in some examples.

Classroom Example
Factor $8x^2 - 2x - 15$.

EXAMPLE 10   Factor $6x^2 - 11x - 10$.

Solution

Step 1   Multiply the coefficient of the x^2 term, 6, and the constant term, -10.

$$(6)(-10) = -60$$

Step 2   Find two integers whose sum is -11 and whose product is -60. It will be helpful to make a listing of the factor pairs for 60.

$(1)(60)$
$(2)(30)$
$(3)(20)$
$(4)(15)$
$(5)(12)$
$(6)(10)$

Because the product from step 1 is -60, we want a pair of factors for which the absolute value of their difference is 11. The factors are 4 and 15. For the sum to be -11 and the product to be -60, we will assign the signs so that we have $+4$ and -15.

Step 3   Rewrite the original problem and express the middle term as a sum of terms using the factors in step 2 as the coefficients of the terms.

Original problem	**Problem rewritten**
$6x^2 - 11x - 10$	$6x^2 - 15x + 4x - 10$

Step 4   Now use factoring by grouping to factor the rewritten problem.

$$6x^2 - 15x + 4x - 10 = 3x(2x - 5) + 2(2x - 5)$$
$$= (2x - 5)(3x + 2)$$

Thus $6x^2 - 11x - 10 = (2x - 5)(3x + 2)$.

Classroom Example
Factor $5x^2 + 38x - 16$.

EXAMPLE 11   Factor $4x^2 - 29x + 30$.

Solution

Step 1   Multiply the coefficient of the x^2 term, 4, and the constant term, 30.

$$(4)(30) = 120$$

Step 2   Find two integers whose sum is -29 and whose product is 120. It will be helpful to make a listing of the factor pairs for 120.

$(1)(120)$	$(5)(24)$
$(2)(60)$	$(6)(20)$
$(3)(40)$	$(8)(15)$
$(4)(30)$	$(10)(12)$

Because our product from step 1 is $+120$, we want a pair of factors for which the absolute value of their sum is 29. The factors are 5 and 24. For the sum to be -29 and the product to be $+120$, we will assign the signs so that we have -5 and -24.

Step 3   Rewrite the original problem and express the middle term as a sum of terms using the factors in step 2 as the coefficients of the terms.

Original problem	**Problem rewritten**
$4x^2 - 29x + 30$	$4x^2 - 5x - 24x + 30$

Step 4   Now use factoring by grouping to factor the rewritten problem.

$$4x^2 - 5x - 24x + 30 = x(4x - 5) - 6(4x - 5)$$
$$= (4x - 5)(x - 6)$$

Thus $4x^2 - 29x + 30 = (4x - 5)(x - 6)$.

The technique presented in Examples 10 and 11 has concrete steps to follow. Examples 7 through 9 were factored by trial-and-error. Both of the techniques we used have their strengths and weaknesses. Which technique to use depends on the complexity of the problem and on your personal preference. The more that you work with both techniques, the more comfortable you will feel using them.

Factoring Perfect Square Trinomials

Before we summarize our work with factoring techniques, let's look at two more special factoring patterns. In Section 3.3 we used the following two patterns to square binomials.

$$(a + b)^2 = a^2 + 2ab + b^2 \qquad \text{and} \qquad (a - b)^2 = a^2 - 2ab + b^2$$

These patterns can also be used for factoring purposes.

$$a^2 + 2ab + b^2 = (a + b)^2 \qquad \text{and} \qquad a^2 - 2ab + b^2 = (a - b)^2$$

The trinomials on the left sides are called **perfect-square trinomials**; they are the result of squaring a binomial. We can always factor perfect-square trinomials using the usual techniques for factoring trinomials. However, they are easily recognized by the nature of their terms. For example, $4x^2 + 12x + 9$ is a perfect-square trinomial because

    1. The first term is a perfect square $(2x)^2$

    2. The last term is a perfect square $(3)^2$

    3. The middle term is twice the product of the quantities $2(2x)(3)$
        being squared in the first and last terms

Likewise, $9x^2 - 30x + 25$ is a perfect-square trinomial because

    1. The first term is a perfect square. $(3x)^2$

    2. The last term is a perfect square. $(5)^2$

    3. The middle term is the negative of twice the product of $-2(3x)(5)$
        the quantities being squared in the first and last terms.

Once we know that we have a perfect-square trinomial, the factors follow immediately from the two basic patterns. Thus

$$4x^2 + 12x + 9 = (2x + 3)^2 \qquad 9x^2 - 30x + 25 = (3x - 5)^2$$

The next example illustrates perfect-square trinomials and their factored forms.

Classroom Example
Factor each of the following:

(a) $x^2 + 18x + 81$
(b) $n^2 - 14n + 49$
(c) $4a^2 - 28ab + 49b^2$
(d) $9x^2 + 6xy + y^2$

EXAMPLE 12   Factor each of the following:

    (a) $x^2 + 14x + 49$ **(b)** $n^2 - 16n + 64$
    (c) $36a^2 + 60ab + 25b^2$ **(d)** $16x^2 - 8xy + y^2$

Solution

    (a) $x^2 + 14x + 49 = (x)^2 + 2(x)(7) + (7) = (x + 7)^2$

    (b) $n^2 - 16n + 64 = (n)^2 - 2(n)(8) + (8)^2 = (n - 8)^2$

    (c) $36a^2 + 60ab + 25b^2 = (6a)^2 + 2(6a)(5b) + (5b)^2 = (6a + 5b)^2$

    (d) $16x^2 - 8xy + y^2 = (4x)^2 - 2(4x)(y) + (y)^2 = (4x - y)^2$

Summary of Factoring Techniques

As we have indicated, factoring is an important algebraic skill. We learned some basic factoring techniques one at a time, but you must be able to apply whichever is (or are) appropriate to the situation. Let's review the techniques and consider examples that demonstrate their use.

1. As a general guideline, always look for a common factor first. The common factor could be a binomial factor.

$$3x^2y^3 + 27xy = 3xy(xy^2 + 9) \qquad x(y + 2) + 5(y + 2) = (y + 2)(x + 5)$$

2. If the polynomial has two terms, then the pattern could be the difference-of-squares pattern or the sum or difference-of-two cubes pattern.

$$9a^2 - 25 = (3a + 5)(3a - 5) \qquad 8x^3 + 125 = (2x + 5)(4x^2 - 10x + 25)$$

3. If the polynomial has three terms, then the polynomial may factor into the product of two binomials. Examples 10 and 11 presented concrete steps for factoring trinomials. Examples 7 through 9 were factored by trial-and-error. The perfect-square-trinomial pattern is a special case of the technique.

$$30n^2 - 31n + 5 = (5n - 1)(6n - 5) \qquad t^4 + 3t^2 + 2 = (t^2 + 2)(t^2 + 1)$$

4. If the polynomial has four or more terms, then factoring by grouping may apply. It may be necessary to rearrange the terms before factoring.

$$ab + ac + 4b + 4c = a(b + c) + 4(b + c) = (b + c)(a + 4)$$

5. If none of the mentioned patterns or techniques work, then the polynomial may not be factorable using integers.

$$x^2 + 5x + 12 \qquad \text{Not factorable using integers}$$

Concept Quiz 3.6

For Problems 1–10, answer true or false.

1. To factor $x^2 - 4x - 60$ we look for two numbers whose product is -60 and whose sum is -4.
2. To factor $2x^2 - x - 3$ we look for two numbers whose product is -3 and whose sum is -1.
3. A trinomial of the form $x^2 + bx + c$ will never have a common factor other than 1.
4. A trinomial of the form $ax^2 + bx + c$ will never have a common factor other than 1.
5. The polynomial $x^2 + 25x + 72$ is not factorable using integers.
6. The polynomial $x^2 + 27x + 72$ is not factorable using integers.
7. The polynomial $2x^2 + 5x - 3$ is not factorable using integers.
8. The trinomial $49x^2 - 42x + 9$ is a perfect-square trinomial.
9. The trinomial $25x^2 + 80x - 64$ is a perfect-square trinomial.
10. To factor $12x^2 - 38x + 30$ one technique is to rewrite the problem as $12x^2 - 20x - 18x + 30$ and to factor by grouping.

Problem Set 3.6

For Problems 1–30, factor completely each of the trinomials and indicate any that are not factorable using integers. (Objective 1)

1. $x^2 + 9x + 20$
2. $x^2 + 11x + 24$
3. $x^2 - 11x + 28$
4. $x^2 - 8x + 12$
5. $a^2 + 5a - 36$
6. $a^2 + 6a - 40$
7. $y^2 + 20y + 84$
8. $y^2 + 21y + 98$
9. $x^2 - 5x - 14$
10. $x^2 - 3x - 54$
11. $x^2 + 9x + 12$
12. $35 - 2x - x^2$

13. $6 + 5x - x^2$

14. $x^2 + 8x - 24$

15. $x^2 + 15xy + 36y^2$

16. $x^2 - 14xy + 40y^2$

17. $a^2 - ab - 56b^2$

18. $a^2 + 2ab - 63b^2$

19. $x^2 + 25x + 150$

20. $x^2 + 21x + 108$

21. $n^2 - 36n + 320$

22. $n^2 - 26n + 168$

23. $t^2 + 3t - 180$

24. $t^2 - 2t - 143$

25. $t^4 - 5t^2 + 6$

26. $t^4 + 10t^2 + 24$

27. $x^4 - 9x^2 + 8$

28. $x^4 - x^2 - 12$

29. $x^4 - 17x^2 + 16$

30. $x^4 - 13x^2 + 36$

For Problems 31–56, factor completely each of the trinomials and indicate any that are not factorable using integers. (Objective 2)

31. $15x^2 + 23x + 6$

32. $9x^2 + 30x + 16$

33. $12x^2 - x - 6$

34. $20x^2 - 11x - 3$

35. $4a^2 + 3a - 27$

36. $12a^2 + 4a - 5$

37. $3n^2 - 7n - 20$

38. $4n^2 + 7n - 15$

39. $3x^2 + 10x + 4$

40. $4n^2 - 19n + 21$

41. $10n^2 - 29n - 21$

42. $4x^2 - x + 6$

43. $8x^2 + 26x - 45$

44. $6x^2 + 13x - 33$

45. $6 - 35x - 6x^2$

46. $4 - 4x - 15x^2$

47. $20y^2 + 31y - 9$

48. $8y^2 + 22y - 21$

49. $24n^2 - 2n - 5$

50. $3n^2 - 16n - 35$

51. $5n^2 + 33n + 18$

52. $7n^2 + 31n + 12$

53. $10x^4 + 3x^2 - 4$

54. $3x^4 + 7x^2 - 6$

55. $18n^4 + 25n^2 - 3$

56. $4n^4 + 3n^2 - 27$

For Problems 57–62, factor completely each of the perfect-square trinomials. (Objective 3)

57. $y^2 - 16y + 64$

58. $a^2 + 30a + 225$

59. $4x^2 + 12xy + 9y^2$

60. $25x^2 - 60xy + 36y^2$

61. $8y^2 - 8y + 2$

62. $12x^2 + 36x + 27$

Problems 63–100 should help you pull together all of the factoring techniques of this chapter. Factor completely each polynomial, and indicate any that are not factorable using integers. (Objective 4)

63. $2t^2 - 8$

64. $14w^2 - 29w - 15$

65. $12x^2 + 7xy - 10y^2$

66. $8x^2 + 2xy - y^2$

67. $18n^3 + 39n^2 - 15n$

68. $n^2 + 18n + 77$

69. $n^2 - 17n + 60$

70. $(x + 5)^2 - y^2$

71. $36a^2 - 12a + 1$

72. $2n^2 - n - 5$

73. $6x^2 + 54$

74. $x^5 - x$

75. $3x^2 + x - 5$

76. $5x^2 + 42x - 27$

77. $x^2 - (y - 7)^2$

78. $2n^3 + 6n^2 + 10n$

79. $1 - 16x^4$

80. $9a^2 - 30a + 25$

81. $4n^2 + 25n + 36$

82. $x^3 - 9x$

83. $n^3 - 49n$

84. $4x^2 + 16$

85. $x^2 - 7x - 8$

86. $x^2 + 3x - 54$

87. $3x^4 - 81x$

88. $x^3 + 125$

89. $x^4 + 6x^2 + 9$

90. $18x^2 - 12x + 2$

91. $x^4 - 5x^2 - 36$

92. $6x^4 - 5x^2 - 21$

93. $6w^2 - 11w - 35$

94. $10x^3 + 15x^2 + 20x$

95. $25n^2 + 64$

96. $4x^2 - 37x + 40$

97. $2n^3 + 14n^2 - 20n$

98. $25t^2 - 100$

99. $2xy + 6x + y + 3$

100. $3xy + 15x - 2y - 10$

Thoughts Into Words

101. How can you determine that $x^2 + 5x + 12$ is not factorable using integers?

102. Explain your thought process when factoring $30x^2 + 13x - 56$.

103. Consider the following approach to factoring $12x^2 + 54x + 60$:

$$12x^2 + 54x + 60 = (3x + 6)(4x + 10)$$
$$= 3(x + 2)(2)(2x + 5)$$
$$= 6(x + 2)(2x + 5)$$

Is this a correct factoring process? Do you have any suggestion for the person using this approach?

Further Investigations

For Problems 104–109, factor each trinomial and assume that all variables that appear as exponents represent positive integers.

104. $x^{2a} + 2x^a - 24$

105. $x^{2a} + 10x^a + 21$

106. $6x^{2a} - 7x^a + 2$

107. $4x^{2a} + 20x^a + 25$

108. $12x^{2n} + 7x^n - 12$ **109.** $20x^{2n} + 21x^n - 5$

Consider the following approach to factoring the problem $(x - 2)^2 + 3(x - 2) - 10$.

$(x - 2)^2 + 3(x - 2) - 10$

$= y^2 + 3y - 10$ Replace $x - 2$ with y

$= (y + 5)(y - 2)$ Factor

$= (x - 2 + 5)(x - 2 - 2)$ Replace y with $x - 2$

$= (x + 3)(x - 4)$

Use this approach to factor Problems 110–115.

110. $(x - 3)^2 + 10(x - 3) + 24$

111. $(x + 1)^2 - 8(x + 1) + 15$

112. $(2x + 1)^2 + 3(2x + 1) - 28$

113. $(3x - 2)^2 - 5(3x - 2) - 36$

114. $6(x - 4)^2 + 7(x - 4) - 3$

115. $15(x + 2)^2 - 13(x + 2) + 2$

Answers to the Concept Quiz
1. True   **2.** False   **3.** True   **4.** False   **5.** True   **6.** False   **7.** False   **8.** True   **9.** False   **10.** True

---

3.7   Equations and Problem Solving

OBJECTIVES

1 Solve equations by factoring

2 Solve word problems that involve factoring

The techniques for factoring trinomials that were presented in the previous section provide us with more power to solve equations. That is, the property "$ab = 0$ if and only if $a = 0$ or $b = 0$" continues to play an important role as we solve equations that contain factorable trinomials. Let's consider some examples.

Classroom Example
Solve $m^2 + 5m - 36 = 0$.

EXAMPLE 1   Solve $x^2 - 11x - 12 = 0$.

Solution

$x^2 - 11x - 12 = 0$

$(x - 12)(x + 1) = 0$

$x - 12 = 0$ or $x + 1 = 0$

$x = 12$ or $x = -1$

The solution set is $\{-1, 12\}$.

Classroom Example
Solve $21x^2 + x - 2 = 0$.

EXAMPLE 2   Solve $20x^2 + 7x - 3 = 0$.

Solution

$20x^2 + 7x - 3 = 0$

$(4x - 1)(5x + 3) = 0$

$4x - 1 = 0$ or $5x + 3 = 0$

$4x = 1$ or $5x = -3$

$x = \dfrac{1}{4}$ or $x = -\dfrac{3}{5}$

The solution set is $\left\{ -\dfrac{3}{5}, \dfrac{1}{4} \right\}$.

Classroom Example
Solve $-3t^2 + 15t + 72 = 0$.

EXAMPLE 3   Solve $-2n^2 - 10n + 12 = 0$.

Solution

$$-2n^2 - 10n + 12 = 0$$
$$-2(n^2 + 5n - 6) = 0$$
$$n^2 + 5n - 6 = 0 \qquad \text{Multiply both sides by } -\frac{1}{2}$$
$$(n + 6)(n - 1) = 0$$
$$n + 6 = 0 \qquad \text{or} \qquad n - 1 = 0$$
$$n = -6 \qquad \text{or} \qquad n = 1$$

The solution set is $\{-6, 1\}$.

Classroom Example
Solve $9x^2 + 48x + 64 = 0$.

EXAMPLE 4   Solve $16x^2 - 56x + 49 = 0$.

Solution

$$16x^2 - 56x + 49 = 0$$
$$(4x - 7)^2 = 0$$
$$(4x - 7)(4x - 7) = 0$$
$$4x - 7 = 0 \qquad \text{or} \qquad 4x - 7 = 0$$
$$4x = 7 \qquad \text{or} \qquad 4x = 7$$
$$x = \frac{7}{4} \qquad \text{or} \qquad x = \frac{7}{4}$$

The only solution is $\frac{7}{4}$; thus the solution set is $\left\{\frac{7}{4}\right\}$.

Classroom Example
Solve $x(4x + 4) = 15$.

EXAMPLE 5   Solve $9a(a + 1) = 4$.

Solution

$$9a(a + 1) = 4$$
$$9a^2 + 9a = 4$$
$$9a^2 + 9a - 4 = 0$$
$$(3a + 4)(3a - 1) = 0$$
$$3a + 4 = 0 \qquad \text{or} \qquad 3a - 1 = 0$$
$$3a = -4 \qquad \text{or} \qquad 3a = 1$$
$$a = -\frac{4}{3} \qquad \text{or} \qquad a = \frac{1}{3}$$

The solution set is $\left\{-\frac{4}{3}, \frac{1}{3}\right\}$.

EXAMPLE 6   Solve $(x - 1)(x + 9) = 11$.

Solution

$$(x - 1)(x + 9) = 11$$
$$x^2 + 8x - 9 = 11$$
$$x^2 + 8x - 20 = 0$$
$$(x + 10)(x - 2) = 0$$
$$x + 10 = 0 \quad \text{or} \quad x - 2 = 0$$
$$x = -10 \quad \text{or} \quad x = 2$$

The solution set is $\{-10, \ 2\}$.

Solving Word Problems

As you might expect, the increase in our power to solve equations broadens our base for solving problems. Now we are ready to tackle some problems using equations of the types presented in this section.

EXAMPLE 7

A cryptographer needs to arrange 60 numbers in a rectangular array in which the number of columns is two more than twice the number of rows. Find the number of rows and the number of columns.

Solution

Let r represent the numbers of rows. Then $2r + 2$ represents the number of columns.

$$r(2r + 2) = 60 \qquad \text{The number of rows times the number of columns yields}$$
$$2r^2 + 2r = 60 \qquad \text{the total amount of numbers in the array}$$
$$2r^2 + 2r - 60 = 0$$
$$2(r^2 + r - 30) = 0$$
$$2(r + 6)(r - 5) = 0$$
$$r + 6 = 0 \quad \text{or} \quad r - 5 = 0$$
$$r = -6 \quad \text{or} \quad r = 5$$

The solution -6 must be discarded, so there are 5 rows and $2r + 2$ or $2(5) + 2 = 12$ columns.

EXAMPLE 8

A strip of uniform width cut from both sides and both ends of a 5-inch by 7-inch photograph reduces the size of the photo to an area of 15 square inches. Find the width of the strip.

Solution

Let x represent the width of the strip, as indicated in Figure 3.19.

The length of the photograph after the strips of width x are cut from both ends and both sides will be $7 - 2x$, and the width of the newly cropped photo will be $5 - 2x$. Because the area $(A = lw)$ is to be 15 square inches, we can set up and solve the following equation.

$$(7 - 2x)(5 - 2x) = 15$$
$$35 - 24x + 4x^2 = 15$$
$$4x^2 - 24x + 20 = 0$$

$$4(x^2 - 6x + 5) = 0$$

$$4(x - 5)(x - 1) = 0$$

$$x - 5 = 0 \quad \text{or} \quad x - 1 = 0$$

$$x = 5 \quad \text{or} \quad x - 1 = 0$$

The solution of 5 must be discarded because the width of the original photograph is only 5 inches. Therefore, the strip to be cropped from all four sides must be 1 inch wide. (Check this answer!)

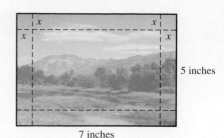

5 inches

7 inches

Figure 3.19

The Pythagorean theorem, an important theorem pertaining to right triangles, can sometimes serve as a guideline for solving problems that deal with right triangles (see Figure 3.20). The Pythagorean theorem states that "in any right triangle, the square of the longest side (called the hypotenuse) is equal to the sum of the squares of the other two sides (called legs)." Let's use this relationship to help solve a problem.

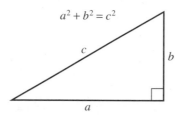

$a^2 + b^2 = c^2$

Figure 3.20

EXAMPLE 9

One leg of a right triangle is 2 centimeters more than twice as long as the other leg. The hypotenuse is 1 centimeter longer than the longer of the two legs. Find the lengths of the three sides of the right triangle.

Solution

Let l represent the length of the shortest leg. Then $2l + 2$ represents the length of the other leg, and $2l + 3$ represents the length of the hypotenuse. Use the Pythagorean theorem as a guideline to set up and solve the following equation.

$$l^2 + (2l + 2)^2 = (2l + 3)^2$$

$$l^2 + 4l^2 + 8l + 4 = 4l^2 + 12l + 9$$

$$l^2 - 4l - 5 = 0$$

$$(l - 5)(l + 1) = 0$$

$$l - 5 = 0 \quad \text{or} \quad l + 1 = 0$$

$$l = 5 \quad \text{or} \quad l = -1$$

The negative solution must be discarded, so the length of one leg is 5 centimeters; the other leg is $2(5) + 2 = 12$ centimeters long, and the hypotenuse is $2(5) + 3 = 13$ centimeters long.

Concept Quiz 3.7

For Problems 1–5, answer true or false.

1. If $xy = 0$, then $x = 0$ or $y = 0$.

2. If the product of three numbers is zero, then at least one of the numbers must be zero.

3. The Pythagorean theorem is true for all triangles.

4. The longest side of a right triangle is called the hypotenuse.

5. If we know the length of any two sides of a right triangle, the third can be determined by using the Pythagorean theorem.

Problem Set 3.7

For Problems 1–54, solve each equation. You will need to use the factoring techniques that we discussed throughout this chapter. (Objective 1)

1. $x^2 + 4x + 3 = 0$

2. $x^2 + 7x + 10 = 0$

3. $x^2 + 18x + 72 = 0$

4. $n^2 + 20n + 91 = 0$

5. $n^2 - 13n + 36 = 0$

6. $n^2 - 10n + 16 = 0$

7. $x^2 + 4x - 12 = 0$

8. $x^2 + 7x - 30 = 0$

9. $w^2 - 4w = 5$

10. $s^2 - 4s = 21$

11. $n^2 + 25n + 156 = 0$

12. $n(n - 24) = -128$

13. $3t^2 + 14t - 5 = 0$

14. $4t^2 - 19t - 30 = 0$

15. $6x^2 + 25x + 14 = 0$

16. $25x^2 + 30x + 8 = 0$

17. $3t(t - 4) = 0$

18. $1 - x^2 = 0$

19. $-6n^2 + 13n - 2 = 0$

20. $(x + 1)^2 - 4 = 0$

21. $2n^3 = 72n$

22. $a(a - 1) = 2$

23. $(x - 5)(x + 3) = 9$

24. $3w^3 - 24w^2 + 36w = 0$

25. $16 - x^2 = 0$

26. $16t^2 - 72t + 81 = 0$

27. $n^2 + 7n - 44 = 0$

28. $2x^3 = 50x$

29. $3x^2 = 75$

30. $x^2 + x - 2 = 0$

31. $15x^2 + 34x + 15 = 0$

32. $20x^2 + 41x + 20 = 0$

33. $8n^2 - 47n - 6 = 0$

34. $7x^2 + 62x - 9 = 0$

35. $28n^2 - 47n + 15 = 0$

36. $24n^2 - 38n + 15 = 0$

37. $35n^2 - 18n - 8 = 0$

38. $8n^2 - 6n - 5 = 0$

39. $-3x^2 - 19x + 14 = 0$

40. $5x^2 = 43x - 24$

41. $n(n + 2) = 360$

42. $n(n + 1) = 182$

43. $9x^4 - 37x^2 + 4 = 0$

44. $4x^4 - 13x^2 + 9 = 0$

45. $3x^2 - 46x - 32 = 0$

46. $x^4 - 9x^2 = 0$

47. $2x^2 + x - 3 = 0$

48. $x^3 + 5x^2 - 36x = 0$

49. $12x^3 + 46x^2 + 40x = 0$

50. $5x(3x - 2) = 0$

51. $(3x - 1)^2 - 16 = 0$

52. $(x + 8)(x - 6) = -24$

53. $4a(a + 1) = 3$

54. $-18n^2 - 15n + 7 = 0$

For Problems 55–70, set up an equation and solve each problem. (Objective 2)

55. Find two consecutive integers whose product is 72.

56. Find two consecutive even whole numbers whose product is 224.

57. Find two integers whose product is 105 such that one of the integers is one more than twice the other integer.

58. Find two integers whose product is 104 such that one of the integers is three less than twice the other integer.

59. The perimeter of a rectangle is 32 inches, and the area is 60 square inches. Find the length and width of the rectangle.

60. Suppose that the length of a certain rectangle is two centimeters more than three times its width. If the area of the rectangle is 56 square centimeters, find its length and width.

61. The sum of the squares of two consecutive integers is 85. Find the integers.

62. The sum of the areas of two circles is 65π square feet. The length of a radius of the larger circle is 1 foot less than twice the length of a radius of the smaller circle. Find the length of a radius of each circle.

63. The combined area of a square and a rectangle is 64 square centimeters. The width of the rectangle is 2 centimeters more than the length of a side of the square, and the length of the rectangle is 2 centimeters more than its width. Find the dimensions of the square and the rectangle.

64. The Ortegas have an apple orchard that contains 90 trees. The number of trees in each row is 3 more than twice the number of rows. Find the number of rows and the number of trees per row.

65. The lengths of the three sides of a right triangle are represented by consecutive whole numbers. Find the lengths of the three sides.

66. The area of the floor of the rectangular room shown in Figure 3.21 is 175 square feet. The length of the room is $1\frac{1}{2}$ feet longer than the width. Find the length of the room.

Area = 175 square feet

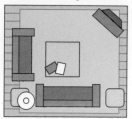

Figure 3.21

67. Suppose that the length of one leg of a right triangle is 3 inches more than the length of the other leg. If the length of the hypotenuse is 15 inches, find the lengths of the two legs.

68. The lengths of the three sides of a right triangle are represented by consecutive even whole numbers. Find the lengths of the three sides.

69. The area of a triangular sheet of paper is 28 square inches. One side of the triangle is 2 inches more than three times the length of the altitude to that side. Find the length of that side and the altitude to the side.

70. A strip of uniform width is shaded along both sides and both ends of a rectangular poster that measures 12 inches by 16 inches (see Figure 3.22). How wide is the shaded strip if one-half of the poster is shaded?

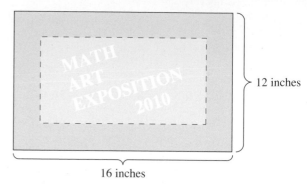

16 inches

12 inches

Figure 3.22

Thoughts Into Words

71. Discuss the role that factoring plays in solving equations.

72. Explain how you would solve the equation $(x + 6)(x - 4) = 0$ and also how you would solve $(x + 6)(x - 4) = -16$.

73. Explain how you would solve the equation $3(x - 1)(x + 2) = 0$ and also how you would solve the equation $x(x - 1)(x + 2) = 0$.

74. Consider the following two solutions for the equation $(x + 3)(x - 4) = (x + 3)(2x - 1)$.

Solution A

$$(x + 3)(x - 4) = (x + 3)(2x - 1)$$
$$(x + 3)(x - 4) - (x + 3)(2x - 1) = 0$$
$$(x + 3)[x - 4 - (2x - 1)] = 0$$
$$(x + 3)(x - 4 - 2x + 1) = 0$$
$$(x + 3)(-x - 3) = 0$$

$$\begin{array}{ccc} x + 3 = 0 & \text{or} & -x - 3 = 0 \\ x = -3 & \text{or} & -x = 3 \\ x = -3 & \text{or} & x = -3 \end{array}$$

The solution set is $\{-3\}$.

Solution B

$$(x + 3)(x - 4) = (x + 3)(2x - 1)$$
$$x^2 - x - 12 = 2x^2 + 5x - 3$$
$$0 = x^2 + 6x + 9$$
$$0 = (x + 3)^2$$
$$x + 3 = 0$$
$$x = -3$$

The solution set is $\{-3\}$.

Are both approaches correct? Which approach would you use, and why?

OBJECTIVE	SUMMARY	EXAMPLE
Find the degree of a polynomial. (Section 3.1/Objective 1)	A polynomial is a monomial or a finite sum (or difference) of monomials. We classify polynomials as follows: Polynomial with one term: Monomial Polynomial with two terms: Binomial Polynomial with three terms: Trinomial The degree of a monomial is the sum of the exponents of the literal factors. The degree of a polynomial is the degree of the term with the highest degree in the polynomial.	Find the degree of the given polynomial: $6x^4 - 7x^3 + 8x^2 + 2x - 10$ **Solution** The degree of the polynomial is 4, because the term with the highest degree, $6x^4$, has a degree of 4.
Add, subtract, and simplify polynomial expressions. (Section 3.1/Objectives 2 and 3)	Similar (or like) terms have the same literal factors. The commutative, associative, and distributive properties provide the basis for rearranging, regrouping, and combining similar terms.	Perform the indicated operations: $4x - [9x^2 - 2(7x - 3x^2)]$ **Solution** $4x - [9x^2 - 2(7x - 3x^2)]$ $\quad = 4x - [9x^2 - 14x + 6x^2]$ $\quad = 4x - [15x^2 - 14x]$ $\quad = 4x - 15x^2 + 14x$ $\quad = -15x^2 + 18x$
Multiply monomials and raise a monomial to an exponent. (Section 3.2/Objectives 1 and 2)	The following properties provide the basis for multiplying monomials: **1.** $b^n \cdot b^m = b^{n+m}$ **2.** $(b^n)^m = b^{mn}$ **3.** $(ab)^n = a^n b^n$	Simplify each of the following: **(a)** $(-5a^4b)(2a^2b^3)$ **(b)** $(-3x^3y)^2$ **Solution** **(a)** $(-5a^4b)(2a^2b^3) = -10a^6b^4$ **(b)** $(-3x^3y)^2 = (-3)^2(x^3)^2(y)^2$ $\qquad\qquad\quad = 9x^6y^2$
Divide monomials. (Section 3.2/Objective 3)	The following properties provide the basis for dividing monomials: **1.** $\dfrac{b^n}{b^m} = b^{n-m}$ if $n > m$ **2.** $\dfrac{b^n}{b^m} = 1$ if $n = m$	Find the quotient: $\dfrac{8x^5y^4}{-8xy^2}$ **Solution** $\dfrac{8x^5y^4}{-8xy^2} = -x^4y^2$
Multiply polynomials. (Section 3.3/Objective 1)	To multiply two polynomials, every term of the first polynomial is multiplied by each term of the second polynomial. Multiplying polynomials often produces similar terms that can be combined to simplify the resulting polynomial.	Find the indicated product: $(3x + 4)(x^2 + 6x - 5)$ **Solution** $(3x + 4)(x^2 + 6x - 5)$ $\quad = 3x(x^2 + 6x - 5)$ $\qquad + 4(x^2 + 6x - 5)$ $\quad = 3x^3 + 18x^2 - 15x + 4x^2$ $\qquad + 24x - 20$ $\quad = 3x^3 + 22x^2 + 9x - 20$

(continued)

OBJECTIVE	SUMMARY	EXAMPLE
Multiply two binomials using a shortcut pattern. (Section 3.3/Objective 2)	A three-step shortcut pattern, often referred to as FOIL, is used to find the product of two binomials.	Find the indicated product: $$(3x + 5)(x - 4)$$ **Solution** $$(3x + 5)(x - 4)$$ $$= 3x^2 + (-12x + 5x) - 20$$ $$= 3x^2 - 7x - 20$$
Find the square of a binomial using a shortcut pattern. (Section 3.3/Objective 3)	The patterns for squaring a binomial are: $$(a + b)^2 = a^2 + 2ab + b^2$$ and $$(a - b)^2 = a^2 - 2ab + b^2$$	Expand $(4x - 3)^2$. **Solution** $$(4x - 3)^2 = (4x)^2 - 2(4x)(3) + (-3)^2$$ $$= 16x^2 - 24x + 9$$
Use a pattern to find the product of $(a + b)(a - b)$. (Section 3.3/Objective 2)	The pattern is $(a + b)(a - b) = a^2 - b^2$.	Find the product: $(x - 3y)(x + 3y)$ **Solution** $$(x - 3y)(x + 3y) = (x)^2 - (3y)^2$$ $$= x^2 - 9y^2$$
Find the cube of a binomial. (Section 3.3/Objective 4)	The patterns for cubing a binomial are: $$(a + b)^3 = a^3 + 3a^2b + 3ab^2 + b^3$$ and $$(a - b)^3 = a^3 - 3a^2b + 3ab^2 - b^3$$	Expand $(2a + 5)^3$. **Solution** $$(2a + 5)^3$$ $$= (2a)^3 + 3(2a)^2(5)$$ $$+ 3(2a)(5)^2 + (5)^3$$ $$= 8a^3 + 60a^2 + 150a + 125$$
Use polynomials in geometry problems. (Section 3.1/Objective 4; Section 3.2/Objective 4; Section 3.3/Objective 5)	Sometimes polynomials are encountered in a geometric setting. A polynomial may be used to represent area or volume.	A rectangular piece of cardboard is 20 inches long and 10 inches wide. From each corner a square piece x inches on a side is cut out. The flaps are turned up to form an open box. Find a polynomial that represents the volume. **Solution** The length of the box will be $20 - 2x$, the width of the box will be $10 - 2x$, and the height will be x, so $$V = (20 - 2x)(10 - 2x)(x).$$ Simplifying the polynomial gives $$V = x^3 - 30x^2 + 200x.$$
Understand the rules about completely factored form. (Section 3.4/Objective 3)	A polynomial with integral coefficients is completely factored if: 1. It is expressed as a product of polynomials with integral coefficients; and 2. No polynomial, other than a monomial, within the factored form can be further factored into polynomials with integral coefficients.	Which of the following is the completely factored form of $2x^3y + 6x^2y^2$? **(a)** $2x^3y + 6x^2y^2 = x^2y(2x + 6y)$ **(b)** $2x^3y + 6x^2y^2 = 6x^2y\left(\dfrac{1}{3}x + y\right)$ **(c)** $2x^3y + 6x^2y^2 = 2x^2y(x + 3y)$ **(d)** $2x^3y + 6x^2y^2 = 2xy(x^2 + 3xy)$ **Solution** Only (c) is completely factored. For parts (a) and (d), the polynomial inside the parentheses can be factored further. For part (b), the coefficients are not integers.

OBJECTIVE	SUMMARY	EXAMPLE
Factor out the greatest common monomial factor. (Section 3.4/Objective 4)	The distributive property in the form $ab + ac = a(b + c)$ is the basis for factoring out the greatest common monomial factor.	Factor $-4x^3y^4 - 2x^4y^3 - 6x^5y^2$. **Solution** $-4x^3y^4 - 2x^4y^3 - 6x^5y^2$ $\quad = -2x^3y^2(2y^2 + xy + 3x^2)$
Factor out a common binomial factor. (Section 3.4/Objective 5)	The common factor can be a binomial factor.	Factor $y(x - 4) + 6(x - 4)$. **Solution** $y(x - 4) + 6(x - 4)$ $\quad = (x - 4)(y + 6)$
Factor by grouping. (Section 3.4/Objective 6)	It may be that the polynomial exhibits no common monomial or binomial factor. However, after factoring common factors from groups of terms, a common factor may be evident.	Factor $2xz + 6x + yz + 3y$. **Solution** $2xz + 6x + yz + 3y$ $\quad = 2x(z + 3) + y(z + 3)$ $\quad = (z + 3)(2x + y)$
Factor the difference of two squares. (Section 3.5/Objective 1)	The factoring pattern for the difference of two squares is: $a^2 - b^2 = (a + b)(a - b)$	Factor $36a^2 - 25b^2$. **Solution** $36a^2 - 25b^2$ $\quad = (6a - 5b)(6a + 5b)$
Factor the sum or difference of two cubes. (Section 3.5/Objective 2)	The factoring patterns $a^3 + b^3 = (a + b)(a^2 - ab + b^2)$ and $a^3 - b^3 = (a - b)(a^2 + ab + b^2)$ are called the sum of two cubes and the difference of two cubes, respectively.	Factor $8x^3 + 27y^3$. **Solution** $8x^3 + 27y^3$ $\quad = (2x + 3y)(4x^2 - 6xy + 9y^2)$
Factor trinomials of the form $x^2 + bx + c$. (Section 3.6/Objective 1)	Expressing a trinomial (for which the coefficient of the squared term is 1) as a product of two binomials is based on the relationship $(x + a)(x + b) = x^2 + (a + b)x + ab$. The coefficient of the middle term is the sum of a and b, and the last term is the product of a and b.	Factor $x^2 - 2x - 35$. **Solution** $x^2 - 2x - 35 = (x - 7)(x + 5)$
Factor trinomials of the form $ax^2 + bx + c$. (Section 3.6/Objective 2)	Two methods were presented for factoring trinomials of the form $ax^2 + bx + c$. One technique is to try the various possibilities of factors and check by multiplying. This method is referred to as trial-and-error. The other method is a structured technique that is shown in Examples 10 and 11 of Section 3.6.	Factor $4x^2 + 16x + 15$. **Solution** Multiply 4 times 15 to get 60. The factors of 60 that add to 16 are 6 and 10. Rewrite the problem and factor by grouping: $4x^2 + 16x + 15$ $\quad = 4x^2 + 10x + 6x + 15$ $\quad = 2x(2x + 5) + 3(2x + 5)$ $\quad = (2x + 5)(2x + 3)$
Factor perfect-square trinomials. (Section 3.6/Objective 3)	A perfect-square trinomial is the result of squaring a binomial. There are two basic perfect-square trinomial factoring patterns, $a^2 + 2ab + b^2 = (a + b)^2$ and $a^2 - 2ab + b^2 = (a - b)^2$	Factor $16x^2 + 40x + 25$. **Solution** $16x^2 + 40x + 25 = (4x + 5)^2$

(continued)

OBJECTIVE	SUMMARY	EXAMPLE
Summarize the factoring techniques. (Section 3.6/Objective 4)	1. As a general guideline, always look for a common factor first. The common factor could be a binomial term. 2. If the polynomial has two terms, then its pattern could be the difference of squares or the sum or difference of two cubes. 3. If the polynomial has three terms, then the polynomial may factor into the product of two binomials. 4. If the polynomial has four or more terms, then factoring by grouping may apply. It may be necessary to rearrange the terms before factoring. 5. If none of the mentioned patterns or techniques work, then the polynomial may not be factorable using integers.	Factor $18x^2 - 50$. **Solution** First factor out a common factor of 2: $18x^2 - 50 = 2(9x^2 - 25)$ Now factor the difference of squares: $18x^2 - 50$ $= 2(9x^2 - 25)$ $= 2(3x - 5)(3x + 5)$
Solve equations. (Section 3.4/Objective 7; Section 3.5/Objective 3; Section 3.7/Objective 1)	The factoring techniques in this chapter, along with the property $ab = 0$, provide the basis for some additional equation-solving skills.	Solve $x^2 - 11x + 28 = 0$. **Solution** $x^2 - 11x + 28 = 0$ $(x - 7)(x - 4) = 0$ $x - 7 = 0$ or $x - 4 = 0$ $x = 7$ or $x = 4$ The solution set is $\{4, 7\}$.
Solve word problems. (Section 3.4/Objective 8; Section 3.5/Objective 4; Section 3.7/Objective 2)	The ability to solve more types of equations increased our capabilities to solve word problems.	Suppose that the area of a square is numerically equal to three times its perimeter. Find the length of a side of the square. **Solution** Let x represent the length of a side of the square. The area is x^2 and the perimeter is $4x$. Because the area is numerically equal to three times the perimeter, we have the equation $x^2 = 3(4x)$. By solving this equation, we can determine that the length of a side of the square is 12 units.

Chapter 3 Review Problem Set

For Problems 1–4, find the degree of the polynomial.

1. $-2x^3 + 4x^2 - 8x + 10$

2. $x^4 + 11x^2 - 15$

3. $5x^3y + 4x^4y^2 - 3x^3y^2$

4. $5xy^3 + 2x^2y^2 - 3x^3y^2$

For Problems 5–40, perform the indicated operations and then simplify.

5. $(3x - 2) + (4x - 6) + (-2x + 5)$

6. $(8x^2 + 9x - 3) - (5x^2 - 3x - 1)$

7. $(6x^2 - 2x - 1) + (4x^2 + 2x + 5) - (-2x^2 + x - 1)$

8. $(-3x^2 - 4x + 8) + (5x^2 + 7x + 2) - (-9x^2 + x + 6)$

9. $[3x - (2x - 3y + 1)] - [2y - (x - 1)]$

10. $[8x - (5x - y + 3)] - [-4y - (2x + 1)]$

11. $(-5x^2y^3)(4x^3y^4)$

12. $(-2a^2)(3ab^2)(a^2b^3)$

13. $\left(\frac{1}{2}ab\right)(8a^3b^2)(-2a^3)$

14. $\left(\frac{3}{4}x^2y^3\right)(12x^3y^2)(3y^3)$

15. $(4x^2y^3)^4$

16. $(-2x^2y^3z)^3$

17. $-(3ab)(2a^2b^3)^2$

18. $(3x^{n+1})(2x^{3n-1})$

19. $\dfrac{-39x^3y^4}{3xy^3}$ **20.** $\dfrac{30x^5y^4}{15x^2y}$

21. $\dfrac{12a^2b^5}{-3a^2b^3}$ **22.** $\dfrac{20a^4b^6}{5ab^3}$

23. $5a^2(3a^2 - 2a - 1)$

24. $-2x^3(4x^2 - 3x - 5)$

25. $(x + 4)(3x^2 - 5x - 1)$

26. $(3x + 2)(2x^2 - 5x + 1)$

27. $(x^2 - 2x - 5)(x^2 + 3x - 7)$

28. $(3x^2 - x - 4)(x^2 + 2x - 5)$

29. $(4x - 3y)(6x + 5y)$

30. $(7x - 9)(x + 4)$

31. $(7 - 3x)(3 + 5x)$

32. $(x^2 - 3)(x^2 + 8)$

33. $(2x - 3)^2$

34. $(5x - 1)^2$

35. $(4x + 3y)^2$

36. $(2x + 5y)^2$

37. $(2x - 7)(2x + 7)$

38. $(3x - 1)(3x + 1)$

39. $(x - 2)^3$

40. $(2x + 5)^3$

41. Find a polynomial that represents the area of the shaded region in Figure 3.23.

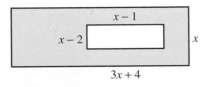

Figure 3.23

42. Find a polynomial that represents the volume of the rectangular solid in Figure 3.24.

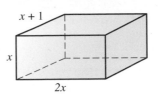

Figure 3.24

For Problems 43–62, factor each polynomial.

43. $10a^2b - 5ab^3 - 15a^3b^2$

44. $3xy - 5x^2y^2 - 15x^3y^3$

45. $a(x + 4) + b(x + 4)$

46. $y(3x - 1) + 7(3x - 1)$

47. $6x^3 + 3x^2y + 2xz^2 + yz^2$

48. $mn + 5n^2 - 4m - 20n$

49. $49a^2 - 25b^2$

50. $36x^2 - y^2$

51. $125a^3 - 8$

52. $27x^3 + 64y^3$

53. $x^2 - 9x + 18$

54. $x^2 + 11x + 28$

55. $x^2 - 4x - 21$

56. $x^2 + 6x - 16$

57. $2x^2 + 9x + 4$

58. $6x^2 - 11x + 4$

59. $12x^2 - 5x - 2$

60. $8x^2 - 10x - 3$

61. $4x^2 - 12xy + 9y^2$

62. $x^2 + 16xy + 64y^2$

For Problems 63–84, factor each polynomial completely. Indicate any that are not factorable using integers.

63. $x^2 + 3x - 28$ **64.** $2t^2 - 18$

65. $4n^2 + 9$ **66.** $12n^2 - 7n + 1$

67. $x^6 - x^2$ **68.** $x^3 - 6x^2 - 72x$

69. $6a^3b + 4a^2b^2 - 2a^2bc$ **70.** $x^2 - (y - 1)^2$

71. $8x^2 + 12$ **72.** $12x^2 + x - 35$

73. $16n^2 - 40n + 25$ **74.** $4n^2 - 8n$

75. $3w^3 + 18w^2 - 24w$ **76.** $20x^2 + 3xy - 2y^2$

77. $16a^2 - 64a$ **78.** $3x^3 - 15x^2 - 18x$

79. $n^2 - 8n - 128$

80. $t^4 - 22t^2 - 75$

81. $35x^2 - 11x - 6$

82. $15 - 14x + 3x^2$

83. $64n^3 - 27$

84. $16x^3 + 250$

For Problems 85–104, solve each equation.

85. $4x^2 - 36 = 0$

86. $x^2 + 5x - 6 = 0$

87. $49n^2 - 28n + 4 = 0$

88. $(3x - 1)(5x + 2) = 0$

89. $(3x - 4)^2 - 25 = 0$

90. $6a^3 = 54a$

91. $x^5 = x$

92. $-n^2 + 2n + 63 = 0$

93. $7n(7n + 2) = 8$

94. $30w^2 - w - 20 = 0$

95. $5x^4 - 19x^2 - 4 = 0$

96. $9n^2 - 30n + 25 = 0$

97. $n(2n + 4) = 96$

98. $7x^2 + 33x - 10 = 0$

99. $(x + 1)(x + 2) = 42$

100. $x^2 + 12x - x - 12 = 0$

101. $2x^4 + 9x^2 + 4 = 0$

102. $30 - 19x - 5x^2 = 0$

103. $3t^3 - 27t^2 + 24t = 0$

104. $-4n^2 - 39n + 10 = 0$

For Problems 105–114, set up an equation and solve each problem.

105. Find three consecutive integers such that the product of the smallest and the largest is one less than 9 times the middle integer.

106. Find two integers whose sum is 2 and whose product is −48.

107. Find two consecutive odd whole numbers whose product is 195.

108. Two cars leave an intersection at the same time, one traveling north and the other traveling east. Some time later, they are 20 miles apart, and the car going east has traveled 4 miles farther than the other car. How far has each car traveled?

109. The perimeter of a rectangle is 32 meters, and its area is 48 square meters. Find the length and width of the rectangle.

110. A room contains 144 chairs. The number of chairs per row is two less than twice the number of rows. Find the number of rows and the number of chairs per row.

111. The area of a triangle is 39 square feet. The length of one side is 1 foot more than twice the altitude to that side. Find the length of that side and the altitude to the side.

112. A rectangular-shaped pool 20 feet by 30 feet has a sidewalk of uniform width around the pool (see Figure 3.25). The area of the sidewalk is 336 square feet. Find the width of the sidewalk.

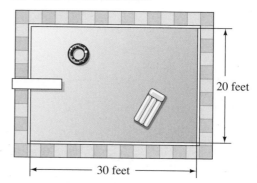

20 feet

30 feet

Figure 3.25

113. The sum of the areas of two squares is 89 square centimeters. The length of a side of the larger square is 3 centimeters more than the length of a side of the smaller square. Find the dimensions of each square.

114. The total surface area of a right circular cylinder is 32π square inches. If the altitude of the cylinder is three times the length of a radius, find the altitude of the cylinder.

Chapter 3 Test

For Problems 1–8, perform the indicated operations and simplify each expression.

1. $(-3x - 1) + (9x - 2) - (4x + 8)$

2. $(-6xy^2)(8x^3y^2)$

3. $(-3x^2y^4)^3$

4. $(5x - 7)(4x + 9)$

5. $(3n - 2)(2n - 3)$

6. $(x - 4y)^3$

7. $(x + 6)(2x^2 - x - 5)$

8. $\dfrac{-70x^4y^3}{5xy^2}$

For Problems 9–14, factor each expression completely.

9. $6x^2 + 19x - 20$

10. $12x^2 - 3$

11. $64 + t^3$

12. $30x + 4x^2 - 16x^3$

13. $x^2 - xy + 4x - 4y$

14. $24n^2 + 55n - 24$

For Problems 15–22, solve each equation.

15. $x^2 + 8x - 48 = 0$

16. $4n^2 = n$

17. $4x^2 - 12x + 9 = 0$

18. $(n - 2)(n + 7) = -18$

19. $3x^3 + 21x^2 - 54x = 0$

20. $12 + 13x - 35x^2 = 0$

21. $n(3n - 5) = 2$

22. $9x^2 - 36 = 0$

For Problems 23–25, set up an equation and solve each problem.

23. The perimeter of a rectangle is 30 inches, and its area is 54 square inches. Find the length of the longest side of the rectangle.

24. A room contains 105 chairs arranged in rows. The number of rows is one more than twice the number of chairs per row. Find the number of rows.

25. The combined area of a square and a rectangle is 57 square feet. The width of the rectangle is 3 feet more than the length of a side of the square, and the length of the rectangle is 5 feet more than the length of a side of the square. Find the length of the rectangle.

4 Rational Expressions

4.1 Simplifying Rational Expressions

4.2 Multiplying and Dividing Rational Expressions

4.3 Adding and Subtracting Rational Expressions

4.4 More on Rational Expressions and Complex Fractions

4.5 Dividing Polynomials

4.6 Fractional Equations

4.7 More Fractional Equations and Applications

Computers often work together to compile large processing jobs. Rational numbers are used to express the rate of the processing speed of a computer.

© Todd Taulman

It takes Pat 12 hours to complete a task. After he had been working on this task for 3 hours, he was joined by his brother, Liam, and together they finished the job in 5 hours. How long would it take Liam to do the job by himself? We can use the *fractional equation* $\frac{5}{12} + \frac{5}{h} = \frac{3}{4}$ to determine that Liam could do the entire job by himself in 15 hours.

Rational expressions are to algebra what rational numbers are to arithmetic. Most of the work we will do with rational expressions in this chapter parallels the work you have previously done with arithmetic fractions. The same basic properties we use to explain reducing, adding, subtracting, multiplying, and dividing arithmetic fractions will serve as a basis for our work with rational expressions. The techniques of factoring that we studied in Chapter 3 will also play an important role in our discussions. At the end of this chapter, we will work with some fractional equations that contain rational expressions.

Video tutorials based on section learning objectives are available in a variety of delivery modes.

| 4.1 | Simplifying Rational Expressions |

OBJECTIVES
1. Reduce rational numbers
2. Simplify rational expressions

We reviewed the basic operations with rational numbers in an informal setting in Chapter 1. In this review, we relied primarily on your knowledge of arithmetic. At this time, we want to become a little more formal with our review so that we can use the work with rational numbers as a basis for operating with rational expressions. We will define a rational expression shortly.

You will recall that any number that can be written in the form $\frac{a}{b}$, where a and b are integers and $b \neq 0$, is called a **rational number**. The following are examples of rational numbers.

$$\frac{1}{2} \qquad \frac{3}{4} \qquad \frac{15}{7} \qquad \frac{-5}{6} \qquad \frac{7}{-8} \qquad \frac{-12}{-17}$$

Numbers such as 6, -4, 0, $4\frac{1}{2}$, 0.7, and 0.21 are also rational, because we can express them as the indicated quotient of two integers. For example,

$$6 = \frac{6}{1} = \frac{12}{2} = \frac{18}{3} \quad \text{and so on} \qquad\qquad 4\frac{1}{2} = \frac{9}{2}$$

$$-4 = \frac{4}{-1} = \frac{-4}{1} = \frac{8}{-2} \quad \text{and so on} \qquad 0.7 = \frac{7}{10}$$

$$0 = \frac{0}{1} = \frac{0}{2} = \frac{0}{3} \quad \text{and so on} \qquad\qquad 0.21 = \frac{21}{100}$$

Because a rational number is the quotient of two integers, our previous work with division of integers can help us understand the various forms of rational numbers. If the signs of the numerator and denominator are different, then the rational number is negative. If the signs of the numerator and denominator are the same, then the rational number is positive. The next examples and Property 4.1 show the equivalent forms of rational numbers. Generally, it is preferred to express the denominator of a rational number as a positive integer.

$$\frac{8}{-2} = \frac{-8}{2} = -\frac{8}{2} = -4 \qquad \frac{12}{3} = \frac{-12}{-3} = 4$$

Observe the following general properties.

Property 4.1

1. $\dfrac{-a}{b} = \dfrac{a}{-b} = -\dfrac{a}{b}$ where $b \neq 0$

2. $\dfrac{-a}{-b} = \dfrac{a}{b}$ where $b \neq 0$

Therefore, a rational number such as $\dfrac{-2}{5}$ can also be written as $\dfrac{2}{-5}$ or $-\dfrac{2}{5}$.

We use the following property, often referred to as the **fundamental principle of fractions**, to reduce fractions to lowest terms or express fractions in simplest or reduced form.

> **Property 4.2 Fundamental Principle of Fractions**
>
> If b and k are nonzero integers and a is any integer, then
>
> $$\frac{a \cdot k}{b \cdot k} = \frac{a}{b}$$

Let's apply Properties 4.1 and 4.2 to the following examples.

Classroom Example
Reduce $\dfrac{14}{21}$ to lowest terms.

EXAMPLE 1 Reduce $\dfrac{18}{24}$ to lowest terms.

Solution

$$\frac{18}{24} = \frac{3 \cdot 6}{4 \cdot 6} = \frac{3}{4}$$

Classroom Example
Change $\dfrac{32}{56}$ to simplest form.

EXAMPLE 2 Change $\dfrac{40}{48}$ to simplest form.

Solution

$$\frac{\overset{5}{\cancel{40}}}{\underset{6}{\cancel{48}}} = \frac{5}{6} \qquad \text{A common factor of 8 was divided out of both numerator and denominator}$$

Classroom Example
Express $\dfrac{-28}{44}$ in reduced form.

EXAMPLE 3 Express $\dfrac{-36}{63}$ in reduced form.

Solution

$$\frac{-36}{63} = -\frac{36}{63} = -\frac{4 \cdot 9}{7 \cdot 9} = -\frac{4}{7}$$

Classroom Example
Reduce $\dfrac{36}{-84}$ to simplest form.

EXAMPLE 4 Reduce $\dfrac{72}{-90}$ to simplest form.

Solution

$$\frac{72}{-90} = -\frac{72}{90} = -\frac{\cancel{2} \cdot 2 \cdot 2 \cdot \cancel{3} \cdot \cancel{3}}{\cancel{2} \cdot \cancel{3} \cdot \cancel{3} \cdot 5} = -\frac{4}{5}$$

Note the different terminology used in Examples 1–4. Regardless of the terminology, keep in mind that the number is not being changed, but the form of the numeral representing the number is being changed. In Example 1, $\dfrac{18}{24}$ and $\dfrac{3}{4}$ are equivalent fractions; they name the same number. Also note the use of prime factors in Example 4.

Simplifying Rational Expressions

A **rational expression** is the indicated quotient of two polynomials. The following are examples of rational expressions.

$$\frac{3x^2}{5} \qquad \frac{x-2}{x+3} \qquad \frac{x^2+5x-1}{x^2-9} \qquad \frac{xy^2+x^2y}{xy} \qquad \frac{a^3-3a^2-5a-1}{a^4+a^3+6}$$

Because we must avoid division by zero, no values that create a denominator of zero can be assigned to variables. Thus the rational expression $\dfrac{x-2}{x+3}$ is meaningful for all values of x except $x = -3$. Rather than making restrictions for each individual expression, we will merely assume that all denominators represent nonzero real numbers.

Property 4.2 $\left(\dfrac{a \cdot k}{b \cdot k} = \dfrac{a}{b}\right)$ serves as the basis for simplifying rational expressions, as the next examples illustrate.

Classroom Example
Simplify $\dfrac{18mn}{45m}$.

EXAMPLE 5

Simplify $\dfrac{15xy}{25y}$.

Solution

$$\frac{15xy}{25y} = \frac{3 \cdot \cancel{5} \cdot x \cdot \cancel{y}}{\cancel{5} \cdot 5 \cdot \cancel{y}} = \frac{3x}{5}$$

Classroom Example
Simplify $\dfrac{-12}{36ab^2}$.

EXAMPLE 6

Simplify $\dfrac{-9}{18x^2y}$.

Solution

$$\frac{-9}{18x^2y} = -\frac{\overset{1}{\cancel{9}}}{\underset{2}{\cancel{18}}x^2y} = -\frac{1}{2x^2y} \qquad \text{A common factor of 9 was divided out of numerator and denominator}$$

Classroom Example
Simplify $\dfrac{-42x^3y^2}{-54x^2y^2}$.

EXAMPLE 7

Simplify $\dfrac{-28a^2b^2}{-63a^2b^3}$.

Solution

$$\frac{-28a^2b^2}{-63a^2b^3} = \frac{4 \cdot \cancel{7} \cdot \cancel{a^2} \cdot \cancel{b^2}}{9 \cdot \cancel{7} \cdot \cancel{a^2} \cdot \underset{b}{\cancel{b^3}}} = \frac{4}{9b}$$

The factoring techniques from Chapter 3 can be used to factor numerators and/or denominators so that we can apply the property $\dfrac{a \cdot k}{b \cdot k} = \dfrac{a}{b}$. Examples 8–12 should clarify this process.

Classroom Example
Simplify $\dfrac{x^2 - 7x}{x^2 - 49}$.

EXAMPLE 8

Simplify $\dfrac{x^2 + 4x}{x^2 - 16}$.

Solution

$$\frac{x^2 + 4x}{x^2 - 16} = \frac{x(\cancel{x+4})}{(x-4)(\cancel{x+4})} = \frac{x}{x-4}$$

Classroom Example
Simplify $\dfrac{9x^2 + 6x + 1}{3x + 1}$.

EXAMPLE 9

Simplify $\dfrac{4a^2 + 12a + 9}{2a + 3}$.

Solution

$$\frac{4a^2 + 12a + 9}{2a + 3} = \frac{(\cancel{2a+3})(2a+3)}{1(\cancel{2a+3})} = \frac{2a+3}{1} = 2a+3$$

Classroom Example

Simplify $\dfrac{7n^2 + 23n + 6}{21n^2 - n - 2}$.

EXAMPLE 10   Simplify $\dfrac{5n^2 + 6n - 8}{10n^2 - 3n - 4}$.

Solution

$$\frac{5n^2 + 6n - 8}{10n^2 - 3n - 4} = \frac{(5n-4)(n + 2)}{(5n-4)(2n + 1)} = \frac{n + 2}{2n + 1}$$

Classroom Example

Simplify $\dfrac{3x^3y - 12xy}{x^2y - xy - 6y}$.

EXAMPLE 11   Simplify $\dfrac{6x^3y - 6xy}{x^3 + 5x^2 + 4x}$.

Solution

$$\frac{6x^3y - 6xy}{x^3 + 5x^2 + 4x} = \frac{6xy(x^2 - 1)}{x(x^2 + 5x + 4)} = \frac{6xy(x+1)(x - 1)}{x(x+1)(x + 4)} = \frac{6y(x - 1)}{x + 4}$$

Note that in Example 11 we left the numerator of the final fraction in factored form. This is often done if expressions other than monomials are involved. Either $\dfrac{6y(x - 1)}{x + 4}$ or $\dfrac{6xy - 6y}{x + 4}$ is an acceptable answer.

Remember that the quotient of any nonzero real number and its opposite is -1. For example, $\dfrac{6}{-6} = -1$ and $\dfrac{-8}{8} = -1$. Likewise, the indicated quotient of any polynomial and its opposite is equal to -1; that is,

$$\frac{a}{-a} = -1 \quad \text{because } a \text{ and } -a \text{ are opposites}$$

$$\frac{a - b}{b - a} = -1 \quad \text{because } a - b \text{ and } b - a \text{ are opposites}$$

$$\frac{x^2 - 4}{4 - x^2} = -1 \quad \text{because } x^2 - 4 \text{ and } 4 - x^2 \text{ are opposites}$$

Example 12 shows how we use this idea when simplifying rational expressions.

Classroom Example

Simplify $\dfrac{6a^2 - 17a + 5}{15a - 6a^2}$.

EXAMPLE 12   Simplify $\dfrac{6a^2 - 7a + 2}{10a - 15a^2}$.

Solution

$$\frac{6a^2 - 7a + 2}{10a - 15a^2} = \frac{(2a - 1)(3a - 2)}{5a(2 - 3a)} \qquad \frac{3a - 2}{2 - 3a} = -1$$

$$= (-1)\left(\frac{2a - 1}{5a}\right)$$

$$= -\frac{2a - 1}{5a} \qquad \text{or} \qquad \frac{1 - 2a}{5a}$$

Concept Quiz 4.1

For Problems 1–10, answer true or false.

1. When a rational number is being reduced, the form of the numeral is being changed but not the number it represents.

2. A rational number is the ratio of two integers where the denominator is not zero.

3. -3 is a rational number.

4. The rational expression $\dfrac{x + 2}{x + 3}$ is meaningful for all values of x except when $x = -2$ and $x = 3$.

5. The binomials $x - y$ and $y - x$ are opposites.

6. The binomials $x + 3$ and $x - 3$ are opposites.

7. The rational expression $\dfrac{2 - x}{x + 2}$ reduces to -1.

8. The rational expression $\dfrac{x - y}{y - x}$ reduces to -1.

9. $\dfrac{x^2 + 5x - 14}{x^2 + 2x + 1} = \dfrac{5x - 14}{2x + 1}$

10. The rational expression $\dfrac{2x - x^2}{x^2 - 4}$ reduces to $\dfrac{x}{x + 2}$.

Problem Set 4.1

For Problems 1–8, express each rational number in reduced form. (Objective 1)

1. $\dfrac{27}{36}$

2. $\dfrac{14}{21}$

3. $\dfrac{45}{54}$

4. $\dfrac{-14}{42}$

5. $\dfrac{24}{-60}$

6. $\dfrac{45}{-75}$

7. $\dfrac{-16}{-56}$

8. $\dfrac{-30}{-42}$

For Problems 9–50, simplify each rational expression. (Objective 2)

9. $\dfrac{12xy}{42y}$

10. $\dfrac{21xy}{35x}$

11. $\dfrac{18a^2}{45ab}$

12. $\dfrac{48ab}{84b^2}$

13. $\dfrac{-14y^3}{56xy^2}$

14. $\dfrac{-14x^2y^3}{63xy^2}$

15. $\dfrac{54c^2d}{-78cd^2}$

16. $\dfrac{60x^3z}{-64xyz^2}$

17. $\dfrac{-40x^3y}{-24xy^4}$

18. $\dfrac{-30x^2y^2z^2}{-35xz^3}$

19. $\dfrac{x^2 - 4}{x^2 + 2x}$

20. $\dfrac{xy + y^2}{x^2 - y^2}$

21. $\dfrac{18x + 12}{12x - 6}$

22. $\dfrac{20x + 50}{15x - 30}$

23. $\dfrac{a^2 + 7a + 10}{a^2 - 7a - 18}$

24. $\dfrac{a^2 + 4a - 32}{3a^2 + 26a + 16}$

25. $\dfrac{2n^2 + n - 21}{10n^2 + 33n - 7}$

26. $\dfrac{4n^2 - 15n - 4}{7n^2 - 30n + 8}$

27. $\dfrac{5x^2 + 7}{10x}$

28. $\dfrac{12x^2 + 11x - 15}{20x^2 - 23x + 6}$

29. $\dfrac{6x^2 + x - 15}{8x^2 - 10x - 3}$

30. $\dfrac{4x^2 + 8x}{x^3 + 8}$

31. $\dfrac{3x^2 - 12x}{x^3 - 64}$

32. $\dfrac{x^2 - 14x + 49}{6x^2 - 37x - 35}$

33. $\dfrac{3x^2 + 17x - 6}{9x^2 - 6x + 1}$

34. $\dfrac{9y^2 - 1}{3y^2 + 11y - 4}$

35. $\dfrac{2x^3 + 3x^2 - 14x}{x^2y + 7xy - 18y}$

36. $\dfrac{3x^3 + 12x}{9x^2 + 18x}$

37. $\dfrac{5y^2 + 22y + 8}{25y^2 - 4}$

38. $\dfrac{16x^3y + 24x^2y^2 - 16xy^3}{24x^2y + 12xy^2 - 12y^3}$

39. $\dfrac{15x^3 - 15x^2}{5x^3 + 5x}$

40. $\dfrac{5n^2 + 18n - 8}{3n^2 + 13n + 4}$

41. $\dfrac{4x^2y + 8xy^2 - 12y^3}{18x^3y - 12x^2y^2 - 6xy^3}$

42. $\dfrac{3 + x - 2x^2}{2 + x - x^2}$

43. $\dfrac{3n^2 + 16n - 12}{7n^2 + 44n + 12}$

44. $\dfrac{x^4 - 2x^2 - 15}{2x^4 + 9x^2 + 9}$

45. $\dfrac{8 + 18x - 5x^2}{10 + 31x + 15x^2}$

46. $\dfrac{6x^4 - 11x^2 + 4}{2x^4 + 17x^2 - 9}$

47. $\dfrac{27x^4 - x}{6x^3 + 10x^2 - 4x}$

48. $\dfrac{64x^4 + 27x}{12x^3 - 27x^2 - 27x}$

49. $\dfrac{-40x^3 + 24x^2 + 16x}{20x^3 + 28x^2 + 8x}$ **50.** $\dfrac{-6x^3 - 21x^2 + 12x}{-18x^3 - 42x^2 + 120x}$

For Problems 51–58, simplify each rational expression. You will need to use factoring by grouping. (Objective 2)

51. $\dfrac{xy + ay + bx + ab}{xy + ay + cx + ac}$ **52.** $\dfrac{xy + 2y + 3x + 6}{xy + 2y + 4x + 8}$

53. $\dfrac{ax - 3x + 2ay - 6y}{2ax - 6x + ay - 3y}$ **54.** $\dfrac{x^2 - 2x + ax - 2a}{x^2 - 2x + 3ax - 6a}$

55. $\dfrac{5x^2 + 5x + 3x + 3}{5x^2 + 3x - 30x - 18}$ **56.** $\dfrac{x^2 + 3x + 4x + 12}{2x^2 + 6x - x - 3}$

57. $\dfrac{2st - 30 - 12s + 5t}{3st - 6 - 18s + t}$ **58.** $\dfrac{nr - 6 - 3n + 2r}{nr + 10 + 2r + 5n}$

For Problems 59–68, simplify each rational expression. You may want to refer to Example 12 of this section. (Objective 2)

59. $\dfrac{5x - 7}{7 - 5x}$ **60.** $\dfrac{4a - 9}{9 - 4a}$

61. $\dfrac{n^2 - 49}{7 - n}$ **62.** $\dfrac{9 - y}{y^2 - 81}$

63. $\dfrac{2y - 2xy}{x^2y - y}$ **64.** $\dfrac{3x - x^2}{x^2 - 9}$

65. $\dfrac{2x^3 - 8x}{4x - x^3}$ **66.** $\dfrac{x^2 - (y - 1)^2}{(y - 1)^2 - x^2}$

67. $\dfrac{n^2 - 5n - 24}{40 + 3n - n^2}$ **68.** $\dfrac{x^2 + 2x - 24}{20 - x - x^2}$

Thoughts Into Words

69. Compare the concept of a rational number in arithmetic to the concept of a rational expression in algebra.

70. What role does factoring play in the simplifying of rational expressions?

71. Why is the rational expression $\dfrac{x + 3}{x^2 - 4}$ undefined for $x = 2$ and $x = -2$ but defined for $x = -3$?

72. How would you convince someone that $\dfrac{x - 4}{4 - x} = -1$ for all real numbers except 4?

Answers to the Concept Quiz

1. True **2.** True **3.** True **4.** False **5.** True **6.** False **7.** False **8.** True **9.** False **10.** False

---

4.2	Multiplying and Dividing Rational Expressions

OBJECTIVES

1 Multiply rational numbers

2 Multiply rational expressions

3 Divide rational numbers

4 Divide rational expressions

5 Simplify problems that involve both multiplication and division of rational expressions

We define multiplication of rational numbers in common fraction form as follows:

> **Definition 4.1 Multiplication of Fractions**
>
> If a, b, c, and d are integers, and b and d are not equal to zero, then
>
> $$\frac{a}{b} \cdot \frac{c}{d} = \frac{a \cdot c}{b \cdot d} = \frac{ac}{bd}$$

To multiply rational numbers in common fraction form, we *multiply numerators and multiply denominators,* as the following examples demonstrate. (The steps in the dashed boxes are usually done mentally.)

$$\frac{2}{3} \cdot \frac{4}{5} = \frac{2 \cdot 4}{3 \cdot 5} = \frac{8}{15}$$

$$\frac{-3}{4} \cdot \frac{5}{7} = \frac{-3 \cdot 5}{4 \cdot 7} = \frac{-15}{28} = -\frac{15}{28}$$

$$-\frac{5}{6} \cdot \frac{13}{3} = \frac{-5}{6} \cdot \frac{13}{3} = \frac{-5 \cdot 13}{6 \cdot 3} = \frac{-65}{18} = -\frac{65}{18}$$

We also agree, when multiplying rational numbers, to express the final product in reduced form. The following examples show some different formats used to multiply and simplify rational numbers.

$$\frac{3}{4} \cdot \frac{4}{7} = \frac{3 \cdot 4}{4 \cdot 7} = \frac{3}{7}$$

$$\frac{\overset{1}{\cancel{8}}}{\underset{1}{\cancel{9}}} \cdot \frac{\overset{3}{\cancel{27}}}{\underset{4}{\cancel{32}}} = \frac{3}{4} \qquad \text{A common factor of 9 was divided out of 9 and 27, and a common factor of 8 was divided out of 8 and 32}$$

$$\left(-\frac{28}{25}\right)\left(-\frac{65}{78}\right) = \frac{2 \cdot 2 \cdot 7 \cdot \cancel{5} \cdot \cancel{13}}{\cancel{5} \cdot 5 \cdot 2 \cdot 3 \cdot \cancel{13}} = \frac{14}{15} \qquad \text{We should recognize that a negative times a negative is positive; also, note the use of prime factors to help us recognize common factors}$$

Multiplying Rational Expressions

Multiplication of rational expressions follows the same basic pattern as multiplication of rational numbers in common fraction form. That is to say, we multiply numerators and multiply denominators and express the final product in simplified or reduced form. Let's consider some examples.

$$\frac{3x}{4y} \cdot \frac{8y^2}{9x} = \frac{3 \cdot \overset{2}{\cancel{8}} \cdot \cancel{x} \cdot \overset{y}{\cancel{y^2}}}{\underset{3}{\cancel{4}} \cdot \cancel{9} \cdot \cancel{x} \cdot \cancel{y}} = \frac{2y}{3} \qquad \text{Note that we use the commutative property of multiplication to rearrange the factors in a form that allows us to identify common factors of the numerator and denominator}$$

$$\frac{-4a}{6a^2b^2} \cdot \frac{9ab}{12a^2} = -\frac{\cancel{4} \cdot \overset{3}{\cancel{9}} \cdot \cancel{a^2} \cdot \cancel{b}}{\underset{2}{\cancel{6}} \cdot \underset{3}{\cancel{12}} \cdot \underset{a^2}{\cancel{a^4}} \cdot \underset{b}{\cancel{b^2}}} = -\frac{1}{2a^2b}$$

$$\frac{12x^2y}{-18xy} \cdot \frac{-24xy^2}{56y^3} = \frac{\overset{2}{\cancel{12}} \cdot \overset{3}{\cancel{24}} \cdot \overset{x^2}{\cancel{x^3}} \cdot \cancel{y^3}}{\underset{3}{\cancel{18}} \cdot \underset{7}{\cancel{56}} \cdot \cancel{x} \cdot \underset{y}{\cancel{y^4}}} = \frac{2x^2}{7y} \qquad \text{You should recognize that the first fraction is negative, and the second fraction is negative. Thus the product is positive.}$$

If the rational expressions contain polynomials (other than monomials) that are factorable, then our work may take on the following format.

Classroom Example
Multiply and simplify $\dfrac{m}{n^2 - 9} \cdot \dfrac{n - 3}{m^3}$.

EXAMPLE 1 Multiply and simplify $\dfrac{y}{x^2 - 4} \cdot \dfrac{x + 2}{y^2}$.

Solution

$$\frac{y}{x^2 - 4} \cdot \frac{x + 2}{y^2} = \frac{\cancel{y}(\cancel{x + 2})}{\underset{y}{\cancel{y^2}}(\cancel{x + 2})(x - 2)} = \frac{1}{y(x - 2)}$$

In Example 1, note that we combined the steps of multiplying numerators and denominators and factoring the polynomials. Also note that we left the final answer in factored form. Either $\dfrac{1}{y(x - 2)}$ or $\dfrac{1}{xy - 2y}$ would be an acceptable answer.

Classroom Example
Multiply and simplify:

$$\frac{m^2 + m}{m + 4} \cdot \frac{m^2 - 4m + 3}{m^4 - m^2}$$

EXAMPLE 2 Multiply and simplify $\dfrac{x^2 - x}{x + 5} \cdot \dfrac{x^2 + 5x + 4}{x^4 - x^2}$.

Solution

$$\frac{x^2 - x}{x + 5} \cdot \frac{x^2 + 5x + 4}{x^4 - x^2} = \frac{x(x - 1)}{x + 5} \cdot \frac{(x + 1)(x + 4)}{x^2(x - 1)(x + 1)}$$

$$= \frac{x(x - 1)(x + 1)(x + 4)}{(x + 5)(x^2)(x - 1)(x + 1)} = \frac{x + 4}{x(x + 5)}$$

Classroom Example
Multiply and simplify:

$$\frac{8x^2 + 10x - 3}{6x^2 + 7x - 3} \cdot \frac{3x^2 + 20x - 7}{8x^2 + 18x - 5}$$

EXAMPLE 3 Multiply and simplify $\dfrac{6n^2 + 7n - 5}{n^2 + 2n - 24} \cdot \dfrac{4n^2 + 21n - 18}{12n^2 + 11n - 15}$.

Solution

$$\frac{6n^2 + 7n - 5}{n^2 + 2n - 24} \cdot \frac{4n^2 + 21n - 18}{12n^2 + 11n - 15}$$

$$= \frac{(3n + 5)(2n - 1)(4n - 3)(n + 6)}{(n + 6)(n - 4)(3n + 5)(4n - 3)} = \frac{2n - 1}{n - 4}$$

Dividing Rational Numbers

We define division of rational numbers in common fraction form as follows:

> **Definition 4.2 Division of Fractions**
>
> If a, b, c, and d are integers, and b, c, and d are not equal to zero, then
>
> $$\frac{a}{b} \div \frac{c}{d} = \frac{a}{b} \cdot \frac{d}{c} = \frac{ad}{bc}$$

Definition 4.2 states that to divide two rational numbers in fraction form, we **invert the divisor and multiply**. We call the numbers $\dfrac{c}{d}$ and $\dfrac{d}{c}$ "reciprocals" or "multiplicative inverses" of each other, because their product is 1. Thus we can describe division by saying "to divide by a fraction, multiply by its reciprocal." The following examples demonstrate the use of Definition 4.2.

$$\frac{7}{8} \div \frac{5}{6} = \frac{7}{8} \cdot \frac{\overset{3}{6}}{5} = \frac{21}{20}, \qquad \frac{-5}{9} \div \frac{15}{18} = -\frac{5}{9} \cdot \frac{\overset{2}{18}}{\underset{3}{15}} = -\frac{2}{3}$$

$$\frac{14}{-19} \div \frac{21}{-38} = \left(-\frac{14}{19}\right) \div \left(-\frac{21}{38}\right) = \left(-\frac{\overset{2}{14}}{19}\right)\left(-\frac{\overset{2}{38}}{\underset{3}{21}}\right) = \frac{4}{3}$$

Dividing Rational Expressions

We define division of algebraic rational expressions in the same way that we define division of rational numbers. That is, the quotient of two rational expressions is the product we obtain when we multiply the first expression by the reciprocal of the second. Consider the following examples.

Classroom Example
Divide and simplify:

$$\frac{18mn^3}{32m^3n^2} \div \frac{9m^3n^2}{12m^2n^2}$$

EXAMPLE 4   Divide and simplify $\dfrac{16x^2y}{24xy^3} \div \dfrac{9xy}{8x^2y^2}$.

Solution

$$\frac{16x^2y}{24xy^3} \div \frac{9xy}{8x^2y^2} = \frac{16x^2y}{24xy^3} \cdot \frac{8x^2y^2}{9xy} = \frac{16 \cdot 8 \cdot \overset{x^2}{\cancel{x^3}} \cdot \cancel{y^3}}{\underset{3}{\cancel{24}} \cdot 9 \cdot \cancel{x^2} \cdot \underset{y}{\cancel{y^4}}} = \frac{16x^2}{27y}$$

Classroom Example
Divide and simplify:

$$\frac{4x^2 + 36}{8x^2 + 4x} \div \frac{x^4 - 81}{2x^2 - 5x - 3}$$

EXAMPLE 5   Divide and simplify $\dfrac{3a^2 + 12}{3a^2 - 15a} \div \dfrac{a^4 - 16}{a^2 - 3a - 10}$.

Solution

$$\frac{3a^2 + 12}{3a^2 - 15a} \div \frac{a^4 - 16}{a^2 - 3a - 10} = \frac{3a^2 + 12}{3a^2 - 15a} \cdot \frac{a^2 - 3a - 10}{a^4 - 16}$$

$$= \frac{3(a^2 + 4)}{3a(a - 5)} \cdot \frac{(a - 5)(a + 2)}{(a^2 + 4)(a + 2)(a - 2)}$$

$$= \frac{\overset{1}{\cancel{3}}(\cancel{a^2 + 4})(\cancel{a - 5})(\cancel{a + 2})}{\underset{1}{\cancel{3}}a(\cancel{a - 5})(\cancel{a^2 + 4})(\cancel{a + 2})(a - 2)}$$

$$= \frac{1}{a(a - 2)}$$

Classroom Example
Divide and simplify:

$$\frac{35x^3 - 8x^2 - 3x}{45x^2 - x - 2} \div (7x - 3)$$

EXAMPLE 6   Divide and simplify $\dfrac{28t^3 - 51t^2 - 27t}{49t^2 + 42t + 9} \div (4t - 9)$.

Solution

$$\frac{28t^3 - 51t^2 - 27t}{49t^2 + 42t + 9} \div \frac{4t - 9}{1} = \frac{28t^3 - 51t^2 - 27t}{49t^2 + 42t + 9} \cdot \frac{1}{4t - 9}$$

$$= \frac{t(7t + 3)(4t - 9)}{(7t + 3)(7t + 3)} \cdot \frac{1}{(4t - 9)}$$

$$= \frac{t(\cancel{7t + 3})(\cancel{4t - 9})}{(\cancel{7t + 3})(7t + 3)(\cancel{4t - 9})}$$

$$= \frac{t}{7t + 3}$$

In a problem such as Example 6, it may be helpful to write the divisor with a denominator of 1. Thus we write $4t - 9$ as $\dfrac{4t - 9}{1}$; its reciprocal is obviously $\dfrac{1}{4t - 9}$.

Let's consider one final example that involves both multiplication and division.

Classroom Example
Perform the indicated operations and simplify:

$$\frac{5x^2 + 13x - 6}{2xy^2 - 3y^2} \cdot \frac{2x^2 + 5x - 12}{x^3 + 3x^2}$$
$$\div \frac{2x^2 + 13x + 20}{x^2y}$$

EXAMPLE 7

Perform the indicated operations and simplify:

$$\frac{x^2 + 5x}{3x^2 - 4x - 20} \cdot \frac{x^2y + y}{2x^2 + 11x + 5} \div \frac{xy^2}{6x^2 - 17x - 10}$$

Solution

$$\frac{x^2 + 5x}{3x^2 - 4x - 20} \cdot \frac{x^2y + y}{2x^2 + 11x + 5} \div \frac{xy^2}{6x^2 - 17x - 10}$$

$$= \frac{x^2 + 5x}{3x^2 - 4x - 20} \cdot \frac{x^2y + y}{2x^2 + 11x + 5} \cdot \frac{6x^2 - 17x - 10}{xy^2}$$

$$= \frac{x(x+5)}{(3x-10)(x+2)} \cdot \frac{y(x^2+1)}{(2x+1)(x+5)} \cdot \frac{(2x+1)(3x-10)}{xy^2}$$

$$= \frac{x(x+5)(y)(x^2+1)(2x+1)(3x-10)}{(3x-10)(x+2)(2x+1)(x+5)(x)(y^2)} = \frac{x^2+1}{y(x+2)}$$

Concept Quiz 4.2

For Problems 1–10, answer true or false.

1. To multiply two rational numbers in fraction form, we need to change to equivalent fractions with a common denominator.

2. When multiplying rational expressions that contain polynomials, the polynomials are factored so that common factors can be divided out.

3. In the division problem $\dfrac{2x^2y}{3z} \div \dfrac{4x^3}{5y^2}$, the fraction $\dfrac{4x^3}{5y^2}$ is the divisor.

4. The numbers $-\dfrac{2}{3}$ and $\dfrac{3}{2}$ are multiplicative inverses.

5. To divide two numbers in fraction form, we invert the divisor and multiply.

6. If $x \neq 0$, then $\left(\dfrac{4xy}{x}\right)\left(\dfrac{3y}{2x}\right) = \dfrac{6y^2}{x}$.

7. $\dfrac{3}{4} \div \dfrac{4}{3} = 1$.

8. If $x \neq 0$ and $y \neq 0$, then $\dfrac{5x^2y}{2y} \div \dfrac{10x^2}{3y} = \dfrac{3}{4}$.

9. If $x \neq 0$ and $y \neq 0$, then $\dfrac{1}{x} \div \dfrac{1}{y} = xy$.

10. If $x \neq y$, then $\dfrac{1}{x-y} \div \dfrac{1}{y-x} = -1$.

Problem Set 4.2

For Problems 1–12, perform the indicated operations involving rational numbers. Express final answers in reduced form. **(Objectives 1 and 3)**

1. $\dfrac{7}{12} \cdot \dfrac{6}{35}$

2. $\dfrac{5}{8} \cdot \dfrac{12}{20}$

3. $\dfrac{-4}{9} \cdot \dfrac{18}{30}$

4. $\dfrac{-6}{9} \cdot \dfrac{36}{48}$

5. $\dfrac{3}{-8} \cdot \dfrac{-6}{12}$

6. $\dfrac{-12}{16} \cdot \dfrac{18}{-32}$

7. $\left(-\dfrac{5}{7}\right) \div \dfrac{6}{7}$

8. $\left(-\dfrac{5}{9}\right) \div \dfrac{10}{3}$

9. $\dfrac{-9}{5} \div \dfrac{27}{10}$

10. $\dfrac{4}{7} \div \dfrac{16}{-21}$

11. $\dfrac{4}{9} \cdot \dfrac{6}{11} \div \dfrac{4}{15}$

12. $\dfrac{2}{3} \cdot \dfrac{6}{7} \div \dfrac{8}{3}$

For Problems 13–50, perform the indicated operations involving rational expressions. Express final answers in simplest form. **(Objectives 2, 4, and 5)**

13. $\dfrac{6xy}{9y^4} \cdot \dfrac{30x^3y}{-48x}$

14. $\dfrac{-14xy^4}{18y^2} \cdot \dfrac{24x^2y^3}{35y^2}$

15. $\dfrac{5a^2b^2}{11ab} \cdot \dfrac{22a^3}{15ab^2}$

16. $\dfrac{10a^2}{5b^2} \cdot \dfrac{15b^3}{2a^4}$

17. $\dfrac{5xy}{8y^2} \cdot \dfrac{18x^2y}{15}$

18. $\dfrac{4x^2}{5y^2} \cdot \dfrac{15xy}{24x^2y^2}$

19. $\dfrac{5x^4}{12x^2y^3} \div \dfrac{9}{5xy}$

20. $\dfrac{7x^2y}{9xy^3} \div \dfrac{3x^4}{2x^2y^2}$

21. $\dfrac{9a^2c}{12bc^2} \div \dfrac{21ab}{14c^3}$

22. $\dfrac{3ab^3}{4c} \div \dfrac{21ac}{12bc^3}$

23. $\dfrac{9x^2y^3}{14x} \cdot \dfrac{21y}{15xy^2} \cdot \dfrac{10x}{12y^3}$

24. $\dfrac{5xy}{7a} \cdot \dfrac{14a^2}{15x} \cdot \dfrac{3a}{8y}$

25. $\dfrac{3x + 6}{5y} \cdot \dfrac{x^2 + 4}{x^2 + 10x + 16}$

26. $\dfrac{5xy}{x + 6} \cdot \dfrac{x^2 - 36}{x^2 - 6x}$

27. $\dfrac{5a^2 + 20a}{a^3 - 2a^2} \cdot \dfrac{a^2 - a - 12}{a^2 - 16}$

28. $\dfrac{2a^2 + 6}{a^2 - a} \cdot \dfrac{a^3 - a^2}{8a - 4}$

29. $\dfrac{3n^2 + 15n - 18}{3n^2 + 10n - 48} \cdot \dfrac{6n^2 - n - 40}{4n^2 + 6n - 10}$

30. $\dfrac{6n^2 + 11n - 10}{3n^2 + 19n - 14} \cdot \dfrac{2n^2 + 6n - 56}{2n^2 - 3n - 20}$

31. $\dfrac{9y^2}{x^2 + 12x + 36} \div \dfrac{12y}{x^2 + 6x}$

32. $\dfrac{7xy}{x^2 - 4x + 4} \div \dfrac{14y}{x^2 - 4}$

33. $\dfrac{x^2 - 4xy + 4y^2}{7xy^2} \div \dfrac{4x^2 - 3xy - 10y^2}{20x^2y + 25xy^2}$

34. $\dfrac{x^2 + 5xy - 6y^2}{xy^2 - y^3} \cdot \dfrac{2x^2 + 15xy + 18y^2}{xy + 4y^2}$

35. $\dfrac{5 - 14n - 3n^2}{1 - 2n - 3n^2} \cdot \dfrac{9 + 7n - 2n^2}{27 - 15n + 2n^2}$

36. $\dfrac{6 - n - 2n^2}{12 - 11n + 2n^2} \cdot \dfrac{24 - 26n + 5n^2}{2 + 3n + n^2}$

37. $\dfrac{3x^4 + 2x^2 - 1}{3x^4 + 14x^2 - 5} \cdot \dfrac{x^4 - 2x^2 - 35}{x^4 - 17x^2 + 70}$

38. $\dfrac{2x^4 + x^2 - 3}{2x^4 + 5x^2 + 2} \cdot \dfrac{3x^4 + 10x^2 + 8}{3x^4 + x^2 - 4}$

39. $\dfrac{3x^2 - 20x + 25}{2x^2 - 7x - 15} \div \dfrac{9x^2 - 3x - 20}{12x^2 + 28x + 15}$

40. $\dfrac{21t^2 + t - 2}{2t^2 - 17t - 9} \div \dfrac{12t^2 - 5t - 3}{8t^2 - 2t - 3}$

41. $\dfrac{10t^3 + 25t}{20t + 10} \cdot \dfrac{2t^2 - t - 1}{t^5 - t}$

42. $\dfrac{t^4 - 81}{t^2 - 6t + 9} \cdot \dfrac{6t^2 - 11t - 21}{5t^2 + 8t - 21}$

43. $\dfrac{4t^2 + t - 5}{t^3 - t^2} \cdot \dfrac{t^4 + 6t^3}{16t^2 + 40t + 25}$

44. $\dfrac{9n^2 - 12n + 4}{n^2 - 4n - 32} \cdot \dfrac{n^2 + 4n}{3n^3 - 2n^2}$

45. $\dfrac{nr + 3n + 2r + 6}{nr + 3n - 3r - 9} \cdot \dfrac{n^2 - 9}{n^3 - 4n}$

46. $\dfrac{xy + xc + ay + ac}{xy - 2xc + ay - 2ac} \cdot \dfrac{2x^3 - 8x}{12x^3 + 20x^2 - 8x}$

47. $\dfrac{x^2 - x}{4y} \cdot \dfrac{10xy^2}{2x - 2} \div \dfrac{3x^2 + 3x}{15x^2y^2}$

48. $\dfrac{4xy^2}{7x} \cdot \dfrac{14x^3y}{12y} \div \dfrac{7y}{9x^3}$

49. $\dfrac{a^2 - 4ab + 4b^2}{6a^2 - 4ab} \cdot \dfrac{3a^2 + 5ab - 2b^2}{6a^2 + ab - b^2} \div \dfrac{a^2 - 4b^2}{8a + 4b}$

50. $\dfrac{2x^2 + 3x}{2x^3 - 10x^2} \cdot \dfrac{x^2 - 8x + 15}{3x^3 - 27x} \div \dfrac{14x + 21}{x^2 - 6x - 27}$

Thoughts Into Words

51. Explain in your own words how to divide two rational expressions.

52. Suppose that your friend missed class the day the material in this section was discussed. How could you draw on her background in arithmetic to explain to her how to multiply and divide rational expressions?

53. Give a step-by-step description of how to do the following multiplication problem.

$$\dfrac{x^2 + 5x + 6}{x^2 - 2x - 8} \cdot \dfrac{x^2 - 16}{16 - x^2}$$

4.3 Adding and Subtracting Rational Expressions

OBJECTIVES
1. Add and subtract rational numbers
2. Add and subtract rational expressions

We can define addition and subtraction of rational numbers as follows:

Definition 4.3 Addition and Subtraction of Fractions

If a, b, and c are integers, and b is not zero, then

$$\frac{a}{b} + \frac{c}{b} = \frac{a + c}{b} \quad \text{Addition}$$

$$\frac{a}{b} - \frac{c}{b} = \frac{a - c}{b} \quad \text{Subtraction}$$

We can add or subtract rational numbers with a common denominator by adding or subtracting the numerators and placing the result over the common denominator. The following examples illustrate Definition 4.3.

$$\frac{2}{9} + \frac{3}{9} = \frac{2 + 3}{9} = \frac{5}{9}$$

$$\frac{7}{8} - \frac{3}{8} = \frac{7 - 3}{8} = \frac{4}{8} = \frac{1}{2} \qquad \text{Don't forget to reduce!}$$

$$\frac{4}{6} + \frac{-5}{6} = \frac{4 + (-5)}{6} = \frac{-1}{6} = -\frac{1}{6}$$

$$\frac{7}{10} + \frac{4}{-10} = \frac{7}{10} + \frac{-4}{10} = \frac{7 + (-4)}{10} = \frac{3}{10}$$

We use this same *common denominator* approach when adding or subtracting rational expressions, as in these next examples.

$$\frac{3}{x} + \frac{9}{x} = \frac{3 + 9}{x} = \frac{12}{x}$$

$$\frac{8}{x - 2} - \frac{3}{x - 2} = \frac{8 - 3}{x - 2} = \frac{5}{x - 2}$$

$$\frac{9}{4y} + \frac{5}{4y} = \frac{9 + 5}{4y} = \frac{14}{4y} = \frac{7}{2y} \qquad \text{Don't forget to simplify the final answer!}$$

$$\frac{n^2}{n - 1} - \frac{1}{n - 1} = \frac{n^2 - 1}{n - 1} = \frac{(n + 1)(n - 1)}{n - 1} = n + 1$$

$$\frac{6a^2}{2a + 1} + \frac{13a + 5}{2a + 1} = \frac{6a^2 + 13a + 5}{2a + 1} = \frac{(2a + 1)(3a + 5)}{2a + 1} = 3a + 5$$

In each of the previous examples that involve rational expressions, we should technically restrict the variables to exclude division by zero. For example, $\frac{3}{x} + \frac{9}{x} = \frac{12}{x}$ is true for all real number values for x, except $x = 0$. Likewise, $\frac{8}{x - 2} - \frac{3}{x - 2} = \frac{5}{x - 2}$ as long as x does not equal 2. Rather than taking the time and space to write down restrictions for each problem, we will merely assume that such restrictions exist.

If rational numbers that do not have a common denominator are to be added or subtracted, then we apply the fundamental principle of fractions $\left(\dfrac{a}{b} = \dfrac{ak}{bk}\right)$ to obtain equivalent fractions with a common denominator. Equivalent fractions are fractions such as $\dfrac{1}{2}$ and $\dfrac{2}{4}$ that name the same number. Consider the following example.

$$\frac{1}{2} + \frac{1}{3} = \frac{3}{6} + \frac{2}{6} = \frac{3 + 2}{6} = \frac{5}{6}$$

$$\left(\begin{array}{c} \frac{1}{2} \text{ and } \frac{3}{6} \\ \text{are equivalent} \\ \text{fractions.} \end{array}\right) \quad \left(\begin{array}{c} \frac{1}{3} \text{ and } \frac{2}{6} \\ \text{are equivalent} \\ \text{fractions.} \end{array}\right)$$

Note that we chose 6 as our common denominator, and 6 is the *least common multiple* of the original denominators 2 and 3. The least common multiple of a set of whole numbers is the smallest nonzero whole number divisible by each of the numbers. In general, we use the least common multiple of the denominators of the fractions to be added or subtracted as a *least common denominator* (LCD).

A least common denominator may be found by inspection or by using the prime-factored forms of the numbers. Let's consider some examples and use each of these techniques.

Classroom Example
Subtract $\dfrac{7}{9} - \dfrac{1}{6}$.

EXAMPLE 1 Subtract $\dfrac{5}{6} - \dfrac{3}{8}$.

Solution

By inspection, we can see that the LCD is 24. Thus both fractions can be changed to equivalent fractions, each with a denominator of 24.

$$\frac{5}{6} - \frac{3}{8} = \left(\frac{5}{6}\right)\left(\frac{4}{4}\right) - \left(\frac{3}{8}\right)\left(\frac{3}{3}\right) = \frac{20}{24} - \frac{9}{24} = \frac{11}{24}$$

$$\uparrow \qquad \uparrow$$
$$\text{Form of 1} \quad \text{Form of 1}$$

In Example 1, note that the fundamental principle of fractions, $\dfrac{a}{b} = \dfrac{a \cdot k}{b \cdot k}$, can be written as $\dfrac{a}{b} = \left(\dfrac{a}{b}\right)\left(\dfrac{k}{k}\right)$. This latter form emphasizes the fact that 1 is the multiplication identity element.

Classroom Example
Perform the indicated operations:
$\dfrac{1}{4} + \dfrac{3}{7} - \dfrac{5}{28}$

EXAMPLE 2 Perform the indicated operations: $\dfrac{3}{5} + \dfrac{1}{6} - \dfrac{13}{15}$.

Solution

Again by inspection, we can determine that the LCD is 30. Thus we can proceed as follows:

$$\frac{3}{5} + \frac{1}{6} - \frac{13}{15} = \left(\frac{3}{5}\right)\left(\frac{6}{6}\right) + \left(\frac{1}{6}\right)\left(\frac{5}{5}\right) - \left(\frac{13}{15}\right)\left(\frac{2}{2}\right)$$

$$= \frac{18}{30} + \frac{5}{30} - \frac{26}{30} = \frac{18 + 5 - 26}{30}$$

$$= \frac{-3}{30} = -\frac{1}{10} \qquad\qquad \text{Don't forget to reduce!}$$

Classroom Example
Add $\dfrac{4}{9} + \dfrac{7}{15}$.

EXAMPLE 3   Add $\dfrac{7}{18} + \dfrac{11}{24}$.

Solution

Let's use the prime-factored forms of the denominators to help find the LCD.

$$18 = 2 \cdot 3 \cdot 3 \qquad 24 = 2 \cdot 2 \cdot 2 \cdot 3$$

The LCD must contain three factors of 2 because 24 contains three 2s. The LCD must also contain two factors of 3 because 18 has two 3s. Thus the LCD $= 2 \cdot 2 \cdot 2 \cdot 3 \cdot 3 = 72$. Now we can proceed as usual.

$$\frac{7}{18} + \frac{11}{24} = \left(\frac{7}{18}\right)\left(\frac{4}{4}\right) + \left(\frac{11}{24}\right)\left(\frac{3}{3}\right) = \frac{28}{72} + \frac{33}{72} = \frac{61}{72}$$

To add and subtract rational expressions with different denominators, follow the same basic routine that you follow when you add or subtract rational numbers with different denominators. Study the following examples carefully and note the similarity to our previous work with rational numbers.

Classroom Example
Add $\dfrac{2x + 3}{5} + \dfrac{x + 4}{2}$.

EXAMPLE 4   Add $\dfrac{x + 2}{4} + \dfrac{3x + 1}{3}$.

Solution

By inspection, we see that the LCD is 12.

$$\frac{x + 2}{4} + \frac{3x + 1}{3} = \left(\frac{x + 2}{4}\right)\left(\frac{3}{3}\right) + \left(\frac{3x + 1}{3}\right)\left(\frac{4}{4}\right)$$

$$= \frac{3(x + 2)}{12} + \frac{4(3x + 1)}{12}$$

$$= \frac{3(x + 2) + 4(3x + 1)}{12}$$

$$= \frac{3x + 6 + 12x + 4}{12}$$

$$= \frac{15x + 10}{12}$$

Note the final result in Example 4. The numerator, $15x + 10$, could be factored as $5(3x + 2)$. However, because this produces no common factors with the denominator, the fraction cannot be simplified. Thus the final answer can be left as $\dfrac{15x + 10}{12}$. It would also be acceptable to express it as $\dfrac{5(3x + 2)}{12}$.

Classroom Example
Subtract $\dfrac{x - 3}{3} - \dfrac{x + 12}{12}$.

EXAMPLE 5   Subtract $\dfrac{a - 2}{2} - \dfrac{a - 6}{6}$.

Solution

By inspection, we see that the LCD is 6.

$$\frac{a - 2}{2} - \frac{a - 6}{6} = \left(\frac{a - 2}{2}\right)\left(\frac{3}{3}\right) - \frac{a - 6}{6}$$

$$= \frac{3(a - 2)}{6} - \frac{a - 6}{6}$$

$$= \frac{3(a-2) - (a-6)}{6}$$ Be careful with this sign as you move to the next step!

$$= \frac{3a - 6 - a + 6}{6}$$

$$= \frac{2a}{6} = \frac{a}{3}$$ Don't forget to simplify

Classroom Example
Perform the indicated operations:
$\frac{x+2}{12} - \frac{x-4}{6} + \frac{3x-5}{20}$

EXAMPLE 6   Perform the indicated operations: $\frac{x+3}{10} + \frac{2x+1}{15} - \frac{x-2}{18}$.

Solution

If you cannot determine the LCD by inspection, then use the prime-factored forms of the denominators.

$$10 = 2 \cdot 5 \qquad 15 = 3 \cdot 5 \qquad 18 = 2 \cdot 3 \cdot 3$$

The LCD must contain one factor of 2, two factors of 3, and one factor of 5. Thus the LCD is $2 \cdot 3 \cdot 3 \cdot 5 = 90$.

$$\frac{x+3}{10} + \frac{2x+1}{15} - \frac{x-2}{18} = \left(\frac{x+3}{10}\right)\left(\frac{9}{9}\right) + \left(\frac{2x+1}{15}\right)\left(\frac{6}{6}\right) - \left(\frac{x-2}{18}\right)\left(\frac{5}{5}\right)$$

$$= \frac{9(x+3)}{90} + \frac{6(2x+1)}{90} - \frac{5(x-2)}{90}$$

$$= \frac{9(x+3) + 6(2x+1) - 5(x-2)}{90}$$

$$= \frac{9x + 27 + 12x + 6 - 5x + 10}{90}$$

$$= \frac{16x + 43}{90}$$

A denominator that contains variables does not create any serious difficulties; our approach remains basically the same.

Classroom Example
Add $\frac{4}{3a} + \frac{2}{7b}$.

EXAMPLE 7   Add $\frac{3}{2x} + \frac{5}{3y}$.

Solution

Using an LCD of $6xy$, we can proceed as follows:

$$\frac{3}{2x} + \frac{5}{3y} = \left(\frac{3}{2x}\right)\left(\frac{3y}{3y}\right) + \left(\frac{5}{3y}\right)\left(\frac{2x}{2x}\right)$$

$$= \frac{9y}{6xy} + \frac{10x}{6xy}$$

$$= \frac{9y + 10x}{6xy}$$

Classroom Example
Subtract $\frac{3}{14x^2} - \frac{5}{21xy}$.

EXAMPLE 8   Subtract $\frac{7}{12ab} - \frac{11}{15a^2}$.

Solution

We can prime factor the numerical coefficients of the denominators to help find the LCD.

$$12ab = 2 \cdot 2 \cdot 3 \cdot a \cdot b \atop 15a^2 = 3 \cdot 5 \cdot a^2 \bigg\} \longrightarrow \text{LCD} = 2 \cdot 2 \cdot 3 \cdot 5 \cdot a^2 \cdot b = 60a^2b$$

$$\frac{7}{12ab} - \frac{11}{15a^2} = \left(\frac{7}{12ab}\right)\left(\frac{5a}{5a}\right) - \left(\frac{11}{15a^2}\right)\left(\frac{4b}{4b}\right)$$

$$= \frac{35a}{60a^2b} - \frac{44b}{60a^2b}$$

$$= \frac{35a - 44b}{60a^2b}$$

Classroom Example

Add $\dfrac{x}{x-4} + \dfrac{2}{x}$.

EXAMPLE 9   Add $\dfrac{x}{x-3} + \dfrac{4}{x}$.

Solution

By inspection, the LCD is $x(x - 3)$.

$$\frac{x}{x-3} + \frac{4}{x} = \left(\frac{x}{x-3}\right)\left(\frac{x}{x}\right) + \left(\frac{4}{x}\right)\left(\frac{x-3}{x-3}\right)$$

$$= \frac{x^2}{x(x-3)} + \frac{4(x-3)}{x(x-3)}$$

$$= \frac{x^2 + 4(x-3)}{x(x-3)}$$

$$= \frac{x^2 + 4x - 12}{x(x-3)} \quad \text{or} \quad \frac{(x+6)(x-2)}{x(x-3)}$$

Classroom Example

Subtract $\dfrac{4x}{x+3} - 5$.

EXAMPLE 10   Subtract $\dfrac{2x}{x+1} - 3$.

Solution

$$\frac{2x}{x+1} - 3 = \frac{2x}{x+1} - 3\left(\frac{x+1}{x+1}\right)$$

$$= \frac{2x}{x+1} - \frac{3(x+1)}{x+1}$$

$$= \frac{2x - 3(x+1)}{x+1}$$

$$= \frac{2x - 3x - 3}{x+1}$$

$$= \frac{-x - 3}{x+1}$$

Concept Quiz 4.3

For Problems 1–10, answer true or false.

1. The addition problem $\dfrac{2x}{x+4} + \dfrac{1}{x+4}$ is equal to $\dfrac{2x+1}{x+4}$ for all values of x except $x = -\dfrac{1}{2}$ and $x = -4$.

2. Any common denominator can be used to add rational expressions, but typically we use the least common denominator.

3. The fractions $\dfrac{2x^2}{3y}$ and $\dfrac{10x^2z}{15yz}$ are equivalent fractions.

4. The least common multiple of the denominators is always the lowest common denominator.

5. To simplify the expression $\dfrac{5}{2x-1} + \dfrac{3}{1-2x}$, we could use $2x-1$ for the common denominator.

6. If $x \neq \dfrac{1}{2}$, then $\dfrac{5}{2x-1} + \dfrac{3}{1-2x} = \dfrac{2}{2x-1}$.

7. $\dfrac{3}{-4} - \dfrac{-2}{3} = \dfrac{17}{12}$

8. $\dfrac{4x-1}{5} + \dfrac{2x+1}{6} = \dfrac{x}{5}$

9. $\dfrac{x}{4} - \dfrac{3x}{2} + \dfrac{5x}{3} = \dfrac{5x}{12}$

10. If $x \neq 0$, then $\dfrac{2}{3x} - \dfrac{3}{2x} - 1 = \dfrac{-5-6x}{6x}$.

Problem Set 4.3

For Problems 1–12, perform the indicated operations involving rational numbers. Be sure to express your answers in reduced form. **(Objective 1)**

1. $\dfrac{1}{4} + \dfrac{5}{6}$

2. $\dfrac{3}{5} + \dfrac{1}{6}$

3. $\dfrac{7}{8} - \dfrac{3}{5}$

4. $\dfrac{7}{9} - \dfrac{1}{6}$

5. $\dfrac{6}{5} + \dfrac{1}{-4}$

6. $\dfrac{7}{8} + \dfrac{5}{-12}$

7. $\dfrac{8}{15} + \dfrac{3}{25}$

8. $\dfrac{5}{9} - \dfrac{11}{12}$

9. $\dfrac{1}{5} + \dfrac{5}{6} - \dfrac{7}{15}$

10. $\dfrac{2}{3} - \dfrac{7}{8} + \dfrac{1}{4}$

11. $\dfrac{1}{3} - \dfrac{1}{4} - \dfrac{3}{14}$

12. $\dfrac{5}{6} - \dfrac{7}{9} - \dfrac{3}{10}$

For Problems 13–66, add or subtract the rational expressions as indicated. Be sure to express your answers in simplest form. **(Objective 2)**

13. $\dfrac{2x}{x-1} + \dfrac{4}{x-1}$

14. $\dfrac{3x}{2x+1} - \dfrac{5}{2x+1}$

15. $\dfrac{4a}{a+2} + \dfrac{8}{a+2}$

16. $\dfrac{6a}{a-3} - \dfrac{18}{a-3}$

17. $\dfrac{3(y-2)}{7y} + \dfrac{4(y-1)}{7y}$

18. $\dfrac{2x-1}{4x^2} + \dfrac{3(x-2)}{4x^2}$

19. $\dfrac{x-1}{2} + \dfrac{x+3}{3}$

20. $\dfrac{x-2}{4} + \dfrac{x+6}{5}$

21. $\dfrac{2a-1}{4} + \dfrac{3a+2}{6}$

22. $\dfrac{a-4}{6} + \dfrac{4a-1}{8}$

23. $\dfrac{n+2}{6} - \dfrac{n-4}{9}$

24. $\dfrac{2n+1}{9} - \dfrac{n+3}{12}$

25. $\dfrac{3x-1}{3} - \dfrac{5x+2}{5}$

26. $\dfrac{4x-3}{6} - \dfrac{8x-2}{12}$

27. $\dfrac{x-2}{5} - \dfrac{x+3}{6} + \dfrac{x+1}{15}$

28. $\dfrac{x+1}{4} + \dfrac{x-3}{6} - \dfrac{x-2}{8}$

29. $\dfrac{3}{8x} + \dfrac{7}{10x}$

30. $\dfrac{5}{6x} - \dfrac{3}{10x}$

31. $\dfrac{5}{7x} - \dfrac{11}{4y}$

32. $\dfrac{5}{12x} - \dfrac{9}{8y}$

33. $\dfrac{4}{3x} + \dfrac{5}{4y} - 1$

34. $\dfrac{7}{3x} - \dfrac{8}{7y} - 2$

35. $\dfrac{7}{10x^2} + \dfrac{11}{15x}$

36. $\dfrac{7}{12a^2} - \dfrac{5}{16a}$

37. $\dfrac{10}{7n} - \dfrac{12}{4n^2}$

38. $\dfrac{6}{8n^2} - \dfrac{3}{5n}$

39. $\dfrac{3}{n^2} - \dfrac{2}{5n} + \dfrac{4}{3}$

40. $\dfrac{1}{n^2} + \dfrac{3}{4n} - \dfrac{5}{6}$

41. $\dfrac{3}{x} - \dfrac{5}{3x^2} - \dfrac{7}{6x}$

42. $\dfrac{7}{3x^2} - \dfrac{9}{4x} - \dfrac{5}{2x}$

43. $\dfrac{6}{5t^2} - \dfrac{4}{7t^3} + \dfrac{9}{5t^3}$

44. $\dfrac{5}{7t} + \dfrac{3}{4t^2} + \dfrac{1}{14t}$

45. $\dfrac{5b}{24a^2} - \dfrac{11a}{32b}$

46. $\dfrac{9}{14x^2y} - \dfrac{4x}{7y^2}$

47. $\dfrac{7}{9xy^3} - \dfrac{4}{3x} + \dfrac{5}{2y^2}$

48. $\dfrac{7}{16a^2b} + \dfrac{3a}{20b^2}$

49. $\dfrac{2x}{x-1} + \dfrac{3}{x}$

50. $\dfrac{3x}{x-4} - \dfrac{2}{x}$

51. $\dfrac{a-2}{a} - \dfrac{3}{a+4}$

52. $\dfrac{a+1}{a} - \dfrac{2}{a+1}$

53. $\dfrac{-3}{4n+5} - \dfrac{8}{3n+5}$

54. $\dfrac{-2}{n-6} - \dfrac{6}{2n+3}$

55. $\dfrac{-1}{x+4} + \dfrac{4}{7x-1}$

56. $\dfrac{-3}{4x+3} + \dfrac{5}{2x-5}$

57. $\dfrac{7}{3x-5} - \dfrac{5}{2x+7}$

58. $\dfrac{5}{x-1} - \dfrac{3}{2x-3}$

59. $\dfrac{5}{3x-2} + \dfrac{6}{4x+5}$

60. $\dfrac{3}{2x+1} + \dfrac{2}{3x+4}$

61. $\dfrac{3x}{2x+5} + 1$

62. $2 + \dfrac{4x}{3x-1}$

63. $\dfrac{4x}{x-5} - 3$

64. $\dfrac{7x}{x+4} - 2$

65. $-1 - \dfrac{3}{2x+1}$

66. $-2 - \dfrac{5}{4x-3}$

67. Recall that the indicated quotient of a polynomial and its opposite is -1. For example, $\dfrac{x-2}{2-x}$ simplifies to -1. Keep this idea in mind as you add or subtract the following rational expressions.

(a) $\dfrac{1}{x-1} - \dfrac{x}{x-1}$ (b) $\dfrac{3}{2x-3} - \dfrac{2x}{2x-3}$

(c) $\dfrac{4}{x-4} - \dfrac{x}{x-4} + 1$ (d) $-1 + \dfrac{2}{x-2} - \dfrac{x}{x-2}$

68. Consider the addition problem $\dfrac{8}{x-2} + \dfrac{5}{2-x}$. Note that the denominators are opposites of each other. If the property $\dfrac{a}{-b} = -\dfrac{a}{b}$ is applied to the second fraction, we have $\dfrac{5}{2-x} = -\dfrac{5}{x-2}$. Thus we proceed as follows:

$$\dfrac{8}{x-2} + \dfrac{5}{2-x} = \dfrac{8}{x-2} - \dfrac{5}{x-2} = \dfrac{8-5}{x-2} = \dfrac{3}{x-2}$$

Use this approach to do the following problems.

(a) $\dfrac{7}{x-1} + \dfrac{2}{1-x}$ (b) $\dfrac{5}{2x-1} + \dfrac{8}{1-2x}$

(c) $\dfrac{4}{a-3} - \dfrac{1}{3-a}$ (d) $\dfrac{10}{a-9} - \dfrac{5}{9-a}$

(e) $\dfrac{x^2}{x-1} - \dfrac{2x-3}{1-x}$ (f) $\dfrac{x^2}{x-4} - \dfrac{3x-28}{4-x}$

Thoughts Into Words

69. What is the difference between the concept of least common multiple and the concept of least common denominator?

70. A classmate tells you that she finds the least common multiple of two counting numbers by listing the multiples of each number and then choosing the smallest number that appears in both lists. Is this a correct procedure? What is the weakness of this procedure?

71. For which real numbers does $\dfrac{x}{x-3} + \dfrac{4}{x}$ equal $\dfrac{(x+6)(x-2)}{x(x-3)}$? Explain your answer.

72. Suppose that your friend does an addition problem as follows:

$$\dfrac{5}{8} + \dfrac{7}{12} = \dfrac{5(12) + 8(7)}{8(12)} = \dfrac{60+56}{96} = \dfrac{116}{96} = \dfrac{29}{24}$$

Is this answer correct? If not, what advice would you offer your friend?

4.4   More on Rational Expressions and Complex Fractions

OBJECTIVES   **1** Add and subtract rational expressions

2 Simplify complex fractions

In this section, we expand our work with adding and subtracting rational expressions, and we discuss the process of simplifying complex fractions. Before we begin, however, this seems like an appropriate time to offer a bit of advice regarding your study of algebra. Success in algebra depends on having a good understanding of the concepts and being able to perform the various computations. As for the computational work, you should adopt a carefully organized format that shows as many steps as you need in order to minimize the chances of making careless errors. Don't be eager to find shortcuts for certain computations before you have a thorough understanding of the steps involved in the process. This advice is especially appropriate at the beginning of this section.

Study Examples 1–4 very carefully. Note that the same basic procedure is followed in solving each problem:

Step 1   Factor the denominators.

Step 2   Find the LCD.

Step 3   Change each fraction to an equivalent fraction that has the LCD as its denominator.

Step 4   Combine the numerators and place over the LCD.

Step 5   Simplify by performing the addition or subtraction.

Step 6   Look for ways to reduce the resulting fraction.

Classroom Example
Add $\dfrac{8}{a^2 - 2a} + \dfrac{4}{a}$.

EXAMPLE 1   Add $\dfrac{8}{x^2 - 4x} + \dfrac{2}{x}$.

Solution

$$\frac{8}{x^2 - 4x} + \frac{2}{x} = \frac{8}{x(x - 4)} + \frac{2}{x}$$ Factor the denominators

The LCD is $x(x - 4)$.   Find the LCD

$$= \frac{8}{x(x - 4)} + \left(\frac{2}{x}\right)\left(\frac{x - 4}{x - 4}\right)$$ Change each fraction to an equivalent fraction that has the LCD as its denominator

$$= \frac{8 + 2(x - 4)}{x(x - 4)}$$ Combine the numerators and place over the LCD

$$= \frac{8 + 2x - 8}{x(x - 4)}$$ Simplify by performing the addition or subtraction

$$= \frac{2x}{x(x - 4)}$$

$$= \frac{2}{x - 4}$$ Reduce

Classroom Example
Subtract $\dfrac{x}{x^2 - 9} - \dfrac{7}{x + 3}$.

EXAMPLE 2   Subtract $\dfrac{a}{a^2 - 4} - \dfrac{3}{a + 2}$.

Solution

$$\frac{a}{a^2 - 4} - \frac{3}{a + 2} = \frac{a}{(a + 2)(a - 2)} - \frac{3}{a + 2}$$ Factor the denominators

The LCD is $(a + 2)(a - 2)$.   Find the LCD

$$= \frac{a}{(a + 2)(a - 2)} - \left(\frac{3}{a + 2}\right)\left(\frac{a - 2}{a - 2}\right)$$ Change each fraction to an equivalent fraction that has the LCD as its denominator

$$= \frac{a - 3(a - 2)}{(a + 2)(a - 2)}$$ Combine numerators and place over the LCD

$$= \frac{a - 3a + 6}{(a + 2)(a - 2)}$$ Simplify by performing the addition or subtraction

$$= \frac{-2a + 6}{(a + 2)(a - 2)} \quad \text{or} \quad \frac{-2(a - 3)}{(a + 2)(a - 2)}$$ ▪

Classroom Example
Add:

$$\frac{2x}{x^2 + 5x + 6} + \frac{5}{x^2 - 5x - 14}$$

EXAMPLE 3   Add $\dfrac{3n}{n^2 + 6n + 5} + \dfrac{4}{n^2 - 7n - 8}$.

Solution

$$\frac{3n}{n^2 + 6n + 5} + \frac{4}{n^2 - 7n - 8}$$

$$= \frac{3n}{(n + 5)(n + 1)} + \frac{4}{(n - 8)(n + 1)}$$ Factor the denominators

The LCD is $(n + 5)(n + 1)(n - 8)$.   Find the LCD

$$= \left(\frac{3n}{(n + 5)(n + 1)}\right)\left(\frac{n - 8}{n - 8}\right)$$

$$+ \left(\frac{4}{(n - 8)(n + 1)}\right)\left(\frac{n + 5}{n + 5}\right)$$ Change each fraction to an equivalent fraction that has the LCD as its denominator

$$= \frac{3n(n - 8) + 4(n + 5)}{(n + 5)(n + 1)(n - 8)}$$ Combine numerators and place over the LCD

$$= \frac{3n^2 - 24n + 4n + 20}{(n + 5)(n + 1)(n - 8)}$$ Simplify by performing the addition or subtraction

$$= \frac{3n^2 - 20n + 20}{(n + 5)(n + 1)(n - 8)}$$ ▪

Classroom Example
Perform the indicated operations:

$$\frac{4x^2}{x^4 - 16} + \frac{x}{x^2 - 4} - \frac{1}{x - 2}$$

EXAMPLE 4   Perform the indicated operations:

$$\frac{2x^2}{x^4 - 1} + \frac{x}{x^2 - 1} - \frac{1}{x - 1}$$

Solution

$$\frac{2x^2}{x^4 - 1} + \frac{x}{x^2 - 1} - \frac{1}{x - 1}$$

$$= \frac{2x^2}{(x^2 + 1)(x + 1)(x - 1)} + \frac{x}{(x + 1)(x - 1)} - \frac{1}{x - 1}$$ Factor the denominators

The LCD is $(x^2 + 1)(x + 1)(x - 1)$.   Find the LCD

$$= \frac{2x^2}{(x^2 + 1)(x + 1)(x - 1)}$$ Change each fraction to an equivalent fraction that has the LCD as its denominator

$$+ \left(\frac{x}{(x + 1)(x - 1)}\right)\left(\frac{x^2 + 1}{x^2 + 1}\right)$$

$$- \left(\frac{1}{x - 1}\right)\frac{(x^2 + 1)(x + 1)}{(x^2 + 1)(x + 1)}$$

$$= \frac{2x^2 + x(x^2 + 1) - (x^2 + 1)(x + 1)}{(x^2 + 1)(x + 1)(x - 1)}$$ Combine numerators and place over the LCD

$$= \frac{2x^2 + x^3 + x - x^3 - x^2 - x - 1}{(x^2 + 1)(x + 1)(x - 1)}$$ Simplify by performing the addition or subtraction

$$= \frac{x^2 - 1}{(x^2 + 1)(x + 1)(x - 1)}$$

$$= \frac{(x + 1)(x - 1)}{(x^2 + 1)(x + 1)(x - 1)}$$

$$= \frac{1}{x^2 + 1}$$ Reduce

Simplifying Complex Fractions

Complex fractions are fractional forms that contain rational numbers or rational expressions in the numerators and/or denominators. The following are examples of complex fractions.

$$\frac{\dfrac{4}{x}}{\dfrac{2}{xy}} \qquad \frac{\dfrac{1}{2} + \dfrac{3}{4}}{\dfrac{5}{6} - \dfrac{3}{8}} \qquad \frac{\dfrac{3}{x} + \dfrac{2}{y}}{\dfrac{5}{x} - \dfrac{6}{y^2}} \qquad \frac{\dfrac{1}{x} + \dfrac{1}{y}}{2} \qquad \frac{-3}{\dfrac{2}{x} - \dfrac{3}{y}}$$

It is often necessary to **simplify** a complex fraction. We will take each of these five examples and examine some techniques for simplifying complex fractions.

Classroom Example

Simplify $\dfrac{\dfrac{6}{m}}{\dfrac{3}{m^2n}}$.

EXAMPLE 5   Simplify $\dfrac{\dfrac{4}{x}}{\dfrac{2}{xy}}$.

Solution

This type of problem is a simple division problem.

$$\frac{\dfrac{4}{x}}{\dfrac{2}{xy}} = \frac{4}{x} \div \frac{2}{xy}$$

$$= \frac{\overset{2}{\cancel{4}}}{\cancel{x}} \cdot \frac{xy}{2} = 2y$$

Classroom Example

Simplify $\dfrac{\dfrac{3}{4} - \dfrac{1}{3}}{\dfrac{5}{6} + \dfrac{2}{9}}$.

EXAMPLE 6   Simplify $\dfrac{\dfrac{1}{2} + \dfrac{3}{4}}{\dfrac{5}{6} - \dfrac{3}{8}}$.

Let's look at two possible ways to simplify such a problem.

Solution A

Here we will simplify the numerator by performing the addition and simplify the denominator by performing the subtraction. Then the problem is a simple division problem as in Example 5.

$$\frac{\dfrac{1}{2}+\dfrac{3}{4}}{\dfrac{5}{6}-\dfrac{3}{8}}=\frac{\dfrac{2}{4}+\dfrac{3}{4}}{\dfrac{20}{24}-\dfrac{9}{24}}$$

$$=\frac{\dfrac{5}{4}}{\dfrac{11}{24}}=\frac{5}{\cancel{4}}\cdot\frac{\overset{6}{\cancel{24}}}{11}$$

$$=\frac{30}{11}$$

Solution B

Here we find the LCD of all four denominators (2, 4, 6, and 8). The LCD is 24. Use this LCD to multiply the entire complex fraction by a form of 1, specifically $\dfrac{24}{24}$.

$$\frac{\dfrac{1}{2}+\dfrac{3}{4}}{\dfrac{5}{6}-\dfrac{3}{8}}=\left(\frac{24}{24}\right)\left(\frac{\dfrac{1}{2}+\dfrac{3}{4}}{\dfrac{5}{6}-\dfrac{3}{8}}\right)$$

$$=\frac{24\left(\dfrac{1}{2}+\dfrac{3}{4}\right)}{24\left(\dfrac{5}{6}-\dfrac{3}{8}\right)}$$

$$=\frac{24\left(\dfrac{1}{2}\right)+24\left(\dfrac{3}{4}\right)}{24\left(\dfrac{5}{6}\right)-24\left(\dfrac{3}{8}\right)}$$

$$=\frac{12+18}{20-9}=\frac{30}{11}$$

Classroom Example

Simplify $\dfrac{\dfrac{1}{x}+\dfrac{3}{y}}{\dfrac{4}{x}-\dfrac{2}{y^2}}$.

EXAMPLE 7   Simplify $\dfrac{\dfrac{3}{x}+\dfrac{2}{y}}{\dfrac{5}{x}-\dfrac{6}{y^2}}$.

Solution A

Simplify the numerator and the denominator. Then the problem becomes a division problem.

$$\frac{\dfrac{3}{x}+\dfrac{2}{y}}{\dfrac{5}{x}-\dfrac{6}{y^2}}=\frac{\left(\dfrac{3}{x}\right)\left(\dfrac{y}{y}\right)+\left(\dfrac{2}{y}\right)\left(\dfrac{x}{x}\right)}{\left(\dfrac{5}{x}\right)\left(\dfrac{y^2}{y^2}\right)-\left(\dfrac{6}{y^2}\right)\left(\dfrac{x}{x}\right)}$$

$$=\frac{\dfrac{3y}{xy}+\dfrac{2x}{xy}}{\dfrac{5y^2}{xy^2}-\dfrac{6x}{xy^2}}$$

$$=\frac{\dfrac{3y+2x}{xy}}{\dfrac{5y^2-6x}{xy^2}}$$

$$= \frac{3y + 2x}{xy} \div \frac{5y^2 - 6x}{xy^2}$$

$$= \frac{3y + 2x}{\cancel{xy}} \cdot \frac{\overset{y}{\cancel{xy^2}}}{5y^2 - 6x}$$

$$= \frac{y(3y + 2x)}{5y^2 - 6x}$$

Solution B

Here we find the LCD of all four denominators (x, y, x, and y^2). The LCD is xy^2. Use this LCD to multiply the entire complex fraction by a form of 1, specifically $\dfrac{xy^2}{xy^2}$.

$$\frac{\dfrac{3}{x} + \dfrac{2}{y}}{\dfrac{5}{x} - \dfrac{6}{y^2}} = \left(\frac{xy^2}{xy^2}\right)\left(\frac{\dfrac{3}{x} + \dfrac{2}{y}}{\dfrac{5}{x} - \dfrac{6}{y^2}}\right)$$

$$= \frac{xy^2\left(\dfrac{3}{x} + \dfrac{2}{y}\right)}{xy^2\left(\dfrac{5}{x} - \dfrac{6}{y^2}\right)}$$

$$= \frac{xy^2\left(\dfrac{3}{x}\right) + xy^2\left(\dfrac{2}{y}\right)}{xy^2\left(\dfrac{5}{x}\right) - xy^2\left(\dfrac{6}{y^2}\right)}$$

$$= \frac{3y^2 + 2xy}{5y^2 - 6x} \qquad \text{or} \qquad \frac{y(3y + 2x)}{5y^2 - 6x}$$

Certainly either approach (Solution A or Solution B) will work with problems such as Examples 6 and 7. Examine Solution B in both examples carefully. This approach works effectively with complex fractions where the LCD of all the denominators is easy to find. (Don't be misled by the length of Solution B for Example 6; we were especially careful to show every step.)

Classroom Example

Simplify $\dfrac{\dfrac{1}{m} - \dfrac{1}{n}}{3}$.

EXAMPLE 8

Simplify $\dfrac{\dfrac{1}{x} + \dfrac{1}{y}}{2}$.

Solution

The number 2 can be written as $\dfrac{2}{1}$; thus the LCD of all three denominators (x, y, and 1) is xy. Therefore, let's multiply the entire complex fraction by a form of 1, specifically $\dfrac{xy}{xy}$.

$$\left(\frac{\dfrac{1}{x} + \dfrac{1}{y}}{\dfrac{2}{1}}\right)\left(\frac{xy}{xy}\right) = \frac{xy\left(\dfrac{1}{x}\right) + xy\left(\dfrac{1}{y}\right)}{2xy}$$

$$= \frac{y + x}{2xy}$$

Classroom Example

Simplify $\dfrac{-5}{\dfrac{4}{x} - \dfrac{8}{y}}$.

EXAMPLE 9   Simplify $\dfrac{-3}{\dfrac{2}{x} - \dfrac{3}{y}}$.

Solution

$$\left(\dfrac{\dfrac{-3}{1}}{\dfrac{2}{x} - \dfrac{3}{y}}\right)\left(\dfrac{xy}{xy}\right) = \dfrac{-3(xy)}{xy\left(\dfrac{2}{x}\right) - xy\left(\dfrac{3}{y}\right)}$$

$$= \dfrac{-3xy}{2y - 3x}$$

Let's conclude this section with an example that has a complex fraction as part of an algebraic expression.

Classroom Example

Simplify $1 + \dfrac{x}{1 + \dfrac{1}{x}}$.

EXAMPLE 10   Simplify $1 - \dfrac{n}{1 - \dfrac{1}{n}}$.

Solution

First simplify the complex fraction $\dfrac{n}{1 - \dfrac{1}{n}}$ by multiplying by $\dfrac{n}{n}$.

$$\left(\dfrac{n}{1 - \dfrac{1}{n}}\right)\left(\dfrac{n}{n}\right) = \dfrac{n^2}{n - 1}$$

Now we can perform the subtraction.

$$1 - \dfrac{n^2}{n - 1} = \left(\dfrac{n - 1}{n - 1}\right)\left(\dfrac{1}{1}\right) - \dfrac{n^2}{n - 1}$$

$$= \dfrac{n - 1}{n - 1} - \dfrac{n^2}{n - 1}$$

$$= \dfrac{n - 1 - n^2}{n - 1} \quad \text{or} \quad \dfrac{-n^2 + n - 1}{n - 1}$$

Concept Quiz 4.4

For Problems 1–7, answer true or false.

1. A complex fraction can be described as a fraction within a fraction.

2. Division can simplify the complex fraction $\dfrac{\dfrac{2y}{x}}{\dfrac{6}{x^2}}$.

3. The complex fraction $\dfrac{\dfrac{3}{x - 2} + \dfrac{2}{x + 2}}{\dfrac{7x}{(x + 2)(x - 2)}}$ simplifies to $\dfrac{5x + 2}{7x}$ for all values of x except $x = 0$.

4. The complex fraction $\dfrac{\dfrac{1}{3} - \dfrac{5}{6}}{\dfrac{1}{6} + \dfrac{5}{9}}$ simplifies to $-\dfrac{9}{13}$.

5. One method for simplifying a complex fraction is to multiply the entire fraction by a form of 1.

6. The complex fraction $\dfrac{\dfrac{3}{4} - \dfrac{1}{2}}{\dfrac{2}{3}}$ simplifies to $\dfrac{3}{8}$.

7. The complex fraction $\dfrac{\dfrac{7}{8} - \dfrac{1}{18}}{\dfrac{5}{6} + \dfrac{4}{15}}$ simplifies to $\dfrac{59}{33}$.

8. Arrange in order the following steps for adding rational expressions.
   A. Combine numerators and place over the LCD.
   B. Find the LCD.
   C. Reduce.
   D. Factor the denominators.
   E. Simplify by performing addition or subtraction.
   F. Change each fraction to an equivalent fraction that has the LCD as its denominator.

Problem Set 4.4

For Problems 1–40, perform the indicated operations, and express your answers in simplest form. (Objective 1)

1. $\dfrac{2x}{x^2 + 4x} + \dfrac{5}{x}$

2. $\dfrac{3x}{x^2 - 6x} + \dfrac{4}{x}.$

3. $\dfrac{4}{x^2 + 7x} - \dfrac{1}{x}$

4. $\dfrac{-10}{x^2 - 9x} - \dfrac{2}{x}$

5. $\dfrac{x}{x^2 - 1} + \dfrac{5}{x + 1}$

6. $\dfrac{2x}{x^2 - 16} + \dfrac{7}{x - 4}$

7. $\dfrac{6a + 4}{a^2 - 1} - \dfrac{5}{a - 1}$

8. $\dfrac{4a - 4}{a^2 - 4} - \dfrac{3}{a + 2}$

9. $\dfrac{2n}{n^2 - 25} - \dfrac{3}{4n + 20}$

10. $\dfrac{3n}{n^2 - 36} - \dfrac{2}{5n + 30}$

11. $\dfrac{5}{x} - \dfrac{5x - 30}{x^2 + 6x} + \dfrac{x}{x + 6}$

12. $\dfrac{3}{x + 1} + \dfrac{x + 5}{x^2 - 1} - \dfrac{3}{x - 1}$

13. $\dfrac{3}{x^2 + 9x + 14} + \dfrac{5}{2x^2 + 15x + 7}$

14. $\dfrac{6}{x^2 + 11x + 24} + \dfrac{4}{3x^2 + 13x + 12}$

15. $\dfrac{1}{a^2 - 3a - 10} - \dfrac{4}{a^2 + 4a - 45}$

16. $\dfrac{6}{a^2 - 3a - 54} - \dfrac{10}{a^2 + 5a - 6}$

17. $\dfrac{3a}{8a^2 - 2a - 3} + \dfrac{1}{4a^2 + 13a - 12}$

18. $\dfrac{2a}{6a^2 + 13a - 5} + \dfrac{a}{2a^2 + a - 10}$

19. $\dfrac{5}{x^2 + 3} - \dfrac{2}{x^2 + 4x - 21}$

20. $\dfrac{7}{x^2 + 1} - \dfrac{3}{x^2 + 7x - 60}$

21. $\dfrac{3x}{x^2 - 6x + 9} - \dfrac{2}{x - 3}$

22. $\dfrac{3}{x + 4} + \dfrac{2x}{x^2 + 8x + 16}$

23. $\dfrac{5}{x^2 - 1} + \dfrac{9}{x^2 + 2x + 1}$ **24.** $\dfrac{6}{x^2 - 9} - \dfrac{9}{x^2 - 6x + 9}$

25. $\dfrac{2}{y^2 + 6y - 16} - \dfrac{4}{y + 8} - \dfrac{3}{y - 2}$

26. $\dfrac{7}{y - 6} - \dfrac{10}{y + 12} + \dfrac{4}{y^2 + 6y - 72}$

27. $x - \dfrac{x^2}{x - 2} + \dfrac{3}{x^2 - 4}$

28. $x + \dfrac{5}{x^2 - 25} - \dfrac{x^2}{x + 5}$

29. $\dfrac{x + 3}{x + 10} + \dfrac{4x - 3}{x^2 + 8x - 20} + \dfrac{x - 1}{x - 2}$

30. $\dfrac{2x - 1}{x + 3} + \dfrac{x + 4}{x - 6} + \dfrac{3x - 1}{x^2 - 3x - 18}$

31. $\dfrac{n}{n - 6} + \dfrac{n + 3}{n + 8} + \dfrac{12n + 26}{n^2 + 2n - 48}$

32. $\dfrac{n - 1}{n + 4} + \dfrac{n}{n + 6} + \dfrac{2n + 18}{n^2 + 10n + 24}$

33. $\dfrac{4x - 3}{2x^2 + x - 1} - \dfrac{2x + 7}{3x^2 + x - 2} - \dfrac{3}{3x - 2}$

34. $\dfrac{2x + 5}{x^2 + 3x - 18} - \dfrac{3x - 1}{x^2 + 4x - 12} + \dfrac{5}{x - 2}$

35. $\dfrac{n}{n^2 + 1} + \dfrac{n^2 + 3n}{n^4 - 1} - \dfrac{1}{n - 1}$

36. $\dfrac{2n^2}{n^4 - 16} - \dfrac{n}{n^2 - 4} + \dfrac{1}{n + 2}$

37. $\dfrac{15x^2 - 10}{5x^2 - 7x + 2} - \dfrac{3x + 4}{x - 1} - \dfrac{2}{5x - 2}$

38. $\dfrac{32x + 9}{12x^2 + x - 6} - \dfrac{3}{4x + 3} - \dfrac{x + 5}{3x - 2}$

39. $\dfrac{t + 3}{3t - 1} + \dfrac{8t^2 + 8t + 2}{3t^2 - 7t + 2} - \dfrac{2t + 3}{t - 2}$

40. $\dfrac{t - 3}{2t + 1} + \dfrac{2t^2 + 19t - 46}{2t^2 - 9t - 5} - \dfrac{t + 4}{t - 5}$

For Problems 41–64, simplify each complex fraction.
(Objective 2)

41. $\dfrac{\dfrac{1}{2} - \dfrac{1}{4}}{\dfrac{5}{8} + \dfrac{3}{4}}$ **42.** $\dfrac{\dfrac{3}{8} + \dfrac{3}{4}}{\dfrac{5}{8} - \dfrac{7}{12}}$

43. $\dfrac{\dfrac{3}{28} - \dfrac{5}{14}}{\dfrac{5}{7} + \dfrac{1}{4}}$ **44.** $\dfrac{\dfrac{5}{9} + \dfrac{7}{36}}{\dfrac{3}{18} - \dfrac{5}{12}}$

45. $\dfrac{\dfrac{5}{6y}}{\dfrac{10}{3xy}}$ **46.** $\dfrac{\dfrac{9}{8xy^2}}{\dfrac{5}{4x^2}}$

47. $\dfrac{\dfrac{3}{x} - \dfrac{2}{y}}{\dfrac{4}{y} - \dfrac{7}{xy}}$ **48.** $\dfrac{\dfrac{9}{x} + \dfrac{7}{x^2}}{\dfrac{5}{y} + \dfrac{3}{y^2}}$

49. $\dfrac{\dfrac{6}{a} - \dfrac{5}{b^2}}{\dfrac{12}{a^2} + \dfrac{2}{b}}$ **50.** $\dfrac{\dfrac{4}{ab} - \dfrac{3}{b^2}}{\dfrac{1}{a} + \dfrac{3}{b}}$

51. $\dfrac{\dfrac{2}{x} - 3}{\dfrac{3}{y} + 4}$ **52.** $\dfrac{1 + \dfrac{3}{x}}{1 - \dfrac{6}{x}}$

53. $\dfrac{3 + \dfrac{2}{n + 4}}{5 - \dfrac{1}{n + 4}}$ **54.** $\dfrac{4 + \dfrac{6}{n - 1}}{7 - \dfrac{4}{n - 1}}$

55. $\dfrac{5 - \dfrac{2}{n - 3}}{4 - \dfrac{1}{n - 3}}$ **56.** $\dfrac{\dfrac{3}{n - 5} - 2}{1 - \dfrac{4}{n - 5}}$

57. $\dfrac{\dfrac{-1}{y - 2} + \dfrac{5}{x}}{\dfrac{3}{x} - \dfrac{4}{xy - 2x}}$ **58.** $\dfrac{\dfrac{-2}{x} - \dfrac{4}{x + 2}}{\dfrac{3}{x^2 + 2x} + \dfrac{3}{x}}$

59. $\dfrac{\dfrac{2}{x - 3} - \dfrac{3}{x + 3}}{\dfrac{5}{x^2 - 9} - \dfrac{2}{x - 3}}$ **60.** $\dfrac{\dfrac{2}{x - y} + \dfrac{3}{x + y}}{\dfrac{5}{x + y} - \dfrac{1}{x^2 - y^2}}$

61. $\dfrac{\dfrac{3a}{2 - \dfrac{1}{a}} - 1}{}$ **62.** $\dfrac{\dfrac{a}{\dfrac{1}{a} + 4} + 1}{}$

63. $2 - \dfrac{x}{3 - \dfrac{2}{x}}$ **64.** $1 + \dfrac{x}{1 + \dfrac{1}{x}}$

Thoughts Into Words

65. Which of the two techniques presented in the text would you use to simplify $\dfrac{\dfrac{1}{4} + \dfrac{1}{3}}{\dfrac{3}{4} - \dfrac{1}{6}}$? Which technique would you use to simplify $\dfrac{\dfrac{3}{8} - \dfrac{5}{7}}{\dfrac{7}{9} + \dfrac{6}{25}}$? Explain your choice for each problem.

66. Give a step-by-step description of how to do the following addition problem.

$$\frac{3x + 4}{8} + \frac{5x - 2}{12}$$

Answers to the Concept Quiz

1. True   **2.** True   **3.** False   **4.** True   **5.** True   **6.** True   **7.** False   **8.** D, B, F, A, E, C

4.5   Dividing Polynomials

OBJECTIVES

1   Divide polynomials

2   Use synthetic division to divide polynomials

In Chapter 3, we saw how the property $\dfrac{b^n}{b^m} = b^{n-m}$, along with our knowledge of dividing integers, is used to divide monomials. For example,

$$\frac{12x^3}{3x} = 4x^2 \qquad \frac{-36x^4y^5}{4xy^2} = -9x^3y^3$$

In Section 4.3, we used $\dfrac{a}{b} + \dfrac{c}{b} = \dfrac{a + c}{b}$ and $\dfrac{a}{b} - \dfrac{c}{b} = \dfrac{a - c}{b}$ as the basis for adding and subtracting rational expressions. These same equalities, viewed as $\dfrac{a + b}{c} = \dfrac{a}{c} + \dfrac{b}{c}$ and $\dfrac{a - c}{b} = \dfrac{a}{b} - \dfrac{c}{b}$, along with our knowledge of dividing monomials, provide the basis for dividing polynomials by monomials. Consider the following examples.

$$\frac{18x^3 + 24x^2}{6x} = \frac{18x^3}{6x} + \frac{24x^2}{6x} = 3x^2 + 4x$$

$$\frac{35x^2y^3 - 55x^3y^4}{5xy^2} = \frac{35x^2y^3}{5xy^2} - \frac{55x^3y^4}{5xy^2} = 7xy - 11x^2y^2$$

To divide a polynomial by a monomial, we divide each term of the polynomial by the monomial. As with many skills, once you feel comfortable with the process, you may then want to perform some of the steps mentally. Your work could take on the following format.

$$\frac{40x^4y^5 + 72x^5y^7}{8x^2y} = 5x^2y^4 + 9x^3y^6 \qquad \frac{36a^3b^4 - 45a^4b^6}{-9a^2b^3} = -4ab + 5a^2b^3$$

In Section 4.1, we saw that a fraction like $\dfrac{3x^2 + 11x - 4}{x + 4}$ can be simplified as follows:

$$\frac{3x^2 + 11x - 4}{x + 4} = \frac{(3x - 1)(x + 4)}{x + 4} = 3x - 1$$

We can obtain the same result by using a dividing process similar to long division in arithmetic.

Step 1   Use the conventional long-division format, and arrange both the dividend and the divisor in descending powers of the variable.

$$x + 4\overline{)3x^2 + 11x - 4}$$

Step 2   Find the first term of the quotient by dividing the first term of the dividend by the first term of the divisor.

$$\begin{array}{r} 3x \\ x + 4\overline{)3x^2 + 11x - 4} \end{array}$$

Step 3   Multiply the entire divisor by the term of the quotient found in step 2, and position the product to be subtracted from the dividend.

$$\begin{array}{r} 3x \\ x + 4\overline{)3x^2 + 11x - 4} \\ 3x^2 + 12x \end{array}$$

Step 4   Subtract.

$$\begin{array}{r} 3x \\ x + 4\overline{)3x^2 + 11x - 4} \\ \underline{3x^2 + 12x } \\ -x - 4 \end{array}$$

Remember to add the opposite! ⟶

$(3x^2 + 11x - 4) - (3x^2 + 12x) = -x - 4$ ⟶

Step 5   Repeat the process beginning with step 2; use the polynomial that resulted from the subtraction in step 4 as a new dividend.

$$\begin{array}{r} 3x - 1 \\ x + 4\overline{)3x^2 + 11x - 4} \\ \underline{3x^2 + 12x } \\ -x - 4 \\ \underline{-x - 4} \end{array}$$

In the next example, let's *think* in terms of the previous step-by-step procedure but arrange our work in a more compact form.

Classroom Example
Divide $3x^2 - 5x - 28$ by $x - 4$.

EXAMPLE 1   Divide $5x^2 + 6x - 8$ by $x + 2$.

Solution

$$\begin{array}{r} 5x - 4 \\ x + 2\overline{)5x^2 + 6x - 8} \\ \underline{5x^2 + 10x } \\ -4x - 8 \\ \underline{-4x - 8} \\ 0 \end{array}$$

Think Steps

1. $\dfrac{5x^2}{x} = 5x$

2. $5x(x + 2) = 5x^2 + 10x$

3. $(5x^2 + 6x - 8) - (5x^2 + 10x) = -4x - 8$

4. $\dfrac{-4x}{x} = -4$

5. $-4(x + 2) = -4x - 8$

Recall that to check a division problem, we can multiply the divisor times the quotient and add the remainder. In other words,

Dividend = (Divisor)(Quotient) + (Remainder)

Sometimes the remainder is expressed as a fractional part of the divisor. The relationship then becomes

$$\frac{\text{Dividend}}{\text{Divisor}} = \text{Quotient} + \frac{\text{Remainder}}{\text{Divisor}}$$

Classroom Example
Divide $2x^2 + 11x + 20$ by $x + 3$.

EXAMPLE 2   Divide $2x^2 - 3x + 1$ by $x - 5$.

Solution

$$
\begin{array}{r}
2x + 7 \\
x - 5\overline{)2x^2 - 3x + 1} \\
\underline{2x^2 - 10x} \\
7x + 1 \\
\underline{7x - 35} \\
36
\end{array}
\quad\longleftarrow\quad \text{Remainder}
$$

Thus

$$\frac{2x^2 - 3x + 1}{x - 5} = 2x + 7 + \frac{36}{x - 5}, \qquad x \neq 5$$

✔ **Check**

$$(x - 5)(2x + 7) + 36 \overset{?}{=} 2x^2 - 3x + 1$$
$$2x^2 - 3x - 35 + 36 \overset{?}{=} 2x^2 - 3x + 1$$
$$2x^2 - 3x + 1 = 2x^2 - 3x + 1$$

Each of the next two examples illustrates another point regarding the division process. Study them carefully, and then you should be ready to work the exercises in the next problem set.

Classroom Example
Divide $t^3 - 1$ by $t - 1$.

EXAMPLE 3   Divide $t^3 - 8$ by $t - 2$.

Solution

$$
\begin{array}{r}
t^2 + 2t + 4 \\
t - 2\overline{)t^3 + 0t^2 + 0t - 8} \\
\underline{t^3 - 2t^2} \\
2t^2 + 0t - 8 \\
\underline{2t^2 - 4t} \\
4t - 8 \\
\underline{4t - 8} \\
0
\end{array}
$$

Note the insertion of a "t-squared" term and a "t term" with zero coefficients

Check this result!

Classroom Example
Divide $x^3 + x^2 - 7x - 2$ by $x^2 - 3x$.

EXAMPLE 4   Divide $y^3 + 3y^2 - 2y - 1$ by $y^2 + 2y$.

Solution

$$
\begin{array}{r}
y + 1 \\
y^2 + 2y\overline{)y^3 + 3y^2 - 2y - 1} \\
\underline{y^3 + 2y^2} \\
y^2 - 2y - 1 \\
\underline{y^2 + 2y} \\
- 4y - 1
\end{array}
\quad\longleftarrow\quad \text{Remainder of } -4y - 1
$$

The division process is complete when the degree of the remainder is less than the degree of the divisor. Thus

$$\frac{y^3 + 3y^2 - 2y - 1}{y^2 + 2y} = y + 1 + \frac{-4y - 1}{y^2 + 2y}$$

If the divisor is of the form $x - k$, where the coefficient of the x term is 1, then the format of the division process described in this section can be simplified by a procedure called **synthetic division**. This procedure is a shortcut for this type of polynomial division. If you are continuing on to study college algebra, then you will want to know synthetic division. If you are not continuing on to college algebra, then you probably will not need a shortcut, and the long-division process will be sufficient.

First, let's consider an example and use the usual division process. Then, in step-by-step fashion, we can observe some shortcuts that will lead us into the synthetic-division procedure. Consider the division problem $(2x^4 + x^3 - 17x^2 + 13x + 2) \div (x - 2)$.

$$
\begin{array}{r}
2x^3 + 5x^2 - 7x - 1 \\
x - 2{\overline{\smash{\big)}\,2x^4 + x^3 - 17x^2 + 13x + 2}} \\
\underline{2x^4 - 4x^3} \\
5x^3 - 17x^2 \\
\underline{5x^3 - 10x^2} \\
-7x^2 + 13x \\
\underline{-7x^2 + 14x} \\
-x + 2 \\
\underline{-x + 2}
\end{array}
$$

Note that because the dividend $(2x^4 + x^3 - 17x^2 + 13x + 2)$ is written in descending powers of x, the quotient $(2x^3 + 5x^2 - 7x - 1)$ is produced, also in descending powers of x. In other words, the numerical coefficients are the important numbers. Thus let's rewrite this problem in terms of its coefficients.

$$
\begin{array}{r}
2 + 5 - 7 - 1 \\
1 - 2{\overline{\smash{\big)}\,2 + 1 - 17 + 13 + 2}} \\
\underline{②- 4} \\
5 ⊂17 \\
\underline{⑤- 10} \\
-7 + ⑬ \\
\underline{⊖+ 14} \\
-1 + ② \\
\underline{⊖+ 2}
\end{array}
$$

Now observe that the numbers that are circled are simply repetitions of the numbers directly above them in the format. Therefore, by removing the circled numbers, we can write the process in a more compact form as

$$
\begin{array}{r}
2\ \ 5 - 7 - 1 \\
-2{\overline{\smash{\big)}\,2\ \ 1 - 17\ \ \ \ 13\ \ \ 2}} \\
\underline{-4\ -10\ \ \ 14\ \ \ 2} \\
5 - 7 - 1\ \ \ 0
\end{array}
$$

$$(1)$$
$$(2)$$
$$(3)$$
$$(4)$$

where the repetitions are omitted and where 1, the coefficient of x in the divisor, is omitted.

Note that line (4) reveals all of the coefficients of the quotient, line (1), except for the first coefficient of 2. Thus we can begin line (4) with the first coefficient and then use the following form.

$$
\begin{array}{r}
-2{\overline{\smash{\big)}\,2\ \ 1 - 17\ \ \ 13\ \ \ 2}} \\
\underline{-4\ -10\ \ \ 14\ \ \ 2} \\
2\ \ 5 - 7 - 1\ \ \ 0
\end{array}
$$

$$(5)$$
$$(6)$$
$$(7)$$

Line (7) contains the coefficients of the quotient, where the 0 indicates the remainder.

Finally, by changing the constant in the divisor to 2 (instead of -2), we can add the corresponding entries in lines (5) and (6) rather than subtract. Thus the final synthetic division form for this problem is

$$
\begin{array}{r}
2{\overline{\smash{\big)}\,2\ \ 1 - 17\ \ \ \ 13\ \ \ \ 2}} \\
\underline{4\ \ \ 10\ -14\ -2} \\
2\ \ 5 - 7 - 1\ \ \ \ 0
\end{array}
$$

Now let's consider another problem that illustrates a step-by-step procedure for carrying out the synthetic-division process. Suppose that we want to divide $3x^3 - 2x^2 + 6x - 5$ by $x + 4$.

Step 1   Write the coefficients of the dividend as follows:

$$\overline{)3 \quad -2 \quad 6 \quad -5}$$

Step 2   In the divisor, $(x + 4)$, use -4 instead of 4 so that later we can add rather than subtract.

$$-4\overline{)3 \quad -2 \quad 6 \quad -5}$$

Step 3   Bring down the first coefficient of the dividend (3).

$$-4\overline{)3 \quad -2 \quad 6 \quad -5}$$
$$\overline{3}$$

Step 4   Multiply $(3)(-4)$, which yields -12; this result is to be added to the second coefficient of the dividend (-2).

$$-4\overline{)3 \quad -2 \quad 6 \quad -5}$$
$$\underline{\quad -12}$$
$$3 \quad -14$$

Step 5   Multiply $(-14)(-4)$, which yields 56; this result is to be added to the third coefficient of the dividend (6).

$$-4\overline{)3 \quad -2 \quad 6 \quad -5}$$
$$\underline{\quad -12 \quad 56}$$
$$3 \quad -14 \quad 62$$

Step 6   Multiply $(62)(-4)$, which yields -248; this result is added to the last term of the dividend (-5).

$$-4\overline{)3 \quad -2 \quad 6 \quad -5}$$
$$\underline{\quad -12 \quad 56 \quad -248}$$
$$3 \quad -14 \quad 62 \quad -253$$

The last row indicates a quotient of $3x^2 - 14x + 62$ and a remainder of -253. Thus we have

$$\frac{3x^3 - 2x^2 + 6x - 5}{x + 4} = 3x^2 - 14x + 62 - \frac{253}{x + 4}$$

We will consider one more example, which shows only the final compact form for synthetic division.

Classroom Example
Find the quotient and remainder for
$(2x^4 - 11x^3 + 17x^2 + 2x - 9) \div (x - 3)$.

EXAMPLE 5

Find the quotient and remainder for $(4x^4 - 2x^3 + 6x - 1) \div (x - 1)$.

Solution

$$1\overline{)4 \quad -2 \quad 0 \quad 6 \quad -1}$$
$$\underline{\quad \quad 4 \quad 2 \quad 2 \quad 8}$$
$$4 \quad \quad 2 \quad 2 \quad 8 \quad 7$$

Note that a zero has been inserted as the coefficient of the missing x^2 term

Therefore,

$$\frac{4x^4 - 2x^3 + 6x - 1}{x - 1} = 4x^3 + 2x^2 + 2x + 8 + \frac{7}{x - 1}$$

Concept Quiz 4.5

For Problems 1–10, answer true or false.

1. A division problem written as $(x^2 - x - 6) \div (x - 1)$ could also be written as $\dfrac{x^2 - x - 6}{x - 1}$.

2. The division of $\dfrac{x^2 + 7x + 12}{x + 3} = x + 4$ could be checked by multiplying $(x + 4)$ by $(x + 3)$.

3. For the division problem $(2x^2 + 5x + 9) \div (2x + 1)$, the remainder is 7. The remainder for the division problem can be expressed as $\dfrac{7}{2x + 1}$.

4. In general, to check a division problem we can multiply the divisor by the quotient and subtract the remainder.

5. If a term is inserted to act as a placeholder, then the coefficient of the term must be zero.

6. When performing division, the process ends when the degree of the remainder is less than the degree of the divisor.

7. Synthetic division is a shortcut process for polynomial division.

8. Synthetic division can be used when the divisor is of the form $x - k$.

9. The fraction $\dfrac{x^2 - x - 6}{x - 3}$ can only be simplified by using synthetic division.

10. Synthetic division cannot be used for the problem $(6x^3 + x - 4) \div (x + 2)$ because there is no x^2 term in the dividend.

Problem Set 4.5

For Problems 1–10, perform the indicated divisions of polynomials by monomials. **(Objective 1)**

1. $\dfrac{9x^4 + 18x^3}{3x}$

2. $\dfrac{12x^3 - 24x^2}{6x^2}$

3. $\dfrac{-24x^6 + 36x^8}{4x^2}$

4. $\dfrac{-35x^5 - 42x^3}{-7x^2}$

5. $\dfrac{15a^3 - 25a^2 - 40a}{5a}$

6. $\dfrac{-16a^4 + 32a^3 - 56a^2}{-8a}$

7. $\dfrac{13x^3 - 17x^2 + 28x}{-x}$

8. $\dfrac{14xy - 16x^2y^2 - 20x^3y^4}{-xy}$

9. $\dfrac{-18x^2y^2 + 24x^3y^2 - 48x^2y^3}{6xy}$

10. $\dfrac{-27a^3b^4 - 36a^2b^3 + 72a^2b^5}{9a^2b^2}$

For Problems 11–52, perform the indicated divisions. **(Objective 1)**

11. $\dfrac{x^2 - 7x - 78}{x + 6}$

12. $\dfrac{x^2 + 11x - 60}{x - 4}$

13. $(x^2 + 12x - 160) \div (x - 8)$

14. $(x^2 - 18x - 175) \div (x + 7)$

15. $\dfrac{2x^2 - x - 4}{x - 1}$

16. $\dfrac{3x^2 - 2x - 7}{x + 2}$

17. $\dfrac{15x^2 + 22x - 5}{3x + 5}$

18. $\dfrac{12x^2 - 32x - 35}{2x - 7}$

19. $\dfrac{3x^3 + 7x^2 - 13x - 21}{x + 3}$

20. $\dfrac{4x^3 - 21x^2 + 3x + 10}{x - 5}$

21. $(2x^3 + 9x^2 - 17x + 6) \div (2x - 1)$

22. $(3x^3 - 5x^2 - 23x - 7) \div (3x + 1)$

23. $(4x^3 - x^2 - 2x + 6) \div (x - 2)$

24. $(6x^3 - 2x^2 + 4x - 3) \div (x + 1)$

25. $(x^4 - 10x^3 + 19x^2 + 33x - 18) \div (x - 6)$

26. $(x^4 + 2x^3 - 16x^2 + x + 6) \div (x - 3)$

27. $\dfrac{x^3 - 125}{x - 5}$

28. $\dfrac{x^3 + 64}{x + 4}$

29. $(x^3 + 64) \div (x + 1)$

30. $(x^3 - 8) \div (x - 4)$

31. $(2x^3 - x - 6) \div (x + 2)$

32. $(5x^3 + 2x - 3) \div (x - 2)$

33. $\dfrac{4a^2 - 8ab + 4b^2}{a - b}$

34. $\dfrac{3x^2 - 2xy - 8y^2}{x - 2y}$

35. $\dfrac{4x^3 - 5x^2 + 2x - 6}{x^2 - 3x}$

36. $\dfrac{3x^3 + 2x^2 - 5x - 1}{x^2 + 2x}$

37. $\dfrac{8y^3 - y^2 - y + 5}{y^2 + y}$

38. $\dfrac{5y^3 - 6y^2 - 7y - 2}{y^2 - y}$

39. $(2x^3 + x^2 - 3x + 1) \div (x^2 + x - 1)$

40. $(3x^3 - 4x^2 + 8x + 8) \div (x^2 - 2x + 4)$

41. $(4x^3 - 13x^2 + 8x - 15) \div (4x^2 - x + 5)$

42. $(5x^3 + 8x^2 - 5x - 2) \div (5x^2 - 2x - 1)$

43. $(5a^3 + 7a^2 - 2a - 9) \div (a^2 + 3a - 4)$

44. $(4a^3 - 2a^2 + 7a - 1) \div (a^2 - 2a + 3)$

45. $(2n^4 + 3n^3 - 2n^2 + 3n - 4) \div (n^2 + 1)$

46. $(3n^4 + n^3 - 7n^2 - 2n + 2) \div (n^2 - 2)$

47. $(x^5 - 1) \div (x - 1)$ **48.** $(x^5 + 1) \div (x + 1)$

49. $(x^4 - 1) \div (x + 1)$ **50.** $(x^4 - 1) \div (x - 1)$

51. $(3x^4 + x^3 - 2x^2 - x + 6) \div (x^2 - 1)$

52. $(4x^3 - 2x^2 + 7x - 5) \div (x^2 + 2)$

For Problems 53–64, use synthetic division to determine the quotient and remainder. **(Objective 2)**

53. $(x^2 - 8x + 12) \div (x - 2)$

54. $(x^2 + 9x + 18) \div (x + 3)$

55. $(x^2 + 2x - 10) \div (x - 4)$

56. $(x^2 - 10x + 15) \div (x - 8)$

57. $(x^3 - 2x^2 - x + 2) \div (x - 2)$

58. $(x^3 - 5x^2 + 2x + 8) \div (x + 1)$

59. $(x^3 - 7x - 6) \div (x + 2)$

60. $(x^3 + 6x^2 - 5x - 1) \div (x - 1)$

61. $(2x^3 - 5x^2 - 4x + 6) \div (x - 2)$

62. $(3x^4 - x^3 + 2x^2 - 7x - 1) \div (x + 1)$

63. $(x^4 + 4x^3 - 7x - 1) \div (x - 3)$

64. $(2x^4 + 3x^2 + 3) \div (x + 2)$

Thoughts Into Words

65. Describe the process of long division of polynomials.

66. Give a step-by-step description of how you would do the following division problem.

$$(4 - 3x - 7x^3) \div (x + 6)$$

67. How do you know by inspection that $3x^2 + 5x + 1$ cannot be the correct answer for the division problem $(3x^3 - 7x^2 - 22x + 8) \div (x - 4)$?

Answers to the Concept Quiz

1. True   **2.** True   **3.** True   **4.** False   **5.** True   **6.** True   **7.** True   **8.** True   **9.** False   **10.** False

---

4.6   Fractional Equations

OBJECTIVES   **1** Solve rational equations

2 Solve proportions

3 Solve word problems involving ratios

The fractional equations used in this text are of two basic types. One type has only constants as denominators, and the other type contains variables in the denominators.

In Chapter 2, we considered fractional equations that involve only constants in the denominators. Let's briefly review our approach to solving such equations, because we will be using that same basic technique to solve any type of fractional equation.

Classroom Example
Solve $\dfrac{x + 5}{2} + \dfrac{x - 3}{6} = \dfrac{2}{3}$.

EXAMPLE 1   Solve $\dfrac{x - 2}{3} + \dfrac{x + 1}{4} = \dfrac{1}{6}$.

Solution

$$\frac{x - 2}{3} + \frac{x + 1}{4} = \frac{1}{6}$$

$$12\left(\frac{x - 2}{3} + \frac{x + 1}{4}\right) = 12\left(\frac{1}{6}\right)$$ Multiply both sides by 12, which is the LCD of all of the denominators

$$4(x - 2) + 3(x + 1) = 2$$

$$4x - 8 + 3x + 3 = 2$$
$$7x - 5 = 2$$
$$7x = 7$$
$$x = 1$$

The solution set is $\{1\}$. Check it!

If an equation contains a variable (or variables) in one or more denominators, then we proceed in essentially the same way as in Example 1 *except that we must avoid any value of the variable that makes a denominator zero.* Consider the following examples.

Classroom Example

Solve $\dfrac{3}{n} + \dfrac{1}{4} = \dfrac{5}{n}$.

EXAMPLE 2   Solve $\dfrac{5}{n} + \dfrac{1}{2} = \dfrac{9}{n}$.

Solution

First, we need to realize that n cannot equal zero. (Let's indicate this restriction so that it is not forgotten!) Then we can proceed.

$$\frac{5}{n} + \frac{1}{2} = \frac{9}{n}, \qquad n \neq 0$$

$$2n\left(\frac{5}{n} + \frac{1}{2}\right) = 2n\left(\frac{9}{n}\right) \qquad \text{Multiply both sides by the LCD, which is } 2n$$

$$10 + n = 18$$

$$n = 8$$

The solution set is $\{8\}$. Check it!

Classroom Example

Solve $\dfrac{27 - x}{x} = 9 - \dfrac{3}{x}$.

EXAMPLE 3   Solve $\dfrac{35 - x}{x} = 7 + \dfrac{3}{x}$.

Solution

$$\frac{35 - x}{x} = 7 + \frac{3}{x}, \qquad x \neq 0$$

$$x\left(\frac{35 - x}{x}\right) = x\left(7 + \frac{3}{x}\right) \qquad \text{Multiply both sides by } x$$

$$35 - x = 7x + 3$$

$$32 = 8x$$

$$4 = x$$

The solution set is $\{4\}$.

Classroom Example

Solve $\dfrac{5}{x - 3} = \dfrac{6}{x + 2}$.

EXAMPLE 4   Solve $\dfrac{3}{a - 2} = \dfrac{4}{a + 1}$.

Solution

$$\frac{3}{a - 2} = \frac{4}{a + 1}, \qquad a \neq 2 \text{ and } a \neq -1$$

$$(a - 2)(a + 1)\left(\frac{3}{a - 2}\right) = (a - 2)(a + 1)\left(\frac{4}{a + 1}\right) \qquad \text{Multiply both sides by } (a - 2)(a + 1)$$

$$3(a + 1) = 4(a - 2)$$

$$3a + 3 = 4a - 8$$

$$11 = a$$

The solution set is $\{11\}$.

Keep in mind that listing the restrictions at the beginning of a problem does not replace checking the potential solutions. In Example 4, the answer 11 needs to be checked in the original equation.

Classroom Example

Solve $\dfrac{x}{x+3} + \dfrac{3}{2} = \dfrac{-3}{x+3}$.

EXAMPLE 5 Solve $\dfrac{a}{a-2} + \dfrac{2}{3} = \dfrac{2}{a-2}$.

Solution

$$\frac{a}{a-2} + \frac{2}{3} = \frac{2}{a-2}, \qquad a \neq 2$$

$$3(a-2)\left(\frac{a}{a-2} + \frac{2}{3}\right) = 3(a-2)\left(\frac{2}{a-2}\right) \qquad \text{Multiply both sides by } 3(a-2)$$

$$3a + 2(a-2) = 6$$

$$3a + 2a - 4 = 6$$

$$5a = 10$$

$$a = 2$$

Because our initial restriction was $a \neq 2$, we conclude that this equation has no solution. Thus the solution set is $\varnothing$.

Solving Proportions

A **ratio** is the comparison of two numbers by division. We often use the fractional form to express ratios. For example, we can write the ratio of a to b as $\dfrac{a}{b}$. A statement of equality between two ratios is called a **proportion**. Thus if $\dfrac{a}{b}$ and $\dfrac{c}{d}$ are two equal ratios, we can form the proportion $\dfrac{a}{b} = \dfrac{c}{d}$ ($b \neq 0$ and $d \neq 0$). We deduce an important property of proportions as follows:

$$\frac{a}{b} = \frac{c}{d}, \qquad b \neq 0 \text{ and } d \neq 0$$

$$bd\left(\frac{a}{b}\right) = bd\left(\frac{c}{d}\right) \qquad \text{Multiply both sides by } bd$$

$$ad = bc$$

Cross-Multiplication Property of Proportions

If $\dfrac{a}{b} = \dfrac{c}{d}$ ($b \neq 0$ and $d \neq 0$), then $ad = bc$.

We can treat some fractional equations as proportions and solve them by using the cross-multiplication idea, as in the next examples.

Classroom Example

Solve $\dfrac{4}{x+3} = \dfrac{9}{x-4}$.

EXAMPLE 6 Solve $\dfrac{5}{x+6} = \dfrac{7}{x-5}$.

Solution

$$\frac{5}{x+6} = \frac{7}{x-5}, \qquad x \neq -6 \text{ and } x \neq 5$$

$$5(x - 5) = 7(x + 6) \qquad \text{Apply the cross-multiplication property}$$
$$5x - 25 = 7x + 42$$
$$-67 = 2x$$
$$-\frac{67}{2} = x$$

The solution set is $\left\{-\dfrac{67}{2}\right\}$.

Classroom Example

Solve $\dfrac{x}{9} = \dfrac{3}{x - 6}$.

EXAMPLE 7   Solve $\dfrac{x}{7} = \dfrac{4}{x + 3}$.

Solution

$$\frac{x}{7} = \frac{4}{x + 3}, \qquad x \neq -3$$
$$x(x + 3) = 7(4) \qquad \text{Cross-multiplication property}$$
$$x^2 + 3x = 28$$
$$x^2 + 3x - 28 = 0$$
$$(x + 7)(x - 4) = 0$$
$$x + 7 = 0 \qquad \text{or} \qquad x - 4 = 0$$
$$x = -7 \qquad \text{or} \qquad x = 4$$

The solution set is $\{-7, 4\}$. Check these solutions in the original equation.

Solving Word Problems Involving Ratios

We can conveniently set up some problems and solve them using the concepts of ratio and proportion. Let's conclude this section with two such examples.

Classroom Example

On a certain map $\dfrac{5}{8}$ inches represents 10 miles. If two cities are $4\dfrac{1}{2}$ inches apart on the map, find the number of miles between the cities.

EXAMPLE 8

On a certain map, $1\dfrac{1}{2}$ inches represents 25 miles. If two cities are $5\dfrac{1}{4}$ inches apart on the map, find the number of miles between the cities (see Figure 4.1).

Solution

Let m represent the number of miles between the two cities. To set up the proportion, we will use a ratio of inches on the map to miles. Be sure to keep the ratio "inches on the map to miles" the same for both sides of the proportion.

$$\frac{1\frac{1}{2}}{25} = \frac{5\frac{1}{4}}{m}, \qquad m \neq 0$$

$$\frac{\frac{3}{2}}{25} = \frac{\frac{21}{4}}{m}$$

$$\frac{3}{2}m = 25\left(\frac{21}{4}\right) \qquad \text{Cross-multiplication property}$$

$$\frac{2}{3}\left(\frac{3}{2}m\right) = \frac{2}{\overset{}{\cancel{3}}}(25)\left(\frac{\overset{7}{\cancel{21}}}{\underset{2}{\cancel{4}}}\right) \qquad \text{Multiply both sides by } \frac{2}{3}$$

$$m = \frac{175}{2} = 87\frac{1}{2}$$

The distance between the two cities is $87\dfrac{1}{2}$ miles.

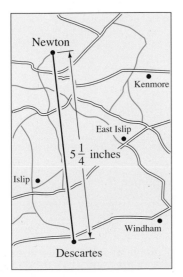

Figure 4.1

Classroom Example
A sum of $3600 is to be divided between two people in the ratio of 3 to 5. How much does each person receive?

EXAMPLE 9

A sum of $750 is to be divided between two people in the ratio of 2 to 3. How much does each person receive?

Solution

Let d represent the amount of money that one person receives. Then $750 - d$ represents the amount for the other person.

$$\frac{d}{750 - d} = \frac{2}{3}, \quad d \neq 750$$

$$3d = 2(750 - d)$$

$$3d = 1500 - 2d$$

$$5d = 1500$$

$$d = 300$$

If $d = 300$, then $750 - d$ equals 450. Therefore, one person receives $300 and the other person receives $450.

Concept Quiz 4.6

For Problems 1–3, answer true or false.

1. In solving rational equations, any value of the variable that makes a denominator zero cannot be a solution of the equation.

2. One method of solving rational equations is to multiply both sides of the equation by the lowest common denominator of the fractions in the equation.

3. In solving a rational equation that is a proportion, cross products can be set equal to each other.

For Problems 4–8, match each equation with its solution set.

Equations

4. $\dfrac{3}{x + 1} = \dfrac{3}{x - 1}$

5. $\dfrac{x}{5} = \dfrac{3x}{15}$

6. $\dfrac{2x + 1}{7} = \dfrac{3x}{7}$

7. $\dfrac{-x + 9}{x - 4} = \dfrac{5}{x - 4}$

8. $\dfrac{4}{x + 2} = \dfrac{4}{2x - 1}$

Solution Sets

A. {All real numbers}
B. $\varnothing$
C. {3}
D. {1}

9. Identify the following equations as a proportion or not a proportion.

(a) $\dfrac{2x}{x + 1} + x = \dfrac{7}{x + 1}$ (b) $\dfrac{x - 8}{2x + 5} = \dfrac{7}{9}$ (c) $5 + \dfrac{2x}{x + 6} = \dfrac{x - 3}{x + 4}$

10. Select all the equations that could represent the following problem: John bought three bottles of energy drink for $5.07. If the price remains the same, what will eight bottles of the energy drink cost?

(a) $\dfrac{3}{5.07} = \dfrac{x}{8}$ (b) $\dfrac{5.07}{8} = \dfrac{x}{3}$ (c) $\dfrac{3}{8} = \dfrac{5.07}{x}$ (d) $\dfrac{5.07}{3} = \dfrac{x}{8}$

Problem Set 4.6

For Problems 1–44, solve each equation. **(Objectives 1 and 2)**

1. $\dfrac{x+1}{4} + \dfrac{x-2}{6} = \dfrac{3}{4}$

2. $\dfrac{x+2}{5} + \dfrac{x-1}{6} = \dfrac{3}{5}$

3. $\dfrac{x+3}{2} - \dfrac{x-4}{7} = 1$

4. $\dfrac{x+4}{3} - \dfrac{x-5}{9} = 1$

5. $\dfrac{5}{n} + \dfrac{1}{3} = \dfrac{7}{n}$

6. $\dfrac{3}{n} + \dfrac{1}{6} = \dfrac{11}{3n}$

7. $\dfrac{7}{2x} + \dfrac{3}{5} = \dfrac{2}{3x}$

8. $\dfrac{9}{4x} + \dfrac{1}{3} = \dfrac{5}{2x}$

9. $\dfrac{3}{4x} + \dfrac{5}{6} = \dfrac{4}{3x}$

10. $\dfrac{5}{7x} - \dfrac{5}{6} = \dfrac{1}{6x}$

11. $\dfrac{47-n}{n} = 8 + \dfrac{2}{n}$

12. $\dfrac{45-n}{n} = 6 + \dfrac{3}{n}$

13. $\dfrac{n}{65-n} = 8 + \dfrac{2}{65-n}$

14. $\dfrac{n}{70-n} = 7 + \dfrac{6}{70-n}$

15. $n + \dfrac{1}{n} = \dfrac{17}{4}$

16. $n + \dfrac{1}{n} = \dfrac{37}{6}$

17. $n - \dfrac{2}{n} = \dfrac{23}{5}$

18. $n - \dfrac{3}{n} = \dfrac{26}{3}$

19. $\dfrac{5}{7x-3} = \dfrac{3}{4x-5}$

20. $\dfrac{3}{2x-1} = \dfrac{5}{3x+2}$

21. $\dfrac{-2}{x-5} = \dfrac{1}{x+9}$

22. $\dfrac{5}{2a-1} = \dfrac{-6}{3a+2}$

23. $\dfrac{x}{x+1} - 2 = \dfrac{3}{x-3}$

24. $\dfrac{x}{x-2} + 1 = \dfrac{8}{x-1}$

25. $\dfrac{a}{a+5} - 2 = \dfrac{3a}{a+5}$

26. $\dfrac{a}{a-3} - \dfrac{3}{2} = \dfrac{3}{a-3}$

27. $\dfrac{5}{x+6} = \dfrac{6}{x-3}$

28. $\dfrac{3}{x-1} = \dfrac{4}{x+2}$

29. $\dfrac{3x-7}{10} = \dfrac{2}{x}$

30. $\dfrac{x}{-4} = \dfrac{3}{12x-25}$

31. $\dfrac{x}{x-6} - 3 = \dfrac{6}{x-6}$

32. $\dfrac{x}{x+1} + 3 = \dfrac{4}{x+1}$

33. $\dfrac{3s}{s+2} + 1 = \dfrac{35}{2(3s+1)}$

34. $\dfrac{s}{2s-1} - 3 = \dfrac{-32}{3(s+5)}$

35. $2 - \dfrac{3x}{x-4} = \dfrac{14}{x+7}$

36. $-1 + \dfrac{2x}{x+3} = \dfrac{-4}{x+4}$

37. $\dfrac{n+6}{27} = \dfrac{1}{n}$

38. $\dfrac{n}{5} = \dfrac{10}{n-5}$

39. $\dfrac{3n}{n-1} - \dfrac{1}{3} = \dfrac{-40}{3n-18}$

40. $\dfrac{n}{n+1} + \dfrac{1}{2} = \dfrac{-2}{n+2}$

41. $\dfrac{-3}{4x+5} = \dfrac{2}{5x-7}$

42. $\dfrac{7}{x+4} = \dfrac{3}{x-8}$

43. $\dfrac{2x}{x-2} + \dfrac{15}{x^2-7x+10} = \dfrac{3}{x-5}$

44. $\dfrac{x}{x-4} - \dfrac{2}{x+3} = \dfrac{20}{x^2-x-12}$

For Problems 45–60, set up an algebraic equation and solve each problem. **(Objective 3)**

45. A sum of $1750 is to be divided between two people in the ratio of 3 to 4. How much does each person receive?

46. A blueprint has a scale in which 1 inch represents 5 feet. Find the dimensions of a rectangular room that measures $3\dfrac{1}{2}$ inches by $5\dfrac{3}{4}$ inches on the blueprint.

47. One angle of a triangle has a measure of 60°, and the measures of the other two angles are in the ratio of 2 to 3. Find the measures of the other two angles.

48. The ratio of the complement of an angle to its supplement is 1 to 4. Find the measure of the angle.

49. If a home valued at $150,000 is assessed $2500 in real estate taxes, then what are the taxes on a home valued at $210,000 if assessed at the same rate?

50. The ratio of male students to female students at a certain university is 5 to 7. If there is a total of 16,200 students, find the number of male students and the number of female students.

51. Suppose that, together, Laura and Tammy sold $120.75 worth of candy for the annual school fair. If the ratio of Tammy's sales to Laura's sales was 4 to 3, how much did each sell?

52. The total value of a house and a lot is $168,000. If the ratio of the value of the house to the value of the lot is 7 to 1, find the value of the house.

53. A 20-foot board is to be cut into two pieces whose lengths are in the ratio of 7 to 3. Find the lengths of the two pieces.

54. An inheritance of $300,000 is to be divided between a son and the local heart fund in the ratio of 3 to 1. How much money will the son receive?

55. Suppose that in a certain precinct, 1150 people voted in the last presidential election. If the ratio of female voters to male voters was 3 to 2, how many females and how many males voted?

56. The perimeter of a rectangle is 114 centimeters. If the ratio of its width to its length is 7 to 12, find the dimensions of the rectangle.

Thoughts Into Words

57. How could you do Problem 53 without using algebra?

58. How can you tell by inspection that the equation $\dfrac{x}{x+2} = \dfrac{-2}{x+2}$ has no solution?

59. How would you help someone solve the equation $\dfrac{3}{x} - \dfrac{4}{x} = \dfrac{-1}{x}$?

Answers to the Concept Quiz
1. True   **2.** True   **3.** True   **4.** B   **5.** A   **6.** D   **7.** B   **8.** C   **9. (a)** Not a proportion
(b) Proportion   **(c)** Not a proportion   **10.** C, D

4.7   More Fractional Equations and Applications

OBJECTIVES

1 Solve rational equations with denominators that require factoring

2 Solve formulas that involve fractional forms

3 Solve rate-time word problems

Let's begin this section by considering a few more fractional equations. We will continue to solve them using the same basic techniques as in the previous section. That is, we will multiply both sides of the equation by the least common denominator of all of the denominators in the equation, with the necessary restrictions to avoid division by zero. Some of the denominators in these problems will require factoring before we can determine a least common denominator.

Classroom Example
Solve $\dfrac{x}{3x+9} + \dfrac{9}{x^2-9} = \dfrac{1}{3}$.

EXAMPLE 1   Solve $\dfrac{x}{2x-8} + \dfrac{16}{x^2-16} = \dfrac{1}{2}$.

Solution

$$\frac{x}{2x-8} + \frac{16}{x^2-16} = \frac{1}{2}$$

$$\frac{x}{2(x-4)} + \frac{16}{(x+4)(x-4)} = \frac{1}{2}, \qquad x \neq 4 \text{ and } x \neq -4$$

$$2(x-4)(x+4)\left(\frac{x}{2(x-4)} + \frac{16}{(x+4)(x-4)}\right) = 2(x+4)(x-4)\left(\frac{1}{2}\right) \qquad \begin{array}{l}\text{Multiply both}\\ \text{sides by the LCD,}\\ 2(x-4)\,(x+4)\end{array}$$

$$x(x+4) + 2(16) = (x+4)(x-4)$$

$$x^2 + 4x + 32 = x^2 - 16$$

$$4x = -48$$

$$x = -12$$

The solution set is $\{-12\}$. Perhaps you should check it!

In Example 1, note that the restrictions were not indicated until the denominators were expressed in factored form. It is usually easier to determine the necessary restrictions at this step.

Classroom Example
Solve
$$\frac{4}{x + 5} + \frac{3}{3x - 2} = \frac{x + 12}{3x^2 + 13x - 10}.$$

EXAMPLE 2   Solve $\dfrac{3}{n - 5} - \dfrac{2}{2n + 1} = \dfrac{n + 3}{2n^2 - 9n - 5}$.

Solution

$$\frac{3}{n - 5} - \frac{2}{2n + 1} = \frac{n + 3}{2n^2 - 9n - 5}$$

$$\frac{3}{n - 5} - \frac{2}{2n + 1} = \frac{n + 3}{(2n + 1)(n - 5)}, \qquad n \neq -\frac{1}{2} \text{ and } n \neq 5$$

$$(2n + 1)(n - 5)\left(\frac{3}{n - 5} - \frac{2}{2n + 1}\right) = (2n + 1)(n - 5)\left(\frac{n + 3}{(2n + 1)(n - 5)}\right)$$

Multiply both sides by the LCD, $(2n + 1) \cdot (n - 5)$

$$3(2n + 1) - 2(n - 5) = n + 3$$
$$6n + 3 - 2n + 10 = n + 3$$
$$4n + 13 = n + 3$$
$$3n = -10$$
$$n = -\frac{10}{3}$$

The solution set is $\left\{-\dfrac{10}{3}\right\}$.

Classroom Example
Solve $3 - \dfrac{9}{x + 3} = \dfrac{27}{x^2 + 3x}$.

EXAMPLE 3   Solve $2 + \dfrac{4}{x - 2} = \dfrac{8}{x^2 - 2x}$.

Solution

$$2 + \frac{4}{x - 2} = \frac{8}{x^2 - 2x}$$

$$2 + \frac{4}{x - 2} = \frac{8}{x(x - 2)}, \qquad x \neq 0 \text{ and } x \neq 2$$

$$x(x - 2)\left(2 + \frac{4}{x - 2}\right) = x(x - 2)\left(\frac{8}{x(x - 2)}\right)$$

Multiply both sides by the LCD, $x(x - 2)$

$$2x(x - 2) + 4x = 8$$
$$2x^2 - 4x + 4x = 8$$
$$2x^2 = 8$$
$$x^2 = 4$$
$$x^2 - 4 = 0$$
$$(x + 2)(x - 2) = 0$$
$$x + 2 = 0 \qquad \text{or} \qquad x - 2 = 0$$
$$x = -2 \qquad \text{or} \qquad x = 2$$

Because our initial restriction indicated that $x \neq 2$, the only solution is -2. Thus the solution set is $\{-2\}$.

Solving Formulas That Involve Fractional Forms

In Section 2.4, we discussed using the properties of equality to change the form of various formulas. For example, we considered the simple interest formula $A = P + Prt$ and changed its form by solving for P as follows:

$$A = P + Prt$$
$$A = P(1 + rt) \qquad \text{Multiply both sides by } \frac{1}{1 + rt}$$
$$\frac{A}{1 + rt} = P$$

If the formula is in the form of a fractional equation, then the techniques of these last two sections are applicable. Consider the following example.

Classroom Example
Solve the future value formula for r:

$$A = P\left(1 + \frac{r}{n}\right)$$

EXAMPLE 4

If the original cost of some business property is C dollars and it is depreciated linearly over N years, then its value, V, at the end of T years is given by

$$V = C\left(1 - \frac{T}{N}\right)$$

Solve this formula for N in terms of V, C, and T.

Solution

$$V = C\left(1 - \frac{T}{N}\right)$$

$$V = C - \frac{CT}{N}$$

$$N(V) = N\left(C - \frac{CT}{N}\right) \qquad \text{Multiply both sides by } N$$

$$NV = NC - CT$$

$$NV - NC = -CT$$

$$N(V - C) = -CT$$

$$N = \frac{-CT}{V - C}$$

$$N = -\frac{CT}{V - C}$$

Solving Rate-Time Word Problems

In Section 2.4 we solved some uniform motion problems. The formula $d = rt$ was used in the analysis of the problems, and we used guidelines that involve distance relationships. Now let's consider some uniform motion problems for which guidelines involving either times or rates are appropriate. These problems will generate fractional equations to solve.

Classroom Example
An airplane travels 2852 miles in the same time that a car travels 299 miles. If the rate of the plane is 555 miles per hour greater than the rate of the car, find the rate of each.

EXAMPLE 5

An airplane travels 2050 miles in the same time that a car travels 260 miles. If the rate of the plane is 358 miles per hour greater than the rate of the car, find the rate of each.

Solution

Let r represent the rate of the car. Then $r + 358$ represents the rate of the plane. The fact that the times are equal can be a guideline. Remember from the basic formula, $d = rt$, that $t = \dfrac{d}{r}$.

$$\underset{\text{Time of plane}}{\frac{\text{Distance of plane}}{\text{Rate of plane}}} \underset{\text{Equals}}{=} \underset{\text{Time of car}}{\frac{\text{Distance of car}}{\text{Rate of car}}}$$

$$\frac{2050}{r + 358} = \frac{260}{r}$$

$$2050r = 260(r + 358)$$
$$2050r = 260r + 93,080$$
$$1790r = 93,080$$
$$r = 52$$

If $r = 52$, then $r + 358$ equals 410. Thus the rate of the car is 52 miles per hour, and the rate of the plane is 410 miles per hour.

■

Classroom Example
It takes a freight train 1 hour longer to travel 180 miles than it takes an express train to travel 195 miles. The rate of the express train is 20 miles per hour greater than the rate of the freight train. Find the times and rates of both trains.

EXAMPLE 6

It takes a freight train 2 hours longer to travel 300 miles than it takes an express train to travel 280 miles. The rate of the express train is 20 miles per hour greater than the rate of the freight train. Find the times and rates of both trains.

Solution

Let t represent the time of the express train. Then $t + 2$ represents the time of the freight train. Let's record the information of this problem in a table.

	Distance	Time	Rate $= \dfrac{\text{distance}}{\text{time}}$
Express train	280	t	$\dfrac{280}{t}$
Freight train	300	$t + 2$	$\dfrac{300}{t + 2}$

The fact that the rate of the express train is 20 miles per hour greater than the rate of the freight train can be a guideline.

Rate of express   Equals   Rate of freight train plus 20

$$\frac{280}{t} = \frac{300}{t + 2} + 20$$

$$t(t + 2)\left(\frac{280}{t}\right) = t(t + 2)\left(\frac{300}{t + 2} + 20\right) \qquad \text{Multiply both sides by } t(t + 2)$$

$$280(t + 2) = 300t + 20t(t + 2)$$
$$280t + 560 = 300t + 20t^2 + 40t$$
$$280t + 560 = 340t + 20t^2$$
$$0 = 20t^2 + 60t - 560$$
$$0 = t^2 + 3t - 28$$
$$0 = (t + 7)(t - 4)$$
$$t + 7 = 0 \qquad \text{or} \qquad t - 4 = 0$$
$$t = -7 \qquad \text{or} \qquad t = 4$$

The negative solution must be discarded, so the time of the express train (t) is 4 hours, and the time of the freight train ($t + 2$) is 6 hours. The rate of the express train $\left(\dfrac{280}{t}\right)$ is $\dfrac{280}{4} = 70$ miles per hour, and the rate of the freight train $\left(\dfrac{300}{t + 2}\right)$ is $\dfrac{300}{6} = 50$ miles per hour.

■

Remark: Note that to solve Example 5 we went directly to a guideline without the use of a table, but for Example 6 we used a table. Remember that this is a personal preference; we are merely acquainting you with a variety of techniques.

Uniform motion problems are a special case of a larger group of problems we refer to as **rate-time problems**. For example, if a certain machine can produce 150 items in 10 minutes, then we say that the machine is producing at a rate of $\dfrac{150}{10} = 15$ items per minute. Likewise, if a person can do a certain job in 3 hours, then, assuming a constant rate of work, we say that the person is working at a rate of $\dfrac{1}{3}$ of the job per hour. In general, if Q is the quantity of something done in t units of time, then the rate, r, is given by $r = \dfrac{Q}{t}$. We state the rate in terms of *so much quantity per unit of time*. (In uniform motion problems the "quantity" is distance.) Let's consider some examples of rate-time problems.

Classroom Example
If Shayla can paint a chair in 45 minutes, and her sister Jamie can paint a similar chair in 60 minutes, how long will it take them to paint a chair if they work together?

EXAMPLE 7

If Jim can mow a lawn in 50 minutes, and his son, Todd, can mow the same lawn in 40 minutes, how long will it take them to mow the lawn if they work together?

Solution

Jim's rate is $\dfrac{1}{50}$ of the lawn per minute, and Todd's rate is $\dfrac{1}{40}$ of the lawn per minute. If we let m represent the number of minutes that they work together, then $\dfrac{1}{m}$ represents their rate when working together. Therefore, because the sum of the individual rates must equal the rate working together, we can set up and solve the following equation.

$$\underset{\text{Jim's rate}}{\dfrac{1}{50}} + \underset{\text{Todd's rate}}{\dfrac{1}{40}} = \underset{\text{Combined rate}}{\dfrac{1}{m}}$$

$$200m\left(\dfrac{1}{50} + \dfrac{1}{40}\right) = 200m\left(\dfrac{1}{m}\right)$$

$$4m + 5m = 200$$

$$9m = 200$$

$$m = \dfrac{200}{9} = 22\dfrac{2}{9}$$

It should take them $22\dfrac{2}{9}$ minutes.

Classroom Example
Working together, Kevin and Casey can wash the windows in $3\dfrac{1}{2}$ hours. Kevin can wash the windows by himself in $6\dfrac{1}{2}$ hours. How long would it take Casey to wash the windows by herself?

EXAMPLE 8

Working together, Linda and Kathy can type a term paper in $3\dfrac{3}{5}$ hours. Linda can type the paper by herself in 6 hours. How long would it take Kathy to type the paper by herself?

Solution

Their rate working together is $\dfrac{1}{3\dfrac{3}{5}} = \dfrac{1}{\dfrac{18}{5}} = \dfrac{5}{18}$ of the job per hour, and Linda's rate is $\dfrac{1}{6}$ of the job per hour. If we let h represent the number of hours that it would take Kathy to do the job by herself, then her rate is $\dfrac{1}{h}$ of the job per hour. Thus we have

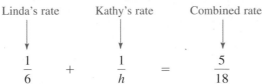

Linda's rate   Kathy's rate   Combined rate

$$\dfrac{1}{6} \quad + \quad \dfrac{1}{h} \quad = \quad \dfrac{5}{18}$$

Solving this equation yields

$$18h\left(\dfrac{1}{6} + \dfrac{1}{h}\right) = 18h\left(\dfrac{5}{18}\right)$$

$$3h + 18 = 5h$$

$$18 = 2h$$

$$9 = h$$

It would take Kathy 9 hours to type the paper by herself. ◼

Our final example of this section illustrates another approach that some people find meaningful for rate-time problems. For this approach, think in terms of fractional parts of the job. For example, if a person can do a certain job in 5 hours, then at the end of 2 hours, he or she has done $\dfrac{2}{5}$ of the job. (Again, assume a constant rate of work.) At the end of 4 hours, he or she has finished $\dfrac{4}{5}$ of the job; and, in general, at the end of h hours, he or she has done $\dfrac{h}{5}$ of the job.

Just as for the motion problems in which distance equals rate times the time, here the fractional part done equals the working rate times the time. Let's see how this works in a problem.

EXAMPLE 9

It takes Pat 12 hours to detail a boat. After he had been working for 3 hours, he was joined by his brother Mike, and together they finished the detailing in 5 hours. How long would it take Mike to detail the boat by himself?

Solution

Let h represent the number of hours that it would take Mike to do the detailing by himself. The fractional part of the job that Pat does equals his working rate times his time. Because it takes Pat 12 hours to do the entire job, his working rate is $\dfrac{1}{12}$. He works for 8 hours (3 hours before Mike and then 5 hours with Mike). Therefore, Pat's part of the job is $\dfrac{1}{12}(8) = \dfrac{8}{12}$. The fractional part of the job that Mike does equals his working rate times his time. Because h represents Mike's time to do the entire job, his working rate is $\dfrac{1}{h}$; he works for 5 hours. Therefore, Mike's part of the job is $\dfrac{1}{h}(5) = \dfrac{5}{h}$. Adding the two fractional parts together results in 1 entire job being done. Let's also show this information in chart form and set up our guideline. Then we can set up and solve the equation.

	Time to do entire job	Working rate	Time working	Fractional part of the job done
Pat	12	$\dfrac{1}{12}$	8	$\dfrac{8}{12}$
Mike	h	$\dfrac{1}{h}$	5	$\dfrac{5}{h}$

$$\underset{\substack{\text{Fractional part of} \\ \text{the job that Pat does}}}{\nearrow} \qquad \underset{\substack{\text{Fractional part of} \\ \text{the job that Mike does}}}{\swarrow}$$

$$\frac{8}{12} + \frac{5}{h} = 1$$

$$12h\left(\frac{8}{12} + \frac{5}{h}\right) = 12h(1)$$

$$12h\left(\frac{8}{12}\right) + 12h\left(\frac{5}{h}\right) = 12h$$

$$8h + 60 = 12h$$

$$60 = 4h$$

$$15 = h$$

It would take Mike 15 hours to detail the boat by himself.   ■

Concept Quiz 4.7

For Problems 1–10, answer true or false.

1. Assuming uniform motion, the rate at which a car travels is equal to the time traveled divided by the distance traveled.

2. If a worker can lay 640 square feet of tile in 8 hours, we can say his rate of work is 80 square feet per hour.

3. If a person can complete two jobs in 5 hours, then the person is working at the rate of $\frac{5}{2}$ of the job per hour.

4. In a time-rate problem involving two workers, the sum of their individual rates must equal the rate working together.

5. If a person works at the rate of $\frac{2}{15}$ of the job per hour, then at the end of 3 hours the job would be $\frac{6}{15}$ completed.

6. If a person can do a job in 7 hours, then at the end of 5 hours he or she will have completed $\frac{5}{7}$ of the job.

7. If a person can do a job in h hours, then at the end of 3 hours he or she will have completed $\frac{h}{3}$ of the job.

8. The equation $A = P + Prt$ cannot be solved for P, because P occurs in two different terms.

9. If Zorka can complete a certain task in 5 hours and Mitzie can complete the same task in 9 hours, then working together they should be able to complete the task in 7 hours.

10. Uniform motion problems are one type of rate-time problem.

Problem Set 4.7

For Problems 1–30, solve each equation. (Objective 1)

1. $\dfrac{x}{4x - 4} + \dfrac{5}{x^2 - 1} = \dfrac{1}{4}$

2. $\dfrac{x}{3x - 6} + \dfrac{4}{x^2 - 4} = \dfrac{1}{3}$

3. $3 + \dfrac{6}{t - 3} = \dfrac{6}{t^2 - 3t}$

4. $2 + \dfrac{4}{t - 1} = \dfrac{4}{t^2 - t}$

5. $\dfrac{3}{n - 5} + \dfrac{4}{n + 7} = \dfrac{2n + 11}{n^2 + 2n - 35}$

6. $\dfrac{2}{n + 3} + \dfrac{3}{n - 4} = \dfrac{2n - 1}{n^2 - n - 12}$

7. $\dfrac{5x}{2x + 6} - \dfrac{4}{x^2 - 9} = \dfrac{5}{2}$

8. $\dfrac{3x}{5x + 5} - \dfrac{2}{x^2 - 1} = \dfrac{3}{5}$

9. $1 + \dfrac{1}{n - 1} = \dfrac{1}{n^2 - n}$

10. $3 + \dfrac{9}{n - 3} = \dfrac{27}{n^2 - 3n}$

11. $\dfrac{2}{n-2} - \dfrac{n}{n+5} = \dfrac{10n+15}{n^2+3n-10}$

12. $\dfrac{n}{n+3} + \dfrac{1}{n-4} = \dfrac{11-n}{n^2-n-12}$

13. $\dfrac{2}{2x-3} - \dfrac{2}{10x^2-13x-3} = \dfrac{x}{5x+1}$

14. $\dfrac{1}{3x+4} + \dfrac{6}{6x^2+5x-4} = \dfrac{x}{2x-1}$

15. $\dfrac{2x}{x+3} - \dfrac{3}{x-6} = \dfrac{29}{x^2-3x-18}$

16. $\dfrac{x}{x-4} - \dfrac{2}{x+8} = \dfrac{63}{x^2+4x-32}$

17. $\dfrac{a}{a-5} + \dfrac{2}{a-6} = \dfrac{2}{a^2-11a+30}$

18. $\dfrac{a}{a+2} + \dfrac{3}{a+4} = \dfrac{14}{a^2+6a+8}$

19. $\dfrac{-1}{2x-5} + \dfrac{2x-4}{4x^2-25} = \dfrac{5}{6x+15}$

20. $\dfrac{-2}{3x+2} + \dfrac{x-1}{9x^2-4} = \dfrac{3}{12x-8}$

21. $\dfrac{7y+2}{12y^2+11y-15} - \dfrac{1}{3y+5} = \dfrac{2}{4y-3}$

22. $\dfrac{5y-4}{6y^2+y-12} - \dfrac{2}{2y+3} = \dfrac{5}{3y-4}$

23. $\dfrac{2n}{6n^2+7n-3} - \dfrac{n-3}{3n^2+11n-4} = \dfrac{5}{2n^2+11n+12}$

24. $\dfrac{x+1}{2x^2+7x-4} - \dfrac{x}{2x^2-7x+3} = \dfrac{1}{x^2+x-12}$

25. $\dfrac{1}{2x^2-x-1} + \dfrac{3}{2x^2+x} = \dfrac{2}{x^2-1}$

26. $\dfrac{2}{n^2+4n} + \dfrac{3}{n^2-3n-28} = \dfrac{5}{n^2-6n-7}$

27. $\dfrac{x+1}{x^3-9x} - \dfrac{1}{2x^2+x-21} = \dfrac{1}{2x^2+13x+21}$

28. $\dfrac{x}{2x^2+5x} - \dfrac{x}{2x^2+7x+5} = \dfrac{2}{x^2+x}$

29. $\dfrac{4t}{4t^2-t-3} + \dfrac{2-3t}{3t^2-t-2} = \dfrac{1}{12t^2+17t+6}$

30. $\dfrac{2t}{2t^2+9t+10} + \dfrac{1-3t}{3t^2+4t-4} = \dfrac{4}{6t^2+11t-10}$

For Problems 31–44, solve each equation for the indicated variable. (Objective 2)

31. $y = \dfrac{5}{6}x + \dfrac{2}{9}$ for x

32. $y = \dfrac{3}{4}x - \dfrac{2}{3}$ for x

33. $\dfrac{-2}{x-4} = \dfrac{5}{y-1}$ for y

34. $\dfrac{7}{y-3} = \dfrac{3}{x+1}$ for y

35. $I = \dfrac{100M}{C}$ for M

36. $V = C\left(1 - \dfrac{T}{N}\right)$ for T

37. $\dfrac{R}{S} = \dfrac{T}{S+T}$ for R

38. $\dfrac{1}{R} = \dfrac{1}{S} + \dfrac{1}{T}$ for R

39. $\dfrac{y-1}{x-3} - \dfrac{b-1}{a-3}$ for y

40. $y = -\dfrac{a}{b}x + \dfrac{c}{d}$ for x

41. $\dfrac{x}{a} + \dfrac{y}{b} = 1$ for y

42. $\dfrac{y-b}{x} = m$ for y

43. $\dfrac{y-1}{x+6} = \dfrac{-2}{3}$ for y

44. $\dfrac{y+5}{x-2} = \dfrac{3}{7}$ for y

Set up an equation and solve each of the following problems. (Objective 3)

45. Kent drives his Mazda 270 miles in the same time that it takes Dave to drive his Nissan 250 miles. If Kent averages 4 miles per hour faster than Dave, find their rates.

46. Suppose that Wendy rides her bicycle 30 miles in the same time that it takes Kim to ride her bicycle 20 miles. If Wendy rides 5 miles per hour faster than Kim, find the rate of each.

47. An inlet pipe can fill a tank (see Figure 4.2) in 10 minutes. A drain can empty the tank in 12 minutes. If the tank is empty, and both the pipe and drain are open, how long will it take before the tank overflows?

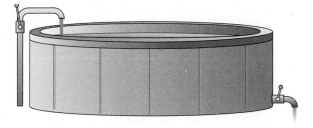

Figure 4.2

48. Barry can do a certain job in 3 hours, whereas it takes Sanchez 5 hours to do the same job. How long would it take them to do the job working together?

49. Connie can type 600 words in 5 minutes less than it takes Katie to type 600 words. If Connie types at a rate of 20 words per minute faster than Katie types, find the typing rate of each woman.

50. Walt can mow a lawn in 1 hour, and his son, Malik, can mow the same lawn in 50 minutes. One day Malik started mowing the lawn by himself and worked for 30 minutes. Then Walt joined him and they finished the lawn. How long did it take them to finish mowing the lawn after Walt started to help?

51. Plane A can travel 1400 miles in 1 hour less time than it takes plane B to travel 2000 miles. The rate of plane B is 50 miles per hour greater than the rate of plane A. Find the times and rates of both planes.

52. To travel 60 miles, it takes Sue, riding a moped, 2 hours less time than it takes Doreen to travel 50 miles riding a bicycle. Sue travels 10 miles per hour faster than Doreen. Find the times and rates of both girls.

53. It takes Amy twice as long to deliver papers as it does Nancy. How long would it take each girl to deliver the papers by herself if they can deliver the papers together in 40 minutes?

54. If two inlet pipes are both open, they can fill a pool in 1 hour and 12 minutes. One of the pipes can fill the pool by itself in 2 hours. How long would it take the other pipe to fill the pool by itself?

55. Rod agreed to mow a vacant lot for $12. It took him an hour longer than he had anticipated, so he earned $1 per hour less than he had originally calculated. How long had he anticipated that it would take him to mow the lot?

56. Last week Al bought some golf balls for $20. The next day they were on sale for $0.50 per ball less, and he bought $22.50 worth of balls. If he purchased 5 more balls on the second day than on the first day, how many did he buy each day and at what price per ball?

57. Debbie rode her bicycle out into the country for a distance of 24 miles. On the way back, she took a much shorter route of 12 miles and made the return trip in one-half hour less time. If her rate out into the country was 4 miles per hour greater than her rate on the return trip, find both rates.

58. Felipe jogs for 10 miles and then walks another 10 miles. He jogs $2\frac{1}{2}$ miles per hour faster than he walks, and the entire distance of 20 miles takes 6 hours. Find the rate at which he walks and the rate at which he jogs.

Thoughts Into Words

59. Why is it important to consider more than one way to do a problem?

60. Write a paragraph or two summarizing the new ideas about problem solving you have acquired thus far in this course.

Answers to the Concept Quiz

1. False   **2.** True   **3.** False   **4.** True   **5.** True   **6.** True   **7.** False   **8.** False   **9.** False   **10.** True

OBJECTIVE	SUMMARY	EXAMPLE
Reduce rational numbers and rational expressions. (Section 4.1/Objectives 1 and 2)	Any number that can be written in the form $\frac{a}{b}$, where a and b are integers and $b \neq 0$, is a rational number. A rational expression is defined as the indicated quotient of two polynomials. The fundamental principle of fractions, $\frac{a \cdot k}{b \cdot k} = \frac{a}{b}$, is used when reducing rational numbers or rational expressions.	Simplify $\dfrac{x^2 - 2x - 15}{x^2 + x - 6}$. Solution $\dfrac{x^2 - 2x - 15}{x^2 + x - 6}$ $= \dfrac{(x + 3)(x - 5)}{(x + 3)(x - 2)} = \dfrac{x - 5}{x - 2}$
Multiply rational numbers and rational expressions. (Section 4.2/Objectives 1 and 2)	Multiplication of rational expressions is based on the following definition: $\dfrac{a}{b} \cdot \dfrac{c}{d} = \dfrac{ac}{bd}$, where $b \neq 0$ and $d \neq 0$	Find the product: $\dfrac{3y^2 + 12y}{y^3 - 2y^2} \cdot \dfrac{y^2 - 3y + 2}{y^2 + 7y + 12}$ Solution $\dfrac{3y^2 + 12y}{y^3 - 2y^2} \cdot \dfrac{y^2 - 3y + 2}{y^2 + 7y + 12}$ $= \dfrac{3y(y + 4)}{y^2(y - 2)} \cdot \dfrac{(y - 2)(y - 1)}{(y + 3)(y + 4)}$ $= \dfrac{3y(y + 4)}{y^2(y - 2)} \cdot \dfrac{(y - 2)(y - 1)}{(y + 3)(y + 4)}$ $= \dfrac{3(y - 1)}{y(y + 3)}$
Divide rational numbers and rational expressions. (Section 4.2/Objectives 3 and 4)	Division of rational expressions is based on the following definition: $\dfrac{a}{b} \div \dfrac{c}{d} = \dfrac{a}{b} \cdot \dfrac{d}{c} = \dfrac{ad}{bc}$, where $b \neq 0$, $c \neq 0$, and $d \neq 0$	Find the quotient: $\dfrac{6xy}{x^2 - 6x + 9} \div \dfrac{18x}{x^2 - 9}$ Solution $\dfrac{6xy}{x^2 - 6x + 9} \div \dfrac{18x}{x^2 - 9}$ $= \dfrac{6xy}{x^2 - 6x + 9} \cdot \dfrac{x^2 - 9}{18x}$ $= \dfrac{6xy}{(x - 3)(x - 3)} \cdot \dfrac{(x + 3)(x - 3)}{18x}$ $= \dfrac{6xy}{(x - 3)(x - 3)} \cdot \dfrac{(x + 3)(x - 3)}{18x}$ $= \dfrac{y(x - 3)}{3(x - 3)}$

(continued)

OBJECTIVE	SUMMARY	EXAMPLE
Simplify problems that involve both multiplication and division of rational expressions. (Section 4.2/Objective 5)	Perform the multiplications and divisions from left to right according to the order of operations. You can change division to multiplication by multiplying by the reciprocal and then finding the product.	Perform the indicated operations: $$\frac{6xy^3}{5x} \div \frac{3xy}{10} \cdot \frac{y}{7x^2}$$ **Solution** $$\frac{6xy^3}{5x} \div \frac{3xy}{10} \cdot \frac{y}{7x^2}$$ $$= \frac{6xy^3}{5x} \cdot \frac{10}{3xy} \cdot \frac{y}{7x^2}$$ $$= \frac{\overset{2}{6}xy^3}{5x} \cdot \frac{\overset{2}{10}}{3xy} \cdot \frac{y}{7x^2}$$ $$= \frac{4y^3}{7x^3}$$
Add and subtract rational numbers or rational expressions. (Section 4.3/Objectives 1 and 2; Section 4.4/Objective 1)	Addition and subtraction of rational expressions are based on the following definitions. $$\frac{a}{b} + \frac{c}{b} = \frac{a+c}{b} \quad \text{Addition}$$ $$\frac{a}{b} - \frac{c}{b} = \frac{a-c}{b} \quad \text{Subtraction}$$ The following basic procedure is used to add or subtract rational expressions. **1.** Factor the denominators. **2.** Find the LCD. **3.** Change each fraction to an equivalent fraction that has the LCD as the denominator. **4.** Combine the numerators and place over the LCD. **5.** Simplify by performing the addition or subtraction in the numerator. **6.** If possible, reduce the resulting fraction.	Subtract: $$\frac{2}{x^2 - 2x - 3} - \frac{5}{x^2 + 5x + 4}$$ **Solution** $$\frac{2}{x^2 - 2x - 3} - \frac{5}{x^2 + 5x + 4}$$ $$= \frac{2}{(x-3)(x+1)}$$ $$\quad - \frac{5}{(x+1)(x+4)}$$ The LCD is $(x-3)(x+1)(x+4)$. $$= \frac{2(x + 4r}{(x-3)(x+1)(x+4)}$$ $$\quad - \frac{5(x-3)}{(x+1)(x+4)(x-3)}$$ $$= \frac{2(x+4) - 5(x-3)}{(x-3)(x+1)(x+4)}$$ $$= \frac{2x + 8 - 5x + 15}{(x-3)(x+1)(x+4)}$$ $$= \frac{-3x + 23}{(x-3)(x+1)(x+4)}$$

OBJECTIVE	SUMMARY	EXAMPLE
Simplify complex fractions. (Section 4.4/Objective 2)	Fractions that contain rational numbers or rational expressions in the numerators or denominators are called complex fractions. In Section 4.4, two methods were shown for simplifying complex fractions.	Simplify $\dfrac{\dfrac{2}{x} - \dfrac{3}{y}}{\dfrac{4}{x^2} + \dfrac{5}{y}}$. **Solution** $$\dfrac{\dfrac{2}{x} - \dfrac{3}{y}}{\dfrac{4}{x^2} + \dfrac{5}{y}}$$ Multiply the numerator and denominator by x^2y: $$\dfrac{x^2y\left(\dfrac{2}{x} - \dfrac{3}{y}\right)}{x^2y\left(\dfrac{4}{x^2} + \dfrac{5}{y}\right)}$$ $$= \dfrac{x^2y\left(\dfrac{2}{x}\right) + x^2y\left(-\dfrac{3}{y}\right)}{x^2y\left(\dfrac{4}{x^2}\right) + x^2y\left(\dfrac{5}{y}\right)}$$ $$= \dfrac{2xy - 3x^2}{4y + 5x^2}.$$
Divide polynomials. (Section 4.5/Objective 1)	1. To divide a polynomial by a monomial, divide each term of the polynomial by the monomial. 2. The procedure for dividing a polynomial by a polynomial resembles the long-division process.	Divide $2x^2 + 11x + 19$ by $x + 3$. **Solution** $\begin{array}{r} 2x + 5 \\ x+3{\overline{\smash{\big)}\,2x^2 + 11x + 19}} \\ \underline{2x^2 + 6x} \\ 5x + 19 \\ \underline{5x + 15} \\ 4 \end{array}$ Thus $\dfrac{2x^2 + 11x + 19}{x + 3}$ $$= 2x + 5 + \dfrac{4}{x + 3}.$$
Use synthetic division to divide polynomials. (Section 4.5/Objective 2)	Synthetic division is a shortcut to the long-division process when the divisor is of the form $x - k$.	Divide $x^4 - 3x^2 + 5x + 6$ by $x + 2$. **Solution** $\begin{array}{r} -2{\overline{\smash{\big)}\,1 \quad 0 \quad -3 \quad 5 \quad 6}} \\ \underline{-2 \quad 4 \quad -2 \quad -6} \\ 1 \quad -2 \quad 1 \quad 3 \quad 0 \end{array}$ Thus $\dfrac{x^4 - 3x^2 + 5x + 6}{x + 2}$ $$= x^3 - 2x^2 + x + 3.$$

(continued)

OBJECTIVE	SUMMARY	EXAMPLE
Solve rational equations. (Section 4.6/Objective 1)	To solve a rational equation, it is often easiest to begin by multiplying both sides of the equation by the LCD of all the denominators in the equation. Recall that any value of the variable that makes the denominators zero cannot be a solution to the equation.	Solve $\dfrac{2}{3x} + \dfrac{5}{12} = \dfrac{1}{4x}$. **Solution** $\dfrac{2}{3x} + \dfrac{5}{12} = \dfrac{1}{4x}, \quad x \neq 0$ Multiply both sides by $12x$: $12x\left(\dfrac{2}{3x} + \dfrac{5}{12}\right) = 12x\left(\dfrac{1}{4x}\right)$ $12x\left(\dfrac{2}{3x}\right) + 12x\left(\dfrac{5}{12}\right)$ $\qquad\qquad = 12x\left(\dfrac{1}{4x}\right)$ $8 + 5x = 3$ $5x = -5$ $x = -1$ The solution set is $\{-1\}$.
Solve proportions. (Section 4.6/Objective 2)	A ratio is the comparison of two numbers by division. A proportion is a statement of equality between two ratios. Proportions can be solved using the cross-multiplication property of proportions.	Solve $\dfrac{5}{2x - 1} = \dfrac{3}{x + 4}$. **Solution** $\dfrac{5}{2x - 1} = \dfrac{3}{x + 4}, \quad x \neq -4, x \neq \dfrac{1}{2}$ $3(2x - 1) = 5(x + 4)$ $6x - 3 = 5x + 20$ $x = 23$ The solution set is $\{23\}$.
Solve rational equations where the denominators require factoring. (Section 4.7/Objective 1)	It may be necessary to factor the denominators in a rational equation in order to determine the LCD of all the denominators.	Solve $\dfrac{7x}{3x + 12} - \dfrac{2}{x^2 - 16} = \dfrac{7}{3}$. **Solution** $\dfrac{7x}{3x + 12} - \dfrac{2}{x^2 - 16} = \dfrac{7}{3}, \quad x \neq -4, x \neq 4$ $\dfrac{7x}{3(x + 4)} - \dfrac{2}{(x - 4)(x + 4)} = \dfrac{7}{3}$ Multiply both sides by $3(x + 4)(x - 4)$: $7x(x - 4) - 2(3) = 7(x + 4)(x - 4)$ $7x^2 - 28x - 6 = 7x^2 - 112$ $-28x = -106$ $x = \dfrac{-106}{-28} = \dfrac{53}{14}$ The solution set is $\left\{\dfrac{53}{14}\right\}$.

OBJECTIVE	SUMMARY	EXAMPLE
Solve formulas that involve fractional forms. (Section 4.7/Objective 2)	The techniques that are used for solving rational equations can also be used to change the form of formulas.	Solve $\dfrac{x}{2a} - \dfrac{y}{2b} = 1$ for y. **Solution** $\dfrac{x}{2a} - \dfrac{y}{2b} = 1$ Multiply both sides by $2ab$: $2ab\left(\dfrac{x}{2a} - \dfrac{y}{2b}\right) = 2ab(1)$ $bx - ay = 2ab$ $-ay = 2ab - bx$ $y = \dfrac{2ab - bx}{-a}$ $y = \dfrac{-2ab + bx}{a}$
Solve word problems involving ratios. (Section 4.6/Objective 3)	Many real-world situations can be solved by using ratios and setting up a proportion to be solved.	At a law firm, the ratio of female attorneys to male attorneys is 1 to 4. If the firm has a total of 125 attorneys, find the number of female attorneys. **Solution** Let x represent the number of female attorneys. Then $125 - x$ represents the numbers of male attorneys. The following proportion can be set up. $\dfrac{x}{125 - x} = \dfrac{1}{4}$ Solve by cross-multiplication: $\dfrac{x}{125 - x} = \dfrac{1}{4}$ $4x = 1(125 - x)$ $4x = 125 - x$ $5x = 125$ $x = 25$ There are 25 female attorneys.

(continued)

OBJECTIVE	SUMMARY	EXAMPLE
Solve rate-time word problems. (Section 4.7/Objective 3)	Uniform motion problems are a special case of rate-time problems. In general, if Q is the quantity of some job done in t time units, then the rate, r, is given by $r = \dfrac{Q}{t}$.	At a veterinarian clinic, it takes Laurie twice as long to feed the animals as it does Janet. How long would it take each person to feed the animals by herself if they can feed the animals together in 60 minutes? **Solution** Let t represent the time it takes Janet to feed the animals. Then $2t$ represents the time it would take Laurie to feed the animals. Laurie's rate plus Janet's rate equals the rate working together. $$\frac{1}{2t} + \frac{1}{t} = \frac{1}{60}$$ Multiply both sides by $60t$: $$60t\left(\frac{1}{2t} + \frac{1}{t}\right) = 60t\left(\frac{1}{60}\right)$$ $$30 + 60 = t$$ $$90 = t$$ It would take Janet 90 minutes working alone to feed the animals, and it would take Laurie 180 minutes working alone to feed the animals.

Chapter 4 Review Problem Set

For Problems 1–6, simplify each rational expression.

1. $\dfrac{26x^2y^3}{39x^4y^2}$

2. $\dfrac{a^2 - 9}{a^2 + 3a}$

3. $\dfrac{n^2 - 3n - 10}{n^2 + n - 2}$

4. $\dfrac{x^4 - 1}{x^3 - x}$

5. $\dfrac{8x^3 - 2x^2 - 3x}{12x^2 - 9x}$

6. $\dfrac{x^4 - 7x^2 - 30}{2x^4 + 7x^2 + 3}$

For Problems 7–10, simplify each complex fraction.

7. $\dfrac{\dfrac{5}{8} - \dfrac{1}{2}}{\dfrac{1}{6} + \dfrac{3}{4}}$

8. $\dfrac{\dfrac{3}{2x} + \dfrac{5}{3y}}{\dfrac{4}{x} - \dfrac{3}{4y}}$

9. $\dfrac{\dfrac{3}{x - 2} - \dfrac{4}{x^2 - 4}}{\dfrac{2}{x + 2} + \dfrac{1}{x - 2}}$

10. $1 - \dfrac{1}{2 - \dfrac{1}{x}}$

For Problems 11–24, perform the indicated operations, and express your answers in simplest form.

11. $\dfrac{6xy^2}{7y^3} \div \dfrac{15x^2y}{5x^2}$

12. $\dfrac{9ab}{3a + 6} \cdot \dfrac{a^2 - 4a - 12}{a^2 - 6a}$

13. $\dfrac{n^2 + 10n + 25}{n^2 - n} \cdot \dfrac{5n^3 - 3n^2}{5n^2 + 22n - 15}$

14. $\dfrac{x^2 - 2xy - 3y^2}{x^2 + 9y^2} \div \dfrac{2x^2 + xy - y^2}{2x^2 - xy}$

15. $\dfrac{2x + 1}{5} + \dfrac{3x - 2}{4}$

16. $\dfrac{3}{2n} + \dfrac{5}{3n} - \dfrac{1}{9}$

17. $\dfrac{3x}{x + 7} - \dfrac{2}{x}$

18. $\dfrac{10}{x^2 - 5x} + \dfrac{2}{x}$

19. $\dfrac{3}{n^2 - 5n - 36} + \dfrac{2}{n^2 + 3n - 4}$

20. $\dfrac{3}{2y+3} + \dfrac{5y-2}{2y^2-9y-18} - \dfrac{1}{y-6}$

21. $\dfrac{2x^2 y}{3x} \cdot \dfrac{xy^2}{6} \div \dfrac{x}{9y}$ **22.** $\dfrac{10x^4 y^3}{8x^2 y} \div \dfrac{5}{xy^2} \cdot \dfrac{3y}{x}$

23. $\dfrac{8x}{2x-6} \div \dfrac{2x-1}{x^2-9} \cdot \dfrac{2x^2+x-1}{x^2+7x+12}$

24. $\dfrac{2-x}{6} \cdot \dfrac{x+1}{x^2-4} \div \dfrac{x^2+2x+1}{10}$

For Problems 25–26, perform the long division.

25. $(18x^2 + 9x - 2) \div (3x + 2)$

26. $(3x^3 + 5x^2 - 6x - 2) \div (x + 4)$

For Problems 27–28, divide using synthetic division.

27. Divide $3x^4 - 14x^3 + 7x^2 + 6x - 8$ by $x - 4$.

28. Divide $2x^4 + x^2 - x + 3$ by $x + 1$.

For Problems 29–40, solve each equation.

29. $\dfrac{4x+5}{3} + \dfrac{2x-1}{5} = 2$ **30.** $\dfrac{3}{4x} + \dfrac{4}{5} = \dfrac{9}{10x}$

31. $\dfrac{a}{a-2} - \dfrac{3}{2} = \dfrac{2}{a-2}$ **32.** $\dfrac{4}{5y-3} = \dfrac{2}{3y+7}$

33. $n + \dfrac{1}{n} = \dfrac{53}{14}$

34. $\dfrac{1}{2x-7} + \dfrac{x-5}{4x^2-49} = \dfrac{4}{6x-21}$

35. $\dfrac{x}{2x+1} - 1 = \dfrac{-4}{7(x-2)}$ **36.** $\dfrac{2x}{-5} = \dfrac{3}{4x-13}$

37. $\dfrac{2n}{2n^2+11n-21} - \dfrac{n}{n^2+5n-14} = \dfrac{3}{n^2+5n-14}$

38. $\dfrac{2}{t^2-t-6} + \dfrac{t+1}{t^2+t-12} = \dfrac{t}{t^2+6t+8}$

39. Solve $\dfrac{y-6}{x+1} = \dfrac{3}{4}$ for y.

40. Solve $\dfrac{x}{a} - \dfrac{y}{b} = 1$ for y.

For Problems 41–47, set up an equation, and solve the problem.

41. A sum of \$1400 is to be divided between two people in the ratio of $\dfrac{3}{5}$. How much does each person receive?

42. At a restaurant the tips are split between the busboy and the waiter in the ratio of 2 to 7. Find the amount each received in tips if there was a total of \$162 in tips.

43. Working together, Dan and Julio can mow a lawn in 12 minutes. Julio can mow the lawn by himself in 10 minutes less time than it takes Dan by himself. How long does it take each of them to mow the lawn alone?

44. Suppose that car A can travel 250 miles in 3 hours less time than it takes car B to travel 440 miles. The rate of car B is 5 miles per hour faster than that of car A. Find the rates of both cars.

45. Mark can overhaul an engine in 20 hours, and Phil can do the same job by himself in 30 hours. If they both work together for a time and then Mark finishes the job by himself in 5 hours, how long did they work together?

46. Kelly contracted to paint a house for \$640. It took him 20 hours longer than he had anticipated, so he earned \$1.60 per hour less than he had calculated. How long had he anticipated that it would take him to paint the house?

47. Nasser rode his bicycle 66 miles in $4\dfrac{1}{2}$ hours. For the first 40 miles he averaged a certain rate, and then for the last 26 miles he reduced his rate by 3 miles per hour. Find his rate for the last 26 miles.

For Problems 1–4, simplify each rational expression.

1. $\dfrac{39x^2y^3}{72x^3y}$

2. $\dfrac{3x^2 + 17x - 6}{x^3 - 36x}$

3. $\dfrac{6n^2 - 5n - 6}{3n^2 + 14n + 8}$

4. $\dfrac{2x - 2x^2}{x^2 - 1}$

For Problems 5–13, perform the indicated operations, and express your answers in simplest form.

5. $\dfrac{5x^2y}{8x} \cdot \dfrac{12y^2}{20xy}$

6. $\dfrac{5a + 5b}{20a + 10b} \cdot \dfrac{a^2 - ab}{2a^2 + 2ab}$

7. $\dfrac{3x^2 + 10x - 8}{5x^2 + 19x - 4} \div \dfrac{3x^2 - 23x + 14}{x^2 - 3x - 28}$

8. $\dfrac{3x - 1}{4} + \dfrac{2x + 5}{6}$

9. $\dfrac{5x - 6}{3} - \dfrac{x - 12}{6}$

10. $\dfrac{3}{5n} + \dfrac{2}{3} - \dfrac{7}{3n}$

11. $\dfrac{3x}{x - 6} + \dfrac{2}{x}$

12. $\dfrac{9}{x^2 - x} - \dfrac{2}{x}$

13. $\dfrac{3}{2n^2 + n - 10} + \dfrac{5}{n^2 + 5n - 14}$

14. Divide $3x^3 + 10x^2 - 9x - 4$ by $x + 4$.

15. Simplify the complex fraction $\dfrac{\dfrac{3}{2x} - \dfrac{1}{6}}{\dfrac{2}{3x} + \dfrac{3}{4}}$.

16. Solve $\dfrac{x + 2}{y - 4} = \dfrac{3}{4}$ for y.

For Problems 17–22, solve each equation.

17. $\dfrac{x - 1}{2} - \dfrac{x + 2}{5} = -\dfrac{3}{5}$

18. $\dfrac{5}{4x} + \dfrac{3}{2} = \dfrac{7}{5x}$

19. $\dfrac{-3}{4n - 1} = \dfrac{-2}{3n + 11}$

20. $n - \dfrac{5}{n} = 4$

21. $\dfrac{6}{x - 4} - \dfrac{4}{x + 3} = \dfrac{8}{x - 4}$

22. $\dfrac{1}{3x - 1} + \dfrac{x - 2}{9x^2 - 1} = \dfrac{7}{6x - 2}$

For Problems 23–25, set up an equation and then solve the problem.

23. The denominator of a rational number is 9 less than three times the numerator. The number in simplest form is $\dfrac{3}{8}$. Find the number.

24. It takes Jodi three times as long to deliver papers as it does Jannie. Together they can deliver the papers in 15 minutes. How long would it take Jodi by herself?

25. René can ride her bike 60 miles in 1 hour less time than it takes Sue to ride 60 miles. René's rate is 3 miles per hour faster than Sue's rate. Find René's rate.

1. Simplify the numerical expression $16 \div 4(2) + 8$.

2. Simplify the numerical expression
$(-2)^2 + (-2)^3 - 3^2$

3. Evaluate $-2xy + 5y^2$ for $x = -3$ and $y = 4$.

4. Evaluate $3(n - 2) + 4(n - 4) - 8(n - 3)$
for $n = -\dfrac{1}{2}$.

For Problems 5–14, perform the indicated operations and then simplify.

5. $(6a^2 + 3a - 4) + (8a + 6) + (a^2 - 1)$

6. $(x^2 + 5x + 2) - (3x^2 - 4x + 6)$

7. $(2x^2y)(-xy^4)$ 8. $(4xy^3)^2$

9. $(-3a^3)^2(4ab^2)$ 10. $(4a^2b)(-3a^3b^2)(2ab)$

11. $-3x^2(6x^2 - x + 4)$ 12. $(5x + 3y)(2x - y)$

13. $(x + 4y)^2$ 14. $(a + 3b)(a^2 - 4ab + b^2)$

For Problems 15–20, factor each polynomial completely.

15. $x^2 - 5x + 6$ 16. $6x^2 - 5x - 4$

17. $2x^2 - 8x + 6$ 18. $3x^2 + 18x - 48$

19. $9m^2 - 16n^2$ 20. $27a^3 + 8$

21. Simplify $\dfrac{-28x^2y^5}{4x^4y}$.   22. Simplify $\dfrac{4x - x^2}{x - 4}$.

For Problems 23–28, perform the indicated operations and express the answer in simplest form.

23. $\dfrac{6xy}{2x + 4} \cdot \dfrac{x^2 - 3x - 10}{3xy - 3y}$

24. $\dfrac{x^2 - 3x - 4}{x^2 - 1} \div \dfrac{x^2 - x - 12}{x^2 + 6x - 7}$

25. $\dfrac{7n - 3}{5} - \dfrac{n + 4}{2}$ 26. $\dfrac{3}{x^2 + x - 6} + \dfrac{5}{x^2 - 9}$

27. $\dfrac{\dfrac{2}{x} + \dfrac{3}{y}}{6}$ 28. $\dfrac{\dfrac{1}{n^2} - \dfrac{1}{m^2}}{\dfrac{1}{m} + \dfrac{1}{n}}$

29. Divide $(6x^3 + 7x^2 + 5x + 12)$ by $(2x + 3)$.

30. Use synthetic division to divide $(2x^3 - 3x^2 - 23x + 14)$ by $(x - 4)$.

For Problems 31–40, solve the equation.

31. $8n - 3(n + 2) = 2n + 12$

32. $0.2(y - 6) = 0.02y + 3.12$

33. $\dfrac{x + 1}{4} + \dfrac{3x + 2}{2} = 5$

34. $\dfrac{5}{8}(x + 2) - \dfrac{1}{2}x = 2$

35. $|3x - 2| = 8$

36. $|x + 8| - 4 = 16$

37. $x^2 + 7x - 8 = 0$

38. $2x^2 + 13x + 15 = 0$

39. $n - \dfrac{3}{n} = \dfrac{26}{3}$

40. $\dfrac{3}{n - 7} + \dfrac{4}{n + 2} = \dfrac{27}{n^2 - 5n - 14}$

41. Solve the formula $A = P + Prt$ for P.

42. Solve the formula $V = \dfrac{1}{3}BH$ for B.

For Problems 43–56, solve the inequality and express the solution in interval notation.

43. $-3x + 2(x - 4) \geq -10$

44. $-10 < 3x + 2 < 8$

45. $|4x + 3| < 15$

46. $|2x + 6| \geq 20$

47. $|x + 4| - 6 > 0$

48. The owner of a local café wants to make a profit of 80% of the cost for each Caesar salad sold. If it costs $3.20 to make a Caesar salad, at what price should each salad be sold?

49. Find the discount sale price of a $920 television that is on sale for 25% off.

50. Suppose that the length of a rectangle is 8 inches less than twice the width. The perimeter of the rectangle is 122 inches. Find the length and width of the rectangle.

51. Two planes leave Kansas City at the same time and fly in opposite directions. If one travels at 450 miles per hour and the other travels at 400 miles per hour, how long will it take for them to be 3400 miles apart?

52. A sum of $68,000 is to be divided between two partners in the ratio of $\dfrac{1}{4}$. How much does each person receive?

53. Victor can rake the lawn in 20 minutes, and his sister Lucia can rake the same lawn in 30 minutes. How long will it take them to rake the lawn if they work together?

54. One leg of a right triangle is 7 inches less than the other leg. The hypotenuse is 1 inch longer than the longer of the two legs. Find the length of the three sides of the right triangle.

55. How long will it take $1500 to double itself at 6% simple interest?

56. A collection of 40 coins consisting of dimes and quarters has a value of $5.95. Find the number of each kind of coin.

5

Exponents and Radicals

5.1 Using Integers as Exponents

5.2 Roots and Radicals

5.3 Combining Radicals and Simplifying Radicals That Contain Variables

5.4 Products and Quotients Involving Radicals

5.5 Equations Involving Radicals

5.6 Merging Exponents and Roots

5.7 Scientific Notation

By knowing the time it takes for the pendulum to swing from one side to the other side and back, the formula, $T = 2\pi\sqrt{\dfrac{L}{32}}$, can be used to find the length of the pendulum.

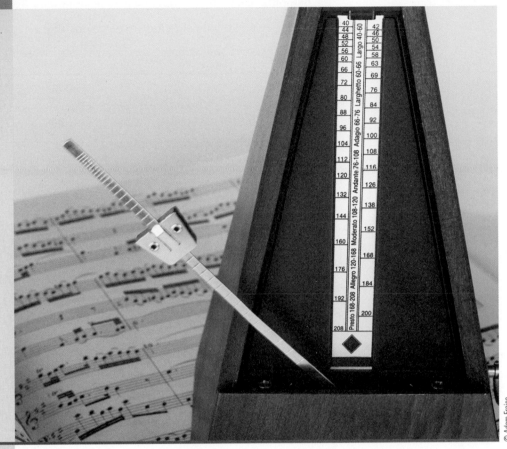

© Adam Fraise

How long will it take a pendulum that is 1.5 feet long to swing from one side to the other side and back? The formula $T = 2\pi\sqrt{\dfrac{L}{32}}$ can be used to determine that it will take approximately 1.4 seconds.

It is not uncommon in mathematics to find two separately developed concepts that are closely related to each other. In this chapter, we will first develop the concepts of exponent and root individually and then show how they merge to become even more functional as a unified idea.

Video tutorials based on section learning objectives are available in a variety of delivery modes.

5.1   Using Integers as Exponents

OBJECTIVES

1 Simplify numerical expressions that have integer exponents

2 Simplify algebraic expressions that have integer exponents

3 Multiply and divide algebraic expressions that have integer exponents

4 Simplify sums and differences of expressions involving integer exponents

Thus far in the text we have used only positive integers as exponents. In Chapter 1 the expression b^n, where b is any real number and n is a positive integer, was defined by

$$b^n = b \cdot b \cdot b \cdot \cdots \cdot b \qquad n \text{ factors of } b$$

Then, in Chapter 3, some of the parts of the following property served as a basis for manipulation with polynomials.

Property 5.1 Properties for Positive Integer Exponents

If m and n are positive integers, and a and b are real numbers (and $b \neq 0$ whenever it appears in a denominator), then

1. $b^n \cdot b^m = b^{n+m}$

2. $(b^n)^m = b^{mn}$

3. $(ab)^n = a^n b^n$

4. $\left(\dfrac{a}{b}\right)^n = \dfrac{a^n}{b^n}$

5. $\dfrac{b^n}{b^m} = b^{n-m}$ when $n > m$

$\dfrac{b^n}{b^m} = 1$ when $n = m$

$\dfrac{b^n}{b^m} = \dfrac{1}{b^{m-n}}$ when $n < m$

We are now ready to extend the concept of an exponent to include the use of zero and the negative integers as exponents.

First, let's consider the use of zero as an exponent. We want to use zero in such a way that the previously listed properties continue to hold. If $b^n \cdot b^m = b^{n+m}$ is to hold, then $x^4 \cdot x^0 = x^{4+0} = x^4$. In other words, x^0 *acts like* 1 because $x^4 \cdot x^0 = x^4$. This line of reasoning suggests the following definition.

Definition 5.1 Exponent of Zero

If b is a nonzero real number, then

$$b^0 = 1$$

According to Definition 5.1, the following statements are all true.

$5^0 = 1$ $(-413)^0 = 1$

$\left(\dfrac{3}{11}\right)^0 = 1$ $n^0 = 1, \quad n \neq 0$

$(x^3 y^4)^0 = 1, \quad x \neq 0, y \neq 0$

We can use a similar line of reasoning to motivate a definition for the use of negative integers as exponents. Consider the example $x^4 \cdot x^{-4}$. If $b^n \cdot b^m = b^{n+m}$ is to hold, then $x^4 \cdot x^{-4} = x^{4+(-4)} = x^0 = 1$. Thus x^{-4} must be the reciprocal of x^4, because their product is 1. That is,

$$x^{-4} = \frac{1}{x^4}$$

This suggests the following general definition.

Definition 5.2 Negative Exponent

If n is a positive integer, and b is a nonzero real number, then

$$b^{-n} = \frac{1}{b^n}$$

According to Definition 5.2, the following statements are all true.

$$x^{-5} = \frac{1}{x^5} \qquad\qquad 2^{-4} = \frac{1}{2^4} = \frac{1}{16}$$

$$10^{-2} = \frac{1}{10^2} = \frac{1}{100} \quad \text{or} \quad 0.01 \qquad\qquad \frac{2}{x^{-3}} = \frac{2}{\frac{1}{x^3}} = (2)\left(\frac{x^3}{1}\right) = 2x^3$$

$$\left(\frac{3}{4}\right)^{-2} = \frac{1}{\left(\frac{3}{4}\right)^2} = \frac{1}{\frac{9}{16}} = \frac{16}{9}$$

It can be verified (although it is beyond the scope of this text) that all of the parts of Property 5.1 hold for *all integers*. In fact, the following equality can replace the three separate statements for part (5).

$$\frac{b^n}{b^m} = b^{n-m} \quad \text{for all integers } n \text{ and } m$$

Let's restate Property 5.1 as it holds for all integers and include, at the right, a "name tag" for easy reference.

Property 5.2 Properties for Integer Exponents

If m and n are integers, and a and b are real numbers (and $b \neq 0$ whenever it appears in a denominator), then

1. $b^n \cdot b^m = b^{n+m}$ Product of two powers

2. $(b^n)^m = b^{mn}$ Power of a power

3. $(ab)^n = a^n b^n$ Power of a product

4. $\left(\dfrac{a}{b}\right)^n = \dfrac{a^n}{b^n}$ Power of a quotient

5. $\dfrac{b^n}{b^m} = b^{n-m}$ Quotient of two powers

Having the use of all integers as exponents enables us to work with a large variety of numerical and algebraic expressions. Let's consider some examples that illustrate the use of the various parts of Property 5.2.

Classroom Example
Simplify each of the following
numerical expressions:

(a) $10^{-5} \cdot 10^2$

(b) $(3^{-2})^{-2}$

(c) $(3^{-1} \cdot 5^2)^{-1}$

(d) $\left(\dfrac{3^{-3}}{5^{-2}}\right)^{-1}$

(e) $\dfrac{10^{-6}}{10^{-9}}$

EXAMPLE 1   Simplify each of the following numerical expressions:

(a) $10^{-3} \cdot 10^2$ **(b)** $(2^{-3})^{-2}$ **(c)** $(2^{-1} \cdot 3^2)^{-1}$

(d) $\left(\dfrac{2^{-3}}{3^{-2}}\right)^{-1}$ **(e)** $\dfrac{10^{-2}}{10^{-4}}$

Solution

(a) $10^{-3} \cdot 10^2 = 10^{-3+2}$ Product of two powers

$\quad\quad = 10^{-1}$

$\quad\quad = \dfrac{1}{10^1} = \dfrac{1}{10}$

(b) $(2^{-3})^{-2} = 2^{(-2)(-3)}$ Power of a power

$\quad\quad = 2^6 = 64$

(c) $(2^{-1} \cdot 3^2)^{-1} = (2^{-1})^{-1}(3^2)^{-1}$ Power of a product

$\quad\quad = 2^1 \cdot 3^{-2}$

$\quad\quad = \dfrac{2^1}{3^2} = \dfrac{2}{9}$

(d) $\left(\dfrac{2^{-3}}{3^{-2}}\right)^{-1} = \dfrac{(2^{-3})^{-1}}{(3^{-2})^{-1}}$ Power of a quotient

$\quad\quad = \dfrac{2^3}{3^2} = \dfrac{8}{9}$

(e) $\dfrac{10^{-2}}{10^{-4}} = 10^{-2-(-4)}$ Quotient of two powers

$\quad\quad = 10^2 = 100$

Classroom Example
Simplify each of the following;
express final results without using
zero or negative integers as exponents:

(a) $x^2 \cdot x^{-7}$

(b) $(x^3)^{-2}$

(c) $(m^4 \cdot n^{-2})^{-3}$

(d) $\left(\dfrac{x^2}{y^{-4}}\right)^{-3}$

(e) $\dfrac{x^{-5}}{x^{-1}}$

EXAMPLE 2

Simplify each of the following; express final results without using zero or negative integers as exponents:

(a) $x^2 \cdot x^{-5}$ **(b)** $(x^{-2})^4$ **(c)** $(x^2 y^{-3})^{-4}$

(d) $\left(\dfrac{a^3}{b^{-5}}\right)^{-2}$ **(e)** $\dfrac{x^{-4}}{x^{-2}}$

Solution

(a) $x^2 \cdot x^{-5} = x^{2+(-5)}$ Product of two powers

$\quad\quad = x^{-3}$

$\quad\quad = \dfrac{1}{x^3}$

(b) $(x^{-2})^4 = x^{4(-2)}$ Power of a power

$\quad\quad = x^{-8}$

$\quad\quad = \dfrac{1}{x^8}$

(c) $(x^2y^{-3})^{-4} = (x^2)^{-4}(y^{-3})^{-4}$ Power of a product

$\phantom{(c)\ (x^2y^{-3})^{-4}} = x^{-4(2)}y^{-4(-3)}$

$\phantom{(c)\ (x^2y^{-3})^{-4}} = x^{-8}y^{12}$

$\phantom{(c)\ (x^2y^{-3})^{-4}} = \dfrac{y^{12}}{x^8}$

(d) $\left(\dfrac{a^3}{b^{-5}}\right)^{-2} = \dfrac{(a^3)^{-2}}{(b^{-5})^{-2}}$ Power of a quotient

$\phantom{(d)\ \left(\dfrac{a^3}{b^{-5}}\right)^{-2}} = \dfrac{a^{-6}}{b^{10}}$

$\phantom{(d)\ \left(\dfrac{a^3}{b^{-5}}\right)^{-2}} = \dfrac{1}{a^6 b^{10}}$

(e) $\dfrac{x^{-4}}{x^{-2}} = x^{-4-(-2)}$ Quotient of two powers

$\phantom{(e)\ \dfrac{x^{-4}}{x^{-2}}} = x^{-2}$

$\phantom{(e)\ \dfrac{x^{-4}}{x^{-2}}} = \dfrac{1}{x^2}$

EXAMPLE 3

Find the indicated products and quotients; express your results using positive integral exponents only:

(a) $(3x^2y^{-4})(4x^{-3}y)$ **(b)** $\dfrac{12a^3b^2}{-3a^{-1}b^5}$ **(c)** $\left(\dfrac{15x^{-1}y^2}{5xy^{-4}}\right)^{-1}$

Solution

(a) $(3x^2y^{-4})(4x^{-3}y) = 12x^{2+(-3)}y^{-4+1}$

$\phantom{(a)\ (3x^2y^{-4})(4x^{-3}y)} = 12x^{-1}y^{-3}$

$\phantom{(a)\ (3x^2y^{-4})(4x^{-3}y)} = \dfrac{12}{xy^3}$

(b) $\dfrac{12a^3b^2}{-3a^{-1}b^5} = -4a^{3-(-1)}b^{2-5}$

$\phantom{(b)\ \dfrac{12a^3b^2}{-3a^{-1}b^5}} = -4a^4b^{-3}$

$\phantom{(b)\ \dfrac{12a^3b^2}{-3a^{-1}b^5}} = -\dfrac{4a^4}{b^3}$

(c) $\left(\dfrac{15x^{-1}y^2}{5xy^{-4}}\right)^{-1} = \left(3x^{-1-1}y^{2-(-4)}\right)^{-1}$ Note that we are first simplifying inside the parentheses

$\phantom{(c)\ \left(\dfrac{15x^{-1}y^2}{5xy^{-4}}\right)^{-1}} = (3x^{-2}y^6)^{-1}$

$\phantom{(c)\ \left(\dfrac{15x^{-1}y^2}{5xy^{-4}}\right)^{-1}} = 3^{-1}x^2y^{-6}$

$\phantom{(c)\ \left(\dfrac{15x^{-1}y^2}{5xy^{-4}}\right)^{-1}} = \dfrac{x^2}{3y^6}$

The final examples of this section show the simplification of numerical and algebraic expressions that involve sums and differences. In such cases, we use Definition 5.2 to change from negative to positive exponents so that we can proceed in the usual way.

Classroom Example
Simplify $3^{-2} + 5^{-1}$.

EXAMPLE 4   Simplify $2^{-3} + 3^{-1}$.

Solution

$$2^{-3} + 3^{-1} = \frac{1}{2^3} + \frac{1}{3^1}$$

$$= \frac{1}{8} + \frac{1}{3}$$

$$= \frac{3}{24} + \frac{8}{24} \qquad \text{Use 24 as the LCD}$$

$$= \frac{11}{24}$$

Classroom Example
Simplify $(6^{-1} - 2^{-3})^{-1}$.

EXAMPLE 5   Simplify $(4^{-1} - 3^{-2})^{-1}$.

Solution

$$(4^{-1} - 3^{-2})^{-1} = \left(\frac{1}{4^1} - \frac{1}{3^2}\right)^{-1} \qquad \text{Apply } b^{-n} = \frac{1}{b^n} \text{ to } 4^{-1} \text{ and to } 3^{-2}$$

$$= \left(\frac{1}{4} - \frac{1}{9}\right)^{-1}$$

$$= \left(\frac{9}{36} - \frac{4}{36}\right)^{-1} \qquad \text{Use 36 as the LCD}$$

$$= \left(\frac{5}{36}\right)^{-1}$$

$$= \frac{1}{\left(\frac{5}{36}\right)^1} \qquad \text{Apply } b^{-n} = \frac{1}{b^n}$$

$$= \frac{1}{\dfrac{5}{36}} = \frac{36}{5}$$

Classroom Example
Express $a^{-2} + b^{-1}$ as a single fraction involving positive exponents only.

EXAMPLE 6

Express $a^{-1} + b^{-2}$ as a single fraction involving positive exponents only.

Solution

$$a^{-1} + b^{-2} = \frac{1}{a^1} + \frac{1}{b^2} \qquad \text{Use } ab^2 \text{ as the common denominator}$$

$$= \left(\frac{1}{a}\right)\left(\frac{b^2}{b^2}\right) + \left(\frac{1}{b^2}\right)\left(\frac{a}{a}\right) \qquad \text{Change to equivalent fractions with } ab^2 \text{ as the common denominator}$$

$$= \frac{b^2}{ab^2} + \frac{a}{ab^2}$$

$$= \frac{b^2 + a}{ab^2}$$

Concept Quiz 5.1

For Problems 1–10, answer true or false.

1. $\left(\dfrac{2}{5}\right)^{-2} = \left(\dfrac{5}{2}\right)^{2}$

2. $(3)^0(3)^2 = 9^2$

3. $(2)^{-4}(2)^4 = 2$

4. $(4^{-2})^{-1} = 16$

5. $(2^{-2} \cdot 2^{-3})^{-1} = \dfrac{1}{16}$

6. $\left(\dfrac{3^{-2}}{3^{-1}}\right)^2 = \dfrac{1}{9}$

7. $\dfrac{1}{\left(\dfrac{2}{3}\right)^{-3}} = \dfrac{8}{27}$

8. $(10^4)(10^{-6}) = \dfrac{1}{100}$

9. $\dfrac{x^{-6}}{x^{-3}} = x^2$

10. $x^{-1} - x^{-2} = \dfrac{x-1}{x^2}$

Problem Set 5.1

For Problems 1–42, simplify each numerical expression. (Objective 1)

1. 3^{-3}

2. 2^{-4}

3. -10^{-2}

4. 10^{-3}

5. $\dfrac{1}{3^{-4}}$

6. $\dfrac{1}{2^{-6}}$

7. $-\left(\dfrac{1}{3}\right)^{-3}$

8. $\left(\dfrac{1}{2}\right)^{-3}$

9. $\left(-\dfrac{1}{2}\right)^{-3}$

10. $\left(\dfrac{2}{7}\right)^{-2}$

11. $\left(-\dfrac{3}{4}\right)^{0}$

12. $\dfrac{1}{\left(\dfrac{4}{5}\right)^{-2}}$

13. $\dfrac{1}{\left(\dfrac{3}{7}\right)^{-2}}$

14. $-\left(\dfrac{5}{6}\right)^{0}$

15. $2^7 \cdot 2^{-3}$

16. $3^{-4} \cdot 3^6$

17. $10^{-5} \cdot 10^2$

18. $10^4 \cdot 10^{-6}$

19. $10^{-1} \cdot 10^{-2}$

20. $10^{-2} \cdot 10^{-2}$

21. $(3^{-1})^{-3}$

22. $(2^{-2})^{-4}$

23. $(5^3)^{-1}$

24. $(3^{-1})^3$

25. $(2^3 \cdot 3^{-2})^{-1}$

26. $(2^{-2} \cdot 3^{-1})^{-3}$

27. $(4^2 \cdot 5^{-1})^2$

28. $(2^{-3} \cdot 4^{-1})^{-1}$

29. $\left(\dfrac{2^{-1}}{5^{-2}}\right)^{-1}$

30. $\left(\dfrac{2^{-4}}{3^{-2}}\right)^{-2}$

31. $\left(\dfrac{2^{-1}}{3^{-2}}\right)^{2}$

32. $\left(\dfrac{3^2}{5^{-1}}\right)^{-1}$

33. $\dfrac{3^3}{3^{-1}}$

34. $\dfrac{2^{-2}}{2^3}$

35. $\dfrac{10^{-2}}{10^2}$

36. $\dfrac{10^{-2}}{10^{-5}}$

37. $2^{-2} + 3^{-2}$

38. $2^{-4} + 5^{-1}$

39. $\left(\dfrac{1}{3}\right)^{-1} - \left(\dfrac{2}{5}\right)^{-1}$

40. $\left(\dfrac{3}{2}\right)^{-1} - \left(\dfrac{1}{4}\right)^{-1}$

41. $(2^{-3} + 3^{-2})^{-1}$

42. $(5^{-1} - 2^{-3})^{-1}$

For Problems 43–62, simplify each expression. Express final results without using zero or negative integers as exponents. **(Objective 2)**

43. $x^2 \cdot x^{-8}$

44. $x^{-3} \cdot x^{-4}$

45. $a^3 \cdot a^{-5} \cdot a^{-1}$

46. $b^{-2} \cdot b^3 \cdot b^{-6}$

47. $(a^{-4})^2$

48. $(b^4)^{-3}$

49. $(x^2 y^{-6})^{-1}$

50. $(x^5 y^{-1})^{-3}$

51. $(ab^3 c^{-2})^{-4}$

52. $(a^3 b^{-3} c^{-2})^{-5}$

53. $(2x^3 y^{-4})^{-3}$

54. $(4x^5 y^{-2})^{-2}$

55. $\left(\dfrac{x^{-1}}{y^{-4}}\right)^{-3}$

56. $\left(\dfrac{y^3}{x^{-4}}\right)^{-2}$

57. $\left(\dfrac{3a^{-2}}{2b^{-1}}\right)^{-2}$

58. $\left(\dfrac{2xy^2}{5a^{-1}b^{-2}}\right)^{-1}$

59. $\dfrac{x^{-6}}{x^{-4}}$

60. $\dfrac{a^{-2}}{a^2}$

61. $\dfrac{a^3 b^{-2}}{a^{-2} b^{-4}}$

62. $\dfrac{x^{-3} y^{-4}}{x^2 y^{-1}}$

For Problems 63–74, find the indicated products and quotients. Express final results using positive integral exponents only. **(Objective 3)**

63. $(2xy^{-1})(3x^{-2}y^4)$

64. $(-4x^{-1}y^2)(6x^3 y^{-4})$

65. $(-7a^2 b^{-5})(-a^{-2}b^7)$

66. $(-9a^{-3}b^{-6})(-12a^{-1}b^4)$

67. $\dfrac{28x^{-2}y^{-3}}{4x^{-3}y^{-1}}$

68. $\dfrac{63x^2 y^{-4}}{7xy^{-4}}$

69. $\dfrac{-72a^2 b^{-4}}{6a^3 b^{-7}}$

70. $\dfrac{108a^{-5}b^{-4}}{9a^{-2}b}$

71. $\left(\dfrac{35x^{-1}y^{-2}}{7x^4 y^3}\right)^{-1}$

72. $\left(\dfrac{-48ab^2}{-6a^3 b^5}\right)^{-2}$

73. $\left(\dfrac{-36a^{-1}b^{-6}}{4a^{-1}b^4}\right)^{-2}$

74. $\left(\dfrac{8xy^3}{-4x^4 y}\right)^{-3}$

For Problems 75–84, express each of the following as a single fraction involving positive exponents only. **(Objective 4)**

75. $x^{-2} + x^{-3}$

76. $x^{-1} + x^{-5}$

77. $x^{-3} - y^{-1}$

78. $2x^{-1} - 3y^{-2}$

79. $3a^{-2} + 4b^{-1}$

80. $a^{-1} + a^{-1}b^{-3}$

81. $x^{-1}y^{-2} - xy^{-1}$

82. $x^2 y^{-2} - x^{-1}y^{-3}$

83. $2x^{-1} - 3x^{-2}$

84. $5x^{-2}y + 6x^{-1}y^{-2}$

Thoughts Into Words

85. Is the following simplification process correct?

$$(3^{-2})^{-1} = \left(\dfrac{1}{3^2}\right)^{-1} = \left(\dfrac{1}{9}\right)^{-1} = \dfrac{1}{\left(\dfrac{1}{9}\right)^1} = 9$$

Could you suggest a better way to do the problem?

86. Explain how to simplify $(2^{-1} \cdot 3^{-2})^{-1}$ and also how to simplify $(2^{-1} + 3^{-2})^{-1}$.

Further Investigations

87. Use a calculator to check your answers for Problems 1–42.

88. Use a calculator to simplify each of the following numerical expressions. Express your answers to the nearest hundredth.

(a) $(2^{-3} + 3^{-3})^{-2}$

(b) $(4^{-3} - 2^{-1})^{-2}$

(c) $(5^{-3} - 3^{-5})^{-1}$

(d) $(6^{-2} + 7^{-4})^{-2}$

(e) $(7^{-3} - 2^{-4})^{-2}$

(f) $(3^{-4} + 2^{-3})^{-3}$

5.2   Roots and Radicals

OBJECTIVES

1   Evaluate roots of numbers

2   Express a radical in simplest radical form

3   Rationalizing the denominator to simplify radicals

4   Applications of radicals

To **square a number** means to raise it to the second power—that is, to use the number as a factor twice.

$$4^2 = 4 \cdot 4 = 16 \qquad \text{Read ``four squared equals sixteen''}$$

$$10^2 = 10 \cdot 10 = 100$$

$$\left(\frac{1}{2}\right)^2 = \frac{1}{2} \cdot \frac{1}{2} = \frac{1}{4}$$

$$(-3)^2 = (-3)(-3) = 9$$

A **square root of a number** is one of its two equal factors. Thus 4 is a square root of 16 because $4 \cdot 4 = 16$. Likewise, -4 is also a square root of 16 because $(-4)(-4) = 16$. In general, a is a square root of b if $a^2 = b$. The following generalizations are a direct consequence of the previous statement.

1. Every positive real number has two square roots; one is positive and the other is negative. They are opposites of each other.

2. Negative real numbers have no real number square roots because any real number, except zero, is positive when squared.

3. The square root of 0 is 0.

The symbol $\sqrt{}$, called a **radical sign**, is used to designate the nonnegative or principal square root. The number under the radical sign is called the **radicand**. The entire expression, such as $\sqrt{16}$, is called a **radical**.

$$\sqrt{16} = 4 \qquad\qquad \sqrt{16} \text{ indicates the nonnegative or principal square root of } 16$$

$$-\sqrt{16} = -4 \qquad\quad -\sqrt{16} \text{ indicates the negative square root of } 16$$

$$\sqrt{0} = 0 \qquad\qquad \text{Zero has only one square root. Technically, we could write } -\sqrt{0} = -0 = 0$$

$$\sqrt{-4} \text{ is not a real number}$$

$$-\sqrt{-4} \text{ is not a real number}$$

In general, the following definition is useful.

> **Definition 5.3 Principal Square Root**
>
> If $a \geq 0$ and $b \geq 0$, then $\sqrt{b} = a$ if and only if $a^2 = b$; a is called the **principal square root of b**.

To **cube a number** means to raise it to the third power—that is, to use the number as a factor three times.

$$2^3 = 2 \cdot 2 \cdot 2 = 8 \qquad \text{Read ``two cubed equals eight''}$$

$$4^3 = 4 \cdot 4 \cdot 4 = 64$$

$$\left(\frac{2}{3}\right)^3 = \frac{2}{3} \cdot \frac{2}{3} \cdot \frac{2}{3} = \frac{8}{27}$$

$$(-2)^3 = (-2)(-2)(-2) = -8$$

A **cube root of a number** is one of its three equal factors. Thus 2 is a cube root of 8 because $2 \cdot 2 \cdot 2 = 8$. (In fact, 2 is the only real number that is a cube root of 8.) Furthermore, -2 is a cube root of -8 because $(-2)(-2)(-2) = -8$. (In fact, -2 is the only real number that is a cube root of -8.)

In general, a is a cube root of b if $a^3 = b$. The following generalizations are a direct consequence of the previous statement.

1. Every positive real number has one positive real number cube root.
2. Every negative real number has one negative real number cube root.
3. The cube root of 0 is 0.

Remark: Technically, every nonzero real number has three cube roots, but only one of them is a real number. The other two roots are classified as imaginary numbers. We are restricting our work at this time to the set of real numbers.

The symbol $\sqrt[3]{}$ designates the cube root of a number. Thus we can write

$$\sqrt[3]{8} = 2 \qquad \sqrt[3]{\frac{1}{27}} = \frac{1}{3}$$

$$\sqrt[3]{-8} = -2 \qquad \sqrt[3]{-\frac{1}{27}} = -\frac{1}{3}$$

In general, the following definition is useful.

> **Definition 5.4 Cube Root of a Number**
>
> $\sqrt[3]{b} = a$ if and only if $a^3 = b$.

In Definition 5.4, if b is a positive number, then a, the cube root, is a positive number; whereas if b is a negative number, then a, the cube root, is a negative number. The number a is called the principal cube root of b or simply the cube root of b.

The concept of root can be extended to fourth roots, fifth roots, sixth roots, and, in general, nth roots.

> **Definition 5.5 nth Root of a Number**
>
> The nth root of b is a if and only if $a^n = b$.

We can make the following generalizations.

If n is an even positive integer, then the following statements are true.

1. Every positive real number has exactly two real nth roots—one positive and one negative. For example, the real fourth roots of 16 are 2 and -2.
2. Negative real numbers do not have real nth roots. For example, there are no real fourth roots of -16.

If n is an odd positive integer greater than 1, then the following statements are true.

1. Every real number has exactly one real nth root.
2. The real nth root of a positive number is positive. For example, the fifth root of 32 is 2.
3. The real nth root of a negative number is negative. For example, the fifth root of -32 is -2.

The symbol $\sqrt[n]{}$ designates the principal nth root. To complete our terminology, the n in the radical $\sqrt[n]{b}$ is called the index of the radical. If $n = 2$, we commonly write $\sqrt{b}$ instead of $\sqrt[2]{b}$.

The following chart can help summarize this information with respect to $\sqrt[n]{b}$, where n is a positive integer greater than 1.

	If b is positive	If b is zero	If b is negative
n is even	$\sqrt[n]{b}$ is a positive real number	$\sqrt[n]{b} = 0$	$\sqrt[n]{b}$ is not a real number
n is odd	$\sqrt[n]{b}$ is a positive real number	$\sqrt[n]{b} = 0$	$\sqrt[n]{b}$ is a negative real number

Consider the following examples.

$\sqrt[4]{81} = 3$ because $3^4 = 81$

$\sqrt[5]{32} = 2$ because $2^5 = 32$

$\sqrt[5]{-32} = -2$ because $(-2)^5 = -32$

$\sqrt[4]{-16}$ is not a real number   because any real number, except zero, is positive when raised to the fourth power

The following property is a direct consequence of Definition 5.5.

> **Property 5.3**
>
> 1. $\left(\sqrt[n]{b}\right)^n = b$ n is any positive integer greater than 1
> 2. $\sqrt[n]{b^n} = b$ n is any positive integer greater than 1 if $b \geq 0$; n is an odd positive integer greater than 1 if $b < 0$

Because the radical expressions in parts (1) and (2) of Property 5.3 are both equal to b, by the transitive property they are equal to each other. Hence $\sqrt[n]{b^n} = \left(\sqrt[n]{b}\right)^n$. The arithmetic is usually easier to simplify when we use the form $\left(\sqrt[n]{b}\right)^n$. The following examples demonstrate the use of Property 5.3.

$$\sqrt{144^2} = \left(\sqrt{144}\right)^2 = 12^2 = 144$$

$$\sqrt[3]{64^3} = \left(\sqrt[3]{64}\right)^3 = 4^3 = 64$$

$$\sqrt[3]{(-8)^3} = \left(\sqrt[3]{-8}\right)^3 = (-2)^3 = -8$$

$$\sqrt[4]{16^4} = \left(\sqrt[4]{16}\right)^4 = 2^4 = 16$$

Let's use some examples to lead into the next very useful property of radicals.

$\sqrt{4 \cdot 9} = \sqrt{36} = 6$ and $\sqrt{4} \cdot \sqrt{9} = 2 \cdot 3 = 6$

$\sqrt{16 \cdot 25} = \sqrt{400} = 20$ and $\sqrt{16} \cdot \sqrt{25} = 4 \cdot 5 = 20$

$\sqrt[3]{8 \cdot 27} = \sqrt[3]{216} = 6$ and $\sqrt[3]{8} \cdot \sqrt[3]{27} = 2 \cdot 3 = 6$

$\sqrt[3]{(-8)(27)} = \sqrt[3]{-216} = -6$ and $\sqrt[3]{-8} \cdot \sqrt[3]{27} = (-2)(3) = -6$

In general, we can state the following property.

> **Property 5.4**
>
> $\sqrt[n]{bc} = \sqrt[n]{b}\sqrt[n]{c}$, when $\sqrt[n]{b}$ and $\sqrt[n]{c}$ are real numbers

Property 5.4 states that the nth root of a product is equal to the product of the nth roots.

Expressing a Radical in Simplest Radical Form

The definition of nth root, along with Property 5.4, provides the basis for changing radicals to simplest radical form. The concept of **simplest radical form** takes on additional meaning as we encounter more complicated expressions, but for now it simply means that the radicand is not to contain any perfect powers of the index. Let's consider some examples to clarify this idea.

Classroom Example
Express each of the following in simplest radical form:

(a) $\sqrt{12}$
(b) $\sqrt{32}$
(c) $\sqrt[3]{48}$
(d) $\sqrt[3]{40}$

EXAMPLE 1   Express each of the following in simplest radical form:

(a) $\sqrt{8}$ (b) $\sqrt{45}$ (c) $\sqrt[3]{24}$ (d) $\sqrt[3]{54}$

Solution

(a) $\sqrt{8} = \sqrt{4 \cdot 2} = \sqrt{4}\sqrt{2} = 2\sqrt{2}$ 4 is a perfect square

(b) $\sqrt{45} = \sqrt{9 \cdot 5} = \sqrt{9}\sqrt{5} = 3\sqrt{5}$ 9 is a perfect square

(c) $\sqrt[3]{24} = \sqrt[3]{8 \cdot 3} = \sqrt[3]{8}\sqrt[3]{3} = 2\sqrt[3]{3}$ 8 is a perfect cube

(d) $\sqrt[3]{54} = \sqrt[3]{27 \cdot 2} = \sqrt[3]{27}\sqrt[3]{2} = 3\sqrt[3]{2}$ 27 is a perfect cube

The first step in each example is to express the radicand of the given radical as the product of two factors, one of which must be a perfect nth power other than 1. Also, observe the radicands of the final radicals. In each case, the radicand cannot have a factor that is a perfect nth power other than 1. We say that the final radicals $2\sqrt{2}, 3\sqrt{5}, 2\sqrt[3]{3}$, and $3\sqrt[3]{2}$ are in *simplest radical form.*

You may vary the steps somewhat in changing to simplest radical form, but the final result should be the same. Consider some different approaches to changing $\sqrt{72}$ to simplest form:

$$\sqrt{72} = \sqrt{9}\sqrt{8} = 3\sqrt{8} = 3\sqrt{4}\sqrt{2} = 3 \cdot 2\sqrt{2} = 6\sqrt{2} \qquad \text{or}$$

$$\sqrt{72} = \sqrt{4}\sqrt{18} = 2\sqrt{18} = 2\sqrt{9}\sqrt{2} = 2 \cdot 3\sqrt{2} = 6\sqrt{2} \qquad \text{or}$$

$$\sqrt{72} = \sqrt{36}\sqrt{2} = 6\sqrt{2}$$

Another variation of the technique for changing radicals to simplest form is to prime factor the radicand and then to look for perfect nth powers in exponential form. The following example illustrates the use of this technique.

Classroom Example
Express each of the following in simplest radical form:

(a) $\sqrt{48}$
(b) $5\sqrt{72}$
(c) $\sqrt[3]{200}$

EXAMPLE 2   Express each of the following in simplest radical form:

(a) $\sqrt{50}$ (b) $3\sqrt{80}$ (c) $\sqrt[3]{108}$

Solution

(a) $\sqrt{50} = \sqrt{2 \cdot 5 \cdot 5} = \sqrt{5^2}\sqrt{2} = 5\sqrt{2}$

(b) $3\sqrt{80} = 3\sqrt{2 \cdot 2 \cdot 2 \cdot 2 \cdot 5} = 3\sqrt{2^4}\sqrt{5} = 3 \cdot 2^2\sqrt{5} = 12\sqrt{5}$

(c) $\sqrt[3]{108} = \sqrt[3]{2 \cdot 2 \cdot 3 \cdot 3 \cdot 3} = \sqrt[3]{3^3}\sqrt[3]{4} = 3\sqrt[3]{4}$

Another property of *n*th roots is demonstrated by the following examples.

$$\sqrt{\frac{36}{9}} = \sqrt{4} = 2 \qquad \text{and} \qquad \frac{\sqrt{36}}{\sqrt{9}} = \frac{6}{3} = 2$$

$$\sqrt[3]{\frac{64}{8}} = \sqrt[3]{8} = 2 \qquad \text{and} \qquad \frac{\sqrt[3]{64}}{\sqrt[3]{8}} = \frac{4}{2} = 2$$

$$\sqrt[3]{\frac{-8}{64}} = \sqrt[3]{-\frac{1}{8}} = -\frac{1}{2} \qquad \text{and} \qquad \frac{\sqrt[3]{-8}}{\sqrt[3]{64}} = \frac{-2}{4} = -\frac{1}{2}$$

In general, we can state the following property.

Property 5.5

$$\sqrt[n]{\frac{b}{c}} = \frac{\sqrt[n]{b}}{\sqrt[n]{c}}, \text{ when } \sqrt[n]{b} \text{ and } \sqrt[n]{c} \text{ are real numbers, and } c \neq 0$$

Property 5.5 states that the *n*th root of a quotient is equal to the quotient of the *n*th roots.

To evaluate radicals such as $\sqrt{\frac{4}{25}}$ and $\sqrt[3]{\frac{27}{8}}$, for which the numerator and denominator of the fractional radicand are perfect *n*th powers, you may use Property 5.5 or merely rely on the definition of *n*th root.

$$\sqrt{\frac{4}{25}} = \frac{\sqrt{4}}{\sqrt{25}} = \frac{2}{5} \qquad \text{or} \qquad \sqrt{\frac{4}{25}} = \frac{2}{5} \quad \text{because } \frac{2}{5} \cdot \frac{2}{5} = \frac{4}{25}$$

↑   ↑

Property 5.5   Definition of *n*th root

↓   ↓

$$\sqrt[3]{\frac{27}{8}} = \frac{\sqrt[3]{27}}{\sqrt[3]{8}} = \frac{3}{2} \qquad \text{or} \qquad \sqrt[3]{\frac{27}{8}} = \frac{3}{2} \quad \text{because } \frac{3}{2} \cdot \frac{3}{2} \cdot \frac{3}{2} = \frac{27}{8}$$

Radicals such as $\sqrt{\frac{28}{9}}$ and $\sqrt[3]{\frac{24}{27}}$, in which only the denominators of the radicand are perfect *n*th powers, can be simplified as follows:

$$\sqrt{\frac{28}{9}} = \frac{\sqrt{28}}{\sqrt{9}} = \frac{\sqrt{28}}{3} = \frac{\sqrt{4}\sqrt{7}}{3} = \frac{2\sqrt{7}}{3}$$

$$\sqrt[3]{\frac{24}{27}} = \frac{\sqrt[3]{24}}{\sqrt[3]{27}} = \frac{\sqrt[3]{24}}{3} = \frac{\sqrt[3]{8}\sqrt[3]{3}}{3} = \frac{2\sqrt[3]{3}}{3}$$

Before we consider more examples, let's summarize some ideas that pertain to the simplifying of radicals. A radical is said to be in *simplest radical form* if the following conditions are satisfied.

1. No fraction appears with a radical sign. $\sqrt{\frac{3}{4}}$ violates this condition

2. No radical appears in the denominator. $\frac{\sqrt{2}}{\sqrt{3}}$ violates this condition

3. No radicand, when expressed in prime-factored form, contains a factor raised to a power equal to or greater than the index. $\sqrt{2^3 \cdot 5}$ violates this condition

Rationalizing the Denominator to Simplify Radicals

Now let's consider an example in which neither the numerator nor the denominator of the radicand is a perfect nth power.

Classroom Example

Simplify $\sqrt{\dfrac{5}{7}}$.

EXAMPLE 3

Simplify $\sqrt{\dfrac{2}{3}}$.

Solution

$$\sqrt{\frac{2}{3}} = \frac{\sqrt{2}}{\sqrt{3}} = \frac{\sqrt{2}}{\sqrt{3}} \cdot \frac{\sqrt{3}}{\sqrt{3}} = \frac{\sqrt{6}}{3}$$

$\uparrow$
Form of 1

We refer to the process we used to simplify the radical in Example 3 as **rationalizing the denominator**. Note that the denominator becomes a rational number. The process of rationalizing the denominator can often be accomplished in more than one way, as we will see in the next example.

Classroom Example

Simplify $\dfrac{\sqrt{7}}{\sqrt{12}}$.

EXAMPLE 4

Simplify $\dfrac{\sqrt{5}}{\sqrt{8}}$.

Solution A

$$\frac{\sqrt{5}}{\sqrt{8}} = \frac{\sqrt{5}}{\sqrt{8}} \cdot \frac{\sqrt{8}}{\sqrt{8}} = \frac{\sqrt{40}}{8} = \frac{\sqrt{4}\sqrt{10}}{8} = \frac{2\sqrt{10}}{8} = \frac{\sqrt{10}}{4}$$

Solution B

$$\frac{\sqrt{5}}{\sqrt{8}} = \frac{\sqrt{5}}{\sqrt{8}} \cdot \frac{\sqrt{2}}{\sqrt{2}} = \frac{\sqrt{10}}{\sqrt{16}} = \frac{\sqrt{10}}{4}$$

Solution C

$$\frac{\sqrt{5}}{\sqrt{8}} = \frac{\sqrt{5}}{\sqrt{4}\sqrt{2}} = \frac{\sqrt{5}}{2\sqrt{2}} = \frac{\sqrt{5}}{2\sqrt{2}} \cdot \frac{\sqrt{2}}{\sqrt{2}} = \frac{\sqrt{10}}{2\sqrt{4}} = \frac{\sqrt{10}}{2(2)} = \frac{\sqrt{10}}{4}$$

The three approaches to Example 4 again illustrate the need to think first and only then push the pencil. You may find one approach easier than another. To conclude this section, study the following examples and check the final radicals against the three conditions previously listed for simplest radical form.

Classroom Example

Simplify each of the following:

(a) $\dfrac{3\sqrt{5}}{4\sqrt{3}}$ (b) $\dfrac{6\sqrt{11}}{5\sqrt{27}}$

(c) $\sqrt[3]{\dfrac{7}{25}}$ (d) $\dfrac{\sqrt[3]{3}}{\sqrt[3]{36}}$

EXAMPLE 5

Simplify each of the following:

(a) $\dfrac{3\sqrt{2}}{5\sqrt{3}}$ (b) $\dfrac{3\sqrt{7}}{2\sqrt{18}}$ (c) $\sqrt[3]{\dfrac{5}{9}}$ (d) $\dfrac{\sqrt[3]{5}}{\sqrt[3]{16}}$

Solution

(a) $\dfrac{3\sqrt{2}}{5\sqrt{3}} = \dfrac{3\sqrt{2}}{5\sqrt{3}} \cdot \dfrac{\sqrt{3}}{\sqrt{3}} = \dfrac{3\sqrt{6}}{5\sqrt{9}} = \dfrac{3\sqrt{6}}{15} = \dfrac{\sqrt{6}}{5}$

$\uparrow$
Form of 1

(b) $\dfrac{3\sqrt{7}}{2\sqrt{18}} = \dfrac{3\sqrt{7}}{2\sqrt{18}} \cdot \dfrac{\sqrt{2}}{\sqrt{2}} = \dfrac{3\sqrt{14}}{2\sqrt{36}} = \dfrac{3\sqrt{14}}{12} = \dfrac{\sqrt{14}}{4}$

Form of 1

(c) $\sqrt[3]{\dfrac{5}{9}} = \dfrac{\sqrt[3]{5}}{\sqrt[3]{9}} = \dfrac{\sqrt[3]{5}}{\sqrt[3]{9}} \cdot \dfrac{\sqrt[3]{3}}{\sqrt[3]{3}} = \dfrac{\sqrt[3]{15}}{\sqrt[3]{27}} = \dfrac{\sqrt[3]{15}}{3}$

Form of 1

(d) $\dfrac{\sqrt[3]{5}}{\sqrt[3]{16}} = \dfrac{\sqrt[3]{5}}{\sqrt[3]{16}} \cdot \dfrac{\sqrt[3]{4}}{\sqrt[3]{4}} = \dfrac{\sqrt[3]{20}}{\sqrt[3]{64}} = \dfrac{\sqrt[3]{20}}{4}$

Form of 1

Applications of Radicals

Many real-world applications involve radical expressions. For example, police often use the formula $S = \sqrt{30Df}$ to estimate the speed of a car on the basis of the length of the skid marks at the scene of an accident. In this formula, S represents the speed of the car in miles per hour, D represents the length of the skid marks in feet, and f represents a coefficient of friction. For a particular situation, the coefficient of friction is a constant that depends on the type and condition of the road surface.

Classroom Example
Using 0.46 as a coefficient of friction, determine how fast a car was traveling if it skidded 275 feet.

EXAMPLE 6

Using 0.35 as a coefficient of friction, determine how fast a car was traveling if it skidded 325 feet.

Solution

Substitute 0.35 for f and 325 for D in the formula.

$$S = \sqrt{30Df} = \sqrt{30(325)(0.35)} - 58 \quad \text{to the nearest whole number}$$

The car was traveling at approximately 58 miles per hour.

The **period** of a pendulum is the time it takes to swing from one side to the other side and back. The formula

$$T = 2\pi\sqrt{\dfrac{L}{32}}$$

where T represents the time in seconds and L the length in feet, can be used to determine the period of a pendulum (see Figure 5.1).

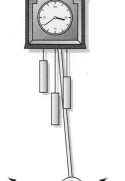

Figure 5.1

Classroom Example
Find, to the nearest tenth of a second, the period of a pendulum of length 2.1 feet.

EXAMPLE 7

Find, to the nearest tenth of a second, the period of a pendulum of length 3.5 feet.

Solution

Let's use 3.14 as an approximation for π and substitute 3.5 for L in the formula.

$$T = 2\pi\sqrt{\dfrac{L}{32}} = 2(3.14)\sqrt{\dfrac{3.5}{32}} = 2.1 \quad \text{to the nearest tenth}$$

The period is approximately 2.1 seconds.

Radical expressions are also used in some geometric applications. For example, the area of a triangle can be found by using a formula that involves a square root. If a, b, and c represent the lengths of the three sides of a triangle, the formula $K = \sqrt{s(s-a)(s-b)(s-c)}$, known as Heron's formula, can be used to determine the area (K) of the triangle. The letter s represents the semiperimeter of the triangle; that is, $s = \dfrac{a+b+c}{2}$.

Classroom Example
Find the area of a triangular piece of sheet metal that has sides of lengths 34 cm, 32 cm, and 60 cm.

EXAMPLE 8

Find the area of a triangular piece of sheet metal that has sides of lengths 17 inches, 19 inches, and 26 inches.

Solution

First, let's find the value of s, the semiperimeter of the triangle.

$$s = \frac{17 + 19 + 26}{2} = 31$$

Now we can use Heron's formula.

$$K = \sqrt{s(s-a)(s-b)(s-c)} = \sqrt{31(31-17)(31-19)(31-26)}$$
$$= \sqrt{31(14)(12)(5)}$$
$$= \sqrt{20{,}640}$$
$$= 161.4 \quad \text{to the nearest tenth}$$

Thus the area of the piece of sheet metal is approximately 161.4 square inches.

Remark: Note that in Examples 6–8, we did not simplify the radicals. When one is using a calculator to approximate the square roots, there is no need to simplify first.

Concept Quiz 5.2

For Problems 1–10, answer true or false.

1. The cube root of a number is one of its three equal factors.
2. Every positive real number has one positive real number square root.
3. The principal square root of a number is the positive square root of the number.
4. The symbol $\sqrt{}$ is called a radical.
5. The square root of 0 is not a real number.
6. The number under the radical sign is called the radicand.
7. Every positive real number has two square roots.
8. The n in the radical $\sqrt[n]{a}$ is called the index of the radical.
9. If n is an odd integer greater than 1 and b is a negative real number, then $\sqrt[n]{b}$ is a negative real number.
10. $\dfrac{3\sqrt{24}}{8}$ is in simplest radical form.

Problem Set 5.2

For Problems 1–20, evaluate each of the following. For example, $\sqrt{25} = 5$. **(Objective 1)**

1. $\sqrt{64}$

2. $\sqrt{49}$

3. $-\sqrt{100}$

4. $-\sqrt{81}$

5. $\sqrt[3]{27}$

6. $\sqrt[3]{216}$

7. $\sqrt[3]{-64}$

8. $\sqrt[3]{-125}$

9. $\sqrt[4]{81}$

10. $-\sqrt[4]{16}$

11. $\sqrt{\dfrac{16}{25}}$

12. $\sqrt{\dfrac{25}{64}}$

13. $-\sqrt{\dfrac{36}{49}}$

14. $\sqrt{\dfrac{16}{64}}$

15. $\sqrt{\dfrac{9}{36}}$

16. $\sqrt{\dfrac{144}{36}}$

17. $\sqrt[3]{\dfrac{27}{64}}$

18. $\sqrt[3]{-\dfrac{8}{27}}$

19. $\sqrt[3]{8^3}$

20. $\sqrt[4]{16^4}$

For Problems 21–74, change each radical to simplest radical form. (Objectives 2 and 3)

21. $\sqrt{27}$

22. $\sqrt{48}$

23. $\sqrt{32}$

24. $\sqrt{98}$

25. $\sqrt{80}$

26. $\sqrt{125}$

27. $\sqrt{160}$

28. $\sqrt{112}$

29. $4\sqrt{18}$

30. $5\sqrt{32}$

31. $-6\sqrt{20}$

32. $-4\sqrt{54}$

33. $\dfrac{2}{5}\sqrt{75}$

34. $\dfrac{1}{3}\sqrt{90}$

35. $\dfrac{3}{2}\sqrt{24}$

36. $\dfrac{3}{4}\sqrt{45}$

37. $-\dfrac{5}{6}\sqrt{28}$

38. $-\dfrac{2}{3}\sqrt{96}$

39. $\sqrt{\dfrac{19}{4}}$

40. $\sqrt{\dfrac{22}{9}}$

41. $\sqrt{\dfrac{27}{16}}$

42. $\sqrt{\dfrac{8}{25}}$

43. $\sqrt{\dfrac{75}{81}}$

44. $\sqrt{\dfrac{24}{49}}$

45. $\sqrt{\dfrac{2}{7}}$

46. $\sqrt{\dfrac{3}{8}}$

47. $\sqrt{\dfrac{2}{3}}$

48. $\sqrt{\dfrac{7}{12}}$

49. $\dfrac{\sqrt{5}}{\sqrt{12}}$

50. $\dfrac{\sqrt{3}}{\sqrt{7}}$

51. $\dfrac{\sqrt{11}}{\sqrt{24}}$

52. $\dfrac{\sqrt{5}}{\sqrt{48}}$

53. $\dfrac{\sqrt{18}}{\sqrt{27}}$

54. $\dfrac{\sqrt{10}}{\sqrt{20}}$

55. $\dfrac{\sqrt{35}}{\sqrt{7}}$

56. $\dfrac{\sqrt{42}}{\sqrt{6}}$

57. $\dfrac{2\sqrt{3}}{\sqrt{7}}$

58. $\dfrac{3\sqrt{2}}{\sqrt{6}}$

59. $-\dfrac{4\sqrt{12}}{\sqrt{5}}$

60. $\dfrac{-6\sqrt{5}}{\sqrt{18}}$

61. $\dfrac{3\sqrt{2}}{4\sqrt{3}}$

62. $\dfrac{6\sqrt{5}}{5\sqrt{12}}$

63. $\dfrac{-8\sqrt{18}}{10\sqrt{50}}$

64. $\dfrac{4\sqrt{45}}{-6\sqrt{20}}$

65. $\sqrt[3]{16}$

66. $\sqrt[3]{40}$

67. $2\sqrt[3]{81}$

68. $-3\sqrt[3]{54}$

69. $\dfrac{2}{\sqrt[3]{9}}$

70. $\dfrac{3}{\sqrt[3]{3}}$

71. $\dfrac{\sqrt[3]{27}}{\sqrt[3]{4}}$

72. $\dfrac{\sqrt[3]{8}}{\sqrt[3]{16}}$

73. $\dfrac{\sqrt[3]{6}}{\sqrt[3]{4}}$

74. $\dfrac{\sqrt[3]{4}}{\sqrt[3]{2}}$

For Problems 75–80, use radicals to solve the problems. (Objective 4)

75. Use a coefficient of friction of 0.4 in the formula from Example 6 and find the speeds of cars that left skid marks of lengths 150 feet, 200 feet, and 350 feet. Express your answers to the nearest mile per hour.

76. Use the formula from Example 7, and find the periods of pendulums of lengths 2 feet, 3 feet, and 4.5 feet. Express your answers to the nearest tenth of a second.

77. Find, to the nearest square centimeter, the area of a triangle that measures 14 centimeters by 16 centimeters by 18 centimeters.

78. Find, to the nearest square yard, the area of a triangular plot of ground that measures 45 yards by 60 yards by 75 yards.

79. Find the area of an equilateral triangle, each of whose sides is 18 inches long. Express the area to the nearest square inch.

80. Find, to the nearest square inch, the area of the quadrilateral in Figure 5.2.

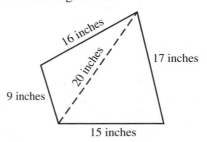

16 inches

20 inches

17 inches

9 inches

15 inches

Figure 5.2

81. Why is $\sqrt{-9}$ not a real number?

82. Why is it that we say 25 has two square roots (5 and -5), but we write $\sqrt{25} = 5$?

83. How is the multiplication property of 1 used when simplifying radicals?

84. How <u>could</u> you find a whole number approximation for $\sqrt{2750}$ if you did not have a calculator or table available?

85. Use your calculator to find a rational approximation, to the nearest thousandth, for (a) through (i).

(a) $\sqrt{2}$ (b) $\sqrt{75}$

(c) $\sqrt{156}$ (d) $\sqrt{691}$

(e) $\sqrt{3249}$ (f) $\sqrt{45,123}$

(g) $\sqrt{0.14}$ (h) $\sqrt{0.023}$

(i) $\sqrt{0.8649}$

86. Sometimes a fairly good estimate can be made of a radical expression by using whole number approximations. For example, $5\sqrt{35} + 7\sqrt{50}$ is approximately $5(6) + 7(7) = 79$. Using a calculator, we find that

$5\sqrt{35} + 7\sqrt{50} = 79.1$, to the nearest tenth. In this case our whole number estimate is very good. For (a) through (f), first make a whole number estimate, and then use your calculator to see how well you estimated.

(a) $3\sqrt{10} - 4\sqrt{24} + 6\sqrt{65}$

(b) $9\sqrt{27} + 5\sqrt{37} - 3\sqrt{80}$

(c) $12\sqrt{5} + 13\sqrt{18} + 9\sqrt{47}$

(d) $3\sqrt{98} - 4\sqrt{83} - 7\sqrt{120}$

(e) $4\sqrt{170} + 2\sqrt{198} + 5\sqrt{227}$

(f) $-3\sqrt{256} - 6\sqrt{287} + 11\sqrt{321}$

Answers to the Concept Quiz

1. True   **2.** True   **3.** True   **4.** False   **5.** False   **6.** True   **7.** True   **8.** True   **9.** True   **10.** False

---

5.3   Combining Radicals and Simplifying Radicals That Contain Variables

OBJECTIVES
1. Simplify expressions by combining radicals
2. Simplify radicals that contain variables

Recall our use of the distributive property as the basis for combining similar terms. For example,

$3x + 2x = (3 + 2)x = 5x$

$8y - 5y = (8 - 5)y = 3y$

$$\frac{2}{3}a^2 + \frac{3}{4}a^2 = \left(\frac{2}{3} + \frac{3}{4}\right)a^2 = \left(\frac{8}{12} + \frac{9}{12}\right)a^2 = \frac{17}{12}a^2$$

In a like manner, expressions that contain radicals can often be simplified by using the distributive property, as follows:

$3\sqrt{2} + 5\sqrt{2} = (3 + 5)\sqrt{2} = 8\sqrt{2}$

$7\sqrt[3]{5} - 3\sqrt[3]{5} = (7 - 3)\sqrt[3]{5} = 4\sqrt[3]{5}$

$4\sqrt{7} + 5\sqrt{7} + 6\sqrt{11} - 2\sqrt{11} = (4 + 5)\sqrt{7} + (6 - 2)\sqrt{11} = 9\sqrt{7} + 4\sqrt{11}$

Note that *in order to be added or subtracted, radicals must have the same index and the same radicand.* Thus we cannot simplify an expression such as $5\sqrt{2} + 7\sqrt{11}$.

Simplifying by combining radicals sometimes requires that you first express the given radicals in simplest form and then apply the distributive property. The following examples illustrate this idea.

Classroom Example
Simplify $2\sqrt{12} + 5\sqrt{48} - 7\sqrt{3}$.

EXAMPLE 1   Simplify $3\sqrt{8} + 2\sqrt{18} - 4\sqrt{2}$.

Solution

$$
\begin{aligned}
3\sqrt{8} + 2\sqrt{18} - 4\sqrt{2} &= 3\sqrt{4}\sqrt{2} + 2\sqrt{9}\sqrt{2} - 4\sqrt{2} \\
&= 3 \cdot 2 \cdot \sqrt{2} + 2 \cdot 3 \cdot \sqrt{2} - 4\sqrt{2} \\
&= 6\sqrt{2} + 6\sqrt{2} - 4\sqrt{2} \\
&= (6 + 6 - 4)\sqrt{2} = 8\sqrt{2}
\end{aligned}
$$

Classroom Example
Simplify $\dfrac{3}{4}\sqrt{98} - \dfrac{2}{5}\sqrt{50}$.

EXAMPLE 2   Simplify $\dfrac{1}{4}\sqrt{45} + \dfrac{1}{3}\sqrt{20}$.

Solution

$$
\begin{aligned}
\frac{1}{4}\sqrt{45} + \frac{1}{3}\sqrt{20} &= \frac{1}{4}\sqrt{9}\sqrt{5} + \frac{1}{3}\sqrt{4}\sqrt{5} \\
&= \frac{1}{4} \cdot 3 \cdot \sqrt{5} + \frac{1}{3} \cdot 2 \cdot \sqrt{5} \\
&= \frac{3}{4}\sqrt{5} + \frac{2}{3}\sqrt{5} = \left(\frac{3}{4} + \frac{2}{3}\right)\sqrt{5} \\
&= \left(\frac{9}{12} + \frac{8}{12}\right)\sqrt{5} = \frac{17}{12}\sqrt{5}
\end{aligned}
$$

Classroom Example
Simplify $3\sqrt[3]{4} + 5\sqrt[3]{32} - 2\sqrt[3]{108}$.

EXAMPLE 3   Simplify $5\sqrt[3]{2} - 2\sqrt[3]{16} - 6\sqrt[3]{54}$.

Solution

$$
\begin{aligned}
5\sqrt[3]{2} - 2\sqrt[3]{16} - 6\sqrt[3]{54} &= 5\sqrt[3]{2} - 2\sqrt[3]{8}\sqrt[3]{2} - 6\sqrt[3]{27}\sqrt[3]{2} \\
&= 5\sqrt[3]{2} - 2 \cdot 2 \cdot \sqrt[3]{2} - 6 \cdot 3 \cdot \sqrt[3]{2} \\
&= 5\sqrt[3]{2} - 4\sqrt[3]{2} - 18\sqrt[3]{2} \\
&= (5 - 4 - 18)\sqrt[3]{2} \\
&= -17\sqrt[3]{2}
\end{aligned}
$$

Simplifying Radicals That Contain Variables

Before we discuss the process of simplifying radicals that contain variables, there is one technicality that we should call to your attention. Let's look at some examples to clarify the point. Consider the radical $\sqrt{x^2}$.

Let $x = 3$; then $\sqrt{x^2} = \sqrt{3^2} = \sqrt{9} = 3$.

Let $x = -3$; then $\sqrt{x^2} = \sqrt{(-3)^2} = \sqrt{9} = 3$.

Thus if $x \geq 0$, then $\sqrt{x^2} = x$, *but if $x < 0$, then* $\sqrt{x^2} = -x$. Using the concept of absolute value, we can state that for all real numbers, $\sqrt{x^2} = |x|$.

Now consider the radical $\sqrt{x^3}$. Because x^3 is negative when x is negative, we need to restrict x to the nonnegative real numbers when working with $\sqrt{x^3}$. Thus we can write, "if $x \geq 0$, then $\sqrt{x^3} = \sqrt{x^2}\sqrt{x} - x\sqrt{x}$," and no absolute-value sign is necessary. Finally, let's consider the radical $\sqrt[3]{x^3}$.

Let $x = 2$; then $\sqrt[3]{x^3} = \sqrt[3]{2^3} = \sqrt[3]{8} = 2$.

Let $x = -2$; then $\sqrt[3]{x^3} = \sqrt[3]{(-2)^3} = \sqrt[3]{-8} = -2$.

Thus it is correct to write, "$\sqrt[3]{x^3} = x$ for all real numbers," and again no absolute-value sign is necessary.

The previous discussion indicates that technically, every radical expression involving variables in the radicand needs to be analyzed individually in terms of any necessary restrictions imposed on the variables. To help you gain experience with this skill, examples and problems are discussed under *Further Investigations* in the problem set. For now, however, to avoid considering such restrictions on a problem-to-problem basis, we shall merely assume that all variables represent positive real numbers. Let's consider the process of simplifying radicals that contain variables in the radicand. Study the following examples, and note that the same basic approach we used in Section 5.2 is applied here.

Classroom Example
Simplify each of the following:

(a) $\sqrt{125m^3}$

(b) $\sqrt{28m^5n^9}$

(c) $\sqrt{147x^6y^7}$

(d) $\sqrt[3]{128m^{10}n^5}$

EXAMPLE 4   Simplify each of the following:

(a) $\sqrt{8x^3}$ (b) $\sqrt{45x^3y^7}$ (c) $\sqrt{180a^4b^3}$ (d) $\sqrt[3]{40x^4y^8}$

Solution

(a) $\sqrt{8x^3} = \sqrt{4x^2}\sqrt{2x} = 2x\sqrt{2x}$ $4x^2$ is a perfect square

(b) $\sqrt{45x^3y^7} = \sqrt{9x^2y^6}\sqrt{5xy} = 3xy^3\sqrt{5xy}$ $9x^2y^6$ is a perfect square

(c) If the numerical coefficient of the radicand is quite large, you may want to look at it in the prime-factored form.

$$\sqrt{180a^4b^3} = \sqrt{2 \cdot 2 \cdot 3 \cdot 3 \cdot 5 \cdot a^4 \cdot b^3}$$

$$= \sqrt{36 \cdot 5 \cdot a^4 \cdot b^3}$$

$$= \sqrt{36a^4b^2}\sqrt{5b}$$

$$= 6a^2b\sqrt{5b}$$

(d) $\sqrt[3]{40x^4y^8} = \sqrt[3]{8x^3y^6}\sqrt[3]{5xy^2} = 2xy^2\sqrt[3]{5xy^2}$ $8x^3y^6$ is a perfect cube

Before we consider more examples, let's restate (in such a way that includes radicands containing variables) the conditions necessary for a radical to be in simplest radical form.

1. A radicand contains no polynomial factor raised to a power equal to or greater than the index of the radical. $\sqrt{x^3}$ violates this condition

2. No fraction appears within a radical sign. $\sqrt{\dfrac{2x}{3y}}$ violates this condition

3. No radical appears in the denominator. $\dfrac{3}{\sqrt[3]{4x}}$ violates this condition

EXAMPLE 5   Express each of the following in simplest radical form:

(a) $\sqrt{\dfrac{2x}{3y}}$ (b) $\dfrac{\sqrt{5}}{\sqrt{12a^3}}$ (c) $\dfrac{\sqrt{8x^2}}{\sqrt{27y^5}}$ (d) $\dfrac{3}{\sqrt[3]{4x}}$ (e) $\dfrac{\sqrt[3]{16x^2}}{\sqrt[3]{9y^5}}$

Classroom Example

Express each of the following in simplest radical form:

(a) $\sqrt{\dfrac{5m}{7n}}$ (b) $\dfrac{\sqrt{3}}{\sqrt{8x^5}}$

(c) $\dfrac{\sqrt{125m^7}}{\sqrt{48n^4}}$

(d) $\dfrac{7}{\sqrt[3]{9y}}$

(e) $\dfrac{\sqrt[3]{81a^7}}{\sqrt[3]{32b^2}}$

Solution

(a) $\sqrt{\dfrac{2x}{3y}} = \dfrac{\sqrt{2x}}{\sqrt{3y}} = \dfrac{\sqrt{2x}}{\sqrt{3y}} \cdot \underset{\underset{\text{Form of 1}}{\uparrow}}{\dfrac{\sqrt{3y}}{\sqrt{3y}}} = \dfrac{\sqrt{6xy}}{3y}$

(b) $\dfrac{\sqrt{5}}{\sqrt{12a^3}} = \dfrac{\sqrt{5}}{\sqrt{12a^3}} \cdot \underset{\underset{\text{Form of 1}}{\uparrow}}{\dfrac{\sqrt{3a}}{\sqrt{3a}}} = \dfrac{\sqrt{15a}}{\sqrt{36a^4}} = \dfrac{\sqrt{15a}}{6a^2}$

(c) $\dfrac{\sqrt{8x^2}}{\sqrt{27y^5}} = \dfrac{\sqrt{4x^2}\sqrt{2}}{\sqrt{9y^4}\sqrt{3y}} = \dfrac{2x\sqrt{2}}{3y^2\sqrt{3y}} = \dfrac{2x\sqrt{2}}{3y^2\sqrt{3y}} \cdot \dfrac{\sqrt{3y}}{\sqrt{3y}} = \dfrac{2x\sqrt{6y}}{(3y^2)(3y)} = \dfrac{2x\sqrt{6y}}{9y^3}$

(d) $\dfrac{3}{\sqrt[3]{4x}} = \dfrac{3}{\sqrt[3]{4x}} \cdot \dfrac{\sqrt[3]{2x^2}}{\sqrt[3]{2x^2}} = \dfrac{3\sqrt[3]{2x^2}}{\sqrt[3]{8x^3}} = \dfrac{3\sqrt[3]{2x^2}}{2x}$

(e) $\dfrac{\sqrt[3]{16x^2}}{\sqrt[3]{9y^5}} = \dfrac{\sqrt[3]{16x^2}}{\sqrt[3]{9y^5}} \cdot \dfrac{\sqrt[3]{3y}}{\sqrt[3]{3y}} = \dfrac{\sqrt[3]{48x^2y}}{\sqrt[3]{27y^6}} = \dfrac{\sqrt[3]{8}\sqrt[3]{6x^2y}}{3y^2} = \dfrac{2\sqrt[3]{6x^2y}}{3y^2}$

Note that in part (c) we did some simplifying first before rationalizing the denominator, whereas in part (b) we proceeded immediately to rationalize the denominator. This is an individual choice, and you should probably do it both ways a few times to decide which you prefer.

Concept Quiz 5.3

For Problems 1–10, answer true or false.

1. In order to be combined when adding, radicals must have the same index and the same radicand.
2. If $x \geq 0$, then $\sqrt{x^2} = x$.
3. For all real numbers, $\sqrt{x^2} = x$.
4. For all real numbers, $\sqrt[3]{x^3} = x$.
5. A radical is not in simplest radical form if it has a fraction within the radical sign.
6. If a radical contains a factor raised to a power that is equal to the index of the radical, then the radical is not in simplest radical form.
7. The radical $\dfrac{1}{\sqrt{x}}$ is in simplest radical form.
8. $3\sqrt{2} + 4\sqrt{3} = 7\sqrt{5}$.
9. If $x > 0$, then $\sqrt{45x^3} = 3x^2\sqrt{5x}$.
10. If $x > 0$, then $\dfrac{4\sqrt{x^5}}{3\sqrt{4x^2}} = \dfrac{2x\sqrt{x}}{3}$.

Problem Set 5.3

For Problems 1–20, use the distributive property to help simplify each of the following. (Objective 1)
For example,

$$3\sqrt{8} - \sqrt{32} = 3\sqrt{4}\sqrt{2} - \sqrt{16}\sqrt{2}$$
$$= 3(2)\sqrt{2} - 4\sqrt{2}$$
$$= 6\sqrt{2} - 4\sqrt{2}$$
$$= (6 - 4)\sqrt{2} = 2\sqrt{2}$$

1. $5\sqrt{18} - 2\sqrt{2}$
2. $7\sqrt{12} + 4\sqrt{3}$
3. $7\sqrt{12} + 10\sqrt{48}$
4. $6\sqrt{8} - 5\sqrt{18}$
5. $-2\sqrt{50} - 5\sqrt{32}$
6. $-2\sqrt{20} - 7\sqrt{45}$
7. $3\sqrt{20} - \sqrt{5} - 2\sqrt{45}$

8. $6\sqrt{12} + \sqrt{3} - 2\sqrt{48}$

9. $-9\sqrt{24} + 3\sqrt{54} - 12\sqrt{6}$

10. $13\sqrt{28} - 2\sqrt{63} - 7\sqrt{7}$

11. $\dfrac{3}{4}\sqrt{7} - \dfrac{2}{3}\sqrt{28}$

12. $\dfrac{3}{5}\sqrt{5} - \dfrac{1}{4}\sqrt{80}$

13. $\dfrac{3}{5}\sqrt{40} + \dfrac{5}{6}\sqrt{90}$

14. $\dfrac{3}{8}\sqrt{96} - \dfrac{2}{3}\sqrt{54}$

15. $\dfrac{3\sqrt{18}}{5} - \dfrac{5\sqrt{72}}{6} + \dfrac{3\sqrt{98}}{4}$

16. $\dfrac{-2\sqrt{20}}{3} + \dfrac{3\sqrt{45}}{4} - \dfrac{5\sqrt{80}}{6}$

17. $5\sqrt[3]{3} + 2\sqrt[3]{24} - 6\sqrt[3]{81}$

18. $-3\sqrt[3]{2} - 2\sqrt[3]{16} + \sqrt[3]{54}$

19. $-\sqrt[3]{16} + 7\sqrt[3]{54} - 9\sqrt[3]{2}$

20. $4\sqrt[3]{24} - 6\sqrt[3]{3} + 13\sqrt[3]{81}$

For Problems 21–64, express each of the following in simplest radical form. All variables represent positive real numbers. (Objective 2)

21. $\sqrt{32x}$

22. $\sqrt{50y}$

23. $\sqrt{75x^2}$

24. $\sqrt{108y^2}$

25. $\sqrt{20x^2y}$

26. $\sqrt{80xy^2}$

27. $\sqrt{64x^3y^7}$

28. $\sqrt{36x^5y^6}$

29. $\sqrt{54a^4b^3}$

30. $\sqrt{96a^7b^8}$

31. $\sqrt{63x^6y^8}$

32. $\sqrt{28x^4y^{12}}$

33. $2\sqrt{40a^3}$

34. $4\sqrt{90a^5}$

35. $\dfrac{2}{3}\sqrt{96xy^3}$

36. $\dfrac{4}{5}\sqrt{125x^4y}$

37. $\sqrt{\dfrac{2x}{5y}}$

38. $\sqrt{\dfrac{3x}{2y}}$

39. $\sqrt{\dfrac{5}{12x^4}}$

40. $\sqrt{\dfrac{7}{8x^2}}$

41. $\dfrac{5}{\sqrt{18y}}$

42. $\dfrac{3}{\sqrt{12x}}$

43. $\dfrac{\sqrt{7x}}{\sqrt{8y^5}}$

44. $\dfrac{\sqrt{5y}}{\sqrt{18x^3}}$

45. $\dfrac{\sqrt{18y^3}}{\sqrt{16x}}$

46. $\dfrac{\sqrt{2x^3}}{\sqrt{9y}}$

47. $\dfrac{\sqrt{24a^2b^3}}{\sqrt{7ab^6}}$

48. $\dfrac{\sqrt{12a^2b}}{\sqrt{5a^3b^3}}$

49. $\sqrt[3]{24y}$

50. $\sqrt[3]{16x^2}$

51. $\sqrt[3]{16x^4}$

52. $\sqrt[3]{54x^3}$

53. $\sqrt[3]{56x^6y^8}$

54. $\sqrt[3]{81x^5y^6}$

55. $\sqrt[3]{\dfrac{7}{9x^2}}$

56. $\sqrt[3]{\dfrac{5}{2x}}$

57. $\dfrac{\sqrt[3]{3y}}{\sqrt[3]{16x^4}}$

58. $\dfrac{\sqrt[3]{2y}}{\sqrt[3]{3x}}$

59. $\dfrac{\sqrt[3]{12xy}}{\sqrt[3]{3x^2y^5}}$

60. $\dfrac{5}{\sqrt[3]{9xy^2}}$

61. $\sqrt{8x + 12y}$ [Hint: $\sqrt{8x + 12y} = \sqrt{4(2x + 3y)}$]

62. $\sqrt{4x + 4y}$

63. $\sqrt{16x + 48y}$

64. $\sqrt{27x + 18y}$

For Problems 65–74, use the distributive property to help simplify each of the following. All variables represent positive real numbers. (Objective 2)

65. $-3\sqrt{4x} + 5\sqrt{9x} + 6\sqrt{16x}$

66. $-2\sqrt{25x} - 4\sqrt{36x} + 7\sqrt{64x}$

67. $2\sqrt{18x} - 3\sqrt{8x} - 6\sqrt{50x}$

68. $4\sqrt{20x} + 5\sqrt{45x} - 10\sqrt{80x}$

69. $5\sqrt{27n} - \sqrt{12n} - 6\sqrt{3n}$

70. $4\sqrt{8n} + 3\sqrt{18n} - 2\sqrt{72n}$

71. $7\sqrt{4ab} - \sqrt{16ab} - 10\sqrt{25ab}$

72. $4\sqrt{ab} - 9\sqrt{36ab} + 6\sqrt{49ab}$

73. $-3\sqrt{2x^3} + 4\sqrt{8x^3} - 3\sqrt{32x^3}$

74. $2\sqrt{40x^5} - 3\sqrt{90x^5} + 5\sqrt{160x^5}$

Thoughts Into Words

75. Is the expression $3\sqrt{2} + \sqrt{50}$ in simplest radical form? Defend your answer.

76. Your friend simplified $\dfrac{\sqrt{6}}{\sqrt{8}}$ as follows:

$$\dfrac{\sqrt{6}}{\sqrt{8}} \cdot \dfrac{\sqrt{8}}{\sqrt{8}} = \dfrac{\sqrt{48}}{8} = \dfrac{\sqrt{16}\sqrt{3}}{8} = \dfrac{4\sqrt{3}}{8} = \dfrac{\sqrt{3}}{2}$$

Is this a correct procedure? Can you show her a better way to do this problem?

77. Does $\sqrt{x + y}$ equal $\sqrt{x} + \sqrt{y}$? Defend your answer.

Further Investigations

78. Use your calculator and evaluate each expression in Problems 1–16. Then evaluate the simplified expression that you obtained when doing these problems. Your two results for each problem should be the same.

Consider these problems, in which the variables could represent any real number. However, we would still have the restriction that the radical would represent a real number. In other words, the radicand must be nonnegative.

$\sqrt{98x^2} = \sqrt{49x^2}\sqrt{2} = 7|x|\sqrt{2}$ An absolute-value sign is necessary to ensure that the principal root is nonnegative

$\sqrt{24x^4} = \sqrt{4x^4}\sqrt{6} = 2x^2\sqrt{6}$ Because x^2 is nonnegative, there is no need for an absolute-value sign to ensure that the principal root is nonnegative

$\sqrt{25x^3} = \sqrt{25x^2}\sqrt{x} = 5x\sqrt{x}$ Because the radicand is defined to be nonnegative, x must be nonnegative, and there is no need for an absolute-value sign to ensure that the principal root is nonnegative

$\sqrt{18b^5} = \sqrt{9b^4}\sqrt{2b} = 3b^2\sqrt{2b}$ An absolute-value sign is not necessary to ensure that the principal root is nonnegative

$\sqrt{12y^6} = \sqrt{4y^6}\sqrt{3} = 2|y^3|\sqrt{3}$ An absolute-value sign is necessary to ensure that the principal root is nonnegative

79. Do the following problems, in which the variable could be any real number as long as the radical represents a real number. Use absolute-value signs in the answers as necessary.

(a) $\sqrt{125x^2}$ **(b)** $\sqrt{16x^4}$

(c) $\sqrt{8b^3}$ **(d)** $\sqrt{3y^5}$

(e) $\sqrt{288x^6}$ **(f)** $\sqrt{28m^8}$

(g) $\sqrt{128c^{10}}$ **(h)** $\sqrt{18d^7}$

(i) $\sqrt{49x^2}$ **(j)** $\sqrt{80n^{20}}$

(k) $\sqrt{81h^3}$

Answers to the Concept Quiz

1. True   **2.** True   **3.** False   **4.** True   **5.** True   **6.** True   **7.** False   **8.** False   **9.** False   **10.** True

---

5.4   Products and Quotients Involving Radicals

OBJECTIVES

1. Multiply two radicals

2. Use the distributive property to multiply radical expressions

3. Rationalize binomial denominators

As we have seen, Property 5.4 $\left(\sqrt[n]{bc} = \sqrt[n]{b}\sqrt[n]{c}\right)$ is used to express one radical as the product of two radicals and also to express the product of two radicals as one radical. In fact, we have used the property for both purposes within the framework of simplifying radicals. For example,

$$\frac{\sqrt{3}}{\sqrt{32}} = \frac{\sqrt{3}}{\sqrt{16}\sqrt{2}} = \frac{\sqrt{3}}{4\sqrt{2}} = \frac{\sqrt{3}}{4\sqrt{2}} \cdot \frac{\sqrt{2}}{\sqrt{2}} = \frac{\sqrt{6}}{8}$$

$$\underset{\sqrt[n]{bc} = \sqrt[n]{b}\sqrt[n]{c}}{\uparrow\qquad\uparrow} \qquad\qquad \underset{\sqrt[n]{b}\sqrt[n]{c} = \sqrt[n]{bc}}{\uparrow\qquad\uparrow}$$

The following examples demonstrate the use of Property 5.4 to multiply radicals and to express the product in simplest form.

Classroom Example
Multiply and simplify where possible:

(a) $(4\sqrt{2})(6\sqrt{7})$

(b) $(5\sqrt{18})(2\sqrt{2})$

(c) $(2\sqrt{5})(5\sqrt{10})$

(d) $(8\sqrt[3]{9})(5\sqrt[3]{6})$

EXAMPLE 1   Multiply and simplify where possible:

(a) $(2\sqrt{3})(3\sqrt{5})$ (b) $(3\sqrt{8})(5\sqrt{2})$

(c) $(7\sqrt{6})(3\sqrt{8})$ (d) $(2\sqrt[3]{6})(5\sqrt[3]{4})$

Solution

(a) $(2\sqrt{3})(3\sqrt{5}) = 2 \cdot 3 \cdot \sqrt{3} \cdot \sqrt{5} = 6\sqrt{15}$

(b) $(3\sqrt{8})(5\sqrt{2}) = 3 \cdot 5 \cdot \sqrt{8} \cdot \sqrt{2} = 15\sqrt{16} = 15 \cdot 4 = 60$

(c) $(7\sqrt{6})(3\sqrt{8}) = 7 \cdot 3 \cdot \sqrt{6} \cdot \sqrt{8} = 21\sqrt{48} = 21\sqrt{16}\sqrt{3}$

$$= 21 \cdot 4 \cdot \sqrt{3} = 84\sqrt{3}$$

(d) $(2\sqrt[3]{6})(5\sqrt[3]{4}) = 2 \cdot 5 \cdot \sqrt[3]{6} \cdot \sqrt[3]{4} = 10\sqrt[3]{24}$

$$= 10\sqrt[3]{8}\sqrt[3]{3}$$

$$= 10 \cdot 2 \cdot \sqrt[3]{3}$$

$$= 20\sqrt[3]{3}$$

Using the Distributive Property to Multiply Radical Expressions

Recall the use of the distributive property when finding the product of a monomial and a polynomial. For example, $3x^2(2x + 7) = 3x^2(2x) + 3x^2(7) = 6x^3 + 21x^2$. In a similar manner, the distributive property and Property 5.4 provide the basis for finding certain special products that involve radicals. The following examples illustrate this idea.

Classroom Example
Multiply and simplify where possible:

(a) $\sqrt{2}(\sqrt{10} + \sqrt{8})$

(b) $3\sqrt{5}(\sqrt{10} + \sqrt{15})$

(c) $\sqrt{7a}(\sqrt{14a} - \sqrt{28ab})$

(d) $(3\sqrt[3]{12})(4\sqrt[3]{9})$

EXAMPLE 2   Multiply and simplify where possible:

(a) $\sqrt{3}(\sqrt{6} + \sqrt{12})$ (b) $2\sqrt{2}(4\sqrt{3} - 5\sqrt{6})$

(c) $\sqrt{6x}(\sqrt{8x} + \sqrt{12xy})$ (d) $\sqrt[3]{2}(5\sqrt[3]{4} - 3\sqrt[3]{16})$

Solution

(a) $\sqrt{3}(\sqrt{6} + \sqrt{12}) = \sqrt{3}\sqrt{6} + \sqrt{3}\sqrt{12}$

$$= \sqrt{18} + \sqrt{36}$$

$$= \sqrt{9}\sqrt{2} + 6$$

$$= 3\sqrt{2} + 6$$

(b) $2\sqrt{2}(4\sqrt{3} - 5\sqrt{6}) = (2\sqrt{2})(4\sqrt{3}) - (2\sqrt{2})(5\sqrt{6})$

$$= 8\sqrt{6} - 10\sqrt{12}$$

$$= 8\sqrt{6} - 10\sqrt{4}\sqrt{3}$$

$$= 8\sqrt{6} - 20\sqrt{3}$$

(c) $\sqrt{6x}(\sqrt{8x} + \sqrt{12xy}) = (\sqrt{6x})(\sqrt{8x}) + (\sqrt{6x})(\sqrt{12xy})$

$$= \sqrt{48x^2} + \sqrt{72x^2y}$$

$$= \sqrt{16x^2}\sqrt{3} + \sqrt{36x^2}\sqrt{2y}$$

$$= 4x\sqrt{3} + 6x\sqrt{2y}$$

$$\textbf{(d)} \ \ \sqrt[3]{2}(5\sqrt[3]{4} - 3\sqrt[3]{16}) = (\sqrt[3]{2})(5\sqrt[3]{4}) - (\sqrt[3]{2})(3\sqrt[3]{16})$$
$$= 5\sqrt[3]{8} - 3\sqrt[3]{32}$$
$$= 5 \cdot 2 - 3\sqrt[3]{8}\sqrt[3]{4}$$
$$= 10 - 6\sqrt[3]{4}$$

The distributive property also plays a central role in determining the product of two binomials. For example, $(x + 2)(x + 3) = x(x + 3) + 2(x + 3) = x^2 + 3x + 2x + 6 = x^2 + 5x + 6$. Finding the product of two binomial expressions that involve radicals can be handled in a similar fashion, as in the next examples.

Classroom Example
Find the following products and simplify:

(a) $(\sqrt{2} - \sqrt{7})(\sqrt{5} + \sqrt{3})$
(b) $(5\sqrt{5} + \sqrt{3})(4\sqrt{5} - 6\sqrt{3})$
(c) $(\sqrt{10} + \sqrt{3})(\sqrt{10} - \sqrt{3})$
(d) $(\sqrt{m} - \sqrt{n})(\sqrt{m} + \sqrt{n})$

EXAMPLE 3   Find the following products and simplify:

(a) $(\sqrt{3} + \sqrt{5})(\sqrt{2} + \sqrt{6})$ **(b)** $(2\sqrt{2} - \sqrt{7})(3\sqrt{2} + 5\sqrt{7})$

(c) $(\sqrt{8} + \sqrt{6})(\sqrt{8} - \sqrt{6})$ **(d)** $(\sqrt{x} + \sqrt{y})(\sqrt{x} - \sqrt{y})$

Solution

(a) $(\sqrt{3} + \sqrt{5})(\sqrt{2} + \sqrt{6}) = \sqrt{3}(\sqrt{2} + \sqrt{6}) + \sqrt{5}(\sqrt{2} + \sqrt{6})$
$$= \sqrt{3}\sqrt{2} + \sqrt{3}\sqrt{6} + \sqrt{5}\sqrt{2} + \sqrt{5}\sqrt{6}$$
$$= \sqrt{6} + \sqrt{18} + \sqrt{10} + \sqrt{30}$$
$$= \sqrt{6} + 3\sqrt{2} + \sqrt{10} + \sqrt{30}$$

(b) $(2\sqrt{2} - \sqrt{7})(3\sqrt{2} + 5\sqrt{7}) = 2\sqrt{2}(3\sqrt{2} + 5\sqrt{7})$
$$- \sqrt{7}(3\sqrt{2} + 5\sqrt{7})$$
$$= (2\sqrt{2})(3\sqrt{2}) + (2\sqrt{2})(5\sqrt{7})$$
$$-(\sqrt{7})(3\sqrt{2}) - (\sqrt{7})(5\sqrt{7})$$
$$= 12 + 10\sqrt{14} - 3\sqrt{14} - 35$$
$$= -23 + 7\sqrt{14}$$

(c) $(\sqrt{8} + \sqrt{6})(\sqrt{8} - \sqrt{6}) = \sqrt{8}(\sqrt{8} - \sqrt{6}) + \sqrt{6}(\sqrt{8} - \sqrt{6})$
$$= \sqrt{8}\sqrt{8} - \sqrt{8}\sqrt{6} + \sqrt{6}\sqrt{8} - \sqrt{6}\sqrt{6}$$
$$= 8 - \sqrt{48} + \sqrt{48} - 6$$
$$= 2$$

(d) $(\sqrt{x} + \sqrt{y})(\sqrt{x} - \sqrt{y}) = \sqrt{x}(\sqrt{x} - \sqrt{y}) + \sqrt{y}(\sqrt{x} - \sqrt{y})$
$$= \sqrt{x}\sqrt{x} - \sqrt{x}\sqrt{y} + \sqrt{y}\sqrt{x} - \sqrt{y}\sqrt{y}$$
$$= x - \sqrt{xy} + \sqrt{xy} - y$$
$$= x - y$$

Rationalizing Binomial Denominators

Note parts (c) and (d) of Example 3; they fit the special-product pattern $(a + b)(a - b) = a^2 - b^2$. Furthermore, in each case the final product is in rational form. The factors $a + b$ and $a - b$ are called **conjugates**. This suggests a way of rationalizing the denominator in an expression that contains a binomial denominator with radicals. We will multiply by the conjugate of the binomial denominator. Consider the following example.

Classroom Example

Simplify $\dfrac{2}{\sqrt{7} - \sqrt{3}}$ by rationalizing the denominator.

EXAMPLE 4   Simplify $\dfrac{4}{\sqrt{5} + \sqrt{2}}$ by rationalizing the denominator.

Solution

$$\frac{4}{\sqrt{5} + \sqrt{2}} = \frac{4}{\sqrt{5} + \sqrt{2}} \cdot \left(\frac{\sqrt{5} - \sqrt{2}}{\sqrt{5} - \sqrt{2}}\right) \quad \text{Form of 1}$$

$$= \frac{4(\sqrt{5} - \sqrt{2})}{(\sqrt{5} + \sqrt{2})(\sqrt{5} - \sqrt{2})} = \frac{4(\sqrt{5} - \sqrt{2})}{5 - 2}$$

$$= \frac{4(\sqrt{5} - \sqrt{2})}{3} \quad \text{or} \quad \frac{4\sqrt{5} - 4\sqrt{2}}{3}$$

Either answer
is acceptable

The next examples further illustrate the process of rationalizing and simplifying expressions that contain binomial denominators.

Classroom Example

For each of the following, rationalize the denominator and simplify:

(a) $\dfrac{\sqrt{6}}{\sqrt{2} - 8}$

(b) $\dfrac{5}{2\sqrt{5} - 3\sqrt{2}}$

(c) $\dfrac{\sqrt{y} - 6}{\sqrt{y} + 2}$

(d) $\dfrac{8\sqrt{m} + 5\sqrt{n}}{\sqrt{m} - \sqrt{n}}$

EXAMPLE 5

For each of the following, rationalize the denominator and simplify:

(a) $\dfrac{\sqrt{3}}{\sqrt{6} - 9}$ (b) $\dfrac{7}{3\sqrt{5} + 2\sqrt{3}}$ (c) $\dfrac{\sqrt{x} + 2}{\sqrt{x} - 3}$ (d) $\dfrac{2\sqrt{x} - 3\sqrt{y}}{\sqrt{x} + \sqrt{y}}$

Solution

(a) $\dfrac{\sqrt{3}}{\sqrt{6} - 9} = \dfrac{\sqrt{3}}{\sqrt{6} - 9} \cdot \dfrac{\sqrt{6} + 9}{\sqrt{6} + 9}$

$$= \frac{\sqrt{3}(\sqrt{6} + 9)}{(\sqrt{6} - 9)(\sqrt{6} + 9)}$$

$$= \frac{\sqrt{18} + 9\sqrt{3}}{6 - 81}$$

$$= \frac{3\sqrt{2} + 9\sqrt{3}}{-75}$$

$$= \frac{3(\sqrt{2} + 3\sqrt{3})}{(-3)(25)}$$

$$= -\frac{\sqrt{2} + 3\sqrt{3}}{25} \quad \text{or} \quad \frac{-\sqrt{2} - 3\sqrt{3}}{25}$$

(b) $\dfrac{7}{3\sqrt{5} + 2\sqrt{3}} = \dfrac{7}{3\sqrt{5} + 2\sqrt{3}} \cdot \dfrac{3\sqrt{5} - 2\sqrt{3}}{3\sqrt{5} - 2\sqrt{3}}$

$$= \frac{7(3\sqrt{5} - 2\sqrt{3})}{(3\sqrt{5} + 2\sqrt{3})(3\sqrt{5} - 2\sqrt{3})}$$

$$= \frac{7(3\sqrt{5} - 2\sqrt{3})}{45 - 12}$$

$$= \frac{7(3\sqrt{5} - 2\sqrt{3})}{33} \quad \text{or} \quad \frac{21\sqrt{5} - 14\sqrt{3}}{33}$$

(c) $\dfrac{\sqrt{x}+2}{\sqrt{x}-3} = \dfrac{\sqrt{x}+2}{\sqrt{x}-3} \cdot \dfrac{\sqrt{x}+3}{\sqrt{x}+3} = \dfrac{(\sqrt{x}+2)(\sqrt{x}+3)}{(\sqrt{x}-3)(\sqrt{x}+3)}$

$$= \dfrac{x+3\sqrt{x}+2\sqrt{x}+6}{x-9}$$

$$= \dfrac{x+5\sqrt{x}+6}{x-9}$$

(d) $\dfrac{2\sqrt{x}-3\sqrt{y}}{\sqrt{x}+\sqrt{y}} = \dfrac{2\sqrt{x}-3\sqrt{y}}{\sqrt{x}+\sqrt{y}} \cdot \dfrac{\sqrt{x}-\sqrt{y}}{\sqrt{x}-\sqrt{y}}$

$$= \dfrac{(2\sqrt{x}-3\sqrt{y})(\sqrt{x}-\sqrt{y})}{(\sqrt{x}+\sqrt{y})(\sqrt{x}-\sqrt{y})}$$

$$= \dfrac{2x-2\sqrt{xy}-3\sqrt{xy}+3y}{x-y}$$

$$= \dfrac{2x-5\sqrt{xy}+3y}{x-y}$$

Concept Quiz 5.4

For Problems 1–10, answer true or false.

1. The property $\sqrt[n]{x}\sqrt[n]{y} = \sqrt[n]{xy}$ can be used to express the product of two radicals as one radical.

2. The product of two radicals always results in an expression that has a radical even after simplifying.

3. The conjugate of $5 + \sqrt{3}$ is $-5 - \sqrt{3}$.

4. The product of $2 - \sqrt{7}$ and $2 + \sqrt{7}$ is a rational number.

5. To rationalize the denominator for the expression $\dfrac{2\sqrt{5}}{4 - \sqrt{5}}$, we would multiply by $\dfrac{\sqrt{5}}{\sqrt{5}}$.

6. To rationalize the denominator for the expression $\dfrac{\sqrt{x}+8}{\sqrt{x}-4}$, we would multiply the numerator and denominator by $\sqrt{x} - 4$.

7. $\dfrac{\sqrt{8}+\sqrt{12}}{\sqrt{2}} = 2 + \sqrt{6}$

8. $\dfrac{\sqrt{2}}{\sqrt{8}+\sqrt{12}} = \dfrac{1}{2+\sqrt{6}}$

9. The product of $5 + \sqrt{3}$ and $-5 - \sqrt{3}$ is -28.

10. The product of $\sqrt{5} - 1$ and $\sqrt{5} + 1$ is 24.

Problem Set 5.4

For Problems 1–14, multiply and simplify where possible. (Objective 1)

1. $\sqrt{6}\sqrt{12}$

2. $\sqrt{8}\sqrt{6}$

3. $(3\sqrt{3})(2\sqrt{6})$

4. $(5\sqrt{2})(3\sqrt{12})$

5. $(4\sqrt{2})(-6\sqrt{5})$

6. $(-7\sqrt{3})(2\sqrt{5})$

7. $(-3\sqrt{3})(-4\sqrt{8})$

8. $(-5\sqrt{8})(-6\sqrt{7})$

9. $(5\sqrt{6})(4\sqrt{6})$

10. $(3\sqrt{7})(2\sqrt{7})$

11. $(2\sqrt[3]{4})(6\sqrt[3]{2})$

12. $(4\sqrt[3]{3})(5\sqrt[3]{9})$

13. $(4\sqrt[3]{6})(7\sqrt[3]{4})$

14. $(9\sqrt[3]{6})(2\sqrt[3]{9})$

For Problems 15–52, find the following products and express answers in simplest radical form. All variables represent nonnegative real numbers. **(Objective 2)**

15. $\sqrt{2}(\sqrt{3} + \sqrt{5})$

16. $\sqrt{3}(\sqrt{7} + \sqrt{10})$

17. $3\sqrt{5}(2\sqrt{2} - \sqrt{7})$

18. $5\sqrt{6}(2\sqrt{5} - 3\sqrt{11})$

19. $2\sqrt{6}(3\sqrt{8} - 5\sqrt{12})$

20. $4\sqrt{2}(3\sqrt{12} + 7\sqrt{6})$

21. $-4\sqrt{5}(2\sqrt{5} + 4\sqrt{12})$

22. $-5\sqrt{3}(3\sqrt{12} - 9\sqrt{8})$

23. $3\sqrt{x}(5\sqrt{2} + \sqrt{y})$

24. $\sqrt{2x}(3\sqrt{y} - 7\sqrt{5})$

25. $\sqrt{xy}(5\sqrt{xy} - 6\sqrt{x})$

26. $4\sqrt{x}(2\sqrt{xy} + 2\sqrt{x})$

27. $\sqrt{5y}(\sqrt{8x} + \sqrt{12y^2})$

28. $\sqrt{2x}(\sqrt{12xy} - \sqrt{8y})$

29. $5\sqrt{3}(2\sqrt{8} - 3\sqrt{18})$

30. $2\sqrt{2}(3\sqrt{12} - \sqrt{27})$

31. $(\sqrt{3} + 4)(\sqrt{3} - 7)$

32. $(\sqrt{2} + 6)(\sqrt{2} - 2)$

33. $(\sqrt{5} - 6)(\sqrt{5} - 3)$

34. $(\sqrt{7} - 2)(\sqrt{7} - 8)$

35. $(3\sqrt{5} - 2\sqrt{3})(2\sqrt{7} + \sqrt{2})$

36. $(\sqrt{2} + \sqrt{3})(\sqrt{5} - \sqrt{7})$

37. $(2\sqrt{6} + 3\sqrt{5})(\sqrt{8} - 3\sqrt{12})$

38. $(5\sqrt{2} - 4\sqrt{6})(2\sqrt{8} + \sqrt{6})$

39. $(2\sqrt{6} + 5\sqrt{5})(3\sqrt{6} - \sqrt{5})$

40. $(7\sqrt{3} - \sqrt{7})(2\sqrt{3} + 4\sqrt{7})$

41. $(3\sqrt{2} - 5\sqrt{3})(6\sqrt{2} - 7\sqrt{3})$

42. $(\sqrt{8} - 3\sqrt{10})(2\sqrt{8} - 6\sqrt{10})$

43. $(\sqrt{6} + 4)(\sqrt{6} - 4)$

44. $(\sqrt{7} - 2)(\sqrt{7} + 2)$

45. $(\sqrt{2} + \sqrt{10})(\sqrt{2} - \sqrt{10})$

46. $(2\sqrt{3} + \sqrt{11})(2\sqrt{3} - \sqrt{11})$

47. $(\sqrt{2x} + \sqrt{3y})(\sqrt{2x} - \sqrt{3y})$

48. $(2\sqrt{x} - 5\sqrt{y})(2\sqrt{x} + 5\sqrt{y})$

49. $2\sqrt[3]{3}(5\sqrt[3]{4} + \sqrt[3]{6})$

50. $2\sqrt[3]{2}(3\sqrt[3]{6} - 4\sqrt[3]{5})$

51. $3\sqrt[3]{4}(2\sqrt[3]{2} - 6\sqrt[3]{4})$

52. $3\sqrt[3]{3}(4\sqrt[3]{9} + 5\sqrt[3]{7})$

For Problems 53–76, rationalize the denominator and simplify. All variables represent positive real numbers. **(Objective 3)**

53. $\dfrac{2}{\sqrt{7} + 1}$

54. $\dfrac{6}{\sqrt{5} + 2}$

55. $\dfrac{3}{\sqrt{2} - 5}$

56. $\dfrac{-4}{\sqrt{6} - 3}$

57. $\dfrac{1}{\sqrt{2} + \sqrt{7}}$

58. $\dfrac{3}{\sqrt{3} + \sqrt{10}}$

59. $\dfrac{\sqrt{2}}{\sqrt{10} - \sqrt{3}}$

60. $\dfrac{\sqrt{3}}{\sqrt{7} - \sqrt{2}}$

61. $\dfrac{\sqrt{3}}{2\sqrt{5} + 4}$

62. $\dfrac{\sqrt{7}}{3\sqrt{2} - 5}$

63. $\dfrac{6}{3\sqrt{7} - 2\sqrt{6}}$

64. $\dfrac{5}{2\sqrt{5} + 3\sqrt{7}}$

65. $\dfrac{\sqrt{6}}{3\sqrt{2} + 2\sqrt{3}}$

66. $\dfrac{3\sqrt{6}}{5\sqrt{3} - 4\sqrt{2}}$

67. $\dfrac{2}{\sqrt{x} + 4}$

68. $\dfrac{3}{\sqrt{x} + 7}$

69. $\dfrac{\sqrt{x}}{\sqrt{x} - 5}$

70. $\dfrac{\sqrt{x}}{\sqrt{x} - 1}$

71. $\dfrac{\sqrt{x} - 2}{\sqrt{x} + 6}$

72. $\dfrac{\sqrt{x} + 1}{\sqrt{x} - 10}$

73. $\dfrac{\sqrt{x}}{\sqrt{x} + 2\sqrt{y}}$

74. $\dfrac{\sqrt{y}}{2\sqrt{x} - \sqrt{y}}$

75. $\dfrac{3\sqrt{y}}{2\sqrt{x} - 3\sqrt{y}}$

76. $\dfrac{2\sqrt{x}}{3\sqrt{x} + 5\sqrt{y}}$

Thoughts Into Words

77. How would you help someone rationalize the denominator and simplify $\dfrac{4}{\sqrt{8} + \sqrt{12}}$?

78. Discuss how the distributive property has been used thus far in this chapter.

79. How would you simplify the expression $\dfrac{\sqrt{8} + \sqrt{12}}{\sqrt{2}}$?

Further Investigations

80. Use your calculator to evaluate each expression in Problems 53–66. Then evaluate the results you obtained when you did the problems.

Answers to the Concept Quiz
1. True   **2.** False   **3.** False   **4.** True   **5.** False   **6.** False   **7.** True   **8.** False   **9.** False   **10.** False

---

5.5   Equations Involving Radicals

OBJECTIVES

1 Solve radical equations

2 Solve radical equations for real-world problems

We often refer to equations that contain radicals with variables in a radicand as **radical equations**. In this section we discuss techniques for solving such equations that contain one or more radicals. To solve radical equations, we need the following property of equality.

> ### Property 5.6
> Let a and b be real numbers and n be a positive integer.
> If $a = b$ then $a^n = b^n$

Property 5.6 states that we can raise both sides of an equation to a positive integral power. However, raising both sides of an equation to a positive integral power sometimes produces results that do not satisfy the original equation. Let's consider two examples to illustrate this point.

Classroom Example
Solve $\sqrt{2x - 1} = 3$.

EXAMPLE 1   Solve $\sqrt{2x - 5} = 7$.

Solution

$$\sqrt{2x - 5} = 7$$
$$\left(\sqrt{2x - 5}\right)^2 = 7^2 \qquad \text{Square both sides}$$
$$2x - 5 = 49$$
$$2x = 54$$
$$x = 27$$

✔ **Check**

$$\sqrt{2x - 5} = 7$$
$$\sqrt{2(27) - 5} \overset{?}{=} 7$$
$$\sqrt{49} \overset{?}{=} 7$$
$$7 = 7$$

The solution set for $\sqrt{2x - 5} = 7$ is $\{27\}$.

Classroom Example
Solve $\sqrt{5y + 9} = -8$.

EXAMPLE 2   Solve $\sqrt{3a + 4} = -4$.

Solution

$$\sqrt{3a + 4} = -4$$

$$\left(\sqrt{3a + 4}\right)^2 = (-4)^2 \qquad \text{Square both sides}$$

$$3a + 4 = 16$$

$$3a = 12$$

$$a = 4$$

✔ **Check**

$$\sqrt{3a + 4} = -4$$

$$\sqrt{3(4) + 4} \stackrel{?}{=} -4$$

$$\sqrt{16} \stackrel{?}{=} -4$$

$$4 \neq -4$$

Because 4 does not check, the original equation has no real number solution. Thus the solution set is $\varnothing$.

In general, raising both sides of an equation to a positive integral power produces an equation that has all of the solutions of the original equation, but it may also have some extra solutions that do not satisfy the original equation. Such extra solutions are called **extraneous solutions**. Therefore, when using Property 5.6, you *must* check each potential solution in the original equation.

Let's consider some examples to illustrate different situations that arise when we are solving radical equations.

Classroom Example
Solve $\sqrt{2x + 6} = x + 3$.

EXAMPLE 3   Solve $\sqrt{2t - 4} = t - 2$.

Solution

$$\sqrt{2t - 4} = t - 2$$

$$\left(\sqrt{2t - 4}\right)^2 = (t - 2)^2 \qquad \text{Square both sides}$$

$$2t - 4 = t^2 - 4t + 4$$

$$0 = t^2 - 6t + 8$$

$$0 = (t - 2)(t - 4) \qquad \text{Factor the right side}$$

$$t - 2 = 0 \quad \text{or} \quad t - 4 = 0 \qquad \text{Apply: } ab = 0 \text{ if and only if } a = 0 \text{ or } b = 0$$

$$t = 2 \quad \text{or} \quad t = 4$$

✔ **Check**

$$\sqrt{2t - 4} = t - 2 \qquad\qquad\qquad \sqrt{2t - 4} = t - 2$$

$$\sqrt{2(2) - 4} \stackrel{?}{=} 2 - 2 \quad \text{when } t = 2 \quad \text{or} \quad \sqrt{2(4) - 4} \stackrel{?}{=} 4 - 2 \quad \text{when } t = 4$$

$$\sqrt{0} \stackrel{?}{=} 0 \qquad\qquad\qquad\qquad \sqrt{4} \stackrel{?}{=} 2$$

$$0 = 0 \qquad\qquad\qquad\qquad\qquad 2 = 2$$

The solution set is $\{2, 4\}$.

Classroom Example
Solve $\sqrt{m+2} = m$.

EXAMPLE 4 Solve $\sqrt{y+6} = y$.

Solution

$$\sqrt{y+6} = y$$
$$\sqrt{y} = y - 6$$
$$(\sqrt{y})^2 = (y-6)^2 \qquad \text{Square both sides}$$
$$y = y^2 - 12y + 36$$
$$0 = y^2 - 13y + 36$$
$$0 = (y-4)(y-9) \qquad \text{Factor the right side}$$

$$y - 4 = 0 \quad \text{or} \quad y - 9 = 0 \qquad \begin{array}{l}\text{Apply: } ab = 0 \text{ if and} \\ \text{only if } a = 0 \text{ or } b = 0\end{array}$$

$$y = 4 \quad \text{or} \quad y - 9$$

✔ **Check**

$$\sqrt{y+6} = y \qquad\qquad \sqrt{y+6} = y$$
$$\sqrt{4}+6 \overset{?}{=} 4 \quad \text{when } y = 4 \quad \text{or} \quad \sqrt{9}+6 \overset{?}{=} 9 \quad \text{when } y = 9$$
$$2 + 6 \overset{?}{=} 4 \qquad\qquad\qquad 3 + 6 \overset{?}{=} 9$$
$$8 \neq 4 \qquad\qquad\qquad\qquad 9 = 9$$

The only solution is 9; the solution set is $\{9\}$.

In Example 4, note that we changed the form of the original equation $\sqrt{y+6} = y$ to $\sqrt{y} = y - 6$ before we squared both sides. Squaring both sides of $\sqrt{y+6} = y$ produces $y + 12\sqrt{y} + 36 = y^2$, which is a much more complex equation that still contains a radical. Here again, it pays to think ahead before carrying out all the steps. Now let's consider an example involving a cube root.

Classroom Example
Solve $\sqrt[3]{x^2+2} = 3$.

EXAMPLE 5 Solve $\sqrt[3]{n^2-1} = 2$.

Solution

$$\sqrt[3]{n^2-1} = 2$$
$$\left(\sqrt[3]{n^2-1}\right)^3 = 2^3 \qquad \text{Cube both sides}$$
$$n^2 - 1 = 8$$
$$n^2 - 9 = 0$$
$$(n+3)(n-3) = 0$$

$$n + 3 = 0 \quad \text{or} \quad n - 3 = 0$$
$$n = -3 \quad \text{or} \quad n = 3$$

✔ **Check**

$$\sqrt[3]{n^2-1} = 2 \qquad\qquad \sqrt[3]{n^2-1} = 2$$
$$\sqrt[3]{(-3)^2-1} \overset{?}{=} 2 \quad \text{when } n = -3 \quad \text{or} \quad \sqrt[3]{3^2-1} \overset{?}{=} 2 \quad \text{when } n = 3$$
$$\sqrt[3]{8} \overset{?}{=} 2 \qquad\qquad\qquad \sqrt[3]{8} \overset{?}{=} 2$$
$$2 = 2 \qquad\qquad\qquad\qquad 2 = 2$$

The solution set is $\{-3, 3\}$.

It may be necessary to square both sides of an equation, simplify the resulting equation, and then square both sides again. The next example illustrates this type of problem.

Classroom Example
Solve $\sqrt{x + 4} = 1 + \sqrt{x - 1}$.

EXAMPLE 6   Solve $\sqrt{x + 2} = 7 - \sqrt{x + 9}$.

Solution

$$\sqrt{x + 2} = 7 - \sqrt{x + 9}$$

$$\left(\sqrt{x + 2}\right)^2 = \left(7 - \sqrt{x + 9}\right)^2 \qquad \text{Square both sides}$$

$$x + 2 = 49 - 14\sqrt{x + 9} + x + 9$$

$$x + 2 = x + 58 - 14\sqrt{x + 9}$$

$$-56 = -14\sqrt{x + 9}$$

$$4 = \sqrt{x + 9}$$

$$(4)^2 = \left(\sqrt{x + 9}\right)^2 \qquad \text{Square both sides}$$

$$16 = x + 9$$

$$7 = x$$

✔ Check

$$\sqrt{x + 2} = 7 - \sqrt{x + 9}$$

$$\sqrt{7 + 2} \overset{?}{=} 7 - \sqrt{7 + 9} \quad \text{when } x = 7$$

$$\sqrt{9} \overset{?}{=} 7 - \sqrt{16}$$

$$3 \overset{?}{=} 7 - 4$$

$$3 = 3$$

The solution set is $\{7\}$.

Solving Radical Equations for Real-World Problems

In Section 5.1 we used the formula $S = \sqrt{30Df}$ to approximate how fast a car was traveling on the basis of the length of skid marks. (Remember that S represents the speed of the car in miles per hour, D represents the length of the skid marks in feet, and f represents a coefficient of friction.) This same formula can be used to estimate the length of skid marks that are produced by cars traveling at different rates on various types of road surfaces. To use the formula for this purpose, let's change the form of the equation by solving for D.

$$\sqrt{30Df} = S$$

$$30Df = S^2 \qquad \text{The result of squaring both sides of the original equation}$$

$$D = \frac{S^2}{30f} \qquad \begin{array}{l}D, S, \text{ and } f \text{ are positive numbers, so this final equation and the} \\ \text{original one are equivalent}\end{array}$$

Classroom Example
Suppose that for a particular road surface, the coefficient of friction is 0.27. How far will a car skid when the brakes are applied at 65 miles per hour?

EXAMPLE 7

Suppose that for a particular road surface, the coefficient of friction is 0.35. How far will a car skid when the brakes are applied at 60 miles per hour?

Solution

We can substitute 0.35 for f and 60 for S in the formula $D = \dfrac{S^2}{30f}$.

$$D = \frac{60^2}{30(0.35)} = 343 \quad \text{to the nearest whole number}$$

The car will skid approximately 343 feet.

Remark: Pause for a moment and think about the result in Example 7. The coefficient of friction 0.35 refers to a wet concrete road surface. Note that a car traveling at 60 miles per hour on such a surface will skid more than the length of a football field.

Concept Quiz 5.5

For Problems 1–10, answer true or false.

1. To solve a radical equation, we can raise each side of the equation to a positive integer power.
2. Solving the equation that results from squaring each side of an original equation may not give all the solutions of the original equation.
3. The equation $\sqrt[3]{x} - 1 = -2$ has a solution.
4. Potential solutions that do not satisfy the original equation are called extraneous solutions.
5. The equation $\sqrt{x + 1} = -2$ has no real number solutions.
6. The solution set for $\sqrt{x + 2} = x$ is $\{1, 4\}$.
7. The solution set for $\sqrt{x + 1} + \sqrt{x - 2} = -3$ is the null set.
8. The solution set for $\sqrt[3]{x + 2} = -2$ is the null set.
9. The solution set for the equation $\sqrt{x^2 - 2x + 1} = x - 3$ is $\{2\}$.
10. The solution set for the equation $\sqrt{5x + 1} + \sqrt{x + 4} = 3$ is $\{0\}$.

Problem Set 5.5

For Problems 1–56, solve each equation. Don't forget to check each of your potential solutions. **(Objective 1)**

1. $\sqrt{5x} = 10$
2. $\sqrt{3x} = 9$
3. $\sqrt{2x} + 4 = 0$
4. $\sqrt{4x} + 5 = 0$
5. $2\sqrt{n} = 5$
6. $5\sqrt{n} = 3$
7. $3\sqrt{n} - 2 = 0$
8. $2\sqrt{n} - 7 = 0$
9. $\sqrt{3y + 1} = 4$
10. $\sqrt{2y - 3} = 5$
11. $\sqrt{4y - 3} - 6 = 0$
12. $\sqrt{3y + 5} - 2 = 0$
13. $\sqrt{3x - 1} + 1 = 4$
14. $\sqrt{4x - 1} - 3 = 2$
15. $\sqrt{2n + 3} - 2 = -1$
16. $\sqrt{5n + 1} - 6 = -4$
17. $\sqrt{2x - 5} = -1$
18. $\sqrt{4x - 3} = -4$
19. $\sqrt{5x + 2} = \sqrt{6x + 1}$
20. $\sqrt{4x + 2} = \sqrt{3x + 4}$
21. $\sqrt{3x + 1} = \sqrt{7x - 5}$
22. $\sqrt{6x + 5} = \sqrt{2x + 10}$
23. $\sqrt{3x - 2} - \sqrt{x + 4} = 0$
24. $\sqrt{7x - 6} - \sqrt{5x + 2} = 0$
25. $5\sqrt{t - 1} = 6$
26. $4\sqrt{t + 3} = 6$
27. $\sqrt{x^2 + 7} = 4$
28. $\sqrt{x^2 + 3} - 2 = 0$
29. $\sqrt{x^2 + 13x + 37} = 1$
30. $\sqrt{x^2 + 5x - 20} = 2$
31. $\sqrt{x^2 - x + 1} = x + 1$
32. $\sqrt{n^2 - 2n - 4} = n$
33. $\sqrt{x^2 + 3x + 7} = x + 2$
34. $\sqrt{x^2 + 2x + 1} = x + 3$

35. $\sqrt{-4x + 17} = x - 3$
36. $\sqrt{2x - 1} = x - 2$
37. $\sqrt{n + 4} = n + 4$
38. $\sqrt{n + 6} = n + 6$
39. $\sqrt{3y} = y - 6$
40. $2\sqrt{n} = n - 3$
41. $4\sqrt{x + 5} = x$
42. $\sqrt{-x - 6} = x$
43. $\sqrt[3]{x - 2} = 3$
44. $\sqrt[3]{x + 1} = 4$
45. $\sqrt[3]{2x + 3} = -3$
46. $\sqrt[3]{3x - 1} = -4$
47. $\sqrt[3]{2x + 5} = \sqrt[3]{4 - x}$
48. $\sqrt[3]{3x - 1} = \sqrt[3]{2 - 5x}$
49. $\sqrt{x + 19} - \sqrt{x + 28} = -1$
50. $\sqrt{x + 4} = \sqrt{x - 1} + 1$
51. $\sqrt{3x + 1} + \sqrt{2x + 4} = 3$
52. $\sqrt{2x - 1} - \sqrt{x + 3} = 1$
53. $\sqrt{n - 4} + \sqrt{n + 4} = 2\sqrt{n - 1}$
54. $\sqrt{n - 3} + \sqrt{n + 5} = 2\sqrt{n}$
55. $\sqrt{t + 3} - \sqrt{t - 2} = \sqrt{7 - t}$
56. $\sqrt{t + 7} - 2\sqrt{t - 8} = \sqrt{t - 5}$

For Problems 57–59, use the appropriate formula to solve the problems. **(Objective 2)**

57. Use the formula given in Example 7 with a coefficient of friction of 0.95. How far will a car skid at 40 miles per hour? at 55 miles per hour? at 65 miles per hour? Express the answers to the nearest foot.

58. Solve the formula $T = 2\pi\sqrt{\dfrac{L}{32}}$ for L. (Remember that in this formula, which was used in Section 5.2, T represents the period of a pendulum expressed in seconds, and L represents the length of the pendulum in feet.)

59. In Problem 58, you should have obtained the equation $L = \dfrac{8T^2}{\pi^2}$. What is the length of a pendulum that has a period of 2 seconds? of 2.5 seconds? of 3 seconds? Express your answers to the nearest tenth of a foot.

Thoughts Into Words

60. Your friend makes an effort to solve the equation $3 + 2\sqrt{x} = x$ as follows:

$$(3 + 2\sqrt{x})^2 = x^2$$
$$9 + 12\sqrt{x} + 4x = x^2$$

At this step he stops and doesn't know how to proceed. What help would you give him?

61. Explain why possible solutions for radical equations *must* be checked.

62. Explain the concept of extraneous solutions.

Answers to the Concept Quiz
1. True   **2.** False   **3.** True   **4.** True   **5.** True   **6.** False   **7.** True   **8.** False   **9.** False   **10.** True

---

5.6   Merging Exponents and Roots

OBJECTIVES

1. Evaluate a number raised to a rational exponent

2. Write an expression with rational exponents as a radical

3. Write radical expressions as expressions with rational exponents

4. Simplify algebraic expressions that have rational exponents

5. Multiply and divide radicals with different indexes

Recall that the basic properties of positive integral exponents led to a definition for the use of negative integers as exponents. In this section, the properties of integral exponents are used to form definitions for the use of rational numbers as exponents. These definitions will tie together the concepts of exponent and root.

Let's consider the following comparisons.

From our study of radicals, we know that

$$(\sqrt{5})^2 = 5$$
$$(\sqrt[3]{8})^3 = 8$$
$$(\sqrt[4]{21})^4 = 21$$

If $(b^n)^m = b^{mn}$ is to hold when n equals a rational number of the form $\dfrac{1}{p}$, where p is a positive integer greater than 1, then

$$(5^{\frac{1}{2}})^2 = 5^{2(\frac{1}{2})} = 5^1 = 5$$
$$(8^{\frac{1}{3}})^3 = 8^{3(\frac{1}{3})} = 8^1 = 8$$
$$(21^{\frac{1}{4}})^4 = 21^{4(\frac{1}{4})} = 21^1 = 21$$

It would seem reasonable to make the following definition.

Definition 5.6

If b is a real number, n is a positive integer greater than 1, and $\sqrt[n]{b}$ exists, then

$$b^{\frac{1}{n}} = \sqrt[n]{b}$$

Definition 5.6 states that $b^{\frac{1}{n}}$ means the nth root of b. We shall assume that b and n are chosen so that $\sqrt[n]{b}$ exists. For example, $(-25)^{\frac{1}{2}}$ is not meaningful at this time because $\sqrt{-25}$ is not a real number. Consider the following examples, which demonstrate the use of Definition 5.6.

$$25^{\frac{1}{2}} = \sqrt{25} = 5 \qquad\qquad 16^{\frac{1}{4}} = \sqrt[4]{16} = 2$$

$$8^{\frac{1}{3}} = \sqrt[3]{8} = 2 \qquad\qquad \left(\frac{36}{49}\right)^{\frac{1}{2}} = \sqrt{\frac{36}{49}} = \frac{6}{7}$$

$$(-27)^{\frac{1}{3}} = \sqrt[3]{-27} = -3$$

The following definition provides the basis for the use of *all* rational numbers as exponents.

> **Definition 5.7**
>
> If $\dfrac{m}{n}$ is a rational number, where n is a positive integer greater than 1, and b is a real number such that $\sqrt[n]{b}$ exists, then
>
> $$b^{\frac{m}{n}} = \sqrt[n]{b^m} = \left(\sqrt[n]{b}\right)^m$$

In Definition 5.7, note that the denominator of the exponent is the index of the radical and that the numerator of the exponent is either the exponent of the radicand or the exponent of the root.

Whether we use the form $\sqrt[n]{b^m}$ or the form $\left(\sqrt[n]{b}\right)^m$ for computational purposes depends somewhat on the magnitude of the problem. Let's use both forms on two problems to illustrate this point.

$$8^{\frac{2}{3}} = \sqrt[3]{8^2} \qquad \text{or} \qquad 8^{\frac{2}{3}} = \left(\sqrt[3]{8}\right)^2$$
$$= \sqrt[3]{64} \qquad\qquad\qquad = 2^2$$
$$= 4 \qquad\qquad\qquad\qquad = 4$$

$$27^{\frac{2}{3}} = \sqrt[3]{27^2} \qquad \text{or} \qquad 27^{\frac{2}{3}} = \left(\sqrt[3]{27}\right)^2$$
$$= \sqrt[3]{729} \qquad\qquad\qquad = 3^2$$
$$= 9 \qquad\qquad\qquad\qquad = 9$$

To compute $8^{\frac{2}{3}}$, either form seems to work about as well as the other one. However, to compute $27^{\frac{2}{3}}$, it should be obvious that $\left(\sqrt[3]{27}\right)^2$ is much easier to handle than $\sqrt[3]{27^2}$.

Classroom Example
Simplify each of the following numerical expressions:
(a) $49^{\frac{3}{2}}$ (b) $81^{\frac{3}{4}}$
(c) $8^{-\frac{5}{3}}$ (d) $(-27)^{\frac{4}{3}}$
(e) $-64^{\frac{1}{3}}$

EXAMPLE 1   Simplify each of the following numerical expressions:

(a) $25^{\frac{3}{2}}$ (b) $16^{\frac{3}{4}}$ (c) $(32)^{-\frac{2}{5}}$ (d) $(-64)^{\frac{2}{3}}$ (e) $-8^{\frac{1}{3}}$

Solution

(a) $25^{\frac{3}{2}} = \left(\sqrt{25}\right)^3 = 5^3 = 125$

(b) $16^{\frac{3}{4}} = \left(\sqrt[4]{16}\right)^3 = 2^3 = 8$

(c) $(32)^{-\frac{2}{5}} = \dfrac{1}{(32)^{\frac{2}{5}}} = \dfrac{1}{\left(\sqrt[5]{32}\right)^2} = \dfrac{1}{2^2} = \dfrac{1}{4}$

(d) $(-64)^{\frac{2}{3}} = \left(\sqrt[3]{-64}\right)^2 = (-4)^2 = 16$

(e) $-8^{\frac{1}{3}} = -\sqrt[3]{8} = -2$

The basic laws of exponents that we stated in Property 5.2 are true for all rational exponents. Therefore, from now on we will use Property 5.2 for rational as well as integral exponents.

Some problems can be handled better in exponential form and others in radical form. Thus we must be able to switch forms with a certain amount of ease. Let's consider some examples that require a switch from one form to the other.

Classroom Example
Write each of the following expressions in radical form:
(a) $m^{\frac{2}{5}}$ (b) $6a^{\frac{4}{7}}$
(c) $m^{\frac{1}{3}}n^{\frac{2}{3}}$ (d) $(a+b)^{\frac{3}{4}}$

EXAMPLE 2   Write each of the following expressions in radical form:

(a) $x^{\frac{3}{4}}$ (b) $3y^{\frac{2}{5}}$ (c) $x^{\frac{1}{4}}y^{\frac{3}{4}}$ (d) $(x+y)^{\frac{2}{3}}$

Solution

(a) $x^{\frac{3}{4}} = \sqrt[4]{x^3}$ (b) $3y^{\frac{2}{5}} = 3\sqrt[5]{y^2}$

(c) $x^{\frac{1}{4}}y^{\frac{3}{4}} = (xy^3)^{\frac{1}{4}} = \sqrt[4]{xy^3}$ (d) $(x+y)^{\frac{2}{3}} = \sqrt[3]{(x+y)^2}$

Classroom Example
Write each of the following using positive rational exponents:
(a) $\sqrt{ab}$ (b) $\sqrt[3]{m^2n}$
(c) $5\sqrt[4]{x^3}$ (d) $\sqrt[6]{(m+n)^5}$

EXAMPLE 3   Write each of the following using positive rational exponents:

(a) $\sqrt{xy}$ (b) $\sqrt[4]{a^3b}$ (c) $4\sqrt[3]{x^2}$ (d) $\sqrt[5]{(x+y)^4}$

Solution

(a) $\sqrt{xy} = (xy)^{\frac{1}{2}} = x^{\frac{1}{2}}y^{\frac{1}{2}}$ (b) $\sqrt[4]{a^3b} = (a^3b)^{\frac{1}{4}} = a^{\frac{3}{4}}b^{\frac{1}{4}}$

(c) $4\sqrt[3]{x^2} = 4x^{\frac{2}{3}}$ (d) $\sqrt[5]{(x+y)^4} = (x+y)^{\frac{4}{5}}$

The properties of exponents provide the basis for simplifying algebraic expressions that contain rational exponents, as these next examples illustrate.

Classroom Example
Simplify each of the following. Express final results using positive exponents only:
(a) $\left(5x^{\frac{1}{3}}\right)\left(2x^{\frac{3}{5}}\right)$ (b) $\left(3m^{\frac{1}{4}}n^{\frac{1}{6}}\right)^3$
(c) $\dfrac{18y^{\frac{1}{6}}}{9y^{\frac{1}{4}}}$ (d) $\left(\dfrac{5x^{\frac{1}{7}}}{8y^{\frac{3}{5}}}\right)^3$

EXAMPLE 4

Simplify each of the following. Express final results using positive exponents only:

(a) $\left(3x^{\frac{1}{2}}\right)\left(4x^{\frac{2}{3}}\right)$ (b) $\left(5a^{\frac{1}{3}}b^{\frac{1}{2}}\right)^2$ (c) $\dfrac{12y^{\frac{1}{3}}}{6y^{\frac{1}{2}}}$ (d) $\left(\dfrac{3x^{\frac{2}{5}}}{2y^{\frac{2}{3}}}\right)^4$

Solution

(a) $\left(3x^{\frac{1}{2}}\right)\left(4x^{\frac{2}{3}}\right) = 3 \cdot 4 \cdot x^{\frac{1}{2}} \cdot x^{\frac{2}{3}}$

$= 12x^{\frac{1}{2}+\frac{2}{3}}$ $b^n \cdot b^m = b^{n+m}$

$= 12x^{\frac{3}{6}+\frac{4}{6}}$ Use 6 as LCD

$= 12x^{\frac{7}{6}}$

(b) $\left(5a^{\frac{1}{3}}b^{\frac{1}{2}}\right)^2 = 5^2 \cdot \left(a^{\frac{1}{3}}\right)^2 \cdot \left(b^{\frac{1}{2}}\right)^2$ $(ab)^n = a^nb^n$

$= 25a^{\frac{2}{3}}b$ $(b^n)^m = b^{mn}$

(c) $\dfrac{12y^{\frac{1}{3}}}{6y^{\frac{1}{2}}} = 2y^{\frac{1}{3}-\frac{1}{2}}$ $\dfrac{b^n}{b^m} = b^{n-m}$

$= 2y^{\frac{2}{6}-\frac{3}{6}}$

$= 2y^{-\frac{1}{6}}$

$= \dfrac{2}{y^{\frac{1}{6}}}$

(d) $\left(\dfrac{3x^{\frac{2}{5}}}{2y^{\frac{2}{3}}}\right)^4 = \dfrac{\left(3x^{\frac{2}{5}}\right)^4}{\left(2y^{\frac{2}{3}}\right)^4}$ $\left(\dfrac{a}{b}\right)^n = \dfrac{a^n}{b^n}$

$= \dfrac{3^4 \cdot \left(x^{\frac{2}{5}}\right)^4}{2^4 \cdot \left(y^{\frac{2}{3}}\right)^4}$ $(ab)^n = a^nb^n$

$= \dfrac{81x^{\frac{8}{5}}}{16y^{\frac{8}{3}}}$ $(b^n)^m = b^{mn}$

Multiplying and Dividing Radicals with Different Indexes

The link between exponents and roots also provides a basis for multiplying and dividing some radicals even if they have different indexes. The general procedure is as follows:

1. Change from radical form to exponential form.
2. Apply the properties of exponents.
3. Then change back to radical form.

The three parts of Example 5 illustrate this process.

Classroom Example
Perform the indicated operations and express the answers in simplest radical form:

(a) $\sqrt[3]{3} \cdot \sqrt[4]{3}$

(b) $\dfrac{\sqrt[3]{2}}{\sqrt{2}}$

(c) $\dfrac{\sqrt{9}}{\sqrt[3]{3}}$

EXAMPLE 5

Perform the indicated operations and express the answers in simplest radical form:

(a) $\sqrt{2}\sqrt[3]{2}$ (b) $\dfrac{\sqrt{5}}{\sqrt[3]{5}}$ (c) $\dfrac{\sqrt{4}}{\sqrt[3]{2}}$

Solution

(a) $\sqrt{2}\sqrt[3]{2} = 2^{\frac{1}{2}} \cdot 2^{\frac{1}{3}}$

$= 2^{\frac{1}{2}+\frac{1}{3}}$

$= 2^{\frac{3}{6}+\frac{2}{6}}$ Use 6 as LCD

$= 2^{\frac{5}{6}}$

$= \sqrt[6]{2^5} = \sqrt[6]{32}$

(b) $\dfrac{\sqrt{5}}{\sqrt[3]{5}} = \dfrac{5^{\frac{1}{2}}}{5^{\frac{1}{3}}}$

$= 5^{\frac{1}{2}-\frac{1}{3}}$

$= 5^{\frac{3}{6}-\frac{2}{6}}$ Use 6 as LCD

$= 5^{\frac{1}{6}} = \sqrt[6]{5}$

(c) $\dfrac{\sqrt{4}}{\sqrt[3]{2}} = \dfrac{4^{\frac{1}{2}}}{2^{\frac{1}{3}}}$

$= \dfrac{(2^2)^{\frac{1}{2}}}{2^{\frac{1}{3}}}$

$= \dfrac{2^1}{2^{\frac{1}{3}}}$

$= 2^{1-\frac{1}{3}}$

$= 2^{\frac{2}{3}} = \sqrt[3]{2^2} = \sqrt[3]{4}$

Concept Quiz 5.6

For Problems 1–10, answer true or false.

1. Assuming the nth root of x exists, $\sqrt[n]{x}$ can be written as $x^{\frac{1}{n}}$.

2. An exponent of $\dfrac{1}{3}$ means that we need to find the cube root of the number.

3. To evaluate $16^{\frac{2}{3}}$ we would find the square root of 16 and then cube the result.

4. When an expression with a rational exponent is written as a radical expression, the denominator of the rational exponent is the index of the radical.

5. The expression $\sqrt[n]{x^m}$ is equivalent to $\left(\sqrt[n]{x}\right)^m$.

6. $-16^{-3} = \dfrac{1}{64}$

7. $\dfrac{\sqrt{7}}{\sqrt[3]{7}} = \sqrt[6]{7}$

8. $(16)^{-\frac{3}{4}} = \dfrac{1}{8}$

9. $\dfrac{\sqrt[3]{16}}{\sqrt{2}} = 2\sqrt{2}$

10. $\sqrt[3]{64^2} = 16$

Problem Set 5.6

For Problems 1–30, evaluate each numerical expression. (Objective 1)

1. $81^{\frac{1}{2}}$

2. $64^{\frac{1}{2}}$

3. $27^{\frac{1}{3}}$

4. $(-32)^{\frac{1}{5}}$

5. $(-8)^{\frac{1}{3}}$

6. $\left(-\frac{27}{8}\right)^{\frac{1}{3}}$

7. $-25^{\frac{1}{2}}$

8. $-64^{\frac{1}{3}}$

9. $36^{-\frac{1}{2}}$

10. $81^{-\frac{1}{2}}$

11. $\left(\frac{1}{27}\right)^{-\frac{1}{3}}$

12. $\left(-\frac{8}{27}\right)^{-\frac{1}{3}}$

13. $4^{\frac{3}{2}}$

14. $64^{\frac{2}{3}}$

15. $27^{\frac{4}{3}}$

16. $4^{\frac{7}{2}}$

17. $(-1)^{\frac{7}{3}}$

18. $(-8)^{\frac{4}{3}}$

19. $-4^{\frac{5}{2}}$

20. $-16^{\frac{3}{2}}$

21. $\left(\frac{27}{8}\right)^{\frac{4}{3}}$

22. $\left(\frac{8}{125}\right)^{\frac{2}{3}}$

23. $\left(\frac{1}{8}\right)^{-\frac{2}{3}}$

24. $\left(-\frac{1}{27}\right)^{-\frac{2}{3}}$

25. $64^{-\frac{7}{6}}$

26. $32^{-\frac{4}{5}}$

27. $-25^{\frac{3}{2}}$

28. $-16^{\frac{3}{4}}$

29. $125^{\frac{4}{3}}$

30. $81^{\frac{5}{4}}$

For Problems 31–44, write each of the following in radical form. (Objective 2)
For example,

$$3x^{\frac{2}{3}} = 3\sqrt[3]{x^2}$$

31. $x^{\frac{4}{3}}$

32. $x^{\frac{2}{5}}$

33. $3x^{\frac{1}{2}}$

34. $5x^{\frac{1}{4}}$

35. $(2y)^{\frac{1}{3}}$

36. $(3xy)^{\frac{1}{2}}$

37. $(2x - 3y)^{\frac{1}{2}}$

38. $(5x + y)^{\frac{1}{3}}$

39. $(2a - 3b)^{\frac{2}{3}}$

40. $(5a + 7b)^{\frac{3}{5}}$

41. $x^{\frac{2}{3}}y^{\frac{1}{3}}$

42. $x^{\frac{3}{7}}y^{\frac{5}{7}}$

43. $-3x^{\frac{1}{5}}y^{\frac{2}{5}}$

44. $-4x^{\frac{3}{4}}y^{\frac{1}{4}}$

For Problems 45–58, write each of the following using positive rational exponents. (Objective 3)
For example,

$$\sqrt{ab} = (ab)^{\frac{1}{2}} = a^{\frac{1}{2}}b^{\frac{1}{2}}$$

45. $\sqrt{5y}$

46. $\sqrt{2xy}$

47. $3\sqrt{y}$

48. $5\sqrt{ab}$

49. $\sqrt[3]{xy^2}$

50. $\sqrt[5]{x^2y^4}$

51. $\sqrt[4]{a^2b^3}$

52. $\sqrt[6]{ab^5}$

53. $\sqrt[5]{(2x - y)^3}$

54. $\sqrt[7]{(3x - y)^4}$

55. $5x\sqrt{y}$

56. $4y\sqrt[3]{x}$

57. $-\sqrt[3]{x + y}$

58. $-\sqrt[5]{(x - y)^2}$

For Problems 59–80, simplify each of the following. Express final results using positive exponents only. (Objective 4)
For example,

$$\left(2x^{\frac{1}{2}}\right)\left(3x^{\frac{1}{3}}\right) = 6x^{\frac{5}{6}}$$

59. $\left(2x^{\frac{2}{5}}\right)\left(6x^{\frac{1}{4}}\right)$

60. $\left(3x^{\frac{1}{4}}\right)\left(5x^{\frac{1}{3}}\right)$

61. $\left(y^{\frac{2}{3}}\right)\left(y^{-\frac{1}{4}}\right)$

62. $\left(y^{\frac{3}{4}}\right)\left(y^{-\frac{1}{2}}\right)$

63. $\left(x^{\frac{2}{5}}\right)\left(4x^{-\frac{1}{2}}\right)$

64. $\left(2x^{\frac{1}{3}}\right)\left(x^{-\frac{1}{2}}\right)$

65. $\left(4x^{\frac{1}{2}}y\right)^2$

66. $\left(3x^{\frac{1}{4}}y^{\frac{1}{5}}\right)^3$

67. $(8x^6y^3)^{\frac{1}{3}}$

68. $(9x^2y^4)^{\frac{1}{2}}$

69. $\dfrac{24x^{\frac{3}{5}}}{6x^{\frac{1}{3}}}$

70. $\dfrac{18x^{\frac{1}{2}}}{9x^{\frac{1}{3}}}$

71. $\dfrac{48b^{\frac{1}{3}}}{12b^{\frac{3}{4}}}$

72. $\dfrac{56a^{\frac{1}{6}}}{8a^{\frac{1}{4}}}$

73. $\left(\dfrac{6x^{\frac{2}{5}}}{7y^{\frac{2}{3}}}\right)^2$

74. $\left(\dfrac{2x^{\frac{1}{3}}}{3y^{\frac{1}{4}}}\right)^4$

75. $\left(\dfrac{x^2}{y^3}\right)^{-\frac{1}{2}}$

76. $\left(\dfrac{a^3}{b^{-2}}\right)^{-\frac{1}{3}}$

77. $\left(\dfrac{18x^{\frac{1}{3}}}{9x^{\frac{1}{4}}}\right)^2$

78. $\left(\dfrac{72x^{\frac{3}{4}}}{6x^{\frac{1}{2}}}\right)^2$

79. $\left(\dfrac{60a^{\frac{1}{5}}}{15a^{\frac{3}{4}}}\right)^2$

80. $\left(\dfrac{64a^{\frac{1}{3}}}{16a^{\frac{5}{9}}}\right)^3$

For Problems 81–90, perform the indicated operations and express answers in simplest radical form. (Objective 5) (See Example 5.)

81. $\sqrt[3]{3}\sqrt{3}$

82. $\sqrt{2}\sqrt[4]{2}$

83. $\sqrt[4]{6}\sqrt{6}$

84. $\sqrt[3]{5}\sqrt{5}$

85. $\dfrac{\sqrt[3]{3}}{\sqrt[4]{3}}$ **86.** $\dfrac{\sqrt{2}}{\sqrt[3]{2}}$ **87.** $\dfrac{\sqrt[3]{8}}{\sqrt[4]{4}}$ **88.** $\dfrac{\sqrt{9}}{\sqrt[3]{3}}$ **89.** $\dfrac{\sqrt[4]{27}}{\sqrt{3}}$ **90.** $\dfrac{\sqrt[3]{16}}{\sqrt[6]{4}}$

Thoughts Into Words

91. Your friend keeps getting an error message when evaluating $-4^{\frac{5}{2}}$ on his calculator. What error is he probably making?

92. Explain how you would evaluate $27^{\frac{2}{3}}$ without a calculator.

Further Investigations

93. Use your calculator to evaluate each of the following.

(a) $\sqrt[3]{1728}$ (b) $\sqrt[3]{5832}$

(c) $\sqrt[4]{2401}$ (d) $\sqrt[4]{65,536}$

(e) $\sqrt[5]{161,051}$ (f) $\sqrt[5]{6,436,343}$

94. Definition 5.7 states that

$$b^{\frac{m}{n}} = \sqrt[n]{b^m} = \left(\sqrt[n]{b}\right)^m$$

Use your calculator to verify each of the following.

(a) $\sqrt[3]{27^2} = \left(\sqrt[3]{27}\right)^2$ (b) $\sqrt[3]{8^5} = \left(\sqrt[3]{8}\right)^5$

(c) $\sqrt[4]{16^3} = \left(\sqrt[4]{16}\right)^3$ (d) $\sqrt[3]{16^2} = \left(\sqrt[3]{16}\right)^2$

(e) $\sqrt[5]{9^4} = \left(\sqrt[5]{9}\right)^4$ (f) $\sqrt[3]{12^4} = \left(\sqrt[3]{12}\right)^4$

95. Use your calculator to evaluate each of the following.

(a) $16^{\frac{5}{2}}$ (b) $25^{\frac{7}{2}}$ (c) $16^{\frac{9}{4}}$

(d) $27^{\frac{5}{3}}$ (e) $343^{\frac{2}{3}}$ (f) $512^{\frac{4}{3}}$

96. Use your calculator to estimate each of the following to the nearest one-thousandth.

(a) $7^{\frac{4}{3}}$ (b) $10^{\frac{4}{5}}$

(c) $12^{\frac{3}{5}}$ (d) $19^{\frac{2}{5}}$

(e) $7^{\frac{3}{4}}$ (f) $10^{\frac{5}{4}}$

97. (a) Because $\dfrac{4}{5} = 0.8$, we can evaluate $10^{\frac{4}{5}}$ by evaluating $10^{0.8}$, which involves a shorter sequence of "calculator steps." Evaluate parts (b), (c), (d), (e), and (f) of Problem 96 and take advantage of decimal exponents.

(b) What problem is created when we try to evaluate $7^{\frac{4}{3}}$ by changing the exponent to decimal form?

Answers to the Concept Quiz

1. True   **2.** True   **3.** False   **4.** True   **5.** True   **6.** False   **7.** True   **8.** True   **9.** False   **10.** True

5.7   Scientific Notation

OBJECTIVES

1 Write numbers in scientific notation

2 Convert numbers from scientific notation to ordinary decimal notation

3 Perform calculations with numbers using scientific notation

Many applications of mathematics involve the use of very large or very small numbers:

1. The speed of light is approximately 29,979,200,000 centimeters per second.

2. A light year—the distance that light travels in 1 year—is approximately 5,865,696,000,000 miles.

3. A millimicron equals 0.000000001 of a meter.

Working with numbers of this type in standard decimal form is quite cumbersome. It is much more convenient to represent very small and very large numbers in *scientific notation*. Although negative numbers can be written in scientific form, we will restrict our discussion to positive numbers. The expression $(N)(10^k)$, where N is a number greater than or equal to 1 and less than 10, written in decimal form, and k is any integer, is commonly called **scientific notation** or the scientific form of a number. Consider the following examples, which show a comparison between ordinary decimal notation and scientific notation.

Ordinary notation	Scientific notation
2.14	$(2.14)(10^0)$
31.78	$(3.178)(10^1)$
412.9	$(4.129)(10^2)$
8,000,000	$(8)(10^6)$
0.14	$(1.4)(10^{-1})$
0.0379	$(3.79)(10^{-2})$
0.00000049	$(4.9)(10^{-7})$

To switch from ordinary notation to scientific notation, you can use the following procedure.

> Write the given number as the product of a number greater than or equal to 1 and less than 10, and a power of 10. The exponent of 10 is determined by counting the number of places that the decimal point was moved when going from the original number to the number greater than or equal to 1 and less than 10. This exponent is (a) negative if the original number is less than 1, (b) positive if the original number is greater than 10, and (c) 0 if the original number itself is between 1 and 10.

Thus we can write

$$0.00467 = (4.67)(10^{-3})$$
$$87,000 \ = (8.7)(10^4)$$
$$3.1416 \ = (3.1416)(10^0)$$

We can express the applications given earlier in scientific notation as follows:

Speed of light $29,979,200,000 = (2.99792)(10^{10})$ centimeters per second

Light year $5,865,696,000,000 = (5.865696)(10^{12})$ miles

Metric units   A millimicron is $0.000000001 = (1)(10^{-9})$ meter

To switch from scientific notation to ordinary decimal notation, you can use the following procedure.

> Move the decimal point the number of places indicated by the exponent of 10. The decimal point is moved to the right if the exponent is positive and to the left if the exponent is negative.

Thus we can write

$$(4.78)(10^4) = 47,800$$
$$(8.4)(10^{-3}) = 0.0084$$

Scientific notation can frequently be used to simplify numerical calculations. We merely change the numbers to scientific notation and use the appropriate properties of exponents. Consider the following examples.

Classroom Example
Perform the indicated operations:
(a) $(0.00051)(4000)$
(b) $\dfrac{8,600,000}{0.00043}$
(c) $\dfrac{(0.000052)(0.032)}{(0.000016)(0.00104)}$
(d) $\sqrt{0.000025}$

EXAMPLE 1

Convert each number to scientific notation and perform the indicated operations. Express the result in ordinary decimal notation:

(a) $(0.00024)(20,000)$ **(b)** $\dfrac{7,800,000}{0.0039}$

(c) $\dfrac{(0.00069)(0.0034)}{(0.0000017)(0.023)}$ **(d)** $\sqrt{0.000004}$

Solution

$$
\begin{aligned}
\textbf{(a)} \quad (0.00024)(20,000) &= (2.4)(10^{-4})(2)(10^{4}) \\
&= (2.4)(2)(10^{-4})(10^{4}) \\
&= (4.8)(10^{0}) \\
&= (4.8)(1) \\
&= 4.8
\end{aligned}
$$

$$
\begin{aligned}
\textbf{(b)} \quad \frac{7,800,000}{0.0039} &= \frac{(7.8)(10^{6})}{(3.9)(10^{-3})} \\
&= (2)(10^{9}) \\
&= 2,000,000,000
\end{aligned}
$$

$$
\begin{aligned}
\textbf{(c)} \quad \frac{(0.00069)(0.0034)}{(0.0000017)(0.023)} &= \frac{(6.9)(10^{-4})(3.4)(10^{-3})}{(1.7)(10^{-6})(2.3)(10^{-2})} \\
&= \frac{\overset{3}{\cancel{(6.9)}}\overset{2}{\cancel{(3.4)}}(10^{-7})}{\cancel{(1.7)}\cancel{(2.3)}(10^{-8})} \\
&= (6)(10^{1}) \\
&= 60
\end{aligned}
$$

$$
\begin{aligned}
\textbf{(d)} \quad \sqrt{0.000004} &= \sqrt{(4)(10^{-6})} \\
&= ((4)(10^{-6}))^{\frac{1}{2}} \\
&= (4)^{\frac{1}{2}}(10^{-6})^{\frac{1}{2}} \\
&= (2)(10^{-3}) \\
&= 0.002
\end{aligned}
$$

■

Classroom Example
The speed of light is approximately $(1.86)(10^{5})$ miles per second. When Saturn is $(8.9)(10^{8})$ miles away from the sun, how long does it take light from the sun to reach Saturn?

EXAMPLE 2

The speed of light is approximately $(1.86)(10^{5})$ miles per second. When Earth is $(9.3)(10^{7})$ miles away from the sun, how long does it take light from the sun to reach Earth?

Solution

We will use the formula $t = \dfrac{d}{r}$.

$$
t = \frac{(9.3)(10^{7})}{(1.86)(10^{5})}
$$

$$t = \frac{(9.3)}{(1.86)}(10^2) \qquad \text{Subtract exponents}$$

$$t = (5)(10^2) = 500 \text{ seconds}$$

At this distance it takes light about 500 seconds to travel from the sun to Earth. To find the answer in minutes, divide 500 seconds by 60 seconds/minute. That gives a result of approximately 8.33 minutes.

————————————————————————— ■

Many calculators are equipped to display numbers in scientific notation. The display panel shows the number between 1 and 10 and the appropriate exponent of 10. For example, evaluating $(3,800,000^2)$ yields

$\boxed{1.444\text{E}13}$

Thus $(3,800,000^2) = (1.444)(10^{13}) = 14,440,000,000,000$.

Similarly, the answer for (0.000168^2) is displayed as

$\boxed{2.8224\text{E-}8}$

Thus $(0.000168^2) = (2.8224)(10^{-8}) = 0.000000028224$.

Calculators vary as to the number of digits displayed in the number between 1 and 10 when scientific notation is used. For example, we used two different calculators to estimate (6729^6) and obtained the following results.

$\boxed{9.2833\text{E}22}$

$\boxed{9.283316768\text{E}22}$

Obviously, you need to know the capabilities of your calculator when working with problems in scientific notation. Many calculators also allow the entry of a number in scientific notation. Such calculators are equipped with an enter-the-exponent key (often labeled as $\boxed{\text{EE}}$ or $\boxed{\text{EEX}}$). Thus a number such as $(3.14)(10^8)$ might be entered as follows:

Enter	Press	Display		Enter	Press	Display
3.14	$\boxed{\text{EE}}$	3.14E	or	3.14	$\boxed{\text{EE}}$	3.14^{00}
8		3.14E8		8		3.14^{08}

A $\boxed{\text{MODE}}$ key is often used on calculators to let you choose normal decimal notation, scientific notation, or engineering notation. (The abbreviations Norm, Sci, and Eng are commonly used.) If the calculator is in scientific mode, then a number can be entered and changed to scientific form by pressing the $\boxed{\text{ENTER}}$ key. For example, when we enter 589 and press the $\boxed{\text{ENTER}}$ key, the display will show 5.89E2. Likewise, when the calculator is in scientific mode, the answers to computational problems are given in scientific form. For example, the answer for $(76)(533)$ is given as 4.0508E4.

It should be evident from this brief discussion that even when you are using a calculator, you need to have a thorough understanding of scientific notation.

Concept Quiz 5.7

For Problems 1–10, answer true or false.

1. A positive number written in scientific notation has the form $(N)(10^k)$, where $1 \leq N < 10$ and k is an integer.

2. A number is less than zero if the exponent is negative when the number is written in scientific notation.

3. $(3.11)(10^{-2}) = 311$

4. $(5.24)(10^{-1}) = 0.524$

5. $(8.91)(10^2) = 89.1$

6. $(4.163)(10^{-5}) = 0.00004163$

7. $(0.00715) = (7.15)(10^{-3})$

8. Scientific notation provides a way of working with numbers that are very large or very small in magnitude.

9. $(0.0012)(5000) = 60$

10. $\dfrac{6{,}200{,}000}{0.0031} = 2{,}000{,}000{,}000$

Problem Set 5.7

For Problems 1–18, write each of the following in scientific notation. (Objective 1)

For example,

$$27{,}800 = (2.78)(10^4)$$

1. 89

2. 117

3. 4290

4. 812,000

5. 6,120,000

6. 72,400,000

7. 40,000,000

8. 500,000,000

9. 376.4

10. 9126.21

11. 0.347

12. 0.2165

13. 0.0214

14. 0.0037

15. 0.00005

16. 0.00000082

17. 0.00000000194

18. 0.00000000003

For Problems 19–32, write each of the following in ordinary decimal notation. (Objective 2)

For example,

$$(3.18)(10^2) = 318$$

19. $(2.3)(10^1)$

20. $(1.62)(10^2)$

21. $(4.19)(10^3)$

22. $(7.631)(10^4)$

23. $(5)(10^8)$

24. $(7)(10^9)$

25. $(3.14)(10^{10})$

26. $(2.04)(10^{12})$

27. $(4.3)(10^{-1})$

28. $(5.2)(10^{-2})$

29. $(9.14)(10^{-4})$

30. $(8.76)(10^{-5})$

31. $(5.123)(10^{-8})$

32. $(6)(10^{-9})$

For Problems 33–50, convert each number to scientific notation and perform the indicated operations. Express the result in ordinary decimal notation. (Objective 3)

33. $(0.0037)(0.00002)$

34. $(0.00003)(0.00025)$

35. $(0.00007)(11,000)$

36. $(0.000004)(120,000)$

37. $\dfrac{360{,}000{,}000}{0.0012}$

38. $\dfrac{66{,}000{,}000{,}000}{0.022}$

39. $\dfrac{0.000064}{16{,}000}$

40. $\dfrac{0.00072}{0.0000024}$

41. $\dfrac{(60{,}000)(0.006)}{(0.0009)(400)}$

42. $\dfrac{(0.00063)(960{,}000)}{(3{,}200)(0.0000021)}$

43. $\dfrac{(0.0045)(60{,}000)}{(1800)(0.00015)}$

44. $\dfrac{(0.00016)(300)(0.028)}{0.064}$

45. $\sqrt{9{,}000{,}000}$

46. $\sqrt{0.00000009}$

47. $\sqrt[3]{8000}$

48. $\sqrt[3]{0.001}$

49. $90{,}000^{\frac{3}{2}}$

50. $8000^{\frac{2}{3}}$

51. Avogadro's number, 602,000,000,000,000,000,000,000, is the number of atoms in 1 mole of a substance. Express this number in scientific notation.

52. The Social Security program paid out approximately 49,000,000,000 dollars in benefits in December 2007. Express this number in scientific notation.

53. Carlos' first computer had a processing speed of $(1.6)(10^6)$ hertz. He recently purchased a laptop computer with a processing speed of $(1.33)(10^9)$ hertz. Approximately how many times faster is the processing speed of his laptop than that of his first computer? Express the result in decimal form.

54. Alaska has an area of approximately $(6.15)(10^5)$ square miles. In 2006 the state had a population of approximately 670,000 people. Compute the population density to the nearest hundredth. Population density is the number of people per square mile. Express the result in decimal form rounded to the nearest hundredth.

55. In the year 2008 the public debt of the United States was approximately \$10,600,000,000,000. For July 2008, the census reported that 303,000,000 people lived in the United States. Convert these figures to scientific notation, and compute the average debt per person. Express the result in scientific notation.

56. The space shuttle can travel at approximately 410,000 miles per day. If the shuttle could travel to Mars, and Mars was 140,000,000 miles away, how many days would it take the shuttle to travel to Mars? Express the result in decimal form.

57. A square pixel on a computer screen has a side of length $(1.17)(10^{-2})$ inches. Find the approximate area of the pixel in inches. Express the result in decimal form.

58. The field of view of a microscope is $(4)(10^{-4})$ meters. If a single cell organism occupies $\dfrac{1}{5}$ of the field of view, find the length of the organism in meters. Express the result in scientific notation.

59. The mass of an electron is $(9.11)(10^{-31})$ kilogram, and the mass of a proton is $(1.67)(10^{-27})$ kilogram.

Approximately how many times more is the mass of a proton than is the mass of an electron? Express the result in decimal form.

60. Atomic masses are measured in atomic mass units (amu). The amu, $(1.66)(10^{-27})$ kilogram, is defined as $\dfrac{1}{12}$ the mass of a common carbon atom. Find the mass of a carbon atom in kilograms. Express the result in scientific notation.

Thoughts Into Words

61. Explain the importance of scientific notation.

62. Why do we need scientific notation even when using calculators and computers?

Further Investigations

63. Sometimes it is more convenient to express a number as a product of a power of 10 and a number that is not between 1 and 10. For example, suppose that we want to calculate $\sqrt{640{,}000}$. We can proceed as follows:

$$\sqrt{640{,}000} = \sqrt{(64)(10^4)}$$
$$= ((64)(10^4))^{\frac{1}{2}}$$
$$= (64)^{\frac{1}{2}}(10^4)^{\frac{1}{2}}$$
$$= (8)(10^2)$$
$$= 8(100) = 800$$

Compute each of the following without a calculator, and then use a calculator to check your answers.

(a) $\sqrt{49{,}000{,}000}$ **(b)** $\sqrt{0.0025}$
(c) $\sqrt{14{,}400}$ **(d)** $\sqrt{0.000121}$
(e) $\sqrt[3]{27{,}000}$ **(f)** $\sqrt[3]{0.000064}$

64. Use your calculator to evaluate each of the following. Express final answers in ordinary notation.

(a) $27{,}000^2$ **(b)** $450{,}000^2$

(c) $14{,}800^2$ **(d)** 1700^3
(e) 900^4 **(f)** 60^5
(g) 0.0213^2 **(h)** 0.000213^2
(i) 0.000198^2 **(j)** 0.000009^3

65. Use your calculator to estimate each of the following. Express final answers in scientific notation with the number between 1 and 10 rounded to the nearest one-thousandth.

(a) 4576^4 **(b)** 719^{10}
(c) 28^{12} **(d)** 8619^6
(e) 314^5 **(f)** $145{,}723^2$

66. Use your calculator to estimate each of the following. Express final answers in ordinary notation rounded to the nearest one-thousandth.

(a) 1.09^5 **(b)** 1.08^{10}
(c) 1.14^7 **(d)** 1.12^{20}
(e) 0.785^4 **(f)** 0.492^5

Answers to the Concept Quiz
1. True   **2.** False   **3.** False   **4.** True   **5.** False   **6.** True   **7.** True   **8.** True   **9.** False   **10.** True

OBJECTIVE	SUMMARY	EXAMPLE
Simplify numerical expressions that have integer exponents. (Section 5.1/Objective 1)	The concept of exponent is expanded to include negative exponents and exponents of zero. If b is a nonzero number, then $b^0 = 1$. If n is a positive integer and b is a nonzero number, then $b^{-n} = \dfrac{1}{b^n}$.	Simplify $\left(\dfrac{2}{5}\right)^{-2}$. **Solution** $\left(\dfrac{2}{5}\right)^{-2} = \dfrac{2^{-2}}{5^{-2}} = \dfrac{5^2}{2^2} = \dfrac{25}{4}$
Simplify algebraic expressions that have integer exponents. (Section 5.1/Objective 2)	The properties for integer exponents listed on page 223 form the basis for manipulating with integer exponents. These properties, along with Definition 5.2; that is, $b^{-n} = \dfrac{1}{b^n}$, enable us to simplify algebraic expressions and express the results with positive exponents.	Simplify $(2x^{-3}y)^{-2}$ and express the final result using positive exponents. **Solution** $(2x^{-3}y)^{-2} = 2^{-2}x^6y^{-2}$ $\qquad = \dfrac{x^6}{2^2y^2} = \dfrac{x^6}{4y^2}$
Multiply and divide algebraic expressions that have integer exponents. (Section 5.1/Objective 3)	The previous remark also applies to simplifying multiplication and division problems that involve integer exponents.	Simplify $(-3x^5y^{-2})(4x^{-1}y^{-1})$ and express the final result using positive exponents. **Solution** $(-3x^5y^{-2})(4x^{-1}y^{-1}) = -12x^4y^{-3}$ $\qquad = -\dfrac{12x^4}{y^3}$
Simplify sums and differences of expressions involving integer exponents. (Section 5.1/Objective 4)	Find the sum or difference of expressions involving integer exponents, change all expressions having negative or zero exponents to equivalent expressions with positive exponents only. To find the sum or difference, it may be necessary to find a common denominator.	Simplify $5x^{-2} + 6y^{-1}$ and express the result as a single fraction involving positive exponents only. **Solution** $5x^{-2} + 6y^{-1} = \dfrac{5}{x^2} + \dfrac{6}{y}$ $\qquad = \dfrac{5}{x^2} \cdot \dfrac{y}{y} + \dfrac{6}{y} \cdot \dfrac{x^2}{x^2}$ $\qquad = \dfrac{5y + 6x^2}{x^2y}$
Express a radical in simplest radical form. (Section 5.2/Objective 2)	The principal nth root of b is designated by $\sqrt[n]{b}$, where n is the index and b is the radicand. A radical expression is in simplest form if: 1. A radicand contains no polynomial factor raised to a power equal to or greater than the index of the radical; 2. No fraction appears within a radical sign; and 3. No radical appears in the denominator. The following properties are used to express radicals in simplest form: $$\sqrt[n]{bc} = \sqrt[n]{b}\sqrt[n]{c} \quad \text{and} \quad \sqrt[n]{\dfrac{b}{c}} = \dfrac{\sqrt[n]{b}}{\sqrt[n]{c}}$$	Simplify $\sqrt{150a^3b^2}$. Assume all variables represent nonnegative values. **Solution** $\sqrt{150a^3b^2} = \sqrt{25a^2b^2}\sqrt{6b}$ $\qquad = 5ab\sqrt{6b}$

(continued)

OBJECTIVE	SUMMARY	EXAMPLE
Rationalize the denominator to simplify radicals. (Section 5.2/Objective 3)	If a radical appears in the denominator, it will be necessary to rationalize the denominator for the expression to be in simplest form.	Simplify $\dfrac{2\sqrt{18}}{\sqrt{5}}$. **Solution** $\dfrac{2\sqrt{18}}{\sqrt{5}} = \dfrac{2\sqrt{9}\sqrt{2}}{\sqrt{5}}$ $= \dfrac{2(3)\sqrt{2}}{\sqrt{5}} = \dfrac{6\sqrt{2}}{\sqrt{5}}$ $= \dfrac{6\sqrt{2}}{\sqrt{5}} \cdot \dfrac{\sqrt{5}}{\sqrt{5}} = \dfrac{6\sqrt{10}}{\sqrt{25}}$ $= \dfrac{6\sqrt{10}}{5}$
Simplify expressions by combining radicals. (Section 5.3/Objective 1)	Simplifying by combining radicals sometimes requires that we first express the given radicals in simplest form.	Simplify $\sqrt{24} - \sqrt{54} + 8\sqrt{6}$. **Solution** $\sqrt{24} - \sqrt{54} + 8\sqrt{6}$ $= \sqrt{4}\sqrt{6} - \sqrt{9}\sqrt{6} + 8\sqrt{6}$ $= 2\sqrt{6} - 3\sqrt{6} + 8\sqrt{6}$ $= (2 - 3 + 8)(\sqrt{6})$ $= 7\sqrt{6}$
Multiply two radicals. (Section 5.4/Objective 1)	The property $\sqrt[n]{b}\sqrt[n]{c} = \sqrt[n]{bc}$ is used to find the product of two radicals.	Multiply $\sqrt[3]{4x^2y}\sqrt[3]{6x^2y^2}$. **Solution** $\sqrt[3]{4x^2y}\sqrt[3]{6x^2y^2} = \sqrt[3]{24x^4y^3}$ $= \sqrt[3]{8x^3y^3}\sqrt[3]{3x}$ $= 2xy\sqrt[3]{3x}$
Use the distributive property to multiply radical expressions. (Section 5.4/Objective 2)	The distributive property and the property $\sqrt[n]{b}\sqrt[n]{c} = \sqrt[n]{bc}$ are used to find products of radical expressions.	Multiply $\sqrt{2x}(\sqrt{6x} + \sqrt{18xy})$ and simplify where possible. **Solution** $\sqrt{2x}(\sqrt{6x} + \sqrt{18xy})$ $= \sqrt{12x^2} + \sqrt{36x^2y}$ $= \sqrt{4x^2}\sqrt{3} + \sqrt{36x^2}\sqrt{y}$ $= 2x\sqrt{3} + 6x\sqrt{y}$
Rationalize binomial denominators. (Section 5.4/Objective 3)	The factors $(a - b)$ and $(a + b)$ are called conjugates. To rationalize a binomial denominator involving radicals, multiply the numerator or denominator by the conjugate of the denominator.	Simplify $\dfrac{3}{\sqrt{7} - \sqrt{5}}$ by rationalizing the denominator. **Solution** $\dfrac{3}{\sqrt{7} - \sqrt{5}}$ $= \dfrac{3}{(\sqrt{7} - \sqrt{5})} \cdot \dfrac{(\sqrt{7} + \sqrt{5})}{(\sqrt{7} + \sqrt{5})}$ $= \dfrac{3(\sqrt{7} + \sqrt{5})}{\sqrt{49} - \sqrt{25}} = \dfrac{3(\sqrt{7} + \sqrt{5})}{7 - 5}$ $= \dfrac{3(\sqrt{7} + \sqrt{5})}{2}$

OBJECTIVE	SUMMARY	EXAMPLE
Solve radical equations. (Section 5.5/Objective 1)	Equations with variables in a radicand are called radical equations. Radical equations are solved by raising each side of the equation to the appropriate power. However, raising both sides of the equation to a power may produce extraneous roots. Therefore, you must check each potential solution.	Solve $\sqrt{x} + 20 = x$. **Solution** $$\sqrt{x} + 20 = x$$ $$\sqrt{x} = x - 20 \quad \text{Isolate the radical}$$ $$(\sqrt{x})^2 = (x - 20)^2$$ $$x = x^2 - 40x + 400$$ $$0 = x^2 - 41x + 400$$ $$0 = (x - 25)(x - 16)$$ $$x = 25 \quad \text{or} \quad x = 16$$ ✔ **Check** $$\sqrt{x} + 20 = x$$ **If $x = 25$**	**If $x = 16$** $\sqrt{25} + 20 = 25$	$\sqrt{16} + 20 = 16$ $25 = 25$	$24 \neq 16$ The solution set is $\{25\}$.
Solve radical equations for real-world problems. (Section 5.5/Objective 2)	Various formulas involve radical equations. These formulas are solved in the same manner as radical equations.	Use the formula $\sqrt{30Df} = S$ (given in Section 5.5) to determine the coefficient of friction, to the nearest hundredth, if a car traveling at 50 miles per hour skidded 300 feet. **Solution** Solve $\sqrt{30Df} = S$ for f. $$(\sqrt{30Df})^2 = S^2$$ $$30Df = S^2$$ $$f = \frac{S^2}{30D}$$ Substituting the values for S and D gives $$f = \frac{50^2}{30(300)}$$ $$= 0.28$$
Evaluate a number raised to a rational exponent. (Section 5.6/Objective 1)	To simplify a number raised to a rational exponent, we apply either the property $b^{\frac{1}{n}} = \sqrt[n]{b}$ or the property $b^{\frac{m}{n}} = \sqrt[n]{b^m} = (\sqrt[n]{b})^m$. When simplifying $b^{\frac{m}{n}}$, the arithmetic computations are usually easiest using the form $(\sqrt[n]{b})^m$, where the nth root is taken first, and that result is raised to the m power.	Simplify $16^{\frac{3}{2}}$. **Solution** $$16^{\frac{3}{2}} = (16^{\frac{1}{2}})^3$$ $$= 4^3$$ $$= 64$$
Write an expression with rational exponents as a radical. (Section 5.6/Objective 2)	If $\frac{m}{n}$ is a rational number, n is a positive integer greater than 1, and b is a real number such that $\sqrt[n]{b}$ exists, then $b^{\frac{m}{n}} = \sqrt[n]{b^m} = (\sqrt[n]{b})^m$.	Write $x^{\frac{3}{5}}$ in radical form. **Solution** $$x^{\frac{3}{5}} = \sqrt[5]{x^3}$$

(continued)

OBJECTIVE	SUMMARY	EXAMPLE
Write radical expressions as expressions with rational exponents. (Section 5.6/Objective 3)	The index of the radical will be the denominator of the rational exponent.	Write $\sqrt[4]{x^3y}$ using positive rational exponents. **Solution** $\sqrt[4]{x^3y} = x^{\frac{3}{4}}y^{\frac{1}{4}}$
Simplify algebraic expressions that have rational exponents. (Section 5.6/Objective 4)	Properties of exponents are used to simplify products and quotients involving rational exponents.	Simplify $\left(4x^{\frac{1}{3}}\right)\left(-3x^{-\frac{3}{4}}\right)$ and express the result with positive exponents only. **Solution** $\left(4x^{\frac{1}{3}}\right)\left(-3x^{-\frac{3}{4}}\right) = -12x^{\frac{1}{3}-\frac{3}{4}}$ $= -12x^{-\frac{5}{12}}$ $= \dfrac{-12}{x^{\frac{5}{12}}}$
Multiply and divide radicals with different indexes. (Section 5.6/Objective 5)	The link between rational exponents and roots provides the basis for multiplying and dividing radicals with different indexes.	Multiply $\sqrt[3]{y^2}\sqrt{y}$ and express in simplest radical form. **Solution** $\sqrt[3]{y^2}\sqrt{y} = y^{\frac{2}{3}}y^{\frac{1}{2}}$ $= y^{\frac{2}{3}+\frac{1}{2}} = y^{\frac{7}{6}}$ $= \sqrt[6]{y^7} = y\sqrt[6]{y}$
Write numbers in scientific notation. (Section 5.7/Objective 1)	Scientific notation is often used to write numbers that are very small or very large in magnitude. The scientific form of a number is expressed as $(N)(10^k)$, where the absolute value of N is a number greater than or equal to 1 and less than 10, written in decimal form, and k is an integer.	Write each of the following in scientific notation: **(a)** 0.000000843 **(b)** 456,000,000,000 **Solution** **(a)** $0.000000843 = (8.43)(10^{-7})$ **(b)** $456,000,000,000 = (4.56)(10^{11})$
Convert numbers from scientific notation to ordinary decimal notation. (Section 5.7/Objective 2)	To switch from scientific notation to ordinary notation, move the decimal point the number of places indicated by the exponent of 10. The decimal point is moved to the right if the exponent is positive and to the left if the exponent is negative.	Write each of the following in ordinary decimal notation: **(a)** $(8.5)(10^{-5})$ **(b)** $(3.4)(10^6)$ **Solution** **(a)** $(8.5)(10^{-5}) = 0.000085$ **(b)** $(3.4)(10^6) = 3,400,000$
Perform calculations with numbers using scientific notation. (Section 5.7/Objective 3)	Scientific notation can often be used to simplify numerical calculations.	Use scientific notation and the properties of exponents to simplify $\dfrac{0.0000084}{0.002}$. **Solution** Change the numbers to scientific notation and use the appropriate properties of exponents. Express the result in standard decimal notation. $\dfrac{0.0000084}{0.002} = \dfrac{(8.4)(10^{-6})}{(2)(10^{-3})}$ $= (4.2)(10^{-3}) = 0.0042$

Chapter 5 Review Problem Set

For Problems 1–6, evaluate the numerical expression.

1. 4^{-3}

2. $\left(\dfrac{2}{3}\right)^{-2}$

3. $(3^2 \cdot 3^{-3})^{-1}$

4. $(4^{-2} \cdot 4^2)^{-1}$

5. $\left(\dfrac{3^{-1}}{3^2}\right)^{-1}$

6. $\left(\dfrac{5^2}{5^{-1}}\right)^{-1}$

For Problems 7–18, simplify and express the final result using positive exponents.

7. $(x^{-3}y^4)^{-2}$

8. $\left(\dfrac{2a^{-1}}{3b^4}\right)^{-3}$

9. $\left(\dfrac{4a^{-2}}{3b^{-2}}\right)^{-2}$

10. $(5x^3y^{-2})^{-3}$

11. $\left(\dfrac{6x^{-2}}{2x^4}\right)^{-2}$

12. $\left(\dfrac{8y^2}{2y^{-1}}\right)^{-1}$

13. $(-5x^{-3})(2x^6)$

14. $(a^{-4}b^3)(3ab^2)$

15. $\dfrac{a^{-1}b^{-2}}{a^4b^{-5}}$

16. $\dfrac{x^3y^5}{x^{-1}y^6}$

17. $\dfrac{-12x^3}{6x^5}$

18. $\dfrac{10a^2b^3}{-5ab^4}$

For Problems 19–22, express as a single fraction involving positive exponents only.

19. $x^{-2} + y^{-1}$

20. $a^{-2} - 2a^{-1}b^{-1}$

21. $2x^{-1} + 3y^{-2}$

22. $(2x)^{-1} + 3y^{-2}$

For Problems 23–34, express the radical in simplest radical form. Assume the variables represent positive real numbers.

23. $\sqrt{54}$

24. $\sqrt{48x^3y}$

25. $\sqrt[3]{56}$

26. $\sqrt[3]{108x^4y^8}$

27. $\dfrac{3}{4}\sqrt{150}$

28. $\dfrac{2}{3}\sqrt{45xy^3}$

29. $\dfrac{4\sqrt{3}}{\sqrt{6}}$

30. $\sqrt{\dfrac{5}{12x^3}}$

31. $\dfrac{\sqrt[3]{2}}{\sqrt[3]{9}}$

32. $\sqrt{\dfrac{9}{5}}$

33. $\sqrt{\dfrac{3x^3}{7}}$

34. $\dfrac{\sqrt{8x^2}}{\sqrt{2x}}$

For Problems 35–38, use the distributive property to help simplify the expression.

35. $3\sqrt{45} - 2\sqrt{20} - \sqrt{80}$

36. $4\sqrt[3]{24} + 3\sqrt[3]{3} - 2\sqrt[3]{81}$

37. $3\sqrt{24} - \dfrac{2\sqrt{54}}{5} + \dfrac{\sqrt{96}}{4}$

38. $-2\sqrt{12x} + 3\sqrt{27x} - 5\sqrt{48x}$

For Problems 39–48, multiply and simplify. Assume the variables represent nonnegative real numbers.

39. $(3\sqrt{8})(4\sqrt{5})$

40. $(5\sqrt[3]{2})(6\sqrt[3]{4})$

41. $(\sqrt{6xy})(\sqrt{10x})$

42. $(-3\sqrt{6xy^3})(\sqrt{6y})$

43. $3\sqrt{2}(4\sqrt{6} - 2\sqrt{7})$

44. $(\sqrt{x} + 3)(\sqrt{x} - 5)$

45. $(2\sqrt{5} - \sqrt{3})(2\sqrt{5} + \sqrt{3})$

46. $(3\sqrt{2} + \sqrt{6})(5\sqrt{2} - 3\sqrt{6})$

47. $(2\sqrt{a} + \sqrt{b})(3\sqrt{a} - 4\sqrt{b})$

48. $(4\sqrt{8} - \sqrt{2})(\sqrt{8} + 3\sqrt{2})$

For Problems 49–52, rationalize the denominator and simplify.

49. $\dfrac{4}{\sqrt{7} - 1}$

50. $\dfrac{\sqrt{3}}{\sqrt{8} + \sqrt{5}}$

51. $\dfrac{3}{2\sqrt{3} + 3\sqrt{5}}$

52. $\dfrac{3\sqrt{2}}{2\sqrt{6} - \sqrt{10}}$

For Problems 53–60, solve the equation.

53. $\sqrt{7x - 3} = 4$

54. $\sqrt{2y + 1} = \sqrt{5y - 11}$

55. $\sqrt{2x} = x - 4$

56. $\sqrt{n^2 - 4n - 4} = n$

57. $\sqrt[3]{2x - 1} = 3$

58. $\sqrt{t^2 + 9t - 1} = 3$

59. $\sqrt{x^2 + 3x - 6} = x$

60. $\sqrt{x + 1} - \sqrt{2x} = -1$

61. The formula $S = \sqrt{30Df}$ is used to approximate the speed S, where D represents the length of the skid marks in feet and f represents the coefficient of friction for the road surface. Suppose that the coefficient of friction is 0.38. How far will a car skid, to the nearest foot, when the brakes are applied at 75 miles per hour?

62. The formula $T = 2\pi\sqrt{\dfrac{L}{32}}$ is used for pendulum motion, where T represents the period of the pendulum in seconds, and L represents the length of the pendulum in feet. Find the length of a pendulum, to the nearest tenth of a foot, if the period is 2.4 seconds.

For Problems 63–70, simplify.

63. $4^{\frac{5}{2}}$

64. $(-1)^{\frac{2}{3}}$

65. $\left(\frac{8}{27}\right)^{\frac{2}{3}}$

66. $-16^{\frac{3}{2}}$

67. $(27)^{-\frac{2}{3}}$

68. $(32)^{-\frac{2}{5}}$

69. $9^{\frac{3}{2}}$

70. $16^{\frac{3}{4}}$

For Problems 71–74, write the expression in radical form.

71. $x^{\frac{1}{3}}y^{\frac{2}{3}}$

72. $a^{\frac{3}{4}}$

73. $4y^{\frac{1}{2}}$

74. $(x+5y)^{\frac{2}{3}}$

For Problems 75–78, write the expression using positive rational exponents.

75. $\sqrt[5]{x^3y}$

76. $\sqrt[3]{4a^2}$

77. $6\sqrt[4]{y^2}$

78. $\sqrt[3]{(3a+b)^5}$

For Problems 79–84, simplify and express the final result using positive exponents.

79. $\left(4x^{\frac{1}{2}}\right)\left(5x^{\frac{1}{5}}\right)$

80. $\frac{42a^{\frac{3}{4}}}{6a^{\frac{1}{3}}}$

81. $\left(\frac{x^3}{y^4}\right)^{-\frac{1}{3}}$

82. $\left(-3a^{\frac{1}{4}}\right)\left(2a^{-\frac{1}{2}}\right)$

83. $\left(x^{\frac{4}{5}}\right)^{-\frac{1}{2}}$

84. $\frac{-24y^{\frac{2}{3}}}{4y^{\frac{1}{4}}}$

For Problems 85–88, perform the indicated operation and express the answer in simplest radical form.

85. $\sqrt[4]{3}\sqrt{3}$

86. $\sqrt[3]{9}\sqrt{3}$

87. $\frac{\sqrt[3]{5}}{\sqrt[4]{5}}$

88. $\frac{\sqrt[3]{16}}{\sqrt{2}}$

For Problems 89–92, write the number in scientific notation.

89. 540,000,000

90. 84,000

91. 0.000000032

92. 0.000768

For Problems 93–96, write the number in ordinary decimal notation.

93. $(1.4)(10^{-6})$

94. $(6.38)(10^{-4})$

95. $(4.12)(10^{7})$

96. $(1.25)(10^{5})$

For Problems 97–104, use scientific notation and the properties of exponents to help perform the calculations.

97. $(0.00002)(0.0003)$

98. $(120,000)(300,000)$

99. $(0.000015)(400,000)$

100. $\frac{0.000045}{0.0003}$

101. $\frac{(0.00042)(0.0004)}{0.006}$

102. $\sqrt{0.000004}$

103. $\sqrt[3]{0.000000008}$

104. $4,000,000^{\frac{3}{2}}$

For Problems 1–4, simplify each of the numerical expressions.

1. $(4)^{-\frac{5}{2}}$

2. $-16^{\frac{5}{4}}$

3. $\left(\dfrac{2}{3}\right)^{-4}$

4. $\left(\dfrac{2^{-1}}{2^{-2}}\right)^{-2}$

For Problems 5–9, express each radical expression in simplest radical form. Assume the variables represent positive real numbers.

5. $\sqrt{63}$

6. $\sqrt[3]{108}$

7. $\sqrt{52x^4y^3}$

8. $\dfrac{5\sqrt{18}}{3\sqrt{12}}$

9. $\sqrt{\dfrac{7}{24x^3}}$

10. Multiply and simplify: $(4\sqrt{6})(3\sqrt{12})$

11. Multiply and simplify: $(3\sqrt{2} + \sqrt{3})(\sqrt{2} - 2\sqrt{3})$

12. Simplify by combining similar radicals:

$2\sqrt{50} - 4\sqrt{18} - 9\sqrt{32}$

13. Rationalize the denominator and simplify:

$\dfrac{3\sqrt{2}}{4\sqrt{3} - \sqrt{8}}$

14. Simplify and express the answer using positive

exponents: $\left(\dfrac{2x^{-1}}{3y}\right)^{-2}$

15. Simplify and express the answer using positive

exponents: $\dfrac{-84a^{\frac{1}{2}}}{7a^{\frac{4}{5}}}$

16. Express $x^{-1} + y^{-3}$ as a single fraction involving positive exponents.

17. Multiply and express the answer using positive exponents: $\left(3x^{-\frac{1}{2}}\right)\left(-4x^{\frac{3}{4}}\right)$

18. Multiply and simplify:

$(3\sqrt{5} - 2\sqrt{3})(3\sqrt{5} + 2\sqrt{3})$

For Problems 19 and 20, use scientific notation and the properties of exponents to help with the calculations.

19. $\dfrac{(0.00004)(300)}{0.00002}$

20. $\sqrt{0.000009}$

For Problems 21–25, solve each equation.

21. $\sqrt{3x + 1} = 3$

22. $\sqrt[3]{3x + 2} = 2$

23. $\sqrt{x} = x - 2$

24. $\sqrt{5x - 2} = \sqrt{3x + 8}$

25. $\sqrt{x^2 - 10x + 28} = 2$

6

Quadratic Equations and Inequalities

6.1 Complex Numbers

6.2 Quadratic Equations

6.3 Completing the Square

6.4 Quadratic Formula

6.5 More Quadratic Equations and Applications

6.6 Quadratic and Other Nonlinear Inequalities

The Pythagorean theorem is applied throughout the construction industry when right angles are involved.

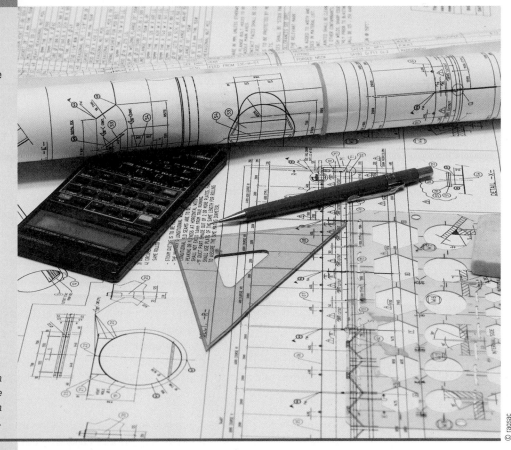

© ragsac

A crime scene investigator must record the dimensions of a rectangular bedroom. Because the access to one wall is blocked, the investigator can only measure the other wall and the diagonal of the rectangular room. The investigator determines that one wall measures 12 feet and the diagonal of the room measures 15 feet. By applying the Pythagorean theorem and solving the resulting quadratic equation, $a^2 + 12^2 = 15^2$, the investigator can determine that the room measures 12 feet by 9 feet.

Solving equations is one of the central themes of this text. Let's pause for a moment and reflect on the different types of equations that we have solved in the last five chapters.

As the chart on the next page shows, we have solved second-degree equations in one variable, but only those for which the polynomial is factorable. In this chapter we will expand our work to include more general types of second-degree equations, as well as inequalities in one variable.

Video tutorials based on section learning objectives are available in a variety of delivery modes.

Type of equation	Example	Solution set
First-degree equations in one variable	$3(x + 4) = -2x + 4x - 10$	$\{-22\}$
Second-degree equations in one variable *that are factorable*	$x^2 - x - 6 = 0$	$\{-2, 3\}$
Fractional equations	$\dfrac{2}{x^2 - 9} + \dfrac{3}{x + 3} = \dfrac{4}{x - 3}$	$\{-19\}$
Radical equations	$\sqrt{3x - 2} = 5$	$\{9\}$

6.1   Complex Numbers

OBJECTIVES

1 Know about the set of complex numbers

2 Add and subtract complex numbers

3 Simplify radicals involving negative numbers

4 Perform operations on radicals involving negative numbers

5 Multiply complex numbers

6 Divide complex numbers

Because the square of any real number is nonnegative, a simple equation such as $x^2 = -4$ has no solutions in the set of real numbers. To handle this situation, we can expand the set of real numbers into a larger set called the *complex numbers*. In this section we will instruct you on how to manipulate complex numbers.

To provide a solution for the equation $x^2 + 1 = 0$, we use the number i, such that

$$i^2 = -1$$

The number i is not a real number and is often called the **imaginary unit**, but the number i^2 is the real number -1. The imaginary unit i is used to define a complex number as follows:

> **Definition 6.1**
>
> A **complex number** is any number that can be expressed in the form
>
> $a + bi$
>
> where a and b are real numbers.

The form $a + bi$ is called the **standard form** of a complex number. The real number a is called the **real part** of the complex number, and b is called the **imaginary part**. (Note that b is a real number even though it is called the imaginary part.) The following list exemplifies this terminology.

1. The number $7 + 5i$ is a complex number that has a real part of 7 and an imaginary part of 5.

2. The number $\dfrac{2}{3} + i\sqrt{2}$ is a complex number that has a real part of $\dfrac{2}{3}$ and an imaginary part of $\sqrt{2}$. (It is easy to mistake $\sqrt{2i}$ for $\sqrt{2}i$. Thus we commonly write $i\sqrt{2}$ instead of $\sqrt{2}i$ to avoid any difficulties with the radical sign.)

3. The number $-4 - 3i$ can be written in the standard form $-4 + (-3i)$ and therefore is a complex number that has a real part of -4 and an imaginary part of -3. [The form $-4 - 3i$ is often used, but we know that it means $-4 + (-3i)$.]

4. The number $-9i$ can be written as $0 + (-9i)$; thus it is a complex number that has a real part of 0 and an imaginary part of -9. (Complex numbers, such as $-9i$, for which $a = 0$ and $b \neq 0$ are called *pure imaginary numbers*.)

5. The real number 4 can be written as $4 + 0i$ and is thus a complex number that has a real part of 4 and an imaginary part of 0.

Look at item 5 in this list. We see that the set of real numbers is a subset of the set of complex numbers. The following diagram indicates the organizational format of the complex numbers.

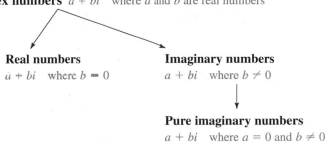

Complex numbers $a + bi$ where a and b are real numbers

Real numbers
$a + bi$ where $b = 0$

Imaginary numbers
$a + bi$ where $b \neq 0$

Pure imaginary numbers
$a + bi$ where $a = 0$ and $b \neq 0$

Two complex numbers $a + bi$ and $c + di$ are said to be **equal** if and only if $a = c$ and $b = d$.

Adding and Subtracting Complex Numbers

To *add complex numbers*, we simply add their real parts and add their imaginary parts. Thus

$$(a + bi) + (c + di) = (a + c) + (b + d)i$$

The following example shows addition of two complex numbers.

Classroom Example
Add the complex numbers:
(a) $(2 + 7i) + (4 + i)$
(b) $(5 - 2i) + (-3 + 9i)$
(c) $\left(\frac{2}{3} + \frac{1}{5}i\right) + \left(\frac{1}{4} + \frac{5}{6}i\right)$

EXAMPLE 1   Add the complex numbers:

(a) $(4 + 3i) + (5 + 9i)$ **(b)** $(-6 + 4i) + (8 - 7i)$

(c) $\left(\frac{1}{2} + \frac{3}{4}i\right) + \left(\frac{2}{3} + \frac{1}{5}i\right)$

Solution

(a) $(4 + 3i) + (5 + 9i) = (4 + 5) + (3 + 9)i = 9 + 12i$

(b) $(-6 + 4i) + (8 - 7i) = (-6 + 8) + (4 - 7)i$
$$= 2 - 3i$$

(c) $\left(\frac{1}{2} + \frac{3}{4}i\right) + \left(\frac{2}{3} + \frac{1}{5}i\right) = \left(\frac{1}{2} + \frac{2}{3}\right) + \left(\frac{3}{4} + \frac{1}{5}\right)i$

$$= \left(\frac{3}{6} + \frac{4}{6}\right) + \left(\frac{15}{20} + \frac{4}{20}\right)i$$

$$= \frac{7}{6} + \frac{19}{20}i$$

The set of complex numbers is closed with respect to addition; that is, the sum of two complex numbers is a complex number. Furthermore, the commutative and associative properties of addition hold for all complex numbers. The addition identity element is $0 + 0i$

(or simply the real number 0). The additive inverse of $a + bi$ is $-a - bi$, because

$$(a + bi) + (-a - bi) = 0$$

To *subtract complex numbers*, $c + di$ from $a + bi$, add the additive inverse of $c + di$. Thus

$$(a + bi) - (c + di) = (a + bi) + (-c - di)$$
$$= (a - c) + (b - d)i$$

In other words, we subtract the real parts and subtract the imaginary parts, as in the next examples.

1. $(9 + 8i) - (5 + 3i) = (9 - 5) + (8 - 3)i$
$$= 4 + 5i$$

2. $(3 - 2i) - (4 - 10i) = (3 - 4) + (-2 - (-10))i$
$$= -1 + 8i$$

Simplifying Radicals Involving Negative Numbers

Because $i^2 = -1$, i is a square root of -1, so we let $i = \sqrt{-1}$. It should be evident that $-i$ is also a square root of -1, because

$$(-i)^2 = (-i)(-i) = i^2 = -1$$

Thus, in the set of complex numbers, -1 has two square roots, i and $-i$. We express these symbolically as

$$\sqrt{-1} = i \qquad \text{and} \qquad -\sqrt{-1} = -i$$

Let us extend our definition so that in the set of complex numbers every negative real number has two square roots. We simply define $\sqrt{-b}$, where b is a positive real number, to be the number whose square is $-b$. Thus

$$\left(\sqrt{-b}\right)^2 = -b, \quad \text{for } b > 0$$

Furthermore, because $\left(i\sqrt{b}\right)\left(i\sqrt{b}\right) = i^2(b) = -1(b) = -b$, we see that

$$\sqrt{-b} = i\sqrt{b}$$

In other words, a square root of any negative real number can be represented as the product of a real number and the imaginary unit i. Consider the following examples.

Classroom Example
Simplify each of the following:

(a) $\sqrt{-9}$

(b) $\sqrt{-19}$

(c) $\sqrt{-32}$

EXAMPLE 2   Simplify each of the following:

(a) $\sqrt{-4}$ **(b)** $\sqrt{-17}$ **(c)** $\sqrt{-24}$

Solution

(a) $\sqrt{-4} = i\sqrt{4} = 2i$

(b) $\sqrt{-17} = i\sqrt{17}$

(c) $\sqrt{-24} = i\sqrt{24} = i\sqrt{4}\sqrt{6} = 2i\sqrt{6}$ Note that we simplified the radical $\sqrt{24}$ to $2\sqrt{6}$

We should also observe that $-\sqrt{-b}$ (where $b > 0$) is a square root of $-b$ because

$$\left(-\sqrt{-b}\right)^2 = \left(-i\sqrt{b}\right)^2 = i^2(b) = -1(b) = -b$$

Thus in the set of complex numbers, $-b$ (where $b > 0$) has two square roots, $i\sqrt{b}$ and $-i\sqrt{b}$. We express these symbolically as

$$\sqrt{-b} = i\sqrt{b} \qquad \text{and} \qquad -\sqrt{-b} = -i\sqrt{b}$$

Performing Operations on Radicals Involving Negative Numbers

We must be very careful with the use of the symbol $\sqrt{-b}$, where $b > 0$. Some real number properties that involve the square root symbol do not hold if the square root symbol does not represent a real number. For example, $\sqrt{a}\sqrt{b} = \sqrt{ab}$ does not hold if a and b are both negative numbers.

Correct $\sqrt{-4}\sqrt{-9} = (2i)(3i) = 6i^2 = 6(-1) = -6$

Incorrect $\sqrt{-4}\sqrt{-9} = \sqrt{(-4)(-9)} = \sqrt{36} = 6$

To avoid difficulty with this idea, you should rewrite all expressions of the form $\sqrt{-b}$ (where $b > 0$) in the form $i\sqrt{b}$ before doing any computations. The following example further demonstrates this point.

Classroom Example
Simplify each of the following:
(a) $\sqrt{-10}\sqrt{-5}$
(b) $\sqrt{-5}\sqrt{-20}$
(c) $\dfrac{\sqrt{-27}}{\sqrt{-3}}$
(d) $\dfrac{\sqrt{-39}}{\sqrt{13}}$

EXAMPLE 3   Simplify each of the following:

(a) $\sqrt{-6}\sqrt{-8}$ (b) $\sqrt{-2}\sqrt{-8}$ (c) $\dfrac{\sqrt{-75}}{\sqrt{-3}}$ (d) $\dfrac{\sqrt{-48}}{\sqrt{12}}$

Solution

(a) $\sqrt{-6}\sqrt{-8} = (i\sqrt{6})(i\sqrt{8}) = i^2\sqrt{48} = (-1)\sqrt{16}\sqrt{3} = -4\sqrt{3}$

(b) $\sqrt{-2}\sqrt{-8} = (i\sqrt{2})(i\sqrt{8}) = i^2\sqrt{16} = (-1)(4) = -4$

(c) $\dfrac{\sqrt{-75}}{\sqrt{-3}} = \dfrac{i\sqrt{75}}{i\sqrt{3}} = \dfrac{\sqrt{75}}{\sqrt{3}} = \sqrt{\dfrac{75}{3}} = \sqrt{25} = 5$

(d) $\dfrac{\sqrt{-48}}{\sqrt{12}} = \dfrac{i\sqrt{48}}{\sqrt{12}} = i\sqrt{\dfrac{48}{12}} = i\sqrt{4} = 2i$

Multiplying Complex Numbers

Complex numbers have a binomial form, so we find the product of two complex numbers in the same way that we find the product of two binomials. Then, by replacing i^2 with -1, we are able to simplify and express the final result in standard form. Consider the following example.

Classroom Example
Simplify each of the following:
(a) $(5 + 2i)(1 + 7i)$
(b) $(3 - 7i)(-2 + 3i)$
(c) $(4 - 7i)^2$
(d) $(4 - 6i)(4 + 6i)$

EXAMPLE 4   Find the product of each of the following:

(a) $(2 + 3i)(4 + 5i)$ (b) $(-3 + 6i)(2 - 4i)$

(c) $(1 - 7i)^2$ (d) $(2 + 3i)(2 - 3i)$

Solution

(a) $(2 + 3i)(4 + 5i) = 2(4 + 5i) + 3i(4 + 5i)$
$= 8 + 10i + 12i + 15i^2$
$= 8 + 22i + 15i^2$
$= 8 + 22i + 15(-1) = -7 + 22i$

(b) $(-3 + 6i)(2 - 4i) = -3(2 - 4i) + 6i(2 - 4i)$
$= -6 + 12i + 12i - 24i^2$
$= -6 + 24i - 24(-1)$
$= -6 + 24i + 24 = 18 + 24i$

(c) $(1 - 7i)^2 = (1 - 7i)(1 - 7i)$
$= 1(1 - 7i) - 7i(1 - 7i)$
$= 1 - 7i - 7i + 49i^2$

$$= 1 - 14i + 49(-1)$$
$$= 1 - 14i - 49$$
$$= -48 - 14i$$

(d) $(2 + 3i)(2 - 3i) = 2(2 - 3i) + 3i(2 - 3i)$
$$= 4 - 6i + 6i - 9i^2$$
$$= 4 - 9(-1)$$
$$= 4 + 9$$
$$= 13$$

■

Example 4(d) illustrates an important situation: The complex numbers $2 + 3i$ and $2 - 3i$ are conjugates of each other. In general, we say that two complex numbers $a + bi$ and $a - bi$ are called **conjugates** of each other. *The product of a complex number and its conjugate is always a real number*, which can be shown as follows:

$$(a + bi)(a - bi) = a(a - bi) + bi(a - bi)$$
$$= a^2 - abi + abi - b^2i^2$$
$$= a^2 - b^2(-1)$$
$$= a^2 + b^2$$

Dividing Complex Numbers

We use conjugates to simplify expressions such as $\dfrac{3i}{5 + 2i}$ that indicate the quotient of two complex numbers. To eliminate i in the denominator and change the indicated quotient to the standard form of a complex number, we can multiply both the numerator and the denominator by the conjugate of the denominator as follows:

$$\frac{3i}{5 + 2i} = \frac{3i(5 - 2i)}{(5 + 2i)(5 - 2i)}$$
$$= \frac{15i - 6i^2}{25 - 4i^2}$$
$$= \frac{15i - 6(-1)}{25 - 4(-1)}$$
$$= \frac{15i + 6}{29}$$
$$= \frac{6}{29} + \frac{15}{29}i$$

The following example further clarifies the process of dividing complex numbers.

Classroom Example
Find the quotient of each of the following:

(a) $\dfrac{2 + 4i}{2 - 5i}$

(b) $\dfrac{9 - 2i}{4i}$

EXAMPLE 5   Find the quotient of each of the following:

(a) $\dfrac{2 - 3i}{4 - 7i}$ **(b)** $\dfrac{4 - 5i}{2i}$

Solution

(a) $\dfrac{2 - 3i}{4 - 7i} = \dfrac{(2 - 3i)(4 + 7i)}{(4 - 7i)(4 + 7i)}$ $4 + 7i$ is the conjugate of $4 - 7i$

$$= \frac{8 + 14i - 12i - 21i^2}{16 - 49i^2}$$

$$= \frac{8 + 2i - 21(-1)}{16 - 49(-1)}$$

$$= \frac{8 + 2i + 21}{16 + 49}$$

$$= \frac{29 + 2i}{65}$$

$$= \frac{29}{65} + \frac{2}{65}i$$

(b) $\dfrac{4 - 5i}{2i} = \dfrac{(4 - 5i)(-2i)}{(2i)(-2i)}$ $-2i$ is the conjugate of $2i$

$$= \frac{-8i + 10i^2}{-4i^2}$$

$$= \frac{-8i + 10(-1)}{-4(-1)}$$

$$= \frac{-8i - 10}{4}$$

$$= -\frac{5}{2} - 2i$$

In Example 5(b), in which the denominator is a pure imaginary number, we can change to standard form by choosing a multiplier other than the conjugate. Consider the following alternative approach for Example 5(b).

$$\frac{4 - 5i}{2i} = \frac{(4 - 5i)(i)}{(2i)(i)}$$

$$= \frac{4i - 5i^2}{2i^2}$$

$$= \frac{4i - 5(-1)}{2(-1)}$$

$$= \frac{4i + 5}{-2}$$

$$= -\frac{5}{2} - 2i$$

Concept Quiz 6.1

For Problems 1–10, answer true or false.

1. The number i is a real number and is called the imaginary unit.
2. The number $4 + 2i$ is a complex number that has a real part of 4.
3. The number $-3 - 5i$ is a complex number that has an imaginary part of 5.
4. Complex numbers that have a real part of 0 are called pure imaginary numbers.
5. The set of real numbers is a subset of the set of complex numbers.
6. Any real number x can be written as the complex number $x + 0i$.
7. By definition, i^2 is equal to -1.
8. The complex numbers $-2 + 5i$ and $2 - 5i$ are conjugates.
9. The product of two complex numbers is never a real number.
10. In the set of complex numbers, -16 has two square roots.

Problem Set 6.1

For Problems 1–8, label each statement true or false. **(Objective 1)**

1. Every complex number is a real number.

2. Every real number is a complex number.

3. The real part of the complex number $6i$ is 0.

4. Every complex number is a pure imaginary number.

5. The sum of two complex numbers is always a complex number.

6. The imaginary part of the complex number 7 is 0.

7. The sum of two complex numbers is sometimes a real number.

8. The sum of two pure imaginary numbers is always a pure imaginary number.

For Problems 9–26, add or subtract as indicated. **(Objective 2)**

9. $(6 + 3i) + (4 + 5i)$ **10.** $(5 + 2i) + (7 + 10i)$

11. $(-8 + 4i) + (2 + 6i)$ **12.** $(5 - 8i) + (-7 + 2i)$

13. $(3 + 2i) - (5 + 7i)$ **14.** $(1 + 3i) - (4 + 9i)$

15. $(-7 + 3i) - (5 - 2i)$ **16.** $(-8 + 4i) - (9 - 4i)$

17. $(-3 - 10i) + (2 - 13i)$ **18.** $(-4 - 12i) + (-3 + 16i)$

19. $(4 - 8i) - (8 - 3i)$ **20.** $(12 - 9i) - (14 - 6i)$

21. $(-1 - i) - (-2 - 4i)$ **22.** $(-2 - 3i) - (-4 - 14i)$

23. $\left(\dfrac{3}{2} + \dfrac{1}{3}i\right) + \left(\dfrac{1}{6} - \dfrac{3}{4}i\right)$ **24.** $\left(\dfrac{2}{3} - \dfrac{1}{5}i\right) + \left(\dfrac{3}{5} - \dfrac{3}{4}i\right)$

25. $\left(-\dfrac{5}{9} + \dfrac{3}{5}i\right) - \left(\dfrac{4}{3} - \dfrac{1}{6}i\right)$ **26.** $\left(\dfrac{3}{8} - \dfrac{5}{2}i\right) - \left(\dfrac{5}{6} + \dfrac{1}{7}i\right)$

For Problems 27–42, write each of the following in terms of i and simplify. **(Objective 3)** For example,

$$\sqrt{-20} = i\sqrt{20} = i\sqrt{4}\sqrt{5} = 2i\sqrt{5}$$

27. $\sqrt{-81}$ **28.** $\sqrt{-49}$

29. $\sqrt{-14}$ **30.** $\sqrt{-33}$

31. $\sqrt{-\dfrac{16}{25}}$ **32.** $\sqrt{-\dfrac{64}{36}}$

33. $\sqrt{-18}$ **34.** $\sqrt{-84}$

35. $\sqrt{-75}$ **36.** $\sqrt{-63}$

37. $3\sqrt{-28}$ **38.** $5\sqrt{-72}$

39. $-2\sqrt{-80}$ **40.** $-6\sqrt{-27}$

41. $12\sqrt{-90}$ **42.** $9\sqrt{-40}$

For Problems 43–60, write each of the following in terms of i, perform the indicated operations, and simplify. **(Objective 4)** For example,

$$\sqrt{-3}\sqrt{-8} = (i\sqrt{3})(i\sqrt{8})$$
$$= i^2\sqrt{24}$$
$$= (-1)\sqrt{4}\sqrt{6}$$
$$= -2\sqrt{6}$$

43. $\sqrt{-4}\sqrt{-16}$ **44.** $\sqrt{-81}\sqrt{-25}$

45. $\sqrt{-3}\sqrt{-5}$ **46.** $\sqrt{-7}\sqrt{-10}$

47. $\sqrt{-9}\sqrt{-6}$ **48.** $\sqrt{-8}\sqrt{-16}$

49. $\sqrt{-15}\sqrt{-5}$ **50.** $\sqrt{-2}\sqrt{-20}$

51. $\sqrt{-2}\sqrt{-27}$ **52.** $\sqrt{-3}\sqrt{-15}$

53. $\sqrt{6}\sqrt{-8}$ **54.** $\sqrt{-75}\sqrt{3}$

55. $\dfrac{\sqrt{-25}}{\sqrt{-4}}$ **56.** $\dfrac{\sqrt{-81}}{\sqrt{-9}}$

57. $\dfrac{\sqrt{-56}}{\sqrt{-7}}$ **58.** $\dfrac{\sqrt{-72}}{\sqrt{-6}}$

59. $\dfrac{\sqrt{-24}}{\sqrt{6}}$ **60.** $\dfrac{\sqrt{-96}}{\sqrt{2}}$

For Problems 61–84, find each of the products and express the answers in the standard form of a complex number. **(Objective 5)**

61. $(5i)(4i)$ **62.** $(-6i)(9i)$

63. $(7i)(-6i)$ **64.** $(-5i)(-12i)$

65. $(3i)(2 - 5i)$ **66.** $(7i)(-9 + 3i)$

67. $(-6i)(-2 - 7i)$ **68.** $(-9i)(-4 - 5i)$

69. $(3 + 2i)(5 + 4i)$ **70.** $(4 + 3i)(6 + i)$

71. $(6 - 2i)(7 - i)$ **72.** $(8 - 4i)(7 - 2i)$

73. $(-3 - 2i)(5 + 6i)$ **74.** $(-5 - 3i)(2 - 4i)$

75. $(9 + 6i)(-1 - i)$ **76.** $(10 + 2i)(-2 - i)$

77. $(4 + 5i)^2$ **78.** $(5 - 3i)^2$

79. $(-2 - 4i)^2$ **80.** $(-3 - 6i)^2$

81. $(6 + 7i)(6 - 7i)$ **82.** $(5 - 7i)(5 + 7i)$

83. $(-1 + 2i)(-1 - 2i)$ **84.** $(-2 - 4i)(-2 + 4i)$

For Problems 85–100, find each of the following quotients, and express the answers in the standard form of a complex number. (Objective 6)

85. $\dfrac{3i}{2 + 4i}$

86. $\dfrac{4i}{5 + 2i}$

87. $\dfrac{-2i}{3 - 5i}$

88. $\dfrac{-5i}{2 - 4i}$

89. $\dfrac{-2 + 6i}{3i}$

90. $\dfrac{-4 - 7i}{6i}$

91. $\dfrac{2}{7i}$

92. $\dfrac{3}{10i}$

93. $\dfrac{2 + 6i}{1 + 7i}$

94. $\dfrac{5 + i}{2 + 9i}$

95. $\dfrac{3 + 6i}{4 - 5i}$

96. $\dfrac{7 - 3i}{4 - 3i}$

97. $\dfrac{-2 + 7i}{-1 + i}$

98. $\dfrac{-3 + 8i}{-2 + i}$

99. $\dfrac{-1 - 3i}{-2 - 10i}$

100. $\dfrac{-3 - 4i}{-4 - 11i}$

101. Some of the solution sets for quadratic equations in the next sections in this chapter will contain complex numbers such as $(-4 + \sqrt{-12})/2$ and $(-4 - \sqrt{-12})/2$. We can simplify the first number as follows.

$$\frac{-4 + \sqrt{-12}}{2} = \frac{-4 + i\sqrt{12}}{2}$$

$$= \frac{-4 + 2i\sqrt{3}}{2} = \frac{\cancel{2}(-2 + i\sqrt{3})}{\cancel{2}}$$

$$= -2 + i\sqrt{3}$$

Simplify each of the following complex numbers. (Objective 3)

(a) $\dfrac{-4 - \sqrt{-12}}{2}$

(b) $\dfrac{6 + \sqrt{-24}}{4}$

(c) $\dfrac{-1 - \sqrt{-18}}{2}$

(d) $\dfrac{-6 + \sqrt{-27}}{3}$

(e) $\dfrac{10 + \sqrt{-45}}{4}$

(f) $\dfrac{4 - \sqrt{-48}}{2}$

Thoughts Into Words

102. Why is the set of real numbers a subset of the set of complex numbers?

103. Can the sum of two nonreal complex numbers be a real number? Defend your answer.

104. Can the product of two nonreal complex numbers be a real number? Defend your answer.

Answers to the Concept Quiz

1. False   **2.** True   **3.** False   **4.** True   **5.** True   **6.** True   **7.** True   **8.** False   **9.** False   **10.** True

---

6.2   Quadratic Equations

OBJECTIVES

1 Solve quadratic equations by factoring

2 Solve quadratic equations of the form $x^2 = a$

3 Solve problems pertaining to right triangles and 30°–60° triangles

A second-degree equation in one variable contains the variable with an exponent of 2, but no higher power. Such equations are also called *quadratic equations*. The following are examples of quadratic equations.

$$x^2 = 36 \qquad\qquad y^2 + 4y = 0 \qquad x^2 + 5x - 2 = 0$$

$$3n^2 + 2n - 1 = 0 \qquad 5x^2 + x + 2 = 3x^2 - 2x - 1$$

A **quadratic equation** in the variable x can also be defined as any equation that can be written in the form

$$ax^2 + bx + c = 0$$

where a, b, and c are real numbers and $a \neq 0$. The form $ax^2 + bx + c = 0$ is called the *standard form* of a quadratic equation.

In previous chapters you solved quadratic equations (the term *quadratic* was not used at that time) by factoring and applying the property, $ab = 0$ if and only if $a = 0$ or $b = 0$. Let's review a few such examples.

Classroom Example
Solve $4x^2 + 11x - 3 = 0$.

EXAMPLE 1   Solve $3n^2 + 14n - 5 = 0$.

Solution

$$3n^2 + 14n - 5 = 0$$
$$(3n - 1)(n + 5) = 0 \qquad\qquad \text{Factor the left side}$$
$$3n - 1 = 0 \quad \text{or} \quad n + 5 = 0 \qquad \text{Apply: } ab = 0 \text{ if and only if } a = 0 \text{ or } b = 0$$
$$3n = 1 \quad \text{or} \quad n = -5$$
$$n = \frac{1}{3} \quad \text{or} \quad n = -5$$

The solution set is $\left\{-5, \dfrac{1}{3}\right\}$.

Classroom Example
Solve $2\sqrt{y} = y - 3$.

EXAMPLE 2   Solve $2\sqrt{x} = x - 8$.

Solution

$$2\sqrt{x} = x - 8$$
$$(2\sqrt{x})^2 = (x - 8)^2 \qquad\qquad \text{Square both sides}$$
$$4x = x^2 - 16x + 64$$
$$0 = x^2 - 20x + 64$$
$$0 = (x - 16)(x - 4) \qquad\qquad \text{Factor the right side}$$
$$x - 16 = 0 \quad \text{or} \quad x - 4 = 0 \qquad \text{Apply: } ab = 0 \text{ if and only if } a = 0 \text{ or } b = 0$$
$$x = 16 \quad \text{or} \quad x = 4$$

✓ **Check**

If $x = 16$	**If $x = 4$**
$2\sqrt{x} = x - 8$	$2\sqrt{x} = x - 8$
$2\sqrt{16} \stackrel{?}{=} 16 - 8$	$2\sqrt{4} \stackrel{?}{=} 4 - 8$
$2(4) \stackrel{?}{=} 8$	$2(2) \stackrel{?}{=} -4$
$8 = 8$	$4 \neq -4$

The solution set is $\{16\}$.

We should make two comments about Example 2. First, remember that applying the property, if $a = b$, then $a^n = b^n$, might produce extraneous solutions. Therefore, we *must* check all potential solutions. Second, the equation $2\sqrt{x} = x - 8$ is said to be of *quadratic form* because it can be written as $2x^{\frac{1}{2}} = \left(x^{\frac{1}{2}}\right)^2 - 8$. More will be said about the phrase *quadratic form* later.

Solving Quadratic Equations of the Form $x^2 = a$

Let's consider quadratic equations of the form $x^2 = a$, where x is the variable and a is any real number. We can solve $x^2 = a$ as follows:

$$x^2 = a$$
$$x^2 - a = 0$$
$$x^2 - (\sqrt{a})^2 = 0 \qquad\qquad a = (\sqrt{a})^2$$
$$(x - \sqrt{a})(x + \sqrt{a}) = 0 \qquad \text{Factor the left side}$$
$$x - \sqrt{a} = 0 \qquad \text{or} \qquad x + \sqrt{a} = 0 \qquad \text{Apply: } ab = 0 \text{ if and only if } a = 0 \text{ or } b = 0$$
$$x = \sqrt{a} \qquad \text{or} \qquad x = -\sqrt{a}$$

The solutions are $\sqrt{a}$ and $-\sqrt{a}$. We can state this result as a general property and use it to solve certain types of quadratic equations.

> **Property 6.1**
>
> For any real number a,
> $$x^2 = a \quad \text{if and only if } x = \sqrt{a} \text{ or } x = -\sqrt{a}$$
> (The statement $x = \sqrt{a}$ or $x = -\sqrt{a}$ can be written as $x = \pm\sqrt{a}$.)

Property 6.1, along with our knowledge of square roots, makes it very easy to solve quadratic equations of the form $x^2 = a$.

Classroom Example
Solve $m^2 = 48$.

EXAMPLE 3   Solve $x^2 = 45$.

Solution

$$x^2 = 45$$
$$x = \pm\sqrt{45}$$
$$x = \pm 3\sqrt{5} \qquad\qquad \sqrt{45} = \sqrt{9}\sqrt{5} = 3\sqrt{5}$$

The solution set is $\{\pm 3\sqrt{5}\}$.

Classroom Example
Solve $n^2 = -25$.

EXAMPLE 4   Solve $x^2 = -9$.

Solution

$$x^2 = -9$$
$$x = \pm\sqrt{-9}$$
$$x = \pm 3i \qquad\qquad \sqrt{-9} = i\sqrt{9} = 3i$$

Thus the solution set is $\{\pm 3i\}$.

Classroom Example
Solve $5x^2 = 16$.

EXAMPLE 5   Solve $7n^2 = 12$.

Solution

$$7n^2 = 12$$
$$n^2 = \frac{12}{7}$$

$$n = \pm\sqrt{\frac{12}{7}}$$

$$n = \pm\frac{2\sqrt{21}}{7} \qquad \sqrt{\frac{12}{7}} = \frac{\sqrt{12}}{\sqrt{7}} \cdot \frac{\sqrt{7}}{\sqrt{7}} = \frac{\sqrt{84}}{7} = \frac{\sqrt{4}\sqrt{21}}{7} = \frac{2\sqrt{21}}{7}$$

The solution set is $\left\{\pm\dfrac{2\sqrt{21}}{7}\right\}$.

Classroom Example
Solve $(4x - 3)^2 = 49$.

EXAMPLE 6   Solve $(3n + 1)^2 = 25$.

Solution

$$(3n + 1)^2 = 25$$
$$(3n + 1) = \pm\sqrt{25}$$
$$3n + 1 = \pm 5$$
$$3n + 1 = 5 \quad \text{or} \quad 3n + 1 = -5$$
$$3n = 4 \quad \text{or} \quad 3n = -6$$
$$n = \frac{4}{3} \quad \text{or} \quad n = -2$$

The solution set is $\left\{-2, \dfrac{4}{3}\right\}$.

Classroom Example
Solve $(x + 4)^2 = -18$.

EXAMPLE 7   Solve $(x - 3)^2 = -10$.

Solution

$$(x - 3)^2 = -10$$
$$x - 3 = \pm\sqrt{-10}$$
$$x - 3 = \pm i\sqrt{10}$$
$$x = 3 \pm i\sqrt{10}$$

Thus the solution set is $\{3 \pm i\sqrt{10}\}$.

Remark: Take another look at the equations in Examples 4 and 7. We should immediately realize that the solution sets will consist only of nonreal complex numbers, because any nonzero real number squared is positive.

Sometimes it may be necessary to change the form before we can apply Property 6.1. Let's consider one example to illustrate this idea.

Classroom Example
Solve $2(5x - 1)^2 + 9 = 53$.

EXAMPLE 8   Solve $3(2x - 3)^2 + 8 = 44$.

Solution

$$3(2x - 3)^2 + 8 = 44$$
$$3(2x - 3)^2 = 36$$
$$(2x - 3)^2 = 12$$
$$2x - 3 = \pm\sqrt{12}$$
$$2x - 3 = \pm 2\sqrt{3}$$

$$2x = 3 \pm 2\sqrt{3}$$

$$x = \frac{3 \pm 2\sqrt{3}}{2}$$

The solution set is $\left\{ \dfrac{3 \pm 2\sqrt{3}}{2} \right\}$.

Solving Problems Pertaining to Right Triangles and 30°–60° Triangles

Our work with radicals, Property 6.1, and the Pythagorean theorem form a basis for solving a variety of problems that pertain to right triangles.

EXAMPLE 9

A 50-foot rope hangs from the top of a flagpole. When pulled taut to its full length, the rope reaches a point on the ground 18 feet from the base of the pole. Find the height of the pole to the nearest tenth of a foot.

Solution

Let's make a sketch (Figure 6.1) and record the given information. Use the Pythagorean theorem to solve for p as follows:

$$p^2 + 18^2 = 50^2$$
$$p^2 + 324 = 2500$$
$$p^2 = 2176$$
$$p = \sqrt{2176} = 46.6 \quad \text{to the nearest tenth}$$

The height of the flagpole is approximately 46.6 feet.

There are two special kinds of right triangles that we use extensively in later mathematics courses. The first is the **isosceles right triangle**, which is a right triangle that has both legs of the same length. Let's consider a problem that involves an isosceles right triangle.

EXAMPLE 10

Find the length of each leg of an isosceles right triangle that has a hypotenuse of length 5 meters.

Solution

Let's sketch an isosceles right triangle and let x represent the length of each leg (Figure 6.2). Then we can apply the Pythagorean theorem.

$$x^2 + x^2 = 5^2$$
$$2x^2 = 25$$
$$x^2 = \frac{25}{2}$$
$$x = \pm\sqrt{\frac{25}{2}} = \pm\frac{5}{\sqrt{2}} = \pm\frac{5\sqrt{2}}{2}$$

Each leg is $\dfrac{5\sqrt{2}}{2}$ meters long.

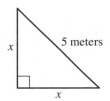

Figure 6.2

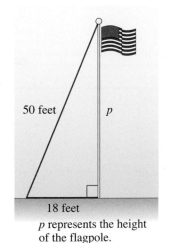

p represents the height of the flagpole.

Figure 6.1

Remark: In Example 9 we made no attempt to express $\sqrt{2176}$ in simplest radical form because the answer was to be given as a rational approximation to the nearest tenth. However, in Example 10 we left the final answer in radical form and therefore expressed it in simplest radical form.

The second special kind of right triangle that we use frequently is one that contains acute angles of 30° and 60°. In such a right triangle, which we refer to as a **30°–60° right triangle**, the side opposite the 30° angle is equal in length to one-half of the length of the hypotenuse. This relationship, along with the Pythagorean theorem, provides us with another problem-solving technique.

Classroom Example
Suppose that a 30-foot ladder is leaning against a building and makes an angle of 60° with the ground. How far up the building does the top of the ladder reach? Express your answer to the nearest tenth of a foot.

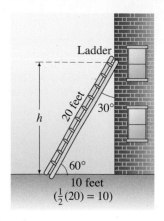

Figure 6.3

EXAMPLE 11

Suppose that a 20-foot ladder is leaning against a building and makes an angle of 60° with the ground. How far up the building does the top of the ladder reach? Express your answer to the nearest tenth of a foot.

Solution

Figure 6.3 depicts this situation. The side opposite the 30° angle equals one-half of the hypotenuse, so it is of length $\frac{1}{2}(20) = 10$ feet. Now we can apply the Pythagorean theorem.

$$h^2 + 10^2 = 20^2$$
$$h^2 + 100 = 400$$
$$h^2 = 300$$
$$h = \sqrt{300} = 17.3 \quad \text{to the nearest tenth}$$

The ladder touches the building at a point approximately 17.3 feet from the ground.

Concept Quiz 6.2

For Problems 1–10, answer true or false.

1. The quadratic equation $-3x^2 + 5x - 8 = 0$ is in standard form.
2. The solution set of the equation $(x + 1)^2 = -25$ will consist only of nonreal complex numbers.
3. An isosceles right triangle is a right triangle that has a hypotenuse of the same length as one of the legs.
4. In a 30°–60° right triangle, the hypotenuse is equal in length to twice the length of the side opposite the 30° angle.
5. The equation $2x^2 + x^3 - x + 4 = 0$ is a quadratic equation.
6. The solution set for $4x^2 = 8x$ is $\{2\}$.
7. The solution set for $3x^2 = 8x$ is $\left\{0, \frac{8}{3}\right\}$.
8. The solution set for $x^2 - 8x - 48 = 0$ is $\{-12, 4\}$.
9. If the length of each leg of an isosceles right triangle is 4 inches, then the hypotenuse is of length $4\sqrt{2}$ inches.
10. If the length of the leg opposite the 30° angle in a right triangle is 6 centimeters, then the length of the other leg is 12 centimeters.

Problem Set 6.2

For Problems 1–20, solve each of the quadratic equations by factoring and applying the property, $ab = 0$ if and only if $a = 0$ or $b = 0$. If necessary, return to Chapter 3 and review the factoring techniques presented there. (**Objective 1**)

1. $x^2 - 9x = 0$
2. $x^2 + 5x = 0$
3. $x^2 = -3x$
4. $x^2 = 15x$
5. $3y^2 + 12y = 0$
6. $6y^2 - 24y = 0$

7. $5n^2 - 9n = 0$ **8.** $4n^2 + 13n = 0$

9. $x^2 + x - 30 = 0$ **10.** $x^2 - 8x - 48 = 0$

11. $x^2 - 19x + 84 = 0$ **12.** $x^2 - 21x + 104 = 0$

13. $2x^2 + 19x + 24 = 0$ **14.** $4x^2 + 29x + 30 = 0$

15. $15x^2 + 29x - 14 = 0$ **16.** $24x^2 + x - 10 = 0$

17. $25x^2 - 30x + 9 = 0$ **18.** $16x^2 - 8x + 1 = 0$

19. $6x^2 - 5x - 21 = 0$ **20.** $12x^2 - 4x - 5 = 0$

For Problems 21–26, solve each radical equation. Don't forget, you *must* check potential solutions. **(Objective 1)**

21. $3\sqrt{x} = x + 2$ **22.** $3\sqrt{2x} = x + 4$

23. $\sqrt{2x} = x - 4$ **24.** $\sqrt{x} = x - 2$

25. $\sqrt{3x + 6} = x$ **26.** $\sqrt{5x + 10} = x$

For Problems 27–62, use Property 6.1 to help solve each quadratic equation. **(Objective 2)**

27. $x^2 = 1$ **28.** $x^2 = 81$

29. $x^2 = -36$ **30.** $x^2 = -49$

31. $x^2 = 14$ **32.** $x^2 = 22$

33. $n^2 - 28 = 0$ **34.** $n^2 - 54 = 0$

35. $3t^2 = 54$ **36.** $4t^2 = 108$

37. $2t^2 = 7$ **38.** $3t^2 = 8$

39. $15y^2 = 20$ **40.** $14y^2 = 80$

41. $10x^2 + 48 = 0$ **42.** $12x^2 + 50 = 0$

43. $24x^2 = 36$ **44.** $12x^2 = 49$

45. $(x - 2)^2 = 9$ **46.** $(x + 1)^2 = 16$

47. $(x + 3)^2 = 25$ **48.** $(x - 2)^2 = 49$

49. $(x + 6)^2 = -4$ **50.** $(3x + 1)^2 = 9$

51. $(2x - 3)^2 = 1$ **52.** $(2x + 5)^2 = -4$

53. $(n - 4)^2 = 5$ **54.** $(n - 7)^2 = 6$

55. $(t + 5)^2 = 12$ **56.** $(t - 1)^2 = 18$

57. $(3y - 2)^2 = -27$ **58.** $(4y + 5)^2 = 80$

59. $3(x + 7)^2 + 4 = 79$ **60.** $2(x + 6)^2 - 9 = 63$

61. $2(5x - 2)^2 + 5 = 25$ **62.** $3(4x - 1)^2 + 1 = -17$

For Problems 63–68, a and b represent the lengths of the legs of a right triangle, and c represents the length of the hypotenuse. Express answers in simplest radical form. **(Objective 3)**

63. Find c if $a = 4$ centimeters and $b = 6$ centimeters.

64. Find c if $a = 3$ meters and $b = 7$ meters.

65. Find a if $c = 12$ inches and $b = 8$ inches.

66. Find a if $c = 8$ feet and $b = 6$ feet.

67. Find b if $c = 17$ yards and $a = 15$ yards.

68. Find b if $c = 14$ meters and $a = 12$ meters.

For Problems 69–72, use the isosceles right triangle in Figure 6.4. Express your answers in simplest radical form. **(Objective 3)**

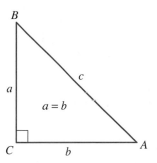

Figure 6.4

69. If $b = 6$ inches, find c.

70. If $a = 7$ centimeters, find c.

71. If $c = 8$ meters, find a and b.

72. If $c = 9$ feet, find a and b.

For Problems 73–78, use the triangle in Figure 6.5. Express your answers in simplest radical form. **(Objective 3)**

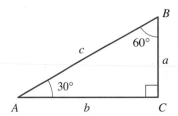

Figure 6.5

73. If $a = 3$ inches, find b and c.

74. If $a = 6$ feet, find b and c.

75. If $c = 14$ centimeters, find a and b.

76. If $c = 9$ centimeters, find a and b.

77. If $b = 10$ feet, find a and c.

78. If $b = 8$ meters, find a and c.

79. A 24-foot ladder resting against a house reaches a windowsill 16 feet above the ground. How far is the foot of the ladder from the foundation of the house? Express your answer to the nearest tenth of a foot.

80. A 62-foot guy-wire makes an angle of 60° with the ground and is attached to a telephone pole (see Figure 6.6). Find the distance from the base of the pole to the point on the pole where the wire is attached. Express your answer to the nearest tenth of a foot.

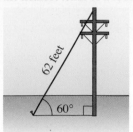

Figure 6.6

81. A rectangular plot measures 16 meters by 34 meters. Find, to the nearest meter, the distance from one corner of the plot to the corner diagonally opposite.

82. Consecutive bases of a square-shaped baseball diamond are 90 feet apart (see Figure 6.7). Find, to the nearest tenth of a foot, the distance from first base diagonally across the diamond to third base.

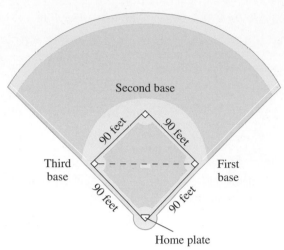

Figure 6.7

83. A diagonal of a square parking lot is 75 meters. Find, to the nearest meter, the length of a side of the lot.

Thoughts Into Words

84. Explain why the equation $(x + 2)^2 + 5 = 1$ has no real number solutions.

85. Suppose that your friend solved the equation $(x + 3)^2 = 25$ as follows:

$$(x + 3)^2 = 25$$
$$x^2 + 6x + 9 = 25$$
$$x^2 + 6x - 16 = 0$$

$$(x + 8)(x - 2) = 0$$
$$x + 8 = 0 \quad \text{or} \quad x - 2 = 0$$
$$x = -8 \quad \text{or} \quad x = 2$$

Is this a correct approach to the problem? Would you offer any suggestion about an easier approach to the problem?

Further Investigations

86. Suppose that we are given a cube with edges 12 centimeters in length. Find the length of a diagonal from a lower corner to the diagonally opposite upper corner. Express your answer to the nearest tenth of a centimeter.

87. Suppose that we are given a rectangular box with a length of 8 centimeters, a width of 6 centimeters, and a height of 4 centimeters. Find the length of a diagonal from a lower corner to the upper corner diagonally opposite. Express your answer to the nearest tenth of a centimeter.

88. The converse of the Pythagorean theorem is also true. It states, "If the measures a, b, and c of the sides of a triangle are such that $a^2 + b^2 = c^2$, then the triangle is a right triangle with a and b the measures of the legs and c the measure of the hypotenuse." Use the converse

of the Pythagorean theorem to determine which of the triangles with sides of the following measures are right triangles.

(a) 9, 40, 41   (b) 20, 48, 52

(c) 19, 21, 26   (d) 32, 37, 49

(e) 65, 156, 169   (f) 21, 72, 75

89. Find the length of the hypotenuse (h) of an isosceles right triangle if each leg is s units long. Then use this relationship to redo Problems 69–72.

90. Suppose that the side opposite the 30° angle in a 30°–60° right triangle is s units long. Express the length of the hypotenuse and the length of the other leg in terms of s. Then use these relationships and redo Problems 73–78.

Answers to the Concept Quiz

1. True   **2.** True   **3.** False   **4.** True   **5.** False   **6.** False   **7.** True   **8.** False   **9.** True   **10.** False

6.3   Completing the Square

OBJECTIVE 1 Solve quadratic equations by completing the square

Thus far we have solved quadratic equations by factoring and applying the property, $ab = 0$ if and only if $a = 0$ or $b = 0$, or by applying the property, $x^2 = a$ if and only if $x = \pm\sqrt{a}$. In this section we examine another method called *completing the square*, which will give us the power to solve any quadratic equation.

A factoring technique we studied in Chapter 3 relied on recognizing *perfect-square trinomials*. In each of the following, the perfect-square trinomial on the right side is the result of squaring the binomial on the left side.

$$(x + 4)^2 = x^2 + 8x + 16 \qquad (x - 6)^2 = x^2 - 12x + 36$$
$$(x + 7)^2 = x^2 + 14x + 49 \qquad (x - 9)^2 = x^2 - 18x + 81$$
$$(x + a)^2 = x^2 + 2ax + a^2$$

Note that in each of the square trinomials, the constant term is equal to the square of one-half of the coefficient of the x term. This relationship enables us to form a perfect-square trinomial by adding a proper constant term. To find the constant term, take one-half of the coefficient of the x term and then square the result. For example, suppose that we want to form a perfect-square trinomial from $x^2 + 10x$. The coefficient of the x term is 10. Because $\frac{1}{2}(10) = 5$, and $5^2 = 25$, the constant term should be 25. The perfect-square trinomial that can be formed is $x^2 + 10x + 25$. This perfect-square trinomial can be factored and expressed as $(x + 5)^2$. Let's use the previous ideas to help solve some quadratic equations.

Classroom Example
Solve $x^2 + 8x - 5 = 0$.

EXAMPLE 1   Solve $x^2 + 10x - 2 = 0$.

Solution

$$x^2 + 10x - 2 = 0$$
$$x^2 + 10x = 2 \qquad \text{Isolate the } x^2 \text{ and } x \text{ terms}$$
$$\frac{1}{2}(10) = 5 \quad \text{and} \quad 5^2 = 25 \qquad \text{Take } \frac{1}{2} \text{ of the coefficient of the } x \text{ term and then square the result}$$
$$x^2 + 10x + 25 = 2 + 25 \qquad \text{Add 25 to } both \text{ sides of the equation}$$
$$(x + 5)^2 = 27 \qquad \text{Factor the perfect-square trinomial}$$
$$x + 5 = \pm\sqrt{27} \qquad \text{Now solve by applying Property 6.1}$$
$$x + 5 = \pm 3\sqrt{3}$$
$$x = -5 \pm 3\sqrt{3}$$

The solution set is $\{-5 \pm 3\sqrt{3}\}$.

The method of completing the square to solve a quadratic equation is merely what the name implies. A perfect-square trinomial is formed, then the equation can be changed to the necessary form for applying the property "$x^2 = a$ if and only if $x = \pm\sqrt{a}$." Let's consider another example.

Classroom Example
Solve $x(x + 10) = -33$.

EXAMPLE 2   Solve $x(x + 8) = -23$.

Solution

$$x(x + 8) = -23$$
$$x^2 + 8x = -23 \qquad \text{Apply the distributive property}$$

$$\frac{1}{2}(8) = 4 \qquad \text{and} \qquad 4^2 = 16$$

Take $\frac{1}{2}$ of the coefficient of the x term and then square the result

$$x^2 + 8x + 16 = -23 + 16$$

Add 16 to *both* sides of the equation

$$(x + 4)^2 = -7$$

Factor the perfect-square trinomial

$$x + 4 = \pm\sqrt{-7}$$

Now solve by applying Property 6.1

$$x + 4 = \pm i\sqrt{7}$$

$$x = -4 \pm i\sqrt{7}$$

The solution set is $\{-4 \pm i\sqrt{7}\}$.

Classroom Example
Solve $m^2 - 3m - 5 = 0$.

EXAMPLE 3   Solve $x^2 - 3x + 1 = 0$.

Solution

$$x^2 - 3x + 1 = 0$$

$$x^2 - 3x = -1$$

$$x^2 - 3x + \frac{9}{4} = -1 + \frac{9}{4} \qquad\qquad \frac{1}{2}(3) = \frac{3}{2} \text{ and } \left(\frac{3}{2}\right)^2 = \frac{9}{4}$$

$$\left(x - \frac{3}{2}\right)^2 = \frac{5}{4}$$

$$x - \frac{3}{2} = \pm\sqrt{\frac{5}{4}}$$

$$x - \frac{3}{2} = \pm\frac{\sqrt{5}}{2}$$

$$x = \frac{3}{2} \pm \frac{\sqrt{5}}{2}$$

$$x = \frac{3 \pm \sqrt{5}}{2}$$

The solution set is $\left\{\dfrac{3 \pm \sqrt{5}}{2}\right\}$.

In Example 3 note that because the coefficient of the x term is odd, we are forced into the realm of fractions. Using common fractions rather than decimals enables us to apply our previous work with radicals.

The relationship for a perfect-square trinomial that states that the constant term is equal to the square of one-half of the coefficient of the x term holds only if the coefficient of x^2 is 1. Thus we must make an adjustment when solving quadratic equations that have a coefficient of x^2 other than 1. We will need to apply the multiplication property of equality so that the coefficient of the x^2 term becomes 1. The next example shows how to make this adjustment.

Classroom Example
Solve $3y^2 - 24y + 26 = 0$.

EXAMPLE 4   Solve $2x^2 + 12x - 5 = 0$.

Solution

$$2x^2 + 12x - 5 = 0$$

$$2x^2 + 12x = 5$$

$$x^2 + 6x = \frac{5}{2} \qquad\qquad \text{Multiply both sides by } \frac{1}{2}$$

$$x^2 + 6x + 9 = \frac{5}{2} + 9 \qquad\qquad \frac{1}{2}(6) = 3, \text{ and } 3^2 = 9$$

$$x^2 + 6x + 9 = \frac{23}{2}$$

$$(x + 3)^2 = \frac{23}{2}$$

$$x + 3 = \pm\sqrt{\frac{23}{2}}$$

$$x + 3 = \pm\frac{\sqrt{46}}{2} \qquad\qquad \sqrt{\frac{23}{2}} = \frac{\sqrt{23}}{\sqrt{2}} \cdot \frac{\sqrt{2}}{\sqrt{2}} = \frac{\sqrt{46}}{2}$$

$$x = -3 \pm \frac{\sqrt{46}}{2}$$

$$x = \frac{-6}{2} \pm \frac{\sqrt{46}}{2} \qquad\qquad \text{Common denominator of 2}$$

$$x = \frac{-6 \pm \sqrt{46}}{2}$$

The solution set is $\left\{ \dfrac{-6 \pm \sqrt{46}}{2} \right\}$.

As we mentioned earlier, we can use the method of completing the square to solve *any* quadratic equation. To illustrate, let's use it to solve an equation that could also be solved by factoring.

Classroom Example
Solve $t^2 - 10t + 21 = 0$ by completing the square.

EXAMPLE 5   Solve $x^2 - 2x - 8 = 0$ by completing the square.

Solution

$$x^2 - 2x - 8 = 0$$

$$x^2 - 2x = 8$$

$$x^2 - 2x + 1 = 8 + 1 \qquad\qquad \frac{1}{2}(-2) = -1 \text{ and } (-1)^2 = 1$$

$$(x - 1)^2 = 9$$

$$x - 1 = \pm 3$$

$$x - 1 = 3 \qquad \text{or} \qquad x - 1 = -3$$

$$x = 4 \qquad \text{or} \qquad x = -2$$

The solution set is $\{-2, 4\}$.

Solving the equation in Example 5 by factoring would be easier than completing the square. Remember, however, that the method of completing the square will work with any quadratic equation.

Concept Quiz 6.3

For Problems 1–10, answer true or false.

1. In a perfect-square trinomial, the constant term is equal to one-half the coefficient of the x term.

2. The method of completing the square will solve any quadratic equation.

3. Every quadratic equation solved by completing the square will have real number solutions.

4. The completing-the-square method cannot be used if factoring could solve the quadratic equation.

5. To use the completing-the-square method for solving the equation $3x^2 + 2x = 5$, we would first divide both sides of the equation by 3.

6. The equation $x^2 + 2x = 0$ cannot be solved by using the method of completing the square.

7. To solve the equation $x^2 - 5x = 1$ by completing the square, we would start by adding $\dfrac{25}{4}$ to both sides of the equation.

8. To solve the equation $x^2 - 2x = 14$ by completing the square, we must first change the form of the equation to $x^2 - 2x - 14 = 0$.

9. The solution set of the equation $x^2 - 2x = 14$ is $\left\{1 \pm \sqrt{15}\right\}$.

10. The solution set of the equation $x^2 - 5x - 1 = 0$ is $\left\{\dfrac{5 \pm \sqrt{29}}{2}\right\}$.

Problem Set 6.3

For Problems 1–14, solve each quadratic equation by using (a) the factoring method and (b) the method of completing the square. **(Objective 1)**

1. $x^2 - 4x - 60 = 0$

2. $x^2 + 6x - 16 = 0$

3. $x^2 - 14x = -40$

4. $x^2 - 18x = -72$

5. $x^2 - 5x - 50 = 0$

6. $x^2 + 3x - 18 = 0$

7. $x(x + 7) = 8$

8. $x(x - 1) = 30$

9. $2n^2 - n - 15 = 0$

10. $3n^2 + n - 14 = 0$

11. $3n^2 + 7n - 6 = 0$

12. $2n^2 + 7n - 4 = 0$

13. $n(n + 6) = 160$

14. $n(n - 6) = 216$

For Problems 15–38, use the method of completing the square to solve each quadratic equation. **(Objective 1)**

15. $x^2 + 4x - 2 = 0$

16. $x^2 + 2x - 1 = 0$

17. $x^2 + 6x - 3 = 0$

18. $x^2 + 8x - 4 = 0$

19. $y^2 - 10y = 1$

20. $y^2 - 6y = -10$

21. $n^2 - 8n + 17 = 0$

22. $n^2 - 4n + 2 = 0$

23. $n(n + 12) = -9$

24. $n(n + 14) = -4$

25. $n^2 + 2n + 6 = 0$

26. $n^2 + n - 1 = 0$

27. $x^2 + 3x - 2 = 0$

28. $x^2 + 5x - 3 = 0$

29. $x^2 + 5x + 1 = 0$

30. $x^2 + 7x + 2 = 0$

31. $y^2 - 7y + 3 = 0$

32. $y^2 - 9y + 30 = 0$

33. $2x^2 + 4x - 3 = 0$

34. $2t^2 - 4t + 1 = 0$

35. $3n^2 - 6n + 5 = 0$

36. $3x^2 + 12x - 2 = 0$

37. $3x^2 + 5x - 1 = 0$

38. $2x^2 + 7x - 3 = 0$

For Problems 39–60, solve each quadratic equation using the method that seems most appropriate.

39. $x^2 + 8x - 48 = 0$

40. $x^2 + 5x - 14 = 0$

41. $2n^2 - 8n = -3$

42. $3x^2 + 6x = 1$

43. $(3x - 1)(2x + 9) = 0$

44. $(5x + 2)(x - 4) = 0$

45. $(x + 2)(x - 7) = 10$

46. $(x - 3)(x + 5) = -7$

47. $(x - 3)^2 = 12$

48. $x^2 = 16x$

49. $3n^2 - 6n + 4 = 0$

50. $2n^2 - 2n - 1 = 0$

51. $n(n + 8) = 240$

52. $t(t - 26) = -160$

53. $3x^2 + 5x = -2$

54. $2x^2 - 7x = -5$

55. $4x^2 - 8x + 3 = 0$

56. $9x^2 + 18x + 5 = 0$

57. $x^2 + 12x = 4$

58. $x^2 + 6x = -11$

59. $4(2x + 1)^2 - 1 = 11$

60. $5(x + 2)^2 + 1 = 16$

61. Use the method of completing the square to solve $ax^2 + bx + c = 0$ for x, where a, b, and c are real numbers and $a \neq 0$.

Thoughts Into Words

62. Explain the process of completing the square to solve a quadratic equation.

63. Give a step-by-step description of how to solve $3x^2 + 9x - 4 = 0$ by completing the square.

Further Investigations

Solve Problems 64–67 for the indicated variable. Assume that all letters represent positive numbers.

64. $\dfrac{x^2}{a^2} - \dfrac{y^2}{b^2} = 1$ for y

65. $\dfrac{x^2}{a^2} + \dfrac{y^2}{b^2} = 1$ for x

66. $s = \dfrac{1}{2}gt^2$ for t

67. $A = \pi r^2$ for r

Solve each of the following equations for x.

68. $x^2 + 8ax + 15a^2 = 0$

69. $x^2 - 5ax + 6a^2 = 0$

70. $10x^2 - 31ax - 14a^2 = 0$

71. $6x^2 + ax - 2a^2 = 0$

72. $4x^2 + 4bx + b^2 = 0$

73. $9x^2 - 12bx + 4b^2 = 0$

Answers to the Concept Quiz

1. False   **2.** True   **3.** False   **4.** False   **5.** True   **6.** False   **7.** True   **8.** False   **9.** True   **10.** True

---

6.4   Quadratic Formula

OBJECTIVES

1. Use the quadratic formula to solve quadratic equations

2. Determine the nature of roots to quadratic equations

As we saw in the last section, the method of completing the square can be used to solve any quadratic equation. Thus if we apply the method of completing the square to the equation $ax^2 + bx + c = 0$, where a, b, and c are real numbers and $a \neq 0$, we can produce a formula for solving quadratic equations. This formula can then be used to solve any quadratic equation. Let's solve $ax^2 + bx + c = 0$ by completing the square.

$$ax^2 + bx + c = 0$$

$$ax^2 + bx = -c \qquad \text{Isolate the } x^2 \text{ and } x \text{ terms}$$

$$x^2 + \frac{b}{a}x = -\frac{c}{a} \qquad \text{Multiply both sides by } \frac{1}{a}$$

$$x^2 + \frac{b}{a}x + \frac{b^2}{4a^2} = -\frac{c}{a} + \frac{b^2}{4a^2} \qquad \frac{1}{2}\left(\frac{b}{a}\right) = \frac{b}{2a} \quad \text{and} \quad \left(\frac{b}{2a}\right)^2 = \frac{b^2}{4a^2}$$

Complete the square by adding $\dfrac{b^2}{4a^2}$ to both sides

$$x^2 + \frac{b}{a}x + \frac{b^2}{4a^2} = -\frac{4ac}{4a^2} + \frac{b^2}{4a^2} \qquad \text{Common denominator of } 4a^2 \text{ on right side}$$

$$x^2 + \frac{b}{a}x + \frac{b^2}{4a^2} = \frac{b^2}{4a^2} - \frac{4ac}{4a^2} \qquad \text{Commutative property}$$

$$\left(x + \frac{b}{2a}\right)^2 = \frac{b^2 - 4ac}{4a^2} \qquad \begin{array}{l}\text{The right side is combined into a}\\\text{single fraction}\end{array}$$

$$x + \frac{b}{2a} = \pm\sqrt{\frac{b^2 - 4ac}{4a^2}}$$

$$x + \frac{b}{2a} = \pm\frac{\sqrt{b^2 - 4ac}}{\sqrt{4a^2}}$$

$$x + \frac{b}{2a} = \pm \frac{\sqrt{b^2 - 4ac}}{2a} \qquad \sqrt{4a^2} = |2a| \text{ but } 2a \text{ can be used because of the use of } \pm$$

$$x + \frac{b}{2a} = \frac{\sqrt{b^2 - 4ac}}{2a} \qquad \text{or} \qquad x + \frac{b}{2a} = -\frac{\sqrt{b^2 - 4ac}}{2a}$$

$$x = -\frac{b}{2a} + \frac{\sqrt{b^2 - 4ac}}{2a} \qquad \text{or} \qquad x = -\frac{b}{2a} - \frac{\sqrt{b^2 - 4ac}}{2a}$$

$$x = \frac{-b + \sqrt{b^2 - 4ac}}{2a} \qquad \text{or} \qquad x = \frac{-b - \sqrt{b^2 - 4ac}}{2a}$$

The quadratic formula is usually stated as follows:

Quadratic Formula

$$x = \frac{-b \pm \sqrt{b^2 - 4ac}}{2a}, \qquad a \neq 0$$

We can use the quadratic formula to solve *any* quadratic equation by expressing the equation in the standard form $ax^2 + bx + c = 0$ and substituting the values for a, b, and c into the formula. Let's consider some examples.

Classroom Example
Solve $n^2 - 5n - 9 = 0$.

EXAMPLE 1   Solve $x^2 + 5x + 2 = 0$.

Solution

$$x^2 + 5x + 2 = 0$$

The given equation is in standard form with $a = 1$, $b = 5$, and $c = 2$. Let's substitute these values into the formula and simplify.

$$x = \frac{-b \pm \sqrt{b^2 - 4ac}}{2a}$$

$$x = \frac{-5 \pm \sqrt{5^2 - 4(1)(2)}}{2(1)}$$

$$x = \frac{-5 \pm \sqrt{25 - 8}}{2}$$

$$x = \frac{-5 \pm \sqrt{17}}{2}$$

The solution set is $\left\{ \dfrac{-5 \pm \sqrt{17}}{2} \right\}$.

Classroom Example
Solve $a^2 + 8a + 5 = 0$.

EXAMPLE 2   Solve $x^2 - 2x - 4 = 0$.

Solution

$$x^2 - 2x - 4 = 0$$

We need to think of $x^2 - 2x - 4 = 0$ as $x^2 + (-2)x + (-4) = 0$ to determine the values $a = 1$, $b = -2$, and $c = -4$. Let's substitute these values into the quadratic formula and simplify.

$$x = \frac{-b \pm \sqrt{b^2 - 4ac}}{2a}$$

$$x = \frac{-(-2) \pm \sqrt{(-2)^2 - 4(1)(-4)}}{2(1)}$$

$$x = \frac{2 \pm \sqrt{4 + 16}}{2}$$

$$x = \frac{2 \pm \sqrt{20}}{2}$$

$$x = \frac{2 \pm 2\sqrt{5}}{2}$$

$$x = \frac{2(1 \pm \sqrt{5})}{2} \qquad \text{Factor out a 2 in the numerator}$$

$$x = \frac{2(1 \pm \sqrt{5})}{2} = 1 \pm \sqrt{5}$$

The solution set is $\{1 \pm \sqrt{5}\}$.

Classroom Example
Solve $f^2 - 8f + 18 = 0$.

EXAMPLE 3   Solve $x^2 - 2x + 19 = 0$.

Solution

$$x^2 - 2x + 19 = 0$$

We can substitute $a = 1$, $b = -2$, and $c = 19$.

$$x = \frac{-b \pm \sqrt{b^2 - 4ac}}{2a}$$

$$x = \frac{-(-2) \pm \sqrt{(-2)^2 - 4(1)(19)}}{2(1)}$$

$$x = \frac{2 \pm \sqrt{4 - 76}}{2}$$

$$x = \frac{2 \pm \sqrt{-72}}{2}$$

$$x = \frac{2 \pm 6i\sqrt{2}}{2} \qquad \sqrt{-72} = i\sqrt{72} = i\sqrt{36}\sqrt{2} = 6i\sqrt{2}$$

$$x = \frac{2(1 \pm 3i)}{2} \qquad \text{Factor out a 2 in the numerator}$$

$$x = \frac{2(1 \pm 3i\sqrt{2})}{2} = 1 \pm 3i\sqrt{2}$$

The solution set is $\{1 \pm 3i\sqrt{2}\}$.

Classroom Example
Solve $2b^2 + 6b - 5 = 0$.

EXAMPLE 4   Solve $2x^2 + 4x - 3 = 0$.

Solution

$$2x^2 + 4x - 3 = 0$$

Here $a = 2$, $b = 4$, and $c = -3$. Solving by using the quadratic formula is unlike solving by completing the square in that there is no need to make the coefficient of x^2 equal to 1.

$$x = \frac{-b \pm \sqrt{b^2 - 4ac}}{2a}$$

$$x = \frac{-4 \pm \sqrt{4^2 - 4(2)(-3)}}{2(2)}$$

$$x = \frac{-4 \pm \sqrt{16 + 24}}{4}$$

$$x = \frac{-4 \pm \sqrt{40}}{4}$$

$$x = \frac{-4 \pm 2\sqrt{10}}{4}$$

$$x = \frac{2(-2 \pm \sqrt{10})}{4} \qquad \text{Factor out a 2 in the numerator}$$

$$x = \frac{\cancel{2}(-2 \pm \sqrt{10})}{\underset{2}{\cancel{4}}} = \frac{-2 \pm \sqrt{10}}{2}$$

The solution set is $\left\{ \dfrac{-2 \pm \sqrt{10}}{2} \right\}$.

Classroom Example
Solve $x(5x - 7) = 6$.

EXAMPLE 5　　Solve $n(3n - 10) = 25$.

Solution

$$n(3n - 10) = 25$$

First, we need to change the equation to the standard form $an^2 + bn + c = 0$.

$$n(3n - 10) = 25$$
$$3n^2 - 10n = 25$$
$$3n^2 - 10n - 25 = 0$$

Now we can substitute $a = 3$, $b = -10$, and $c = -25$ into the quadratic formula.

$$n = \frac{-b \pm \sqrt{b^2 - 4ac}}{2a}$$

$$n = \frac{-(-10) \pm \sqrt{(-10)^2 - 4(3)(-25)}}{2(3)}$$

$$n = \frac{10 \pm \sqrt{100 + 300}}{2(3)}$$

$$n = \frac{10 \pm \sqrt{400}}{6}$$

$$n = \frac{10 \pm 20}{6}$$

$$n = \frac{10 + 20}{6} \qquad \text{or} \qquad n = \frac{10 - 20}{6}$$

$$n = 5 \qquad \text{or} \qquad n = -\frac{5}{3}$$

The solution set is $\left\{ -\dfrac{5}{3}, 5 \right\}$.

In Example 5, note that we used the variable n. The quadratic formula is usually stated in terms of x, but it certainly can be applied to quadratic equations in other variables. Also note in Example 5 that the polynomial $3n^2 - 10n - 25$ can be factored as $(3n + 5)(n - 5)$. Therefore, we could also solve the equation $3n^2 - 10n - 25 = 0$ by using the factoring approach. Section 6.5 will offer some guidance about which approach to use for a particular equation.

Determining the Nature of Roots of Quadratic Equations

The quadratic formula makes it easy to determine the nature of the roots of a quadratic equation without completely solving the equation. The number

$$b^2 - 4ac$$

which appears under the radical sign in the quadratic formula, is called the **discriminant** of the quadratic equation. The discriminant is the indicator of the kind of roots the equation has. For example, suppose that you start to solve the equation $x^2 - 4x + 7 = 0$ as follows:

$$x = \frac{-b \pm \sqrt{b^2 - 4ac}}{2a}$$

$$x = \frac{-(-4) \pm \sqrt{(-4)^2 - 4(1)(7)}}{2(1)}$$

$$x = \frac{4 \pm \sqrt{16 - 28}}{2}$$

$$x = \frac{4 \pm \sqrt{-12}}{2}$$

At this stage you should be able to look ahead and realize that you will obtain two nonreal complex solutions for the equation. (Note, by the way, that these solutions are complex conjugates.) In other words, the discriminant (-12) indicates what type of roots you will obtain.

We make the following general statements relative to the roots of a quadratic equation of the form $ax^2 + bx + c = 0$.

> **1.** If $b^2 - 4ac < 0$, then the equation has two nonreal complex solutions.
>
> **2.** If $b^2 - 4ac = 0$, then the equation has one real solution.
>
> **3.** If $b^2 - 4ac > 0$, then the equation has two real solutions.

The following examples illustrate each of these situations. (You may want to solve the equations completely to verify the conclusions.)

Equation	Discriminant	Nature of roots
$x^2 - 3x + 7 = 0$	$b^2 - 4ac = (-3)^2 - 4(1)(7)$ $= 9 - 28$ $= -19$	Two nonreal complex solutions
$9x^2 - 12x + 4 = 0$	$b^2 - 4ac = (-12)^2 - 4(9)(4)$ $= 144 - 144$ $= 0$	One real solution
$2x^2 + 5x - 3 = 0$	$b^2 - 4ac = (5)^2 - 4(2)(-3)$ $= 25 + 24$ $= 49$	Two real solutions

Remark: A clarification is called for at this time. Previously, we made the statement that if $b^2 - 4ac = 0$, then the equation has one real solution. Technically, such an equation has two solutions, but they are equal. For example, each factor of $(x - 7)(x - 7) = 0$ produces a solution, but both solutions are the number 7. We sometimes refer to this as one real solution with a *multiplicity of two*. Using the idea of multiplicity of roots, we can say that every quadratic equation has two roots.

EXAMPLE 6

Use the discriminant to determine if the equation $5x^2 + 2x + 7 = 0$ has two nonreal complex solutions, one real solution with a multiplicity of two, or two real solutions.

Solution

For the equation $5x^2 + 2x + 7 = 0$, $a = 5$, $b = 2$, and $c = 7$.

$$b^2 - 4ac = (2)^2 - 4(5)(7)$$
$$= 4 - 140$$
$$= -136$$

Because the discriminant is negative, the solutions will be two nonreal complex numbers. ∎

Most students become very adept at applying the quadratic formula to solve quadratic equations but make errors when reducing the answers. The next example shows two different methods for simplifying the answers.

EXAMPLE 7   Solve $3x^2 - 8x + 2 = 0$.

Solution

Here $a = 3$, $b = -8$, and $c = 2$. Let's substitute these values into the quadratic formula and simplify.

$$x = \frac{-b \pm \sqrt{b^2 - 4ac}}{2a}$$

$$x = \frac{-(-8) \pm \sqrt{(-8)^2 - 4(3)(2)}}{2(3)}$$

$$x = \frac{8 \pm \sqrt{64 - 24}}{6}$$

$$x = \frac{8 \pm \sqrt{40}}{6} = \frac{8 \pm 2\sqrt{10}}{6} \qquad \sqrt{40} = \sqrt{4}\sqrt{10} = 2\sqrt{10}$$

Now to simplify, one method is to factor 2 out of the numerator and reduce.

$$x = \frac{8 \pm 2\sqrt{10}}{6} = \frac{2(4 \pm \sqrt{10})}{6} = \frac{2(4 \pm \sqrt{10})}{\overset{6}{\underset{3}{}}} = \frac{4 \pm \sqrt{10}}{3}$$

Another method for simplifying the answer is to write the result as two separate fractions and reduce each fraction.

$$x = \frac{8 \pm 2\sqrt{10}}{6} = \frac{8}{6} \pm \frac{2\sqrt{10}}{6} = \frac{4}{3} \pm \frac{\sqrt{10}}{3} = \frac{4 \pm \sqrt{10}}{3}$$

Be very careful when simplifying your result because that is a common source of incorrect answers. ∎

Concept Quiz 6.4

For Problems 1–10, answer true or false.

1. The quadratic formula can be used to solve any quadratic equation.

2. The number $\sqrt{b^2 - 4ac}$ is called the discriminant of the quadratic equation.

3. Every quadratic equation will have two solutions.

4. The quadratic formula cannot be used if the quadratic equation can be solved by factoring.

5. To use the quadratic formula for solving the equation $3x^2 + 2x - 5 = 0$, you must first divide both sides of the equation by 3.

6. The equation $9x^2 + 30x + 25 = 0$ has one real solution with a multiplicity of 2.

7. The equation $2x^2 + 3x + 4 = 0$ has two nonreal complex solutions.

8. The equation $x^2 + 9 = 0$ has two real solutions.

9. Because the quadratic formula has a denominator, it could be simplified and written as
$$x = -b \pm \frac{\sqrt{b^2 - 4ac}}{2a}.$$

10. Rachel reduced the result $x = \dfrac{6 \pm 5\sqrt{7}}{2}$ to obtain $x = 3 \pm \dfrac{5\sqrt{7}}{2}$. Her result is correct.

Problem Set 6.4

For Problems 1–10, simplify and reduce each expression.

1. $\dfrac{2 \pm \sqrt{20}}{4}$

2. $\dfrac{4 \pm \sqrt{20}}{6}$

3. $\dfrac{-6 \pm \sqrt{27}}{3}$

4. $\dfrac{-9 \pm \sqrt{54}}{3}$

5. $\dfrac{6 \pm \sqrt{18}}{9}$

6. $\dfrac{12 \pm \sqrt{32}}{8}$

7. $\dfrac{-10 \pm \sqrt{75}}{10}$

8. $\dfrac{-4 \pm \sqrt{8}}{4}$

9. $\dfrac{-6 \pm \sqrt{48}}{4}$

10. $\dfrac{-8 \pm \sqrt{72}}{4}$

For Problems 11–50, use the quadratic formula to solve each of the quadratic equations. (Objective 1)

11. $x^2 + 2x - 1 = 0$

12. $x^2 + 4x - 1 = 0$

13. $n^2 + 5n - 3 = 0$

14. $n^2 + 3n - 2 = 0$

15. $a^2 - 8a = 4$

16. $a^2 - 6a = 2$

17. $n^2 + 5n + 8 = 0$

18. $2n^2 - 3n + 5 = 0$

19. $x^2 - 18x + 80 = 0$

20. $x^2 + 19x + 70 = 0$

21. $-y^2 = -9y + 5$

22. $-y^2 + 7y = 4$

23. $2x^2 + x - 4 = 0$

24. $2x^2 + 5x - 2 = 0$

25. $4x^2 + 2x + 1 = 0$

26. $3x^2 - 2x + 5 = 0$

27. $3a^2 - 8a + 2 = 0$

28. $2a^2 - 6a + 1 = 0$

29. $-2n^2 + 3n + 5 = 0$

30. $-3n^2 - 11n + 4 = 0$

31. $3x^2 + 19x + 20 = 0$

32. $2x^2 - 17x + 30 = 0$

33. $36n^2 - 60n + 25 = 0$

34. $9n^2 + 42n + 49 = 0$

35. $4x^2 - 2x = 3$

36. $6x^2 - 4x = 3$

37. $5x^2 - 13x = 0$

38. $7x^2 + 12x = 0$

39. $3x^2 = 5$

40. $4x^2 = 3$

41. $6t^2 + t - 3 = 0$

42. $2t^2 + 6t - 3 = 0$

43. $n^2 + 32n + 252 = 0$

44. $n^2 - 4n - 192 = 0$

45. $12x^2 - 73x + 110 = 0$

46. $6x^2 + 11x - 255 = 0$

47. $-2x^2 + 4x - 3 = 0$

48. $-2x^2 + 6x - 5 = 0$

49. $-6x^2 + 2x + 1 = 0$

50. $-2x^2 + 4x + 1 = 0$

For each quadratic equation in Problems 51–60, first use the discriminant to determine whether the equation has two nonreal complex solutions, one real solution with a multiplicity of two, or two real solutions. Then solve the equation. (Objective 2)

51. $x^2 + 4x - 21 = 0$ **52.** $x^2 - 3x - 54 = 0$

53. $9x^2 - 6x + 1 = 0$ **54.** $4x^2 + 20x + 25 = 0$

55. $x^2 - 7x + 13 = 0$ **56.** $2x^2 - x + 5 = 0$

57. $15x^2 + 17x - 4 = 0$ **58.** $8x^2 + 18x - 5 = 0$

59. $3x^2 + 4x = 2$ **60.** $2x^2 - 6x = -1$

Thoughts Into Words

61. Your friend states that the equation $-2x^2 + 4x - 1 = 0$ must be changed to $2x^2 - 4x + 1 = 0$ (by multiplying both sides by -1) before the quadratic formula can be applied. Is she right about this? If not, how would you convince her she is wrong?

62. Another of your friends claims that the quadratic formula can be used to solve the equation $x^2 - 9 = 0$. How would you react to this claim?

63. Why must we change the equation $3x^2 - 2x = 4$ to $3x^2 - 2x - 4 = 0$ before applying the quadratic formula?

Further Investigations

The solution set for $x^2 - 4x - 37 = 0$ is $\{2 \pm \sqrt{41}\}$. With a calculator, we found a rational approximation, to the nearest one-thousandth, for each of these solutions.

$$2 - \sqrt{41} = -4.403 \quad \text{and} \quad 2 + \sqrt{41} = 8.403$$

Thus the solution set is $\{-4.403, 8.403\}$, with the answers rounded to the nearest one-thousandth.

Solve each of the equations in Problems 64–73, expressing solutions to the nearest one-thousandth.

64. $x^2 - 6x - 10 = 0$ **65.** $x^2 - 16x - 24 = 0$

66. $x^2 + 6x - 44 = 0$ **67.** $x^2 + 10x - 46 = 0$

68. $x^2 + 8x + 2 = 0$ **69.** $x^2 + 9x + 3 = 0$

70. $4x^2 - 6x + 1 = 0$ **71.** $5x^2 - 9x + 1 = 0$

72. $2x^2 - 11x - 5 = 0$ **73.** $3x^2 - 12x - 10 = 0$

For Problems 74–76, use the discriminant to help solve each problem.

74. Determine k so that the solutions of $x^2 - 2x + k = 0$ are complex but nonreal.

75. Determine k so that $4x^2 - kx + 1 = 0$ has two equal real solutions.

76. Determine k so that $3x^2 - kx - 2 = 0$ has real solutions.

Answers to the Concept Quiz

1. True   **2.** False   **3.** True   **4.** False   **5.** False   **6.** True   **7.** True   **8.** False   **9.** False   **10.** True

6.5   More Quadratic Equations and Applications

OBJECTIVES   **1** Solve quadratic equations selecting the most appropriate method

2 Solve word problems involving quadratic equations

Which method should be used to solve a particular quadratic equation? There is no hard and fast answer to that question; it depends on the type of equation and on your personal preference. In the following examples we will state reasons for choosing a specific technique. However, keep in mind that usually this is a decision you must make as the need arises. That's why you need to be familiar with the strengths and weaknesses of each method.

Classroom Example
Solve $3x^2 - x - 5 = 0$.

EXAMPLE 1   Solve $2x^2 - 3x - 1 = 0$.

Solution

Because of the leading coefficient of 2 and the constant term of -1, there are very few factoring possibilities to consider. Therefore, with such problems, first try the factoring approach. Unfortunately, this particular polynomial is not factorable using integers. Let's use the quadratic formula to solve the equation.

$$x = \frac{-b \pm \sqrt{b^2 - 4ac}}{2a}$$

$$x = \frac{-(-3) \pm \sqrt{(-3)^2 - 4(2)(-1)}}{2(2)}$$

$$x = \frac{3 \pm \sqrt{9 + 8}}{4}$$

$$x = \frac{3 \pm \sqrt{17}}{4}$$

The solution set is $\left\{ \dfrac{3 \pm \sqrt{17}}{4} \right\}$. ■

Classroom Example
Solve $\dfrac{2}{x} + \dfrac{6}{x + 3} = 1$.

EXAMPLE 2   Solve $\dfrac{3}{n} + \dfrac{10}{n + 6} = 1$.

Solution

$$\frac{3}{n} + \frac{10}{n + 6} = 1, \qquad n \neq 0 \text{ and } n \neq -6$$

$$n(n + 6)\left(\frac{3}{n} + \frac{10}{n + 6} \right) = 1(n)(n + 6) \qquad \text{Multiply both sides by } n(n + 6), \text{ which is the LCD}$$

$$3(n + 6) + 10n = n(n + 6)$$

$$3n + 18 + 10n = n^2 + 6n$$

$$13n + 18 = n^2 + 6n$$

$$0 = n^2 - 7n - 18$$

This equation is an easy one to consider for possible factoring, and it factors as follows:

$$0 = (n - 9)(n + 2)$$

$$n - 9 = 0 \qquad \text{or} \qquad n + 2 = 0$$

$$n = 9 \qquad \text{or} \qquad n = -2$$

The solution set is $\{-2, 9\}$. ■

We should make a comment about Example 2. Note the indication of the initial restrictions $n \neq 0$ and $n \neq -6$. Remember that we need to do this when solving fractional equations.

Classroom Example
Solve $m^2 + 20m + 96 = 0$.

EXAMPLE 3   Solve $x^2 + 22x + 112 = 0$.

Solution

The size of the constant term makes the factoring approach a little cumbersome for this problem. Furthermore, because the leading coefficient is 1 and the coefficient of the x term is even, the method of completing the square will work effectively.

$$x^2 + 22x + 112 = 0$$
$$x^2 + 22x = -112$$
$$x^2 + 22x + 121 = -112 + 121$$
$$(x + 11)^2 = 9$$
$$x + 11 = \pm\sqrt{9}$$
$$x + 11 = \pm 3$$
$$x + 11 = 3 \quad \text{or} \quad x + 11 = -3$$
$$x = -8 \quad \text{or} \quad x = -14$$

The solution set is $\{-14, -8\}$.

Classroom Example
Solve $x^4 + 2x^2 - 360 = 0$.

EXAMPLE 4　　Solve $x^4 - 4x^2 - 96 = 0$.

Solution

An equation such as $x^4 - 4x^2 - 96 = 0$ is not a quadratic equation, but we can solve it using the techniques that we use on quadratic equations. That is, we can factor the polynomial and apply the property "$ab = 0$ if and only if $a = 0$ or $b = 0$" as follows:

$$x^4 - 4x^2 - 96 = 0$$
$$(x^2 - 12)(x^2 + 8) = 0$$
$$x^2 - 12 = 0 \quad \text{or} \quad x^2 + 8 = 0$$
$$x^2 = 12 \quad \text{or} \quad x^2 = -8$$
$$x = \pm\sqrt{12} \quad \text{or} \quad x = \pm\sqrt{-8}$$
$$x = \pm 2\sqrt{3} \quad \text{or} \quad x = \pm 2i\sqrt{2}$$

The solution set is $\left\{\pm 2\sqrt{3}, \pm 2i\sqrt{2}\right\}$.

Remark: Another approach to Example 4 would be to substitute y for x^2 and y^2 for x^4. The equation $x^4 - 4x^2 - 96 = 0$ becomes the quadratic equation $y^2 - 4y - 96 = 0$. Thus we say that $x^4 - 4x^2 - 96 = 0$ is of *quadratic form*. Then we could solve the quadratic equation $y^2 - 4y - 96 = 0$ and use the equation $y = x^2$ to determine the solutions for x.

Solving Word Problems Involving Quadratic Equations

Before we conclude this section with some word problems that can be solved using quadratic equations, let's restate the suggestions we made in an earlier chapter for solving word problems.

Suggestions for Solving Word Problems

1. Read the problem carefully, and make certain that you understand the meanings of all the words. Be especially alert for any technical terms used in the statement of the problem.

2. Read the problem a second time (perhaps even a third time) to get an overview of the situation being described and to determine the known facts, as well as what is to be found.

3. Sketch any figure, diagram, or chart that might be helpful in analyzing the problem.

4. Choose a meaningful variable to represent an unknown quantity in the problem (perhaps l, if the length of a rectangle is an unknown quantity), and represent any other unknowns in terms of that variable.

5. Look for a guideline that you can use to set up an equation. A guideline might be a formula such as $A = lw$ or a relationship such as "the fractional part of a job done by Bill plus the fractional part of the job done by Mary equals the total job."

6. Form an equation that contains the variable and that translates the conditions of the guideline from English to algebra.

7. Solve the equation and use the solutions to determine all facts requested in the problem.

8. **Check all answers back into the original statement of the problem.**

Keep these suggestions in mind as we now consider some word problems.

Classroom Example
A margin of 1 inch surrounds the front of a card, which leaves 39 square inches for graphics. If the height of the card is three times the width, what are the dimensions of the card?

EXAMPLE 5

A page for a magazine contains 70 square inches of type. The height of a page is twice the width. If the margin around the type is to be 2 inches uniformly, what are the dimensions of a page?

Solution

Let x represent the width of a page. Then $2x$ represents the height of a page. Now let's draw and label a model of a page (Figure 6.8).

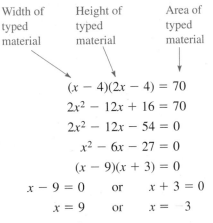

Width of typed material   Height of typed material   Area of typed material

$$(x - 4)(2x - 4) = 70$$
$$2x^2 - 12x + 16 = 70$$
$$2x^2 - 12x - 54 = 0$$
$$x^2 - 6x - 27 = 0$$
$$(x - 9)(x + 3) = 0$$
$$x - 9 = 0 \quad \text{or} \quad x + 3 = 0$$
$$x = 9 \quad \text{or} \quad x = -3$$

Disregard the negative solution; the page must be 9 inches wide, and its height is $2(9) = 18$ inches.

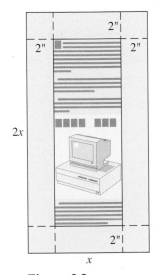

Figure 6.8

Let's use our knowledge of quadratic equations to analyze some applications of the business world. For example, if P dollars is invested at r rate of interest compounded annually for t years, then the amount of money, A, accumulated at the end of t years is given by the formula

$$A = P(1 + r)^t$$

This compound interest formula serves as a guideline for the next problem.

Classroom Example
Suppose that $2500 is invested at a certain rate of interest compounded annually for 2 years. If the accumulated value at the end of 2 years is $2704, find the rate of interest.

EXAMPLE 6

Suppose that $2000 is invested at a certain rate of interest compounded annually for 2 years. If the accumulated value at the end of 2 years is $2205, find the rate of interest.

Solution

Let r represent the rate of interest. Substitute the known values into the compound interest formula to yield

$$A = P(1 + r)^t$$
$$2205 = 2000(1 + r)^2$$

Solving this equation, we obtain

$$\frac{2205}{2000} = (1 + r)^2$$

$$1.1025 = (1 + r)^2$$

$$\pm\sqrt{1.1025} = 1 + r$$

$$\pm 1.05 = 1 + r$$

$$1 + r = 1.05 \qquad \text{or} \qquad 1 + r = -1.05$$

$$r = -1 + 1.05 \qquad \text{or} \qquad r = -1 - 1.05$$

$$r = 0.05 \qquad \text{or} \qquad r = -2.05$$

We must disregard the negative solution, so that $r = 0.05$ is the only solution. Change 0.05 to a percent, and the rate of interest is 5%.

Classroom Example
After hiking 9 miles of a 10-mile hike, Sam hurt his foot. For the remainder of the hike, his rate was two miles per hour slower than before he hurt his foot. The entire hike took $2\frac{3}{4}$ hours. How fast did he hike before hurting his foot?

EXAMPLE 7

On a 130-mile trip from Orlando to Sarasota, Roberto encountered a heavy thunderstorm for the last 40 miles of the trip. During the thunderstorm he drove an average of 20 miles per hour slower than before the storm. The entire trip took $2\frac{1}{2}$ hours. How fast did he drive before the storm?

Solution

Let x represent Roberto's rate before the thunderstorm. Then $x - 20$ represents his speed during the thunderstorm. Because $t = \dfrac{d}{r}$, then $\dfrac{90}{x}$ represents the time traveling before the storm, and $\dfrac{40}{x - 20}$ represents the time traveling during the storm. The following guideline sums up the situation.

Time traveling before the storm	+	Time traveling after the storm	=	Total time
↓		↓		↓
$\dfrac{90}{x}$	$+$	$\dfrac{40}{x - 20}$	$=$	$\dfrac{5}{2}$

Solving this equation, we obtain

$$2x(x - 20)\left(\frac{90}{x} + \frac{40}{x - 20}\right) = 2x(x - 20)\left(\frac{5}{2}\right)$$

$$2x(x - 20)\left(\frac{90}{x}\right) + 2x(x - 20)\left(\frac{40}{x - 20}\right) = 2x(x - 20)\left(\frac{5}{2}\right)$$

$$180(x - 20) + 2x(40) = 5x(x - 20)$$

$$180x - 3600 + 80x = 5x^2 - 100x$$

$$0 = 5x^2 - 360x + 3600$$

$$0 = 5(x^2 - 72x + 720)$$

$$0 = 5(x - 60)(x - 12)$$

$$x - 60 = 0 \qquad \text{or} \qquad x - 12 = 0$$

$$x = 60 \qquad \text{or} \qquad x = 12$$

We discard the solution of 12 because it would be impossible to drive 20 miles per hour slower than 12 miles per hour; thus Roberto's rate before the thunderstorm was 60 miles per hour.

Classroom Example
James bought a shipment of monitors for $6000. When he had sold all but 10 monitors at a profit of $100 per monitor, he had regained the entire cost of the shipment. How many monitors were sold and at what price per monitor?

EXAMPLE 8

A computer installer agreed to do an installation for $150. It took him 2 hours longer than he expected, and therefore he earned $2.50 per hour less than he anticipated. How long did he expect the installation would take?

Solution

Let x represent the number of hours he expected the installation to take. Then $x + 2$ represents the number of hours the installation actually took. The rate of pay is represented by the pay divided by the number of hours. The following guideline is used to write the equation.

Anticipated rate of pay	−	$2.50	=	Actual rate of pay
$\dfrac{150}{x}$	−	$\dfrac{5}{2}$	=	$\dfrac{150}{x + 2}$

Solving this equation, we obtain

$$2x(x + 2)\left(\frac{150}{x} - \frac{5}{2}\right) = 2x(x + 2)\left(\frac{150}{x + 2}\right)$$
$$2(x + 2)(150) - x(x + 2)(5) = 2x(150)$$
$$300(x + 2) - 5x(x + 2) = 300x$$
$$300x + 600 - 5x^2 - 10x = 300x$$
$$-5x^2 - 10x + 600 = 0$$
$$-5(x^2 + 2x - 120) = 0$$
$$-5(x + 12)(x - 10) = 0$$
$$x = -12 \quad \text{or} \quad x = 10$$

Disregard the negative answer. Therefore he anticipated that the installation would take 10 hours. ∎

This next problem set contains a large variety of word problems. Not only are there some business applications similar to those we discussed in this section, but there are also more problems of the types we discussed in Chapters 3 and 4. Try to give them your best shot without referring to the examples in earlier chapters.

Concept Quiz 6.5

For Problems 1–5, choose the method that you think is most appropriate for solving the given equation.

1. $2x^2 + 6x - 3 = 0$
2. $(x + 1)^2 = 36$
3. $x^2 - 3x + 2 = 0$
4. $x^2 + 6x = 19$
5. $4x^2 + 2x - 5 = 0$

A. Factoring
B. Square-root property (Property 6.1)
C. Completing the square
D. Quadratic formula

Problem Set 6.5

For Problems 1–20, solve each quadratic equation using the method that seems most appropriate to you. **(Objective 1)**

1. $x^2 - 4x - 6 = 0$
2. $x^2 - 8x - 4 = 0$
3. $3x^2 + 23x - 36 = 0$
4. $n^2 + 22n + 105 = 0$
5. $x^2 - 18x = 9$
6. $x^2 + 20x = 25$
7. $2x^2 - 3x + 4 = 0$
8. $3y^2 - 2y + 1 = 0$
9. $135 + 24n + n^2 = 0$
10. $28 - x - 2x^2 = 0$

11. $(x - 2)(x + 9) = -10$
12. $(x + 3)(2x + 1) = -3$

13. $2x^2 - 4x + 7 = 0$
14. $3x^2 - 2x + 8 = 0$

15. $x^2 - 18x + 15 = 0$
16. $x^2 - 16x + 14 = 0$

17. $20y^2 + 17y - 10 = 0$
18. $12x^2 + 23x - 9 = 0$

19. $4t^2 + 4t - 1 = 0$
20. $5t^2 + 5t - 1 = 0$

For Problems 21–40, solve each equation. **(Objective 1)**

21. $n + \dfrac{3}{n} = \dfrac{19}{4}$
22. $n - \dfrac{2}{n} = -\dfrac{7}{3}$

23. $\dfrac{3}{x} + \dfrac{7}{x - 1} = 1$
24. $\dfrac{2}{x} + \dfrac{5}{x + 2} = 1$

25. $\dfrac{12}{x - 3} + \dfrac{8}{x} = 14$
26. $\dfrac{16}{x + 5} - \dfrac{12}{x} = -2$

27. $\dfrac{3}{x - 1} - \dfrac{2}{x} = \dfrac{5}{2}$
28. $\dfrac{4}{x + 1} + \dfrac{2}{x} = \dfrac{5}{3}$

29. $\dfrac{6}{x} + \dfrac{40}{x + 5} = 7$
30. $\dfrac{12}{t} + \dfrac{18}{t + 8} = \dfrac{9}{2}$

31. $\dfrac{5}{n - 3} - \dfrac{3}{n + 3} = 1$
32. $\dfrac{3}{t + 2} + \dfrac{4}{t - 2} = 2$

33. $x^4 - 18x^2 + 72 = 0$
34. $x^4 - 21x^2 + 54 = 0$

35. $3x^4 - 35x^2 + 72 = 0$
36. $5x^4 - 32x^2 + 48 = 0$

37. $3x^4 + 17x^2 + 20 = 0$
38. $4x^4 + 11x^2 - 45 = 0$

39. $6x^4 - 29x^2 + 28 = 0$
40. $6x^4 - 31x^2 + 18 = 0$

For Problems 41–68, set up an equation and solve each problem. **(Objective 2)**

41. Find two consecutive whole numbers such that the sum of their squares is 145.

42. Find two consecutive odd whole numbers such that the sum of their squares is 74.

43. Two positive integers differ by 3, and their product is 108. Find the numbers.

44. Suppose that the sum of two numbers is 20, and the sum of their squares is 232. Find the numbers.

45. Find two numbers such that their sum is 10 and their product is 22.

46. Find two numbers such that their sum is 6 and their product is 7.

47. Suppose that the sum of two whole numbers is 9, and the sum of their reciprocals is $\dfrac{1}{2}$. Find the numbers.

48. The difference between two whole numbers is 8, and the difference between their reciprocals is $\dfrac{1}{6}$. Find the two numbers.

49. The sum of the lengths of the two legs of a right triangle is 21 inches. If the length of the hypotenuse is 15 inches, find the length of each leg.

50. The length of a rectangular floor is 1 meter less than twice its width. If a diagonal of the rectangle is 17 meters, find the length and width of the floor.

51. A rectangular plot of ground measuring 12 meters by 20 meters is surrounded by a sidewalk of a uniform width (see Figure 6.9). The area of the sidewalk is 68 square meters. Find the width of the walk.

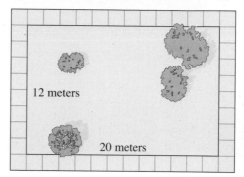

Figure 6.9

52. A 5-inch by 7-inch picture is surrounded by a frame of uniform width. The area of the picture and frame together is 80 square inches. Find the width of the frame.

53. The perimeter of a rectangle is 44 inches, and its area is 112 square inches. Find the length and width of the rectangle.

54. A rectangular piece of cardboard is 2 units longer than it is wide. From each of its corners a square piece 2 units on a side is cut out. The flaps are then turned up to form an open box that has a volume of 70 cubic units. Find the length and width of the original piece of cardboard.

55. Charlotte's time to travel 250 miles is 1 hour more than Lorraine's time to travel 180 miles. Charlotte drove 5 miles per hour faster than Lorraine. How fast did each one travel?

56. Larry's time to travel 156 miles is 1 hour more than Terrell's time to travel 108 miles. Terrell drove 2 miles per hour faster than Larry. How fast did each one travel?

57. On a 570-mile trip, Andy averaged 5 miles per hour faster for the last 240 miles than he did for the first 330 miles. The entire trip took 10 hours. How fast did he travel for the first 330 miles?

58. On a 135-mile bicycle excursion, Maria averaged 5 miles per hour faster for the first 60 miles than she did for the last 75 miles. The entire trip took 8 hours. Find her rate for the first 60 miles.

59. It takes Terry 2 hours longer to do a certain job than it takes Tom. They worked together for 3 hours; then Tom left and Terry finished the job in 1 hour. How long would it take each of them to do the job alone?

60. Suppose that Arlene can mow the entire lawn in 40 minutes less time with the power mower than she can with the push mower. One day the power mower broke down after she had been mowing for 30 minutes. She finished the lawn with the push mower in 20 minutes. How long does it take Arlene to mow the entire lawn with the power mower?

61. A student did a word processing job for $24. It took him 1 hour longer than he expected, and therefore he earned $4 per hour less than he anticipated. How long did he expect that it would take to do the job?

62. A group of students agreed that each would chip in the same amount to pay for a party that would cost $100. Then they found 5 more students interested in the party and in sharing the expenses. This decreased the amount each had to pay by $1. How many students were involved in the party and how much did each student have to pay?

63. A group of students agreed that each would contribute the same amount to buy their favorite teacher an $80 birthday gift. At the last minute, 2 of the students decided not to chip in. This increased the amount that the remaining students had to pay by $2 per student. How many students actually contributed to the gift?

64. The formula $D = \dfrac{n(n-3)}{2}$ yields the number of diagonals, D, in a polygon of n sides. Find the number of sides of a polygon that has 54 diagonals.

65. The formula $S = \dfrac{n(n+1)}{2}$ yields the sum, S, of the first n natural numbers $1, 2, 3, 4, \ldots$. How many consecutive natural numbers starting with 1 will give a sum of 1275?

66. At a point 16 yards from the base of a tower, the distance to the top of the tower is 4 yards more than the height of the tower (see Figure 6.10). Find the height of the tower.

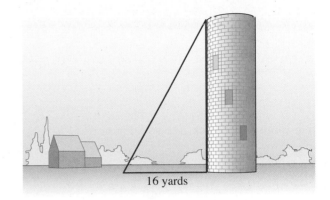

16 yards

Figure 6.10

67. Suppose that $500 is invested at a certain rate of interest compounded annually for 2 years. If the accumulated value at the end of 2 years is $594.05, find the rate of interest.

68. Suppose that $10,000 is invested at a certain rate of interest compounded annually for 2 years. If the accumulated value at the end of 2 years is $12,544, find the rate of interest.

Thoughts Into Words

69. How would you solve the equation $x^2 - 4x = 252$? Explain your choice of the method that you would use.

70. Explain how you would solve $(x-2)(x-7) = 0$ and also how you would solve $(x-2)(x-7) = 4$.

71. One of our problem-solving suggestions is to look for a guideline that can be used to help determine an equation. What does this suggestion mean to you?

72. Can a quadratic equation with integral coefficients have exactly one nonreal complex solution? Explain your answer.

Further Investigations

For Problems 73–79, solve each equation.

73. $x - 9\sqrt{x} + 18 = 0$ [*Hint:* Let $y = \sqrt{x}$.]

74. $x - 4\sqrt{x} + 3 = 0$

75. $x + \sqrt{x} - 2 = 0$

76. $x^{\frac{2}{3}} + x^{\frac{1}{3}} - 6 = 0$ [*Hint:* Let $y = x^{\frac{1}{3}}$.]

77. $6x^{\frac{2}{3}} - 5x^{\frac{1}{3}} - 6 = 0$ **78.** $x^{-2} + 4x^{-1} - 12 = 0$

79. $12x^{-2} - 17x^{-1} - 5 = 0$

The following equations are also quadratic in form. To solve, begin by raising each side of the equation to the appropriate power so that the exponent will become an integer. Then, to solve the resulting quadratic equation, you may use the square-root property, factoring, or the quadratic formula—whichever is most appropriate. Be aware that raising each side of the equation to a power may introduce extraneous roots; therefore, be sure to check your solutions. Study the following example before you begin the problems.

Solve

$$(x + 3)^{\frac{2}{3}} = 1$$

$$[(x + 3)^{\frac{2}{3}}]^3 = 1^3 \qquad \text{Raise both sides to the third power}$$

$$(x + 3)^2 = 1$$

$$x^2 + 6x + 9 = 1$$

$$x^2 + 6x + 8 = 0$$

$$(x + 4)(x + 2) = 0$$

$$x + 4 = 0 \qquad \text{or} \qquad x + 2 = 0$$

$$x = -4 \qquad \text{or} \qquad x = -2$$

Both solutions do check. The solution set is $\{-4, -2\}$.

For problems 80–88, solve each equation.

80. $(5x + 6)^{\frac{1}{2}} = x$

81. $(3x + 4)^{\frac{1}{2}} = x$

82. $x^{\frac{2}{3}} = 2$

83. $x^{\frac{2}{5}} = 2$

84. $(2x + 6)^{\frac{1}{2}} = x$

85. $(2x - 4)^{\frac{2}{3}} = 1$

86. $(4x + 5)^{\frac{2}{3}} = 2$

87. $(6x + 7)^{\frac{1}{2}} = x + 2$

88. $(5x + 21)^{\frac{1}{2}} = x + 3$

Answers to the Concept Quiz

Answers for Problems 1–5 may vary. **1.** D   **2.** B   **3.** A   **4.** C   **5.** D

6.6   Quadratic and Other Nonlinear Inequalities

OBJECTIVES   **1** Solve quadratic inequalities

2 Solve inequalities of quotients

We refer to the equation $ax^2 + bx + c = 0$ as the standard form of a quadratic equation in one variable. Similarly, the following forms express **quadratic inequalities** in one variable.

$$ax^2 + bx + c > 0 \qquad\qquad ax^2 + bx + c < 0$$

$$ax^2 + bx + c \geq 0 \qquad\qquad ax^2 + bx + c \leq 0$$

We can use the number line very effectively to help solve quadratic inequalities for which the quadratic polynomial is factorable. Let's consider some examples to illustrate the procedure.

Classroom Example
Solve and graph the solutions for $x^2 + 4x - 21 \geq 0$.

EXAMPLE 1   Solve and graph the solutions for $x^2 + 2x - 8 > 0$.

Solution

First, let's factor the polynomial:

$$x^2 + 2x - 8 > 0$$

$$(x + 4)(x - 2) > 0$$

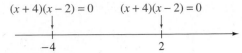

Figure 6.11

On a number line (Figure 6.11), we indicate that at $x = 2$ and $x = -4$, the product $(x + 4) \cdot (x - 2)$ equals zero. The numbers -4 and 2 divide the number line into three intervals: (1) the numbers less than -4, (2) the numbers between -4 and 2, and (3) the numbers greater than 2. We can choose a *test number* from each of these intervals and see how it affects the signs of the factors $x + 4$ and $x - 2$ and, consequently, the sign of the product of these factors. For example, if $x < -4$ (try $x = -5$), then $x + 4$ is negative and $x - 2$ is negative, so their product is positive. If $-4 < x < 2$ (try $x = 0$), then $x + 4$ is positive and $x - 2$ is negative, so their product is negative. If $x > 2$ (try $x = 3$), then $x + 4$ is positive and $x - 2$ is positive, so their product is positive. This information can be conveniently arranged using a number line, as shown in Figure 6.12. Note the open circles at -4 and 2 to indicate that they are not included in the solution set.

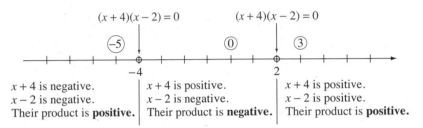

Figure 6.12

Thus the given inequality, $x^2 + 2x - 8 > 0$, is satisfied by numbers less than -4 along with numbers greater than 2. Using interval notation, the solution set is $(-\infty, -4) \cup (2, \infty)$. These solutions can be shown on a number line (Figure 6.13).

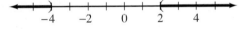

Figure 6.13

We refer to numbers such as -4 and 2 in the preceding example (where the given polynomial or algebraic expression equals zero or is undefined) as **critical numbers**. Let's consider some additional examples that make use of critical numbers and test numbers.

Classroom Example
Solve and graph the solutions for
$x^2 + 3x - 10 < 0$.

EXAMPLE 2   Solve and graph the solutions for $x^2 + 2x - 3 \leq 0$.

Solution

First, factor the polynomial:

$$x^2 + 2x - 3 \leq 0$$
$$(x + 3)(x - 1) \leq 0$$

Second, locate the values for which $(x + 3)(x - 1)$ equals zero. We put dots at -3 and 1 to remind ourselves that these two numbers are to be included in the solution set because the given statement includes equality. Now let's choose a test number from each of the three intervals, and record the sign behavior of the factors $(x + 3)$ and $(x - 1)$ (Figure 6.14).

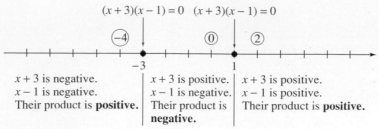

Figure 6.14

Therefore, the solution set is $[-3, 1]$, and it can be graphed as in Figure 6.15.

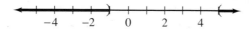

Figure 6.15

Solving Inequalities of Quotients

Examples 1 and 2 have indicated a systematic approach for solving quadratic inequalities when the polynomial is factorable. This same type of number line analysis can also be used to solve indicated quotients such as $\dfrac{x + 1}{x - 5} > 0$.

Classroom Example
Solve and graph the solutions for $\dfrac{x - 2}{x + 6} \geq 0$.

EXAMPLE 3   Solve and graph the solutions for $\dfrac{x + 1}{x - 5} > 0$.

Solution

First, indicate that at $x = -1$ the given quotient equals zero, and at $x = 5$ the quotient is undefined. Second, choose test numbers from each of the three intervals, and record the sign behavior of $(x + 1)$ and $(x - 5)$ as in Figure 6.16.

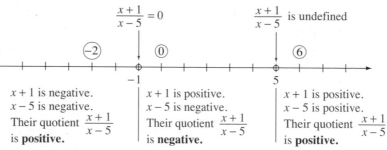

Figure 6.16

Therefore, the solution set is $(-\infty, -1) \cup (5, \infty)$, and its graph is shown in Figure 6.17.

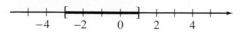

Figure 6.17

Classroom Example
Solve $\dfrac{m + 1}{m + 3} \leq 0$.

EXAMPLE 4   Solve $\dfrac{x + 2}{x + 4} \leq 0$.

Solution

The indicated quotient equals zero at $x = -2$ and is undefined at $x = -4$. (Note that -2 is to be included in the solution set, but -4 is not to be included.) Now let's choose some test numbers and record the sign behavior of $(x + 2)$ and $(x + 4)$ as in Figure 6.18.

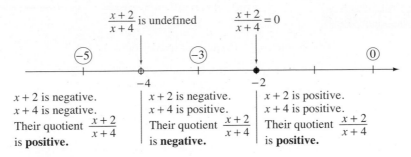

Figure 6.18

Therefore, the solution set is $(-4, -2]$.

The final example illustrates that sometimes we need to change the form of the given inequality before we use the number line analysis.

EXAMPLE 5   Solve $\dfrac{x}{x + 2} \geq 3.$

Solution

First, let's change the form of the given inequality as follows:

$$\frac{x}{x + 2} \geq 3$$

$$\frac{x}{x + 2} - 3 \geq 0 \qquad \text{Add } -3 \text{ to both sides}$$

$$\frac{x - 3(x + 2)}{x + 2} \geq 0 \qquad \text{Express the left side over a common denominator}$$

$$\frac{x - 3x - 6}{x + 2} \geq 0$$

$$\frac{-2x - 6}{x + 2} \geq 0$$

Now we can proceed as we did with the previous examples. If $x = -3$, then $\dfrac{-2x - 6}{x + 2}$ equals zero; and if $x = -2$, then $\dfrac{-2x - 6}{x + 2}$ is undefined. Then, choosing test numbers, we can record the sign behavior of $(-2x - 6)$ and $(x + 2)$ as in Figure 6.19.

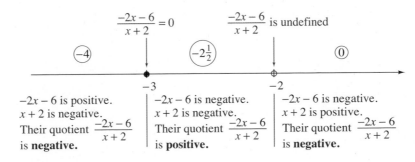

Figure 6.19

Therefore, the solution set is $[-3, -2)$. Perhaps you should check a few numbers from this solution set back into the original inequality!

Concept Quiz 6.6

For Problems 1–10, answer true or false.

1. When solving the inequality $(x + 3)(x - 2) > 0$, we are looking for values of x that make the product of $(x + 3)$ and $(x - 2)$ a positive number.
2. The solution set of the inequality $x^2 + 4 > 0$ is all real numbers.
3. The solution set of the inequality $x^2 \leq 0$ is the null set.
4. The critical numbers for the inequality $(x + 4)(x - 1) \leq 0$ are -4 and -1.
5. The number 2 is included in the solution set of the inequality $\dfrac{x + 4}{x - 2} \geq 0$.
6. The solution set of $(x - 2)^2 \geq 0$ is the set of all real numbers.
7. The solution set of $\dfrac{x + 2}{x - 3} \leq 0$ is $(-2, 3)$.
8. The solution set of $\dfrac{x - 1}{x} > 2$ is $(-1, 0)$.
9. The solution set of the inequality $(x - 2)^2(x + 1)^2 < 0$ is $\varnothing$.
10. The solution set of the inequality $(x - 4)(x + 3)^2 \leq 0$ is $(-\infty, 4]$.

Problem Set 6.6

For Problems 1–12, solve each inequality and graph its solution set on a number line. **(Objective 1)**

1. $(x + 2)(x - 1) > 0$
2. $(x - 2)(x + 3) > 0$
3. $(x + 1)(x + 4) < 0$
4. $(x - 3)(x - 1) < 0$
5. $(2x - 1)(3x + 7) \geq 0$
6. $(3x + 2)(2x - 3) \geq 0$
7. $(x + 2)(4x - 3) \leq 0$
8. $(x - 1)(2x - 7) \leq 0$
9. $(x + 1)(x - 1)(x - 3) > 0$
10. $(x + 2)(x + 1)(x - 2) > 0$
11. $x(x + 2)(x - 4) \leq 0$
12. $x(x + 3)(x - 3) \leq 0$

For Problems 13–38, solve each inequality. **(Objective 1)**

13. $x^2 + 2x - 35 < 0$
14. $x^2 + 3x - 54 < 0$
15. $x^2 - 11x + 28 > 0$
16. $x^2 + 11x + 18 > 0$
17. $3x^2 + 13x - 10 \leq 0$
18. $4x^2 - x - 14 \leq 0$
19. $8x^2 + 22x + 5 \geq 0$
20. $12x^2 - 20x + 3 \geq 0$
21. $x(5x - 36) > 32$
22. $x(7x + 40) < 12$
23. $x^2 - 14x + 49 \geq 0$
24. $(x + 9)^2 \geq 0$
25. $4x^2 + 20x + 25 \leq 0$
26. $9x^2 - 6x + 1 \leq 0$
27. $(x + 1)(x - 3)^2 > 0$
28. $(x - 4)^2(x - 1) \leq 0$
29. $4 - x^2 < 0$
30. $2x^2 - 18 \geq 0$
31. $4(x^2 - 36) < 0$
32. $-4(x^2 - 36) \geq 0$
33. $5x^2 + 20 > 0$
34. $-3x^2 - 27 \geq 0$
35. $x^2 - 2x \geq 0$
36. $2x^2 + 6x < 0$
37. $3x^3 + 12x^2 > 0$
38. $2x^3 + 4x^2 \leq 0$

For Problems 39–56, solve each inequality. **(Objective 2)**

39. $\dfrac{x + 1}{x - 2} > 0$
40. $\dfrac{x - 1}{x + 2} > 0$
41. $\dfrac{x - 3}{x + 2} < 0$
42. $\dfrac{x + 2}{x - 4} < 0$
43. $\dfrac{2x - 1}{x} \geq 0$
44. $\dfrac{x}{3x + 7} \geq 0$
45. $\dfrac{-x + 2}{x - 1} \leq 0$
46. $\dfrac{3 - x}{x + 4} \leq 0$
47. $\dfrac{2x}{x + 3} > 4$
48. $\dfrac{x}{x - 1} > 2$
49. $\dfrac{x - 1}{x - 5} \leq 2$
50. $\dfrac{x + 2}{x + 4} \leq 3$
51. $\dfrac{x + 2}{x - 3} > -2$
52. $\dfrac{x - 1}{x - 2} < -1$
53. $\dfrac{3x + 2}{x + 4} \leq 2$
54. $\dfrac{2x - 1}{x + 2} \geq -1$
55. $\dfrac{x + 1}{x - 2} < 1$
56. $\dfrac{x + 3}{x - 4} \geq 1$

Thoughts Into Words

57. Explain how to solve the inequality $(x + 1)(x - 2) \cdot (x - 3) > 0$.

58. Explain how to solve the inequality $(x - 2)^2 > 0$ by inspection.

59. Your friend looks at the inequality $1 + \dfrac{1}{x} > 2$ and, without any computation, states that the solution set is all real numbers between 0 and 1. How can she do that?

60. Why is the solution set for $(x - 2)^2 \geq 0$ the set of all real numbers?

61. Why is the solution set for $(x - 2)^2 \leq 0$ the set $\{2\}$?

Further Investigations

62. The product $(x - 2)(x + 3)$ is positive if both factors are negative *or* if both factors are positive. Therefore, we can solve $(x - 2)(x + 3) > 0$ as follows:

$(x - 2 < 0 \text{ and } x + 3 < 0)$ or $(x - 2 > 0 \text{ and } x + 3 > 0)$

$(x < 2 \text{ and } x < -3)$ or $(x > 2 \text{ and } x > -3)$

$x < -3$ or $x > 2$

The solution set is $(-\infty, -3) \cup (2, \infty)$. Use this type of analysis to solve each of the following.

(a) $(x - 2)(x + 7) > 0$

(b) $(x - 3)(x + 9) \geq 0$

(c) $(x + 1)(x - 6) \leq 0$

(d) $(x + 4)(x - 8) < 0$

(e) $\dfrac{x + 4}{x - 7} > 0$

(f) $\dfrac{x - 5}{x + 8} \leq 0$

Chapter 6 Summary

OBJECTIVE	SUMMARY	EXAMPLE
Know the set of complex numbers. (Section 6.1/ Objective 1)	A number of the form $a + bi$, where a and b are real numbers and i is the imaginary unit defined by $i = \sqrt{-1}$, is a complex number. Two complex numbers are said to be equal if and only if $a = c$ and $b = d$.	
Add and subtract complex numbers. (Section 6.1/ Objective 2)	We describe the addition and subtraction of complex numbers as follows: $(a + bi) + (c + di) = (a + c) + (b + d)i$ and $(a + bi) - (c + di) = (a - c) + (b - d)i$	Add the complex numbers: $(3 - 6i) + (-7 - 3i)$. **Solution** $(3 - 6i) + (-7 - 3i)$ $= (3 - 7) + (-6 - 3)i$ $= -4 - 9i$
Simplify radicals involving negative numbers. (Section 6.1/Objective 3)	We can represent a square root of any negative real number as the product of a real number and the imaginary unit i, That is, $\sqrt{-b} = i\sqrt{b}$, where b is a positive real number.	Write $\sqrt{-48}$ in terms of i and simplify. **Solution** $\sqrt{-48} = \sqrt{-1}\sqrt{48}$ $= i\sqrt{16}\sqrt{3}$ $= 4i\sqrt{3}$
Perform operations on radicals involving negative numbers. (Section 6.1/Objective 4)	Before performing any operations, represent the square root of any negative real number as the product of a real number and the imaginary unit i.	Perform the indicated operation and simplify: $\dfrac{\sqrt{-28}}{\sqrt{-4}}$ **Solution** $\dfrac{\sqrt{-28}}{\sqrt{-4}} = \dfrac{i\sqrt{28}}{i\sqrt{4}} = \dfrac{\sqrt{28}}{\sqrt{4}} = \sqrt{\dfrac{28}{4}} = \sqrt{7}$
Multiply complex numbers. (Section 6.1/Objective 5)	The product of two complex numbers follows the same pattern as the product of two binomials. The conjugate of $a + bi$ is $a - bi$. The product of a complex number and its conjugate is a real number. When simplifying, replace any i^2 with -1.	Find the product $(2 + 3i)(4 - 5i)$ and express the answer in standard form of a complex number. **Solution** $(2 + 3i)(4 - 5i) = 8 + 2i - 15i^2$ $= 8 + 2i - 15(-1)$ $= 23 + 2i$
Divide complex numbers. (Section 6.1/Objective 6)	To simplify expressions that indicate the quotient of complex numbers, such as $\dfrac{4 + 3i}{5 - 2i}$, multiply the numerator and denominator by the conjugate of the denominator.	Find the quotient $\dfrac{2 + 3i}{4 - i}$ and express the answer in standard form of a complex number. **Solution** Multiply the numerator and denominator by $4 + i$, the conjugate of the denominator. $\dfrac{2 + 3i}{4 - i} = \dfrac{(2 + 3i)}{(4 - i)} \cdot \dfrac{(4 + i)}{(4 + i)}$ $= \dfrac{8 + 14i + 3i^2}{16 - i^2}$ $= \dfrac{8 + 14i + 3(-1)}{16 - (-1)}$ $= \dfrac{5 + 14i}{17} = \dfrac{5}{17} + \dfrac{14}{17}i$

OBJECTIVE	SUMMARY	EXAMPLE
Solve quadratic equations by factoring. (Section 6.2/Objective 1)	The standard form for a quadratic equation in one variable is $ax^2 + bx + c = 0$, where a, b, and c are real numbers and $a \neq 0$. Some quadratic equations can be solved by factoring and applying the property, $ab = 0$ if and only if $a = 0$ or $b = 0$.	Solve $2x^2 + x - 3 = 0$. **Solution** $$2x^2 + x - 3 = 0$$ $$(2x + 3)(x - 1) = 0$$ $2x + 3 = 0 \quad$ or $\quad x - 1 = 0$ $$x = -\frac{3}{2} \quad \text{or} \quad x = 1$$ The solution set is $\left\{ -\dfrac{3}{2}, 1 \right\}$.
Solve quadratic equations of the form $x^2 - a$. (Section 6.2/Objective 2)	We can solve some quadratic equations by applying the property, $x^2 = a$ if and only if $x = \pm\sqrt{a}$.	Solve $3(x + 7)^2 = 24$. **Solution** $3(x + 7)^2 = 24$ First divide both sides of the equation by 3: $$(x + 7)^2 = 8$$ $$x + 7 = \pm\sqrt{8}$$ $$x + 7 = \pm 2\sqrt{2}$$ $$x = -7 \pm 2\sqrt{2}$$ The solution set is $\{-7 \pm 2\sqrt{2}\}$.
Solve quadratic equations by completing the square. (Section 6.3/Objective 1)	To solve a quadratic equation by completing the square, first put the equation in the form $x^2 + bx = k$. Then (1) take one-half of b, square that result, and add to each side of the equation; (2) factor the left side; and (3) apply the property, $x^2 = a$ if and only if $x = \pm\sqrt{a}$.	Solve $x^2 + 12x - 2 = 0$. **Solution** $$x^2 + 12x - 2 = 0$$ $$x^2 + 12x = 2$$ $$x^2 + 12x + 36 = 2 + 36$$ $$(x + 6)^2 = 38$$ $$x + 6 = \pm\sqrt{38}$$ $$x = -6 \pm \sqrt{38}$$ The solution set is $\{-6 \pm \sqrt{38}\}$.
Use the quadratic formula to solve quadratic equations. (Section 6.4/Objective 1)	Any quadratic equation of the form $ax^2 + bx + c = 0$, where $a \neq 0$, can be solved by the quadratic formula, which is usually stated as $$x = \frac{-b \pm \sqrt{b^2 - 4ac}}{2a}$$	Solve $3x^2 - 5x - 6 = 0$. **Solution** $3x^2 - 5x - 6 = 0$ $a = 3$, $b = -5$, and $c = -6$ $$x = \frac{-(-5) \pm \sqrt{(-5)^2 - 4(3)(-6)}}{2(3)}$$ $$x = \frac{5 \pm \sqrt{97}}{6}$$ The solution set is $\left\{ \dfrac{5 \pm \sqrt{97}}{6} \right\}$.

(continued)

OBJECTIVE	SUMMARY	EXAMPLE
Determine the nature of roots to quadratic equations. (Section 6.4/Objective 2)	The discriminant, $b^2 - 4ac$, can be used to determine the nature of the roots of a quadratic equation. **1.** If $b^2 - 4ac$ is less than zero, then the equation has two nonreal complex solutions. **2.** If $b^2 - 4ac$ is equal to zero, then the equation has two equal real solutions. **3.** If $b^2 - 4ac$ is greater than zero, then the equation has two unequal real solutions.	Use the discriminant to determine the nature of the solutions for the equation $2x^2 + 3x + 5 = 0$. **Solution** $2x^2 + 3x + 5 = 0$ For $a = 2$, $b = 3$, and $c = 5$, $b^2 - 4ac = (3)^2 - 4(2)(5) = -31$. Because the discriminant is less than zero, the equation has two nonreal complex solutions.
Solve quadratic equations by selecting the most appropriate method. (Section 6.5/Objective 1)	There are three major methods for solving a quadratic equation. **1.** Factoring **2.** Completing the square **3.** Quadratic formula Consider which method is most appropriate before you begin solving the equation.	Solve $x^2 - 4x + 9 = 0$. **Solution** This equation does not factor. This equation can easily be solved by completing the square, because $a = 1$ and b is an even number. $$x^2 - 4x + 9 = 0$$ $$x^2 - 4x = -9$$ $$x^2 - 4x + 4 = -9 + 4$$ $$(x + 4)^2 = -5$$ $$x + 4 = \pm\sqrt{-5}$$ $$x = -4 \pm i\sqrt{5}$$ The solution set is $\{-4 \pm i\sqrt{5}\}$.
Solve problems pertaining to right triangles and $30°-60°$ triangles. (Section 6.2/Objective 3)	There are two special kinds of right triangles that are used in later mathematics courses. The **isosceles right triangle** is a right triangle that has both legs of the same length. In a **$30°-60°$ right triangle**, the side opposite the $30°$ angle is equal in length to one-half the length of the hypotenuse.	Find the length of each leg of an isosceles right triangle that has a hypotenuse of length 6 inches. **Solution** Let x represent the length of each leg: $$x^2 + x^2 = 6^2$$ $$2x^2 = 36$$ $$x^2 = 18$$ $$x = \pm\sqrt{18} = \pm 3\sqrt{2}$$ Disregard the negative solution. The length of each leg is $3\sqrt{2}$ inches.
Solve word problems involving quadratic equations. (Section 6.5/Objective 2)	Keep the following suggestions in mind as you solve word problems. **1.** Read the problem carefully. **2.** Sketch any figure, diagram, or chart that might help you organize and analyze the problem. **3.** Choose a meaningful variable. **4.** Look for a guideline that can be used to set up an equation.	Find two consecutive odd whole numbers such that the sum of their squares is 290. **Solution** Let x represent the first whole number. Then $x + 2$ would represent the next consecutive odd whole number. $$x^2 + (x + 2)^2 = 290$$ $$x^2 + x^2 + 4x + 4 = 290$$ $$2x^2 + 4x - 286 = 0$$

OBJECTIVE	SUMMARY	EXAMPLE
	5. Form an equation that translates the guideline from English into algebra. **6.** Solve the equation and answer the question posed in the problem. **7.** Check all answers back into the original statement of the problem.	$$2(x^2 + 2x - 143) = 0$$ $$2(x + 13)(x - 11) = 0$$ $$x = -13 \quad \text{or} \quad x = 11$$ Disregard the solution of -13 because it is not a whole number. The whole numbers are 11 and 13.
Solve quadratic inequalities. (Section 6.6/Objective 1)	To solve quadratic inequalities that are factorable polynomials, the critical numbers are found by factoring the polynomial. The critical numbers partition the number line into regions. A test point from each region is used to determine if the values in that region make the inequality a true statement. The answer is usually expressed in interval notation.	Solve $x^2 + x - 6 \le 0$. **Solution** Solve the equation $x^2 + x - 6 = 0$ to find the critical numbers. $$x^2 + x - 6 = 0$$ $$(x + 3)(x - 2) = 0$$ $$x = -3 \quad \text{or} \quad x = 2$$ The critical numbers are -3 and 2. Choose a test point from each of the intervals $(-\infty, -3)$, $(-3, 2)$, and $(2, \infty)$. Evaluating the inequality $x^2 + x - 6 \le 0$ for each of the test points shows that $(-3, 2)$ is the only interval of values that makes the inequality a true statement. Because the inequality includes the endpoints of the interval, the solution is $[-3, 2]$.
Solve inequalities of quotients. (Section 6.6/Objective 2)	To solve inequalities involving quotients, use the same basic approach as for solving quadratic equations. Be careful to avoid any values that make the denominator zero.	Solve $\dfrac{x + 1}{2x - 3} \ge 0$. **Solution** Set the numerator equal to zero and then set the denominator equal to zero to find the critical numbers. $$x + 1 = 0 \quad \text{and} \quad 2x - 3 = 0$$ $$x = -1 \quad \text{and} \quad x = \frac{3}{2}$$ The critical numbers are -1 and $\frac{3}{2}$. Evaluate the inequality with a test point from each of the intervals $(-\infty, -1)$, $\left(-1, \frac{3}{2}\right)$, and $\left(\frac{3}{2}, \infty\right)$; this shows that the values in the intervals $(-\infty, -1)$ and $\left(\frac{3}{2}, \infty\right)$ make the inequality a true statement. Because the inequality includes the "equal to" statement, the solution should include -1 but not $\frac{3}{2}$, because $\frac{3}{2}$ would make the quotient undefined. The solution set is $(-\infty, -1] \cup \left(\frac{3}{2}, \infty\right)$.

Chapter 6   Review Problem Set

For Problems 1–4, perform the indicated operations and express the answers in the standard form of a complex number.

1. $(-7 + 3i) + (9 - 5i)$ **2.** $(4 - 10i) - (7 - 9i)$

3. $(6 - 3i) - (-2 + 5i)$ **4.** $(-4 + i) - (2 + 3i)$

For Problems 5–8, write each expression in terms of i and simplify.

5. $\sqrt{-8}$ **6.** $\sqrt{-25}$

7. $3\sqrt{-16}$ **8.** $2\sqrt{-18}$

For Problems 9–18, perform the indicated operation and simplify.

9. $\sqrt{-2}\sqrt{-6}$ **10.** $\sqrt{-2}\sqrt{18}$

11. $\dfrac{\sqrt{-42}}{\sqrt{-6}}$ **12.** $\dfrac{\sqrt{-6}}{\sqrt{2}}$

13. $5i(3 - 6i)$ **14.** $(5 - 7i)(6 + 8i)$

15. $(-2 - 3i)(4 - 8i)$ **16.** $(4 - 3i)(4 + 3i)$

17. $\dfrac{4 + 3i}{6 - 2i}$ **18.** $\dfrac{-1 - i}{-2 + 5i}$

For Problems 19 and 20, perform the indicated operations and express the answer in the standard form of a complex number.

19. $\dfrac{3 + 4i}{2i}$ **20.** $\dfrac{-6 + 5i}{-i}$

For Problems 21–24, solve each of the quadratic equations by factoring.

21. $x^2 + 8x = 0$ **22.** $x^2 = 6x$

23. $x^2 - 3x - 28 = 0$ **24.** $2x^2 + x - 3 = 0$

For Problems 25–28, use Property 6.1 to help solve each quadratic equation.

25. $2x^2 = 90$ **26.** $(y - 3)^2 = -18$

27. $(2x + 3)^2 = 24$ **28.** $a^2 - 27 = 0$

For Problems 29–32, use the method of completing the square to solve the quadratic equation.

29. $y^2 + 18y - 10 = 0$ **30.** $n^2 + 6n + 20 = 0$

31. $x^2 - 10x + 1 = 0$ **32.** $x^2 + 5x - 2 = 0$

For Problems 33–36, use the quadratic formula to solve the equation.

33. $x^2 + 6x + 4 = 0$ **34.** $x^2 + 4x + 6 = 0$

35. $3x^2 - 2x + 4 = 0$ **36.** $5x^2 - x - 3 = 0$

For Problems 37–40, find the discriminant of each equation and determine whether the equation has (1) two nonreal complex solutions, (2) one real solution with a multiplicity of 2, or (3) two real solutions. Do not solve the equations.

37. $4x^2 - 20x + 25 = 0$ **38.** $5x^2 - 7x + 31 = 0$

39. $7x^2 - 2x - 14 = 0$ **40.** $5x^2 - 2x = 4$

For Problems 41–59, solve each equation.

41. $x^2 - 17x = 0$ **42.** $(x - 2)^2 = 36$

43. $(2x - 1)^2 = -64$ **44.** $x^2 - 4x - 21 = 0$

45. $x^2 + 2x - 9 = 0$ **46.** $x^2 - 6x = -34$

47. $4\sqrt{x} = x - 5$ **48.** $3n^2 + 10n - 8 = 0$

49. $n^2 - 10n = 200$ **50.** $3a^2 + a - 5 = 0$

51. $x^2 - x + 3 = 0$ **52.** $2x^2 - 5x + 6 = 0$

53. $2a^2 + 4a - 5 = 0$ **54.** $t(t + 5) = 36$

55. $x^2 + 4x + 9 = 0$ **56.** $(x - 4)(x - 2) = 80$

57. $\dfrac{3}{x} + \dfrac{2}{x + 3} = 1$ **58.** $2x^4 - 23x^2 + 56 = 0$

59. $\dfrac{3}{n - 2} = \dfrac{n + 5}{4}$

For Problems 60–70, set up an equation and solve each problem.

60. The wing of an airplane is in the shape of a $30°-60°$ right triangle. If the side opposite the $30°$ angle measures 20 feet, find the measure of the other two sides of the wing. Round the answers to the nearest tenth of a foot.

61. An agency is using photo surveillance of a rectangular plot of ground that measures 40 meters by 25 meters. If during the surveillance, someone is observed moving from one corner of the plot to the corner diagonally opposite, how far has the observed person moved? Round the answer to the nearest tenth of a meter.

62. One leg of an isosceles right triangle measures 4 inches. Find the length of the hypotenuse of the triangle. Express the answer in radical form.

63. Find two numbers whose sum is 6 and whose product is 2.

64. A landscaper agreed to design and plant a flower bed for $40. It took him three hours less than he anticipated, and therefore he earned $3 per hour more than he anticipated. How long did he expect it would take to design and plant the flower bed?

65. Andre traveled 270 miles in 1 hour more than it took Sandy to travel 260 miles. Sandy drove 7 miles per hour faster than Andre. How fast did each one travel?

66. The area of a square is numerically equal to twice its perimeter. Find the length of a side of the square.

67. Find two consecutive even whole numbers such that the sum of their squares is 164.

68. The perimeter of a rectangle is 38 inches, and its area is 84 square inches. Find the length and width of the rectangle.

69. It takes Billy 2 hours longer to do a certain job than it takes Reena. They worked together for 2 hours; then Reena left, and Billy finished the job in 1 hour. How long would it take each of them to do the job alone?

70. A company has a rectangular parking lot 40 meters wide and 60 meters long. The company plans to increase the area of the lot by 1100 square meters by adding a strip of equal width to one side and one end. Find the width of the strip to be added.

For Problems 71–78, solve each inequality and express the solution set using interval notation.

71. $x^2 + 3x - 10 > 0$

72. $2x^2 + x - 21 \leq 0$

73. $4x^2 - 1 \leq 0$

74. $x^2 - 7x + 10 > 0$

75. $\dfrac{x - 4}{x + 6} \geq 0$

76. $\dfrac{2x - 1}{x + 1} > 4$

77. $\dfrac{3x + 1}{x - 4} < 2$

78. $\dfrac{3x + 1}{x - 1} \leq 0$

1. Find the product $(3 - 4i)(5 + 6i)$, and express the result in the standard form of a complex number.

2. Find the quotient $\dfrac{2 - 3i}{3 + 4i}$, and express the result in the standard form of a complex number.

For Problems 3–15, solve each equation.

3. $x^2 = 7x$

4. $(x - 3)^2 = 16$

5. $x^2 + 3x - 18 = 0$

6. $x^2 - 2x - 1 = 0$

7. $5x^2 - 2x + 1 = 0$

8. $x^2 + 30x = -224$

9. $(3x - 1)^2 + 36 = 0$

10. $(5x - 6)(4x + 7) = 0$

11. $(2x + 1)(3x - 2) = 55$

12. $n(3n - 2) = 40$

13. $x^4 + 12x^2 - 64 = 0$

14. $\dfrac{3}{x} + \dfrac{2}{x + 1} = 4$

15. $3x^2 - 2x - 3 = 0$

16. Does the equation $4x^2 + 20x + 25 = 0$ have (a) two nonreal complex solutions, (b) two equal real solutions, or (c) two unequal real solutions?

17. Does the equation $4x^2 - 3x = -5$ have (a) two nonreal complex solutions, (b) two equal real solutions, or (c) two unequal real solutions?

For Problems 18–20, solve each inequality and express the solution set using interval notation.

18. $x^2 - 3x - 54 \le 0$

19. $\dfrac{3x - 1}{x + 2} > 0$

20. $\dfrac{x - 2}{x + 6} \ge 3$

For Problems 21–25, set up an equation and solve each problem.

21. A 24-foot ladder leans against a building and makes an angle of 60° with the ground. How far up on the building does the top of the ladder reach? Express your answer to the nearest tenth of a foot.

22. A rectangular plot of ground measures 16 meters by 24 meters. Find, to the nearest meter, the distance from one corner of the plot to the diagonally opposite corner.

23. Amy agreed to clean her brother's room for $36. It took her 1 hour longer than she expected, and therefore she earned $3 per hour less than she anticipated. How long did she expect it would take to clean the room?

24. The perimeter of a rectangle is 41 inches, and its area is 91 square inches. Find the length of its shortest side.

25. The sum of two numbers is 6 and their product is 4. Find the larger of the two numbers.

For Problems 1–6, evaluate each of the numerical expressions.

1. $\left(\dfrac{3}{2}\right)^{-3}$

2. $16^{-\frac{1}{2}}$

3. $\dfrac{2^{-5}}{2^{-6}}$

4. $\sqrt[3]{\dfrac{1}{8}}$

5. $\dfrac{1}{\left(\dfrac{1}{3}\right)^{-2}}$

6. $(4^{-3} \cdot 4)^{-1}$

For Problems 7–14, evaluate each algebraic expression for the given values of the variable.

7. $\dfrac{1}{2x} + \dfrac{2}{3x} + \dfrac{3}{x}$ for $x = 5$

8. $\dfrac{3m^2n}{11mn^2}$ for $m = 2$ and $n = -1$

9. $(2a + 3b) - 2(6a - 7b)$ for $a = -4$ and $b = -2$

10. $4x^2 - y^2$ for $x = \dfrac{1}{2}$ and $y = -2$

11. $(3x + 2y)^2$ for $x = -3$ and $y = \dfrac{1}{2}$

12. $\dfrac{x^2 + 2y^3}{5x + y}$ for $x = 3$ and $y = -1$

13. $\dfrac{1}{3}n + \dfrac{1}{2}n - \dfrac{1}{5}n$ for $n = \dfrac{2}{3}$

14. $3x^2y$ for $x = 1.2$ and $y = 0.2$

For Problems 15–26, perform the indicated operations and express the answers in simplified form.

15. $(3ab^2)(-a^3b^3)(4a^2b)$

16. $\left(-\dfrac{4}{3}c^3d^2\right)\left(-\dfrac{1}{4}cd\right)$

17. $(-3mn^3)^4$

18. $(a - 2)(3a^2 - a + 7)$

19. $-\dfrac{25t^2k^3}{5tk}$

20. $(3x + y)(4x - 5y)$

21. $(7m - 6n)^2$

22. $\dfrac{9a^2b}{4ab} \cdot \dfrac{6a^3b^2}{27ab}$

23. $\dfrac{2x^3 + 2x^2 - 24x}{2x^2 + 19x + 35} \div \dfrac{4x^3 + 4x^2 - 48x}{2x^2 - x - 15}$

24. $\dfrac{11x - 3}{2} - \dfrac{6x + 5}{3}$

25. $(3x^3 - 7x^2 + x - 6) \div (x - 2)$

26. $2 - \dfrac{x}{4x - 1}$

27. Simplify the complex fraction.

$$\dfrac{\dfrac{3}{4x} + \dfrac{7}{9}}{\dfrac{1}{12} - \dfrac{5}{3x}}$$

For Problems 28–35, factor completely.

28. $2ax - 2ay + 3cx - 3cy$

29. $81m^2 - 9n^2$

30. $2x^2 - 13x - 7$

31. $12y^2 + 28y - 5$

32. $6t^2 + 34t - 56$

33. $c^2 - y^6$

34. $8h^2 - 14h - 15$

35. $a^3 + 8b^3$

For Problems 36–58, solve each equation.

36. $-7(a + 4) - 3(2a - 9) = 5(3a + 11)$

37. $-8(a + 5) = -2(4a - 3)$

38. $\dfrac{t}{5} + \dfrac{t}{3} - \dfrac{t}{30} = 1$

39. $\dfrac{4}{5}(a - 2) + \dfrac{1}{2}(a + 3) = 4$

40. $0.035(2000 - x) + 0.04x = 77.50$

41. $A = P + Prt$ for t

42. $\sqrt{3x - 4} = 4$

43. $\sqrt[3]{10x - 3} = 3$

44. $4c^2 = \dfrac{4}{3}$

45. $\sqrt{x + 3} + 5 = \sqrt{x + 48}$

46. $\dfrac{1}{2}(3x - 5)^2 - 25 = 25$

47. $3\sqrt{x} = x - 10$

48. $(4x - 3)^2 - 5 = 20$

49. $6x^2 + 7x - 20 = 0$

50. $(2x + 1)(x - 3) = 9$

51. $P = 2l + 2w$ for w

52. $|9x - 2| = 0$

53. $|4x + 7| - 3 = 12$

54. $\dfrac{2x - 5}{12} + \dfrac{3x + 1}{4} = \dfrac{x - 4}{6}$

55. $\dfrac{4}{9x + 2} = \dfrac{7}{3x - 1}$

56. $\dfrac{a + 4}{4} = \dfrac{3}{a}$

57. $\dfrac{x}{x - 4} - \dfrac{1}{x + 5} = \dfrac{1}{x^2 + x - 20}$

58. $\dfrac{n}{n - 5} - \dfrac{5}{2n + 9} = \dfrac{25}{2n^2 - n - 45}$

For Problems 59–70, solve each inequality and express the solution set using interval notation.

59. $-5x > 10 - x$

60. $3(4x - 5) \geq 4(1 - 2x)$

61. $9x - 2 < 3(3x + 10)$

62. $\dfrac{2x + 7}{12} - \dfrac{3x - 8}{8} \leq \dfrac{1}{3}$

63. $0.04x + 0.055(x + 10{,}000) \geq 645$

64. $|3x - 4| < 8$

65. $\left|5x + \dfrac{2}{3}\right| < -4$

66. $\dfrac{1}{3}a - \dfrac{3}{8}a > \dfrac{1}{6}$

67. $2x^2 + x - 15 \geq 0$

68. $\dfrac{3x}{x - 5} < 2$

69. $3x + 7 > 10$ or $4x + 1 \leq -19$

70. $-3 \leq 5x + 7 \leq 27$

For Problems 71–80, solve by setting up and solving an appropriate equation or inequality.

71. Greg leaves Moose Lodge at 1:00 P.M. on snow shoes traveling east at 2.5 miles per hour. His wife, Tricia, leaves the lodge at the same time on cross country skis traveling west at 5 miles per hour. At what time will they be 10 miles apart?

72. Sean has $1000 he wants to invest at 4% interest. How much should he invest at 5% annual interest so that both the investments earn at least $120 in total annual interest?

73. The measure of the smallest angle of a triangle is half the measure of the middle angle. The measure of the largest angle is 5° more than twice the measure of the middle angle. Find the measures of the angles of the triangle.

74. Weed-no-More Landscape Company was hired to clean a lot for $100. The company took 2 hours longer than the estimate indicated, so they earned $2.50 per hour less than they thought. How many hours did the company estimate it would take to clean the lot?

75. A rectangular dog-agility field has a length of 110 feet and a width of 90 feet. The judge stands in one corner and the starting line is in the corner located diagonally across the field. Find the distance between the judge and the starting line to the nearest tenth of a foot.

76. Betty Ann invested $2500 at a certain rate of interest compounded annually. After 2 years, the accumulated value is $2704. Find the annual rate of interest.

77. Together Camden and Aidan can repair a van in 5 hours. If Aidan can complete the job himself in $8\dfrac{1}{3}$ hours, how long would it take Camden to fix the van by himself?

78. The deck of a house is in the shape of a right triangle. The longest side of the deck measures 17 feet. The sum of the measures of the two sides (legs) of the deck is 23 feet. Find the measure of each of the two sides of the deck.

79. It takes Samuel 2 hours longer to paddle his canoe 8 miles than it takes him to paddle his kayak 12 miles. His rate when paddling the kayak is $2\dfrac{2}{5}$ miles per hour greater than his rate when paddling the canoe. Find his rate when paddling each vessel.

80. The length of the side of a square is the same as the radius of a circle. The perimeter of the square is numerically equal to 4 times the area of the circle. Find the radius of the circle. Use 3.14 as the value for π. Round the answer to the nearest hundredth.

7

Linear Equations and Inequalities in Two Variables

7.1 Rectangular Coordinate System and Linear Equations

7.2 Linear Inequalities in Two Variables

7.3 Distance and Slope

7.4 Determining the Equation of a Line

7.5 Graphing Nonlinear Equations

René Descartes, a philosopher and mathematician, developed a system for locating a point on a plane. This system is our current rectangular coordinate grid used for graphing; it is named the Cartesian coordinate system.

© Mark Yuill

René Descartes, a French mathematician of the 17th century, was able to transform geometric problems into an algebraic setting so that he could use the tools of algebra to solve the problems. This connecting of algebraic and geometric ideas is the foundation of a branch of mathematics called *analytic geometry*, today more commonly called *coordinate geometry*. Basically, there are two kinds of problems in coordinate geometry: Given an algebraic equation, find its geometric graph; and given a set of conditions pertaining to a geometric graph, find its algebraic equation. We discuss problems of both types in this chapter.

Video tutorials based on section learning objectives are available in a variety of delivery modes.

| | 7.1 | Rectangular Coordinate System and Linear Equations |

OBJECTIVES

1 Find solutions for linear equations in two variables

2 Review the rectangular coordinate system

3 Graph the solutions for linear equations

4 Graph linear equations by finding the x and y intercepts

5 Graph lines passing through the origin, vertical lines, and horizontal lines

6 Apply graphing to linear relationships

7 Introduce graphing utilities

In this chapter we want to solve equations in two variables. Let's begin by considering the solutions for the equation $y = 3x + 2$. A **solution** of an equation in two variables is an ordered pair of real numbers that satisfies the equation. When using the variables x and y, we agree that the first number of an ordered pair is a value of x and the second number is a value of y. We see that $(1, 5)$ is a solution for $y = 3x + 2$, because if x is replaced by 1 and y by 5, the result is the true numerical statement $5 = 3(1) + 2$. Likewise, $(2, 8)$ is a solution because $8 = 3(2) + 2$ is a true numerical statement. We can find infinitely many pairs of real numbers that satisfy $y = 3x + 2$ by arbitrarily choosing values for x, and then, for each chosen value of x, determining a corresponding value for y. Let's use a table to record some of the solutions for $y = 3x + 2$.

x value	y value determined from $y = 3x + 2$	Ordered pair
-3	-7	$(-3, -7)$
-1	-1	$(-1, -1)$
0	2	$(0, 2)$
1	5	$(1, 5)$
2	8	$(2, 8)$
4	14	$(4, 14)$

Classroom Example
Determine some ordered-pair solutions for the equation $y = 3x - 4$.

EXAMPLE 1

Determine some ordered-pair solutions for the equation $y = 2x - 5$ and record the values in a table.

Solution

We can start by arbitrarily choosing values for x and then determine the corresponding y value. And even though you can arbitrarily choose values for x, it is good practice to choose some negative values, zero, and some positive values.

Let $x = -4$; then, according to our equation, $y = 2(-4) - 5 = -13$.

Let $x = -1$; then, according to our equation, $y = 2(-1) - 5 = -7$.

Let $x = 0$; then, according to our equation, $y = 2(0) - 5 = -5$.

Let $x = 2$; then, according to our equation, $y = 2(2) - 5 = -1$.

Let $x = 4$; then, according to our equation, $y = 2(4) - 5 = 3$.

Organizing this information in a chart gives the following table.

x value	y value determined from $y = 2x - 5$	Ordered pair
-4	-13	$(-4, -13)$
-1	-7	$(-1, -7)$
0	-5	$(0, -5)$
2	-1	$(2, -1)$
4	3	$(4, 3)$

A table can show an infinite number of solutions for a linear equation in two variables, but a graph can display visually the solutions plotted on a coordinate system. Let's review the rectangular coordinate system and then we can use a graph to display the solutions of an equation in two variables.

Review of the Rectangular Coordinate System

Consider two number lines, one vertical and one horizontal, perpendicular to each other at the point we associate with zero on both lines (Figure 7.1). We refer to these number lines as the **horizontal and vertical axes** or, together, as the **coordinate axes**. They partition the plane into four regions called **quadrants**. The quadrants are numbered with Roman numerals from I through IV counterclockwise as indicated in Figure 7.1. The point of intersection of the two axes is called the **origin**.

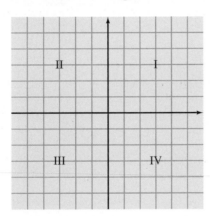

Figure 7.1

It is now possible to set up a one-to-one correspondence between **ordered pairs** of real numbers and the points in a plane. To each ordered pair of real numbers there corresponds a unique point in the plane, and to each point in the plane there corresponds a unique ordered pair of real numbers. A part of this correspondence is illustrated in Figure 7.2. The ordered

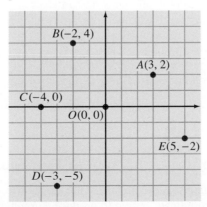

Figure 7.2

pair $(3, 2)$ denotes that the point A is located three units to the right of, and two units up from, the origin. (The ordered pair $(0, 0)$ is associated with the origin O.) The ordered pair $(-3, -5)$ denotes that the point D is located three units to the left and five units down from the origin.

Remark: The notation $(-2, 4)$ was used earlier in this text to indicate an interval of the real number line. Now we are using the same notation to indicate an ordered pair of real numbers. This double meaning should not be confusing because the context of the material will always indicate which meaning of the notation is being used. Throughout this chapter, we will be using the ordered-pair interpretation.

In general we refer to the real numbers a and b in an ordered pair (a, b) associated with a point as the **coordinates of the point**. The first number, a, called the **abscissa**, is the directed distance of the point from the vertical axis measured parallel to the horizontal axis. The second number, b, called the **ordinate**, is the directed distance of the point from the horizontal axis measured parallel to the vertical axis (Figure 7.3a). Thus in the first quadrant, all points have a positive abscissa and a positive ordinate. In the second quadrant, all points have a negative abscissa and a positive ordinate. We have indicated the sign situations for all four quadrants in Figure 7.3(b). This system of associating points in a plane with pairs of real numbers is called the **rectangular coordinate system** or the **Cartesian coordinate system**.

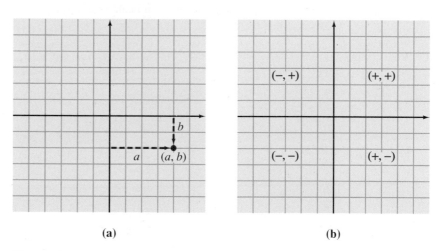

(a)   (b)

Figure 7.3

Historically, the rectangular coordinate system provided the basis for the development of the branch of mathematics called **analytic geometry**, or what we presently refer to as **coordinate geometry**. In this discipline, René Descartes, a French 17th-century mathematician, was able to transform geometric problems into an algebraic setting and then use the tools of algebra to solve the problems. Basically, there are two kinds of problems to solve in coordinate geometry:

1. Given an algebraic equation, find its geometric graph.

2. Given a set of conditions pertaining to a geometric figure, find its algebraic equation.

In this chapter we will discuss problems of both types. Let's begin by plotting the graph of an algebraic equation.

Graphing the Solutions for Linear Equations

Let's begin by determining some solutions for the equation $y = x + 2$ and then plot the solutions on a rectangular coordinate system to produce a graph of the equation. Let's use a table to record some of the solutions.

Choose x	Determine y from $y = x + 2$	Solutions for $y = x + 2$
0	2	(0, 2)
1	3	(1, 3)
3	5	(3, 5)
5	7	(5, 7)
-2	0	$(-2, 0)$
-4	-2	$(-4, -2)$
-6	-4	$(-6, -4)$

We can plot the ordered pairs as points in a coordinate plane and use the horizontal axis as the x axis and the vertical axis as the y axis, as in Figure 7.4(a). The straight line that contains the points in Figure 7.4(b) is called the **graph of the equation** $y = x + 2$. Every point on the line has coordinates that are solutions of the equation $y = x + 2$. The graph provides a visual display of the infinite solutions for the equation.

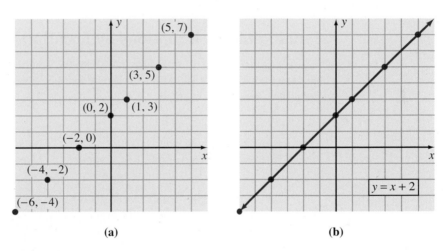

(a)   (b)

Figure 7.4

Classroom Example
Graph the equation $y = -3x + 2$.

EXAMPLE 2   Graph the equation $y = -x + 4$.

Solution

Let's begin by determining some solutions for the equation $y = -x + 4$ and then plot the solutions on a rectangular coordinate system to produce a graph of the equation.

Let's use a table to record some of the solutions.

x value	y value determined from $y = -x + 4$	Ordered pair
-3	7	$(-3, 7)$
-1	5	$(-1, 5)$
0	4	(0, 4)
2	2	(2, 2)
4	0	(4, 0)
6	-2	$(6, -2)$

We can plot the ordered pairs on a coordinate system as shown in Figure 7.5(a). The graph of the equation was created by drawing a straight line through the plotted points as in Figure 7.5(b).

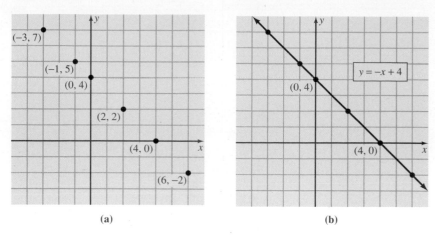

(a)   (b)

Figure 7.5

Graphing Linear Equations by Locating the *x* and *y* Intercepts

The points (4, 0) and (0, 4) in Figure 7.5(b) are the points of the graph that are on the coordinate axes. That is, they yield the *x* intercept and the *y* intercept of the graph. Let's define in general the *intercepts* of a graph.

> The *x* coordinates of the points that a graph has in common with the *x* axis are called the **x intercepts** of the graph. (To compute the *x* intercepts, let $y = 0$ and solve for *x*.)
>
> The *y* coordinates of the points that a graph has in common with the *y* axis are called the **y intercepts** of the graph. (To compute the *y* intercepts, let $x = 0$ and solve for *y*.)

It is advantageous to be able to recognize the kind of graph that a certain type of equation produces. For example, if we recognize that the graph of $3x + 2y = 12$ is a straight line, then it becomes a simple matter to find two points and sketch the line. Let's pursue the graphing of straight lines in a little more detail.

In general, any equation of the form $Ax + By = C$, where *A*, *B*, and *C* are constants (*A* and *B* not both zero) and *x* and *y* are variables, is a **linear equation**, and its graph is a straight line. Two points of clarification about this description of a linear equation should be made. First, the choice of *x* and *y* for variables is arbitrary. Any two letters could be used to represent the variables. For example, an equation such as $3r + 2s = 9$ can be considered a linear equation in two variables. So that we are not constantly changing the labeling of the coordinate axes when graphing equations, however, it is much easier to use the same two variables in all equations. Thus we will go along with convention and use *x* and *y* as variables. Second, the phrase "any equation of the form $Ax + By = C$" technically means "any equation of the form $Ax + By = C$ or equivalent to that form." For example, the equation $y = 2x - 1$ is equivalent to $-2x + y = -1$ and thus is linear and produces a straight-line graph.

The knowledge that any equation of the form $Ax + By = C$ produces a straight-line graph, along with the fact that two points determine a straight line, makes graphing linear equations a simple process. We merely find two solutions (such as the intercepts), plot the corresponding points, and connect the points with a straight line. It is wise to find a third point as a check point. Let's consider an example.

Classroom Example
Graph $2x - y = 4$.

EXAMPLE 3   Graph $3x - 2y = 12$.

Solution

First, let's find the intercepts. Let $x = 0$; then

$$3(0) - 2y = 12$$
$$-2y = 12$$
$$y = -6$$

Thus $(0, -6)$ is a solution. Let $y = 0$; then

$$3x - 2(0) = 12$$
$$3x = 12$$
$$x = 4$$

Thus $(4, 0)$ is a solution. Now let's find a third point to serve as a check point. Let $x = 2$; then

$$3(2) - 2y = 12$$
$$6 - 2y = 12$$
$$-2y = 6$$
$$y = -3$$

Thus $(2, -3)$ is a solution. Plot the points associated with these three solutions and connect them with a straight line to produce the graph of $3x - 2y = 12$ in Figure 7.6.

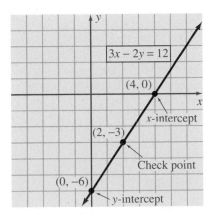

Figure 7.6

Let's review our approach to Example 3. Note that we did not solve the equation for y in terms of x or for x in terms of y. Because we know the graph is a straight line, there is no need for any extensive table of values; thus there is no need to change the form of the original equation. Furthermore, the solution $(2, -3)$ served as a check point. If it had not been on the line determined by the two intercepts, then we would have known that an error had been made.

Classroom Example
Graph $4x + 3y = 6$.

EXAMPLE 4   Graph $2x + 3y = 7$.

Solution

Without showing all of our work, the following table indicates the intercepts and a check point. The points from the table are plotted, and the graph of $2x + 3y = 7$ is shown in Figure 7.7.

x	y	
0	$\dfrac{7}{3}$	
$\dfrac{7}{2}$	0	Intercepts
2	1	Check point

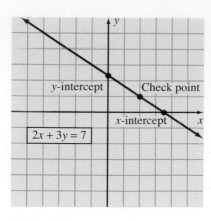

Figure 7.7

Graphing Lines That Pass through the Origin, Vertical Lines, and Horizontal Lines

It is helpful to recognize some *special* straight lines. For example, the graph of any equation of the form $Ax + By = C$, where $C = 0$ (the constant term is zero), is a straight line that contains the origin. Let's consider an example.

Classroom Example
Graph $y = -3x$.

EXAMPLE 5 Graph $y = 2x$.

Solution

Obviously $(0, 0)$ is a solution. (Also, notice that $y = 2x$ is equivalent to $-2x + y = 0$; thus it fits the condition $Ax + By = C$, where $C = 0$.) Because both the x intercept and the y intercept are determined by the point $(0, 0)$, another point is necessary to determine the line. Then a third point should be found as a check point. The graph of $y = 2x$ is shown in Figure 7.8.

x	y	
0	0	Intercepts
2	4	Additional point
−1	−2	Check point

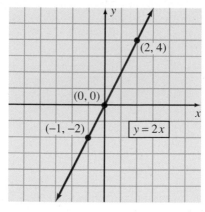

Figure 7.8

Classroom Example
Graph $x = -3$.

EXAMPLE 6 Graph $x = 2$.

Solution

Because we are considering linear equations in *two variables*, the equation $x = 2$ is equivalent to $x + 0(y) = 2$. Now we can see that any value of y can be used, but the x value must always be 2. Therefore, some of the solutions are $(2, 0)$, $(2, 1)$, $(2, 2)$, $(2, -1)$, and $(2, -2)$. The graph of all solutions of $x = 2$ is the vertical line in Figure 7.9.

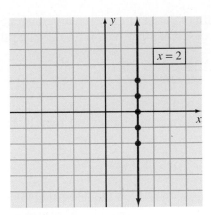

Figure 7.9

Classroom Example
Graph $y = 2$.

EXAMPLE 7   Graph $y = -3$.

Solution

The equation $y = -3$ is equivalent to $0(x) + y = -3$. Thus any value of x can be used, but the value of y must be -3. Some solutions are $(0, -3)$, $(1, -3)$, $(2, -3)$, $(-1, -3)$, and $(-2, -3)$. The graph of $y = -3$ is the horizontal line in Figure 7.10.

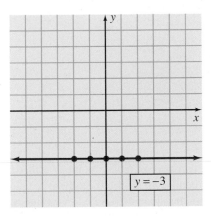

Figure 7.10

In general, the graph of any equation of the form $Ax + By = C$, where $A = 0$ or $B = 0$ (not both), is a line parallel to one of the axes. More specifically, any equation of the form $x = a$, where a is a constant, is a line parallel to the y axis that has an x intercept of a. Any equation of the form $y = b$, where b is a constant, is a line parallel to the x axis that has a y intercept of b.

Graphing Linear Relationships

There are numerous applications of linear relationships. For example, suppose that a retailer has a number of items that she wants to sell at a profit of 30% of the cost of each item. If we let s represent the selling price and c the cost of each item, then the equation

$$s = c + 0.3c = 1.3c$$

can be used to determine the selling price of each item based on the cost of the item. In other words, if the cost of an item is $4.50, then it should be sold for $s = (1.3)(4.5) = \$5.85$.

The equation $s = 1.3c$ can be used to determine the following table of values. Reading from the table, we see that if the cost of an item is $15, then it should be sold for $19.50

in order to yield a profit of 30% of the cost. Furthermore, because this is a linear relationship, we can obtain exact values between values given in the table.

c	1	5	10	15	20
s	1.3	6.5	13	19.5	26

For example, a c value of 12.5 is halfway between c values of 10 and 15, so the corresponding s value is halfway between the s values of 13 and 19.5. Therefore, a c value of 12.5 produces an s value of

$$s = 13 + \frac{1}{2}(19.5 - 13) = 16.25$$

Thus, if the cost of an item is $12.50, it should be sold for $16.25.

Now let's graph this linear relationship. We can label the horizontal axis c, label the vertical axis s, and use the origin along with one ordered pair from the table to produce the straight-line graph in Figure 7.11. (Because of the type of application, we use only nonnegative values for c and s.)

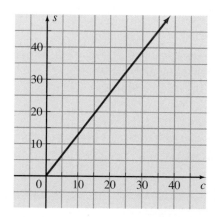

Figure 7.11

From the graph we can approximate s values on the basis of given c values. For example, if $c = 30$, then by reading up from 30 on the c axis to the line and then across to the s axis, we see that s is a little less than 40. (An exact s value of 39 is obtained by using the equation $s = 1.3c$.)

Many formulas that are used in various applications are linear equations in two variables. For example, the formula $C = \frac{5}{9}(F - 32)$, which is used to convert temperatures from the Fahrenheit scale to the Celsius scale, is a linear relationship. Using this equation, we can determine that $14°F$ is equivalent to $C = \frac{5}{9}(14 - 32) = \frac{5}{9}(-18) = -10°C$. Let's use the equation $C = \frac{5}{9}(F - 32)$ to complete the following table.

F	-22	-13	5	32	50	68	86
C	-30	-25	-15	0	10	20	30

Reading from the table, we see, for example, that $-13°F = -25°C$ and $68°F = 20°C$.

To graph the equation $C = \frac{5}{9}(F - 32)$ we can label the horizontal axis F, label the vertical axis C, and plot two ordered pairs (F, C) from the table. Figure 7.12 shows the graph of the equation.

From the graph we can approximate C values on the basis of given F values. For example, if F = 80°, then by reading up from 80 on the F axis to the line and then across to the C axis, we see that C is approximately 25°. Likewise, we can obtain approximate F values on the basis of given C values. For example, if C = −25°, then by reading across from −25 on the C axis to the line and then up to the F axis, we see that F is approximately −15°.

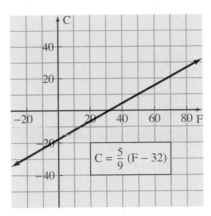

Figure 7.12

Graphing Utilities

The term **graphing utility** is used in current literature to refer to either a graphing calculator (see Figure 7.13) or a computer with a graphing software package. (We use the phrase *use a graphing calculator* to mean "use a graphing calculator or a computer with the appropriate software.")

These devices have a range of capabilities that enable the user not only to obtain a quick sketch of a graph but also to study various characteristics of it, such as the *x* intercepts, *y* intercepts, and turning points of a curve. We will introduce some of these features of graphing utilities as we need them in the text. Because there are so many different types of graphing utilities available, we will use generic terminology and let you consult your user's manual for specific key-punching instructions. We urge you to study the graphing utility examples in this text even if you do not have access to a graphing calculator or a computer. The examples were chosen to reinforce concepts under discussion.

Courtesy Texas Instruments

Figure 7.13

EXAMPLE 8

Use a graphing utility to obtain a graph of the line $2.1x + 5.3y = 7.9$.

Solution

First, let's solve the equation for y in terms of x.

$$2.1x + 5.3y = 7.9$$
$$5.3y = 7.9 - 2.1x$$
$$y = \frac{7.9 - 2.1x}{5.3}$$

Now we can enter the expression $\dfrac{7.9 - 2.1x}{5.3}$ for Y_1 and obtain the graph shown in Figure 7.14.

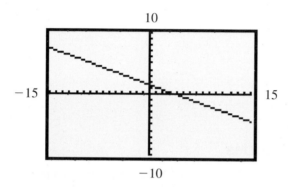

Figure 7.14

Concept Quiz 7.1

For Problems 1–10, answer true or false.

1. In a rectangular coordinate system, the coordinate axes partition the plane into four parts called quadrants.

2. Quadrants are named with Roman numerals and are numbered clockwise.

3. The real numbers in an ordered pair are referred to as the coordinates of the point.

4. If the abscissa of an ordered pair is negative, then the point is in either the third or fourth quadrant.

5. The equation $y = x + 3$ has an infinite number of ordered pairs that satisfy the equation.

6. The graph of $y = x^2$ is a straight line.

7. The y intercept of the graph of $3x + 4y = -4$ is -4.

8. The graph of $y = 4$ is a vertical line.

9. The graph of $x = 4$ has an x intercept of 4.

10. The graph of every linear equation has a y intercept.

Problem Set 7.1

For Problems 1–4, determine which of the ordered pairs are solutions to the given equation. (Objective 1)

1. $y = 3x - 2$ $(2, 4), (-1, -5), (0, 1)$

2. $y = 2x + 3$ $(2, 5), (1, 5), (-1, 1)$

3. $2x + y = 6$ $(-2, 10), (-1, 5), (3, 0)$

4. $-3x + 2y = 2$ $\left(3, \dfrac{11}{2}\right), (-2, -2)\left(-1, -\dfrac{1}{2}\right)$

For Problems 5–8, complete the table of values for the equation and graph the equation. (Objective 3)

5. $y = -x + 3$

x	−2	−1	0	4
y				

6. $y = 2x - 1$

x	−3	−1	0	2
y				

7. $2x - y = 6$

x	−2	0	2	4
y				

8. $2x - 3y = -6$

x	−3	0	2	3
y				

For Problems 9–28, graph each of the linear equations by finding the x and y intercepts. (Objective 4)

9. $x + 2y = 4$

10. $2x + y = 6$

11. $2x - y = 2$

12. $3x - y = 3$

13. $3x + 2y = 6$

14. $2x + 3y = 6$

15. $5x - 4y = 20$

16. $4x - 3y = -12$

17. $x + 4y = -6$

18. $5x + y = -2$

19. $-x - 2y = 3$

20. $-3x - 2y = 12$

21. $y = x + 3$

22. $y = x - 1$

23. $y = -2x - 1$

24. $y = 4x + 3$

25. $y = \frac{1}{2}x + \frac{2}{3}$

26. $y = \frac{2}{3}x - \frac{3}{4}$

27. $-3y = -x + 3$

28. $2y = x - 2$

For Problems 29–40, graph each of the linear equations. (Objective 5)

29. $y = -x$

30. $y = x$

31. $y = 3x$

32. $y = -4x$

33. $2x - 3y = 0$

34. $3x + 4y = 0$

35. $x = 0$

36. $y = 0$

37. $y = 2$

38. $x = -3$

39. $x = -4$

40. $y = -1$

For Problems 41–47, apply graphing to linear relationships. (Objective 6)

41. (a) Digital Solutions charges for help-desk services according to the equation $c = 0.25m + 10$, where c represents the cost in dollars and m represents the minutes of service. Complete the following table.

m	5	10	15	20	30	60
c						

(b) Label the horizontal axis m and the vertical axis c, and graph the equation $c = 0.25m + 10$ for non-negative values of m.

(c) Use the graph from part (b) to approximate values for c when $m = 25, 40$, and 45.

(d) Check the accuracy of your readings from the graph in part (c) by using the equation $c = 0.25m + 10$.

42. (a) The equation $F = \frac{9}{5}C + 32$ can be used to convert from degrees Celsius to degrees Fahrenheit. Complete the following table.

C	0	5	10	15	20	−5	−10	−15	−20	−25
F										

(b) Graph the equation $F = \frac{9}{5}C + 32$.

(c) Use your graph from part (b) to approximate values for F when $C = 25°, 30°, -30°$, and $-40°$.

(d) Check the accuracy of your readings from the graph in part (c) by using the equation $F = \frac{9}{5}C + 32$.

43. (a) A doctor's office wants to chart and graph the linear relationship between the hemoglobin A1c reading and the average blood glucose level. The equation $G = 30h - 60$ describes the relationship, in which h is the hemoglobin A1c reading and G is the average blood glucose reading. Complete this chart of values:

Hemoglobin A1c, h	6.0	6.5	7.0	8.0	8.5	9.0	10.0
Blood glucose, G							

(b) Label the horizontal axis h and the vertical axis G, then graph the equation $G = 30h - 60$ for h values between 4.0 and 12.0.

(c) Use the graph from part (b) to approximate values for G when $h = 5.5$ and 7.5.

(d) Check the accuracy of your readings from the graph in part (c) by using the equation $G = 30h - 60$.

44. Suppose that the daily profit from an ice cream stand is given by the equation $p = 2n - 4$, where n represents the gallons of ice cream mix used in a day and p represents the dollars of profit. Label the horizontal axis n and the vertical axis p, and graph the equation $p = 2n - 4$ for nonnegative values of n.

45. The cost (c) of playing an online computer game for a time (t) in hours is given by the equation $c = 3t + 5$. Label the horizontal axis t and the vertical axis c, and graph the equation for nonnegative values of t.

46. The area of a sidewalk whose width is fixed at 3 feet can be given by the equation $A = 3l$, where A represents the area in square feet and l represents the length in feet. Label the horizontal axis l and the vertical axis A, and graph the equation $A = 3l$ for nonnegative values of l.

47. An online grocery store charges for delivery based on the equation $C = 0.30p$, where C represents the cost of delivery in dollars and p represents the weight of the groceries in pounds. Label the horizontal axis p and the vertical axis C, and graph the equation $C = 0.30p$ for nonnegative values of p.

Thoughts Into Words

48. How do we know that the graph of $y = -3x$ is a straight line that contains the origin?

49. How do we know that the graphs of $2x - 3y = 6$ and $-2x + 3y = -6$ are the same line?

50. What is the graph of the conjunction $x = 2$ and $y = 4$? What is the graph of the disjunction $x = 2$ or $y = 4$? Explain your answers.

51. Your friend claims that the graph of the equation $x = 2$ is the point $(2, 0)$. How do you react to this claim?

Further Investigations

From our work with absolute value, we know that $|x + y| = 1$ is equvalent to $x + y = 1$ or $x + y = -1$. Therefore, the graph of $|x + y| = 1$ consists of the two lines $x + y = 1$ and $x + y = -1$. Graph each of the following.

52. $|x + y| = 1$

53. $|x - y| = 4$

54. $|2x - y| = 4$

55. $|3x + 2y| = 6$

Graphing Calculator Activities

This is the first of many appearances of a group of problems called graphing calculator activities. These problems are specifically designed for those of you who have access to a graphing calculator or a computer with an appropriate software package. Within the framework of these problems, you will be given the opportunity to reinforce concepts we discussed in the text; lay groundwork for concepts we will introduce later in the text; predict shapes and locations of graphs on the basis of your previous graphing experiences; solve problems that are unreasonable or perhaps impossible to solve without a graphing utility; and in general become familiar with the capabilities and limitations of your graphing utility. (Objective 7)

56. (a) Graph $y = 3x + 4$, $y = 2x + 4$, $y = -4x + 4$, and $y = -2x + 4$ on the same set of axes.

(b) Graph $y = \dfrac{1}{2}x - 3$, $y = 5x - 3$, $y = 0.1x - 3$, and $y = -7x - 3$ on the same set of axes.

(c) What characteristic do all lines of the form $y = ax + 2$ (where a is any real number) share?

57. (a) Graph $y = 2x - 3$, $y = 2x + 3$, $y = 2x - 6$, and $y = 2x + 5$ on the same set of axes.

(b) Graph $y = -3x + 1$, $y = -3x + 4$, $y = -3x - 2$, and $y = -3x - 5$ on the same set of axes.

(c) Graph $y = \dfrac{1}{2}x + 3$, $y = \dfrac{1}{2}x - 4$, $y = \dfrac{1}{2}x + 5$, and $y = \dfrac{1}{2}x - 2$ on the same set of axes.

(d) What relationship exists among all lines of the form $y = 3x + b$, where b is any real number?

58. (a) Graph $2x + 3y = 4$, $2x + 3y = -6$, $4x - 6y = 7$, and $8x + 12y = -1$ on the same set of axes.

(b) Graph $5x - 2y = 4$, $5x - 2y = -3$, $10x - 4y = 3$, and $15x - 6y = 30$ on the same set of axes.

(c) Graph $x + 4y = 8$, $2x + 8y = 3$, $x - 4y = 6$, and $3x + 12y = 10$ on the same set of axes.

(d) Graph $3x - 4y = 6$, $3x + 4y = 10$, $6x - 8y = 20$, and $6x - 8y = 24$ on the same set of axes.

(e) For each of the following pairs of lines, (a) predict whether they are parallel lines, and (b) graph each pair of lines to check your prediction.

(1) $5x - 2y = 10$	and	$5x - 2y = -4$
(2) $x + y = 6$	and	$x - y = 4$
(3) $2x + y = 8$	and	$4x + 2y = 2$
(4) $y = 0.2x + 1$	and	$y = 0.2x - 4$
(5) $3x - 2y = 4$	and	$3x + 2y = 4$
(6) $4x - 3y = 8$	and	$8x - 6y = 3$
(7) $2x - y = 10$	and	$6x - 3y = 6$
(8) $x + 2y = 6$	and	$3x - 6y = 6$

59. Now let's use a graphing calculator to get a graph of $C = \dfrac{5}{9}(F - 32)$. By letting $F = x$ and $C = y$, we obtain Figure 7.15. Pay special attention to the boundaries on x. These values were chosen so that the fraction

$$\frac{(\text{Maximum value of } x) \text{ minus } (\text{Minimum value of } x)}{95}$$

would be equal to 1. The viewing window of the graphing calculator used to produce Figure 7.15 is 95 pixels (dots) wide. Therefore, we use 95 as the denominator of the fraction. We chose the boundaries for y to make sure that the cursor would be visible on the screen when we looked for certain values.

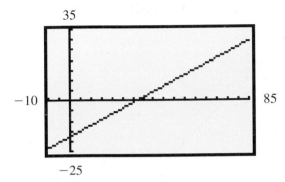

Figure 7.15

Now let's use the TRACE feature of the graphing calculator to complete the following table. Note that the cursor moves in increments of 1 as we trace along the graph.

F	−5	5	9	11	12	20	30	45	60
C									

(This was accomplished by setting the aforementioned fraction equal to 1.) By moving the cursor to each of the F values, we can complete the table as follows.

F	−5	5	9	11	12	20	30	45	60
C	−21	−15	−13	−12	−11	−7	−1	7	16

The C values are expressed to the nearest degree. Use your calculator and check the values in the table by using the equation $C = \dfrac{5}{9}(F - 32)$.

60. (a) Use your graphing calculator to display the graph of $F = \dfrac{9}{5}C + 32$. Be sure to set boundaries on the horizontal axis so that when you are using the trace feature, the cursor will move in increments of 1.

(b) Use the TRACE feature and check your answers for part (a) of Problem 42.

Answers to the Concept Quiz

1. True   **2.** False   **3.** True   **4.** False   **5.** True   **6.** False   **7.** False   **8.** False   **9.** True   **10.** False

---

7.2   Linear Inequalities in Two Variables

OBJECTIVE   **1**   Graph linear inequalities in two variables

Linear inequalities in two variables are of the form $Ax + By > C$ or $Ax + By < C$, where A, B, and C are real numbers. (Combined linear equality and inequality statements are of the form $Ax + By \geq C$ or $Ax + By \leq C$.)

Graphing linear inequalities is almost as easy as graphing linear equations. The following discussion leads into a simple, step-by-step process. Let's consider the following equation and related inequalities.

$$x + y = 2 \qquad x + y > 2 \qquad x + y < 2$$

The graph of $x + y = 2$ is shown in Figure 7.16. The line divides the plane into two half planes, one above the line and one below the line. In Figure 7.17(a) we indicated several points in the half-plane above the line. Note that for each point, the ordered pair of real numbers satisfies the inequality $x + y > 2$. This is true for *all points* in the half-plane above the line. Therefore, the graph of $x + y > 2$ is the half-plane above the line, as indicated by the shaded portion in Figure 7.17(b). We use a dashed line to indicate that points on the line do *not* satisfy $x + y > 2$. We would use a solid line if we were graphing $x + y \geq 2$.

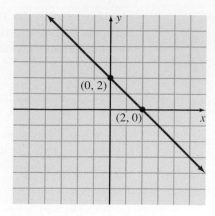

Figure 7.16

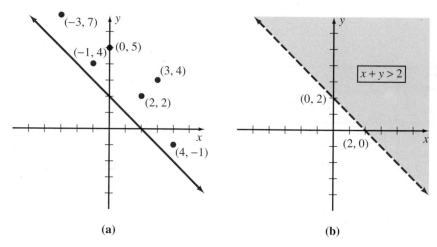

(a)   (b)

Figure 7.17

In Figure 7.18(a), several points are indicated in the half-plane below the line, $x + y = 2$. Note that for each point, the ordered pair of real numbers satisfies the inequality $x + y < 2$. This is true for *all points* in the half-plane below the line. Thus the graph of $x + y < 2$ is the half-plane below the line, as indicated in Figure 7.18(b).

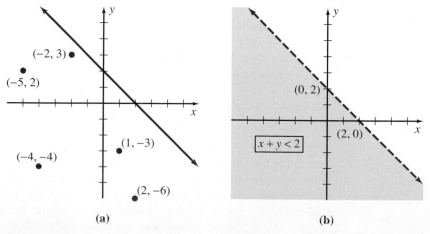

(a)   (b)

Figure 7.18

To graph a linear inequality, we suggest the following steps.

1. First, graph the corresponding equality. Use a solid line if equality is included in the original statement. Use a dashed line if equality is not included.
2. Choose a "test point" not on the line and substitute its coordinates into the inequality. (The origin is a convenient point to use if it is not on the line.)
3. The graph of the original inequality is
   (a) the half-plane that contains the test point if the inequality is satisfied by that point, or
   (b) the half-plane that does not contain the test point if the inequality is not satisfied by the point.

Let's apply these steps to some examples.

Classroom Example
Graph $2x + 3y < 6$.

EXAMPLE 1   Graph $x - 2y > 4$.

Solution

Step 1   Graph $x - 2y = 4$ as a dashed line because equality is not included in $x - 2y > 4$ (Figure 7.19).

Step 2   Choose the origin as a test point, and substitute its coordinates into the inequality.

$$x - 2y > 4 \quad \text{becomes } 0 - 2(0) > 4, \text{ which is false}$$

Step 3   Because the test point did not satisfy the given inequality, the graph is the half-plane that does not contain the test point. Thus the graph of $x - 2y > 4$ is the half-plane below the line, as indicated in Figure 7.19.

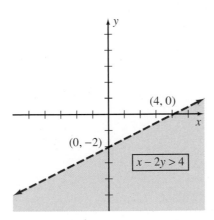

Figure 7.19

Classroom Example
Graph $x - 4y \geq 8$.

EXAMPLE 2   Graph $3x + 2y \leq 6$.

Solution

Step 1   Graph $3x + 2y = 6$ as a solid line because equality is included in $3x + 2y \leq 6$ (Figure 7.20).

Step 2   Choose the origin as a test point and substitute its coordinates into the given statement.

$$3x + 2y \leq 6 \quad \text{becomes } 3(0) + 2(0) \leq 6, \text{ which is true}$$

Step 3   Because the test point satisfies the given statement, all points in the same half-plane as the test point satisfy the statement. Thus the graph of $3x + 2y \leq 6$ consists of the line and the half-plane below the line (Figure 7.20).

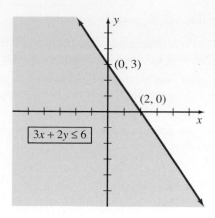

Figure 7.20

Classroom Example
Graph $y < -4x$.

EXAMPLE 3   Graph $y \leq 3x$.

Solution

Step 1 Graph $y = 3x$ as a solid line because equality is included in the statement $y \leq 3x$ (Figure 7.21).

Step 2 The origin is on the line, so we must choose some other point as a test point. Let's try $(2, 1)$.

$$y \leq 3x \quad \text{becomes } 1 \leq 3(2), \text{ which is a true statement}$$

Step 3 Because the test point satisfies the given inequality, the graph is the half-plane that contains the test point. Thus the graph of $y \leq 3x$ consists of the line and the half-plane below the line, as indicated in Figure 7.21.

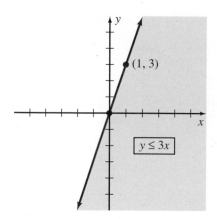

Figure 7.21

Concept Quiz 7.2

For Problems 1–10, answer true or false.

1. The ordered pair $(2, -3)$ satisfies the inequality $2x + y > 1$.

2. A dashed line on the graph indicates that the points on the line do not satisfy the inequality.

3. Any point can be used as a test point to determine the half-plane that is the solution of the inequality.

4. The ordered pair $(3, -2)$ satisfies the inequality $5x - 2y \geq 19$.

5. The ordered pair $(1, -3)$ satisfies the inequality $-2x - 3y < 4$.

6. The graph of $x > 0$ is the half-plane above the x axis.

7. The graph of $y < 0$ is the half-plane below the x axis.

8. The graph of $-x + y > 4$ is the half-plane above the line $-x + y = 4$.

9. The origin can serve as a test point to determine the half-plane that satisfies the inequality $3y > 2x$.

10. The ordered pair $(-2, -1)$ can be used as a test point to determine the half-plane that satisfies the inequality $y < -3x - 7$.

Problem Set 7.2

For Problems 1–24, graph each of the inequalities.
(Objective 1)

1. $x - y > 2$
2. $x + y > 4$
3. $x + 3y < 3$
4. $2x - y > 6$
5. $2x + 5y \geq 10$
6. $3x + 2y \leq 4$
7. $y \leq -x + 2$
8. $y \geq -2x - 1$
9. $y > -x$
10. $y < x$
11. $2x - y \geq 0$
12. $x + 2y \geq 0$
13. $-x + 4y - 4 \leq 0$
14. $-2x + y - 3 \leq 0$
15. $y > -\dfrac{3}{2}x - 3$
16. $2x + 5y > -4$
17. $y < -\dfrac{1}{2}x + 2$
18. $y < -\dfrac{1}{3}x + 1$
19. $x \leq 3$
20. $y \geq -2$
21. $x > 1$ and $y < 3$
22. $x > -2$ and $y > -1$
23. $x \leq -1$ and $y < 1$
24. $x < 2$ and $y \geq -2$

Thoughts Into Words

25. Why is the point $(-4, 1)$ not a good test point to use when graphing $5x - 2y > -22$?

26. Explain how you would graph the inequality
$$-3 > x - 3y.$$

Further Investigations

27. Graph $|x| < 2$. [*Hint*: Remember that $|x| < 2$ is equivalent to $-2 < x < 2$.]

28. Graph $|y| > 1$.

29. Graph $|x + y| < 1$.

30. Graph $|x - y| > 2$.

Graphing Calculator Activities

31. This is a good time for you to become acquainted with the DRAW features of your graphing calculator. Again, you may need to consult your user's manual for specific key-punching instructions. Return to Examples 1, 2, and 3 of this section, and use your graphing calculator to graph the inequalities.

32. Use a graphing calculator to check your graphs for Problems 1–24.

33. Use the DRAW feature of your graphing calculator to draw each of the following.
(a) A line segment between $(-2, -4)$ and $(-2, 5)$
(b) A line segment between $(2, 2)$ and $(5, 2)$
(c) A line segment between $(2, 3)$ and $(5, 7)$
(d) A triangle with vertices at $(1, -2)$, $(3, 4)$, and $(-3, 6)$

Answers to the Concept Quiz

1. False   **2.** True   **3.** False   **4.** True   **5.** False   **6.** False   **7.** True   **8.** True   **9.** False   **10.** False

7.3   Distance and Slope

OBJECTIVES

1 Find the distance between two points

2 Find the slope of a line

3 Use slope to graph lines

4 Apply slope to solve problems

As we work with the rectangular coordinate system, it is sometimes necessary to express the length of certain line segments. In other words, we need to be able to find the distance between two points. Let's first consider two specific examples and then develop the general distance formula.

Classroom Example
Find the distance between the points $A(-3, 1)$ and $B(-3, 7)$ and also between the points $C(2, 5)$ and $D(-1, 5)$.

EXAMPLE 1

Find the distance between the points $A(2, 2)$ and $B(5, 2)$ and also between the points $C(-2, 5)$ and $D(-2, -4)$.

Solution

Let's plot the points and draw $\overline{AB}$ as in Figure 7.22. Because $\overline{AB}$ is parallel to the x axis, its length can be expressed as $|5 - 2|$ or $|2 - 5|$. (The absolute-value symbol is used to ensure a nonnegative value.) Thus the length of $\overline{AB}$ is 3 units. Likewise, the length of $\overline{CD}$ is $|5 - (-4)| = |-4 - 5| = 9$ units.

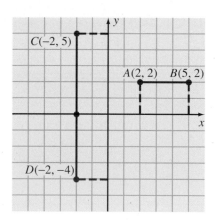

Figure 7.22

Classroom Example
Find the distance between the points $A(-2, 2)$ and $B(6, -4)$.

EXAMPLE 2   Find the distance between the points $A(2, 3)$ and $B(5, 7)$.

Solution

Let's plot the points and form a right triangle as indicated in Figure 7.23. Note that the coordinates of point C are $(5, 3)$. Because $\overline{AC}$ is parallel to the horizontal axis, its length is easily determined to be 3 units. Likewise, $\overline{CB}$ is parallel to the vertical axis, and its length is 4 units. Let d represent the length of $\overline{AB}$, and apply the Pythagorean theorem to obtain

$$d^2 = 3^2 + 4^2$$
$$d^2 = 9 + 16$$

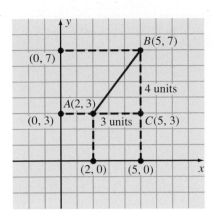

$$d^2 = 25$$
$$d = \pm\sqrt{25} = \pm 5$$

"Distance between" is a nonnegative value, so the length of $\overline{AB}$ is 5 units.

Figure 7.23

The approach we used in Example 2 becomes the basis for a general distance formula for finding the distance between any two points in a coordinate plane:

1. Let $P_1(x_1, y_1)$ and $P_2(x_2, y_2)$ represent any two points in a coordinate plane.
2. Form a right triangle as indicated in Figure 7.24. The coordinates of the vertex of the right angle, point R, are (x_2, y_1).

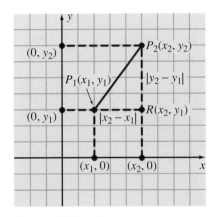

Figure 7.24

The length of $\overline{P_1R}$ is $|x_2 - x_1|$, and the length of $\overline{RP_2}$ is $|y_2 - y_1|$. (The absolute-value symbol is used to ensure a nonnegative value.) Let d represent the length of $\overline{P_1P_2}$ and apply the Pythagorean theorem to obtain

$$d^2 = |x_2 - x_1|^2 + |y_2 - y_1|^2$$

Because $|a|^2 = a^2$, the **distance formula** can be stated as

$$d = \sqrt{(x_2 - x_1)^2 + (y_2 - y_1)^2}$$

It makes no difference which point you call P_1 or P_2 when using the distance formula. If you forget the formula, don't panic. Just form a right triangle and apply the Pythagorean theorem as we did in Example 2. Let's consider an example that demonstrates the use of the distance formula.

EXAMPLE 3   Find the distance between $(-1, 4)$ and $(1, 2)$.

Solution

Let $(-1, 4)$ be P_1 and $(1, 2)$ be P_2. Using the distance formula, we obtain

$$
\begin{aligned}
d &= \sqrt{[1 - (-1)]^2 + (2 - 4)^2} \\
&= \sqrt{2^2 + (-2)^2} \\
&= \sqrt{4 + 4} \\
&= \sqrt{8} = 2\sqrt{2} \qquad \text{Express the answer in simplest radical form}
\end{aligned}
$$

The distance between the two points is $2\sqrt{2}$ units. ∎

In Example 3, we did not sketch a figure because of the simplicity of the problem. However, sometimes it is helpful to use a figure to organize the given information and aid in the analysis of the problem, as we see in the next example.

EXAMPLE 4

Verify that the points $(-3, 6)$, $(3, 4)$, and $(1, -2)$ are vertices of an isosceles triangle. (An isosceles triangle has two sides of the same length.)

Solution

Let's plot the points and draw the triangle (Figure 7.25). Use the distance formula to find the lengths d_1, d_2, and d_3, as follows:

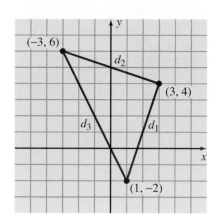

$$
\begin{aligned}
d_1 &= \sqrt{(3 - 1)^2 + (4 - (-2))^2} \\
&= \sqrt{2^2 + 6^2} = \sqrt{40} = 2\sqrt{10}
\end{aligned}
$$

$$
\begin{aligned}
d_2 &= \sqrt{(-3 - 3)^2 + (6 - 4)^2} \\
&= \sqrt{(-6)^2 + 2^2} = \sqrt{40} = 2\sqrt{10}
\end{aligned}
$$

$$
\begin{aligned}
d_3 &= \sqrt{(-3 - 1)^2 + (6 - (-2))^2} \\
&= \sqrt{(-4)^2 + 8^2} = \sqrt{80} = 4\sqrt{5}
\end{aligned}
$$

Figure 7.25

Because $d_1 = d_2$, we know that it is an isosceles triangle. ∎

Finding the Slope of a Line

In coordinate geometry, the concept of *slope* is used to describe the "steepness" of lines. The **slope** of a line is the ratio of the vertical change to the horizontal change as we move from one point on a line to another point. This is illustrated in Figure 7.26 with points P_1 and P_2.

A precise definition for slope can be given by considering the coordinates of the points P_1, P_2, and R as indicated in Figure 7.27. The horizontal change as we move from P_1 to P_2 is $x_2 - x_1$, and the vertical change is $y_2 - y_1$. Thus the following definition for slope is given.

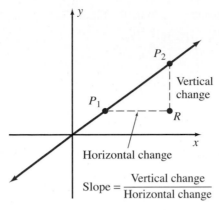

Figure 7.26

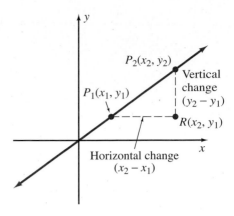

Figure 7.27

> ### Definition 7.1 Slope of a Line
>
> If points P_1 and P_2 with coordinates (x_1, y_1) and (x_2, y_2), respectively, are any two dif-
> ferent points on a line, then the slope of the line (denoted by m) is
>
> $$m = \frac{y_2 - y_1}{x_2 - x_1}, \qquad x_2 \neq x_1$$

Because $\dfrac{y_2 - y_1}{x_2 - x_1} = \dfrac{y_1 - y_2}{x_1 - x_2}$, how we designate P_1 and P_2 is not important. Let's use
Definition 7.1 to find the slopes of some lines.

EXAMPLE 5

Find the slope of the line determined by each of the following pairs of points, and graph the
lines:

(a) $(-1, 1)$ and $(3, 2)$ **(b)** $(4, -2)$ and $(-1, 5)$
(c) $(2, -3)$ and $(-3, -3)$

Solution

(a) Let $(-1, 1)$ be P_1 and $(3, 2)$ be P_2 (Figure 7.28).

$$m = \frac{y_2 - y_1}{x_2 - x_1} = \frac{2 - 1}{3 - (-1)} = \frac{1}{4}$$

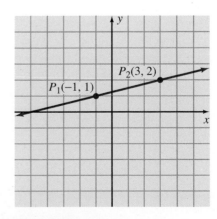

Figure 7.28

(b) Let $(4, -2)$ be P_1 and $(-1, 5)$ be P_2 (Figure 7.29).

$$m = \frac{y_2 - y_1}{x_2 - x_1} = \frac{5 - (-2)}{-1 - 4} = \frac{7}{-5} = -\frac{7}{5}$$

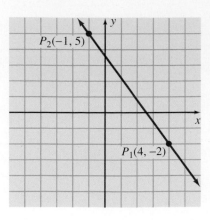

Figure 7.29

(c) Let $(2, -3)$ be P_1 and $(-3, -3)$ be P_2 (Figure 7.30).

$$m = \frac{y_2 - y_1}{x_2 - x_1}$$

$$= \frac{-3 - (-3)}{-3 - 2}$$

$$= \frac{0}{-5} = 0$$

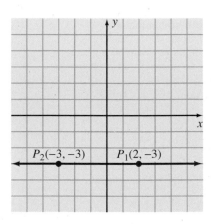

Figure 7.30

The three parts of Example 5 represent the three basic possibilities for slope; that is, the slope of a line can be positive, negative, or zero. A line that has a positive slope rises as we move from left to right, as in Figure 7.28. A line that has a negative slope falls as we move from left to right, as in Figure 7.29. A horizontal line, as in Figure 7.30, has a slope of zero. Finally, we need to realize that *the concept of slope is undefined for vertical lines*. This is due to the fact that for any vertical line, the horizontal change as we move from one point on the line to another is zero. Thus the ratio $\dfrac{y_2 - y_1}{x_2 - x_1}$ will have a denominator of zero and be undefined. Accordingly, the restriction $x_2 \neq x_1$ is imposed in Definition 7.1.

One final idea pertaining to the concept of slope needs to be emphasized. The slope of a line is a *ratio*, the ratio of vertical change to horizontal change. A slope of $\dfrac{2}{3}$ means that for every 2 units of vertical change there must be a corresponding 3 units of horizontal change. Thus starting at some point on a line that has a slope of $\dfrac{2}{3}$, we could locate other points on the line as follows:

$$\frac{2}{3} = \frac{4}{6} \qquad \longrightarrow \quad \text{by moving 4 units } up \text{ and 6 units to the } right$$

$$\frac{2}{3} = \frac{8}{12} \qquad \longrightarrow \quad \text{by moving 8 units } up \text{ and 12 units to the } right$$

$$\frac{2}{3} = \frac{-2}{-3} \qquad \longrightarrow \quad \text{by moving 2 units } down \text{ and 3 units to the } left$$

Likewise, if a line has a slope of $-\dfrac{3}{4}$, then by starting at some point on the line we could locate other points on the line as follows:

$$-\frac{3}{4} = \frac{-3}{4}$$ → by moving 3 units *down* and 4 units to the *right*

$$-\frac{3}{4} = \frac{3}{-4}$$ → by moving 3 units *up* and 4 units to the *left*

$$-\frac{3}{4} = \frac{-9}{12}$$ → by moving 9 units *down* and 12 units to the *right*

$$-\frac{3}{4} = \frac{15}{-20}$$ → by moving 15 units *up* and 20 units to the *left*

Using Slope to Graph Lines

Classroom Example

Graph the line that passes through the point (0, 3) and has a slope of $m = -\dfrac{2}{5}$.

EXAMPLE 6

Graph the line that passes through the point $(0, -2)$ and has a slope of $\dfrac{1}{3}$.

Solution

To graph, plot the point $(0, -2)$. Because the slope $= \dfrac{\text{vertical change}}{\text{horizontal change}} = \dfrac{1}{3}$, we can locate another point on the line by starting from the point $(0, -2)$ and moving 1 unit up and 3 units to the right to obtain the point $(3, -1)$. Because two points determine a line, we can draw the line (Figure 7.31).

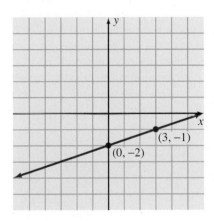

Figure 7.31

Remark: Because $m = \dfrac{1}{3} = \dfrac{-1}{-3}$, we can locate another point by moving 1 unit down and 3 units to the left from the point $(0, -2)$.

Classroom Example

Graph the line that passes through the point (−1, 2) and has a slope of −3.

EXAMPLE 7

Graph the line that passes through the point $(1, 3)$ and has a slope of -2.

Solution

To graph the line, plot the point $(1, 3)$. We know that $m = -2 = \dfrac{-2}{1}$. Furthermore, because the slope $= \dfrac{\text{vertical change}}{\text{horizontal change}} = \dfrac{-2}{1}$, we can locate another point on the line by starting from the point (1, 3) and moving 2 units down and 1 unit to the right to obtain the point (2, 1). Because two points determine a line, we can draw the line (Figure 7.32).

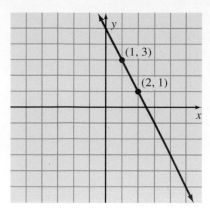

Figure 7.32

Remark: Because $m = -2 = \dfrac{-2}{1} = \dfrac{2}{-1}$, we can locate another point by moving 2 units up and 1 unit to the left from the point (1, 3).

Applying Slope to Solve Problems

The concept of slope has many real-world applications even though the word *slope* is often not used. The concept of slope is used in most situations that involve an incline. Hospital beds are hinged in the middle so that both the head end and the foot end can be raised or lowered; that is, the slope of either end of the bed can be changed. Likewise, treadmills are designed so that the incline (slope) of the platform can be adjusted. A roofer, when making an estimate to replace a roof, is concerned not only about the total area to be covered but also about the pitch of the roof. (Contractors do not define *pitch* according to the mathematical definition of slope, but both concepts refer to "steepness.") In Figure 7.33, the two roofs might require the same amount of shingles, but the roof on the left will take longer to complete because the pitch is so great that scaffolding will be required.

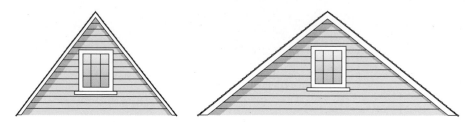

Figure 7.33

The concept of slope is also used in the construction of flights of stairs (Figure 7.34). The terms *rise* and *run* are commonly used, and the steepness (slope) of the stairs can be expressed as the ratio of rise to run. In Figure 7.34, the stairs on the left, which have a ratio of rise to run of $\dfrac{10}{11}$, are steeper than the stairs on the right, which have a ratio of $\dfrac{7}{11}$.

In highway construction, the word *grade* is used for the concept of slope. For example, in Figure 7.35, the highway is said to have a grade of 17%. This means that for every horizontal distance of 100 feet, the highway rises or drops 17 feet. In other words, the slope of the highway is $\dfrac{17}{100}$.

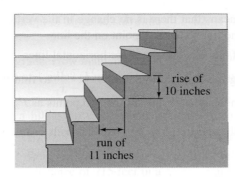
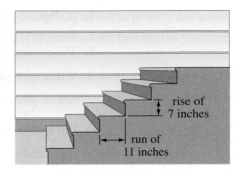

Figure 7.34

Figure 7.35

Classroom Example
A certain highway has a 4% grade.
How many feet does it rise in a hori-
zontal distance of 2 miles?

EXAMPLE 8

A certain highway has a 3% grade. How many feet does it rise in a horizontal distance of 1 mile?

Solution

A 3% grade means a slope of $\dfrac{3}{100}$. Therefore, if we let y represent the unknown vertical distance, and use the fact that 1 mile = 5280 feet, we can set up and solve the following proportion.

$$\frac{3}{100} = \frac{y}{5280}$$

$$100y = 3(5280) = 15{,}840$$

$$y = 158.4$$

The highway rises 158.4 feet in a horizontal distance of 1 mile.

Concept Quiz 7.3

For Problems 1–10, answer true or false.

1. When applying the distance formula $d = \sqrt{(x_2 - x_1)^2 + (y_2 - y_1)^2}$ to find the distance between two points, you can designate either of the two points as P_1.

2. An isosceles triangle has two sides of the same length.

3. The distance between the points $(-1, 4)$ and $(-1, -2)$ is 2 units.

4. The distance between the points $(3, -4)$ and $(3, 2)$ is undefined.

5. The slope of a line is the ratio of the vertical change to the horizontal change when moving from one point on the line to another point on the line.

6. The slope of a line is always positive.

Similarly, $\overline{CB}$ can be treated as a segment of a number line, as shown in Figure 7.38. Therefore,

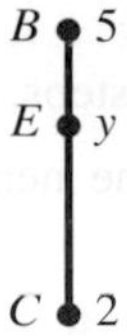

$$y = 2 + \frac{2}{3}(5 - 2) = 2 + \frac{2}{3}(3) = 4$$

The coordinates of point P are (5, 4).

Figure 7.38

For each of the following, find the coordinates of the indicated point in the xy plane.

(a) One-third of the distance from (2, 3) to (5, 9)
(b) Two-thirds of the distance from (1, 4) to (7, 13)
(c) Two-fifths of the distance from (−2, 1) to (8, 11)
(d) Three-fifths of the distance from (2, −3) to (−3, 8)
(e) Five-eighths of the distance from (−1, −2) to (4, −10)
(f) Seven-eighths of the distance from (−2, 3) to (−1, −9)

70. Suppose we want to find the coordinates of the midpoint of a line segment. Let $P(x, y)$ represent the midpoint of the line segment from $A(x_1, y_1)$ to $B(x_2, y_2)$. Using the method from Problem 68, the formula for the x coordinate of the midpoint is $x = x_1 + \frac{1}{2}(x_2 - x_1)$. This formula can be simplified algebraically to produce a simpler formula.

$$x = x_1 + \frac{1}{2}(x_2 - x_1)$$

$$x = x_1 + \frac{1}{2}x_2 - \frac{1}{2}x_1$$

$$x = \frac{1}{2}x_1 + \frac{1}{2}x_2$$

$$x = \frac{x_1 + x_2}{2}$$

Hence the x coordinate of the midpoint can be interpreted as the average of the x coordinates of the endpoints of the line segment. A similar argument for the y coordinate of the midpoint gives the following formula.

$$y = \frac{y_1 + y_2}{2}$$

For each of the pairs of points, use the formula to find the midpoint of the line segment between the points.

(a) (3, 1) and (7, 5)
(b) (−2, 8) and (6, 4)
(c) (−3, 2) and (5, 8)
(d) (4, 10) and (9, 25)
(e) (−4, −1) and (−10, 5)
(f) (5, 8) and (−1, 7)

Graphing Calculator Activities

71. Remember that we did some work with parallel lines back in the graphing calculator activities in Problem Set 7.1. Now let's do some work with perpendicular lines. Be sure to set your boundaries so that the distance between tic marks is the same on both axes.

(a) Graph $y = 4x$ and $y = -\frac{1}{4}x$ on the same set of axes. Do they appear to be perpendicular lines?

(b) Graph $y = 3x$ and $y = \frac{1}{3}x$ on the same set of axes. Do they appear to be perpendicular lines?

(c) Graph $y = \frac{2}{5}x - 1$ and $y = -\frac{5}{2}x + 2$ on the same set of axes. Do they appear to be perpendicular lines?

(d) Graph $y = \frac{3}{4}x - 3$, $y = \frac{4}{3}x + 2$, and $y = -\frac{4}{3}x + 2$ on the same set of axes. Does there appear to be a pair of perpendicular lines?

(e) On the basis of your results in parts (a) through (d), make a statement about how we can recognize perpendicular lines from their equations.

72. For each of the following pairs of equations, (1) predict whether they represent parallel lines, perpendicular lines, or lines that intersect but are not perpendicular, and (2) graph each pair of lines to check your prediction.

(a) $5.2x + 3.3y = 9.4$ and $5.2x + 3.3y = 12.6$
(b) $1.3x - 4.7y = 3.4$ and $1.3x - 4.7y = 11.6$
(c) $2.7x + 3.9y = 1.4$ and $2.7x - 3.9y = 8.2$
(d) $5x - 7y = 17$ and $7x + 5y = 19$
(e) $9x + 2y = 14$ and $2x + 9y = 17$
(f) $2.1x + 3.4y = 11.7$ and $3.4x - 2.1y = 17.3$

Answers to the Concept Quiz

1. True **2.** True **3.** False **4.** False **5.** True **6.** False **7.** True **8.** False **9.** True **10.** False

7.4   Determining the Equation of a Line

OBJECTIVES

1. Find the equation of a line given a point and a slope

2. Find the equation of a line given two points

3. Find the equation of a line given the slope and y intercept

4. Use the point-slope form to write equations of lines

5. Apply the slope-intercept form of an equation

6. Find equations for parallel or perpendicular lines

To review, there are basically two types of problems to solve in coordinate geometry:

1. Given an algebraic equation, find its geometric graph.

2. Given a set of conditions pertaining to a geometric figure, find its algebraic equation.

Problems of type 1 have been our primary concern thus far in this chapter. Now let's analyze some problems of type 2 that deal specifically with straight lines. Given certain facts about a line, we need to be able to determine its algebraic equation. Let's consider some examples.

Classroom Example
Find the equation of the line that has a slope of $m = \dfrac{1}{4}$ and contains the point (2, 5).

EXAMPLE 1

Find the equation of the line that has a slope of $\dfrac{2}{3}$ and contains the point (1, 2).

Solution

First, let's draw the line and record the given information. Then choose a point (x, y) that represents any point on the line other than the given point (1, 2). (See Figure 7.39.)

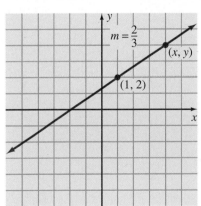

The slope determined by (1, 2) and (x, y) is $\dfrac{2}{3}$. Thus

$$\frac{y - 2}{x - 1} = \frac{2}{3}$$

$$2(x - 1) = 3(y - 2)$$

$$2x - 2 = 3y - 6$$

$$2x - 3y = -4$$

Figure 7.39

Finding the Equation of a Line, Given Two Points

Classroom Example
Find the equation of the line that contains (−4, 3) and (2, −2).

EXAMPLE 2   Find the equation of the line that contains (3, 2) and (−2, 5).

Solution

First, let's draw the line determined by the given points (Figure 7.40); if we know two points, we can find the slope.

$$m = \frac{y_2 - y_1}{x_2 - x_1} = \frac{3}{-5} = -\frac{3}{5}$$

Now we can use the same approach as in Example 1.

Form an equation using a variable point (x, y), one of the two given points, and the slope of $-\dfrac{3}{5}$.

$$\frac{y - 5}{x + 2} = \frac{3}{-5} \qquad \left(-\frac{3}{5} = \frac{3}{-5}\right)$$
$$3(x + 2) = -5(y - 5)$$
$$3x + 6 = -5y + 25$$
$$3x + 5y = 19$$

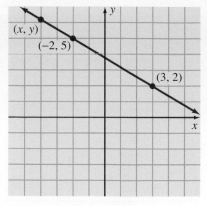

Figure 7.40

Finding the Equation of a Line, Given the Slope and *y* Intercept

EXAMPLE 3

Find the equation of the line that has a slope of $\dfrac{1}{4}$ and a y intercept of 2.

Solution

A y intercept of 2 means that the point $(0, 2)$ is on the line (Figure 7.41).

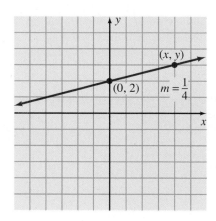

Figure 7.41

Choose a variable point (x, y) and proceed as in the previous examples.

$$\frac{y - 2}{x - 0} = \frac{1}{4}$$
$$1(x - 0) = 4(y - 2)$$
$$x = 4y - 8$$
$$x - 4y = -8$$

Perhaps it would be helpful to pause a moment and look back over Examples 1, 2, and 3. Note that we used the same basic approach in all three situations. We chose a variable point (x, y) and used it to determine the equation that satisfies the conditions given in the problem. The approach we took in the previous examples can be generalized to produce some special forms of equations of straight lines.

Using the Point-Slope Form to Write Equations of Lines

Generalizing from the previous examples, let's find the equation of a line that has a slope of m and contains the point (x_1, y_1). To use the slope formula we will need two points. Choosing a point (x, y) to represent any other point on the line (Figure 7.42) and using the given point (x_1, y_1), we can determine the slope to be

$$m = \frac{y - y_1}{x - x_1} \quad \text{where } x \neq x_1$$

Simplifying gives us the equation $y - y_1 = m(x - x_1)$.
    We refer to the equation

$$y - y_1 = m(x - x_1)$$

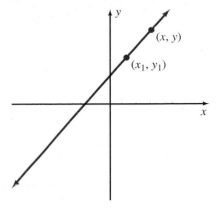

Figure 7.42

as the **point-slope form** of the equation of a straight line. Instead of the approach we used in Example 1, we could use the point-slope form to write the equation of a line with a given slope that contains a given point.

Classroom Example
Use the point-slope form to find the equation of a line that has a slope of $\frac{2}{3}$ and contains the point $(1, -6)$.

EXAMPLE 4

Use the point-slope form to find the equation of a line that has a slope of $\frac{3}{5}$ and contains the point $(2, 4)$.

Solution

We can determine the equation by substituting $\frac{3}{5}$ for m and $(2, 4)$ for (x_1, y_1) in the point-slope form.

$$y - y_1 = m(x - x_1)$$
$$y - 4 = \frac{3}{5}(x - 2)$$
$$5(y - 4) = 3(x - 2)$$
$$5y - 20 = 3x - 6$$
$$-14 = 3x - 5y$$

Thus the equation of the line is $3x - 5y = -14$.

Applying the Slope-Intercept Form of an Equation

Another special form of the equation of a line is the slope-intercept form. Let's use the point-slope form to find the equation of a line that has a slope of m and a y intercept of b. A y intercept of b means that the line contains the point $(0, b)$, as in Figure 7.43. Therefore, we can use the point-slope form as follows:

$$y - y_1 = m(x - x_1)$$
$$y - b = m(x - 0)$$
$$y - b = mx$$
$$y = mx + b$$

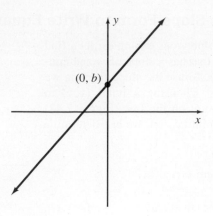

Figure 7.43

We refer to the equation

$$y = mx + b$$

as the **slope-intercept form** of the equation of a straight line. We use it for three primary purposes, as the next three examples illustrate.

EXAMPLE 5

Find the equation of the line that has a slope of $\dfrac{1}{4}$ and a y intercept of 2.

Solution

This is a restatement of Example 3, but this time we will use the slope-intercept form ($y = mx + b$) of a line to write its equation. Because $m = \dfrac{1}{4}$ and $b = 2$, we can substitute these values into $y = mx + b$.

$$y = mx + b$$

$$y = \frac{1}{4}x + 2$$

$$4y = x + 8 \qquad \text{Multiply both sides by 4}$$

$$x - 4y = -8 \qquad \text{Same result as in Example 3}$$

EXAMPLE 6

Find the slope of the line when the equation is $3x + 2y = 6$.

Solution

We can solve the equation for y in terms of x and then compare it to the slope-intercept form to determine its slope. Thus

$$3x + 2y = 6$$

$$2y = -3x + 6$$

$$y = -\frac{3}{2}x + 3$$

$$y = -\frac{3}{2}x + 3 \qquad y = mx + b$$

The slope of the line is $-\dfrac{3}{2}$. Furthermore, the y intercept is 3.

Classroom Example
Graph the line determined by the
equation $y = -\frac{1}{3}x + 2$.

EXAMPLE 7   Graph the line determined by the equation $y = \frac{2}{3}x - 1$.

Solution

Comparing the given equation to the general slope-intercept form, we see that the slope of the line is $\frac{2}{3}$, and the y intercept is -1. Because the y intercept is -1, we can plot the point $(0, -1)$. Because the slope is $\frac{2}{3}$, let's move 3 units to the right and 2 units up from $(0, -1)$ to locate the point $(3, 1)$. The two points $(0, -1)$ and $(3, 1)$ determine the line in Figure 7.44. (Consider picking a third point as a check point.)

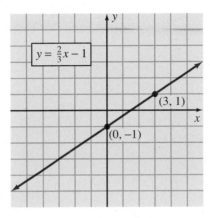

Figure 7.44

> In general, if the equation of a nonvertical line is written in slope-intercept form ($y = mx + b$), the coefficient of x is the slope of the line, and the constant term is the y intercept. (Remember that the concept of slope is not defined for a vertical line.)

We use two forms of equations of straight lines extensively. They are the **standard form** and the **slope-intercept form**, and we describe them as follows.

Standard Form $Ax + By = C$, where B and C are integers, and A is a nonnegative integer (A and B not both zero).

Slope-Intercept Form $y = mx + b$, where m is a real number representing the slope, and b is a real number representing the y intercept.

Finding Equations for Parallel and Perpendicular Lines

We can use two important relationships between lines and their slopes to solve certain kinds of problems. It can be shown that nonvertical parallel lines have the same slope and that two nonvertical lines are perpendicular if the product of their slopes is -1. (Details for verifying these facts are left to another course.) In other words, if two lines have slopes m_1 and m_2, respectively, then

1. The two lines are parallel if and only if $m_1 = m_2$.
2. The two lines are perpendicular if and only if $(m_1)(m_2) = -1$.

The following examples demonstrate the use of these properties.

Classroom Example
(a) Verify that the graphs of
$4x - 2y = 10$ and $2x - y = 6$
are parallel lines.
(b) Verify that the graphs
of $5x + 2y = 14$ and
$4x - 10y = -3$ are
perpendicular lines.

EXAMPLE 8

(a) Verify that the graphs of $2x + 3y = 7$ and $4x + 6y = 11$ are parallel lines.

(b) Verify that the graphs of $8x - 12y = 3$ and $3x + 2y = 2$ are perpendicular lines.

Solution

(a) Let's change each equation to slope-intercept form.

$$2x + 3y = 7 \quad \longrightarrow \quad 3y = -2x + 7$$

$$y = -\frac{2}{3}x + \frac{7}{3}$$

$$4x + 6y = 11 \quad \longrightarrow \quad 6y = -4x + 11$$

$$y = -\frac{4}{6}x + \frac{11}{6}$$

$$y = -\frac{2}{3}x + \frac{11}{6}$$

Both lines have a slope of $-\dfrac{2}{3}$, but they have different y intercepts. Therefore, the two lines are parallel.

(b) Solving each equation for y in terms of x, we obtain

$$8x - 12y = 3 \quad \longrightarrow \quad -12y = -8x + 3$$

$$y = \frac{8}{12}x - \frac{3}{12}$$

$$y = \frac{2}{3}x - \frac{1}{4}$$

$$3x + 2y = 2 \quad \longrightarrow \quad 2y = -3x + 2$$

$$y = -\frac{3}{2}x + 1$$

Because $\left(\dfrac{2}{3}\right)\left(-\dfrac{3}{2}\right) = -1$ (the product of the two slopes is -1), the lines are therefore perpendicular.

Remark: The statement "the product of two slopes is -1" has the same meaning as the statement "the two slopes are negative reciprocals of each other"; that is, $m_1 = -\dfrac{1}{m_2}$.

Classroom Example
Find the equation of the line that
contains the point $(4, -5)$ and is
parallel to the line determined by
$8x + 2y = 12$.

EXAMPLE 9

Find the equation of the line that contains the point $(1, 4)$ and is parallel to the line determined by $x + 2y = 5$.

Solution

First, let's draw a figure to help in our analysis of the problem (Figure 7.45). Because the line through $(1, 4)$ is to be parallel to the line determined by $x + 2y = 5$, it must have the same slope. Let's find the slope by changing $x + 2y = 5$ to the slope-intercept form.

$$x + 2y = 5$$

$$2y = -x + 5$$

$$y = -\frac{1}{2}x + \frac{5}{2}$$

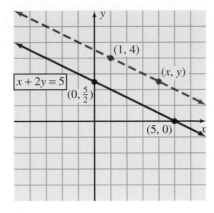

Figure 7.45

The slope of both lines is $-\dfrac{1}{2}$. Now we can choose a variable point (x, y) on the line through $(1, 4)$ and proceed as we did in earlier examples.

$$\frac{y - 4}{x - 1} = \frac{1}{-2}$$
$$1(x - 1) = -2(y - 4)$$
$$x - 1 = -2y + 8$$
$$x + 2y = 9$$

EXAMPLE 10

Classroom Example
Find the equation of the line that contains the point (3, 5) and is perpendicular to the line determined by $3x - 4y = 8$.

Find the equation of the line that contains the point $(-1, -2)$ and is perpendicular to the line determined by $2x - y = 6$.

Solution

First, let's draw a figure to help in our analysis of the problem (Figure 7.46). Because the line through $(-1, -2)$ is to be perpendicular to the line determined by $2x - y = 6$, its slope must be the negative reciprocal of the slope of $2x - y = 6$. Let's find the slope of $2x - y = 6$ by changing it to the slope-intercept form.

$$2x - y = 6$$
$$-y = -2x + 6$$
$$y = 2x - 6 \qquad \text{The slope is 2}$$

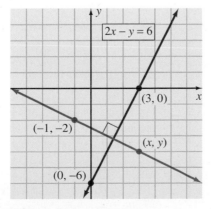

Figure 7.46

The slope of the desired line is $-\dfrac{1}{2}$ (the negative reciprocal of 2), and we can proceed as before by using a variable point (x, y).

$$\frac{y + 2}{x + 1} = \frac{1}{-2}$$
$$1(x + 1) = -2(y + 2)$$
$$x + 1 = -2y - 4$$
$$x + 2y = -5$$

Concept Quiz 7.4

For Problems 1–10, answer true or false.

1. If two distinct lines have the same slope, then the lines are parallel.
2. If the slopes of two lines are reciprocals, then the lines are perpendicular.
3. In the standard form of the equation of a line $Ax + By = C$, A can be a rational number in fractional form.
4. In the slope-intercept form of an equation of a line $y = mx + b$, m is the slope.
5. In the standard form of the equation of a line $Ax + By = C$, A is the slope.
6. The slope of the line determined by the equation $3x - 2y = -4$ is $\dfrac{3}{2}$.
7. The concept of a slope is not defined for the line $y = 2$.
8. The concept of slope is not defined for the line $x = 2$.
9. The lines determined by the equations $x - 3y = 4$ and $2x - 6y = 11$ are parallel lines.
10. The lines determined by the equations $x - 3y = 4$ and $x + 3y = 4$ are perpendicular lines.

Problem Set 7.4

For Problems 1–14, write the equation of the line that has the indicated slope and contains the indicated point. Express final equations in standard form. **(Objective 1)**

1. $m = \dfrac{1}{2}$, $(3, 5)$
2. $m = \dfrac{1}{3}$, $(2, 3)$
3. $m = 3$, $(-2, 4)$
4. $m = -2$, $(-1, 6)$
5. $m = -\dfrac{3}{4}$, $(-1, -3)$
6. $m = -\dfrac{3}{5}$, $(-2, -4)$
7. $m = \dfrac{5}{4}$, $(4, -2)$
8. $m = \dfrac{3}{2}$, $(8, -2)$
9. $m = \dfrac{5}{2}$, $(-3, 4)$
10. $m = \dfrac{2}{3}$, $(1, -4)$
11. $m = -2$, $(5, 8)$
12. $m = -1$, $(-6, 2)$
13. $m = -\dfrac{1}{3}$, $(5, 0)$
14. $m = -\dfrac{3}{4}$, $(0, 1)$

For Problems 15–24, write the equation of the line that contains the indicated pair of points. Express final equations in standard form. **(Objective 2)**

15. $(2, 1)$, $(6, 5)$
16. $(-1, 2)$, $(2, 5)$
17. $(-2, -3)$, $(2, 7)$
18. $(-3, -4)$, $(1, 2)$
19. $(-3, 2)$, $(4, 1)$
20. $(-2, 5)$, $(3, -3)$
21. $(-1, -4)$, $(3, -6)$
22. $(3, 8)$, $(7, 2)$
23. $(0, 0)$, $(5, 7)$
24. $(0, 0)$, $(-5, 9)$

For Problems 25–32, write the equation of the line that has the indicated slope (m) and y intercept (b). Express final equations in slope-intercept form. **(Objective 3)**

25. $m = \dfrac{3}{7}$, $b = 4$
26. $m = \dfrac{2}{9}$, $b = 6$
27. $m = 2$, $b = -3$
28. $m = -3$, $b = -1$

29. $m = -\dfrac{2}{5}, \quad b = 1$ **30.** $m = -\dfrac{3}{7}, \quad b = 4$

31. $m = 0, \quad b = -4$ **32.** $m = \dfrac{1}{5}, \quad b = 0$

For Problems 33–48, write the equation of the line that satisfies the given conditions. Express final equations in standard form. (Objectives 1, 2, and 6)

33. x intercept of 2 and y intercept of -4

34. x intercept of -1 and y intercept of -3

35. x intercept of -3 and slope of $-\dfrac{5}{8}$

36. x intercept of 5 and slope of $-\dfrac{3}{10}$

37. Contains the point $(2, -4)$ and is parallel to the y axis

38. Contains the point $(-3, -7)$ and is parallel to the x axis

39. Contains the point $(5, 6)$ and is perpendicular to the y axis

40. Contains the point $(-4, 7)$ and is perpendicular to the x axis

41. Contains the point $(1, 3)$ and is parallel to the line $x + 5y = 9$

42. Contains the point $(-1, 4)$ and is parallel to the line $x - 2y = 6$

43. Contains the origin and is parallel to the line $4x - 7y = 3$

44. Contains the origin and is parallel to the line $-2x - 9y = 4$

45. Contains the point $(-1, 3)$ and is perpendicular to the line $2x - y = 4$

46. Contains the point $(-2, -3)$ and is perpendicular to the line $x + 4y = 6$

47. Is perpendicular to the line $-2x + 3y = 8$ and contains the origin.

48. Contains the origin and is perpendicular to the line $y = -5x$

For Problems 49–54, change the equation to slope-intercept form and determine the slope and y intercept of the line. (Objective 5)

49. $3x + y = 7$ **50.** $5x - y = 9$

51. $3x + 2y = 9$ **52.** $x - 4y = 3$

53. $x = 5y + 12$ **54.** $-4x - 7y = 14$

For Problems 55–62, use the slope-intercept form to graph the following lines. (Objective 5)

55. $y = \dfrac{2}{3}x - 4$ **56.** $y = \dfrac{1}{4}x + 2$

57. $y = 2x + 1$ **58.** $y = 3x - 1$

59. $y = -\dfrac{3}{2}x + 4$ **60.** $y = -\dfrac{5}{3}x + 3$

61. $y = -x + 2$ **62.** $y = -2x + 4$

For Problems 63–72, graph the following lines using the technique that seems most appropriate.

63. $y = -\dfrac{2}{5}x - 1$ **64.** $y = -\dfrac{1}{2}x + 3$

65. $x + 2y = 5$ **66.** $2x - y = 7$

67. $-y = -4x + 7$ **68.** $3x = 2y$

69. $7y = -2x$ **70.** $y = -3$

71. $x = 2$ **72.** $y = -x$

For Problems 73–78, the situations can be described by the use of linear equations in two variables. If two pairs of values are known, then we can determine the equation by using the approach we used in Example 2 of this section. For each of the following, assume that the relationship can be expressed as a linear equation in two variables, and use the given information to determine the equation. Express the equation in slope-intercept form. (Objectives 2 and 5)

73. A diabetic patient was told by her doctor that her hemoglobin A1c reading of 6.5 corresponds to an average blood glucose level of 135. At her next checkup, three months later, the patient was told that her hemoglobin A1c reading of 6.0 corresponds to an average blood glucose level of 120. Let y represent the average blood glucose level, and x represent the hemoglobin A1c reading.

74. Hal purchased a 500-minute calling card for \$17.50. After he used all the minutes on that card, he purchased another card from the same company at a price of \$26.25 for 750 minutes. Let y represent the cost of the card in dollars and x represent the number of minutes.

75. A company uses 7 pounds of fertilizer for a lawn that measures 5000 square feet and 12 pounds for a lawn that measures 10,000 square feet. Let y represent the pounds of fertilizer and x the square footage of the lawn.

76. A new diet guideline claims that a person weighing 140 pounds should consume 1490 daily calories and that a 200-pound person should consume 1700 calories. Let y represent the calories and x the weight of the person in pounds.

77. Two banks on opposite corners of a town square had signs that displayed the current temperature. One bank displayed the temperature in degrees Celsius and the other in degrees Fahrenheit. A temperature of 10°C was displayed at the same time as a temperature of 50°F.

On another day, a temperature of $-5°C$ was displayed at the same time as a temperature of $23°F$. Let y represent the temperature in degrees Fahrenheit and x the temperature in degrees Celsius.

78. An accountant has a schedule of depreciation for some business equipment. The schedule shows that after 12 months the equipment is worth $7600 and that after 20 months it is worth $6000. Let y represent the worth and x represent the time in months.

Thoughts Into Words

79. What does it mean to say that two points determine a line?

80. How would you help a friend determine the equation of the line that is perpendicular to $x - 5y = 7$ and contains the point $(5, 4)$?

81. Explain how you would find the slope of the line $y = 4$.

Further Investigations

82. The equation of a line that contains the two points (x_1, y_1) and (x_2, y_2) is $\dfrac{y - y_1}{x - x_1} = \dfrac{y_2 - y_1}{x_2 - x_1}$. We often refer to this as the **two-point form** of the equation of a straight line. Use the two-point form and write the equation of the line that contains each of the indicated pairs of points. Express final equations in standard form.
   (a) $(1, 1)$ and $(5, 2)$
   (b) $(2, 4)$ and $(-2, -1)$
   (c) $(-3, 5)$ and $(3, 1)$
   (d) $(-5, 1)$ and $(2, -7)$

83. Let $Ax + By = C$ and $A'x + B'y = C'$ represent two lines. Change both of these equations to slope-intercept form, and then verify each of the following properties.
   (a) If $\dfrac{A}{A'} = \dfrac{B}{B'} \neq \dfrac{C}{C'}$, then the lines are parallel.
   (b) If $AA' = -BB'$, then the lines are perpendicular.

84. The properties in Problem 83 provide us with another way to write the equation of a line parallel or perpendicular to a given line that contains a given point not on the line. For example, suppose that we want the equation of the line perpendicular to $3x + 4y = 6$ that contains the point $(1, 2)$. The form $4x - 3y = k$, where k is a constant, represents a family of lines perpendicular to $3x + 4y = 6$ because we have satisfied the condition $AA' = -BB'$. Therefore, to find what specific line of the family contains $(1, 2)$, we substitute 1 for x and 2 for y to determine k.

$$4x - 3y = k$$
$$4(1) - 3(2) = k$$
$$-2 = k$$

Thus the equation of the desired line is $4x - 3y = -2$.

Use the properties from Problem 83 to help write the equation of each of the following lines.

(a) Contains $(1, 8)$ and is parallel to $2x + 3y = 6$

(b) Contains $(-1, 4)$ and is parallel to $x - 2y = 4$

(c) Contains $(2, -7)$ and is perpendicular to $3x - 5y = 10$

(d) Contains $(-1, -4)$ and is perpendicular to $2x + 5y = 12$

85. The problem of finding the perpendicular bisector of a line segment presents itself often in the study of analytic geometry. As with any problem of writing the equation of a line, you must determine the slope of the line and a point that the line passes through. A perpendicular bisector passes through the midpoint of the line segment and has a slope that is the negative reciprocal of the slope of the line segment. The problem can be solved as follows:

Find the perpendicular bisector of the line segment between the points $(1, -2)$ and $(7, 8)$.

The midpoint of the line segment is $\left(\dfrac{1 + 7}{2}, \dfrac{-2 + 8}{2}\right)$ $= (4, 3)$.

The slope of the line segment is $m = \dfrac{8 - (-2)}{7 - 1}$ $= \dfrac{10}{6} = \dfrac{5}{3}$.

Hence the perpendicular bisector will pass through the point $(4, 3)$ and have a slope of $m = -\dfrac{3}{5}$.

$$y - 3 = -\frac{3}{5}(x - 4)$$
$$5(y - 3) = -3(x - 4)$$
$$5y - 15 = -3x + 12$$
$$3x + 5y = 27$$

Thus the equation of the perpendicular bisector of the line segment between the points $(1, -2)$ and $(7, 8)$ is $3x + 5y = 27$.

Find the perpendicular bisector of the line segment between the points for the following. Write the equation in standard form.

(a) $(-1, 2)$ and $(3, 0)$

(b) $(6, -10)$ and $(-4, 2)$

(c) $(-7, -3)$ and $(5, 9)$

(d) $(0, 4)$ and $(12, -4)$

Graphing Calculator Activities

86. Predict whether each of the following pairs of equations represents parallel lines, perpendicular lines, or lines that intersect but are not perpendicular. Then graph each pair of lines to check your predictions. (The properties presented in Problem 83 should be very helpful.)

(a) $5.2x + 3.3y = 9.4$ and $5.2x + 3.3y = 12.6$

(b) $1.3x - 4.7y = 3.4$ and $1.3x - 4.7y = 11.6$

(c) $2.7x + 3.9y = 1.4$ and $2.7x - 3.9y = 8.2$

(d) $5x - 7y = 17$ and $7x + 5y = 19$

(e) $9x + 2y = 14$ and $2x + 9y = 17$

(f) $2.1x + 3.4y = 11.7$ and $3.4x - 2.1y = 17.3$

(g) $7.1x - 2.3y = 6.2$ and $2.3x + 7.1y = 9.9$

(h) $-3x + 9y = 12$ and $9x - 3y = 14$

(i) $2.6x - 5.3y = 3.4$ and $5.2x - 10.6y = 19.2$

(j) $4.8x - 5.6y = 3.4$ and $6.1x + 7.6y = 12.3$

Answers to the Concept Quiz

1. True   **2.** False   **3.** False   **4.** True   **5.** False   **6.** True   **7.** False   **8.** True   **9.** True   **10.** False

7.5   Graphing Nonlinear Equations

OBJECTIVES

1 Graph nonlinear equations

2 Determine if the graph of an equation is symmetric to the x axis, the y axis, or the origin

Equations such as $y = x^2 - 4$, $x = y^2$, $y = \dfrac{1}{x}$, $x^2y = -2$, and $x = y^3$ are all examples of non-linear equations. The graphs of these equations are figures other than straight lines, which can be determined by plotting a sufficient number of points. Let's plot the points and observe some characteristics of these graphs that we then can use to supplement the point-plotting process.

Classroom Example
Graph $y = x^2 + 3$.

EXAMPLE 1   Graph $y = x^2 - 4$

Solution

Let's begin by finding the intercepts. If $x = 0$, then

$$y = 0^2 - 4 = -4$$

The point $(0, -4)$ is on the graph. If $y = 0$, then

$$0 = x^2 - 4$$
$$0 = (x + 2)(x - 2)$$
$$x + 2 = 0 \qquad \text{or} \qquad x - 2 = 0$$
$$x = -2 \qquad \text{or} \qquad x = 2$$

The points $(-2, 0)$ and $(2, 0)$ are on the graph. The given equation is in a convenient form for setting up a table of values.

Plotting these points and connecting them with a smooth curve produces Figure 7.47.

x	y	
0	−4	
−2	0	Intercepts
2	0	
1	−3	
−1	−3	
3	5	Other points
−3	5	

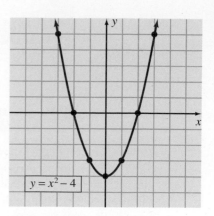

$y = x^2 - 4$

Figure 7.47

The curve in Figure 7.47 is called a parabola; we will study parabolas in more detail in a later chapter. At this time we want to emphasize that the parabola in Figure 7.47 is said to be *symmetric with respect to the y axis*. In other words, the y axis is a line of symmetry. Each half of the curve is a mirror image of the other half through the y axis. Note, in the table of values, that for each ordered pair (x, y), the ordered pair $(-x, y)$ is also a solution. A general test for y-axis symmetry can be stated as follows:

> ### y-Axis Symmetry
>
> The graph of an equation is symmetric with respect to the y axis if replacing x with $-x$ results in an equivalent equation.

The equation $y = x^2 - 4$ exhibits symmetry with respect to the y axis because replacing x with $-x$ produces $y = (-x)^2 - 4 = x^2 - 4$. Let's test some equations for such symmetry. We will replace x with $-x$ and check for an equivalent equation.

Equation	Test for symmetry with respect to the y axis	Equivalent equation	Symmetric with respect to the y axis
$y = -x^2 + 2$	$y = -(-x)^2 + 2 = -x^2 + 2$	Yes	Yes
$y = 2x^2 + 5$	$y = 2(-x)^2 + 5 = 2x^2 + 5$	Yes	Yes
$y = x^4 + x^2$	$y = (-x)^4 + (-x)^2$ $= x^4 + x^2$	Yes	Yes
$y = x^3 + x^2$	$y = (-x)^3 + (-x)^2$ $= -x^3 + x^2$	No	No
$y = x^2 + 4x + 2$	$y = (-x)^2 + 4(-x) + 2$ $= x^2 - 4x + 2$	No	No

Classroom Example
Graph $x = \dfrac{1}{2} y^2$.

Some equations yield graphs that have x-axis symmetry. In the next example we will see the graph of a parabola that is symmetric with respect to the x axis.

EXAMPLE 2   Graph $x = y^2$.

Solution

First, we see that $(0, 0)$ is on the graph and determines both intercepts. Second, the given equation is in a convenient form for setting up a table of values.

Plotting these points and connecting them with a smooth curve produces Figure 7.48.

x	y	
0	0	Intercepts
1	1	
1	-1	Other points
4	2	
4	-2	

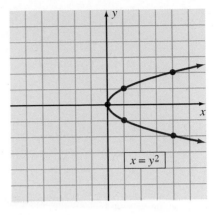

Figure 7.48

The parabola in Figure 7.48 is said to be *symmetric with respect to the x axis*. Each half of the curve is a mirror image of the other half through the *x* axis. Also note in the table of values, that for each ordered pair (x, y), the ordered pair $(x, -y)$ is a solution. A general test for *x*-axis symmetry can be stated as follows:

x-Axis Symmetry

The graph of an equation is symmetric with respect to the *x* axis if replacing *y* with $-y$ results in an equivalent equation.

The equation $x = y^2$ exhibits *x*-axis symmetry because replacing *y* with $-y$ produces $x = (-y)^2 = y^2$. Let's test some equations for *x*-axis symmetry. We will replace *y* with $-y$ and check for an equivalent equation.

Equation	Test for symmetry with respect to the x axis	Equivalent equation	Symmetric with respect to the x axis
$x = y^2 + 5$	$x = (-y)^2 + 5 = y^2 + 5$	Yes	Yes
$x = -3y^2$	$x = -3(-y)^2 = -3y^2$	Yes	Yes
$x = y^3 + 2$	$x = (-y)^3 + 2 = -y^3 + 2$	No	No
$x = y^2 - 5y + 6$	$x = (-y)^2 - 5(-y) + 6$ $= y^2 + 5y + 6$	No	No

In addition to *y*-axis and *x*-axis symmetry, some equations yield graphs that have symmetry with respect to the origin. In the next example we will see a graph that is symmetric with respect to the origin.

Classroom Example

Graph $y = \dfrac{2}{x}$.

EXAMPLE 3   Graph $y = \dfrac{1}{x}$.

Solution

First, let's find the intercepts. Let $x = 0$; then $y = \dfrac{1}{x}$ becomes $y = \dfrac{1}{0}$, and $\dfrac{1}{0}$ is undefined. Thus there is no *y* intercept. Let $y = 0$; then $y = \dfrac{1}{x}$ becomes $0 = \dfrac{1}{x}$, and there are no values of *x*

x	y
$\dfrac{1}{2}$	2
1	1
2	$\dfrac{1}{2}$
3	$\dfrac{1}{3}$
$-\dfrac{1}{2}$	-2
-1	-1
-2	$-\dfrac{1}{2}$
-3	$-\dfrac{1}{3}$

that will satisfy this equation. In other words, this graph has no points on either the x axis or the y axis. Second, let's set up a table of values and keep in mind that neither x nor y can equal zero.

In Figure 7.49(a) we plotted the points associated with the solutions from the table. Because the graph does not intersect either axis, it must consist of two branches. Thus connecting the points in the first quadrant with a smooth curve and then connecting the points in the third quadrant with a smooth curve, we obtain the graph shown in Figure 7.49(b).

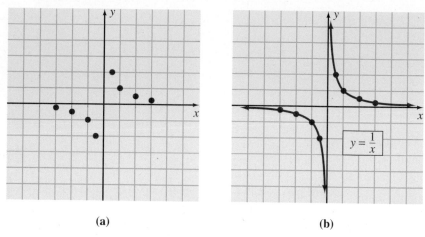

         (a)   (b)

Figure 7.49

The curve in Figure 7.49 is said to be *symmetric with respect to the origin*. Each half of the curve is a mirror image of the other half through the origin. Note in the table of values, that for each ordered pair (x, y), the ordered pair $(-x, -y)$ is also a solution. A general test for origin symmetry can be stated as follows:

Origin Symmetry

The graph of an equation is symmetric with respect to the origin if replacing x with $-x$ and y with $-y$ results in an equivalent equation.

The equation $y = \dfrac{1}{x}$ exhibits symmetry with respect to the origin because replacing y with $-y$ and x with $-x$ produces $-y = \dfrac{1}{-x}$, which is equivalent to $y = \dfrac{1}{x}$. Let's test some equations for symmetry with respect to the origin. We will replace y with $-y$, replace x with $-x$, and then check for an equivalent equation.

Equation	Test for symmetry with respect to the origin	Equivalent equation	Symmetric with respect to the origin
$y = x^3$	$(-y) = (-x)^3$ $-y = -x^3$ $y = x^3$	Yes	Yes
$x^2 + y^2 = 4$	$(-x)^2 + (-y)^2 = 4$ $x^2 + y^2 = 4$	Yes	Yes
$y = x^2 - 3x + 4$	$(-y) = (-x)^2 - 3(-x) + 4$ $-y = x^2 + 3x + 4$ $y = -x^2 - 3x - 4$	No	No

Let's pause for a moment and pull together the graphing techniques that we have introduced thus far. The following list is a set of graphing suggestions. The order of the suggestions indicates the order in which we usually attack a new graphing problem.

1. Determine what type of symmetry the equation exhibits.
2. Find the intercepts.
3. Solve the equation for y in terms of x or for x in terms of y if it is not already in such a form.
4. Set up a table of ordered pairs that satisfy the equation. The type of symmetry will affect your choice of values in the table. (We will illustrate this in a moment.)
5. Plot the points associated with the ordered pairs from the table, and connect them with a smooth curve. Then, if appropriate, reflect this part of the curve according to the symmetry shown by the equation.

Classroom Example
Graph $x^2 y = 3$.

EXAMPLE 4   Graph $x^2 y = -2$.

Solution

Because replacing x with $-x$ produces $(-x)^2 y = -2$ or, equivalently, $x^2 y = -2$, the equation exhibits y-axis symmetry. There are no intercepts because neither x nor y can equal 0. Solving the equation for y produces $y = \dfrac{-2}{x^2}$. The equation exhibits y-axis symmetry, so let's use only positive values for x and then reflect the curve across the y axis.

Let's plot the points determined by the table, connect them with a smooth curve, and reflect this portion of the curve across the y axis. Figure 7.50 is the result of this process.

x	y
1	-2
2	$-\dfrac{1}{2}$
3	$-\dfrac{2}{9}$
4	$-\dfrac{1}{8}$
$\dfrac{1}{2}$	-8

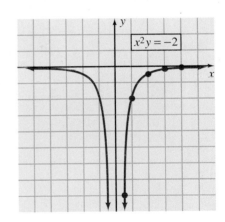

Figure 7.50

Classroom Example
Graph $x = \dfrac{1}{2} y^3$.

EXAMPLE 5   Graph $x = y^3$.

Solution

Because replacing x with $-x$ and y with $-y$ produces $-x = (-y)^3 = -y^3$, which is equivalent to $x = y^3$, the given equation exhibits origin symmetry. If $x = 0$, then $y = 0$, so the origin is a point of the graph. The given equation is in an easy form for deriving a table of values.

x	y
0	0
1	1
8	2
$\dfrac{1}{8}$	$\dfrac{1}{2}$

Let's plot the points determined by the table, connect them with a smooth curve, and reflect this portion of the curve through the origin to produce Figure 7.51.

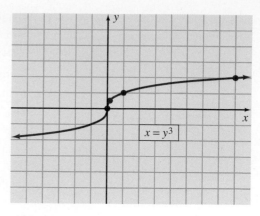

Figure 7.51

Classroom Example
Use a graphing utility to obtain a
graph of the equation $x = \dfrac{1}{2}y^3$.

EXAMPLE 6 Use a graphing utility to obtain a graph of the equation $x = y^3$.

Solution

First, we may need to solve the equation for y in terms of x. (We say we "may need to" because some graphing utilities are capable of graphing two-variable equations without solving for y in terms of x.)

$$y = \sqrt[3]{x} = x^{1/3}$$

Now we can enter the expression $x^{1/3}$ for Y_1 and obtain the graph shown in Figure 7.52.

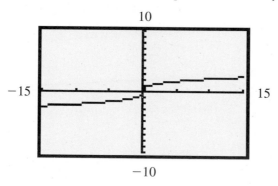

Figure 7.52

As indicated in Figure 7.52, the **viewing rectangle** of a graphing utility is a portion of the xy plane shown on the display of the utility. In this display, the boundaries were set so that $-15 \leq x \leq 15$ and $-10 \leq y \leq 10$. These boundaries were set automatically; however, boundaries can be reassigned as necessary, which is an important feature of graphing utilities.

Concept Quiz 7.5

For Problems 1–10, answer true or false.

1. The equation $y = \sqrt{x}$ is a nonlinear equation.

2. If a graph is symmetric with respect to the y axis, then the x axis is a line of symmetry for the graph.

3. When replacing y with $-y$ in an equation results in an equivalent equation, then the graph of the equation is symmetric with respect to the x axis.

4. If a parabola is symmetric with respect to the x axis, then each half of the curve is a mirror image of the other half through the x axis.

5. If the graph of an equation is symmetric with respect to the x axis, then it cannot be symmetric with respect to the y axis.

6. If the point $(-2, 5)$ is on a graph that is symmetric with respect to the y axis, then the point $(-2, -5)$ is also on the graph.

7. If for each ordered pair (x, y) that is a solution of the equation, the ordered pair $(-x, -y)$ is also a solution, then the graph of the equation is symmetric with respect to the origin.

8. The graph of the line $y = 3x$ is symmetric with respect to the y axis.

9. The graph of a straight line is symmetric with respect to the origin only if the line passes through the origin.

10. Every straight line that passes through the origin is symmetric with respect to the origin.

Problem Set 7.5

For each of the points in Problems 1–5, determine the points that are symmetric with respect to (a) the x axis, (b) the y axis, and (c) the origin. (Objective 2)

1. $(-3, 1)$
2. $(-2, -4)$
3. $(7, -2)$
4. $(0, -4)$
5. $(5, 0)$

For Problems 6–25, determine the type(s) of symmetry (symmetry with respect to the x axis, y axis, and/or origin) exhibited by the graph of each of the following equations. Do not sketch the graph. (Objective 2)

6. $x^2 + 2y = 4$
7. $-3x + 2y^2 = -4$
8. $x = -y^2 + 5$
9. $y = 4x^2 + 13$
10. $xy = -6$
11. $2x^2y^2 = 5$
12. $2x^2 + 3y^2 = 9$
13. $x^2 - 2x - y^2 = 4$
14. $y = x^2 - 6x - 4$
15. $y = 2x^2 - 7x - 3$
16. $y = x$
17. $y = 2x$
18. $y = x^4 + 4$
19. $y = x^4 - x^2 + 2$
20. $x^2 + y^2 = 13$
21. $x^2 - y^2 = -6$
22. $y = -4x^2 - 2$
23. $x = -y^2 + 9$
24. $x^2 + y^2 - 4x - 12 = 0$
25. $2x^2 + 3y^2 + 8y + 2 = 0$

For Problems 26–59, graph each of the equations. (Objective 1)

26. $y = x + 1$
27. $y = x - 4$
28. $y = 3x - 6$
29. $y = 2x + 4$
30. $y = -2x + 1$
31. $y = -3x - 1$
32. $y = \dfrac{2}{3}x - 1$
33. $y = -\dfrac{1}{3}x + 2$
34. $y = \dfrac{1}{3}x$
35. $y = \dfrac{1}{2}x$
36. $2x + y = 6$
37. $2x - y = 4$
38. $x + 3y = -3$
39. $x - 2y = 2$
40. $y = x^2 - 1$
41. $y = x^2 + 2$
42. $y = -x^3$
43. $y = x^3$
44. $y = \dfrac{2}{x^2}$
45. $y = \dfrac{-1}{x^2}$
46. $y = 2x^2$
47. $y = -3x^2$
48. $xy = -3$
49. $xy = 2$
50. $x^2y = 4$
51. $xy^2 = -4$
52. $y^3 = x^2$
53. $y^2 = x^3$
54. $y = \dfrac{-2}{x^2 + 1}$
55. $y = \dfrac{4}{x^2 + 1}$
56. $x = -y^3$
57. $y = x^4$
58. $y = -x^4$
59. $x = -y^3 + 2$

Thoughts Into Words

60. How would you convince someone that there are infinitely many ordered pairs of real numbers that satisfy $x + y = 7$?

61. What is the graph of $x = 0$? What is the graph of $y = 0$? Explain your answers.

62. Is a graph symmetric with respect to the origin if it is symmetric with respect to both axes? Defend your answer.

63. Is a graph symmetric with respect to both axes if it is symmetric with respect to the origin? Defend your answer.

Graphing Calculator Activities

This set of activities is designed to help you get started with your graphing utility by setting different boundaries for the viewing rectangle; you will notice the effect on the graphs produced. These boundaries are usually set by using a menu displayed by a key marked either WINDOW or RANGE. You may need to consult the user's manual for specific key-punching instructions.

64. Graph the equation $y = \dfrac{1}{x}$ (Example 3) using the following boundaries.
   (a) $-15 \leq x \leq 15$ and $-10 \leq y \leq 10$
   (b) $-10 \leq x \leq 10$ and $-10 \leq y \leq 10$
   (c) $-5 \leq x \leq 5$ and $-5 \leq y \leq 5$

65. Graph the equation $y = \dfrac{-2}{x^2}$ (Example 4), using the following boundaries.
   (a) $-15 \leq x \leq 15$ and $-10 \leq y \leq 10$
   (b) $-5 \leq x \leq 5$ and $-10 \leq y \leq 10$
   (c) $-5 \leq x \leq 5$ and $-10 \leq y \leq 1$

66. Graph the two equations $y = \pm\sqrt{x}$ (Example 2) on the same set of axes, using the following boundaries. (Let $Y_1 = \sqrt{x}$ and $Y_2 = -\sqrt{x}$)
   (a) $-15 \leq x \leq 15$ and $-10 \leq y \leq 10$
   (b) $-1 \leq x \leq 15$ and $-10 \leq y \leq 10$
   (c) $-1 \leq x \leq 15$ and $-5 \leq y \leq 5$

67. Graph $y = \dfrac{1}{x}$, $y = \dfrac{5}{x}$, $y = \dfrac{10}{x}$, and $y = \dfrac{20}{x}$ on the same set of axes. (Choose your own boundaries.) What effect does increasing the constant seem to have on the graph?

68. Graph $y = \dfrac{10}{x}$ and $y = \dfrac{-10}{x}$ on the same set of axes. What relationship exists between the two graphs?

69. Graph $y = \dfrac{10}{x^2}$ and $y = \dfrac{-10}{x^2}$ on the same set of axes. What relationship exists between the two graphs?

Answers to the Concept Quiz

1. True   **2.** False   **3.** True   **4.** True   **5.** False   **6.** False   **7.** True   **8.** False   **9.** True   **10.** True

OBJECTIVE	SUMMARY	EXAMPLE
Find solutions for linear equations in two variables. (Section 7.1/Objective 1)	A solution of an equation in two variables is an ordered pair of real numbers that satisfies the equation.	Find a solution for the equation $2x - 3y = -6$. **Solution** Choose an arbitrary value for x and determine the corresponding y value. Let $x = 3$; then substitute 3 for x in the equation. $$2(3) - 3y = -6$$ $$6 - 3y = -6$$ $$-3y = -12$$ $$y = 4$$ Therefore, the ordered pair $(3, 4)$ is a solution.
Graph the solutions for linear equations. (Section 7.1/Objective 3)	A graph provides a visual display of the infinite solutions of an equation in two variables. The ordered-pair solutions for a linear equation can be plotted as points on a rectangular coordinate system. Connecting the points with a straight line produces a graph of the equation. Any equation of the form $Ax + By = C$, where A, B, and C are constants (A and B not both zero) and x and y are variables, is a linear equation, and its graph is a straight line.	Graph $y = 2x - 3$. **Solution** Find at least three ordered-pair solutions for the equation. We can determine that $(-1, -5)$, $(0, -3)$, and $(1, -1)$ are solutions. The graph is shown below. 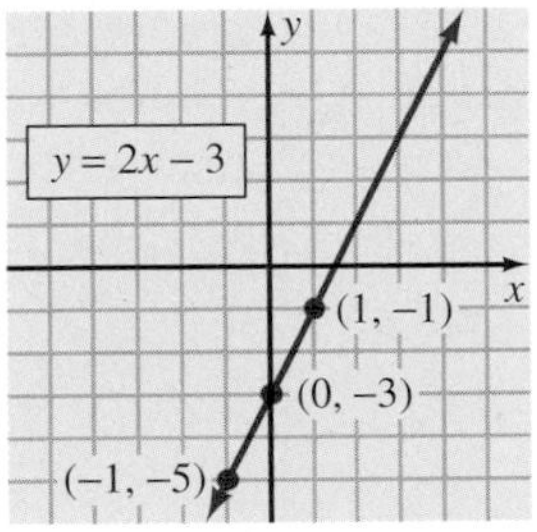
Graph linear equations by finding the x and y intercepts. (Section 7.1/Objective 4)	The x intercept is the x coordinate of the point where the graph intersects the x axis. The y intercept is the y coordinate of the point where the graph intersects the y axis. To find the x intercept, substitute 0 for y in the equation and then solve for x. To find the y intercept, substitute 0 for x in the equation and then solve for y. Plot the intercepts and connect them with a straight line to produce the graph.	Graph $x - 2y = 4$. **Solution** Let $y = 0$. $$x - 2(0) = 4$$ $$x = 4$$ Let $x = 0$. $$0 - 2y = 4$$ $$y = -2$$ 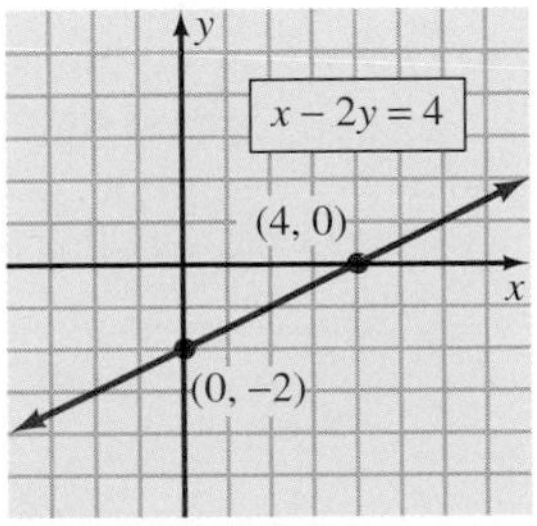

(continued)

OBJECTIVE	SUMMARY	EXAMPLE
Graph lines passing through the origin, vertical lines, and horizontal lines. (Section 7.1/Objective 5)	The graph of any equation of the form $Ax + By = C$, where $C = 0$, is a straight line that passes through the origin. Any equation of the form $x = a$, where a is a constant, is a vertical line. Any equation of the form $y = b$, where b is a constant, is a horizontal line.	Graph $3x + 2y = 0$. **Solution** The equation indicates that the graph will be a line passing through the origin. Solving the equation for y gives us $y = -\dfrac{3}{2}x$. Find at least three ordered-pair solutions for the equation. We can determine that $(-2, 3)$, $(0, 0)$ and $(2, -3)$ are solutions. The graph is shown below. 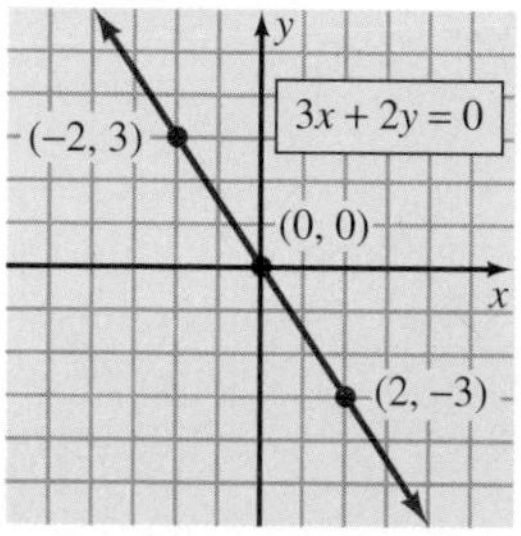
Apply graphing to linear relationships. (Section 7.1/Objective 6)	Many relationships between two quantities are linear relationships. Graphs of these relationships can be used to present information about the relationship.	Let c represent the cost in dollars, and let w represent the gallons of water used; then the equation $c = 0.004w + 20$ can be used to determine the cost of a water bill for a household. Graph the relationship. **Solution** Label the vertical axis c and the horizontal axis w. Because of the type of application, we use only nonnegative values for w. 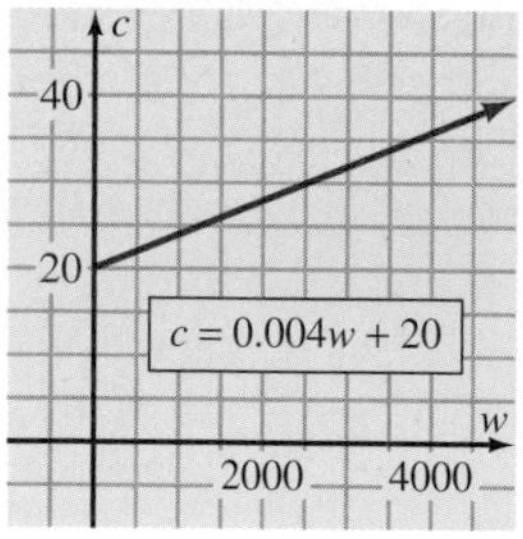
Graph linear inequalities in two variables. (Section 7.2/Objective 1)	To graph a linear inequality, first graph the line for the corresponding equality. Use a solid line if the equality is included in the given statement or a dashed line if the equality is not included. Then a test point is used to determine which half-plane is	Graph $x - 2y \leq -4$. **Solution** First graph $x - 2y = -4$. Choose $(0, 0)$ as a test point. Substituting $(0, 0)$ into the inequality yields $0 \leq -4$. Because the test

OBJECTIVE	SUMMARY	EXAMPLE
	included in the solution set. See page 339 for the detailed steps.	point $(0, 0)$ makes the inequality a false statement, the half-plane not containing the point $(0, 0)$ is in the solution.
Find the distance between two points. (Section 7.3/Objective 1)	The distance between any two points (x_1, y_1) and (x_2, y_2) is given by the distance formula $d = \sqrt{(x_2 - x_1)^2 + (y_2 - y_1)^2}$.	Find the distance between $(1, -5)$ and $(4, 2)$. **Solution** $$d = \sqrt{(x_2 - x_1)^2 + (y_2 - y_1)^2}$$ $$d = \sqrt{(4 - 1)^2 + (2 - (-5))^2}$$ $$d = \sqrt{(3)^2 + (7)^2}$$ $$d = \sqrt{9 + 49} = \sqrt{58}$$
Find the slope of a line. (Section 7.3/Objective 2)	The slope (denoted by m) of a line determined by the points (x_1, y_1) and (x_2, y_2) is given by the slope formula $m = \dfrac{y_2 - y_1}{x_2 - x_1}$ where $x_2 \neq x_1$.	Find the slope of a line that contains the points $(-1, 2)$ and $(7, 8)$. **Solution** Use the slope formula: $$m = \frac{8 - 2}{7 - (-1)} = \frac{6}{8} = \frac{3}{4}$$ Thus the slope of the line is $\dfrac{3}{4}$.
Use slope to graph lines. (Section 7.3/Objective 3)	A line can be graphed if a point on the line and the slope is known; simply plot the point and from that point use the slope to locate another point on the line. Then those two points can be connected with a straight line to produce the graph.	Graph the line that contains the point $(-3, -2)$ and has a slope of $\dfrac{5}{2}$. **Solution** From the point $(-3, -2)$, locate another point by moving up 5 units and to the right 2 units to obtain the point $(-1, 3)$. Then draw the line.

OBJECTIVE	SUMMARY	EXAMPLE
Apply slope to solve problems. (Section 7.3/Objective 4)	The concept of slope is used in most situations where an incline is involved. In highway construction the word "grade" is often used instead of "slope."	A certain highway has a grade of 2%. How many feet does it rise in a horizontal distance of one-third of a mile (1760 feet)? **Solution** A 2% grade is equivalent to a slope of $\dfrac{2}{100}$. We can set up the proportion $\dfrac{2}{100} = \dfrac{y}{1760}$; then solving for y gives us $y = 35.2$. So the highway rises 35.2 feet in one-third of a mile.
Apply the slope-intercept form of an equation of a line. (Section 7.4/Objective 5)	The equation $y = mx + b$ is referred to as the slope-intercept form of the equation of a line. If the equation of a nonvertical line is written in this form, then the coefficient of x is the slope and the constant term is the y intercept.	Change the equation $2x + 7y = -21$ to slope-intercept form and determine the slope and y intercept. **Solution** Solve the equation $2x + 7y = -21$ for y: $$2x + 7y = -21$$ $$7y = -2x - 21$$ $$y = \dfrac{-2}{7}x - 3$$ The slope is $-\dfrac{2}{7}$, and the y intercept is -3.
Find the equation of a line given the slope and a point contained in the line. (Section 7.4/Objective 1)	To determine the equation of a straight line given a set of conditions, we can use the point-slope form $y - y_1 = m(x - x_1)$, or $m = \dfrac{y - y_1}{x - x_1}$. The result can be expressed in standard form or slope-intercept form. **Standard Form** $Ax + By = C$, where B and C are integers, and A is a nonnegative integer (A and B not both zero). **Slope-Intercept Form** $y = mx + b$, where m is a real number representing the slope, and b is a real number representing the y intercept.	Find the equation of a line that contains the point $(1, -4)$ and has a slope of $\dfrac{3}{2}$. **Solution** Substitute $\dfrac{3}{2}$ for m and $(1, -4)$ for (x_1, y_1) into the formula $m = \dfrac{y - y_1}{x - x_1}$: $$\dfrac{3}{2} = \dfrac{y - (-4)}{x - 1}$$ Simplifying the equation yields $3x - 2y = 11$.

OBJECTIVE	SUMMARY	EXAMPLE
Find the equation of a line given two points contained in the line. (Section 7.4/Objective 2)	First calculate the slope of the line. Substitute the slope and the coordinates of one of the points into the following equations. $$y - y_1 = m(x - x_1) \quad \text{or} \quad m = \frac{y - y_1}{x - x_1}.$$	Find the equation of a line that contains the points $(-3, 4)$ and $(-6, 10)$. **Solution** First calculate the slope: $$m = \frac{10 - 4}{-6 - (-3)} = \frac{6}{-3} = -2$$ Now substitute -2 for m and $(-3, 4)$ for (x_1, y_1) in the formula $y - y_1 = m(x - x_1)$: $$y - 4 = -2(x - (-3))$$ Simplifying this equation yields $2x + y = -2$.
Find the equations for parallel and perpendicular lines. (Section 7.4/Objective 6)	If two lines have slopes m_1 and m_2, respectively, then: **1.** The two lines are parallel if and only if $m_1 = m_2$. **2.** The two lines are perpendicular if and only if $(m_1)(m_2) = -1$.	Find the equation of a line that contains the point $(2, 1)$ and is parallel to the line $y = 3x + 4$. **Solution** The slope of the parallel line is 3. Therefore, use this slope and the point $(2, 1)$ to determine the equation: $$y - 1 = 3(x - 2)$$ Simplifying this equation yields $y = 3x - 5$.
Determine if the graph of an equation is symmetric to the x axis, the y axis, or the origin. (Section 7.5/Objective 2)	The graph of an equation is symmetric with respect to the y axis if replacing x with $-x$ results in an equivalent equation. The graph of an equation is symmetric with respect to the x axis if replacing y with $-y$ results in an equivalent equation. The graph of an equation is symmetric with respect to origin if replacing x with $-x$ and y with $-y$ results in an equivalent equation.	Determine the type of symmetry exhibited by the graph of the following equation. $x = y^2 + 4$ **Solution** Replacing x with $-x$ gives $-x = y^2 + 4$. This is not an equivalent equation, so the graph will not exhibit y-axis symmetry. Replacing y with $-y$ gives $x = (-y)^2 + 4 = y^2 + 4$. This is an equivalent equation, so the graph will exhibit x-axis symmetry. Replacing x with $-x$ and y with $-y$ gives: $$(-x) = (-y)^2 + 4$$ $$-x = y^2 + 4$$ This is not an equivalent equation, so the graph will not exhibit symmetry with respect to the origin.

(continued)

OBJECTIVE	SUMMARY	EXAMPLE
Graph nonlinear equations. (Section 7.5/Objective 1)	The following suggestions are offered for graphing an equation in two variables. 1. Determine what type of symmetry the equation exhibits. 2. Find the intercepts. 3. Solve the equation for y or x if it is not already in such a form. 4. Set up a table of ordered pairs that satisfies the equation. The type of symmetry will affect your choice of values in the table. 5. Plot the points associated with the ordered pairs and connect them with a smooth curve. Then, if appropriate, reflect this part of the curve according to the symmetry shown by the equation.	Graph $x \quad y^2 + 4 = 0$. **Solution** Replacing y with $-y$ gives an equivalent equation, so the graph will be symmetric with respect to the x axis. To find the x intercept, let $y = 0$ and solve for x. This gives an x intercept of -4. To find the y intercept, let $x = 0$ and solve for y. This gives y intercepts of 2 and -2. Solving the equation for x gives the equation $x = y^2 - 4$. Choose values for y to obtain the table of points.

x	y
-3	1
0	2
5	3

Chapter 7   Review Problem Set

For Problems 1–4, determine which of the ordered pairs are solutions of the given equation.

1. $4x + y = 6$; $(1, 2)$, $(6, 0)$, $(-1, 10)$

2. $-x + 2y = 4$; $(-4, 1)$, $(-4, -1)$, $(0, 2)$

3. $3x + 2y = 12$; $(2, 3)$, $(-2, 9)$, $(3, 2)$

4. $2x - 3y = -6$; $(0, -2)$, $(-3, 0)$, $(1, 2)$

For Problems 5–8, complete the table of values for the equation and graph the equation.

5. $y = 2x - 5$

x	-1	0	1	4
y				

6. $y = -2x - 1$

x	-3	-1	0	2
y				

7. $y = \dfrac{3x - 4}{2}$

x	-2	0	2	4
y				

8. $2x - 3y = 3$

x	-3	0	3
y			

For Problems 9–12, graph each equation by finding the x and y intercepts.

9. $2x - y = 6$

10. $-3x - 2y = 6$

11. $x - 2y = 4$

12. $5x - y = -5$

For Problems 13–18, graph each equation.

13. $y = -4x$

14. $2x + 3y = 0$

15. $x = 1$

16. $y = -2$

17. $y = 4$

18. $x = -3$

19. (a) An apartment moving company charges according to the equation $c = 75h + 150$, where c represents the charge in dollars and h represents the number of hours for the move. Complete the following table.

h	1	2	3	4
c				

(b) Labeling the horizontal axis h and the vertical axis c, graph the equation $c = 75h + 150$ for nonnegative values of h.

(c) Use the graph from part (b) to approximate values of c when $h = 1.5$ and 3.5.

(d) Check the accuracy of your reading from the graph in part (c) by using the equation $c = 75h + 150$.

20. (a) The value-added tax is computed by the equation $t = 0.15v$ where t represents the tax and v represents the value of the goods. Complete the following table.

v	100	200	350	400
t				

(b) Labeling the horizontal axis v and the vertical axis t, graph the equation $t = 0.15v$ for nonnegative values of v.

(c) Use the graph from part (b) to approximate values of t when $v = 250$ and 300.

(d) Check the accuracy of your reading from the graph in part (c) by using the equation $t = 0.15v$.

For Problems 21–26, graph each inequality.

21. $-x + 3y < -6$

22. $x + 2y \geq 4$

23. $2x - 3y \leq 6$

24. $y > -\dfrac{1}{2}x + 3$

25. $y < 2x - 5$

26. $y \geq \dfrac{2}{3}x$

27. Find the distance between each of the pairs of points.

(a) $(-1, 5)$ and $(1, -2)$

(b) $(5, 0)$ and $(2, 7)$

28. Find the lengths of the sides of a triangle whose vertices are at $(2, 3)$, $(5, -1)$, and $(-4, -5)$.

29. Verify that $(1, 2)$ is the midpoint of the line segment joining $(-3, -1)$ and $(5, 5)$.

30. Find the slope of the line determined by each pair of points.

(a) $(3, 4), (-2, -2)$ **(b)** $(-2, 3), (4, -1)$

31. Find y if the line through $(-4, 3)$ and $(12, y)$ has a slope of $\dfrac{1}{8}$.

32. Find x if the line through $(x, 5)$ and $(3, -1)$ has a slope of $-\dfrac{3}{2}$.

For Problems 33–36, graph the line that has the indicated slope and contains the indicated point.

33. $m = -\dfrac{1}{2}, (0, 3)$ **34.** $m = \dfrac{3}{5}, (0, -4)$

35. $m = 3, (-1, 2)$ **36.** $m = -2, (1, 4)$

37. A certain highway has a 6% grade. How many feet does it rise in a horizontal distance of 1 mile (5280 feet)?

38. If the ratio of rise to run is to be $\dfrac{2}{3}$ for the steps of a staircase, and the run is 12 inches, find the rise.

39. Find the slope of each of the following lines.

(a) $4x + y = 7$ **(b)** $2x - 7y = 3$

40. Find the slope of any line that is perpendicular to the line $-3x + 5y = 7$.

41. Find the slope of any line that is parallel to the line $4x + 5y = 10$.

For Problems 42–49, write the equation of the line that satisfies the stated conditions. Express final equations in standard form.

42. Having a slope of $-\dfrac{3}{7}$ and a y intercept of 4

43. Containing the point $(-1, -6)$ and having a slope of $\dfrac{2}{3}$

44. Containing the point $(3, -5)$ and having a slope of -1

45. Containing the points $(-1, 2)$ and $(3, -5)$

46. Containing the points $(0, 4)$ and $(2, 6)$

47. Containing the point $(2, 5)$ and parallel to the line $x - 2y = 4$

48. Containing the point $(-2, -6)$ and perpendicular to the line $3x + 2y = 12$

49. Containing the point $(-8, 3)$ and parallel to the line $4x + y = 7$

50. The taxes for a primary residence can be described by a linear relationship. Find the equation for the relationship if the taxes for a home valued at $200,000 are $2400, and the taxes are $3150 when the home is valued at $250,000. Let y be the taxes and x the value of the home. Write the equation in slope-intercept form.

51. The freight charged by a trucking firm for a parcel under 200 pounds depends on the distance it is being shipped. To ship a 150-pound parcel 300 miles, it costs $40. If the same parcel is shipped 1000 miles, the cost is $180. Assume the relationship between the cost and distance is linear. Find the equation for the relationship. Let y be the cost and x be the miles. Write the equation in slope-intercept form.

52. On a final exam in math class, the number of points earned has a linear relationship with the number of correct answers. John got 96 points when he answered 12 questions correctly. Kimberly got 144 points when she answered 18 questions correctly. Find the equation for the relationship. Let y be the number of points and x be the number of correct answers. Write the equation in slope-intercept form.

53. The time needed to install computer cables has a linear relationship with the number of feet of cable being installed. It takes $1\frac{1}{2}$ hours to install 300 feet, and 1050 feet can be installed in 4 hours. Find the equation for the relationship. Let y be the feet of cable installed and x be the time in hours. Write the equation in slope-intercept form.

54. Determine the type(s) of symmetry (symmetry with respect to the x axis, y axis, and/or origin) exhibited by the graph of each of the following equations. Do not sketch the graph.

(a) $y = x^2 + 4$ **(b)** $xy = -4$

(c) $y = -x^3$ **(d)** $x = y^4 + 2y^2$

For Problems 55−58, graph each equation.

55. $y = x^3 + 2$ **56.** $y = -x^3$

57. $y = x^2 + 3$ **58.** $y = -2x^2 - 1$

1. Find the slope of the line determined by the points $(-2, 4)$ and $(3, -2)$.

2. Find the slope of the line determined by the equation $3x - 7y = 12$.

3. Find the length of a line segment with endpoints of $(4, 2)$ and $(-3, -1)$. Express the answer in simplest radical form.

4. Find the equation of the line that has a slope of $-\dfrac{3}{2}$ and contains the point $(4, -5)$. Express the equation in standard form.

5. Find the equation of the line that contains the points $(-4, 2)$ and $(2, 1)$. Express the equation in slope-intercept form.

6. Find the equation of the line that is parallel to the line $5x + 2y = 7$ and contains the point $(-2, -4)$. Express the equation in standard form.

7. Find the equation of the line that is perpendicular to the line $x - 6y = 9$ and contains the point $(4, 7)$. Express the equation in standard form.

8. What kind(s) of symmetry does the graph of $y = 9x$ exhibit?

9. What kind(s) of symmetry does the graph of $y^2 = x^2 + 6$ exhibit?

10. What kind(s) of symmetry does the graph of $x^2 + 6x + 2y^2 - 8 = 0$ exhibit?

11. What is the slope of all lines that are parallel to the line $7x - 2y = 9$?

12. What is the slope of all lines that are perpendicular to the line $4x + 9y = -6$?

13. Find the x intercept of the line $y = \dfrac{3}{5}x - \dfrac{2}{3}$.

14. Find the y intercept of the line $\dfrac{3}{4}x - \dfrac{2}{5}y = \dfrac{1}{4}$.

15. The grade of a highway up a hill is 25%. How much change in horizontal distance is there if the vertical height of the hill is 120 feet?

16. Suppose that a highway rises 200 feet in a horizontal distance of 3000 feet. Express the grade of the highway to the nearest tenth of a percent.

17. If the ratio of rise to run is to be $\dfrac{3}{4}$ for the steps of a staircase, and the rise is 32 centimeters, find the run to the nearest centimeter.

For Problems 18–23, graph each equation.

18. $y = -x^2 - 3$

19. $y = -x - 3$

20. $-3x + y = 5$

21. $3y = 2x$

22. $\dfrac{1}{3}x + \dfrac{1}{2}y = 2$

23. $y = \dfrac{-x - 1}{4}$

For Problems 24 and 25, graph each inequality.

24. $2x - y < 4$

25. $3x + 2y \geq 6$

8

Functions

8.1 Concept of a Function

8.2 Linear Functions and Applications

8.3 Quadratic Functions

8.4 More Quadratic Functions and Applications

8.5 Transformations of Some Basic Curves

8.6 Combining Functions

8.7 Direct and Inverse Variation

The price of goods may be decided by using a function to describe the relationship between the price and the demand. Such a function gives us a means of studying the demand when the price is varied.

© Matt Antonio

A golf pro-shop operator finds that she can sell 30 sets of golf clubs in a year at $500 per set. Furthermore, she predicts that for each $25 decrease in price, she could sell three extra sets of golf clubs. At what price should she sell the clubs to maximize gross income? We can use the quadratic function $f(x) = (30 + 3x)(500 - 25x)$ to determine that the clubs should be sold at $375 per set.

One of the fundamental concepts of mathematics is that of a function. Functions unify different areas of mathematics, and they also serve as a meaningful way of applying mathematics to many problems. They provide a means of studying quantities that vary with one another; that is, a change in one produces a corresponding change in another. In this chapter, we will (1) introduce the basic ideas pertaining to functions, (2) use the idea of a function to show how some concepts from previous chapters are related, and (3) discuss some applications in which functions are used.

Video tutorials based on section learning objectives are available in a variety of delivery modes.

| 8.1 | Concept of a Function |

OBJECTIVES

1. Know the definition of a function

2. Apply the vertical line test to determine if a graph represents a function

3. Evaluate a function for a given input value

4. Evaluate a piecewise-defined function for a given input value

5. Find the difference quotient of a function

6. Determine the domain and range of a function

7. Solve application problems involving functions

The notion of correspondence is used in everyday situations and is central to the concept of a function. Consider the following correspondences.

1. To each person in a class, there corresponds an assigned seat.

2. To each day of a year, there corresponds an assigned integer that represents the high temperature for that day in a certain geographic location.

3. To each book in a library, there corresponds a whole number that represents the number of pages in the book.

Such correspondences can be depicted as in Figure 8.1. To each member in set *A*, there corresponds *one and only one* member in set *B*. For example, in the first correspondence, set *A* would consist of the students in a class, and set *B* would be the assigned seats. In the second example, set *A* would consist of the days of a year and set *B* would be a set of integers. Furthermore, the same integer might be assigned to

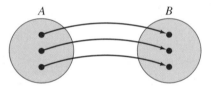

Figure 8.1

more than one day of the year. (Different days might have the same high temperature.) The key idea is that *one and only one* integer is assigned to *each* day of the year. Likewise, in the third example, more than one book may have the same number of pages, but to each book, there is assigned one and only one number that represents the number of pages.

Mathematically, the general concept of a function can be defined as follows:

Definition 8.1

A **function** *f* is a correspondence between two sets *X* and *Y* that assigns to each element *x* of set *X* one and only one element *y* of set *Y*. The element *y* being assigned is called the **image** of *x*. The set *X* is called the **domain** of the function, and the set of all images is called the **range** of the function.

In Definition 8.1, the image *y* is usually denoted by $f(x)$. Thus the symbol $f(x)$, which is read "*f* of *x*" or "the value of *f* at *x*," represents the element in the range associated with the element *x* from the domain. Figure 8.2 depicts this situation. Again we emphasize that each member of the domain has precisely one image in the range; however, different members in the domain, such as *a* and *b* in Figure 8.2, may have the same image.

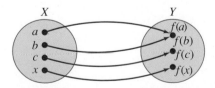

Figure 8.2

In Definition 8.1, we named the function f. It is common to name a function with a single letter, and the letters f, g, and h are often used. We suggest more meaningful choices when functions are used in real-world situations. For example, if a problem involves a profit function, then naming the function p or even P seems natural. Be careful not to confuse f and $f(x)$. Remember that f is used to name a function, whereas $f(x)$ is an element of the range—namely, the element assigned to x by f.

The assignments made by a function are often expressed as ordered pairs. For example, the assignments in Figure 8.2 could be expressed as $(a, f(a))$, $(b, f(b))$, $(c, f(c))$, and $(x, f(x))$, where the first components are from the domain, and the second components are from the range. Thus a function can also be thought of as a set of ordered pairs in which no two of the ordered pairs have the same first component.

Remark: In some texts, the concept of a relation is introduced first, and then functions are defined as special kinds of relations. A **relation** is defined as a set of ordered pairs, and a function is defined as a relation in which no two ordered pairs have the same first element.

The ordered pairs that represent a function can be generated by various means, such as a graph or a chart. However, one of the most common ways of generating ordered pairs is by using equations. For example, the equation $f(x) = 2x + 3$ indicates that to each value of x in the domain, we assign $2x + 3$ from the range. For example,

$f(1) = 2(1) + 3 = 5$ produces the ordered pair $(1, 5)$

$f(4) = 2(4) + 3 = 11$ produces the ordered pair $(4, 11)$

$f(-2) = 2(-2) + 3 = -1$ produces the ordered pair $(-2, -1)$

It may be helpful for you to picture the concept of a function in terms of a function machine, as illustrated in Figure 8.3. Each time a value of x is put into the machine, the equation $f(x) = 2x + 3$ is used to generate one and only one value for $f(x)$.

Using the ordered-pair interpretation of a function, we can define the **graph** of a function f to be the set of all points in a plane of the form $(x, f(x))$, where x is from the domain of f. In other words, the graph of f is the same as the graph of the equation $y = f(x)$. Furthermore, because $f(x)$, or y, takes on only one value for each value of x, we can easily tell whether a given graph represents a function. For example,

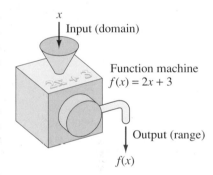

Figure 8.3

in Figure 8.4(a), for any choice of x there is only one value for y. Geometrically this means that no vertical line intersects the curve in more than one point. On the other hand, Figure 8.4(b) does not represent the graph of a function because certain values of x (all positive values) produce more than one value for y. In other words, some vertical lines intersect the curve in more than one point, as illustrated in Figure 8.4(b).

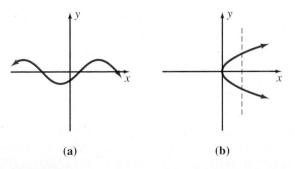

(a)   (b)

Figure 8.4

A vertical-line test for functions can be stated as follows.

> **Vertical-Line Test**
>
> If each vertical line intersects a graph in no more than one point, then the graph represents a function.

Let's consider some examples to illustrate these ideas about functions.

EXAMPLE 1   If $f(x) = x^2 - x + 4$, find $f(3)$, $f(-1)$, $f(a)$, $f(2a)$, and $f(a + 3)$.

Solution

$$f(3) = (3)^2 - (3) + 4 = 9 - 3 + 4 = 10$$
$$f(-1) = (-1)^2 - (-1) + 4 = 1 + 1 + 4 = 6$$
$$f(a) = (a)^2 - (a) + 4 = a^2 - a + 4$$
$$f(2a) = (2a)^2 - (2a) + 4 = 4a^2 - 2a + 4$$
$$f(a + 3) = (a + 3)^2 - (a + 3) + 4 = a^2 + 6a + 9 - a - 3 + 4 = a^2 + 5a + 10$$

Evaluating Piecewise-Defined Functions

Sometimes the rule of assignment for a function consists of more than one part. Different rules are assigned depending on x, the element in the domain. An everyday example of this concept is that the price of admission to a theme park depends on whether you are a child, an adult, or a senior citizen. In mathematics we often refer to such functions as *piecewise-defined functions*. Let's consider examples of such functions.

EXAMPLE 2

A county government collects taxes for schools based on the income of its citizens rather than on real estate taxes. The county uses the following function to determine the amount of tax due; x represents a citizen's annual income in dollars.

$$f(x) = \begin{cases} 0.05x & 0 < x \le 20{,}000 \\ 0.06x & 20{,}000 < x \le 50{,}000 \\ 0.08x & 50{,}000 < x \end{cases}$$

If Darren, Martha, Tonieka, and Caleb earn annual incomes of $23,000, $18,500, $55,000, and $20,000, respectively, find the amount of tax each of them owes.

Solution

Because Darren has an income of $23,000, the function to be used is $f(x) = 0.06x$. Therefore, the tax is figured as $f(23000) = 0.06(23000) = 1380$. Darren will owe $1,380 in tax.

Because Martha has an income of $18,500, the function to be used is $f(x) = 0.05x$. Therefore, the tax is figured as $f(18500) = 0.05(18500) = 925$. Martha will owe $925 in tax.

Because Tonieka has an income of $55,000, the function to be used is $f(x) = 0.08x$. Therefore, the tax is figured as $f(55000) = 0.08(55000) = 4400$. Tonieka will owe $4,400 in tax.

Because Caleb has an income of $20,000, the function to be used is $f(x) = 0.05x$. Therefore, the tax is figured as $f(20000) = 0.05(20000) = 1000$. Caleb will owe $1000 in tax.

EXAMPLE 3   If $f(x) = \begin{cases} 2x + 1 & \text{for } x \geq 0 \\ 3x - 1 & \text{for } x < 0 \end{cases}$ find $f(2), f(4), f(-1)$, and $f(-3)$.

Solution

For $x \geq 0$, we use the assignment $f(x) = 2x + 1$.

$$f(2) = 2(2) + 1 = 5$$
$$f(4) = 2(4) + 1 = 9$$

For $x < 0$, we use the assignment $f(x) = 3x - 1$.

$$f(-1) = 3(-1) - 1 = -4$$
$$f(-3) = 3(-3) - 1 = -10$$

Finding the Difference Quotient

The quotient $\dfrac{f(a + h) - f(a)}{h}$ is often called a **difference quotient**. We use it extensively with functions when we study the limit concept in calculus. The next examples illustrate finding the difference quotient for specific functions.

EXAMPLE 4   Find $\dfrac{f(a + h) - f(a)}{h}$ for each of the following functions.

(a) $f(x) = x^2 + 6$ **(b)** $f(x) = 2x^2 + 3x - 4$ **(c)** $f(x) = \dfrac{1}{x}$

Solutions

(a) $f(a) = a^2 + 6$

$$f(a + h) = (a + h)^2 + 6 = a^2 + 2ah + h^2 + 6$$

Therefore

$$f(a + h) - f(a) = (a^2 + 2ah + h^2 + 6) - (a^2 + 6)$$
$$= a^2 + 2ah + h^2 + 6 - a^2 - 6$$
$$= 2ah + h^2$$

and

$$\frac{f(a + h) - f(a)}{h} = \frac{2ah + h^2}{h} = \frac{h(2a + h)}{h} = 2a + h$$

(b) $f(a) = 2a^2 + 3a - 4$

$$f(a + h) = 2(a + h)^2 + 3(a + h) - 4$$
$$= 2(a^2 + 2ha + h^2) + 3a + 3h - 4$$
$$= 2a^2 + 4ha + 2h^2 + 3a + 3h - 4$$

Therefore

$$f(a + h) - f(a) = (2a^2 + 4ha + 2h^2 + 3a + 3h - 4) - (2a^2 + 3a - 4)$$
$$= 2a^2 + 4ha + 2h^2 + 3a + 3h - 4 - 2a^2 - 3a + 4$$
$$= 4ha + 2h^2 + 3h$$

and

$$\frac{f(a + h) - f(a)}{h} = \frac{4ha + 2h^2 + 3h}{h}$$
$$= \frac{h(4a + 2h + 3)}{h}$$
$$= 4a + 2h + 3$$

(c) $$f(a) = \frac{1}{a}$$

$$f(a + h) = \frac{1}{a + h}$$

Therefore

$$f(a + h) - f(a) = \frac{1}{a + h} - \frac{1}{a}$$

$$= \frac{a}{a(a + h)} - \frac{a + h}{a(a + h)} \qquad \text{Common denominator of } a(a + h)$$

$$= \frac{a - (a + h)}{a(a + h)}$$

$$= \frac{a - a - h}{a(a + h)}$$

$$= \frac{-h}{a(a + h)} \qquad \text{or} \qquad -\frac{h}{a(a + h)}$$

and

$$\frac{f(a + h) - f(a)}{h} = \frac{-\dfrac{h}{a(a + h)}}{h}$$

$$= -\frac{h}{a(a + h)} \cdot \frac{1}{h}$$

$$= -\frac{1}{a(a + h)}$$ ■

Determining the Domain and Range of a Function

For our purposes in this text, if the domain of a function is not specifically indicated or determined by a real-world application, then we will assume the domain is *all real number* replacements for the variable, provided that they represent elements in the domain and produce real number functional values. We have to be careful with functions that involve fractions and radicals. For functions that involve fractions, the domain cannot include any values that would make the denominator of the fraction equal to zero. For functions that involve radicals, the domain cannot include any values for which the radical would not be a real number, such as taking the square root of a negative number.

Classroom Example
For the function $f(x) = \sqrt{2x + 6}$, (a) specify the domain, (b) determine the range, and (c) evaluate $f\left(\frac{3}{2}\right)$, $f(29)$, and $f(6)$.

EXAMPLE 5

For the function $f(x) = \sqrt{x - 1}$, (a) specify the domain, (b) determine the range, and (c) evaluate $f(5)$, $f(50)$, and $f(25)$.

Solutions

(a) The radicand must be nonnegative, so $x - 1 \geq 0$ and thus $x \geq 1$. Therefore the domain (D) is

$$D = \{x \,|\, x \geq 1\}$$

(b) The symbol $\sqrt{}$ indicates the nonnegative square root; thus the range (R) is

$$R = \{f(x) \,|\, f(x) \geq 0\}$$

(c) $f(5) = \sqrt{4} = 2$

$f(50) = \sqrt{49} = 7$

$f(25) = \sqrt{24} = 2\sqrt{6}$ ■

As we will see later, the range of a function is often easier to determine after we have graphed the function. However, our equation- and inequality-solving processes are frequently sufficient to determine the domain of a function. Let's consider some examples.

Classroom Example
Determine the domain for each of the following functions:

(a) $f(x) = \dfrac{7}{3x + 4}$

(b) $f(x) = \dfrac{1}{x^2 - 16}$

(c) $f(x) = \sqrt{x^2 - 5x - 24}$

EXAMPLE 6 Determine the domain for each of the following functions:

(a) $f(x) = \dfrac{3}{2x - 5}$ **(b)** $g(x) = \dfrac{1}{x^2 - 9}$ **(c)** $f(x) = \sqrt{x^2 + 4x - 12}$

Solutions

(a) We need to eliminate any values of x that will make the denominator zero. Therefore let's solve the equation $2x - 5 = 0$:

$$2x - 5 = 0$$
$$2x = 5$$
$$x = \frac{5}{2}$$

We can replace x with any real number except $\frac{5}{2}$ because $\frac{5}{2}$ makes the denominator zero. Thus the domain is

$$D = \left\{x \mid x \neq \frac{5}{2}\right\}$$

(b) We need to eliminate any values of x that will make the denominator zero. Let's solve the equation $x^2 - 9 = 0$:

$$x^2 - 9 = 0$$
$$x^2 = 9$$
$$x = \pm 3$$

The domain is thus the set

$$D = \{x \mid x \neq 3 \text{ and } x \neq -3\}$$

(c) The radicand, $x^2 + 4x - 12$, must be nonnegative. Let's use a number line approach, as we did in Chapter 6, to solve the inequality $x^2 + 4x - 12 \geq 0$ (see Figure 8.5):

$$x^2 + 4x - 12 \geq 0$$
$$(x + 6)(x - 2) \geq 0$$

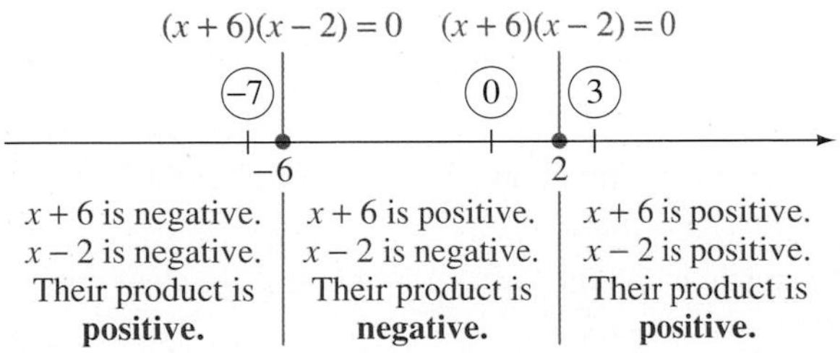

Figure 8.5

The product $(x + 6)(x - 2)$ is nonnegative if $x \leq -6$ or $x \geq 2$. Using interval notation, we can express the domain as $(-\infty, -6] \cup [2, \infty)$.

Functions and function notation provide the basis for describing many real-world relationships. The next example illustrates this point.

EXAMPLE 7

Suppose a factory determines that the overhead for producing a quantity of a certain item is $500 and that the cost for producing each item is $25. Express the total expenses as a function of the number of items produced, and compute the expenses for producing 12, 25, 50, 75, and 100 items.

Solution

Let n represent the number of items produced. Then $25n + 500$ represents the total expenses. Using E to represent the expense function, we have

$$E(n) = 25n + 500, \quad \text{where } n \text{ is a whole number}$$

We obtain

$$E(12) = 25(12) + 500 = 800$$
$$E(25) = 25(25) + 500 = 1125$$
$$E(50) = 25(50) + 500 = 1750$$
$$E(75) = 25(75) + 500 = 2375$$
$$E(100) = 25(100) + 500 = 3000$$

Thus the total expenses for producing 12, 25, 50, 75, and 100 items are $800, $1125, $1750, $2375, and $3000, respectively.

∎

As we stated before, an equation such as $f(x) = 5x - 7$ that is used to determine a function can also be written $y = 5x - 7$. In either form, we refer to x as the **independent variable** and to y, or $f(x)$, as the **dependent variable**. Many formulas in mathematics and other related areas also determine functions. For example, the area formula for a circular region, $A = \pi r^2$, assigns to each positive real value for r a unique value for A. This formula determines a function f, where $f(r) = \pi r^2$. The variable r is the independent variable, and A, or $f(r)$, is the dependent variable.

Concept Quiz 8.1

For Problems 1–10, answer true or false.

1. For a function, each member of the domain has precisely one image in the range.
2. The set of ordered pairs $\{(1, 2), (2, 2), (3, 2), (4, 2)\}$ is a function.
3. The graph of a function g is the set of all points in a plane of the form $(x, g(x))$, where x is from the domain of g.
4. If a vertical line intersects a graph at more than one point, then the graph does not represent a function.
5. A piecewise-defined function assigns different rules to subsets of the domain.
6. The quotient $\dfrac{f(a) - f(a - h)}{a}$ is called the difference quotient.
7. For the function $f(r) = 2\pi r$, r is the dependent variable.
8. The domain of the function $\{(1, 1), (2, 4), (3, 9), (4, 16)\}$ is the set $\{1, 2, 3, 4, 9, 16\}$.
9. The range of the function $\{(-2, 4), (-1, 1), (0, 0), (1, 1), (2, 4)\}$ is the set $\{0, 1, 4\}$.
10. The definition of a relation and the definition of a function are the same.

Problem Set 8.1

For Problems 1–6, state whether or not the set of ordered pairs represents a function. (Objective 1)

1. $\{(1,5),(2,8),(3,11),(4,14)\}$

2. $\{(0,0),(2,10),(4,20),(6,30),(8,40)\}$

3. $\{(0,5),(0,-5),(1,2\sqrt{6}),(1,-2\sqrt{6})\}$

4. $\{(1,1),(1,2),(1,-1),(1,-2),(1,3)\}$

5. $\{(1,2),(2,5),(3,10),(4,17),(5,26)\}$

6. $\{(-1,5),(0,1),(1,-3),(2,-7)\}$

For Problems 7–14 (Figures 8.6–8.13), determine whether the indicated graph represents a function of x. (Objective 2)

7.

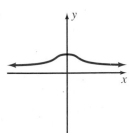

Figure 8.6

8.

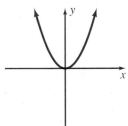

Figure 8.7

9.

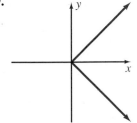

Figure 8.8

10.

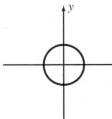

Figure 8.9

11.

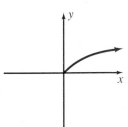

Figure 8.10

12.

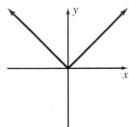

Figure 8.11

13.

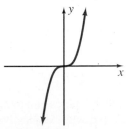

Figure 8.12

14.

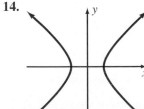

Figure 8.13

For Problems 15–28, evaluate each function for the given values. (Objective 3)

15. If $f(x) = -2x + 5$, find $f(3), f(5)$, and $f(-2)$.

16. If $f(x) = x^2 - 3x - 4$, find $f(2), f(4)$, and $f(-3)$.

17. If $g(x) = -2x^2 + x - 5$, find $g(3), g(-1)$, and $g(2a)$.

18. If $g(x) = -x^2 - 4x + 6$, find $g(0), g(5)$, and $g(-a)$.

19. If $h(x) = \dfrac{2}{3}x - \dfrac{3}{4}$, find $h(3), h(4)$, and $h\left(-\dfrac{1}{2}\right)$.

20. If $h(x) = -\dfrac{1}{2}x + \dfrac{2}{3}$, find $h(-2), h(6)$, and $h\left(-\dfrac{2}{3}\right)$.

21. If $f(x) = \sqrt{2x - 1}$, find $f(5), f\left(\dfrac{1}{2}\right)$, and $f(23)$.

22. If $f(x) = \sqrt{3x + 2}$, find $f\left(\dfrac{14}{3}\right), f(10)$, and $f\left(-\dfrac{1}{3}\right)$.

23. If $f(x) = -2x + 7$, find $f(a), f(a + 2)$, and $f(a + h)$.

24. If $f(x) = x^2 - 7x$, find $f(a), f(a - 3)$, and $f(a + h)$.

25. If $f(x) = x^2 - 4x + 10$, find $f(-a)$, $f(a - 4)$, and $f(a + h)$.

26. If $f(x) = 2x^2 - x - 1$, find $f(-a)$, $f(a + 1)$, and $f(a + h)$.

27. If $f(x) = -x^2 + 3x + 5$, find $f(-a), f(a + 6)$, and $f(-a + 1)$.

28. If $f(x) = -x^2 - 2x - 7$, find $f(-a), f(-a - 2)$, and $f(a + 7)$.

For Problems 29–34, evaluate each piecewise-defined function for the given values. (Objective 4)

29. If $f(x) = \begin{cases} x & \text{for } x \geq 0 \\ x^2 & \text{for } x < 0 \end{cases}$, find $f(4), f(10), f(-3)$, and $f(-5)$.

30. If $f(x) = \begin{cases} 3x + 2 & \text{for } x \geq 0 \\ 5x - 1 & \text{for } x < 0 \end{cases}$, find $f(2), f(6), f(-1)$, and $f(-4)$.

31. If $f(x) = \begin{cases} 2x & \text{for } x \geq 0 \\ -2x & \text{for } x < 0 \end{cases}$, find $f(3), f(5), f(-3)$, and $f(-5)$.

32. If $f(x) = \begin{cases} 2 & \text{for } x < 0 \\ x^2 + 1 & \text{for } 0 \leq x \leq 4, \\ -1 & \text{for } x > 4 \end{cases}$ find $f(3), f(6), f(0)$, and $f(-3)$.

33. If $f(x) = \begin{cases} 1 & \text{for } x > 0 \\ 0 & \text{for } -1 < x \le 0, \\ -1 & \text{for } x \le -1 \end{cases}$ find $f(2), f(0),$ $f\left(-\dfrac{1}{2}\right),$ and $f(-4).$

34. If $f(x) = \begin{cases} -x^2 & \text{for } x < 0 \\ x^2 & \text{for } x \ge 0 \end{cases}$, find $f(3), f(-1), f(-2),$ and $f(1).$

For Problems 35–48, find $\dfrac{f(a+h) - f(a)}{h}$. **(Objective 5)**

35. $f(x) = 3x + 8$ **36.** $f(x) = 4x + 5$

37. $f(x) = -7x - 2$ **38.** $f(x) = -2x + 3$

39. $f(x) = -x^2 + 4x - 2$ **40.** $f(x) = x^2 - 3x$

41. $f(x) = 3x^2 - x - 4$ **42.** $f(x) = 2x^2 + 7x - 4$

43. $f(x) = x^3 - x^2 + 2x - 1$ **44.** $f(x) = x^3$

45. $f(x) = \dfrac{2}{x-1}$ **46.** $f(x) = \dfrac{1}{x+1}$

47. $f(x) = \dfrac{1}{x^2}$ **48.** $f(x) = \dfrac{x}{x+1}$

For Problems 49–62, determine the domain and the range of the given function. **(Objective 6)**

49. $f(x) = \sqrt{3x - 4}$ **50.** $f(x) = \sqrt{x}$

51. $f(x) = x^2 - 2$ **52.** $f(x) = x^2 + 1$

53. $f(x) = |x|$ **54.** $f(x) = x^3$

55. $f(x) = -\sqrt{x}$ **56.** $f(x) = x^4$

57. $f(x) = \sqrt{2x - 5}$

58. $f(x) = \sqrt{x - 2} + 3$

59. $f(x) = \sqrt{x + 4} - 2$

60. $f(x) = |x| + 5$

61. $f(x) = -|x| - 6$

62. $f(x) = |x - 1| - 3$

For Problems 63–76, determine the domain of the given function. **(Objective 6)**

63. $f(x) = \dfrac{-4}{x+2}$ **64.** $f(x) = \dfrac{3}{x-4}$

65. $f(x) = \dfrac{5}{(2x-1)(x+4)}$

66. $f(x) = \dfrac{2x}{(x-2)(x+3)}$

67. $f(x) = \dfrac{1}{x^2 - 4}$

68. $f(x) = \sqrt{5x + 1}$

69. $f(x) = \dfrac{4x}{x^2 - x - 12}$

70. $g(x) = \dfrac{3}{x^2 + 5x + 6}$

71. $g(x) = \dfrac{x}{6x^2 + 13x - 5}$

72. $g(x) = \dfrac{5}{x^2 + 4x}$

73. $f(x) = \dfrac{x + 2}{x^2 + 1}$

74. $f(x) = \sqrt{-3x - 1}$

75. $f(x) = \sqrt{-4x + 3}$

76. $f(x) = \dfrac{2x - 1}{x^2 + 4}$

For Problems 77–86, express the domain of the given function using interval notation. **(Objective 6)**

77. $f(x) = \sqrt{x^2 - 16}$

78. $f(x) = \sqrt{x^2 - 1}$

79. $f(x) = \sqrt{x^2 + 1} - 4$

80. $f(x) = \sqrt{x^2 + 4}$

81. $f(x) = \sqrt{x^2 - 3x - 40}$

82. $f(x) = \sqrt{x^2 - 2x - 24}$

83. $f(x) = -\sqrt{8x^2 + 6x - 35}$

84. $f(x) = \sqrt{12x^2 + x - 6}$

85. $f(x) = \sqrt{1 - x^2}$

86. $f(x) = \sqrt{16 - x^2}$

For Problems 87–96, solve each problem. **(Objective 7)**

87. A copy center charges for copies depending on the number of copies made. The following functions are used to determine the cost in dollars of color or black and white copies, where n is the number of copies.

Color Copies	**Black and White Copies**
$f(n) = \begin{cases} 0.89n & 0 < n \le 20 \\ 0.79n & 20 < n \le 50 \\ 0.69n & 50 < n \end{cases}$	$f(n) = \begin{cases} 0.09n & 0 < n \le 50 \\ 0.08n & 50 < n \le 200 \\ 0.06n & 200 < n \end{cases}$

Isaac is producing a cookbook that requires him to make 20 color copies and 210 black and white copies. What will it cost Isaac to make the copies?

88. An equipment rental agency charges rent in dollars for a small backhoe according to the following function, in which h represents the number of hours the backhoe is rented. Find the rent charged when the backhoe is rented for 6.5 hours; 3 hours; and 10 hours.

$$f(h) = \begin{cases} 100 + 50h & 0 < h \le 3 \\ 160 + 30h & 3 < h \le 8 \\ 200 + 25h & 8 < h \end{cases}$$

89. The equation $A(r) = \pi r^2$ expresses the area of a circular region as a function of the length of a radius (r). Compute $A(2)$, $A(3)$, $A(12)$, and $A(17)$ and express your answers to the nearest hundredth.

90. Suppose that the profit function for selling n items is given by

$$P(n) = -n^2 + 500n - 61{,}500$$

Evaluate $P(200)$, $P(230)$, $P(250)$, and $P(260)$.

91. The height of a projectile fired vertically into the air (neglecting air resistance) at an initial velocity of 64 feet per second is a function of the time (t) and is given by the equation $h(t) = 64t - 16t^2$. Compute $h(1)$, $h(2)$, $h(3)$, and $h(4)$.

92. In a physics experiment, it is found that the equation $V(t) = 1667t - 6940t^2$ expresses the velocity of an object as a function of time (t). Compute $V(0.1)$, $V(0.15)$, and $V(0.2)$.

93. The equation $I(r) = 500r$ expresses the amount of simple interest earned by an investment of \$500 for 1 year as a function of the rate of interest (r). Compute $I(0.11)$, $I(0.12)$, $I(0.135)$, and $I(0.15)$.

94. A car rental agency charges \$50 per day plus \$0.32 a mile. Therefore the daily charge for renting a car is a function of the number of miles traveled (m) and can be expressed as $C(m) = 50 + 0.32m$. Compute $C(75)$, $C(150)$, $C(225)$, and $C(650)$.

95. The equation $A(r) = 2\pi r^2 + 16\pi r$ expresses the total surface area of a right circular cylinder of height 8 centimeters as a function of the length of a radius (r). Compute $A(2)$, $A(4)$, and $A(8)$ and express your answers to the nearest hundredth.

96. Suppose the height of a semielliptical archway is given by the function $h(x) = \sqrt{64 - 4x^2}$, where x is the distance from the center line of the arch. Compute $h(0)$, $h(2)$, and $h(4)$.

Thoughts Into Words

97. What does it mean to say that the domain of a function may be restricted if the function represents a real-world situation? Give three examples of such functions.

98. Expand Definition 8.1 to include a definition for the concept of a relation.

99. Are there any functions for which $f(a + b) = f(a) + f(b)$? Defend your answer.

100. Does $f(a + b) = f(a) + f(b)$ for all functions? Defend your answer.

Answers to the Concept Quiz

1. True   **2.** True   **3.** True   **4.** True   **5.** True   **6.** False   **7.** False   **8.** False   **9.** True   **10.** False

---

8.2   Linear Functions and Applications

OBJECTIVES   **1** Graph linear functions

2 Determine a linear function for specified conditions

3 Solve application problems involving linear functions

As we use the function concept in our study of mathematics, it is helpful to classify certain types of functions and become familiar with their equations, characteristics, and graphs. This will enhance our problem-solving capabilities.

Any function that can be written in the form

$$f(x) = ax + b$$

where a and b are real numbers, is called a **linear function**. The following equations are examples of linear functions.

$$f(x) = -2x + 4 \qquad f(x) = 3x - 6 \qquad f(x) = \frac{2}{3}x + \frac{5}{6}$$

The equation $f(x) = ax + b$ can also be written as $y = ax + b$. From our work in Section 7.5, we know that $y = ax + b$ is the equation of a straight line that has a slope of a and a y intercept of b. This information can be used to graph linear functions, as illustrated by the following example.

Classroom Example
Graph $f(x) = -x - 2$.

EXAMPLE 1   Graph $f(x) = -2x + 4$.

Solution

Because the y intercept is 4, the point $(0, 4)$ is on the line. Furthermore, because the slope is -2, we can move two units down and one unit to the right of $(0, 4)$ to determine the point $(1, 2)$. The line determined by $(0, 4)$ and $(1, 2)$ is drawn in Figure 8.14.

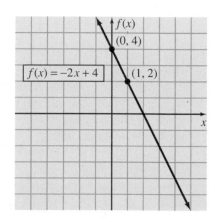

Figure 8.14

Note that in Figure 8.14, we labeled the vertical axis $f(x)$. We could also label it y because $y = f(x)$. We will use the $f(x)$ labeling for most of our work with functions; however, we will continue to refer to y-axis symmetry instead of $f(x)$-axis symmetry.

Recall from Section 7.2 that we can also graph linear equations by finding the two intercepts. This same approach can be used with linear functions, as illustrated by the next two examples.

Classroom Example
Graph $f(x) = 2x + 3$.

EXAMPLE 2   Graph $f(x) = 3x - 6$.

Solution

First, we see that $f(0) = -6$; thus the point $(0, -6)$ is on the graph. Second, by setting $3x - 6$ equal to zero and solving for x, we obtain

$$3x - 6 = 0$$
$$3x = 6$$
$$x = 2$$

Therefore $f(2) = 3(2) - 6 = 0$, and the point $(2, 0)$ is on the graph. The line determined by $(0, -6)$ and $(2, 0)$ is shown in Figure 8.15.

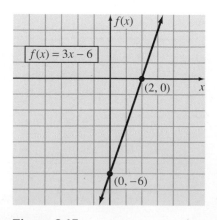

Figure 8.15

EXAMPLE 3   Graph the function $f(x) = \dfrac{2}{3}x + \dfrac{5}{6}$.

Solution

Because $f(0) = \dfrac{5}{6}$, the point $\left(0, \dfrac{5}{6}\right)$ is on the graph. By setting $\dfrac{2}{3}x + \dfrac{5}{6}$ equal to zero and

solving for x, we obtain

$$\frac{2}{3}x + \frac{5}{6} = 0$$

$$\frac{2}{3}x = -\frac{5}{6}$$

$$x = -\frac{5}{4}$$

Therefore $f\left(-\dfrac{5}{4}\right) = 0$, and the point $\left(-\dfrac{5}{4}, 0\right)$ is on

the graph. The line determined by the two points

$\left(0, \dfrac{5}{6}\right)$ and $\left(-\dfrac{5}{4}, 0\right)$ is shown in Figure 8.16.

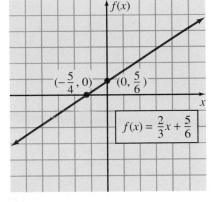

Figure 8.16

As you graph functions using function notation, it is often helpful to think of the ordinate of every point on the graph as the value of the function at a specific value of x. Geometrically the functional value is the directed distance of the point from the x axis. This idea is illustrated in Figure 8.17 for the function $f(x) = x$ and in Figure 8.18 for the function $f(x) = 2$. The linear function $f(x) = x$ is often called the **identity function**. Any linear function of the form $f(x) = ax + b$, where $a = 0$, is called a **constant function**.

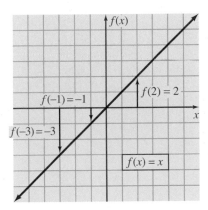

Figure 8.17

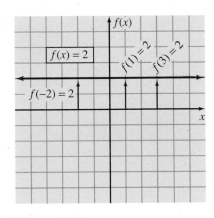

Figure 8.18

From our previous work with linear equations, we know that parallel lines have equal slopes and that two perpendicular lines have slopes that are negative reciprocals of each other. Thus when we work with linear functions of the form $f(x) = ax + b$, it is easy to recognize parallel and perpendicular lines. For example, the lines determined by $f(x) = 0.21x + 4$ and $g(x) = 0.21x - 3$ are parallel lines because both lines have a slope of 0.21 and different y intercepts. Let's use a graphing calculator to graph these two functions along with $h(x) = 0.21x + 2$ and $p(x) = 0.21x - 7$ (Figure 8.19).

The graphs of the functions $f(x) = \dfrac{2}{5}x + 8$ and $g(x) = -\dfrac{5}{2}x - 4$ are perpendicular lines

because the slopes $\left(\dfrac{2}{5} \text{ and } -\dfrac{5}{2}\right)$ of the two lines are negative reciprocals of each other. Again

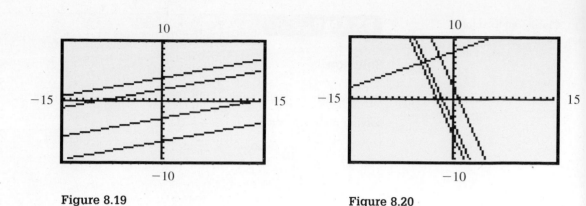

Figure 8.19   **Figure 8.20**

using our graphing calculator, let's graph these two functions along with $h(x) = -\dfrac{5}{2}x + 2$ and $p(x) = -\dfrac{5}{2}x - 6$ (Figure 8.20). If the lines do not appear to be perpendicular, you may want to change the window with a zoom square option.

Remark: A property of plane geometry states that if two or more lines are perpendicular to the same line, then they are parallel lines. Figure 8.20 is a good illustration of that property.

The function notation can also be used to determine linear functions that satisfy certain conditions. Let's see how this works.

Classroom Example
Determine the linear function for a line with a slope of $-\dfrac{2}{3}$ that contains the point $(-3, 4)$.

EXAMPLE 4

Determine the linear function whose graph is a line with a slope of $\dfrac{1}{4}$ that contains the point $(2, 5)$.

Solution

We can substitute $\dfrac{1}{4}$ for a in the equation $f(x) = ax + b$ to obtain $f(x) = \dfrac{1}{4}x + b$. The fact that the line contains the point $(2, 5)$ means that $f(2) = 5$. Therefore

$$f(2) = \frac{1}{4}(2) + b = 5$$

$$b = \frac{9}{2}$$

and the function is $f(x) = \dfrac{1}{4}x + \dfrac{9}{2}$.

Applications of Linear Functions

We worked with some applications of linear equations in Section 7.2. Now let's consider some additional applications that use the concept of a linear function to connect mathematics to the real world.

Classroom Example
The cost for burning a 75-watt bulb is given by the function $c(h) = 0.0045h$, and h represents the number of hours that the bulb is burning.

(a) How much does it cost to burn a 75-watt bulb for 4 hours per night for two weeks?
(b) Graph the function $c(h) = 0.0045h$.

EXAMPLE 5

The cost for burning a 60-watt light bulb is given by the function $c(h) = 0.0036h$, where h represents the number of hours that the bulb is burning.

(a) How much does it cost to burn a 60-watt bulb for 3 hours per night for a 30-day month?
(b) Graph the function $c(h) = 0.0036h$.
(c) Suppose that a 60-watt light bulb is left burning in a closet for a week before it is discovered and turned off. Use the graph from part (b) to approximate the cost of allowing the bulb to burn for a week. Then use the function to find the exact cost.

(c) What is the approximate cost of allowing the bulb to burn continuously for two weeks?

Solutions

(a) $c(90) = 0.0036(90) = 0.324$ The cost, to the nearest cent, is $0.32.

(b) Because $c(0) = 0$ and $c(100) = 0.36$, we can use the points $(0, 0)$ and $(100, 0.36)$ to graph the linear function $c(h) = 0.0036h$ (Figure 8.21).

(c) If the bulb burns for 24 hours per day for a week, it burns for $24(7) = 168$ hours. Reading from the graph, we can approximate 168 on the horizontal axis, read up to the line, and then read across to the vertical axis. It looks as though it will cost approximately 60 cents. Using $c(h) = 0.0036h$, we obtain exactly $c(168) = 0.0036(168) = 0.6048$.

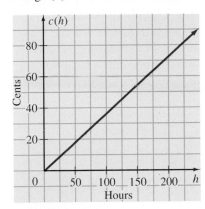

Figure 8.21

Classroom Example
Great Internet Services charges a fixed monthly fee plus an amount for each hour of use. For two different months, the charges were $49.20 for 36 hours of use and $64.40 for 52 hours of use. Determine the linear function that Great Internet Services uses to determine the monthly charge.

EXAMPLE 6

The Clear Call Cellular phone company has a fixed monthly charge plus an amount per minute of airtime. In May, Anna used 720 minutes of airtime and had a bill of $54.80. For the month of June, she used 510 minutes of airtime and had a bill of $46.40. Determine the linear function that Clear Call Cellular uses to determine its monthly bills.

Solution

The linear function $f(x) = ax + b$, where x represents the number of airtime minutes, models this situation. Anna's two monthly bills can be represented by the ordered pairs $(720, 54.80)$ and $(510, 46.40)$. From these two ordered pairs, we can determine a, which is the slope of the line:

$$a = \frac{46.40 - 54.80}{510 - 720} = \frac{-8.4}{-210} = 0.04$$

Thus $f(x) = ax + b$ becomes $f(x) = 0.04x + b$. Now either ordered pair can be used to determine the value of b. Using $(510, 46.40)$, we have $f(510) = 46.40$, so

$$f(510) = 0.04(510) + b = 46.40$$
$$b = 26$$

The linear function is $f(x) = 0.04x + 26$. In other words, Clear Call Cellular charges a monthly fee of $26.00 plus $0.04 per minute of airtime.

Classroom Example
Suppose Janet is considering changing to Super Internet Services, which charges a $39 monthly fee and $0.40 per hour of use. Compared to the internet company in Example 6, which service would charge the least for its services?

EXAMPLE 7

Suppose that Anna (Example 6) is thinking of switching to Simple Cellular phone company, which charges a monthly fee of $14 plus $0.06 per minute of airtime. Should Anna use Clear Cellular from Example 6 or Simple Cellular?

Solution

The linear function $f(x) = 0.06x + 14$, where x represents the number of airtime minutes, can be used to determine the monthly bill from Simple Cellular. Let's graph this function and $f(x) = 0.04x + 26$ from Example 6 on the same set of axes (see Figure 8.22).

Now we see that the two functions have equal values at the point of intersection of the two lines. To find the coordinates of this point, we can set $0.06x + 14$ equal to $0.04x + 26$ and solve for x:

$$0.06x + 14 = 0.04x + 26$$
$$0.02x = 12$$
$$x = 600$$

If $x = 600$, then $0.06(600) + 14 = 50$, and the point of intersection is $(600, 50)$. Again from the lines in Figure 8.22, Anna should switch to Simple Cellular if she uses less than 600 minutes of airtime, but she should stay with Clear Cellular if she plans on using more than 600 minutes of airtime.

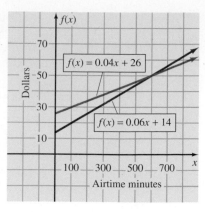

Figure 8.22

Concept Quiz 8.2

For Problems 1–10, answer true or false.

1. Any function of the form $f(x) = ax^n + b$, where a, b, and c are real numbers, is a linear function.
2. Geometrically, the functional value is the directed distance from the y axis.
3. The graph of a horizontal line represents a function.
4. The linear function $f(x) = 1$ is called the identity function.
5. The graphs of $f(x) = mx + b$ and $f(x) = -mx + b$ are perpendicular lines.
6. Every straight line graph represents a function.
7. If a city has a 7% sales tax on the dollars spent for hotel rooms, then the sales tax is a linear function of the dollars spent on hotel rooms.
8. If the amount of a paycheck varies directly as the number of hours worked, then the amount of the paycheck is a linear function of the hours worked.
9. The equation $f(x) = ax + b$ can also be written as $y = ax + b$.
10. The graph of the linear function, $f(x) = -4x + 5$, is a straight line with a slope of -4.

Problem Set 8.2

For Problems 1–16, graph each of the linear functions. (Objective 1)

1. $f(x) = 2x - 4$
2. $f(x) = 3x + 3$
3. $f(x) = -x + 3$
4. $f(x) = -2x + 6$
5. $f(x) = 3x + 9$
6. $f(x) = 2x - 6$
7. $f(x) = -4x - 4$
8. $f(x) = -x - 5$
9. $f(x) = -3x$
10. $f(x) = -4x$
11. $f(x) = -3$
12. $f(x) = -1$
13. $f(x) = \frac{1}{2}x + 3$
14. $f(x) = \frac{2}{3}x + 4$
15. $f(x) = -\frac{3}{4}x - 6$
16. $f(x) = -\frac{1}{2}x - 1$

For Problems 17–22, determine the linear equation for the stated conditions. (Objective 2)

17. Determine the linear function for a graph that is a line with a slope of $\frac{2}{3}$ and contains the point $(-1, 3)$.

18. Determine the linear function for a graph that is a line with a slope of $-\frac{3}{5}$ and contains the point $(4, -5)$.

19. Determine the linear function for a graph that is a line containing the points $(-3, -1)$ and $(2, -6)$.

20. If a graph is a line that contains the points $(-2, -3)$ and $(4, 3)$, determine the linear function.

21. If a graph is a line that is perpendicular to the line $g(x) = 5x - 2$ and contains the point $(6, 3)$, determine the linear function.

22. If a graph is a line that is parallel to the line $g(x) = -3x - 4$ and contains the point $(2, 7)$, determine the linear function.

For Problems 23–30, apply the concepts of linear functions to answer the questions. (Objective 3)

23. The cost of burning a 75-watt bulb is given by the function $c(h) = 0.0045h$, where h represents the number of hours that the bulb burns.
   (a) How much does it cost to burn a 75-watt bulb for 3 hours per night for a 31-day month? Express your answer to the nearest cent.
   (b) Graph the function $c(h) = 0.0045h$.
   (c) Use the graph in part (b) to approximate the cost of burning a 75-watt bulb for 225 hours.
   (d) Use $c(h) = 0.0045h$ to find the exact cost, to the nearest cent, of burning a 75-watt bulb for 225 hours.

24. The Rent-Me Car Rental charges $15 per day plus $0.22 per mile to rent a car. Determine a linear function that can be used to calculate the cost of daily car rentals. Then use that function to determine the cost of renting a car for a day and driving 175 miles; 220 miles; 300 miles; 460 miles.

25. Suppose that ABC Car Rental agency charges a fixed amount per day plus an amount per mile for renting a car. Heidi rented a car one day and paid $80 for 200 miles. On another day she rented a car from the same agency and paid $117.50 for 350 miles. Determine the linear function the agency uses to calculate its daily rental charges.

26. Suppose that Heidi (Problem 25) also has access to Speedy Car Rental, which charges a daily fee of $15.00 plus $0.31 per mile. Should Heidi use ABC Car Rental from Problem 25 or Speedy Car Rental?

27. The Hybrid-Only Car Rental agency uses the function $f(x) = 26$ for any daily use of a car up to and including 200 miles. For driving more than 200 miles per day, it uses the function $g(x) = 26 + 0.15(x - 200)$ to determine the charges. How much would the company charge for daily driving of 150 miles? of 230 miles? of 360 miles? of 430 miles?

28. Zack wants to sell five items that cost him $1.20, $2.30, $6.50, $12, and $15.60. He wants to make a profit of 60% of the cost. Create a function that you can use to determine the selling price of each item, and then use the function to calculate each selling price.

29. "All Items 20% Off Marked Price" is a sign at a local golf pro shop. Create a function and then use it to determine how much one has to pay for each of the following marked items: a $9.50 hat, a $15 umbrella, a $75 pair of golf shoes, a $12.50 golf glove, a $750 set of golf clubs.

30. The linear depreciation method assumes that an item depreciates the same amount each year. Suppose a new piece of machinery costs $32,500, and it depreciates $1950 each year for t years.
   (a) Set up a linear function that yields the value of the machinery after t years.
   (b) Find the value of the machinery after 5 years.
   (c) Find the value of the machinery after 8 years.
   (d) Graph the function from part (a).
   (e) Use the graph from part (d) to approximate how many years it takes for the value of the machinery to become zero.
   (f) Use the function to determine how long it takes for the value of the machinery to become zero.

Thoughts Into Words

31. Is $f(x) = (3x - 2) - (2x + 1)$ a linear function? Explain your answer.

32. Suppose that Bianca walks at a constant rate of 3 miles per hour. Explain what it means that the distance Bianca walks is a linear function of the time that she walks.

Further Investigations

For Problems 33–37, graph each of the functions.

33. $f(x) = |x|$

34. $f(x) = x + |x|$

35. $f(x) = x - |x|$

36. $f(x) = |x| - x$

37. $f(x) = \dfrac{x}{|x|}$

Graphing Calculator Activities

38. Use a graphing calculator to check your graphs for Problems 1–16.

39. Use a graphing calculator to do parts (b) and (c) of Example 5.

40. Use a graphing calculator to check our solution for Example 7.

41. Use a graphing calculator to do parts (b) and (c) of Problem 23.

42. Use a graphing calculator to do parts (d) and (e) of Problem 30.

43. Use a graphing calculator to check your graphs for Problems 33–37.

44. (a) Graph $f(x) = |x|$, $f(x) = 2|x|$, $f(x) = 4|x|$, and $f(x) = \dfrac{1}{2}|x|$ on the same set of axes.

(b) Graph $f(x) = |x|$, $f(x) = -|x|$, $f(x) = -3|x|$, and $f(x) = -\dfrac{1}{2}|x|$ on the same set of axes.

(c) Use your results from parts (a) and (b) to make a conjecture about the graphs of $f(x) = a|x|$, where a is a nonzero real number.

(d) Graph $f(x) = |x|$, $f(x) = |x| + 3$, $f(x) = |x| - 4$, and $f(x) = |x| + 1$ on the same set of axes. Make a conjecture about the graphs of $f(x) = |x| + k$, where k is a nonzero real number.

(e) Graph $f(x) = |x|$, $f(x) = |x - 3|$, $f(x) = |x - 1|$, and $f(x) = |x + 4|$ on the same set of axes. Make a conjecture about the graphs of $f(x) = |x - h|$, where h is a nonzero real number.

(f) On the basis of your results from parts (a) through (e), sketch each of the following graphs. Then use a graphing calculator to check your sketches.

(1) $f(x) = |x - 2| + 3$

(2) $f(x) = |x + 1| - 4$

(3) $f(x) = 2|x - 4| - 1$

(4) $f(x) = -3|x + 2| + 4$

(5) $f(x) = -\dfrac{1}{2}|x - 3| - 2$

Answers to the Concept Quiz

1. False **2.** False **3.** True **4.** False **5.** False **6.** False **7.** True **8.** True **9.** True **10.** True

---

8.3   Quadratic Functions

OBJECTIVES

1 Graph quadratic functions of the form $f(x) = a(x - h)^2 + k$

2 Graph quadratic functions by changing the form $f(x) = ax^2 + bx + c$ to the form $f(x) = a(x - h)^2 + k$

3 Graph piecewise-defined functions

Any function that can be written in the form

$$f(x) = ax^2 + bx + c$$

where a, b, and c are real numbers and $a \neq 0$, is called a **quadratic function**. The graph of any quadratic function is a **parabola**. As we work with parabolas, we will use the vocabulary indicated in Figure 8.23.

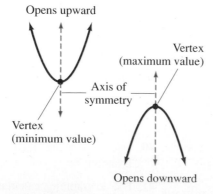

Figure 8.23

Graphing a parabola relies on finding the vertex, determining whether the parabola opens upward or downward, and locating two points on opposite sides of the axis of symmetry. We are also interested in comparing parabolas produced by equations such as $f(x) = x^2 + k$, $f(x) = ax^2$, $f(x) = (x - h)^2$, and $f(x) = a(x - h)^2 + k$ to the basic parabola produced by the equation $f(x) = x^2$. The graph of $f(x) = x^2$ is shown in Figure 8.24. Note that the vertex of the parabola is at the origin, $(0, 0)$, and the graph is symmetric to the y, or $f(x)$, axis. Remember that an equation exhibits y-axis symmetry if replacing x with $-x$ produces an equivalent equation. Therefore, because $f(-x) = (-x)^2 = x^2$, the equation exhibits y-axis symmetry.

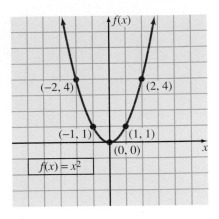

Figure 8.24

Now let's consider an equation of the form $f(x) = x^2 + k$, where k is a constant. (Keep in mind that all such equations exhibit y-axis symmetry.)

Classroom Example
Graph $y = x^2 - 1$.

EXAMPLE 1   Graph $f(x) = x^2 - 2$.

Solution

Let's set up a table to make some comparisons of function values. Because the graph exhibits y-axis symmetry, we will calculate only positive values and then reflect the points across the y axis.

x	$f(x) = x^2$	$f(x) = x^2 - 2$
0	0	-2
1	1	-1
2	4	2
3	9	7

Notice that the functional values for $f(x) = x^2 - 2$ are 2 less than the corresponding functional values for $f(x) = x^2$. Thus the graph of $f(x) = x^2 - 2$ is the same as the parabola of $f(x) = x^2$ except that it is moved down two units (Figure 8.25).

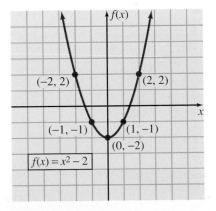

Figure 8.25

In general, the graph of a quadratic function of the form $f(x) = x^2 + k$ is the same as the graph of $f(x) = x^2$, except that it is moved up or down $|k|$ units, depending on whether k is positive or negative. We say that the graph of $f(x) = x^2 + k$ is a **vertical translation** of the graph of $f(x) = x^2$.

Now let's consider some quadratic functions of the form $f(x) = ax^2$, where a is a nonzero constant. (The graphs of these equations also have y-axis symmetry.)

Classroom Example
Graph $y = 4x^2$.

EXAMPLE 2   Graph $f(x) = 2x^2$.

Solution

Let's set up a table to make some comparisons of functional values. Note that in the table, the functional values for $f(x) = 2x^2$ are *twice* the corresponding functional values for $f(x) = x^2$. Thus the parabola associated with $f(x) = 2x^2$ has the same vertex (the origin) as the graph of $f(x) = x^2$, but it is *narrower*, as shown in Figure 8.26.

x	$f(x) = x^2$	$f(x) = 2x^2$
0	0	0
1	1	2
2	4	8
3	9	18

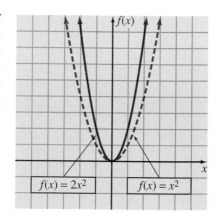

Figure 8.26

Classroom Example
Graph $y = \dfrac{1}{3}x^2$.

EXAMPLE 3   Graph $f(x) = \dfrac{1}{2}x^2$.

Solution

As we see from the table, the functional values for $f(x) = \dfrac{1}{2}x^2$ are *one-half* of the corresponding functional values for $f(x) = x^2$. Therefore the parabola associated with $f(x) = \dfrac{1}{2}x^2$ is *wider* than the basic parabola, as shown in Figure 8.27.

x	$f(x) = x^2$	$f(x) = \frac{1}{2}x^2$
0	0	0
1	1	$\dfrac{1}{2}$
2	4	2
3	9	$\dfrac{9}{2}$
4	16	8

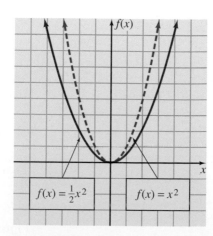

Figure 8.27

| EXAMPLE 4 | Graph $f(x) = -x^2$. |

Solution

It should be evident that the functional values for $f(x) = -x^2$ are the *opposites* of the corresponding functional values for $f(x) = x^2$. Therefore the graph of $f(x) = -x^2$ is a reflection across the x axis of the basic parabola (Figure 8.28).

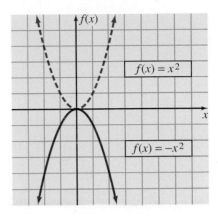

Figure 8.28

In general, the graph of a quadratic function of the form $f(x) = ax^2$ has its vertex at the origin and opens upward if a is positive and downward if a is negative. The parabola is narrower than the basic parabola if $|a| > 1$ and wider if $|a| < 1$.

Let's continue our investigation of quadratic functions by considering those of the form $f(x) = (x - h)^2$, in which h is a nonzero constant.

Classroom Example
Graph $y = (x - 1)^2$.

| EXAMPLE 5 | Graph $f(x) = (x - 3)^2$. |

Solution

A fairly extensive table of values illustrates a pattern. Note that $f(x) = (x - 3)^2$ and $f(x) = x^2$ take on the same functional values but for different values of x. More specifically, if $f(x) = x^2$ achieves a certain functional value at a specific value of x, then $f(x) = (x - 3)^2$ achieves that same functional value at $x + 3$. In other words, the graph of $f(x) = (x - 3)^2$ is the graph of $f(x) = x^2$ *moved three units to the right* (Figure 8.29).

x	$f(x) = x^2$	$f(x) = (x - 3)^2$
-1	1	16
0	0	9
1	1	4
2	4	1
3	9	0
4	16	1
5	25	4
6	36	9
7	49	16

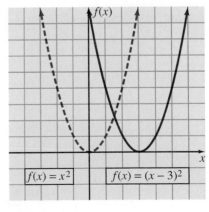

Figure 8.29

In general, the graph of a quadratic function of the form $f(x) = (x - h)^2$ is the same as the graph of $f(x) = x^2$, except that it is moved to the right h units if h is positive or moved to the left $|h|$ units if h is negative. We say that the graph of $f(x) = (x - h)^2$ is a **horizontal translation** of the graph of $f(x) = x^2$.

The following diagram summarizes our work thus far for graphing quadratic functions.

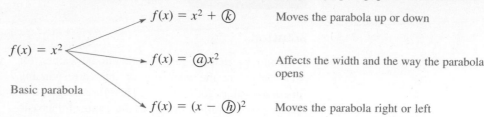

$f(x) = x^2 + \circledR{k}$ Moves the parabola up or down

$f(x) = x^2$
Basic parabola

$f(x) = \circledR{a}x^2$ Affects the width and the way the parabola opens

$f(x) = (x - \circledR{h})^2$ Moves the parabola right or left

We have studied, separately, the effects a, h, and k have on the graph of a quadratic function. However, we need to consider the general form of a quadratic function when all of these effects are present.

In general, the graph of a quadratic function of the form $f(x) = a(x - h)^2 + k$ has its vertex at (h, k) and opens upward if a is positive and downward if a is negative. The parabola is narrower than the basic parabola if $|a| > 1$ and wider if $|a| < 1$.

Classroom Example
Graph $y = 3(x + 2)^2 - 2$.

EXAMPLE 6   Graph $f(x) = 3(x - 2)^2 + 1$.

Solution

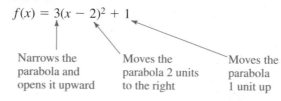

$f(x) = 3(x - 2)^2 + 1$

Narrows the parabola and opens it upward

Moves the parabola 2 units to the right

Moves the parabola 1 unit up

The vertex is $(2, 1)$, and the line $x = 2$ is the axis of symmetry. If $x = 1$, then $f(1) = 3(1 - 2)^2 + 1 = 4$. Thus the point $(1, 4)$ is on the graph, and so is its reflection, $(3, 4)$, across the line of symmetry. The parabola is shown in Figure 8.30.

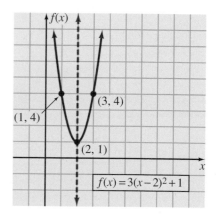

Figure 8.30

Classroom Example
Graph $y = -\dfrac{1}{3}(x - 1)^2 + 3$.

EXAMPLE 7   Graph $f(x) = -\dfrac{1}{2}(x + 1)^2 - 3$.

Solution

$f(x) = -\dfrac{1}{2}[x - (-1)]^2 - 3$

Widens the parabola and opens it downward

Moves the parabola 1 unit to the left

Moves the parabola 3 units down

The vertex is at $(-1, -3)$, and the line $x = -1$ is the axis of symmetry. If $x = 0$, then $f(0) = -\dfrac{1}{2}(0 + 1)^2 - 3 = -\dfrac{7}{2}$. Thus the point $\left(0, -\dfrac{7}{2}\right)$ is on the graph, and so is its reflection, $\left(-2, -\dfrac{7}{2}\right)$, across the line of symmetry. The parabola is shown in Figure 8.31.

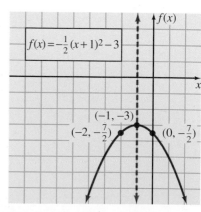

Figure 8.31

Graphing Quadratic Functions of the Form $f(x) = ax^2 + bx + c$

We are now ready to graph quadratic functions of the form $f(x) = ax^2 + bx + c$. The general approach is to change from the form $f(x) = ax^2 + bx + c$ to the form $f(x) = a(x - h)^2 + k$ and then proceed as we did in Examples 6 and 7. The process of *completing the square* serves as the basis for making the change in form. Let's consider two examples to illustrate the details.

Classroom Example
Graph $y = x^2 + 4x + 5$.

EXAMPLE 8   Graph $f(x) = x^2 - 4x + 3$.

Solution

$$f(x) = x^2 - 4x + 3$$
$$= (x^2 - 4x) + 3 \qquad \text{Add 4, which is the square of one-half of the coefficient of } x$$

$$= (x^2 - 4x + 4) + 3 - 4 \longleftarrow \text{Subtract 4 to compensate for the 4 that was added}$$

$$= (x - 2)^2 - 1$$

The graph of $f(x) = (x - 2)^2 - 1$ is the basic parabola moved two units to the right and one unit down (Figure 8.32).

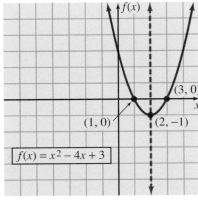

Figure 8.32

Classroom Example
Graph $y = -3x^2 + 6x - 1$.

EXAMPLE 9   Graph $f(x) = -2x^2 - 4x + 1$.

Solution

$$f(x) = -2x^2 - 4x + 1$$
$$= -2(x^2 + 2x) + 1 \qquad \text{Factor } -2 \text{ from the first two terms}$$
$$= -2(x^2 + 2x + 1) - (-2)(1) + 1 \qquad \text{Add 1 inside the parentheses to complete the square}$$

Subtract 1, but it must also be multiplied by a factor of -2

$$= -2(x^2 + 2x + 1) + 2 + 1$$

$$= -2(x + 1)^2 + 3$$

The graph of $f(x) = -2(x + 1)^2 + 3$ is shown in Figure 8.33.

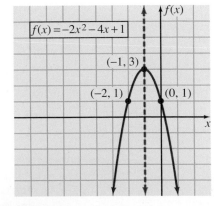

Figure 8.33

Graphing Piecewise-Defined Functions

Now let's graph a piecewise-defined function that involves both linear and quadratic rules of assignment.

EXAMPLE 10   Graph $f(x) = \begin{cases} 2x & \text{for } x \geq 0 \\ x^2 + 1 & \text{for } x < 0 \end{cases}$.

Solution

If $x \geq 0$, then $f(x) = 2x$. Thus for nonnegative values of x, we graph the linear function $f(x) = 2x$. If $x < 0$, then $f(x) = x^2 + 1$. Thus for negative values of x, we graph the quadratic function $f(x) = x^2 + 1$. The complete graph is shown in Figure 8.34.

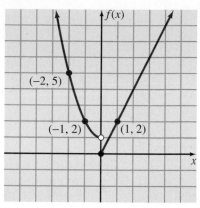

Figure 8.34

What we know about parabolas and the process of completing the square can be helpful when we are using a graphing utility to graph a quadratic function. Consider the following example.

EXAMPLE 11

Use a graphing utility to obtain the graph of the quadratic function $f(x) = -x^2 + 37x - 311$

Solution

First, we know that the parabola opens downward, and its width is the same as that of the basic parabola $f(x) = x^2$. Then we can start the process of completing the square to determine an approximate location of the vertex:

$$\begin{aligned} f(x) &= -x^2 + 37x - 311 \\ &= -(x^2 - 37x) - 311 \\ &= -\left(x^2 - 37x + \left(\frac{37}{2}\right)^2\right) - 311 + \left(\frac{37}{2}\right)^2 \\ &= -(x^2 - 37x + (18.5)^2) - 311 + 342.25 \\ &= -(x - 18.5)^2 + 31.25 \end{aligned}$$

Thus the vertex is near $x = 18$ and $y = 31$. Setting the boundaries of the viewing rectangle so that $-2 \leq x \leq 25$ and $-10 \leq y \leq 35$, we obtain the graph shown in Figure 8.35.

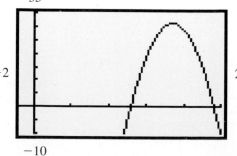

Figure 8.35

Remark: The graph in Figure 8.35 is sufficient for most purposes because it shows the vertex and the x intercepts of the parabola. Certainly we could use other boundaries that would also give this information.

Concept Quiz 8.3

For Problems 1–7, answer true or false.

1. The graph of any quadratic function is a parabola.

2. For the quadratic function $f(x) = ax^2 + bx + c$, the vertex of the parabola is always the minimum value of the function.

3. The graph of $y = \frac{1}{2}x^2$ is a parabola that opens downward.

4. If the vertex of a parabola that opens upward is located at the point (a, b), then the axis of symmetry is $x = a$.

5. If the point $(1, 4)$ is on the graph of a parabola, then the point $(-1, 4)$ is also on the parabola.

6. Every parabola has an axis of symmetry that passes through the vertex.

7. The process of changing the form of $f(x) = ax^2 + bx + c$ to the equivalent form $f(x) = a(x - h)^2 + k$ is called factoring the square.

For Problems 8–10, match the quadratic function with its graph.

8. $y = x^2 + 2$ 9. $y = (x - 2)^2$ 10. $y = 2x^2$

A. 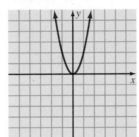   B. 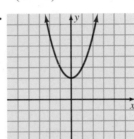   C.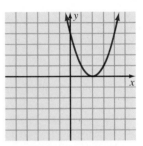

Problem Set 8.3

For Problems 1–14, graph each quadratic function. (Objective 1)

1. $f(x) = x^2 + 1$

2. $f(x) = x^2 - 3$

3. $f(x) = 3x^2$

4. $f(x) = -2x^2$

5. $f(x) = -x^2 + 2$

6. $f(x) = -3x^2 - 1$

7. $f(x) = (x + 2)^2$

8. $f(x) = (x - 1)^2$

9. $f(x) = -2(x + 1)^2$

10. $f(x) = 3(x - 2)^2$

11. $f(x) = (x - 1)^2 + 2$

12. $f(x) = -(x + 2)^2 + 3$

13. $f(x) = \frac{1}{2}(x - 2)^2 - 3$

14. $f(x) = 2(x - 3)^2 - 1$

For Problems 15–26, use completing the square to change the form of the function and then graph each quadratic function. (Objective 2)

15. $f(x) = x^2 + 2x + 4$

16. $f(x) = x^2 - 4x + 2$

17. $f(x) = x^2 - 3x + 1$

18. $f(x) = x^2 + 5x + 5$

19. $f(x) = 2x^2 + 12x + 17$

20. $f(x) = 3x^2 - 6x$

21. $f(x) = -x^2 - 2x + 1$

22. $f(x) = -2x^2 + 12x - 16$

23. $f(x) = 2x^2 - 2x + 3$

24. $f(x) = 2x^2 + 3x - 1$

25. $f(x) = -2x^2 - 5x + 1$

26. $f(x) = -3x^2 + x - 2$

For Problems 27–44, graph each piecewise-defined function. (Objective 3)

27. $f(x) = \begin{cases} x^2 & \text{for } x < 0 \\ x^2 + 3 & \text{for } x \geq 0 \end{cases}$

28. $f(x) = \begin{cases} x^2 & \text{for } x < 0 \\ -x^2 + 2 & \text{for } x \geq 0 \end{cases}$

29. $f(x) = \begin{cases} -x^2 & \text{for } x < 0 \\ x^2 + 1 & \text{for } x \geq 0 \end{cases}$

30. $f(x) = \begin{cases} -x^2 & \text{for } x < 0 \\ x^2 - 3 & \text{for } x \geq 0 \end{cases}$

31. $f(x) = \begin{cases} -x^2 + 2 & \text{for } x < 0 \\ 2 & \text{for } 0 \leq x < 3 \\ x^2 - 7 & \text{for } x \geq 3 \end{cases}$

32. $f(x) = \begin{cases} x^2 + 1 & \text{for } x < 0 \\ 1 & \text{for } 0 \leq x < 3 \\ -x^2 + 10 & \text{for } x \geq 3 \end{cases}$

33. $f(x) = \begin{cases} -x^2 & \text{for } x < -1 \\ x & \text{for } -1 \leq x < 1 \\ x^2 & \text{for } x \geq 1 \end{cases}$

34. $f(x) = \begin{cases} x^2 & \text{for } x < -2 \\ \dfrac{1}{2}x + 5 & \text{for } -2 \le x < 2 \\ x^2 + 2 & \text{for } x \ge 2 \end{cases}$

35. $f(x) = \begin{cases} -x^2 & \text{for } x < 0 \\ x + 2 & \text{for } 0 \le x < 4 \\ 2x & \text{for } x \ge 4 \end{cases}$

36. $f(x) = \begin{cases} -2x & \text{for } x < 0 \\ x^2 & \text{for } 0 \le x < 2 \\ \dfrac{1}{2}x + 2 & \text{for } x \ge 2 \end{cases}$

37. $f(x) = \begin{cases} 3x & \text{for } x < 0 \\ x & \text{for } x \ge 0 \end{cases}$

38. $f(x) = \begin{cases} -4x & \text{for } x < 0 \\ -x & \text{for } x \ge 0 \end{cases}$

39. $f(x) = \begin{cases} x^2 & \text{for } x < 0 \\ 2x + 1 & \text{for } x \ge 0 \end{cases}$

40. $f(x) = \begin{cases} 2x^2 & \text{for } x < 0 \\ -x^2 & \text{for } x \ge 0 \end{cases}$

41. $f(x) = \begin{cases} -1 & \text{for } x < 0 \\ 2 & \text{for } x \ge 0 \end{cases}$

42. $f(x) = \begin{cases} -1 & \text{for } x \le 0 \\ 1 & \text{for } 0 < x \le 2 \\ 2 & \text{for } x > 2 \end{cases}$

43. $f(x) = \begin{cases} 1 & \text{for } 0 \le x < 1 \\ 2 & \text{for } 1 \le x < 2 \\ 3 & \text{for } 2 \le x < 3 \\ 4 & \text{for } 3 \le x < 4 \end{cases}$

44. $f(x) = \begin{cases} 2x + 3 & \text{for } x < 0 \\ \dfrac{3}{2}x & \text{for } 0 \le x < 2 \\ 1 & \text{for } x \ge 2 \end{cases}$

45. The **greatest integer function** is defined by the equation $f(x) = [x]$, where $[x]$ refers to the largest integer less than or equal to x. For example, $[2.6] = 2$, $[\sqrt{2}] = 1$, $[4] = 4$, and $[-1.4] = -2$. Graph $f(x) = [x]$ for $-4 \le x < 4$.

Thoughts Into Words

46. Explain the concept of a piecewise-defined function.

47. Is $f(x) = (3x^2 - 2) - (2x + 1)$ a quadratic function? Explain your answer.

48. Give a step-by-step description of how you would use the ideas presented in this section to graph $f(x) = 5x^2 + 10x + 4$.

Graphing Calculator Activities

49. This problem is designed to reinforce ideas presented in this section. For each part, first predict the shapes and locations of the parabolas, and then use your graphing calculator to graph them on the same set of axes.

 (a) $f(x) = x^2$, $f(x) = x^2 - 4$, $f(x) = x^2 + 1$, $f(x) = x^2 + 5$

 (b) $f(x) = x^2$, $f(x) = (x - 5)^2$, $f(x) = (x + 5)^2$, $f(x) = (x - 3)^2$

 (c) $f(x) = x^2$, $f(x) = 5x^2$, $f(x) = \dfrac{1}{3}x^2$, $f(x) = -2x^2$

 (d) $f(x) = x^2$, $f(x) = (x - 7)^2 - 3$, $f(x) = -(x + 8)^2 + 4$, $f(x) = -3x^2 - 4$

 (e) $f(x) = x^2 - 4x - 2$, $f(x) = -x^2 + 4x + 2$, $f(x) = -x^2 - 16x - 58$, $f(x) = x^2 + 16x + 58$

50. (a) Graph both $f(x) = x^2 - 14x + 51$ and $f(x) = x^2 + 14x + 51$ on the same set of axes. What relationship seems to exist between the two graphs?

 (b) Graph both $f(x) = x^2 + 12x + 34$ and $f(x) = x^2 - 12x + 34$ on the same set of axes. What relationship seems to exist between the two graphs?

 (c) Graph both $f(x) = -x^2 + 8x - 20$ and $f(x) = -x^2 - 8x - 20$ on the same set of axes. What relationship seems to exist between the two graphs?

 (d) Make a statement that generalizes your findings in parts (a) through (c).

51. Use your graphing calculator to graph the piecewise-defined functions in Problems 37 – 44. You may need to consult your user's manual for instructions on graphing these functions.

Answers to the Concept Quiz

1. True   **2.** False   **3.** False   **4.** True   **5.** False   **6.** True   **7.** False   **8.** B   **9.** C   **10.** A

8.4   More Quadratic Functions and Applications

OBJECTIVES
1. Graph parabolas using a formula to locate the vertex
2. Determine the x and y intercepts for a parabola
3. Solve application problems involving quadratic functions

In the previous section, we used the process of completing the square to change a quadratic function such as $f(x) = x^2 - 4x + 3$ to the form $f(x) = (x - 2)^2 - 1$. From the form $f(x) = (x - 2)^2 - 1$, it is easy to identify the vertex $(2, -1)$ and the axis of symmetry $x = 2$ of the parabola. In general, if we complete the square on

$$f(x) = ax^2 + bx + c$$

we obtain

$$f(x) = a\left(x^2 + \frac{b}{a}x\right) + c$$

$$= a\left(x^2 + \frac{b}{a}x + \frac{b^2}{4a^2}\right) + c - \frac{b^2}{4a}$$

$$= a\left(x + \frac{b}{2a}\right)^2 + \frac{4ac - b^2}{4a}$$

Therefore the parabola associated with the function $f(x) = ax^2 + bx + c$ has its vertex at

$$\left(-\frac{b}{2a}, \frac{4ac - b^2}{4a}\right)$$

and the equation of its axis of symmetry is $x = -\dfrac{b}{2a}$. These facts are illustrated in Figure 8.36.

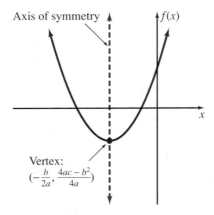

Figure 8.36

By using the information from Figure 8.36, we now have another way of graphing quadratic functions of the form $f(x) = ax^2 + bx + c$, as indicated by the following steps:

Step 1 Determine whether the parabola opens upward (if $a > 0$) or downward (if $a < 0$).

Step 2 Find $-\dfrac{b}{2a}$, which is the x coordinate of the vertex.

Step 3   Find $f\left(-\dfrac{b}{2a}\right)$, which is the y coordinate of the vertex, or find the y coordinate by evaluating

$$\frac{4ac - b^2}{4a}$$

Step 4   Locate another point on the parabola, and also locate its image across the axis of symmetry, which is the line with equation $x = -\dfrac{b}{2a}$.

The three points found in steps 2, 3, and 4 should determine the general shape of the parabola. Let's illustrate this procedure with two examples.

EXAMPLE 1   Graph $f(x) = 3x^2 - 6x + 5$.

Solution

Step 1   Because $a > 0$, the parabola opens upward.

Step 2 $-\dfrac{b}{2a} = -\dfrac{(-6)}{2(3)} = -\dfrac{(-6)}{6} = 1$

Step 3 $f\left(-\dfrac{b}{2a}\right) = f(1) = 3(1)^2 - 6(1) + 5 = 2.$

Thus the vertex is at $(1, 2)$.

Step 4   Letting $x = 2$, we obtain $f(2) = 12 - 12 + 5 = 5$. Thus $(2, 5)$ is on the graph, and so is its reflection, $(0, 5)$, across the line of symmetry, $x = 1$.

The three points $(1, 2)$, $(2, 5)$, and $(0, 5)$ are used to graph the parabola in Figure 8.37.

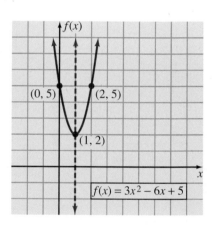

Figure 8.37

EXAMPLE 2   Graph $f(x) = -x^2 - 4x - 7$.

Solution

Step 1   Because $a < 0$, the parabola opens downward.

Step 2 $-\dfrac{b}{2a} = -\dfrac{(-4)}{2(-1)} = -\dfrac{(-4)}{(-2)} = -2$

Step 3 $f\left(-\dfrac{b}{2a}\right) = f(-2) =$
$-(-2)^2 - 4(-2) - 7 = -3$ Thus the vertex is at $(-2, -3)$.

Step 4   Letting $x = 0$, we obtain $f(0) = -7$. Thus $(0, -7)$ is on the graph, and so is its reflection, $(-4, -7)$, across the line of symmetry, $x = -2$.

The three points $(-2, -3)$, $(0, -7)$, and $(-4, -7)$ are used to draw the parabola in Figure 8.38.

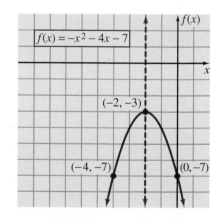

Figure 8.38

In summary, we have two methods to graph a quadratic function:

   1. We can express the function in the form $f(x) = a(x - h)^2 + k$ and use the values of a, h, and k to determine the parabola.

2. We can express the function in the form $f(x) = ax^2 + bx + c$, locate the vertex at $\left(-\dfrac{b}{2a}, f\left(-\dfrac{b}{2a}\right)\right)$, and use the approach demonstrated in Examples 1 and 2.

Parabolas possess various properties that make them useful. For example, if a parabola is rotated about its axis, a parabolic surface is formed, and such surfaces are used for light and sound reflectors. A projectile fired into the air follows the curvature of a parabola. The trend line of profit and cost functions sometimes follows a parabolic curve. In most applications of the parabola, we are primarily interested in the x intercepts and the vertex. Let's consider some examples of finding the x intercepts and the vertex.

Classroom Example
Find the x intercepts and the vertex for each of the following parabolas.

(a) $f(x) = -x^2 + 2x + 15$
(b) $f(x) = x^2 + 6x - 10$
(c) $f(x) = 5x^2 - 2x - 6$

EXAMPLE 3

Find the x intercepts and the vertex for each of the following parabolas:

(a) $f(x) = -x^2 + 11x - 18$ **(b)** $f(x) = x^2 - 8x - 3$ **(c)** $f(x) = 2x^2 - 12x + 23$

Solutions

(a) To find the x intercepts for $f(x) = -x^2 + 11x - 18$, let $f(x) = 0$ and solve the resulting equation:

$$-x^2 + 11x - 18 = 0$$
$$x^2 - 11x + 18 = 0$$
$$(x - 2)(x - 9) = 0$$
$$x - 2 = 0 \quad \text{or} \quad x - 9 = 0$$
$$x = 2 \qquad\qquad x = 9$$

Therefore the x intercepts are 2 and 9. To find the vertex, let's determine the point $\left(-\dfrac{b}{2a}, f\left(-\dfrac{b}{2a}\right)\right)$:

$$f(x) = -x^2 + 11x - 18$$
$$-\frac{b}{2a} = -\frac{11}{2(-1)} = -\frac{11}{-2} = \frac{11}{2}$$
$$f\left(\frac{11}{2}\right) = -\left(\frac{11}{2}\right)^2 + 11\left(\frac{11}{2}\right) - 18$$
$$= -\frac{121}{4} + \frac{121}{2} - 18$$
$$= \frac{-121 + 242 - 72}{4}$$
$$= \frac{49}{4}$$

Therefore the vertex is at $\left(\dfrac{11}{2}, \dfrac{49}{4}\right)$.

(b) To find the x intercepts for $f(x) = x^2 - 8x - 3$, let $f(x) = 0$, and solve the resulting equation:

$$x^2 - 8x - 3 = 0$$
$$x = \frac{-(-8) \pm \sqrt{(-8)^2 - 4(1)(-3)}}{2(1)}$$
$$= \frac{8 \pm \sqrt{76}}{2}$$
$$= \frac{8 \pm 2\sqrt{19}}{2}$$
$$= 4 \pm \sqrt{19}$$

Therefore the x intercepts are $4 + \sqrt{19}$ and $4 - \sqrt{19}$. This time, to find the vertex, let's complete the square on x:

$$f(x) = x^2 - 8x - 3$$
$$= x^2 - 8x + 16 - 3 - 16$$
$$= (x - 4)^2 - 19$$

Therefore the vertex is at $(4, -19)$.

(c) To find the x intercepts for $f(x) = 2x^2 - 12x + 23$, let $f(x) = 0$ and solve the resulting equation:

$$2x^2 - 12x + 23 = 0$$
$$x = \frac{-(-12) \pm \sqrt{(-12)^2 - 4(2)(23)}}{2(2)}$$
$$= \frac{12 \pm \sqrt{-40}}{4}$$

Because these solutions are nonreal complex numbers, there are no x intercepts. To find the vertex, let's determine the point $\left(-\dfrac{b}{2a}, f\left(-\dfrac{b}{2a}\right)\right)$:

$$f(x) = 2x^2 - 12x + 23$$
$$-\frac{b}{2a} = -\frac{-12}{2(2)}$$
$$= 3$$
$$f(3) = 2(3)^2 - 12(3) + 23$$
$$= 18 - 36 + 23$$
$$= 5$$

Therefore the vertex is at $(3, 5)$.

Remark: Note that in parts (a) and (c), we used the general point

$$\left(-\frac{b}{2a}, f\left(-\frac{b}{2a}\right)\right)$$

to find the vertices. In part (b), however, we completed the square and used that form to determine the vertex. Which approach you use is up to you. We chose to complete the square in part (b) because the algebra involved was quite easy.

In part (a) of Example 3, we solved the equation $-x^2 + 11x - 18 = 0$ to determine that 2 and 9 are the x intercepts of the graph of the function $f(x) = -x^2 + 11x - 18$. The numbers 2 and 9 are also called the **real number zeros** of the function. That is to say, $f(2) = 0$ and $f(9) = 0$. In part (b) of Example 3, the real numbers $4 + \sqrt{19}$ and $4 - \sqrt{19}$ are the x intercepts of the graph of the function $f(x) = x^2 - 8x - 3$ and are the real number zeros of the function. Again, this means that $f(4 + \sqrt{19}) = 0$ and $f(4 - \sqrt{19}) = 0$. In part (c) of Example 3, the nonreal complex numbers $\dfrac{12 \pm \sqrt{-40}}{4}$, which simplify to $\dfrac{6 \pm i\sqrt{10}}{2}$, indicate that the graph of the function $f(x) = 2x^2 - 12x + 23$ has no points on the x axis. The complex numbers are zeros of the function, but they have no physical significance for the graph other than indicating that the graph has no points on the x axis.

Figure 8.39 shows our result when we used a graphing calculator to graph the three functions of Example 3 on the same set of axes. This gives us a visual interpretation of the conclusions drawn regarding the x intercepts and vertices.

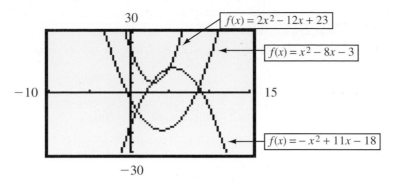

Figure 8.39

Back to Problem Solving

As we have seen, the vertex of the graph of a quadratic function is either the lowest or the highest point on the graph. Thus we often speak of the **minimum value** or **maximum value** of a function when we discuss applications of the parabola. The x value of the vertex indicates where the minimum or maximum occurs, and $f(x)$ yields the minimum or maximum value of the function. Let's consider some examples that illustrate these ideas.

EXAMPLE 4

A farmer has 120 rods of fencing and wants to enclose a rectangular plot of land that requires fencing on only three sides because it is bounded on one side by a river. Find the length and width of the plot that will maximize the area.

Solution

Let x represent the width; then $120 - 2x$ represents the length, as indicated in Figure 8.40.

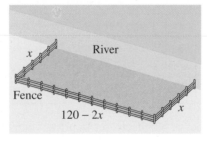

Figure 8.40

The function $A(x) = x(120 - 2x)$ represents the area of the plot in terms of the width x. Because

$$A(x) = x(120 - 2x)$$
$$= 120x - 2x^2$$
$$= -2x^2 + 120x$$

we have a quadratic function with $a = -2$, $b = 120$, and $c = 0$. Therefore the *maximum* value ($a < 0$ so the parabola opens downward) of the function is obtained where the x value is

$$-\frac{b}{2a} = -\frac{120}{2(-2)} = 30$$

If $x = 30$, then $120 - 2x = 120 - 2(30) = 60$. Thus the farmer should make the plot 30 rods wide and 60 rods long to maximize the area at $(30)(60) = 1800$ square rods.

Classroom Example
Find two numbers whose sum is
20, such that the sum of their
squares is a minimum.

EXAMPLE 5

Find two numbers whose sum is 30, such that the sum of their squares is a minimum.

Solution

Let x represent one of the numbers; then $30 - x$ represents the other number. By expressing the sum of their squares as a function of x, we obtain

$$f(x) = x^2 + (30 - x)^2$$

which can be simplified to

$$f(x) = x^2 + 900 - 60x + x^2$$
$$= 2x^2 - 60x + 900$$

This is a quadratic function with $a = 2$, $b = -60$, and $c = 900$. Therefore the x value where the *minimum* occurs is

$$-\frac{b}{2a} = -\frac{-60}{4} = 15$$

If $x = 15$, then $30 - x = 30 - 15 = 15$. Thus the two numbers should both be 15.

Classroom Example
A travel agent can sell 42 tickets
for a 3-day cruise at $450 each.
For each $20 decrease in price,
the number of tickets sold
increases by four. At what price
should the tickets be sold to
maximize gross income?

EXAMPLE 6

A golf pro-shop operator finds that she can sell 30 sets of golf clubs at $500 per set in a year. Furthermore, she predicts that for each $25 decrease in price, she could sell three extra sets of golf clubs. At what price should she sell the clubs to maximize gross income?

Solution

In analyzing such a problem, it sometimes helps to start by setting up a table. We use the fact that three additional sets can be sold for each $25 decrease in price.

Number of sets	×	Price per set	=	Income
30	×	$500	=	$15,000
33	×	$475	=	$15,675
36	×	$450	=	$16,200

Let x represent the number of $25 decreases in price. Then the income can be expressed as a function of x.

$$f(x) = \underset{\substack{\uparrow \\ \text{Number} \\ \text{of sets}}}{(30 + 3x)}\underset{\substack{\uparrow \\ \text{Price per} \\ \text{set}}}{(500 - 25x)}$$

Simplifying this equation, we obtain

$$f(x) = 15{,}000 - 750x + 1500x - 75x^2$$
$$= -75x^2 + 750x + 15{,}000$$

We complete the square in order to analyze the parabola.

$$f(x) = -75x^2 + 750x + 15{,}000$$
$$= -75(x^2 - 10x) + 15{,}000$$
$$= -75(x^2 - 10x + 25) + 15{,}000 + 1875$$
$$= -75(x - 5)^2 + 16{,}875$$

From this form, we know that the vertex of the parabola is at (5, 16,875), and because $a = -75$, we know that a *maximum* occurs at the vertex. Thus five decreases of $25—that is, a $125 reduction in price—will give a maximum income of $16,875. The golf clubs should be sold at $375 per set.

We have determined that the vertex of a parabola associated with $f(x) = ax^2 + bx + c$ is located at $\left(-\dfrac{b}{2a}, f\left(-\dfrac{b}{2a}\right)\right)$ and that the x intercepts of the graph can be found by solving the quadratic equation $ax^2 + bx + c = 0$. Therefore a graphing utility does not provide us with much extra power when we are working with quadratic functions. However, as functions become more complex, a graphing utility becomes more helpful. Let's continue to use our graphing utility at this time, while we have a way of checking our results.

Classroom Example
Use a graphing utility to graph $f(x) = x^2 + 6x - 10$ and find the x intercepts of the graph.

EXAMPLE 7

Use a graphing utility to graph $f(x) = x^2 - 8x - 3$ and find the x intercepts of the graph. (This is the parabola from part (b) of Example 3.)

Solution

A graph of the parabola is shown in Figure 8.41. One x intercept appears to be between 0 and -1 and the other between 8 and 9. Let's zoom in on the x intercept between 8 and 9. This produces a graph like Figure 8.42.

Now we can use the TRACE function to determine that this x intercept is at approximately 8.4. (This agrees with the answer of $4 + \sqrt{19}$ from Example 6.) In a similar fashion, we can determine that the other x intercept is at approximately -0.4.

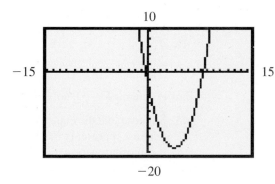

Figure 8.41

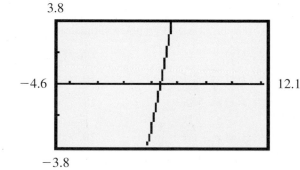

Figure 8.42

Concept Quiz 8.4

For Problems 1–10, answer true or false.

1. The y coordinate of the vertex for the parabola associated with $f(x) = ax^2 + bx + c$ is equal to $-\dfrac{b}{2a}$.

2. The x coordinate of the vertex for the parabola associated with $f(x) = ax^2 + bx + c$ is equal to $-\dfrac{b}{2}$.

3. For the parabola associated with $f(x) = ax^2 + bx + c$, the parabola will always open upward if b is positive.

4. For the quadratic function $f(x) = -4x^2 + 3x + 1$, the vertex of its parabola will be the highest point on the graph.

5. The minimum value of the function $f(x) = 2x^2 + 5x + 8$ is equal to $f\left(\dfrac{-5}{4}\right)$.

6. The x intercepts for the parabola associated with $f(x) = ax^2 + bx + c$ can be found by using the quadratic formula $x = \dfrac{-b \pm \sqrt{b^2 - 4ac}}{2a}$.

7. Every graph of a quadratic function has x intercepts.

8. Every graph of a quadratic function has a y intercept.

9. For the parabola associated with $f(x) = ax^2 + bx + c$, the axis of symmetry is $x = -\dfrac{b}{2a}$.

10. It is possible for the vertex and x intercept of a parabola to coincide. (In other words, for the vertex and x intercept to be the same point.)

Problem Set 8.4

For Problems 1–12, use the approach of Examples 1 and 2 of this section to graph each quadratic function. **(Objective 1)**

1. $f(x) = x^2 - 8x + 15$
2. $f(x) = x^2 + 6x + 11$
3. $f(x) = 2x^2 + 20x + 52$
4. $f(x) = 3x^2 - 6x - 1$
5. $f(x) = -x^2 + 4x - 7$
6. $f(x) = -x^2 - 6x - 5$
7. $f(x) = -3x^2 + 6x - 5$
8. $f(x) = -2x^2 - 4x + 2$
9. $f(x) = x^2 + 3x - 1$
10. $f(x) = x^2 + 5x + 2$
11. $f(x) = -2x^2 + 5x + 1$
12. $f(x) = -3x^2 + 2x - 1$

For Problems 13–20, use the approach that you think is the most appropriate to graph each quadratic function.

13. $f(x) = -x^2 + 3$
14. $f(x) = (x + 1)^2 + 1$
15. $f(x) = x^2 + x - 1$
16. $f(x) = -x^2 + 3x - 4$
17. $f(x) = -2x^2 + 4x + 1$
18. $f(x) = 4x^2 - 8x + 5$
19. $f(x) = -\left(x + \dfrac{5}{2}\right)^2 + \dfrac{3}{2}$
20. $f(x) = x^2 - 4x$

For Problems 21–36, find the x intercepts and the vertex of each parabola. **(Objective 2)**

21. $f(x) = 3x^2 - 12$

22. $f(x) = 6x^2 - 4$

23. $f(x) = 5x^2 - 10x$

24. $f(x) = 3x^2 + 9x$

25. $f(x) = x^2 - 8x + 15$
26. $f(x) = x^2 - 16x + 63$

27. $f(x) = 2x^2 - 28x + 96$
28. $f(x) = 3x^2 - 60x + 297$

29. $f(x) = -x^2 + 10x - 24$

30. $f(x) = -2x^2 + 36x - 160$

31. $f(x) = x^2 - 14x + 44$

32. $f(x) = x^2 - 18x + 68$

33. $f(x) = -x^2 + 9x - 21$

34. $f(x) = 2x^2 + 3x + 3$

35. $f(x) = -4x^2 + 4x + 4$

36. $f(x) = -2x^2 + 3x + 7$

For Problems 37–42, find the zeros of each function.

37. $f(x) = x^2 + 3x - 88$
38. $f(x) = 6x^2 - 5x - 4$

39. $f(x) = 4x^2 - 48x + 108$
40. $f(x) = x^2 - 6x - 6$

41. $f(x) = x^2 - 4x + 11$

42. $f(x) = x^2 - 23x + 126$

For Problems 43–52, solve each problem. **(Objective 3)**

43. Suppose that the equation $p(x) = -2x^2 + 280x - 1000$, where x represents the number of items sold, describes the profit function for a certain business. How many items should be sold to maximize the profit?

44. Suppose that the cost function for the production of a particular item is given by the equation $C(x) = 2x^2 - 320x + 12{,}920$, where x represents the number of items. How many items should be produced to minimize the cost?

45. Neglecting air resistance, the height of a projectile fired vertically into the air at an initial velocity of 96 feet per second is a function of time x and is given by the equation $f(x) = 96x - 16x^2$. Find the highest point reached by the projectile.

46. Find two numbers whose sum is 30, such that the sum of the square of one number plus ten times the other number is a minimum.

47. Find two numbers whose sum is 50 and whose product is a maximum.

48. Find two numbers whose difference is 40 and whose product is a minimum.

49. Two hundred forty meters of fencing is available to enclose a rectangular playground. What should the dimensions of the playground be to maximize the area?

50. An outdoor adventure company advertises that they will provide a guided mountain bike trip and a picnic lunch for $50 per person. They must have a guarantee of 30 people to do the trip. Furthermore, they agree that for each person in excess of 30, they will reduce the price per person for all riders by $0.50. How many people will it take to maximize the company's revenue?

51. A video rental service has 1000 subscribers, each of whom pays $15 per month. On the basis of a survey, the company believes that for each decrease of $0.25 in the monthly rate, it could obtain 20 additional subscribers. At what rate will the maximum revenue be obtained, and how many subscribers will there be at that rate?

52. A manufacturer finds that for the first 500 units of its product that are produced and sold, the profit is $50 per unit. The profit on each of the units beyond 500 is decreased by $0.10 times the number of additional units sold. What level of output will maximize profit?

Thoughts Into Words

53. Suppose your friend was absent the day this section was discussed. How would you explain to her the ideas pertaining to x intercepts of the graph of a function, zeros of the function, and solutions of the equation $f(x) = 0$?

54. Give a step-by-step explanation of how to find the x intercepts of the graph of the function $f(x) = 2x^2 + 7x - 4$.

55. Give a step-by-step explanation of how to find the vertex of the parabola determined by the equation $f(x) = -x^2 - 6x - 5$.

Graphing Calculator Activities

56. Suppose that the viewing window on your graphing calculator is set so that $-15 \leq x \leq 15$ and $-10 \leq y \leq 10$. Now try to graph the function $f(x) = x^2 - 8x + 28$. Nothing appears on the screen, so the parabola must be outside the viewing window. We could arbitrarily expand the window until the parabola appeared. However, let's be a little more systematic and use $\left(-\dfrac{b}{2a}, f\left(-\dfrac{b}{2a}\right)\right)$ to find the vertex. We find the vertex is at $(4, 12)$, so let's change the y values of the window so that $0 \leq y \leq 25$. Now we get a good picture of the parabola.

Graph each of the following parabolas, and keep in mind that you may need to change the dimensions of the viewing window to obtain a good picture.
(a) $f(x) = x^2 - 2x + 12$
(b) $f(x) = -x^2 - 4x - 16$
(c) $f(x) = x^2 + 12x + 44$
(d) $f(x) = x^2 - 30x + 229$
(e) $f(x) = -2x^2 + 8x - 19$

57. Use a graphing calculator to graph each of the following parabolas, and then use the TRACE function to help estimate the x intercepts and the vertex. Finally, use the approach of Example 7 to find the x intercepts and the vertex.
(a) $f(x) = x^2 - 6x + 3$
(b) $f(x) = x^2 - 18x + 66$
(c) $f(x) = -x^2 + 8x - 3$
(d) $f(x) = -x^2 + 24x - 129$
(e) $f(x) = 14x^2 - 7x + 1$
(f) $f(x) = -\dfrac{1}{2}x^2 + 5x - \dfrac{17}{2}$

58. In Problems 21–36, you were asked to find the x intercepts and the vertex of some parabolas. Now use a graphing calculator to graph each parabola and visually justify your answers.

59. For each of the following quadratic functions, use the discriminant to determine the number of real-number zeros, and then graph the function with a graphing calculator to check your answer.
(a) $f(x) = 3x^2 - 15x - 42$
(b) $f(x) = 2x^2 - 36x + 162$
(c) $f(x) = -4x^2 - 48x - 144$
(d) $f(x) = 2x^2 + 2x + 5$
(e) $f(x) = 4x^2 - 4x - 120$
(f) $f(x) = 5x^2 - x + 4$

Answers to the Concept Quiz

1. False   **2.** False   **3.** False   **4.** True   **5.** True   **6.** True   **7.** False   **8.** True   **9.** True   **10.** True

8.5 Transformations of Some Basic Curves

OBJECTIVE

1 Graph functions by applying horizontal and vertical translations, vertical stretchings or shrinkings, or reflections to the basic graphs of $f(x) = x^2$, $f(x) = x^3$, $f(x) = x^4$, $f(x) = \sqrt{x}$, and $f(x) = |x|$

From our work in Section 8.3, we know that the graph of $f(x) = (x - 5)^2$ is the basic parabola $f(x) = x^2$ translated five units to the right. Likewise, we know that the graph of $f(x) = -x^2 - 2$ is the basic parabola reflected across the x axis and translated downward two units. Translations and reflections apply not only to parabolas but also to curves in general. Therefore, if we know the shapes of a few basic curves, then it is easy to sketch numerous variations of these curves by using the concepts of translation and reflection.

Let's begin this section by establishing the graphs of four basic curves and then apply some transformations to these curves. First, let's restate, in terms of function vocabulary, the graphing suggestions offered in Chapter 7. Pay special attention to suggestions 2 and 3, in which we restate the concepts of intercepts and symmetry using function notation.

1. Determine the domain of the function.

2. Find the y intercept (we are labeling the y axis with $f(x)$) by evaluating $f(0)$. Find the x intercept by finding the value(s) of x such that $f(x) = 0$.

3. Determine any types of symmetry that the equation possesses. If $f(-x) = f(x)$, then the function exhibits y-axis symmetry. If $f(-x) = -f(x)$, then the function exhibits origin symmetry. (Note that the definition of a function rules out the possibility that the graph of a function has x-axis symmetry.)

4. Set up a table of ordered pairs that satisfy the equation. The type of symmetry and the domain will affect your choice of values of x in the table.

5. Plot the points associated with the ordered pairs and connect them with a smooth curve. Then, if appropriate, reflect this part of the curve according to any symmetries possessed by the graph.

EXAMPLE 1   Graph $f(x) = x^3$.

Solution

The domain is the set of real numbers. Because $f(0) = 0$, the origin is on the graph. Because $f(-x) = (-x)^3 = -x^3 = -f(x)$, the graph is symmetric with respect to the origin. Therefore, we can concentrate on the positive values of x for our table. By connecting the points associated with the ordered pairs in the table with a smooth curve and then reflecting it through the origin, we get the graph in Figure 8.43.

x	$f(x) = x^3$
0	0
1	1
2	8
$\dfrac{1}{2}$	$\dfrac{1}{8}$

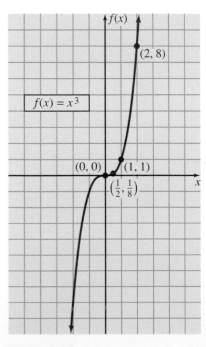

Figure 8.43

EXAMPLE 2   Graph $f(x) = x^4$.

Solution

The domain is the set of real numbers. Because $f(0) = 0$, the origin is on the graph. Because $f(-x) = (-x)^4 = x^4 = f(x)$, the graph has y-axis symmetry, and we can concentrate our table of values on the positive values of x. If we connect the points associated with the ordered pairs in the table with a smooth curve and then reflect across the vertical axis, we get the graph in Figure 8.44.

x	$f(x) = x^4$
0	0
1	1
2	16
$\dfrac{1}{2}$	$\dfrac{1}{16}$

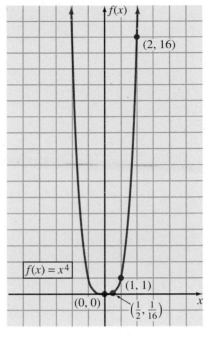

Figure 8.44

Remark: The curve in Figure 8.44 is not a parabola, even though it resembles one; this curve is flatter at the bottom and steeper than a parabola would be.

EXAMPLE 3   Graph $f(x) = \sqrt{x}$.

Solution

The domain of the function is the set of nonnegative real numbers. Because $f(0) = 0$, the origin is on the graph. Because $f(-x) \neq f(x)$ and $f(-x) \neq -f(x)$, there is no symmetry, so let's set up a table of values using nonnegative values for x. Plotting the points determined by the table and connecting them with a smooth curve produces Figure 8.45.

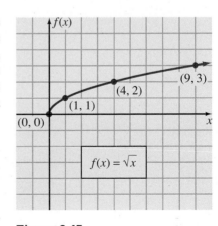

Figure 8.45

x	$f(x) = \sqrt{x}$
0	0
1	1
4	2
9	3

Sometimes a new function is defined in terms of old functions. In such cases, the definition plays an important role in the study of the new function. Consider the following example.

EXAMPLE 4   Graph $f(x) = |x|$.

Solution

The concept of absolute value is defined for all real numbers by

$$|x| = x \quad \text{if } x \geq 0$$
$$|x| = -x \quad \text{if } x < 0$$

Therefore the absolute value function can be expressed as

$$f(x) = |x| = \begin{cases} x & \text{if } x \geq 0 \\ -x & \text{if } x < 0 \end{cases}$$

The graph of $f(x) = x$ for $x \geq 0$ is the ray in the first quadrant, and the graph of $f(x) = -x$ for $x < 0$ is the half line (not including the origin) in the second quadrant, as indicated in Figure 8.46. Note that the graph has y-axis symmetry.

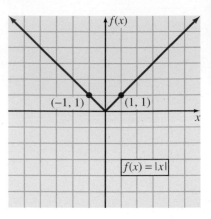

Figure 8.46

Translations of the Basic Curves

From our work in Section 8.3, we know that

1. The graph of $f(x) = x^2 + 3$ is the graph of $f(x) = x^2$ moved up three units.
2. The graph of $f(x) = x^2 - 2$ is the graph of $f(x) = x^2$ moved down two units.

Now let's describe in general the concept of a vertical translation.

> **Vertical Translation**
>
> The graph of $y = f(x) + k$ is the graph of $y = f(x)$ shifted k units upward if $k > 0$ or shifted $|k|$ units downward if $k < 0$.

In Figure 8.47, the graph of $f(x) = |x| + 2$ is obtained by shifting the graph of $f(x) = |x|$ upward two units, and the graph of $f(x) = |x| - 3$ is obtained by shifting the graph of $f(x) = |x|$ downward three units. Remember that $f(x) = |x| - 3$ can be written as $f(x) = |x| + (-3)$.

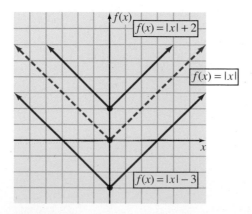

Figure 8.47

We also graphed horizontal translations of the basic parabola in Section 8.3. For example:

1. The graph of $f(x) = (x - 4)^2$ is the graph of $f(x) = x^2$ shifted four units to the right.

2. The graph of $f(x) = (x + 5)^2$ is the graph of $f(x) = x^2$ shifted five units to the left.

The general concept of a horizontal translation can be described as follows.

> ### Horizontal Translation
>
> The graph of $y = f(x - h)$ is the graph of $y = f(x)$ shifted h units to the right if $h > 0$ or shifted $|h|$ units to the left if $h < 0$.

In Figure 8.48, the graph of $f(x) = (x - 3)^3$ is obtained by shifting the graph of $f(x) = x^3$ three units to the right. Likewise, the graph of $f(x) = (x + 2)^3$ is obtained by shifting the graph of $f(x) = x^3$ two units to the left.

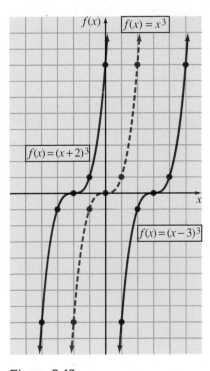

Figure 8.48

Reflections of the Basic Curves

From our work in Section 8.3, we know that the graph of $f(x) = -x^2$ is the graph of $f(x) = x^2$ reflected through the x axis. The general concept of an x-axis reflection can be described as follows:

> ### x-Axis Reflection
>
> The graph of $y = -f(x)$ is the graph of $y = f(x)$ reflected through the x axis.

In Figure 8.49, the graph of $f(x) = -\sqrt{x}$ is obtained by reflecting the graph of $f(x) = \sqrt{x}$ through the x axis. Reflections are sometimes referred to as **mirror images**. Thus if we think of the x axis in Figure 8.49 as a mirror, then the graphs of $f(x) = \sqrt{x}$ and $f(x) = -\sqrt{x}$ are mirror images of each other.

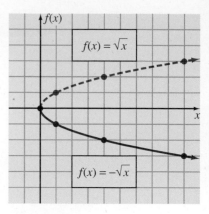

Figure 8.49

In Section 8.3, we did not consider a y-axis reflection of the basic parabola $f(x) = x^2$ because it is symmetric with respect to the y axis. In other words, a y-axis reflection of $f(x) = x^2$ produces the same figure. However, we will describe the general concept of a y-axis reflection.

y-Axis Reflection

The graph of $y = f(-x)$ is the graph of $y = f(x)$ reflected through the y axis.

Now suppose that we want to do a y-axis reflection of $f(x) = \sqrt{x}$. Because the domain for the function $f(x) = \sqrt{x}$ is restricted to values of x, such that $x \geq 0$, the domain for the y-axis reflection is restricted to values of x such that $-x \geq 0$. Simplifying $-x \geq 0$ by multiplying both sides by -1 gives $x \leq 0$. Figure 8.50 shows the y-axis reflection of $f(x) = \sqrt{x}$.

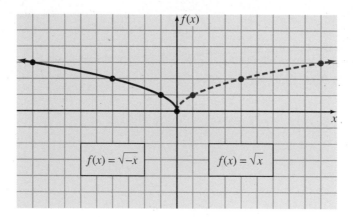

Figure 8.50

Vertical Stretching and Shrinking

Translations and reflections are called **rigid transformations** because the basic shape of the curve being transformed is not changed. In other words, only the positions of the graphs are changed. Now we want to consider some transformations that distort the shape of the original figure somewhat.

In Section 8.3, we graphed the function $f(x) = 2x^2$ by doubling the $f(x)$ values of the ordered pairs that satisfy the function $f(x) = x^2$. We obtained a parabola with its vertex at the origin, symmetric to the y axis, but *narrower* than the basic parabola. Likewise, we graphed the function $f(x) = \dfrac{1}{2}x^2$ by halving the $f(x)$ values of the ordered pairs that satisfy $f(x) = x^2$. In this case, we obtained a parabola with its vertex at the origin, symmetric to the y axis, but *wider* than the basic parabola.

The concepts of *narrower* and *wider* can be used to describe parabolas, but they cannot be used to describe accurately some other curves. Instead, we use the more general concepts of vertical stretching and shrinking.

> ### Vertical Stretching and Shrinking
>
> The graph of $y = cf(x)$ is obtained from the graph of $y = f(x)$ by multiplying the y co-ordinates for $y = f(x)$ by c. If $|c| > 1$, the graph is said to be *stretched* by a factor of $|c|$, and if $0 < |c| < 1$, the graph is said to be *shrunk* by a factor of $|c|$.

In Figure 8.51, the graph of $f(x) = 2\sqrt{x}$ is obtained by doubling the y coordinates of points on the graph of $f(x) = \sqrt{x}$. Likewise, the graph of $f(x) = \dfrac{1}{2}\sqrt{x}$ is obtained by halving the y coordinates of points on the graph of $f(x) = \sqrt{x}$.

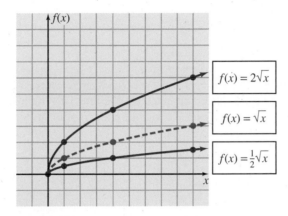

Figure 8.51

Successive Transformations

Some curves are the result of performing more than one transformation on a basic curve. Let's consider the graph of a function that involves a stretching, a reflection, a horizontal translation, and a vertical translation of the basic absolute-value function.

Classroom Example
Graph $f(x) = -\dfrac{1}{2}\sqrt{x + 1} + 2$.

EXAMPLE 5   Graph $f(x) = -2|x - 3| + 1$.

Solution

This is the basic absolute-value curve stretched by a factor of 2, reflected through the x axis, shifted three units to the right, and shifted one unit upward. To sketch the graph, we locate the point $(3, 1)$ and then determine a point on each of the rays. The graph is shown in Figure 8.52.

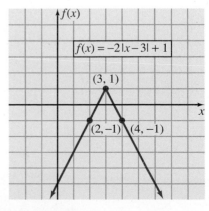

Figure 8.52

Remark: Note that in Example 5 we did not sketch the original basic curve $f(x) = |x|$ or any of the intermediate transformations. However, it is helpful to picture each transformation mentally. This locates the point (3, 1) and establishes the fact that the two rays point downward. Then a point on each ray determines the final graph.

We do need to realize that changing the order of doing the transformations may produce an incorrect graph. In Example 5, performing the translations first, and then performing the stretching and x-axis reflection, would locate the vertex of the graph at (3, −1) instead of (3, 1). *Unless parentheses indicate otherwise, stretchings, shrinkings, and reflections should be performed before translations.*

Classroom Example

Graph $f(x) = \sqrt{-4 - x}$.

EXAMPLE 6   Graph $f(x) = \sqrt{-3 - x}$.

Solution

It appears that this function is a y-axis reflection and a horizontal translation of the basic function $f(x) = \sqrt{x}$. First let's rewrite the expression under the radical.

$$f(x) = \sqrt{-3 - x} = \sqrt{-(3 + x)} = \sqrt{-(x + 3)}$$

Now to graph $f(x) = \sqrt{-(x + 3)}$, we would first reflect the graph of $f(x) = \sqrt{x}$ across the y axis and then shift the graph 3 units to the left. The graph is shown in Figure 8.53. Because it is always a good idea to check your graph by plotting a few points, we have added the points (−7, 2) and (−4, 1) to the graph.

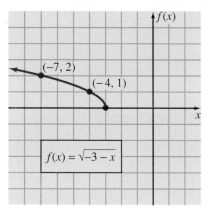

Figure 8.53

Now suppose that we want to graph the following function.

$$f(x) = \frac{2x^2}{x^2 + 4}$$

Because this is neither a basic function that we recognize nor a transformation of a basic function, we must revert to our previous graphing experiences. In other words, we need to find the domain, find the intercepts, check for symmetry, check for any restrictions, set up a table of values, plot the points, and sketch the curve. (If you want to do this now, you can check your result on page 489.) Furthermore, if the new function is defined in terms of an old function, we may be able to apply the definition of the old function and thereby simplify the new function for graphing purposes. Suppose you are asked to graph the function $f(x) = |x| + x$. This function can be simplified by applying the definition of absolute value. We will leave this for you to do in the next problem set.

Finally, let's use a graphing utility to give another illustration of the concept of stretching and shrinking a curve.

Classroom Example

If $f(x) = \sqrt{36 - x^2}$, sketch a

graph of $y = 3f(x)$ and $y = \frac{1}{3}f(x)$.

EXAMPLE 7

If $f(x) = \sqrt{25 - x^2}$, sketch a graph of $y = 2(f(x))$ and $y = \frac{1}{2}(f(x))$.

Solution

If $y = f(x) = \sqrt{25 - x^2}$, then

$$y = 2(f(x)) = 2\sqrt{25 - x^2} \qquad \text{and} \qquad y = \frac{1}{2}(f(x)) = \frac{1}{2}\sqrt{25 - x^2}$$

Graphing all three of these functions on the same set of axes produces Figure 8.54.

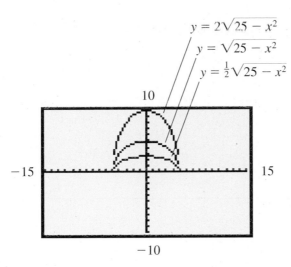

Figure 8.54

Concept Quiz 8.5

1. What is the domain of $f(x) = \sqrt{x}$?
    A. $x > 0$ B. $x \geq 0$ C. All real numbers

2. What is the domain of $f(x) = |x|$?
    A. $x > 0$ B. $x \geq 0$ C. All real numbers

3. If a graph is symmetric to the y axis, then which of the following is equal to $f(2)$?
    A. $-f(2)$ B. $f(-2)$ C. $-f(-2)$

4. Which of the following describes the graph of $f(x) = x^4 + 3$?
    A. The graph of $f(x) = x^4$ shifted up 3 units
    B. The graph of $f(x) = x^4$ shifted to the left 3 units
    C. The graph of $f(x) = x^4$ shifted to the right 3 units

5. For the graph of the function $f(x) = -2|x + 1| - 3$, what are the coordinates of the vertex?
    A. $(-1, 3)$ B. $(1, -3)$ C. $(-1, -3)$ D. $(0, 5)$

For Problems 6–10, answer true or false.

6. When the graph of a parabola is stretched, it is said to be narrower than the basic parabola.

7. A horizontal translation is a rigid transformation, and the shape of the graph does not change.

8. When applying successive transformations to a graph, unless parentheses indicate otherwise, stretchings, shrinkings, or reflections should be performed before translations.

9. The graphs of $f(x) = x^4$ and $f(x) = x^2$ are parabolas.

10. The graph of $y = f(-x)$ is the graph of $y = f(x)$ reflected across the x axis.

Problem Set 8.5

For Problems 1–30, graph each function. (Objective 1)

1. $f(x) = x^4 + 2$

2. $f(x) = -x^4 - 1$

3. $f(x) = (x - 2)^4$

4. $f(x) = (x + 3)^4 + 1$

5. $f(x) = -x^3$

6. $f(x) = x^3 - 2$

7. $f(x) = (x + 2)^3$

8. $f(x) = (x - 3)^3 - 1$

9. $f(x) = |x - 1| + 2$

10. $f(x) = -|x + 2|$

11. $f(x) = |x + 1| - 3$

12. $f(x) = 2|x|$

13. $f(x) = x + |x|$

14. $f(x) = \dfrac{|x|}{x}$

15. $f(x) = -|x - 2| - 1$

16. $f(x) = 2|x + 1| - 4$

17. $f(x) = x - |x|$

18. $f(x) = |x| - x$

19. $f(x) = -2\sqrt{x}$

20. $f(x) = 2\sqrt{x} - 1$

21. $f(x) = \sqrt{x + 2} - 3$

22. $f(x) = -\sqrt{x + 2} + 2$

23. $f(x) = \sqrt{2 - x}$

24. $f(x) = \sqrt{-1 - x}$

25. $f(x) = -2x^4 + 1$

26. $f(x) = 2(x - 2)^4 - 4$

27. $f(x) = -2x^3$

28. $f(x) = 2x^3 + 3$

29. $f(x) = 3(x - 2)^3 - 1$

30. $f(x) = -2(x + 1)^3 + 2$

31. Suppose that the graph of $y = f(x)$ with a domain of $-2 \le x \le 2$ is shown in Figure 8.55.

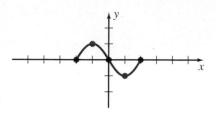

Figure 8.55

Sketch the graph of each of the following transformations of $y = f(x)$.

(a) $y = f(x) + 3$

(b) $y = f(x - 2)$

(c) $y = -f(x)$

(d) $y = f(x + 3) - 4$

Thoughts Into Words

32. Are the graphs of the two functions $f(x) = \sqrt{x - 2}$ and $g(x) = \sqrt{2 - x}$ y-axis reflections of each other? Defend your answer.

33. Are the graphs of $f(x) = 2\sqrt{x}$ and $g(x) = \sqrt{2x}$ identical? Defend your answer.

34. Are the graphs of $f(x) = \sqrt{x + 4}$ and $g(x) = \sqrt{-x + 4}$ y-axis reflections of each other? Defend your answer.

Graphing Calculator Activities

35. Use your graphing calculator to check your graphs for Problems 13–30.

36. Graph $f(x) = \sqrt{x^2 + 8}$, $f(x) = \sqrt{x^2 + 4}$, and $f(x) = \sqrt{x^2 + 1}$ on the same set of axes. Look at these graphs and predict the graph of $f(x) = \sqrt{x^2 - 4}$. Now graph it with the calculator to test your prediction.

37. For each of the following, predict the general shape and location of the graph, and then use your calculator to graph the function to check your prediction.

(a) $f(x) = \sqrt{x^2}$

(b) $f(x) = \sqrt{x^3}$

(c) $f(x) = |x^2|$

(d) $f(x) = |x^3|$

38. Graph $f(x) = x^4 + x^3$. Now predict the graph for each of the following, and check each prediction with your graphing calculator.

(a) $f(x) = x^4 + x^3 - 4$

(b) $f(x) = (x - 3)^4 + (x - 3)^3$

(c) $f(x) = -x^4 - x^3$

(d) $f(x) = x^4 - x^3$

39. Graph $f(x) = \sqrt[3]{x}$. Now predict the graph for each of the following, and check each prediction with your graphing calculator.

(a) $f(x) = 5 + \sqrt[3]{x}$

(b) $f(x) = \sqrt[3]{x + 4}$

(c) $f(x) = -\sqrt[3]{x}$

(d) $f(x) = \sqrt[3]{x - 3} - 5$

(e) $f(x) = \sqrt[3]{-x}$

8.6	Combining Functions

OBJECTIVES
1. Combine functions by finding the sum, difference, product, or quotient
2. Find the composition of two functions
3. Evaluate a composite function for a specified value

In subsequent mathematics courses, it is common to encounter functions that are defined in terms of sums, differences, products, and quotients of simpler functions. For example, if $h(x) = x^2 + \sqrt{x} - 1$, then we may consider the function h as the sum of f and g, where $f(x) = x^2$ and $g(x) = \sqrt{x} - 1$. In general, if f and g are functions, and D is the intersection of their domains, then the following definitions can be made:

Sum $(f + g)(x) = f(x) + g(x)$

Difference $(f - g)(x) = f(x) - g(x)$

Product $(f \cdot g)(x) = f(x) \cdot g(x)$

Quotient $\left(\dfrac{f}{g}\right)(x) = \dfrac{f(x)}{g(x)}, \quad g(x) \neq 0$

Classroom Example
If $f(x) = -3x + 5$ and $g(x) = x^2 - 2x - 8$, find
(a) $(f + g)(x)$
(b) $(f - g)(x)$
(c) $(f \cdot g)(x)$; and
(d) $(f/g)(x)$.
Determine the domain of each.

EXAMPLE 1

If $f(x) = 3x - 1$ and $g(x) = x^2 - x - 2$, find **(a)** $(f + g)(x)$; **(b)** $(f - g)(x)$;   **(c)** $(f \cdot g)(x)$; and **(d)** $(f/g)(x)$. Determine the domain of each.

Solutions

(a) $(f + g)(x) = f(x) + g(x) = (3x - 1) + (x^2 - x - 2) = x^2 + 2x - 3$

(b) $(f - g)(x) = f(x) - g(x)$

$$= (3x - 1) - (x^2 - x - 2)$$

$$= 3x - 1 - x^2 + x + 2$$

$$= -x^2 + 4x + 1$$

(c) $(f \cdot g)(x) = f(x) \cdot g(x)$

$$= (3x - 1)(x^2 - x - 2)$$

$$= 3x^3 - 3x^2 - 6x - x^2 + x + 2$$

$$= 3x^3 - 4x^2 - 5x + 2$$

(d) $\left(\dfrac{f}{g}\right)(x) = \dfrac{f(x)}{g(x)} = \dfrac{3x - 1}{x^2 - x - 2}$

The domain of both f and g is the set of all real numbers. Therefore the domain of $f + g$, $f - g$, and $f \cdot g$ is the set of all real numbers. For f/g, the denominator $x^2 - x - 2$ cannot equal zero. Solving $x^2 - x - 2 = 0$ produces

$$(x - 2)(x + 1) = 0$$

$$x - 2 = 0 \quad \text{or} \quad x + 1 = 0$$

$$x = 2 \qquad\qquad x = -1$$

Therefore the domain for f/g is the set of all real numbers except 2 and -1.

Graphs of functions can help us visually sort out our thought processes. For example, suppose that $f(x) = 0.46x - 4$ and $g(x) = 3$. If we think in terms of ordinate values, it seems reasonable that the graph of $f + g$ is the graph of f moved up three units. Likewise, the graph of $f - g$ should be the graph of f moved down three units. Let's use a graphing calculator to support these conclusions. Letting $Y_1 = 0.46x - 4$, $Y_2 = 3$, $Y_3 = Y_1 + Y_2$, and $Y_4 = Y_1 - Y_2$, we obtain Figure 8.56. Certainly this figure supports our conclusions. This type of graphical analysis becomes more important as the functions become more complex.

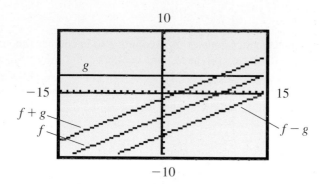

Figure 8.56

Composition of Functions

Besides adding, subtracting, multiplying, and dividing functions, there is another important operation called *composition*. The composition of two functions can be defined as follows:

Definition 8.2

The **composition** of functions f and g is defined by

$$(f \circ g)(x) = f(g(x))$$

for all x in the domain of g such that $g(x)$ is in the domain of f.

The left side, $(f \circ g)(x)$, of the equation in Definition 8.2 is read "the composition of f and g," and the right side is read "f of g of x." It may also be helpful for you to have a mental picture of Definition 8.2 as two function machines hooked together to produce another function (called the **composite function**), as illustrated in Figure 8.57. Note that what comes out of the g function is substituted into the f function. Thus composition is sometimes called the **substitution of functions**.

Figure 8.57 also illustrates the fact that $f \circ g$ is defined for all x in the domain of g such that $g(x)$ is in the domain of f. In other words, what comes out of g must be capable of being fed into f. Let's consider some examples.

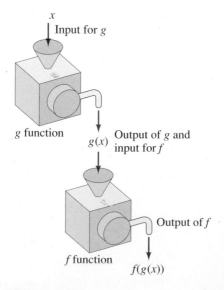

Figure 8.57

EXAMPLE 2

If $f(x) = x^2$ and $g(x) = 3x - 4$, find $(f \circ g)(x)$ and determine its domain.

Solution

Apply Definition 8.2 to obtain

$$(f \circ g)(x) = f(g(x))$$
$$= f(3x - 4)$$
$$= (3x - 4)^2$$
$$= 9x^2 - 24x + 16$$

Because g and f are both defined for all real numbers, so is $f \circ g$. Therefore, the domain of $f \circ g$ is all real numbers. ▪

Definition 8.2, with f and g interchanged, defines the composition of g and f as $(g \circ f)(x) = g(f(x))$.

EXAMPLE 3

If $f(x) = x^2$ and $g(x) = 3x - 4$, find $(g \circ f)(x)$ and determine its domain.

Solution

$$(g \circ f)(x) = g(f(x))$$
$$= g(x^2)$$
$$= 3x^2 - 4$$

Because f and g are defined for all real numbers, so is $g \circ f$. Therefore, the domain of $g \circ f$ is all real numbers. ▪

The results of Examples 2 and 3 demonstrate an important idea: *The composition of functions is not a commutative operation.* In other words, $f \circ g \neq g \circ f$ for all functions f and g. However, as we will see in Section 10.3, there is a special class of functions for which $f \circ g = g \circ f$.

EXAMPLE 4

If $f(x) = \sqrt{x}$ and $g(x) = 2x - 1$, find $(f \circ g)(x)$ and $(g \circ f)(x)$. Also determine the domain of each composite function.

Solution

$$(f \circ g)(x) = f(g(x))$$
$$= f(2x - 1)$$
$$= \sqrt{2x - 1}$$

The domain and range of g are the set of all real numbers, but the domain of f is all *nonnegative* real numbers. Therefore $g(x)$, which is $2x - 1$, must be nonnegative.

$$2x - 1 \geq 0$$
$$2x \geq 1$$
$$x \geq \frac{1}{2}$$

Thus the domain of $f \circ g$ is $D = \left\{x \mid x \geq \dfrac{1}{2}\right\}$.

$$(g \circ f)(x) = g(f(x))$$

$$= g(\sqrt{x})$$

$$= 2\sqrt{x} - 1$$

The domain and range of f are the set of nonnegative real numbers. The domain of g is the set of all real numbers. Therefore the domain of $g \circ f$ is $D = \{x \mid x \geq 0\}$.

Classroom Example

If $f(x) = \dfrac{3}{x + 2}$ and $g(x) = \dfrac{2}{x}$, find $(f \circ g)(x)$ and $(g \circ f)(x)$. Determine the domain for each composite function.

EXAMPLE 5

If $f(x) = \dfrac{3}{x - 1}$ and $g(x) = \dfrac{1}{2x}$, find $(f \circ g)(x)$ and $(g \circ f)(x)$. Determine the domain for each composite function.

Solution

$$(f \circ g)(x) = f(g(x))$$

$$= f\left(\dfrac{1}{2x}\right)$$

$$= \dfrac{3}{\dfrac{1}{2x} - 1} = \dfrac{3}{\dfrac{1}{2x} - \dfrac{2x}{2x}} = \dfrac{3}{\dfrac{1 - 2x}{2x}}$$

$$= \dfrac{6x}{1 - 2x}$$

The domain of g is all real numbers except 0, and the domain of f is all real numbers except 1. Therefore $g(x) \neq 1$. So we need to solve $g(x) = 1$ to find the values of x that will make $g(x) = 1$.

$$g(x) = 1$$

$$\dfrac{1}{2x} = 1$$

$$1 = 2x$$

$$\dfrac{1}{2} = x$$

Therefore $x \neq \dfrac{1}{2}$, so the domain of $f \circ g$ is $D = \left\{x \mid x \neq 0 \text{ and } x \neq \dfrac{1}{2}\right\}$.

$$(g \circ f)(x) = g(f(x))$$

$$= g\left(\dfrac{3}{x - 1}\right)$$

$$= \dfrac{1}{2\left(\dfrac{3}{x - 1}\right)} = \dfrac{1}{\dfrac{6}{x - 1}}$$

$$= \dfrac{x - 1}{6}$$

The domain of f is all real numbers except 1, and the domain of g is all real numbers except 0. Because $f(x)$, which is $3/(x - 1)$, will never equal 0, the domain of $g \circ f$ is $D = \{x \mid x \neq 1\}$.

Classroom Example
If $f(x) = 4x - 1$ and
$g(x) = \sqrt{x + 3}$, find $(g \circ f)\left(\dfrac{1}{2}\right)$.

EXAMPLE 6

If $f(x) = 5x + 2$ and $g(x) = \dfrac{1}{x + 1}$, find $(g \circ f)(-2)$.

Solution A

First determine $(g \circ f)(x)$.

$$\begin{aligned}
(g \circ f)(x) &= g[f(x)] \\
&= g(5x + 2) \\
&= \frac{1}{(5x + 2) + 1} \\
&= \frac{1}{5x + 3}
\end{aligned}$$

Now substitute -2 for x in $(g \circ f)(x)$.

$$(g \circ f)(-2) = \frac{1}{5(-2) + 3} = -\frac{1}{7}$$

Solution B

The composition $(g \circ f)(-2)$ can be rewritten as $g[f(-2)]$. Let's evaluate $f(-2)$.

$$f(-2) = 5(-2) + 2 = -8$$

Now the value -8 can be substituted for $f(-2)$ and $g[f(-2)]$ can be determined.

$$g[f(-2)] = g(-8) = \frac{1}{-8 + 1} = -\frac{1}{7}$$

Depending on the functions given in the problem, you may find one approach simpler than the other approach. ∎

A graphing utility can be used to find the graph of a composite function without actually forming the function algebraically. Let's see how this works.

Classroom Example
If $f(x) = x^2$ and $g(x) = x + 2$, use a graphing utility to obtain the graph of $y = (f \circ g)(x)$ and $y = (g \circ f)(x)$.

EXAMPLE 7

If $f(x) = x^3$ and $g(x) = x - 4$, use a graphing utility to obtain the graphs of $y = (f \circ g)(x)$ and of $y = (g \circ f)(x)$.

Solution

To find the graph of $y = (f \circ g)(x)$, we can make the following assignments:

$$Y_1 = x - 4$$
$$Y_2 = (Y_1)^3$$

(Note that we have substituted Y_1 for x in $f(x)$ and assigned this expression to Y_2, much the same way as we would do it algebraically.) The graph of $y = (f \circ g)(x)$ is shown in Figure 8.58.

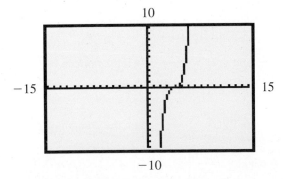

Figure 8.58

To find the graph of $y = (g \circ f)(x)$, we can make the following assignments.

$$Y_1 = x^3$$
$$Y_2 = Y_1 - 4$$

The graph of $y = (g \circ f)(x)$ is shown in Figure 8.59.

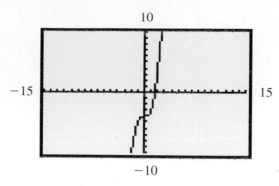

Figure 8.59

Take another look at Figures 8.58 and 8.59. Note that in Figure 8.58, the graph of $y = (f \circ g)(x)$ is the basic cubic curve $f(x) = x^3$ translated four units to the right. Likewise, in Figure 8.59, the graph of $y = (g \circ f)(x)$ is the basic cubic curve translated four units downward. These are examples of a more general concept of using composite functions to represent various geometric transformations.

Concept Quiz 8.6

For Problems 1–10, answer true or false.

1. If $f(x) = \sqrt{x}$ and $g(x) = x^2$, then the domain of $f \circ g$ is all real numbers.

2. If $f(x) = 2x + 6$ and $g(x) = x - 7$, then the domain of $\dfrac{f}{g}$ is all real numbers.

3. The composition of functions is a commutative operation.

4. The sum of two functions is a commutative operation.

5. The composition of two functions $f \circ g$ means to multiply the functions.

6. When forming the composition of two functions $f \circ g$, the range elements of g are members of the domain of f.

7. If $f(x) = \dfrac{1}{x - 6}$ and $g(x) = 2x$, then the domain of $f \circ g$ is all real numbers except 3 and 6.

8. If the domain of f is $x > 0$ and the domain of g is $x < 0$, then the sum $(f + g)(x)$ is not defined.

9. If $f(x) = \dfrac{1}{x - 6}$ and $g(x) = \dfrac{6}{x - 3}$, then the domain of $f \circ g$ is
$$D = \{x \mid x \neq 3 \text{ and } x \neq 4\}.$$

10. If $f(x) = \dfrac{1}{x - 6}$ and $g(x) = \dfrac{6}{x - 3}$, then the domain of $g \circ f$ is
$$D = \left\{ x \mid x \neq 6 \text{ and } x \neq \dfrac{19}{3} \right\}.$$

Problem Set 8.6

For Problems 1–8, find $f + g$, $f - g$, $f \cdot g$, and f/g. Also specify the domain for each. (Objective 1)

1. $f(x) = 3x - 4$, $g(x) = 5x + 2$

2. $f(x) = -6x - 1$, $g(x) = -8x + 7$

3. $f(x) = x^2 - 6x + 4$, $g(x) = -x - 1$

4. $f(x) = 2x^2 - 3x + 5$, $g(x) = x^2 - 4$

5. $f(x) = x^2 - x - 1$, $g(x) = x^2 + 4x - 5$

6. $f(x) = x^2 - 2x - 24$, $g(x) = x^2 - x - 30$

7. $f(x) = \sqrt{x - 1}$, $g(x) = \sqrt{x}$

8. $f(x) = \sqrt{x + 2}$, $g(x) = \sqrt{3x - 1}$

For Problems 9–26, find $(f \circ g)(x)$ and $(g \circ f)(x)$. Also specify the domain for each. (Objective 2)

9. $f(x) = 2x$, $g(x) = 3x - 1$

10. $f(x) = 4x + 1$, $g(x) = 3x$

11. $f(x) = 5x - 3$, $g(x) = 2x + 1$

12. $f(x) = 3 - 2x$, $g(x) = -4x$

13. $f(x) = 3x + 4$, $g(x) = x^2 + 1$

14. $f(x) = 3$, $g(x) = -3x^2 - 1$

15. $f(x) = 3x - 4$, $g(x) = x^2 + 3x - 4$

16. $f(x) = 2x^2 - x - 1$, $g(x) = x + 4$

17. $f(x) = \dfrac{1}{x}$, $g(x) = 2x + 7$

18. $f(x) = \dfrac{1}{x^2}$, $g(x) = x$

19. $f(x) = \sqrt{x - 2}$, $g(x) = 3x - 1$

20. $f(x) = \dfrac{1}{x}$, $g(x) = \dfrac{1}{x^2}$

21. $f(x) = \dfrac{1}{x - 1}$, $g(x) = \dfrac{2}{x}$

22. $f(x) = \dfrac{4}{x + 2}$, $g(x) = \dfrac{3}{2x}$

23. $f(x) = 2x + 1$, $g(x) = \sqrt{x - 1}$

24. $f(x) = \sqrt{x + 1}$, $g(x) = 5x - 2$

25. $f(x) = \dfrac{1}{x - 1}$, $g(x) = \dfrac{x + 1}{x}$

26. $f(x) = \dfrac{x - 1}{x + 2}$, $g(x) = \dfrac{1}{x}$

For Problems 27–32, solve each problem. (Objective 3)

27. If $f(x) = 3x - 2$ and $g(x) = x^2 + 1$, find $(f \circ g)(-1)$ and $(g \circ f)(3)$.

28. If $f(x) = x^2 - 2$ and $g(x) = x + 4$, find $(f \circ g)(2)$ and $(g \circ f)(-4)$.

29. If $f(x) = 2x - 3$ and $g(x) = x^2 - 3x - 4$, find $(f \circ g)(-2)$ and $(g \circ f)(1)$.

30. If $f(x) = 1/x$ and $g(x) = 2x + 1$, find $(f \circ g)(1)$ and $(g \circ f)(2)$.

31. If $f(x) = \sqrt{x}$ and $g(x) = 3x - 1$, find $(f \circ g)(4)$ and $(g \circ f)(4)$.

32. If $f(x) = x + 5$ and $g(x) = |x|$, find $(f \circ g)(-4)$ and $(g \circ f)(-4)$.

For Problems 33–38, show that $(f \circ g)(x) = x$ and that $(g \circ f)(x) = x$.

33. $f(x) = 2x$, $g(x) = \dfrac{1}{2}x$

34. $f(x) = \dfrac{3}{4}x$, $g(x) = \dfrac{4}{3}x$

35. $f(x) = x - 2$, $g(x) = x + 2$

36. $f(x) = 2x + 1$, $g(x) = \dfrac{x - 1}{2}$

37. $f(x) = 3x + 4$ $g(x) = \dfrac{x - 4}{3}$

38. $f(x) = 4x - 3$, $g(x) = \dfrac{x + 3}{4}$

Thoughts Into Words

39. Discuss whether addition, subtraction, multiplication, and division of functions are commutative operations.

40. Explain why the composition of two functions is not a commutative operation.

41. Explain how to find the domain of

$$\left(\frac{f}{g}\right)(x) \text{ if } f(x) = \frac{x - 1}{x + 2} \text{ and } g(x) = \frac{x + 3}{x - 5}.$$

Further Investigations

42. If $f(x) = 3x - 4$ and $g(x) = ax + b$, find conditions on a and b that will guarantee that $f \circ g = g \circ f$.

43. If $f(x) = x^2$ and $g(x) = \sqrt{x}$, with both having a domain of the set of nonnegative real numbers, then show that $(f \circ g)(x) = x$ and $(g \circ f)(x) = x$.

44. If $f(x) = 3x^2 - 2x - 1$ and $g(x) = x$, find $f \circ g$ and $g \circ f$. (Recall that we have previously named $g(x) = x$ the "identity function.")

Graphing Calculator Activities

45. For each of the following, predict the general shape and location of the graph, and then use your calculator to graph the function to check your prediction. (Your knowledge of the graphs of the basic functions that are being added or subtracted should be helpful when you are making your predictions.)

(a) $f(x) = x^4 + x^2$ **(b)** $f(x) = x^3 + x^2$

(c) $f(x) = x^4 - x^2$ **(d)** $f(x) = x^2 - x^4$

(e) $f(x) = x^2 - x^3$ **(f)** $f(x) = x^3 - x^2$

(g) $f(x) = |x| + \sqrt{x}$ **(h)** $f(x) = |x| - \sqrt{x}$

46. For each of the following, find the graph of $y = (f \circ g)(x)$ and of $y = (g \circ f)(x)$.

(a) $f(x) = x^2$ and $g(x) = x + 5$

(b) $f(x) = x^3$ and $g(x) = x + 3$

(c) $f(x) = x - 6$ and $g(x) = -x^3$

(d) $f(x) = x^2 - 4$ and $g(x) = \sqrt{x}$

(e) $f(x) = \sqrt{x}$ and $g(x) = x^2 + 4$

(f) $f(x) = \sqrt[3]{x}$ and $g(x) = x^3 - 5$

Answers to the Concept Quiz

1. True   **2.** False   **3.** False   **4.** True   **5.** False   **6.** True   **7.** False   **8.** True   **9.** True   **10.** True

---

8.7   Direct and Inverse Variation

OBJECTIVES

1 Translate statements of variation into equations

2 Find the value for the constant of variation

3 Solve application problems for direct, inverse, or joint variation

The amount of simple interest earned by a fixed amount of money invested at a certain rate *varies directly* as the time.

At a constant temperature, the volume of an enclosed gas *varies inversely* as the pressure.

Such statements illustrate two basic types of functional relationships, **direct variation** and **inverse variation**, that are widely used, especially in the physical sciences. These relationships can be expressed by equations that determine functions. The purpose of this section is to investigate these special functions.

Direct Variation

The statement "y varies directly as x" means

$$y = kx$$

where k is a nonzero constant called the **constant of variation**. The phrase "y is directly proportional to x" is also used to indicate direct variation; k is then referred to as the **constant of proportionality**.

Remark: Note that the equation $y = kx$ defines a function and can be written $f(x) = kx$. However, in this section, it is more convenient not to use function notation but instead to use variables that are meaningful in terms of the physical entities involved in the particular problem.

Statements that indicate direct variation may also involve powers of a variable. For example, "y varies directly as the square of x" can be written $y = kx^2$. In general, y varies directly as the nth power of x $(n > 0)$ means

$$y = kx^n$$

There are three basic types of problems in which we deal with direct variation:

1. Translating an English statement into an equation expressing the direct variation;
2. Finding the constant of variation from the given values of the variables; and
3. Finding additional values of the variables once the constant of variation has been determined.

Let's consider an example of each type of problem.

Classroom Example
Translate the statement "the distance traveled varies directly as the time traveled" into an equation, and use k as the constant of variation.

EXAMPLE 1

Translate the statement "The tension on a spring varies directly as the distance it is stretched" into an equation, using k as the constant of variation.

Solution

Let t represent the tension and d the distance; the equation is

$$t = kd$$

Classroom Example
If A varies directly as the square root of s, and if $A = 28$ when $s = 49$, find the constant of variation.

EXAMPLE 2

If A varies directly as the square of e, and if $A = 96$ when $e = 4$, find the constant of variation.

Solution

Because A varies directly as the square of e, we have

$$A = ke^2$$

Substitute 96 for A and 4 for e to obtain

$$96 = k(4)^2$$
$$96 = 16k$$
$$6 = k$$

The constant of variation is 6.

Classroom Example
If r is directly proportional to t and if $r = 40$ when $t = 48$, find the value of r when $t = 84$.

EXAMPLE 3

If y is directly proportional to x, and if $y = 6$ when $x = 8$, find the value of y when $x = 24$.

Solution

The statement "y is directly proportional to x" translates into

$$y = kx$$

Let $y = 6$ and $x = 8$; the constant of variation becomes

$$6 = k(8)$$

$$\frac{6}{8} = k$$

$$\frac{3}{4} = k$$

Thus the specific equation is

$$y = \frac{3}{4}x$$

Now let $x = 24$ to obtain

$$y = \frac{3}{4}(24) = 18$$

Inverse Variation

The second basic type of variation is *inverse variation*. The statement "*y* varies inversely as *x*" means

$$y = \frac{k}{x}$$

where k is a nonzero constant, which is again referred to as the constant of variation. The phrase "*y* is inversely proportional to *x*" is also used to express inverse variation. As with direct variation, statements indicating inverse variation may involve powers of x. For example, "*y* varies inversely as the square of *x*" can be written $y = k/x^2$. In general, y varies inversely as the *n*th power of x ($n > 0$) means

$$y = \frac{k}{x^n}$$

The following examples illustrate the three basic kinds of problems that involve inverse variation.

Classroom Example
Translate the statement "the volume of a gas varies inversely as the pressure" into an equation that uses k as the constant of variation.

EXAMPLE 4

Translate the statement "The length of a rectangle of fixed area varies inversely as the width" into an equation, using k as the constant of variation.

Solution

Let l represent the length and w the width; the equation is

$$l = \frac{k}{w}$$

Classroom Example
If m is inversely proportional to n, and if $m = 6$ when $n = 15$, find the constant of variation.

EXAMPLE 5

If y is inversely proportional to x, and if $y = 14$ when $x = 4$, find the constant of variation.

Solution

Because y is inversely proportional to x, we have

$$y = \frac{k}{x}$$

Substitute 4 for x and 14 for y to obtain

$$14 = \frac{k}{4}$$

Solving this equation yields

$$k = 56$$

The constant of variation is 56.

Classroom Example
Suppose that the time traveled a fixed distance varies inversely with the speed. If it takes 4 hours at 70 miles per hour to travel that distance, how long would it take at 56 miles per hour?

EXAMPLE 6

The time required for a car to travel a certain distance varies inversely as the rate at which it travels. If it takes 4 hours at 50 miles per hour to travel the distance, how long will it take at 40 miles per hour?

Solution

Let t represent time and r rate. The phrase "time required . . . varies inversely as the rate" translates into

$$t = \frac{k}{r}$$

Substitute 4 for t and 50 for r to find the constant of variation.

$$4 = \frac{k}{50}$$

$$k = 200$$

Thus the specific equation is

$$t = \frac{200}{r}$$

Now substitute 40 for r to produce

$$t = \frac{200}{40}$$

$$= 5$$

It will take 5 hours at 40 miles per hour.

The terms *direct* and *inverse*, as applied to variation, refer to the relative behavior of the variables involved in the equation. That is, in **direct variation** ($y = kx$), an assignment of *increasing absolute values for x* produces *increasing absolute values for y.* However, in **inverse variation** ($y = k/x$), an assignment of *increasing absolute values for x* produces *decreasing absolute values for y.*

Joint Variation

Variation may involve more than two variables. The following table illustrates some different types of variation statements and their equivalent algebraic equations that use k as the constant of variation. Statements 1, 2, and 3 illustrate the concept of **joint variation**. Statements 4 and 5 show that both direct and inverse variation may occur in the same problem. Statement 6 combines joint variation with inverse variation.

Variation Statement	Algebraic Equation
1. y varies jointly as x and z.	$y = kxz$
2. y varies jointly as x, z, and w.	$y = kxzw$
3. V varies jointly as h and the square of r.	$V = khr^2$
4. h varies directly as V and inversely as w.	$h = \dfrac{kV}{w}$
5. y is directly proportional to x and inversely proportional to the square of z.	$y = \dfrac{kx}{z^2}$
6. y varies jointly as w and z and inversely as x.	$y = \dfrac{kwz}{x}$

The final two examples of this section illustrate different kinds of problems involving some of these variation situations.

EXAMPLE 7

The volume of a pyramid varies jointly as its altitude and the area of its base. If a pyramid with an altitude of 9 feet and a base with an area of 17 square feet has a volume of 51 cubic feet, find the volume of a pyramid with an altitude of 14 feet and a base with an area of 45 square feet.

Solution

Let's use the following variables:

V = volume h = altitude

B = area of base k = constant of variation

The fact that the volume varies jointly as the altitude and the area of the base can be represented by the equation

$V = kBh$

Substitute 51 for V, 17 for B, and 9 for h to obtain

$51 = k(17)(9)$

$51 = 153k$

$\dfrac{51}{153} = k$

$\dfrac{1}{3} = k$

Therefore the specific equation is $V = \dfrac{1}{3}Bh$. Now substitute 45 for B and 14 for h to obtain

$V = \dfrac{1}{3}(45)(14) = (15)(14) = 210$

The volume is 210 cubic feet.

Classroom Example
Suppose that a varies jointly as b and c, and inversely as d. If $a = 2$ when $b = 16$, $c = 7$, and $d = 28$, find a when $b = 10$, $c = 9$, and $d = 45$.

EXAMPLE 8

Suppose that y varies jointly as x and z and inversely as w. If $y = 154$ when $x = 6$, $z = 11$, and $w = 3$, find y when $x = 8$, $z = 9$, and $w = 6$.

Solution

The statement "y varies jointly as x and z and inversely as w" translates into the equation

$$y = \frac{kxz}{w}$$

Substitute 154 for y, 6 for x, 11 for z, and 3 for w to produce

$$154 = \frac{(k)(6)(11)}{3}$$

$$154 = 22k$$

$$7 = k$$

Thus the specific equation is

$$y = \frac{7xz}{w}$$

Now substitute 8 for x, 9 for z, and 6 for w to obtain

$$y = \frac{7(8)(9)}{6}$$

$$= 84$$

Concept Quiz 8.7

For Problems 1–4, match the statement of variation with its equation.

1. y varies inversely as the cube of x.
2. y varies directly as the cube of x.
3. y varies directly as the square of w and inversely as the cube of x.
4. y varies jointly as the square of w and the cube of x.

A. $y = \dfrac{kw^2}{x^3}$ B. $y = \dfrac{k}{x^3}$ C. $y = kw^2x^3$ D. $y = kx^3$

For Problems 5–10, answer true or false.

5. The statement y varies jointly as x and w means that y varies directly as x and inversely as w.
6. The constant of variation is always a positive number.
7. If a worker gets paid \$9.50 for each hour worked, we would say that his pay varies directly with the number of hours worked.
8. If a fast food restaurant loses \$0.25 for each special burger sold, we would say that the amount of money lost varies inversely as the number of special burgers sold.
9. Joint variation means that the variation involves three or more variables.
10. The equation $y = -2x$ is an example of inverse variation because the y values decrease as the x values increase.

Problem Set 8.7

For Problems 1–8, translate each statement of variation into an equation; use k as the constant of variation. **(Objective 1)**

1. y varies directly as the cube of x.

2. a varies inversely as the square of b.

3. A varies jointly as l and w.

4. s varies jointly as g and the square of t.

5. At a constant temperature, the volume (V) of a gas varies inversely as the pressure (P).

6. y varies directly as the square of x and inversely as the cube of w.

7. The volume (V) of a cone varies jointly as its height (h) and the square of a radius (r).

8. l is directly proportional to r and t.

For Problems 9–18, find the constant of variation for each stated condition. **(Objective 2)**

9. y varies directly as x, and $y = 72$ when $x = 3$.

10. y varies inversely as the square of x, and $y = 4$ when $x = 2$.

11. A varies directly as the square of r, and $A = 154$ when $r = 7$.

12. V varies jointly as B and h, and $V = 104$ when $B = 24$ and $h = 13$.

13. A varies jointly as b and h, and $A = 81$ when $b = 9$ and $h = 18$.

14. s varies jointly as g and the square of t, and $s = -108$ when $g = 24$ and $t = 3$.

15. y varies jointly as x and z and inversely as w, and $y = 154$ when $x = 6$, $z = 11$, and $w = 3$.

16. V varies jointly as h and the square of r, and $V = 1100$ when $h = 14$ and $r = 5$.

17. y is directly proportional to the square of x and inversely proportional to the cube of w, and $y = 18$ when $x = 9$ and $w = 3$.

18. y is directly proportional to x and inversely proportional to the square root of w, and $y = \dfrac{1}{5}$ when $x = 9$ and $w = 10$.

For Problems 19–32, solve each problem. **(Objective 3)**

19. If y is directly proportional to x, and $y = 5$ when $x = -15$, find the value of y when $x = -24$.

20. If y is inversely proportional to the square of x, and $y = \dfrac{1}{8}$ when $x = 4$, find y when $x = 8$.

21. If V varies jointly as B and h, and $V = 96$ when $B = 36$ and $h = 8$, find V when $B = 48$ and $h = 6$.

22. If A varies directly as the square of e, and $A = 150$ when $e = 5$, find A when $e = 10$.

23. The time required for a car to travel a certain distance varies inversely as the rate at which it travels. If it takes 3 hours to travel the distance at 50 miles per hour, how long will it take at 30 miles per hour?

24. The distance that a freely falling body falls varies directly as the square of the time it falls. If a body falls 144 feet in 3 seconds, how far will it fall in 5 seconds?

25. The period (the time required for one complete oscillation) of a simple pendulum varies directly as the square root of its length. If a pendulum 12 feet long has a period of 4 seconds, find the period of a pendulum of length 3 feet.

26. Suppose the number of days it takes to complete a construction job varies inversely as the number of people assigned to the job. If it takes 7 people 8 days to do the job, how long will it take 10 people to complete the job?

27. The number of days needed to assemble some machines varies directly as the number of machines and inversely as the number of people working. If it takes 4 people 32 days to assemble 16 machines, how many days will it take 8 people to assemble 24 machines?

28. The volume of a gas at a constant temperature varies inversely as the pressure. What is the volume of a gas under a pressure of 25 pounds if the gas occupies 15 cubic centimeters under a pressure of 20 pounds?

29. The volume (V) of a gas varies directly as the temperature (T) and inversely as the pressure (P). If $V = 48$ when $T = 320$ and $P = 20$, find V when $T = 280$ and $P = 30$.

30. The volume of a cylinder varies jointly as its altitude and the square of the radius of its base. If the volume of a cylinder is 1386 cubic centimeters when the radius of the base is 7 centimeters, and its altitude is 9 centimeters, find the volume of a cylinder that has a base of radius 14 centimeters if the altitude of the cylinder is 5 centimeters.

31. The cost of labor varies jointly as the number of workers and the number of days that they work. If it costs $900 to have 15 people work for 5 days, how much will it cost to have 20 people work for 10 days?

32. The cost of publishing pamphlets varies directly as the number of pamphlets produced. If it costs $96 to publish 600 pamphlets, how much does it cost to publish 800 pamphlets?

Thoughts Into Words

33. How would you explain the difference between direct variation and inverse variation?

34. Suppose that y varies directly as the square of x. Does doubling the value of x also double the value of y? Explain your answer.

35. Suppose that y varies inversely as x. Does doubling the value of x also double the value of y? Explain your answer.

Further Investigations

In the previous problems, we chose numbers to make computations reasonable without the use of a calculator. However, variation-type problems often involve messy computations, and the calculator becomes a very useful tool. Use your calculator to help solve the following problems.

36. The simple interest earned by a certain amount of money varies jointly as the rate of interest and the time (in years) that the money is invested.
  (a) If some money invested at 11% for 2 years earns $385, how much would the same amount earn at 12% for 1 year?
  (b) If some money invested at 12% for 3 years earns $819, how much would the same amount earn at 14% for 2 years?
  (c) If some money invested at 14% for 4 years earns $1960, how much would the same amount earn at 15% for 2 years?

37. The period (the time required for one complete oscillation) of a simple pendulum varies directly as the square root of its length. If a pendulum 9 inches long has a period of 2.4 seconds, find the period of a pendulum of length 12 inches. Express the answer to the nearest tenth of a second.

38. The volume of a cylinder varies jointly as its altitude and the square of the radius of its base. If the volume of a cylinder is 549.5 cubic meters when the radius of the base is 5 meters and its altitude is 7 meters, find the volume of a cylinder that has a base of radius 9 meters and an altitude of 14 meters.

39. If y is directly proportional to x and inversely proportional to the square of z, and if $y = 0.336$ when $x = 6$ and $z = 5$, find the constant of variation.

40. If y is inversely proportional to the square root of x, and $y = 0.08$ when $x = 225$, find y when $x = 625$.

Answers to the Concept Quiz

1. B   **2.** D   **3.** A   **4.** C   **5.** False   **6.** False   **7.** True   **8.** False   **9.** True   **10.** False

Chapter 8 Summary

OBJECTIVE	SUMMARY	EXAMPLE
Know the definition of a function. (Section 8.1/Objective 1)	A function f is a correspondence between two sets X and Y that assigns to each element x of set X one and only one element y of set Y. The element y being assigned is called the image of x. The set X is called the **domain** of the function, and the set of all the images is called the **range** of the function. A function can be thought of as a set of ordered pairs in which no two have the same first component.	Specify the domain and range of the relation, and state whether or not it is a function. $\{(1, 8), (2, 7), (5, 6), (3, 8)\}$ Solution $D = \{1, 2, 3, 5\}$ $R = \{6, 7, 8\}$ Because each element in the domain is assigned one and only element in the range, it is a function.
Apply the vertical line test to determine if a graph represents a function. (Section 8.1/Objective 2)	The vertical line test is used to determine if a graph is the graph of a function. If each vertical line intersects a graph in no more than one point, then the graph represents a function.	Identify the graph as the graph of a function or the graph of a relation that is not a function. Solution It is the graph of a relation that is not a function because a vertical line will intersect the graph in more than one point.
Evaluate a function for a given input value. (Section 8.1/Objective 3)	Single letters such as f, g, and h are commonly used to name functions. The symbol $f(x)$ represents the element in the range associated with x from the domain.	If $f(x) = 2x^2 + 3x - 5$, find $f(4)$. Solution Substitute 4 for x in the equation. $f(4) = 2(4)^2 + 3(4) - 5$ $f(4) = 32 + 12 - 5$ $f(4) = 39$
Evaluate a piecewise-defined function for a given input value. (Section 8.1/Objective 4)	Sometimes the rule of assignment for a function may consist of more than one part. Such a function is called a piecewise-defined function. An everyday example of this concept is that there is a different formula for the fee for legal aid services depending upon the income group to which a client belongs.	If $f(x) = \begin{cases} 2x + 3 & x \le 4 \\ 5x - 1 & x > 4 \end{cases}$, find $f(8)$. Solution Because 8 is greater than 4, we use the function rule $f(x) = 5x - 1$ to find $f(8)$. $f(8) = 5(8) - 1 = 39$
Find the difference quotient of a function. (Section 8.1/Objective 5)	The quotient $\dfrac{f(a + h) - f(a)}{h}$ is called the difference quotient. Being able to determine the difference quotient is an essential skill when studying limits in a calculus course.	If $f(x) = 5x + 7$, find the difference quotient. Solution $\dfrac{f(a + h) - f(a)}{h} = \dfrac{5(a + h) + 7 - (5a + 7)}{h}$ $= \dfrac{5a + 5h + 7 - 5a - 7}{h}$ $= \dfrac{5h}{h}$ $= 5$

OBJECTIVE	SUMMARY	EXAMPLE
Determine the domain and range of a function. (Section 8.1/Objective 6)	The domain of a function is the set of all real number replacements for the variable that will produce real number functional values. Replacement values that make a denominator zero or a radical expression undefined are excluded from the domain. The range of a function is often easier to determine from the graph of the function.	Specify the domain for $f(x) = \sqrt{2x - 5}$. **Solution** The replacement values for x that make the radicand negative must be excluded from the domain. To find those values, set the radicand equal to or greater than zero and solve. $2x - 5 \geq 0$ $x \geq \dfrac{5}{2}$ The domain is the set $\left\{x \middle| x \geq \dfrac{5}{2}\right\}$ or stated in interval notation, $\left[\dfrac{5}{2}, \infty\right)$. For any domain value, all the range elements will be positive or zero because the function is the principal square root.
Graph a linear function. (Section 8.2/Objective 1)	Any function that can be written in the form $f(x) = ax + b$ where a and b are real numbers, is a **linear function**. The graph of a linear function is a straight line.	Graph $f(x) = 3x + 1$. **Solution** Because $f(0) = 1$, the point $(0, 1)$ is on the graph. Also $f(1) = 4$, so the point $(1, 4)$ is on the graph.
Determine a linear function for specified conditions. (Section 8.2/Objective 2)	Knowing two distinct ordered pairs of a linear function makes it possible to determine the equation for the function.	Determine the linear function whose graph is a line that contains the points $(-1, 6)$ and $(1, 12)$. **Solution** The linear function $f(x) = ax + b$ models the situation. From the two ordered pairs we can determine a. $a = \dfrac{12 - 6}{1 - (-1)} = 3$ So $f(x) = ax + b$ becomes $f(x) = 3x + b$. Now substitute either ordered pair into the equation to determine b. $6 = 3(-1) + b$ $b = 9$ The linear function is $f(x) = 3x + 9$.

(continued)

OBJECTIVE	SUMMARY	EXAMPLE
Solve applications involving linear functions. (Section 8.2/Objective 3)	Linear functions and their graphs can be useful when problem solving.	The FixItFast computer repair company uses the equation $C(m) = 2m + 15$, where m is the number of minutes for the service call, to determine the charge for a service call. Graph the function and use the graph to approximate the charge for a 25-minute service call. Then use the function to find the exact charge for a 25-minute service call. **Solution** Compare your approximation to the exact charge $C(25) = 2(25) + 15 = 65$.
Graph quadratic functions. (Section 8.3/Objectives 1, 2 and Section 8.4/Objective 1)	Any function that can be written in the form $f(x) = ax^2 + bx + c$, where a, b, and c are real numbers and $a \neq 0$, is a **quadratic function**. The graph of any quadratic function is a **parabola**, which can be drawn using either of the following methods. 1. Express the function in the form $f(x) = a(x - h)^2 + k$ and use the values of a, h, and k to determine the parabola. 2. Express the function in the form $f(x) = ax^2 + bx + c$ and use the fact that the vertex is at $\left(-\dfrac{b}{2a}, f\left(-\dfrac{b}{2a}\right)\right)$ and the axis of symmetry is $x = -\dfrac{b}{2a}$.	Graph $f(x) = 2x^2 + 8x + 7$. **Solution** $\begin{aligned} f(x) &= 2x^2 + 8x + 7 = 2(x^2 + 4x) + 7 \\ &= 2(x^2 + 4x + 4) - 8 + 7 \\ &= 2(x + 2)^2 - 1 \end{aligned}$ $\boxed{f(x) = 2(x + 2)^2 - 1}$

OBJECTIVE	SUMMARY	EXAMPLE
Solve applications involving quadratic functions. (Section 8.4/Objective 3)	We can solve some applications that involve maximum and minimum values by using our knowledge of parabolas generated by quadratic functions.	Suppose the cost function for producing a particular item is given by the equation $C(x) = 3x^2 - 270x + 15{,}800$, where x represents the number of items. How many items should be produced to minimize the cost? **Solution** The function represents a parabola. The minimum will occur at the vertex, so we want to find the x coordinate of the vertex. $$x = -\frac{b}{2a}$$ $$x = -\frac{-270}{2(3)} = 45$$ Therefore 45 items should be produced to minimize the cost.
Graph piecewise-defined functions. (Section 8.3/Objective 3)	Piecewise-defined functions have different rules of assignment for intervals of the domain. Graph the function for each specified interval of the domain on the same coordinate system.	Graph $f(x) = \begin{cases} -2x & x < -1 \\ 2 & -1 \le x \le 1 \\ 2x & x > 1 \end{cases}$ **Solution** 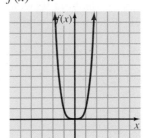

Graph functions by applying translations, stretching or shrinking, and reflections to the basic graphs shown here.
(Section 8.5/Objective 1)

$f(x) = x^2$

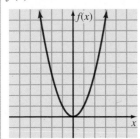

$f(x) = x^3$

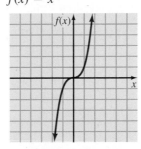

$f(x) = x^4$

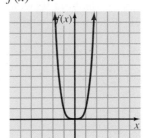

$f(x) = \sqrt{x}$

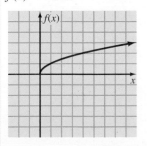

$f(x) = |x|$

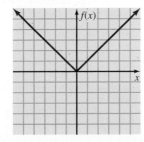

(continued)

OBJECTIVE	SUMMARY	EXAMPLE
Graph by applying horizontal and vertical translations. (Section 8.5/Objective 1)	**Vertical Translation** The graph of $y = f(x) + k$ is the graph of $y = f(x)$ shifted k units upward if k is positive and $\lvert k \rvert$ units downward if k is negative. **Horizontal Translation** The graph of $y = f(x - h)$ is the graph of $y = f(x)$ shifted h units to the right if h is positive and $\lvert h \rvert$ units to the left if h is negative.	Graph $f(x) = \lvert x + 4 \rvert$. **Solution** To fit the form, change the equation to the equivalent form $f(x) = \lvert x - (-4) \rvert$. Because h is negative, the graph of $f(x) = \lvert x \rvert$ is shifted 4 units to the left. $f(x) = \lvert x + 4 \rvert$
Graph by applying reflections. (Section 8.5/Objective 1)	**x-axis reflection** The graph of $y = -f(x)$ is the graph of $y = f(x)$ reflected through the x axis. **y-axis reflection** The graph of $y = f(-x)$ is the graph of $y = f(x)$ reflected through the y axis.	Graph $f(x) = \sqrt{-x}$. **Solution** The graph of $f(x) = \sqrt{-x}$ is the graph of $f(x) = \sqrt{x}$ reflected through the y axis. $f(x) = \sqrt{-x}$
Graph by applying the concepts of vertical stretching or shrinking of a graph. (Section 8.5/Objective 1)	**Vertical Stretching and Shrinking** The graph of $y = cf(x)$ is obtained from the graph of $y = f(x)$ by multiplying the y coordinates of $y = f(x)$ by c. If $\lvert c \rvert > 1$, the graph is said to be **stretched** by a factor of $\lvert c \rvert$, and if $0 < \lvert c \rvert < 1$, the graph is said to be **shrunk** by a factor of $\lvert c \rvert$.	Graph $f(x) = \dfrac{1}{4}x^2$. **Solution** The graph of $f(x) = \dfrac{1}{4}x^2$ is the graph of $f(x) = x^2$ shrunk by a factor of $\dfrac{1}{4}$. $f(x) = \dfrac{1}{4}x^2$

OBJECTIVE	SUMMARY	EXAMPLE
Graph functions by using successive transformations (Section 8.5/Objective 1)	Some curves result from performing more than one transformation on a basic curve. Unless parentheses indicate otherwise, stretchings, shrinkings, and x-axis reflections should be performed before translations.	Graph $f(x) = -2(x + 1)^2 + 3$. **Solution** $$f(x) = -2(x + 1)^2 + 3$$ Narrows the parabola and opens it downward / Moves the parabola 1 unit to the left / Moves the parabola 3 units up $f(x) = -2(x + 1)^2 + 3$
Combine functions by finding the sum, difference, product, or quotient. (Section 8.6/Objective 1)	In general, if f and g are functions, and D is the intersection of their domain, then the following definitions can be stated: **Sum of two functions** $$(f + g)(x) = f(x) + g(x)$$ **Difference of two functions** $$(f - g)(x) = f(x) - g(x)$$ **Product of two functions** $$(f \cdot g)(x) = f(x) \cdot g(x)$$ **Quotient of two functions** $$\left(\frac{f}{g}\right)(x) = \frac{f(x)}{g(x)}, \qquad g(x) \neq 0$$	If $f(x) = -x^3 + 10$ and $g(x) = x - 4$, find $\left(\dfrac{f}{g}\right)(x)$ and determine its domain. **Solution** $$\left(\frac{f}{g}\right)(x) = \frac{-x^3 + 10}{x - 4}$$ The domain of f is all real numbers, and the domain of g is all real numbers except 4. Therefore the domain of $\dfrac{f}{g}$ is all real numbers except 4.
Find the composition of two functions. (Section 8.6/Objective 2)	The **composition** of two functions f and g is defined by $(f \circ g)(x) = f(g(x))$ for all x in the domain of g such that $g(x)$ is in the domain of f. Remember that the composition of functions is not a commutative operation.	If $f(x) = x + 5$ and $g(x) = x^2 + 4x - 6$ find $(g \circ f)(x)$. **Solution** In the function g, substitute $f(x)$ for x. $(g \circ f)(x) = g(f(x))$ $(g \circ f)(x) = (x + 5)^2 + 4(x + 5) - 6$ $\qquad = x^2 + 10x + 25 + 4x + 20 - 6$ $\qquad = x^2 + 14x + 39$

(continued)

OBJECTIVE	SUMMARY	EXAMPLE
Evaluate a composite function for a specified value. (Section 8.6/Objective 3)	Evaluating the composition of functions can be done with two different methods. 1. Given two functions, the composite function could be formed and then evaluated by substituting directly into the composite function. 2. To find $(f \circ g)(a)$, first evaluate $g(a)$ and then substitute the value of $g(a)$ into f. Depending on the functions given in the problem, one method might be simpler than the other method.	If $f(x) = \sqrt{2x + 1}$ and $g(x) = x^2 + 3$, find $(f \circ g)(5)$. **Solution A** The composite function is $(f \circ g)(x) = \sqrt{2x^2 + 7}$ Therefore, $(f \circ g)(5) = \sqrt{2(5)^2 + 7} = \sqrt{57}$ **Solution B** $(f \circ g)(5) = f(g(5))$ $g(5) = (5)^2 + 3 = 28$ Substituting 28 for $g(5)$ gives $f(g(5)) = f(28) = \sqrt{2(28) + 1} = \sqrt{57}$
Translate statements of variation into equations. (Section 8.7/Objective 1)	Relationships that involve direct and inverse variation can be expressed by equations that determine functions. The statement y *varies directly as* x means $y = kx$ where k is the constant of variation. The statement y *varies directly as the nth power of* $x(n > 0)$ means $y = kx^n$. The statement y *varies inversely as* x means $y = \dfrac{k}{x}$. The statement y *varies inversely as the nth power of* $x(n > 0)$ means $y = \dfrac{k}{x^n}$. The statement y *varies jointly as* x *and* w means $y = kxw$.	Translate the statement "w varies inversely as the square of y" into an equation using k as the constant of variation. **Solution** $w = \dfrac{k}{y^2}$
Solve application problems for direct, inverse, or joint variation. (Section 8.7/Objectives 2, 3)	There are basically three steps for solving variation problems. 1. Translate the English statement into an equation of variation. 2. Determine the value for the constant of variation. 3. Substitute k and the given values for the variables into the equation of variation to produce the desired answer.	Andrew's paycheck varies directly with the number of hours he works. If he earned \$400 for working 32 hours, how much will he earn if he works 40 hours? **Solution** Let p represent the pay and h represent the number of hours worked. The equation of variation will be $p = kh$. Substitute \$400 for p and 32 for h to determine k. $400 = 32k$ $k = 12.5$ The equation of variation is $p = 12.5h$. For 40 hours of work, $p = 12.5(40) = 500$. So Andrew will earn \$500 for 40 hours of work.

Chapter 8   **Review Problem Set**

1. If $f(x) = 3x^2 - 2x - 1$, find $f(2)$, $f(-1)$, and $f(-3)$.

2. For each of the following functions, find

$$\frac{f(a + h) - f(a)}{h}$$

   (a) $f(x) = -5x + 4$ **(b)** $f(x) = 2x^2 - x + 4$
   (c) $f(x) = -3x^2 + 2x - 5$

3. Determine the domain and range of the function $f(x) = x^2 + 5$.

4. Determine the domain of the function

$$f(x) = \frac{2}{2x^2 + 7x - 4}$$

5. Express the domain of $f(x) = \sqrt{x^2 - 7x + 10}$ using interval notation.

For Problems 6–23, graph each function.

6. $f(x) = -2x + 2$ **7.** $f(x) = 2x^2 - 1$

8. $f(x) = -\sqrt{x - 2} + 1$ **9.** $f(x) = x^2 - 8x + 17$

10. $f(x) = -x^3 + 2$ **11.** $f(x) = 2|x - 1| + 3$

12. $f(x) = -2x^2 - 12x - 19$ **13.** $f(x) = -\frac{1}{3}x + 1$

14. $f(x) = -\frac{2}{x^2}$ **15.** $f(x) = 2|x| - x$

16. $f(x) = (x - 2)^2$ **17.** $f(x) = \sqrt{-x + 4}$

18. $f(x) = -(x + 1)^2 - 3$ **19.** $f(x) = \sqrt{x + 3} - 2$

20. $f(x) = -|x| + 4$ **21.** $f(x) = (x - 2)^3$

22. $f(x) = \begin{cases} x^2 - 1 & \text{for } x < 0 \\ 3x - 1 & \text{for } x \geq 0 \end{cases}$

23. $f(x) = \begin{cases} 3 & \text{for } x \leq -3 \\ |x| & \text{for } -3 < x < 3 \\ 2x - 3 & \text{for } x \geq 3 \end{cases}$

24. If $f(x) = 2x + 3$ and $g(x) = x^2 - 4x - 3$, find $f + g$, $f - g$, $f \cdot g$, and f/g.

For Problems 25–30, find $(f \circ g)(x)$ and $(g \circ f)(x)$. Also specify the domain for each.

25. $f(x) = 3x - 9$ and $g(x) = -2x + 7$

26. $f(x) = x^2 - 5$ and $g(x) = 5x - 4$

27. $f(x) = \sqrt{x - 5}$ and $g(x) = x + 2$

28. $f(x) = \frac{1}{x}$ and $g(x) = x^2 - x - 6$

29. $f(x) = x^2$ and $g(x) = \sqrt{x - 1}$

30. $f(x) = \frac{1}{x - 3}$ and $g(x) = \frac{1}{x + 2}$

31. If $f(x) = \begin{cases} x^2 - 2 & \text{for } x \geq 0 \\ -3x + 4 & \text{for } x < 0 \end{cases}$
   find $f(5)$, $f(0)$, and $f(-3)$.

32. If $f(x) = -x^2 - x + 4$ and $g(x) = \sqrt{x - 2}$, find $f(g(6))$ and $g(f(-2))$.

33. If $f(x) = |x|$ and $g(x) = x^2 - x - 1$, find $(f \circ g)(1)$ and $(g \circ f)(-3)$.

34. Determine the linear function whose graph is a line that is parallel to the line determined by

$$g(x) = \frac{2}{3}x + 4$$

   and contains the point $(5, -2)$.

35. Determine the linear function whose graph is a line that is perpendicular to the line determined by

$$g(x) = -\frac{1}{2}x - 6$$

   and contains the point $(-6, 3)$.

36. The cost for burning a 100-watt light bulb is given by the function $c(h) = 0.006h$, where h represents the number of hours that the bulb burns. How much, to the nearest cent, does it cost to burn a 100-watt bulb for 4 hours per night for a 30-day month?

37. "All Items 30% Off Marked Price" is a sign in a local department store. Form a function and then use it to determine how much one has to pay for each of the following marked items: a $65 pair of shoes, a $48 pair of slacks, a $15.50 belt.

For Problems 38–40, find the x intercepts and the vertex for each parabola.

38. $f(x) = 3x^2 + 6x - 24$

39. $f(x) = x^2 - 6x - 5$

40. $f(x) = 2x^2 - 28x + 101$

41. Find two numbers whose sum is 10, such that the sum of the square of one number plus four times the other number is a minimum.

42. A group of students is arranging a chartered flight to Europe. The charge per person is $496 if 100 students go on the flight. If more than 100 students go, the charge per student is reduced by an amount equal to $4 times the number of students above 100. How many students should the airline try to get in order to maximize its revenue?

43. If y varies directly as x and inversely as w, and if $y = 27$ when $x = 18$ and $w = 6$, find the constant of variation.

44. If y varies jointly as x and the square root of w, and if $y = 140$ when $x = 5$ and $w = 16$, find y when $x = 9$ and $w = 49$.

45. The weight of a body above the surface of the earth varies inversely as the square of its distance from the center of the earth. Assuming the radius of the earth to be 4000 miles, determine how much a man would weigh 1000 miles above the earth's surface if he weighs 200 pounds on the surface.

46. The number of hours needed to assemble some furniture varies directly as the number of pieces of furniture and inversely as the number of people working. If it takes 3 people 10 hours to assemble 20 pieces of furniture, how many hours will it take 4 people to assemble 40 pieces of furniture?

1. If $f(x) = -\dfrac{1}{2}x + \dfrac{1}{3}$, find $f(-3)$.

2. If $f(x) = -x^2 - 6x + 3$, find $f(-2)$.

3. If $f(x) = 3x^2 + 2x - 5$, find $\dfrac{f(a + h) - f(a)}{h}$.

4. For the function $f(x) = \dfrac{-3}{2x^2 + 7x - 4}$, determine the domain.

5. For the function $f(x) = \sqrt{5 - 3x}$, determine the domain.

6. If $f(x) = 3x - 1$ and $g(x) = 2x^2 - x - 5$, find $f + g$, $f - g$, and $f \cdot g$.

7. If $f(x) = -3x + 4$ and $g(x) = 7x + 2$, find $(f \circ g)(x)$.

8. If $f(x) = 2x + 5$ and $g(x) = 2x^2 - x + 3$, find $(g \circ f)(x)$.

9. If $f(x) = \dfrac{3}{x - 2}$ and $g(x) = \dfrac{2}{x}$, find $(f \circ g)(x)$.

10. If $f(x) = x^2 - 2x - 3$ and $g(x) = |x - 3|$, find $f(g(-2))$ and $g(f(1))$.

11. Determine the linear function whose graph is a line that has a slope of $-\dfrac{5}{6}$ and contains the point $(4, -8)$.

12. If $f(x) = \dfrac{3}{x}$ and $g(x) = \dfrac{2}{x - 1}$, determine the domain of $\left(\dfrac{f}{g}\right)(x)$.

13. If $f(x) = 2x^2 - x + 1$ and $g(x) = x^2 + 3$, find $(f + g)(-2)$, $(f - g)(4)$, and $(g - f)(-1)$.

14. If $f(x) = x^2 + 5x - 6$ and $g(x) = x - 1$, find $(f \cdot g)(x)$ and $\left(\dfrac{f}{g}\right)(x)$.

15. Find two numbers whose sum is 60, such that the sum of the square of one number plus 12 times the other number is a minimum.

16. If y varies jointly as x and z, and if $y = 18$ when $x = 8$ and $z = 9$, find y when $x = 5$ and $z = 12$.

17. If y varies inversely as x, and if $y = \dfrac{1}{2}$ when $x = -8$, find the constant of variation.

18. The simple interest earned by a certain amount of money varies jointly as the rate of interest and the time (in years) that the money is invested. If \$140 is earned for the money invested at 7% for 5 years, how much is earned if the same amount is invested at 8% for 3 years?

19. A retailer has a number of items that he wants to sell at a profit of 35% of the cost. What linear function can be used to determine selling prices of the items? What price should he charge for a tie that cost him \$13?

20. Find the x intercepts and the vertex of the parabola $f(x) = 4x^2 - 16x - 48$.

For Problems 21–25, graph each function.

21. $f(x) = (x - 2)^3 - 3$

22. $f(x) = -2x^2 - 12x - 14$

23. $f(x) = 3|x - 2| - 1$

24. $f(x) = \sqrt{-x + 2}$

25. $f(x) = -x - 1$

For Problems 1–10, evaluate each expression.

1. $(3^{-2})^{-1}$

2. $\left(\dfrac{7}{9}\right)^{-1}$

3. $\dfrac{1}{\left(\dfrac{1}{2}\right)^{-3}}$

4. $8^{-1} + 2^{-3}$

5. $(3^{-2} + 2^{-3})^{-1}$

6. $-\sqrt{0.16}$

7. $\sqrt[3]{3\dfrac{3}{8}}$

8. $9^{3/2}$

9. $8^{2/3}$

10. $(-27)^{4/3}$

For Problems 11–15, evaluate each algebraic expression for the given values of the variables.

11. $-3(x - 1) + 4(2x + 3) - (3x + 5)$ for $x = -9$

12. $\dfrac{3}{n} - \dfrac{5}{n} + \dfrac{9}{n}$ for $n = -7$

13. $\dfrac{4}{x - 2} + \dfrac{7}{x + 1}$ for $x = 6$

14. $(2x + 5y)(2x - 5y)$ for $x = 5$ and $y = -1$

15. $\dfrac{\dfrac{2}{x} - \dfrac{3}{y}}{\dfrac{1}{x} + \dfrac{4}{y}}$ for $x = -3$ and $y = 11$

For Problems 16–19, simplify each rational expression.

16. $\dfrac{12x^3y^2}{27xy}$

17. $\dfrac{6x^2 + 11x - 7}{8x^2 - 22x + 9}$

18. $\dfrac{8x^3 + 64}{4x^2 - 16}$

19. $\dfrac{xy + 4y - 2x - 8}{x^2 + 4x}$

For Problems 20–24, perform the indicated operations involving rational expressions. Express final answers in simplest form.

20. $\dfrac{3a^2b}{4a^3b^2} \div \dfrac{6a}{27b}$

21. $\dfrac{x^2 - x}{x + 5} \cdot \dfrac{x^2 + 5x + 4}{x^4 - x^2}$

22. $\dfrac{x + 3}{10} + \dfrac{2x + 1}{15} - \dfrac{x - 2}{18}$

23. $\dfrac{7}{12ab} - \dfrac{11}{15a^2}$

24. $\dfrac{8}{x^2 - 4x} + \dfrac{2}{x}$

For Problems 25–27, simplify each complex fraction.

25. $\dfrac{\dfrac{2}{x} - 3}{\dfrac{3}{y} + 4}$

26. $\dfrac{\dfrac{5}{x^2} - \dfrac{3}{x}}{\dfrac{1}{y} + \dfrac{2}{y^2}}$

27. $\dfrac{\dfrac{3a}{2} - 1}{2 - \dfrac{1}{a}}$

For Problems 28–30, perform the indicated operations and simplify. Express final answers using positive exponents only.

28. $(-3x^{-1}y^2)(4x^{-2}y^{-3})$

29. $\dfrac{48x^{-4}y^2}{6xy}$

30. $\left(\dfrac{27a^{-4}b^{-3}}{-3a^{-1}b^{-4}}\right)^{-1}$

For Problems 31–36, express each in simplest radical form. All variables represent positive real numbers.

31. $\sqrt{\dfrac{8}{25}}$

32. $\dfrac{4\sqrt{3}}{7\sqrt{6}}$

33. $\sqrt{48x^3y^7}$

34. $\dfrac{4}{\sqrt{5} - \sqrt{3}}$

35. $\sqrt[3]{48x^4y^5}$

36. $\dfrac{\sqrt[3]{4}}{\sqrt[3]{2}}$

For Problems 37–40, find each of the indicated products or quotients. Express answers in the standard form of a complex number.

37. $(5 - 2i)(6 + 5i)$

38. $(-3 - i)(-2 - 4i)$

39. $\dfrac{5}{4i}$

40. $\dfrac{6 + 2i}{3 - 4i}$

For Problems 41–58, solve each equation.

41. $3(2x - 1) - 2(5x + 1) = 4(3x + 4)$

42. $n + \dfrac{3n - 1}{9} - 4 = \dfrac{3n + 1}{3}$

43. $0.92 + 0.9(x - 0.3) = 2x - 5.95$

44. $|4x - 1| = 11$

45. $|2x - 1| = |-x + 4|$

46. $x^3 = 36x$

47. $(3x - 1)^2 = 45$

48. $(2x + 5)^2 = -32$

49. $2x^2 - 3x + 4 = 0$

50. $(n + 4)(n - 6) = 11$ **51.** $(2n - 1)(n + 6) = 0$

52. $(x + 5)(3x - 1) = (x + 5)(2x + 7)$

53. $(x - 4)(2x + 9) = (2x - 1)(x + 2)$

54. $(3x - 1)(x + 1) = (2x + 1)(x - 3)$

55. $\sqrt{3x} - x = -6$

56. $\sqrt{x + 19} - \sqrt{x + 28} = -1$

57. $12x^4 - 19x^2 + 5 = 0$

58. $x^3 - 4x^2 - 3x + 12 = 0$

For Problems 59–68, solve each inequality and express the solution set using interval notation.

59. $|5x - 2| > 13$ **60.** $(x - 2)(x + 4) \leq 0$

61. $|6x + 2| \leq 8$ **62.** $x(x + 5) < 24$

63. $-5(y - 1) + 3 > 3y - 4 - 4y$

64. $\dfrac{x - 2}{5} - \dfrac{3x - 1}{4} \leq \dfrac{3}{10}$

65. $(2x + 1)(x - 2)(x + 5) > 0$

66. $\dfrac{x - 3}{x - 7} \geq 0$ **67.** $\dfrac{2x}{x + 3} > 4$

68. $2x^3 + 5x^2 - 3x < 0$

69. On a number line, find the coordinate of the point that is three-fourths of the distance from -6 to 10.

70. In a Cartesian plane, find the coordinates of a point that is two-thirds of the distance from $(-1, 2)$ to $(8, 11)$.

71. Find the slope of the line determined by the equation $-2x + 5y = 7$.

72. Write the equation of the line that contains the two points $(3, -4)$ and $(-2, -1)$.

73. If $f(x) = 3x - 2$ and $g(x) = x^2 + 2x$, find $f(g(3))$ and $g(f(2))$.

74. If $f(x) = 2x - 1$ and $g(x) = \sqrt{x + 2}$, find $f(g(x))$ and $g(f(x))$.

75. Express the domain of the function $f(x) = \sqrt{x^2 + 7x - 30}$.

76. If $f(x) = -x^2 + 6x - 1$, find $\dfrac{f(a + h) - f(a)}{h}$.

For Problems 77–82, graph each function.

77. $f(x) = -|x - 2| + 4$ **78.** $f(x) = -x^2 - 6x - 10$

79. $f(x) = x - 2$ **80.** $f(x) = (x - 2)^2$

81. $f(x) = (x - 2)^3$ **82.** $f(x) = \sqrt{x - 2}$

For Problems 83–97, use an equation or an inequality to help solve each problem.

83. Find three consecutive odd integers whose sum is 57.

84. Eric has a collection of 63 coins consisting of nickels, dimes, and quarters. The number of dimes is 6 more than the number of nickels, and the number of quarters is 1 more than twice the number of nickels. How many coins of each kind are in the collection?

85. One of two supplementary angles is 4° larger than one-third of the other angle. Find the measure of each of the angles.

86. If a ring costs a jeweler $300, at what price should it be sold to make a profit of 50% on the selling price?

87. Beth invested a certain amount of money at 8% interest and $300 more than that amount at 9%. Her total yearly interest was $316. How much did she invest at each rate?

88. Two trains leave the same depot at the same time, one traveling east and the other west. At the end of $4\frac{1}{2}$ hours, the trains are 639 miles apart. If the rate of the train traveling east is 10 miles per hour faster than the rate of the other train, find their rates.

89. A 10-quart radiator contains a 50% solution of antifreeze. How much needs to be drained out and replaced with pure antifreeze to obtain a 70% antifreeze solution?

90. Sam shot rounds of 70, 73, and 76 on the first three days of a golf tournament. What must he shoot on the fourth day of the tournament to average 72 or lower for the four days?

91. The cube of a number equals nine times the same number. Find the number.

92. A strip of uniform width is to be cut off both sides and both ends of a sheet of paper that is 8 inches by 14 inches to reduce the size of the paper to an area of 72 square inches. Find the width of the strip.

93. A sum of $2450 is to be divided between two people in the ratio of 3 to 4. How much does each person receive?

94. Working together, Sue and Dean can complete a task in $1\frac{1}{5}$ hours. Dean can do the task by himself in 2 hours.

How long would it take Sue to complete the task by herself?

95. A new diet requires that the number of calories from a serving of starchy vegetables be one-half the number of calories from a serving of meat. Also the number of calories from a serving of fruit must be one-third the number of calories from a serving of meat. For a 770-calorie meal consisting of a serving of meat, starchy vegetables, and fruit, find the allotted number of calories for each type of serving.

96. Marge, the office manager, has a budget of $28,000 to furnish the conference room of a hotel with 24 seating arrangements, each consisting of a table with four chairs. The chairs being considered for purchase cost twenty dollars less than one-half the cost of the table. How much money will remain in the budget after the purchase of the tables and chairs?

97. The sum of the two smallest angles of a triangle is 40° less than the other angle. The sum of the smallest and largest angles is twice the other angle. Find the measures of the three angles of the triangle.

9 Polynomial and Rational Functions

9.1 Synthetic Division

9.2 Remainder and Factor Theorems

9.3 Polynomial Equations

9.4 Graphing Polynomial Functions

9.5 Graphing Rational Functions

9.6 More on Graphing Rational Functions

The graphs of polynomial functions are smooth curves that can be used to describe the path of objects such as a roller coaster.

© Racheal Grazias

Earlier in this text we solved linear and quadratic equations and graphed linear and quadratic functions. In this chapter we will expand our equation-solving processes and graphing techniques to include more general polynomial equations and functions. Then our knowledge of polynomial functions will allow us to work with rational functions. The function concept will again serve as a unifying thread throughout the chapter. To facilitate our study in this chapter, we will first review the concept of dividing polynomials, and we will introduce theorems about division.

Video tutorials based on section learning objectives are available in a variety of delivery modes.

9.1 Synthetic Division

OBJECTIVE

1 Use synthetic division to determine the quotient and remainder for polynomial division

In Section 4.5 we discussed the process of dividing polynomials and the simplified process of synthetic division when the divisor is of the form $x - c$. Because polynomial division is central to the study of polynomial functions, we want to review the division process and state the algorithms and theorems for the division of polynomials.

Earlier we discussed the process of dividing polynomials by using the following format:

$$
\begin{array}{r}
x^2 - 2x + 4 \\
3x + 1 \overline{)3x^3 - 5x^2 + 10x + 1} \\
\underline{3x^3 + x^2} \\
-6x^2 + 10x + 1 \\
\underline{-6x^2 - 2x} \\
12x + 1 \\
\underline{12x + 4} \\
-3
\end{array}
$$

We also suggested writing the final result as

$$
\frac{3x^3 - 5x^2 + 10x + 1}{3x + 1} = x^2 - 2x + 4 + \frac{-3}{3x + 1}
$$

Multiplying both sides of this equation by $3x + 1$ produces

$$
3x^3 - 5x^2 + 10x + 1 = (3x + 1)(x^2 - 2x + 4) + (-3)
$$

which is of the familiar form

$$
\text{Dividend} = (\text{Divisor})(\text{Quotient}) + \text{Remainder}
$$

This result is commonly called the **division algorithm for polynomials**, and it can be stated in general terms as follows:

Division Algorithm for Polynomials

If $f(x)$ and $d(x)$ are polynomials and $d(x) \neq 0$, then there exist unique polynomials $q(x)$ and $r(x)$ such that

$$
f(x) = d(x)q(x) + r(x)
$$

Dividend   Divisor   Quotient   Remainder

where $r(x) = 0$ or the degree of $r(x)$ is less than the degree of $d(x)$.

If the divisor is of the form $x - c$, where c is a constant, then the typical long-division algorithm can be conveniently simplified into a process called **synthetic division**. First, let's consider an example using the usual algorithm. Then, in a step-by-step fashion, we will list some shortcuts to use that will lead us into the synthetic-division procedure. Consider the division problem $(3x^4 + x^3 - 15x^2 + 6x - 8) \div (x - 2)$:

$$
\begin{array}{r}
3x^3 + 7x^2 - x + 4 \\
x - 2 \overline{\smash{)}3x^4 + x^3 - 15x^2 + 6x - 8} \\
\underline{3x^4 - 6x^3} \\
7x^3 - 15x^2 \\
\underline{7x^3 - 14x^2} \\
-x^2 + 6x \\
\underline{-x^2 + 2x} \\
4x - 8 \\
\underline{4x - 8}
\end{array}
$$

Note that because the dividend $(3x^4 + x^3 - 15x^2 + 6x - 8)$ is written in descending powers of x, the quotient $(3x^3 + 7x^2 - x + 4)$ is also in descending powers of x. In other words, the numerical coefficients are the key, so let's rewrite this problem in terms of its coefficients.

$$
\begin{array}{r}
3 \quad\; 7 \;\; - 1 \;\; 4 \\
1 - 2 \overline{\smash{)}3 \quad\; 1 \;\; -15 \;\; 6 \;\; -8} \\
\textcircled{3} \, -6 \\
7 \;\; \textcircled{-15} \\
\textcircled{7} \;\; -14 \\
-1 \;\; \textcircled{6} \\
\textcircled{-1} \;\; 2 \\
4 \;\; \textcircled{-8} \\
\textcircled{4} \;\; -8
\end{array}
$$

Now observe that the numbers circled are simply repetitions of the numbers directly above them in the format. Thus the circled numbers could be omitted and the format would be as follows. (Disregard the arrows for the moment.)

$$
\begin{array}{r}
3 \quad\; 7 \;\; - 1 \;\; 4 \\
1 - 2 \overline{\smash{)}3 \quad\; 1 \;\; -15 \;\; 6 \;\; -8} \\
\underline{-6} \\
7 \\
\underline{-14} \\
-1 \\
2 \\
\underline{4} \\
-8
\end{array}
$$

Next, move some numbers up as indicated by the arrows, and omit writing 1 as the coefficient of x in the divisor to yield the following more compact form:

$$
\begin{array}{rl}
3 \quad 7 \;\; - 1 \;\; 4 & \qquad (1) \\
-2 \overline{\smash{)}3 \quad 1 \;\; -15 \;\; 6 \;\; -8} & \qquad (2) \\
\underline{-6 \;\; -14 \;\; 2 \;\; -8} & \qquad (3) \\
7 \;\; - 1 \;\; 4 & \qquad (4)
\end{array}
$$

Note that line (4) reveals all of the coefficients of the quotient in line (1), except for the first coefficient, 3. Thus we can omit line (1), begin line (4) with the first coefficient, and then use the following form:

$$
\begin{array}{rl}
-2 \overline{\smash{)}3 \quad 1 \;\; -15 \;\; 6 \;\; -8} & \qquad (5) \\
\underline{-6 \;\; -14 \;\; 2 \;\; -8} & \qquad (6) \\
3 \;\; 7 \;\; - 1 \;\; 4 \;\; 0 & \qquad (7)
\end{array}
$$

Line (7) contains the coefficients of the quotient; the 0 indicates the remainder. Finally, changing the constant in the divisor to 2 (instead of -2), which will change the signs of the numbers in line (6), allows us to add the corresponding entries in lines (5) and (6) rather than subtract them. Thus the final synthetic-division form for this problem is

$$
\begin{array}{r|rrrr}
2 & 3 & 1 & -15 & 6 & -8 \\
  &   & 6 & 14 & -2 & 8 \\
\hline
  & 3 & 7 & -1 & 4 & 0
\end{array}
$$

Now we will consider another problem and follow a step-by-step procedure for setting up and carrying out the synthetic division. Suppose that we want to do the following division problem.

$$x + 4 \overline{\smash{)}2x^3 + 5x^2 - 13x - 2}$$

1. Write the coefficients of the dividend as follows.

$$\overline{\smash{)}2 \quad 5 \quad -13 \quad -2}$$

2. In the divisor, use -4 instead of 4 so that later we can add rather than subtract.

$$-4\overline{\smash{)}2 \quad 5 \quad -13 \quad -2}$$

3. Bring down the first coefficient of the dividend.

$$
\begin{array}{r|rrrr}
-4 & 2 & 5 & -13 & -2 \\
\hline
   & 2
\end{array}
$$

4. Multiply that first coefficient by the divisor, which yields $2(-4) = -8$. This result is added to the second coefficient of the dividend.

$$
\begin{array}{r|rrrr}
-4 & 2 & 5 & -13 & -2 \\
   &   & -8 & & \\
\hline
   & 2 & -3
\end{array}
$$

5. Multiply $(-3)(-4)$, which yields 12; this result is added to the third coefficient of the dividend.

$$
\begin{array}{r|rrrr}
-4 & 2 & 5 & -13 & -2 \\
   &   & -8 & 12 & \\
\hline
   & 2 & -3 & -1
\end{array}
$$

6. Multiply $(-1)(-4)$, which yields 4; this result is added to the last term of the dividend.

$$
\begin{array}{r|rrrr}
-4 & 2 & 5 & -13 & -2 \\
   &   & -8 & 12 & 4 \\
\hline
   & 2 & -3 & -1 & 2
\end{array}
$$

The last row indicates a quotient of $2x^2 - 3x - 1$ and a remainder of 2.

Let's consider three more examples, showing only the final compact form for synthetic division.

Classroom Example
Find the quotient and remainder for $(3x^3 - 7x^2 + 2x - 8) \div (x - 3)$.

EXAMPLE 1

Find the quotient and remainder for $(2x^3 - 5x^2 + 6x + 4) \div (x - 2)$.

Solution

$$
\begin{array}{r|rrrr}
2 & 2 & -5 & 6 & 4 \\
  &   & 4 & -2 & 8 \\
\hline
  & 2 & -1 & 4 & 12
\end{array}
$$

Therefore the quotient is $2x^2 - x + 4$, and the remainder is 12.

Classroom Example
Find the quotient and remainder for
$(2x^4 - 3x^2 + x - 12) \div (x - 2)$.

EXAMPLE 2

Find the quotient and remainder for $(4x^4 - 2x^3 + 6x - 1) \div (x - 1)$.

Solution

$$
\begin{array}{r}
1\overline{)\,4 \quad -2 \quad 0 \quad 6 \quad -1} \\
\underline{ \quad 4 \quad 2 \quad 2 \quad 8} \\
4 \quad 2 \quad 2 \quad 8 \quad 7
\end{array}
$$

Note that a 0 has been inserted as the
coefficient of the missing x^2 term

Thus the quotient is $4x^3 + 2x^2 + 2x + 8$, and the remainder is 7.

Classroom Example
Find the quotient and remainder for
$(x^3 - 2x^2 + 2x + 5) \div (x + 1)$.

EXAMPLE 3

Find the quotient and remainder for $(x^3 + 8x^2 + 13x - 6) \div (x + 3)$.

Solution

$$
\begin{array}{r}
-3\overline{)\,1 \quad 8 \quad 13 \quad -6} \\
\underline{ \quad -3 \quad -15 \quad 6} \\
1 \quad 5 \quad -2 \quad 0
\end{array}
$$

Thus the quotient is $x^2 + 5x - 2$, and the remainder is 0.

In Example 3, because the remainder is 0, we can say that $x + 3$ is a factor of $x^3 + 8x^2 + 13x - 6$. We will use this idea a bit later when we solve polynomial equations.

Concept Quiz 9.1

For Problems 1–3, given $(x^3 + 6x^2 - 5x - 2) \div (x - 1) = x^2 + 7x + 2$, match the mathematical expression with the correct term.

1. $x^2 + 7x + 2$ **2.** $x^3 + 6x^2 - 5x - 1$ **3.** $x - 1$
A. Dividend   B. Quotient   C. Divisor

For Problems 4–8, answer true or false.

4. For long division of polynomials, the degree of the remainder is always less than the degree of the divisor.

5. The polynomial divisor of $(x + 3)$ would become a divisor of 3 for synthetic division.

6. If a synthetic division problem gave a quotient line of 3   −1   4   7   0, we would know that the remainder is zero.

7. If a synthetic division problem gave a quotient of 2   3   −5   6, we would know that the quotient is $2x^2 + 3x - 5$ with a remainder of 6.

8. If a synthetic division problem gave a quotient line of 4   0   −3   7, we would know that the quotient is $4x - 3$ with a remainder of 7.

Problem Set 9.1

Use synthetic division to determine the quotient and remainder for each problem. (Objective 1)

1. $(4x^2 - 5x - 6) \div (x - 2)$

2. $(5x^2 - 9x + 4) \div (x - 1)$

3. $(2x^2 - x - 21) \div (x + 3)$

4. $(3x^2 + 8x + 4) \div (x + 2)$

5. $(3x^2 - 16x + 17) \div (x - 4)$

6. $(6x^2 - 29x - 8) \div (x - 5)$

7. $(4x^2 + 19x - 32) \div (x + 6)$

8. $(7x^2 + 26x - 2) \div (x + 4)$

9. $(x^3 + 2x^2 - 7x + 4) \div (x - 1)$

10. $(2x^3 - 7x^2 + 2x + 3) \div (x - 3)$

11. $(3x^3 + 8x^2 - 8) \div (x + 2)$

12. $(4x^3 + 17x^2 + 75) \div (x + 5)$

13. $(5x^3 - 9x^2 - 3x - 2) \div (x - 2)$

14. $(x^3 - 6x^2 + 5x + 14) \div (x - 4)$

15. $(x^3 + 6x^2 - 8x + 1) \div (x + 7)$

16. $(2x^3 + 11x^2 - 5x + 1) \div (x + 6)$

17. $(-x^3 + 7x^2 - 14x + 6) \div (x - 3)$

18. $(-2x^3 - 3x^2 + 4x + 5) \div (x + 1)$

19. $(-3x^3 + x^2 + 2x + 2) \div (x + 1)$

20. $(-x^3 + 4x^2 + 31x + 2) \div (x - 8)$

21. $(3x^3 - 2x - 5) \div (x - 2)$

22. $(2x^3 - x - 4) \div (x + 3)$

23. $(2x^4 + x^3 + 3x^2 + 2x - 2) \div (x + 1)$

24. $(x^4 - 3x^3 - 6x^2 + 11x - 12) \div (x - 4)$

25. $(x^4 + 4x^3 - 7x - 1) \div (x - 3)$

26. $(3x^4 - x^3 + 2x^2 - 7x - 1) \div (x + 1)$

27. $(x^4 + 5x^3 - x^2 + 25) \div (x + 5)$

28. $(2x^4 + 3x^2 + 3) \div (x + 2)$

29. $(x^4 - 16) \div (x - 2)$

30. $(x^4 - 16) \div (x + 2)$

31. $(x^5 - 1) \div (x + 1)$

32. $(x^5 - 1) \div (x - 1)$

33. $(x^5 + 1) \div (x + 1)$

34. $(x^5 + 1) \div (x - 1)$

35. $(x^5 + 3x^4 - 5x^3 - 3x^2 + 3x - 4) \div (x + 4)$

36. $(2x^5 + 3x^4 - 4x^3 - x^2 + 5x - 2) \div (x + 2)$

37. $(4x^5 - 6x^4 + 2x^3 + 2x^2 - 5x + 2) \div (x - 1)$

38. $(3x^5 - 8x^4 + 5x^3 + 2x^2 - 9x + 4) \div (x - 2)$

39. $(9x^3 - 6x^2 + 3x - 4) \div \left(x - \dfrac{1}{3}\right)$

40. $(2x^3 + 3x^2 - 2x + 3) \div \left(x + \dfrac{1}{2}\right)$

41. $(3x^4 - 2x^3 + 5x^2 - x - 1) \div \left(x + \dfrac{1}{3}\right)$

42. $(4x^4 - 5x^2 + 1) \div \left(x - \dfrac{1}{2}\right)$

Thoughts Into Words

43. How would you describe what is accomplished with synthetic division to someone who had just completed an elementary algebra course?

44. Why is synthetic division restricted to situations in which the divisor is of the form $x - c$?

9.2   Remainder and Factor Theorems

OBJECTIVES

1   Use the remainder theorem to evaluate a function for a given value

2   Determine if an expression is a factor of a given polynomial

3   Find the linear factors of a polynomial

Let's consider the division algorithm (stated in the previous section) when the dividend, $f(x)$, is divided by a linear polynomial of the form $x - c$. Then the division algorithm

$$f(x) = d(x)q(x) + r(x)$$

Dividend   Divisor   Quotient   Remainder

becomes $f(x) = (x - c)q(x) + r(x)$

Because the degree of the remainder, $r(x)$, must be less than the degree of the divisor, $x - c$, the remainder is a constant. Therefore, letting R represent the remainder, we have

$$f(x) = (x - c)q(x) + R$$

If the functional value at c is found, we obtain

$$f(c) = (c - c)q(c) + R$$
$$= 0 \cdot q(c) + R$$
$$= R$$

In other words, if a polynomial is divided by a linear polynomial of the form $x - c$, then the remainder is given by the value of the polynomial at c. Let's state this result more formally as the **remainder theorem**.

Property 9.1 Remainder theorem

If the polynomial $f(x)$ is divided by $x - c$, then the remainder is equal to $f(c)$.

Classroom Example
If $f(x) = 2x^3 + x^2 - 6x - 9$, find $f(3)$ by (a) using synthetic division and the remainder theorem, and (b) evaluating $f(3)$ directly.

EXAMPLE 1

If $f(x) = x^3 + 2x^2 - 5x - 1$, find $f(2)$ by (a) using synthetic division and the remainder theorem, and (b) evaluating $f(2)$ directly.

Solution

(a)
$$2)\overline{\begin{array}{rrrr} 1 & 2 & -5 & -1 \\ & 2 & 8 & 6 \\ \hline 1 & 4 & 3 & ⑤ \end{array}} \quad \longleftarrow \quad R = f(2)$$

(b) $f(2) = 2^3 + 2(2)^2 - 5(2) - 1 = 8 + 8 - 10 - 1 = 5$

Classroom Example
If $f(x) = x^4 - 6x^3 - 8x^2 + 2x + 7$, find $f(-2)$ by (a) using synthetic division and the remainder theorem, and (b) evaluating $f(-2)$ directly.

EXAMPLE 2

If $f(x) = x^4 + 7x^3 + 8x^2 + 11x + 5$, find $f(-6)$ by (a) using synthetic division and the remainder theorem and (b) evaluating $f(-6)$ directly.

Solution

(a)
$$-6)\overline{\begin{array}{rrrrr} 1 & 7 & 8 & 11 & 5 \\ & -6 & -6 & -12 & 6 \\ \hline 1 & 1 & 2 & -1 & ⑪ \end{array}} \quad \longleftarrow \quad R = f(-6)$$

(b) $f(-6) = (-6)^4 + 7(-6)^3 + 8(-6)^2 + 11(-6) + 5$
$$= 1296 - 1512 + 288 - 66 + 5$$
$$= 11$$

In Example 2, note that the computations involved in finding $f(-6)$ by using synthetic division and the remainder theorem are much easier than those required to evaluate $f(-6)$ directly. This is not always the case, but using synthetic division is often easier than evaluating $f(c)$ directly.

Classroom Example
Find the remainder when $(3x^3 + 5x^2 + 3x + 10)$ is divided by $x + 2$.

EXAMPLE 3   Find the remainder when $x^3 + 3x^2 - 13x - 15$ is divided by $x + 1$.

Solution

Let $f(x) = x^3 + 3x^2 - 13x - 15$, write $x + 1$ as $x - (-1)$, and apply the remainder theorem:
$$f(-1) = (-1)^3 + 3(-1)^2 - 13(-1) - 15 = 0$$

Thus the remainder is 0.

Example 3 illustrates an important aspect of the remainder theorem—the situation in which the remainder is zero. Thus we can say that $x + 1$ is a factor of $x^3 + 3x^2 - 13x - 15$.

Factor Theorem

A general factor theorem can be formulated by considering the equation

$$f(x) = (x - c)q(x) + R$$

If $x - c$ is a factor of $f(x)$, then the remainder R, which is also $f(c)$, must be zero. Conversely, if $R = f(c) = 0$, then $f(x) = (x - c)q(x)$; in other words, $x - c$ is a factor of $f(x)$. The **factor theorem** can be stated as follows:

> **Property 9.2 Factor Theorem**
>
> A polynomial $f(x)$ has a factor $x - c$ if and only if $f(c) = 0$.

Classroom Example
Is $x - 3$ a factor of
$x^3 - 8x^2 + 19x - 12$?

EXAMPLE 4   Is $x - 1$ a factor of $x^3 + 5x^2 + 2x - 8$?

Solution

Let $f(x) = x^3 + 5x^2 + 2x - 8$ and compute $f(1)$ to obtain

$$f(1) = 1^3 + 5(1)^2 + 2(1) - 8 = 0$$

By the factor theorem, therefore, $x - 1$ is a factor of $f(x)$.

Classroom Example
Is $x + 2$ a factor of
$5x^3 + 8x^2 - x + 7$?

EXAMPLE 5   Is $x + 3$ a factor of $2x^3 + 5x^2 - 6x - 7$?

Solution

Use synthetic division to obtain the following:

$$
\begin{array}{r|rrrr}
-3 & 2 & 5 & -6 & -7 \\
   &   & -6 & 3 & 9 \\
\hline
   & 2 & -1 & -3 & 2 \end{array}
\quad \longleftarrow R = f(-3)
$$

Because $R \neq 0$, we know that $x + 3$ is not a factor of the given polynomial.

In Examples 4 and 5, we were concerned only with determining whether a linear polynomial of the form $x - c$ was a factor of another polynomial. For such problems, it is reasonable to compute $f(c)$ either directly or by synthetic division, whichever way seems easier for a particular problem. However, if more information is required, such as the complete factorization of the given polynomial, then the use of synthetic division is appropriate, as the next two examples illustrate.

Classroom Example
Show that $x - 6$ is a factor of
$x^3 - 3x^2 - 16x - 12$, and find
the other linear factors of the
polynomial.

EXAMPLE 6

Show that $x - 1$ is a factor of $x^3 - 2x^2 - 11x + 12$, and find the other linear factors of the polynomial.

Solution

Let's use synthetic division to divide $x^3 - 2x^2 - 11x + 12$ by $x - 1$.

$$
\begin{array}{r|rrrr}
1 & 1 & -2 & -11 & 12 \\
  &   & 1 & -1 & -12 \\
\hline
  & 1 & -1 & -12 & 0 \end{array}
$$

The last line indicates a quotient of $x^2 - x - 12$ and a remainder of 0. The remainder of 0 means that $x - 1$ is a factor. Furthermore, we can write

$$x^3 - 2x^2 - 11x + 12 = (x - 1)(x^2 - x - 12)$$

The quadratic polynomial $x^2 - x - 12$ can be factored as $(x - 4)(x + 3)$ using our conventional factoring techniques. Thus we obtain

$$x^3 - 2x^2 - 11x + 12 = (x - 1)(x - 4)(x + 3)$$

Classroom Example
Show that $x + 7$ is a factor of $x^3 + 3x^2 - 25x + 21$, and complete the factorization of $f(x)$.

EXAMPLE 7

Show that $x + 4$ is a factor of $f(x) = x^3 - 5x^2 - 22x + 56$, and complete the factorization of $f(x)$.

Solution

Use synthetic division to divide $x^3 - 5x^2 - 22x + 56$ by $x + 4$.

$$
\begin{array}{r}
-4)\overline{\,1 \quad -5 \quad -22 \quad 56\,} \\
\underline{\quad -4 \quad\; 36 \quad -56} \\
1 \quad -9 \quad\; 14 \quad\;\; 0
\end{array}
$$

The last line indicates a quotient of $x^2 - 9x + 14$ and a remainder of 0. The remainder of 0 means that $x + 4$ is a factor. Furthermore, we can write

$$x^3 - 5x^2 - 22x + 56 = (x + 4)(x^2 - 9x + 14)$$

and then complete the factoring to obtain

$$x^3 - 5x^2 - 22x + 56 = (x + 4)(x - 7)(x - 2)$$

The factor theorem also plays a significant role in determining some general factorization ideas, as the last example of this section demonstrates.

Classroom Example
Verify that $x - 1$ is a factor of $x^n - 1$ for all integral values of x.

EXAMPLE 8

Verify that $x + 1$ is a factor of $x^n + 1$ for all odd positive integral values of n.

Solution

Let $f(x) = x^n + 1$ and compute $f(-1)$.

$$
\begin{aligned}
f(-1) &= (-1)^n + 1 \\
&= -1 + 1 \qquad \text{Any odd power of } -1 \text{ is } -1 \\
&= 0
\end{aligned}
$$

Because $f(-1) = 0$, we know that $x + 1$ is a factor of $f(x)$.

Concept Quiz 9.2

For Problems 1–6, answer true or false.

1. When a polynomial is divided by a divisor that is a linear factor, the remainder is a constant term.
2. If $f(3) = -12$, then the remainder, when $f(x)$ is divided by $x - 3$, is -12.
3. If $f(-5) = 0$, then $(x - 5)$ is a factor of $f(x)$.
4. If $(x + 3)$ is factor of $f(x)$, then the division of $f(x)$ by $(x + 3)$ has a remainder of 0.
5. For any polynomial of the form $x^n + 1$ where n is an odd positive integer, $(x + 1)$ is a factor.
6. If $f(2) = 8$, then $(x - 2)$ is a factor of $f(x)$.

Problem Set 9.2

For Problems 1–10, find $f(c)$ by (a) evaluating $f(c)$ directly, and (b) using synthetic division and the remainder theorem. (Objective 1)

1. $f(x) = x^2 + 2x - 6$ and $c = 3$

2. $f(x) = x^2 - 7x + 4$ and $c = 2$

3. $f(x) = x^3 - 2x^2 + 3x - 1$ and $c = -1$

4. $f(x) = x^3 + 3x^2 - 4x - 7$ and $c = -2$

5. $f(x) = 2x^4 - x^3 - 3x^2 + 4x - 1$ and $c = 2$

6. $f(x) = 3x^4 - 4x^3 + 5x^2 - 7x + 6$ and $c = 1$

7. $f(n) = 6n^3 - 35n^2 + 8n - 10$ and $c = 6$

8. $f(n) = 8n^3 - 39n^2 - 7n - 1$ and $c = 5$

9. $f(n) = 2n^5 - 1$ and $c = -2$

10. $f(n) = 3n^4 - 2n^3 + 4n - 1$ and $c = 3$

For Problems 11–20, find $f(c)$ either by using synthetic division and the remainder theorem or by evaluating $f(c)$ directly. (Objective 1)

11. $f(x) = 6x^5 - 3x^3 + 2$ and $c = -1$

12. $f(x) = -4x^4 + x^3 - 2x^2 - 5$ and $c = 2$

13. $f(x) = 2x^4 - 15x^3 - 9x^2 - 2x - 3$ and $c = 8$

14. $f(x) = x^4 - 8x^3 + 9x^2 - 15x + 2$ and $c = 7$

15. $f(n) = 4n^7 + 3$ and $c = 3$

16. $f(n) = -3n^6 - 2$ and $c = -3$

17. $f(n) = 3n^5 + 17n^4 - 4n^3 + 10n^2 - 15n + 13$ and $c = -6$

18. $f(n) = -2n^5 - 9n^4 + 7n^3 + 14n^2 + 19n - 38$ and $c = -5$

19. $f(x) = -4x^4 - 6x^2 + 7$ and $c = 4$

20. $f(x) = 3x^5 - 7x^3 - 6$ and $c = 5$

For Problems 21–34, use the factor theorem to help answer some questions about factors. (Objective 2)

21. Is $x - 2$ a factor of $5x^2 - 17x + 14$?

22. Is $x + 1$ a factor of $3x^2 - 5x - 8$?

23. Is $x + 3$ a factor of $6x^2 + 13x - 14$?

24. Is $x - 5$ a factor of $8x^2 - 47x + 32$?

25. Is $x - 1$ a factor of $4x^3 - 13x^2 + 21x - 12$?

26. Is $x - 4$ a factor of $2x^3 - 11x^2 + 10x + 8$?

27. Is $x + 2$ a factor of $x^3 + 7x^2 + x - 18$?

28. Is $x + 3$ a factor of $x^3 + x^2 - 14x - 24$?

29. Is $x - 3$ a factor of $3x^3 - 5x^2 - 17x + 17$?

30. Is $x + 4$ a factor of $2x^3 + 9x^2 - 5x - 39$?

31. Is $x + 2$ a factor of $x^3 + 8$?

32. Is $x - 2$ a factor of $x^3 - 8$?

33. Is $x - 3$ a factor of $x^4 - 81$?

34. Is $x + 3$ a factor of $x^4 - 81$?

For Problems 35–44, use synthetic division to show that $g(x)$ is a factor of $f(x)$, and complete the factorization of $f(x)$. (Objectives 2, 3)

35. $g(x) = x - 2$, $f(x) = x^3 - 6x^2 - 13x + 42$

36. $g(x) = x + 1$, $f(x) = x^3 + 6x^2 - 31x - 36$

37. $g(x) = x + 2$, $f(x) = 12x^3 + 29x^2 + 8x - 4$

38. $g(x) = x - 3$, $f(x) = 6x^3 - 17x^2 - 5x + 6$

39. $g(x) = x + 1$, $f(x) = x^3 - 2x^2 - 7x - 4$

40. $g(x) = x - 5$, $f(x) = 2x^3 + x^2 - 61x + 30$

41. $g(x) = x - 6$, $f(x) = x^5 - 6x^4 - 16x + 96$

42. $g(x) = x + 3$, $f(x) = x^5 + 3x^4 - x - 3$

43. $g(x) = x + 5$, $f(x) = 9x^3 + 21x^2 - 104x + 80$

44. $g(x) = x + 4$, $f(x) = 4x^3 + 4x^2 - 39x + 36$

For Problems 45–48, find the value(s) of k that makes the second polynomial a factor of the first.

45. $k^2x^4 + 3kx^2 - 4$; $x - 1$

46. $x^3 - kx^2 + 5x + k$; $x - 2$

47. $kx^3 + 19x^2 + x - 6$; $x + 3$

48. $x^3 + 4x^2 - 11x + k$; $x + 2$

49. Argue that $f(x) = 3x^4 + 2x^2 + 5$ has no factor of the form $x - c$, where c is a real number.

50. Show that $x + 2$ is a factor of $x^{12} - 4096$.

51. Verify that $x + 1$ is a factor of $x^n - 1$ for all even positive integral values of n.

52. Verify that $x - 1$ is a factor of $x^n - 1$ for all positive integral values of n.

53. (a) Verify that $x - y$ is a factor of $x^n - y^n$ for all positive integral values of n.

(b) Verify that $x + y$ is a factor of $x^n - y^n$ for all even positive integral values of n.

(c) Verify that $x + y$ is a factor of $x^n + y^n$ for all odd positive integral values of n.

Thoughts Into Words

54. State the remainder theorem in your own words.

55. Discuss some of the uses of the factor theorem.

Further Investigations

The remainder and factor theorems are true for any complex value of c. Therefore, for Problems 56–58, find $f(c)$ by (a) using synthetic division and the remainder theorem, and (b) evaluating $f(c)$ directly.

56. $f(x) = x^3 - 5x^2 + 2x + 1$ and $c = i$

57. $f(x) = x^2 + 4x - 2$ and $c = 1 + i$

58. $f(x) = x^3 + 2x^2 + x - 2$ and $c = 2 - 3i$

59. Show that $x - 2i$ is a factor of $f(x) = x^4 + 6x^2 + 8$.

60. Show that $x + 3i$ is a factor of $f(x) = x^4 + 14x^2 + 45$.

61. Consider changing the form of the polynomial $f(x) = x^3 + 4x^2 - 3x + 2$ as follows:

$$f(x) = x^3 + 4x^2 - 3x + 2$$

$$= x(x^2 + 4x - 3) + 2$$

$$= x[x(x + 4) - 3] + 2$$

The final form $f(x) = x[x(x + 4) - 3] + 2$ is called the **nested form** of the polynomial. It is particularly well suited for evaluating functional values of f either by hand or with a calculator. For each of the following, find the indicated functional values using the nested form of the given polynomial.

(a) $f(4)$, $f(-5)$, and $f(7)$ for $f(x) = x^3 + 5x^2 - 2x + 1$

(b) $f(3)$, $f(6)$, and $f(-7)$ for $f(x) = 2x^3 - 4x^2 - 3x + 2$

(c) $f(4)$, $f(5)$, and $f(-3)$ for $f(x) = -2x^3 + 5x^2 - 6x - 7$

(d) $f(5)$, $f(6)$, and $f(-3)$ for $f(x) = x^4 + 3x^3 - 2x^2 + 5x - 1$

9.3   Polynomial Equations

OBJECTIVES

1 Understand the concept of multiplicity of roots

2 Solve polynomial equations using the rational root theorem and the factor theorem

3 Use Descartes' rule of signs

We have solved a large variety of linear equations of the form $ax + b = 0$ and quadratic equations of the form $ax^2 + bx + c = 0$. Linear and quadratic equations are special cases of a general class of equations we refer to as **polynomial equations**. The equation

$$a_n x^n + a_{n-1} x^{n-1} + \cdots + a_1 x + a_0 = 0$$

where the coefficients $a_0, a_1, \ldots, a_n$ are real numbers and n is a positive integer, is called a **polynomial equation of degree n**. The following are examples of polynomial equations:

$$\sqrt{2}x - 6 = 0 \qquad\qquad \text{Degree 1}$$

$$\frac{3}{4}x^2 - \frac{2}{3}x + 5 = 0 \qquad\qquad \text{Degree 2}$$

$$4x^3 - 3x^2 - 7x - 9 = 0 \qquad\qquad \text{Degree 3}$$

$$5x^4 - x + 6 = 0 \qquad\qquad \text{Degree 4}$$

Remark: The most general polynomial equation would allow complex numbers as coefficients. However, for our purposes in this text, we will restrict the coefficients to real numbers. We often refer to such equations as *polynomial equations over the reals*.

In general, solving polynomial equations of degree greater than 2 can be very difficult and often requires mathematics beyond the scope of this text. However, there are some general properties pertaining to the solving of polynomial equations that you should be familiar with; furthermore, there are certain types of polynomial equations that we can solve using the techniques available to us at this time. We can also use a graphical approach to approximate solutions, which, in some cases, is shorter than using an algebraic approach.

Let's begin by listing some polynomial equations and corresponding solution sets that we have already encountered in this text.

Equation	Solution set
$3x + 4 = 7$	$\{1\}$
$x^2 + x - 6 = 0$	$\{-3, 2\}$
$2x^3 - 3x^2 - 2x + 3 = 0$	$\left\{-1, 1, \dfrac{3}{2}\right\}$
$x^4 - 16 = 0$	$\{-2, 2, -2i, 2i\}$

Note that in each of these examples, the number of solutions corresponds to the degree of the equation. The first-degree equation has one solution, the second-degree equation has two solutions, the third-degree equation has three solutions, and the fourth-degree equation has four solutions. Now consider the equation

$$(x - 4)^2(x + 5)^3 = 0$$

It can be written as

$$(x - 4)(x - 4)(x + 5)(x + 5)(x + 5) = 0$$

which implies that

$$x - 4 = 0 \quad \text{or} \quad x - 4 = 0 \quad \text{or} \quad x + 5 = 0 \quad \text{or}$$
$$x + 5 = 0 \quad \text{or} \quad x + 5 = 0$$

Therefore

$$x = 4 \quad \text{or} \quad x = 4 \quad \text{or} \quad x = -5 \quad \text{or} \quad x = -5 \quad \text{or} \quad x = -5$$

We state that the solution set of the original equation is $\{-5, 4\}$, but we also say that the equation has a solution of 4 with a *multiplicity of two* and a solution of -5 with a *multiplicity of three.* Furthermore, note that the sum of the multiplicities is 5, which agrees with the degree of the equation. The following general property can be stated:

> ### Property 9.3
>
> A polynomial equation of degree n has n solutions, and any solution of multiplicity p is counted p times.

Finding Rational Solutions

Although solving polynomial equations of degree greater than 2 can, in general, be very difficult, *rational solutions of polynomial equations with integral coefficients* can be found using techniques presented in this chapter. The following property restricts the potential rational solutions of such equations:

> ### Property 9.4 Rational Root Theorem
>
> Consider the polynomial equation
>
> $$a_n x^n + a_{n-1} x^{n-1} + \cdots + a_1 x + a_0 = 0$$
>
> in which the coefficients $a_0, a_1, \ldots, a_n$ are *integers*. If the rational number $\dfrac{c}{d}$, reduced to lowest terms, is a solution of the equation, then c is a factor of the constant term a_0, and d is a factor of the leading coefficient a_n.

The "why" behind the rational root theorem is based on some simple factoring ideas, as indicated by the following outline of a proof for the theorem.

Outline of Proof   If $\dfrac{c}{d}$ is to be a solution, then

$$a_n \left(\frac{c}{d}\right)^n + a_{n-1} \left(\frac{c}{d}\right)^{n-1} + \cdots + a_1 \left(\frac{c}{d}\right) + a_0 = 0$$

Multiply both sides of this equation by d^n and add $-a_0 d^n$ to both sides to yield

$$a_n c^n + a_{n-1} c^{n-1} d + \cdots + a_1 c d^{n-1} = -a_0 d^n$$

Because c is a factor of the left side of this equation, c must also be a factor of $-a_0 d^n$. Furthermore, because $\dfrac{c}{d}$ is in reduced form, c and d have no common factors other than -1 or 1. Thus c is a factor of a_0. In the same way, from the equation

$$a_{n-1} c^{n-1} d + \cdots + a_1 c d^{n-1} + a_0 d^n = -a_n c^n$$

we can conclude that d is a factor of the left side, and therefore d is also a factor of a_n.

The rational root theorem, a graph, synthetic division, the factor theorem, and some previous knowledge pertaining to solving linear and quadratic equations form a basis for finding rational solutions. Let's consider some examples.

Classroom Example
Find all rational solutions of
$2x^3 - 9x^2 - 20x + 12 = 0.$

EXAMPLE 1   Find all rational solutions of $3x^3 + 8x^2 - 15x + 4 = 0$.

Solution

If $\dfrac{c}{d}$ is a rational solution, then c must be a factor of 4, and d must be a factor of 3.

Therefore, the possible values for c and d are as follows:

For c	$\pm 1, \pm 2, \pm 4$
For d	$\pm 1, \pm 3$

Thus the possible values for $\dfrac{c}{d}$ are

$$\pm 1, \; \pm\frac{1}{3}, \; \pm 2, \; \pm\frac{2}{3}, \; \pm 4, \; \pm\frac{4}{3}$$

Now let's use a graph of $y = 3x^3 + 8x^2 - 15x + 4$ to shorten the list of possible rational solutions (see Figure 9.1).

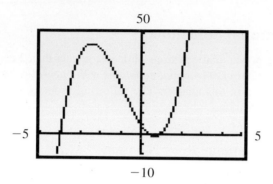

Figure 9.1

The x intercepts appear to be at -4, at 1, and between 0 and 1. Using synthetic division,

$$
\begin{array}{r|rrrr}
1) & 3 & 8 & -15 & 4 \\
  &   & 3 & 11 & -4 \\
\hline
  & 3 & 11 & -4 & 0
\end{array}
$$

we can show that $x - 1$ is a factor of the given polynomial, and therefore 1 is a rational solution of the equation. Furthermore, the result of the synthetic division also indicates that we can factor the given polynomial as follows:

$$3x^3 + 8x^2 - 15x + 4 = 0$$
$$(x - 1)(3x^2 + 11x - 4) = 0$$

The quadratic factor can be factored further using our previous techniques; we can proceed as follows:

$$(x - 1)(3x^2 + 11x - 4) = 0$$
$$(x - 1)(3x - 1)(x + 4) = 0$$
$$x - 1 = 0 \quad\text{or}\quad 3x - 1 = 0 \quad\text{or}\quad x + 4 = 0$$
$$x = 1 \quad\text{or}\quad x = \frac{1}{3} \quad\text{or}\quad x = -4$$

Thus the entire solution set consists of rational numbers, which can be listed as $\left\{ -4, \dfrac{1}{3}, 1 \right\}$.

Remark: The graphs used in this section are done with a graphing utility. In the next section, we will discuss some special situations for which freehand sketches of the graphs are easily obtained.

In Example 1 we used a graph to help shorten the list of possible rational solutions determined by the rational root theorem. Without using a graph, one needs to conduct an organized search of the list of possible rational solutions, as the next example demonstrates.

EXAMPLE 2   Find all rational solutions of $3x^3 + 7x^2 - 22x - 8 = 0$.

Solution

If $\dfrac{c}{d}$ is a rational solution, then c must be a factor of -8, and d must be a factor of 3.

Therefore, the possible values for c and d are as follows:

For c $\pm 1, \pm 2, \pm 4, \pm 8$
For d $\pm 1, \pm 3$

Thus the possible values for $\dfrac{c}{d}$ are

$$\pm 1, \pm \frac{1}{3}, \pm 2, \pm \frac{2}{3}, \pm 4, \pm \frac{4}{3}, \pm 8, \pm \frac{8}{3}$$

Let's begin our search for rational solutions; we will try the integers first.

$$\begin{array}{r|rrrr} 1 & 3 & 7 & -22 & -8 \\ & & 3 & 10 & -12 \\ \hline & 3 & 10 & -12 & \boxed{-20} \end{array}$$

← This remainder indicates that $x - 1$ is not a factor, and thus 1 is not a solution

$$\begin{array}{r|rrrr} -1 & 3 & 7 & -22 & -8 \\ & & -3 & -4 & 26 \\ \hline & 3 & 4 & -26 & \boxed{18} \end{array}$$

← This remainder indicates that -1 is not a solution

$$\begin{array}{r|rrrr} 2 & 3 & 7 & -22 & -8 \\ & & 6 & 26 & 8 \\ \hline & 3 & 13 & 4 & 0 \end{array}$$

Now we know that $x - 2$ is a factor; we can proceed as follows:

$$3x^3 + 7x^2 - 22x - 8 = 0$$

$$(x - 2)(3x^2 + 13x + 4) = 0$$

$$(x - 2)(3x + 1)(x + 4) = 0$$

$x - 2 = 0$	or	$3x + 1 = 0$	or	$x + 4 = 0$
$x = 2$	or	$3x = -1$	or	$x = -4$
$x = 2$	or	$x = -\dfrac{1}{3}$	or	$x = -4$

The solution set is $\left\{ -4, -\dfrac{1}{3}, 2 \right\}$

In Examples 1 and 2, we were solving third-degree equations. Therefore, after finding one linear factor by synthetic division, we were able to factor the remaining quadratic factor in the usual way. However, if the given equation is of degree 4 or more, we may need to find more than one linear factor by synthetic division, as the next example illustrates.

EXAMPLE 3   Solve $x^4 - 6x^3 + 22x^2 - 30x + 13 = 0$.

Solution

The possible values for $\dfrac{c}{d}$ are as follows:

For $\dfrac{c}{d}$ $\pm 1, \pm 13$

By synthetic division, we find that

$$
\begin{array}{r|rrrr}
1) & 1 & -6 & 22 & -30 & 13 \\
  &   & 1 & -5 & 17 & -13 \\
\hline
  & 1 & -5 & 17 & -13 & 0
\end{array}
$$

which indicates that $x - 1$ is a factor of the given polynomial. The bottom line of the synthetic division indicates that the given polynomial can be factored as follows:

$$x^4 - 6x^3 + 22x^2 - 30x + 13 = 0$$

$$(x - 1)(x^3 - 5x^2 + 17x - 13) = 0$$

Therefore

$$x - 1 = 0 \quad \text{or} \quad x^3 - 5x^2 + 17x - 13 = 0$$

Now we can use the same approach to look for rational solutions of the expression $x^3 - 5x^2 + 17x - 13 = 0$. The possible values for $\dfrac{c}{d}$ are as follows:

For $\dfrac{c}{d}$ $\quad \pm 1, \pm 13$

By synthetic division, we find that

$$
\begin{array}{r|rrrr}
1) & 1 & -5 & 17 & -13 \\
  &   & 1 & -4 & 13 \\
\hline
  & 1 & -4 & 13 & 0
\end{array}
$$

which indicates that $x - 1$ is a factor of $x^3 - 5x^2 + 17x - 13$ and that the other factor is $x^2 - 4x + 13$.

Now we can solve the original equation as follows:

$$x^4 - 6x^3 + 22x^2 - 30x + 13 = 0$$

$$(x - 1)(x^3 - 5x^2 + 17x - 13) = 0$$

$$(x - 1)(x - 1)(x^2 - 4x + 13) = 0$$

$$x - 1 = 0 \quad \text{or} \quad x - 1 = 0 \quad \text{or} \quad x^2 - 4x + 13 = 0$$

$$x = 1 \quad \text{or} \quad x = 1 \quad \text{or} \quad x^2 - 4x + 13 = 0$$

Use the quadratic formula on $x^2 - 4x + 13 = 0$:

$$x = \frac{4 \pm \sqrt{16 - 52}}{2} = \frac{4 \pm \sqrt{-36}}{2}$$

$$= \frac{4 \pm 6i}{2} = 2 \pm 3i$$

Thus the original equation has a rational solution of 1 with a multiplicity of two and two complex solutions, $2 + 3i$ and $2 - 3i$. The solution set is listed as $\{1, 2 \pm 3i\}$. ▪

Let's graph the equation $y = x^4 - 6x^3 + 22x^2 - 30x + 13$ to give some visual support for our work in Example 3. The graph in Figure 9.2 indicates only an x intercept at 1. This is consistent with the solution set of $\{1, 2 \pm 3i\}$.

Example 3 illustrates two general properties. First, note that the coefficient of x^4 is 1, and thus the possible rational solutions must be integers. In general, the possible rational solutions of $x^n + a_{n-1}x^{n-1} + \cdots + a_1x + a_0 = 0$ are the integral factors of a_0. Second, note that the

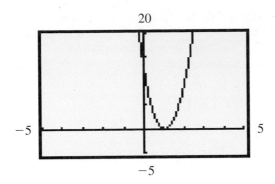

Figure 9.2

complex solutions of Example 3 are conjugates of each other. The following general property can be stated:

> **Property 9.5**
>
> Nonreal complex solutions of polynomial equations with real coefficients, if they exist, must occur in conjugate pairs.

Each of Properties 9.3, 9.4, and 9.5 yields some information about the solutions of a polynomial equation. Before we state the final property of this section, which will give us some additional information, we need to consider two ideas.

First, in a polynomial that is arranged in descending powers of x, if two successive terms differ in sign, then there is said to be a **variation in sign**. (We disregard terms with zero coefficients when sign variations are counted.) For example, the polynomial

$$3x^3 - 2x^2 + 4x + 7$$

has *two* sign variations, whereas the polynomial

$$x^5 - 4x^3 + x - 5$$

has *three* variations.

Second, the solutions of

$$a_n(-x)^n + a_{n-1}(-x)^{n-1} + \cdots + a_1(-x) + a_0 = 0$$

are the opposites of the solutions of

$$a_n x^n + a_{n-1} x^{n-1} + \cdots + a_1 x + a_0 = 0$$

In other words, if a new equation is formed by replacing x with $-x$ in a given equation, then the solutions of the newly formed equation are the opposites of the solutions of the given equation. For example, the solution set of $x^2 + 7x + 12 = 0$ is $\{-4, -3\}$, and the solution set of $(-x)^2 + 7(-x) + 12 = 0$, which simplifies to $x^2 - 7x + 12 = 0$, is $\{3, 4\}$.

Now we can state a property that can help us to determine the nature of the solutions of a polynomial equation without actually solving the equation.

> **Property 9.6 Descartes' Rule of Signs**
>
> Let $a_n x^n + a_{n-1} x^{n-1} + \cdots + a_1 x + a_0 = 0$ be a polynomial equation with real coefficients.
>
> 1. The number of *positive real solutions* of the given equation either is equal to the number of variations in sign of the polynomial or is less than the number of variations by a positive even integer.
>
> 2. The number of *negative real solutions* of the given equation either is equal to the number of variations in sign of the polynomial $a_n(-x)^n + a_{n-1}(-x)^{n-1} + \cdots + a_1(-x) + a_0$ or is less than the number of variations by a positive even integer.

Property 9.6 (Descartes' rule of signs), along with Properties 9.3 and 9.5, allow us to acquire some information about the solutions of a polynomial equation without actually solving the equation. Let's consider some equations and see how much we know about their solutions without solving them.

1. $x^3 + 3x^2 + 5x + 4 = 0$
   (a) No variations of sign in $x^3 + 3x^2 + 5x + 4$ means that there are *no positive solutions.*
   (b) Replacing x with $-x$ in the given polynomial produces $(-x)^3 + 3(-x)^2 + 5(-x) + 4$, which simplifies to $-x^3 + 3x^2 - 5x + 4$ and contains three variations of sign; thus there are *three (or one) negative solution(s).*
   Conclusion   The given equation has three negative real solutions or else one negative real solution and two nonreal complex solutions.

2. $2x^4 + 3x^2 - x - 1 = 0$
   (a) There is one variation of sign; thus the equation has *one positive solution.*
   (b) Replacing x with $-x$ produces $2(-x)^4 + 3(-x)^2 - (-x) - 1$, which simplifies to $2x^4 + 3x^2 + x - 1$ and contains one variation of sign. Thus the equation has *one negative solution.*
   Conclusion   The given equation has one positive, one negative, and two nonreal complex solutions.

3. $3x^4 + 2x^2 + 5 = 0$
   (a) No variations of sign in the given polynomial means that there are *no positive solutions.*
   (b) Replacing x with $-x$ produces $3(-x)^4 + 2(-x)^2 + 5$, which simplifies to $3x^4 + 2x^2 + 5$ and contains no variations of sign. Thus there are *no negative solutions.*
   Conclusion   The given equation contains four nonreal complex solutions. These solutions will appear in conjugate pairs.

4. $2x^5 - 4x^3 + 2x - 5 = 0$
   (a) The fact that there are three variations of sign in the given polynomial implies that there are *three or one positive solutions.*
   (b) Replacing x with $-x$ produces $2(-x)^5 - 4(-x)^3 + 2(-x) - 5$, which simplifies to $-2x^5 + 4x^3 - 2x - 5$ and contains two variations of sign. Thus there are *two (or zero) negative solution(s).*
   Conclusion   The given equation has either three positive and two negative solutions; three positive and two nonreal complex solutions; one positive, two negative, and two nonreal complex solutions; or one positive and four nonreal complex solution(s).

It should be evident from the previous discussions that sometimes we can truly pinpoint the nature of the solutions of a polynomial equation. However, for some equations (such as in the last example), the best we can do with the properties discussed in this section is to restrict the possibilities for the nature of the solutions. It might be helpful for you to review Examples 1, 2, and 3 of this section and show that the solution sets do satisfy Properties 9.3, 9.5, and 9.6.

Finally, let's consider a situation for which the graphing calculator becomes a very useful tool.

EXAMPLE 4   Find the real number solutions of the equation $x^4 - 2x^3 - 5 = 0$.

Solution

First, let's use a graphing calculator to get a graph of $y = x^4 - 2x^3 - 5$, as shown in Figure 9.3. Obviously, there are two x intercepts, one between -2 and -1 and another between 2 and 3. From the rational root theorem, we know that the only possible rational roots of the given equation are ± 1 and ± 5. Therefore these x intercepts must be irrational numbers. We can use the ZOOM and TRACE features of the graphing calculator to approximate these values at -1.2 and 2.4, to the nearest tenth. Thus the real number solutions of $x^4 - 2x^3 - 5 = 0$ are approximately -1.2 and 2.4. The other two solutions must be conjugate complex numbers.

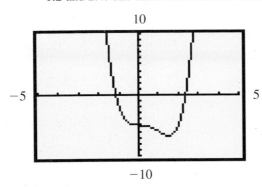

Figure 9.3

Concept Quiz 9.3

For Problems 1–8, answer true or false.

1. For a polynomial equation, the number of solutions is equal to the degree of the polynomial.
2. The equation $(x - 7)^3(x + 1)^2 = 0$ has a solution of 7 with a multiplicity of 3 and a solution of -1 with a multiplicity of 2.
3. Given $2x^4 - 3x^2 + 8 = 0$, the only possible rational solutions are $\pm\dfrac{1}{8}$, $\pm\dfrac{1}{2}$, and $\pm\dfrac{1}{4}$.
4. According to the rational root theorem, $\dfrac{1}{3}$ is a possible rational solution of the equation $3x^3 - 4x^2 + x + 5 = 0$.
5. The rational root theorem can identify all possible real number roots of a polynomial equation.
6. If $-3 + 5i$ is a solution to a polynomial equation, then $-3 - 5i$ is also a solution of the equation.
7. The equation $2x^3 + 4x^2 + x + 6 = 0$ has no positive solutions.
8. The equation $x^4 + x^2 + 4 = 0$ has no real number solutions.

Problem Set 9.3

For Problems 1–20, use the rational root theorem and the factor theorem to help solve each equation. Be sure that the number of solutions for each equation agrees with Property 9.3, taking into account multiplicity of solutions. (Objectives 1, 2)

1. $x^3 - 2x^2 - 11x + 12 = 0$
2. $x^3 + x^2 - 4x - 4 = 0$
3. $15x^3 + 14x^2 - 3x - 2 = 0$
4. $3x^3 + 13x^2 - 52x + 28 = 0$
5. $8x^3 - 2x^2 - 41x - 10 = 0$
6. $6x^3 + x^2 - 10x + 3 = 0$
7. $x^3 - x^2 - 8x + 12 = 0$

8. $x^3 - 2x^2 - 7x - 4 = 0$

9. $x^3 - 4x^2 + 8 = 0$

10. $x^3 - 10x - 12 = 0$

11. $x^4 + 4x^3 - x^2 - 16x - 12 = 0$

12. $x^4 - 4x^3 - 7x^2 + 34x - 24 = 0$

13. $x^4 + x^3 - 3x^2 - 17x - 30 = 0$

14. $x^4 - 3x^3 + 2x^2 + 2x - 4 = 0$

15. $x^3 - x^2 + x - 1 = 0$

16. $6x^4 - 13x^3 - 19x^2 + 12x = 0$

17. $2x^4 + 3x^3 - 11x^2 - 9x + 15 = 0$

18. $3x^4 - x^3 - 8x^2 + 2x + 4 = 0$

19. $4x^4 + 12x^3 + x^2 - 12x + 4 = 0$

20. $2x^5 - 5x^4 + x^3 + x^2 - x + 6 = 0$

For Problems 21–26, verify that the equations do not have any rational number solutions. (Objective 2)

21. $x^4 + 3x - 2 = 0$

22. $x^4 - x^3 - 8x^2 - 3x + 1 = 0$

23. $3x^4 - 4x^3 - 10x^2 + 3x - 4 = 0$

24. $2x^4 - 3x^3 + 6x^2 - 24x + 5 = 0$

25. $x^5 + 2x^4 - 2x^3 + 5x^2 - 2x - 3 = 0$

26. $x^5 - 2x^4 + 3x^3 + 4x^2 + 7x - 1 = 0$

For Problems 27–30, solve each equation by first applying the multiplication property of equality to produce an equivalent equation with integral coefficients. (Objective 2)

27. $\dfrac{1}{10}x^3 + \dfrac{1}{5}x^2 - \dfrac{1}{2}x - \dfrac{3}{5} = 0$

28. $\dfrac{1}{10}x^3 + \dfrac{1}{2}x^2 + \dfrac{1}{5}x - \dfrac{4}{5} = 0$

29. $x^3 - \dfrac{5}{6}x^2 - \dfrac{22}{3}x + \dfrac{5}{2} = 0$

30. $x^3 + \dfrac{9}{2}x^2 - x - 12 = 0$

For Problems 31–40, use Descartes' rule of signs (Property 9.6) to help list the possibilities for the nature of the solutions for each equation. *Do not* solve the equations. (Objective 3)

31. $6x^2 + 7x - 20 = 0$

32. $8x^2 - 14x + 3 = 0$

33. $2x^3 + x - 3 = 0$

34. $4x^3 + 3x + 7 = 0$

35. $3x^3 - 2x^2 + 6x + 5 = 0$

36. $4x^3 + 5x^2 - 6x - 2 = 0$

37. $x^5 - 3x^4 + 5x^3 - x^2 + 2x - 1 = 0$

38. $2x^5 + 3x^3 - x + 1 = 0$

39. $x^5 + 32 = 0$

40. $2x^6 + 3x^4 - 2x^2 - 1 = 0$

Thoughts Into Words

41. Explain what it means to say that the equation $(x + 3)^2 = 0$ has a solution of -3 with a multiplicity of two.

42. Describe how to use the rational root theorem to show that the equation $x^2 - 3 = 0$ has no rational solutions.

Further Investigations

43. Use the rational root theorem to argue that $\sqrt{2}$ is not a rational number. [*Hint*: The solutions of $x^2 - 2 = 0$ are $\pm\sqrt{2}$.]

44. Use the rational root theorem to argue that $\sqrt{12}$ is not a rational number.

45. Defend this statement: "Every polynomial equation of odd degree with real coefficients has at least one real number solution."

46. The following synthetic division shows that 2 is a solution of $x^4 + x^3 + x^2 - 9x - 10 = 0$:

$$2\,\overline{)\,1 \quad 1 \quad 1 \quad -9 \quad -10}$$
$$\underline{2 \quad 6 \quad 14 \quad 10}$$
$$1 \quad 3 \quad 7 \quad 5 \quad 0 \quad \leftarrow$$

Note that the new quotient row (indicated by the arrow) consists entirely of nonnegative numbers. This indicates that searching for solutions greater than 2 would be a waste of time because larger divisors would continue to increase each of the numbers (except the one on the far left) in the new quotient row. (Try 3 as a divisor!) Thus we say that 2 is an *upper bound* for the real number solutions of the given equation.

Now consider the following synthetic division, which shows that -1 is also a solution of $x^4 + x^3 + x^2 - 9x - 10 = 0$:

$$-1\,\overline{)\,1 \quad 1 \quad 1 \quad -9 \quad -10}$$
$$\underline{-1 \quad 0 \quad -1 \quad 10}$$
$$1 \quad 0 \quad 1 \quad -10 \quad 0 \quad \leftarrow$$

The new quotient row (indicated by the arrow) shows that there is no need to look for solutions less than -1, because any divisor less than -1 would increase the absolute value of each number (except the one on the far left) in the new quotient row. (Try -2 as a divisor!) Thus we say that -1 is a *lower bound* for the real number solutions of the given equation.

The following general property can be stated:

If $a_nx^n + a_{n-1}x^{n-1} + \cdots + a_1x + a_0 = 0$ is a polynomial equation with real coefficients, where $a_n > 0$, and if the polynomial is divided synthetically by $x - c$, then

1. If $c > 0$ and all numbers in the new quotient row of the synthetic division are nonnegative, then c is an upper bound of the solutions of the given equation.

2. If $c < 0$ and the numbers in the new quotient row alternate in sign (with 0 considered either positive or negative, as needed), then c is a lower bound of the solutions of the given equation.

Find the smallest positive integer and the largest negative integer that are upper and lower bounds, respectively, for the real number solutions of each of the following equations. Keep in mind that the integers that serve as bounds do not necessarily have to be solutions of the equation.

(a) $x^3 - 3x^2 + 25x - 75 = 0$

(b) $x^3 + x^2 - 4x - 4 = 0$

(c) $x^4 + 4x^3 - 7x^2 - 22x + 24 = 0$

(d) $3x^3 + 7x^2 - 22x - 8 = 0$

(e) $x^4 - 2x^3 - 9x^2 + 2x + 8 = 0$

Graphing Calculator Activities

47. Solve each of the following equations, using a graphing calculator whenever it seems to be helpful. Express all irrational solutions in lowest radical form.

(a) $x^3 + 2x^2 - 14x - 40 = 0$
(b) $x^3 + x^2 - 7x + 65 = 0$
(c) $x^4 - 6x^3 - 6x^2 + 32x + 24 = 0$
(d) $x^4 + 3x^3 - 39x^2 + 11x + 24 = 0$
(e) $x^3 - 14x^2 + 26x - 24 = 0$
(f) $x^4 + 2x^3 - 3x^2 - 4x + 4 = 0$

48. Find approximations, to the nearest hundredth, of the real number solutions of each of the following equations:

(a) $x^2 - 4x + 1 = 0$
(b) $3x^3 - 2x^2 + 12x - 8 = 0$
(c) $x^4 - 8x^3 + 14x^2 - 8x + 13 = 0$
(d) $x^4 + 6x^3 - 10x^2 - 22x + 161 = 0$
(e) $7x^5 - 5x^4 + 35x^3 - 25x^2 + 28x - 20 = 0$

Answers to the Concept Quiz

1. True   **2.** True   **3.** False   **4.** True   **5.** False   **6.** True   **7.** True   **8.** True

9.4   Graphing Polynomial Functions

OBJECTIVES

1 Know the patterns for the graphs of $f(x) = ax^n$

2 Graph polynomial functions

3 Identify the intervals in which a polynomial function is positive or negative

The terms with which we classify functions are analogous to those with which we describe the linear equations, quadratic equations, and polynomial equations. In Chapter 8 we defined a linear function in terms of the equation

$$f(x) = ax + b$$

and a quadratic function in terms of the equation

$$f(x) = ax^2 + bx + c$$

Both are special cases of a general class of functions called polynomial functions. Any function of the form

$$f(x) = a_n x^n + a_{n-1} x^{n-1} + \cdots + a_1 x + a_0$$

is called a **polynomial function of degree n**, where a_n is a nonzero real number, $a_{n-1}, \ldots,$ a_1, a_0 are real numbers, and n is a nonnegative integer. The following are examples of polynomial functions:

$$f(x) = 5x^3 - 2x^2 + x - 4 \qquad \text{Degree 3}$$

$$f(x) = -2x^4 - 5x^3 + 3x^2 + 4x - 1 \qquad \text{Degree 4}$$

$$f(x) = 3x^5 + 2x^2 - 3 \qquad \text{Degree 5}$$

Remark: Our previous work with polynomial equations is sometimes presented as "finding zeros of polynomial functions." The *solutions*, or *roots*, of a polynomial equation are also called the **zeros** of the polynomial function. For example, -2 and 2 are solutions of $x^2 - 4 = 0$, and they are zeros of $f(x) = x^2 - 4$. That is, $f(-2) = 0$ and $f(2) = 0$.

For a complete discussion of graphing polynomial functions, we would need some tools from calculus. However, the graphing techniques that we have discussed in this text will allow us to graph certain kinds of polynomial functions. For example, polynomial functions of the form $f(x) = ax^n$ are quite easy to graph. We know from our previous work that if $n = 1$, then functions such as $f(x) = 2x$, $f(x) = -3x$, and $f(x) = \dfrac{1}{2}x$ are lines through the origin that have slopes of 2, -3, and $\dfrac{1}{2}$, respectively.

Furthermore, if $n = 2$, we know that the graphs of functions of the form $f(x) = ax^2$ are parabolas that are symmetric with respect to the y axis and have their vertices at the origin.

We have also previously graphed the special case of $f(x) = ax^n$, where $a = 1$ and $n = 3$; namely, the function $f(x) = x^3$. This graph is shown in Figure 9.4.

The graphs of functions of the form $f(x) = ax^3$, where $a \neq 1$, are slight variations of $f(x) = x^3$ and can be determined easily by plotting a few points. The graphs of $f(x) = \dfrac{1}{2}x^3$ and $f(x) = -x^3$ appear in Figure 9.5(a) and 9.5(b).

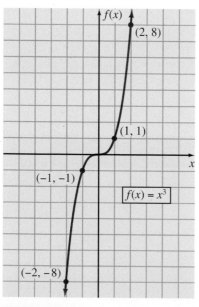

Figure 9.4

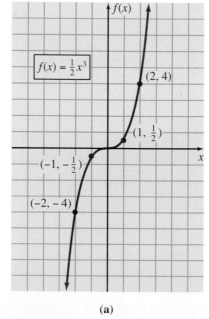

(a)

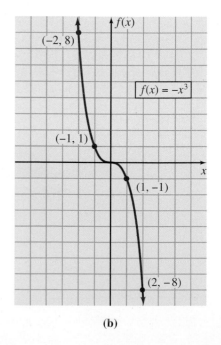

(b)

Figure 9.5

Two general patterns emerge from studying functions of the form $f(x) = x^n$. If n is odd and greater than 3, the graphs closely resemble Figure 9.4. The graph of $f(x) = x^5$ is shown in Figure 9.6. Note that the curve "flattens out" a little more around the origin than it does in the graph of $f(x) = x^3$; it increases and decreases more rapidly because of the larger exponent. If n is even and greater than 2, the graphs of $f(x) = x^n$ are not parabolas. They resemble the basic parabola, but they are flatter at the bottom and steeper on the sides. Figure 9.7 shows the graph of $f(x) = x^4$.

Graphs of functions of the form $f(x) = ax^n$, where n is an integer greater than 2 and $a \neq 1$, are variations of those shown in Figures 9.4 and 9.7. If n is odd, the curve is symmetric about the origin. If n is even, the graph is symmetric about the y axis.

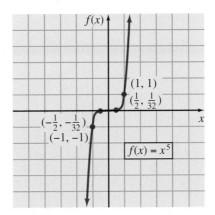

Figure 9.6

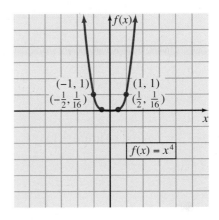

Figure 9.7

Remember from our work in Chapter 8 that transformations of basic curves are easy to sketch. For example, in Figure 9.8, we translated the graph of $f(x) = x^3$ upward two units to produce the graph of $f(x) = x^3 + 2$. Figure 9.9 shows the graph of $f(x) = (x - 1)^5$, obtained by translating the graph of $f(x) = x^5$ one unit to the right. In Figure 9.10, we sketched the graph of $f(x) = -x^4$ as the x-axis reflection of $f(x) = x^4$.

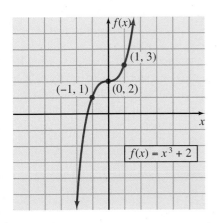

Figure 9.8

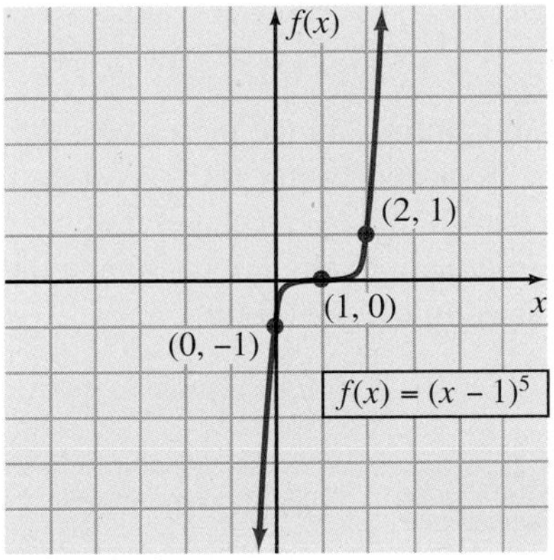

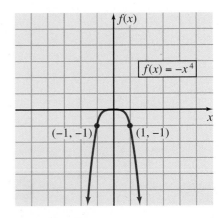

Figure 9.9

Figure 9.10

Graphing Polynomial Functions in Factored Form

As the degree of the polynomial increases, the graphs often become more complicated. We do know, however, that polynomial functions produce smooth continuous curves with a number of turning points, as illustrated in Figures 9.11 and 9.12. Some typical graphs of polynomial functions of odd degree are shown in Figure 9.11. As the graphs suggest, every polynomial function of odd degree has at least one *real zero*—that is, at least one real number c such that $f(c) = 0$. Geometrically, the zeros of the function are the x intercepts of the graph. Figure 9.12 illustrates some possible graphs of polynomial functions of even degree.

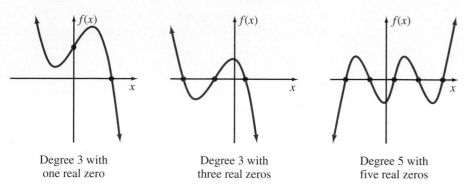

Degree 3 with   Degree 3 with   Degree 5 with
one real zero   three real zeros   five real zeros

Figure 9.11

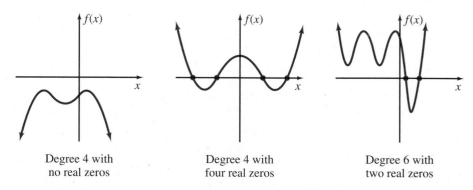

Degree 4 with   Degree 4 with   Degree 6 with
no real zeros   four real zeros   two real zeros

Figure 9.12

The **turning points** are the places where the function changes either from increasing to decreasing or from decreasing to increasing. Using calculus, we are able to verify that a polynomial function of degree n has at most $n - 1$ turning points. Now let's illustrate how we can use this information, along with some other techniques, to graph polynomial functions that are expressed in factored form.

Classroom Example
Graph $f(x) = (x + 1)(x - 4)(x - 2)$.

EXAMPLE 1   Graph $f(x) = (x + 2)(x - 1)(x - 3)$.

Solution

First, let's find the x intercepts (zeros of the function) by setting each factor equal to zero and solving for x:

$$x + 2 = 0 \quad \text{or} \quad x - 1 = 0 \quad \text{or} \quad x - 3 = 0$$
$$x = -2 \qquad\qquad x = 1 \qquad\qquad x = 3$$

Thus the points $(-2, 0)$, $(1, 0)$, and $(3, 0)$ are on the graph. Second, the points associated with the x intercepts divide the x axis into four intervals as shown in Figure 9.13.

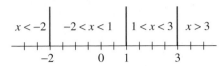

Figure 9.13

In each of these intervals, $f(x)$ is either always positive or always negative. That is to say, the graph is either above or below the x axis. Selecting a test value for x in each of the intervals will determine whether $f(x)$ is positive or negative. Any additional points that are easily obtained improve the accuracy of the graph. The table summarizes these results.

Interval	Test value	Sign of $f(x)$	Location of graph
$x < -2$	$f(-3) = -24$	Negative	Below x axis
$-2 < x < 1$	$f(0) = 6$	Positive	Above x axis
$1 < x < 3$	$f(2) = -4$	Negative	Below x axis
$x > 3$	$f(4) = 18$	Positive	Above x axis

Additional values: $f(-1) = 8$

Making use of the x intercepts and the information in the table, we can sketch the graph in Figure 9.14. The points $(-3, -24)$ and $(4, 18)$ are not shown, but they are used to indicate a rapid decrease and increase of the curve in those regions.

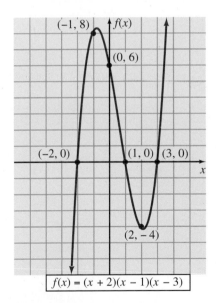

$$f(x) = (x + 2)(x - 1)(x - 3)$$

Figure 9.14

Remark: In Figure 9.14, the approximate turning points of the graph are indicated at $(2, -4)$ and $(-1, 8)$. Keep in mind that these are only integral approximations. Using the ZOOM and TRACE features of a graphing calculator, we found that the points $(-0.8, 8.2)$ and $(2.1, -4.1)$ are approximations to the nearest tenth. Again, the tools of calculus are needed to find the exact turning points.

EXAMPLE 2   Graph $f(x) = -x^4 + 3x^3 - 2x^2$.

Solution

The polynomial can be factored as follows:

$$f(x) = -x^4 + 3x^3 - 2x^2$$
$$= -x^2(x^2 - 3x + 2)$$
$$= -x^2(x - 1)(x - 2)$$

Now we can find the x intercepts.

$$-x^2 = 0 \quad \text{or} \quad x - 1 = 0 \quad \text{or} \quad x - 2 = 0$$
$$x = 0 \quad \text{or} \quad x = 1 \quad \text{or} \quad x = 2$$

The points $(0, 0)$, $(1, 0)$, and $(2, 0)$ are on the graph and divide the x axis into four intervals as shown in Figure 9.15.

Figure 9.15

In the following table, we determine some points and summarize the sign behavior of $f(x)$.

Interval	Test value	Sign of $f(x)$	Location of graph
$x < 0$	$f(-1) = -6$	Negative	Below x axis
$0 < x < 1$	$f\left(\dfrac{1}{2}\right) = -\dfrac{3}{16}$	Negative	Below x axis
$1 < x < 2$	$f\left(\dfrac{3}{2}\right) = \dfrac{9}{16}$	Positive	Above x axis
$x > 2$	$f(3) = -18$	Negative	Below x axis

Making use of the table and the x intercepts, we can draw the graph, as illustrated in Figure 9.16.

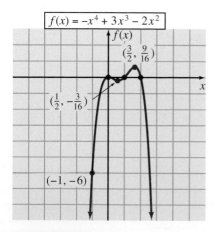

Figure 9.16

EXAMPLE 3   Graph $f(x) = x^3 + 3x^2 - 4$.

Solution

Use the rational root theorem, synthetic division, and the factor theorem to factor the given polynomial as follows.

$$f(x) = x^3 + 3x^2 - 4$$
$$= (x - 1)(x^2 + 4x + 4)$$
$$= (x - 1)(x + 2)^2$$

Now we can find the x intercepts.

$$x - 1 = 0 \qquad \text{or} \qquad (x + 2)^2 = 0$$
$$x = 1 \qquad \text{or} \qquad x = -2$$

The points $(-2, 0)$ and $(1, 0)$ are on the graph and divide the x axis into three intervals as shown in Figure 9.17.

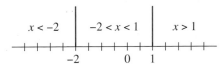

Figure 9.17

In the following table, we determine some points and summarize the sign behavior of $f(x)$.

Interval	Test value	Sign of $f(x)$	Location of graph
$x < -2$	$f(-3) = -4$	Negative	Below x axis
$-2 < x < 1$	$f(0) = -4$	Negative	Below x axis
$x > 1$	$f(2) = 16$	Positive	Above x axis

Additional values: $f(-1) = -2$
$f(-4) = -20$

As a result of the table and the x intercepts, we can sketch the graph as shown in Figure 9.18.

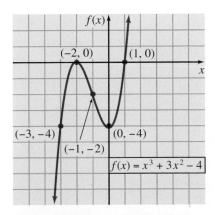

Figure 9.18

Finally, let's use a graphical approach to solve a problem involving a polynomial function.

EXAMPLE 4

Suppose that we have a rectangular piece of cardboard that measures 20 inches by 14 inches. From each corner, a square piece is cut out, and then the flaps are turned up to form an open box (see Figure 9.19). Determine the length of a side of the square pieces to be cut out so that the volume of the box is as large as possible.

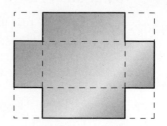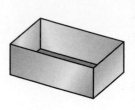

Figure 9.19

Solution

Let x represent the length of a side of the squares to be cut from each corner. Then $20 - 2x$ represents the length of the open box, and $14 - 2x$ represents the width. The volume of a rectangular box is given by the formula $V = lwh$, so the volume of this box can be represented by $V = x(20 - 2x)(14 - 2x)$. Now let $y = V$, and graph the function $y = x(20 - 2x)(14 - 2x)$ as shown in Figure 9.20. For this problem, we are interested only in the part of the graph between $x = 0$ and $x = 7$ because the length of a side of the squares has to be less than 7 inches for a box to be formed. Figure 9.21 gives us a view of that part of the graph. Now we can use the ZOOM and TRACE features to determine that when x equals approximately 2.7, the value of y is a maximum of approximately 339.0. Thus square pieces of length approximately 2.7 inches on a side should be cut from each corner of the rectangular piece of cardboard. The open box formed will have a volume of approximately 339.0 cubic inches.

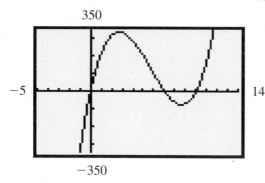

Figure 9.20

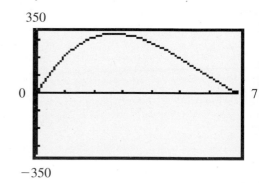

Figure 9.21

Concept Quiz 9.4

For Problems 1–4, match the function with its graph.

1. $f(x) = -x^4$ **2.** $f(x) = 2x^3$ **3.** $f(x) = (x + 2)^3$ **4.** $f(x) = x^3 + 2$

A.

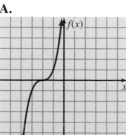

B.

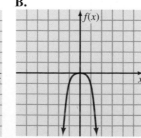

C.

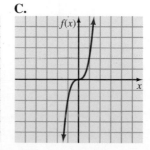

D.

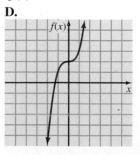

For Problems 5–8, answer true or false.

5. The solutions of a polynomial equation are called the zeros of the polynomial function.

6. The graphs of $f(x) = x^4$ and $f(x) = x^6$ are parabolas.

7. Every polynomial function of odd degree has at least one real number zero.

8. Turning points of polynomial functions are where the function crosses the x axis.

Problem Set 9.4

For Problems 1–22, graph each of the polynomial functions. (Objective 2)

1. $f(x) = -(x - 3)^3$

2. $f(x) = (x - 2)^3 + 1$

3. $f(x) = (x + 1)^3$

4. $f(x) = x^3 - 3$

5. $f(x) = (x + 3)^4$

6. $f(x) = x^4 - 2$

7. $f(x) = -(x - 2)^4$

8. $f(x) = (x - 1)^5 + 2$

9. $f(x) = (x + 1)^4 + 3$

10. $f(x) = -x^5$

11. $f(x) = (x - 2)(x + 1)(x + 3)$

12. $f(x) = (x - 1)(x + 1)(x - 3)$

13. $f(x) = x(x + 2)(2 - x)$

14. $f(x) = (x + 4)(x + 1)(1 - x)$

15. $f(x) = -x^2(x - 1)(x + 1)$

16. $f(x) = -x(x + 3)(x - 2)$

17. $f(x) = (2x - 1)(x - 2)(x - 3)$

18. $f(x) = x(x - 2)^2(x - 1)$

19. $f(x) = (x - 2)(x - 1)(x + 1)(x + 2)$

20. $f(x) = (x - 1)^2(x + 2)$

21. $f(x) = x(x - 2)^2(x + 1)$

22. $f(x) = (x + 1)^2(x - 1)^2$

For Problems 23–34, graph each polynomial function by first factoring the given polynomial. You may need to use some factoring techniques from Chapter 3 as well as the rational root theorem and the factor theorem. (Objective 2)

23. $f(x) = -x^3 - x^2 + 6x$

24. $f(x) = x^3 + x^2 - 2x$

25. $f(x) = x^4 - 5x^3 + 6x^2$

26. $f(x) = -x^4 - 3x^3 - 2x^2$

27. $f(x) = x^3 + 2x^2 - x - 2$

28. $f(x) = x^3 - x^2 - 4x + 4$

29. $f(x) = x^3 - 8x^2 + 19x - 12$

30. $f(x) = x^3 + 6x^2 + 11x + 6$

31. $f(x) = 2x^3 - 3x^2 - 3x + 2$

32. $f(x) = x^3 + 2x^2 - x - 2$

33. $f(x) = x^4 - 5x^2 + 4$

34. $f(x) = -x^4 + 5x^2 - 4$

For Problems 35–42, (a) find the y intercepts, (b) find the x intercepts, and (c) find the intervals of x where $f(x) > 0$ and those where $f(x) < 0$. *Do not* sketch the graphs. (Objective 3)

35. $f(x) = (x + 3)(x - 6)(8 - x)$

36. $f(x) = (x - 5)(x + 4)(x - 3)$

37. $f(x) = (x + 3)^4(x - 1)^3$

38. $f(x) = (x - 4)^2(x + 3)^3$

39. $f(x) = x(x - 6)^2(x + 4)$

40. $f(x) = (x + 2)^2(x - 1)^3(x - 2)$

41. $f(x) = x^2(2 - x)(x + 3)$

42. $f(x) = (x + 2)^5(x - 4)^2$

43. A rectangular piece of cardboard is 13 inches long and 9 inches wide. From each corner, a square piece is cut out, and then the flaps are turned up to form an open box. Use a graphing utility to determine the length (to the nearest tenth) of a side of one of the square pieces so that the volume of the box is as large as possible.

44. A company determines that its weekly profit from manufacturing and selling x units of a certain item is given by $P(x) = -x^3 + 3x^2 + 2880x - 500$. Use a graphing utility to find the weekly production rate that will maximize the profit.

Thoughts Into Words

45. How would you defend the statement that the equation $2x^4 + 3x^3 + x^2 + 5 = 0$ has no positive solutions? Does it have any negative solutions? Defend your answer.

46. How do you know by inspection that the graph of $f(x) = (x + 1)^2(x - 2)^2$ in Figure 9.22 is incorrect?

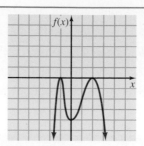

Figure 9.22

Further Investigations

47. A polynomial function with real coefficients is continuous everywhere; that is, its graph has no holes or breaks. This is the basis for the following property: If $f(x)$ is a polynomial with real coefficients, and if $f(a)$ and $f(b)$ are of opposite sign, then there is at least one real zero between a and b. This property, along with our knowledge of polynomial functions, provides the basis for locating and approximating irrational solutions of a polynomial equation.

Consider the equation $x^3 + 2x - 4 = 0$. Applying Descartes' rule of signs, we can determine that this equation has one positive real solution and two nonreal complex solutions. (You may want to confirm this!) The rational root theorem indicates that the only possible rational solutions are 1, 2, and 4. Using a little more compact format for synthetic division, we obtain the following results when testing for 1 and 2 as possible solutions:

	1	0	2	−4
1	1	1	3	−1
2	1	2	6	8

Because $f(1) = -1$ and $f(2) = 8$, there must be an irrational solution between 1 and 2. Furthermore, -1 is closer to 0 than is 8, so our guess is that the solution is closer to 1 than to 2. Let's start looking at 1.0, 1.1, 1.2, and so on, until we can place the solution between two numbers.

	1	0	2	−4	
1.0	1	1	3	−1	A calculator is very
1.1	1	1.1	3.21	−0.469	helpful at this time
1.2	1	1.2	3.44	0.128	

Because $f(1.1) = -0.469$ and $f(1.2) = 0.128$, the irrational solution must be between 1.1 and 1.2. Furthermore, because 0.128 is closer to 0 than is -0.469, our guess is that the solution is closer to 1.2 than to 1.1. Let's start looking at 1.15, 1.16, and so on.

	1	0	2	−4
1.15	1	1.15	3.3225	−0.179
1.16	1	1.16	3.3456	−0.119
1.17	1	1.17	3.3689	−0.058
1.18	1	1.18	3.3924	0.003

Because $f(1.17) = -0.058$ and $f(1.18) = 0.003$, the irrational solution must be between 1.17 and 1.18. Therefore we can use 1.2 as a rational approximation to the nearest tenth.

For each of the following equations, (a) verify that the equation has exactly one irrational solution, and (b) find an approximation, to the nearest tenth, of that solution.

(a) $x^3 + x - 6 = 0$

(b) $x^3 - 6x - 6 = 0$

(c) $x^3 - 27x - 60 = 0$

(d) $x^3 - x^2 - x - 1 = 0$

(e) $x^3 - 2x - 10 = 0$

(f) $x^3 - 5x^2 - 1 = 0$

Graphing Calculator Activities

48. Graph $f(x) = x^3$. Now predict the graphs for $f(x) = x^3 + 2$, $f(x) = -x^3 + 2$, and $f(x) = -x^3 - 2$. Graph these three functions on the same set of axes with the graph of $f(x) = x^3$.

49. Draw a rough sketch of the graphs of the functions $f(x) = x^3 - x^2$, $f(x) = -x^3 + x^2$, and $f(x) = -x^3 - x^2$. Now graph these three functions to check your sketches.

50. Graph $f(x) = x^4 + x^3 + x^2$. What should the graphs of $f(x) = x^4 - x^3 + x^2$ and $f(x) = -x^4 - x^3 - x^2$ look like? Graph them to see if you were right.

51. How should the graphs of $f(x) = x^3$, $f(x) = x^5$, and $f(x) = x^7$ compare? Graph these three functions on the same set of axes.

52. How should the graphs of $f(x) = x^2$, $f(x) = x^4$, and $f(x) = x^6$ compare? Graph these three functions on the same set of axes.

53. For each of the following functions, find the x intercepts, and find the intervals of x where $f(x) > 0$ and those where $f(x) < 0$.

(a) $f(x) = x^3 - 3x^2 - 6x + 8$
(b) $f(x) = x^3 - 8x^2 - x + 8$
(c) $f(x) = x^3 - 7x^2 + 16x - 12$
(d) $f(x) = x^3 - 19x^2 + 90x - 72$
(e) $f(x) = x^4 + 3x^3 - 3x^2 - 11x - 6$
(f) $f(x) = x^4 + 12x^2 - 64$

54. Find the coordinates of the turning points of each of the following graphs. Express x and y values to the nearest integer.

(a) $f(x) = 2x^3 - 3x^2 - 12x + 40$
(b) $f(x) = 2x^3 - 33x^2 + 60x + 1050$
(c) $f(x) = -2x^3 - 9x^2 + 24x + 100$
(d) $f(x) = x^4 - 4x^3 - 2x^2 + 12x + 3$
(e) $f(x) = x^3 - 30x^2 + 288x - 900$
(f) $f(x) = x^5 - 2x^4 - 3x^3 - 2x^2 + x - 1$

55. For each of the following functions, find the x intercepts and find the turning points. Express your answers to the nearest tenth.

(a) $f(x) = x^3 + 2x^2 - 3x + 4$
(b) $f(x) = 42x^3 - x^2 - 246x - 35$
(c) $f(x) = x^4 - 4x^2 - 4$

9.5 Graphing Rational Functions

OBJECTIVES

1 Find the vertical asymptote(s) for a rational function

2 Find the horizontal asymptote for a rational function

3 Graph rational functions

Let's begin this section by using a graphing calculator to graph the function $f(x) = \dfrac{x^2}{x^2 - x - 2}$ twice using different boundaries, as indicated in Figures 9.23 and 9.24. It should be evident from the two figures that we really cannot tell what the graph of the function looks like. This happens frequently in graphing rational functions with a graphing calculator. Thus we need to do a careful analysis of rational functions, emphasizing the use

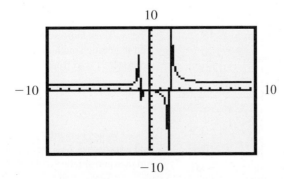

Figure 9.23

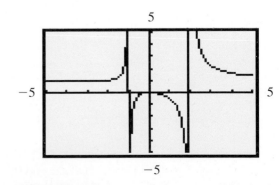

Figure 9.24

of hand-drawn graphs. (By the way, if you are interested in seeing the complete graph of this function, turn to the first example of the next section.)

A function of the form

$$f(x) = \frac{p(x)}{q(x)}, \quad q(x) \neq 0$$

where $p(x)$ and $q(x)$ are polynomials, is called a **rational function**.

The following are examples of rational functions:

$$f(x) = \frac{2}{x-1} \qquad f(x) = \frac{x}{x-2}$$

$$f(x) = \frac{x^2}{x^2-x-6} \qquad f(x) = \frac{x^3-8}{x+4}$$

In each of these examples, the domain of the rational function is the set of all real numbers except those that make the denominator zero. For example, the domain of $f(x) = \frac{2}{x-1}$ is the set of all real numbers except 1. As we will soon see, these exclusions from the domain are important numbers from a graphing standpoint; they represent breaks in an otherwise continuous curve.

Let's set the stage for graphing rational functions by considering in detail the function $f(x) = \frac{1}{x}$. First, note that at $x = 0$ the function is undefined. Second, let's consider a rather extensive table of values to find some number trends and to build a basis for defining the concept of an asymptote.

x	$f(x) = \frac{1}{x}$	
1	1	
2	0.5	These values indicate that the value of $f(x)$ is
10	0.1	positive and approaches zero from above as x
100	0.01	gets larger and larger
1000	0.001	
0.5	2	
0.1	10	These values indicate that $f(x)$ is positive and is
0.01	100	getting larger and larger as x approaches zero
0.001	1000	from the right
0.0001	10,000	
-0.5	-2	
-0.1	-10	These values indicate that $f(x)$ is negative
-0.01	-100	and is getting smaller and smaller as x
-0.001	-1000	approaches zero from the left
-0.0001	$-10,000$	
-1	-1	
-2	-0.5	These values indicate that $f(x)$ is negative
-10	-0.1	and approaches zero from below as x gets
-100	-0.01	smaller and smaller without bound
-1000	-0.001	

Figure 9.25 shows a sketch of $f(x) = \dfrac{1}{x}$, which is drawn using a few points from this table and the patterns discussed. Note that the graph approaches but does not touch either axis. We say that the y axis (or the $f(x)$ axis) is a **vertical asymptote** and that the x axis is a **horizontal asymptote**.

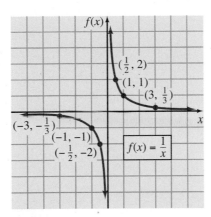

Figure 9.25

Remark: We know that the equation $f(x) = \dfrac{1}{x}$ exhibits origin symmetry because $f(-x) = -f(x)$. Thus the graph in Figure 9.25 could have been drawn by first determining the part of the curve in the first quadrant and then reflecting that curve through the origin.

Now let's define the concepts of vertical and horizontal asymptotes.

Vertical Asymptote

A line $x = a$ is a vertical asymptote for the graph of a function f if:

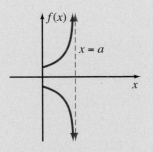

1. $f(x)$ either increases or decreases without bound as x approaches a from the left, as in Figure 9.26,

Figure 9.26

or

2. $f(x)$ either increases or decreases without bound as x approaches a from the right, as in Figure 9.27.

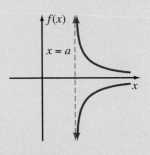

Figure 9.27

Horizontal Asymptote

A line $y = b$ (or $f(x) = b$) is a horizontal asymptote for the graph of a function f if:

1. $f(x)$ approaches b from above or below as x gets infinitely small, as in Figure 9.28,

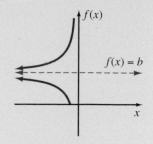

Figure 9.28

or

2. $f(x)$ approaches b from above or below as x gets infinitely large, as in Figure 9.29.

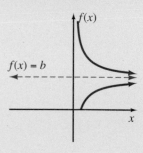

Figure 9.29

Following are some suggestions for graphing rational functions of the type we are considering in this section.

1. Check for y-axis and origin symmetry.
2. Find any vertical asymptote by setting the denominator equal to zero and solving for x.
3. Find any horizontal asymptote by studying the behavior of $f(x)$ as x gets infinitely large or as x gets infinitely small.
4. Study the behavior of the graph when it is close to the asymptotes.
5. Plot as many points as necessary to determine the shape of the graph. The number needed may be affected by whether or not the graph has any kind of symmetry.

Keep these suggestions in mind as you study the following examples.

Classroom Example

Graph $f(x) = \dfrac{3}{x-2}$.

EXAMPLE 1

Graph $f(x) = \dfrac{-2}{x-1}$.

Solution

Because $x = 1$ makes the denominator zero, the line $x = 1$ is a vertical asymptote. We have indicated this with a dashed line in Figure 9.30. Now let's look for a horizontal asymptote by checking some large and some small values of x.

x	f(x)
10	$-\dfrac{2}{9}$
100	$-\dfrac{2}{99}$
1000	$-\dfrac{2}{999}$

x	f(x)
-10	$\dfrac{2}{11}$
-100	$\dfrac{2}{101}$
-1000	$\dfrac{2}{1001}$

This table shows that as x gets very large, the value of $f(x)$ approaches zero from below

This table shows that as x gets very small, the value of $f(x)$ approaches zero from above

Therefore the x axis is a horizontal asymptote.

Finally, let's check the behavior of the graph near the vertical asymptote.

x	$f(x)$
2	-2
1.5	-4
1.1	-20
1.01	-200
1.001	-2000

As x approaches 1 from the right side, the value of $f(x)$ gets smaller and smaller

x	$f(x)$
0	2
0.5	4
0.9	20
0.99	200
0.999	2000

As x approaches 1 from the left side, the value of $f(x)$ gets larger and larger

The graph of $f(x) = \dfrac{-2}{x - 1}$ is shown in Figure 9.30.

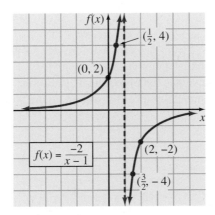

Figure 9.30

Classroom Example

Graph $f(x) = \dfrac{x}{x + 4}$.

EXAMPLE 2

Graph $f(x) = \dfrac{x}{x + 2}$.

Solution

Because $x = -2$ makes the denominator zero, the line $x = -2$ is a vertical asymptote. To study the behavior of $f(x)$ as x gets very large or very small, let's change the form of the rational expression by dividing numerator and denominator by x:

$$f(x) = \frac{x}{x + 2} = \frac{\dfrac{x}{x}}{\dfrac{x + 2}{x}} = \frac{1}{\dfrac{x}{x} + \dfrac{2}{x}} = \frac{1}{1 + \dfrac{2}{x}}$$

Now we can see that as x gets larger and larger, the value of $f(x)$ approaches 1 from below; as x gets smaller and smaller, the value of $f(x)$ approaches 1 from above. (Perhaps you should check these claims by plugging in some values for x.) Thus the line $f(x) = 1$ is a horizontal asymptote. Drawing the asymptotes (dashed lines) and plotting a few points, we complete the graph in Figure 9.31.

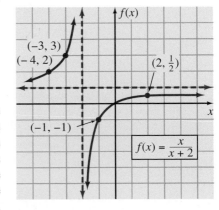

Figure 9.31

In the next two examples, pay special attention to the role of symmetry. It will allow us to direct our efforts toward quadrants I and IV and then to reflect those portions of the curve across the vertical axis to complete the graph.

EXAMPLE 3   Graph $f(x) = \dfrac{2x^2}{x^2 + 4}$.

Solution

First, note that $f(-x) = f(x)$; therefore this graph is symmetric with respect to the vertical axis. Second, the denominator $x^2 + 4$ cannot equal zero for any real number value of x; thus there is no vertical asymptote. Third, dividing both numerator and denominator of the rational expression by x^2 produces

$$f(x) = \frac{2x^2}{x^2 + 4} = \frac{\dfrac{2x^2}{x^2}}{\dfrac{x^2 + 4}{x^2}} = \frac{2}{\dfrac{x^2}{x^2} + \dfrac{4}{x^2}} = \frac{2}{1 + \dfrac{4}{x^2}}$$

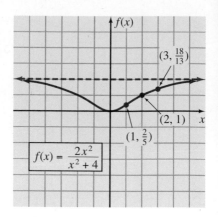

Now we can see that as x gets larger and larger, the value of $f(x)$ approaches 2 from below. Therefore the line $f(x) = 2$ is a horizontal asymptote. We can plot a few points using positive values for x, sketch this part of the curve, and then reflect across the $f(x)$ axis to obtain the complete graph, as shown in Figure 9.32.

Figure 9.32

EXAMPLE 4   Graph $f(x) = \dfrac{3}{x^2 - 4}$.

Solution

First, note that $f(-x) = f(x)$; therefore this graph is symmetric about the y axis. Thus, by setting the denominator equal to zero and solving for x, we obtain

$$x^2 - 4 = 0$$
$$x^2 = 4$$
$$x = \pm 2$$

The lines $x = 2$ and $x = -2$ are vertical asymptotes. Next, we can see that $\dfrac{3}{x^2 - 4}$ approaches zero from above as x gets larger and larger. Finally, we can plot a few points using positive values for x (other than 2), sketch this part of the curve, and then reflect it across the $f(x)$ axis to obtain the complete graph shown in Figure 9.33.

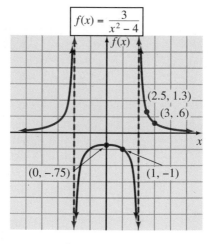

Figure 9.33

Now suppose that we are going to use a graphing utility to obtain a graph of the function $f(x) = \dfrac{4x^2}{x^4 - 16}$. Before we enter this function into a graphing utility, let's analyze what we know about the graph.

1. Because $f(0) = 0$, the origin is a point on the graph.
2. Because $f(-x) = f(x)$, the graph is symmetric with respect to the y axis.

3. By setting the denominator equal to zero and solving for x, we can determine the vertical asymptotes.

$$x^4 - 16 = 0$$
$$(x^2 + 4)(x^2 - 4) = 0$$
$$x^2 + 4 = 0 \qquad \text{or} \qquad x^2 - 4 = 0$$
$$x^2 = -4 \qquad\qquad\qquad x^2 = 4$$
$$x = \pm 2i \qquad\qquad\qquad x = \pm 2$$

Remember that we are working with ordered pairs of real numbers. Thus the lines $x = -2$ and $x = 2$ are vertical asymptotes.

4. Divide both the numerator and the denominator of the rational expression by x^4 to produce

$$\frac{4x^2}{x^4 - 16} = \frac{\dfrac{4x^2}{x^4}}{\dfrac{x^4 - 16}{x^4}} = \frac{\dfrac{4}{x^2}}{1 - \dfrac{16}{x^4}}$$

From the last expression, we see that as $|x|$ gets larger and larger, the value of $f(x)$ approaches zero from above. Therefore the x axis is a horizontal asymptote.

Now let's enter the function into a graphing calculator and set the boundaries so that we show the behavior of the function close to the asymptotes. Note that the graph shown in Figure 9.34 is consistent with all of the information that we determined before using the graphing calculator. In other words, our knowledge of graphing techniques enhances our use of a graphing utility.

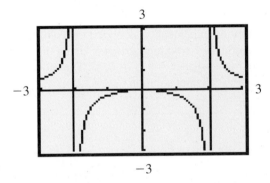

Figure 9.34

Back in Section 2.4 we solved problems of the following type: How much pure alcohol should be added to 6 liters of a 40% alcohol solution to raise it to a 60% alcohol solution? The answer of 3 liters can be found by solving the following equation, in which x represents the amount of pure alcohol to be added:

Pure alcohol to start with	$+$	Pure alcohol added	$=$	Pure alcohol in final solution
$\downarrow$		$\downarrow$		$\downarrow$
$0.40(6)$	$+$	x	$=$	$0.60(6 + x)$

Now let's consider this problem in a more general setting by writing a function in which x represents the amount of pure alcohol to be added, and y represents the concentration of pure alcohol in the final solution.

$$0.40(6) + x = y(6 + x)$$
$$2.4 + x = y(6 + x)$$
$$\frac{2.4 + x}{6 + x} = y$$

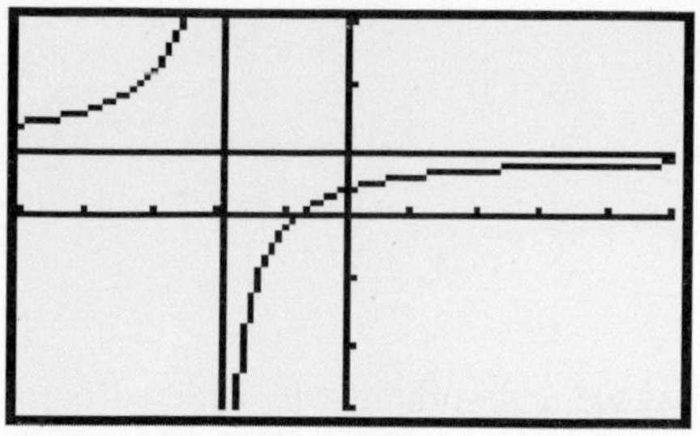

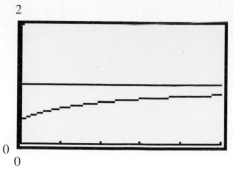

Figure 9.35

Figure 9.36

We can graph the rational function $y = \dfrac{2.4 + x}{6 + x}$ as shown in Figure 9.35. For this particular problem, x is nonnegative, so we are interested only in the part of the graph that is in the first quadrant. We change the boundaries of the viewing rectangle so that $0 \leq x \leq 15$ and $0 \leq y \leq 2$ to obtain Figure 9.36. Now we are ready to answer questions about this situation.

1. How much pure alcohol needs to be added to raise the 40% solution to a 60% solution? [*Hint*: We are looking for the value of x when y is 0.60.] *Answer*: Using the TRACE feature of the graphing utility, we find that when $y = 0.60$, $x = 3$. Therefore 3 liters of pure alcohol need to be added.

2. How much pure alcohol needs to be added to raise the 40% solution to a 70% solution? *Answer*: Using the TRACE feature of the graphing utility, we find that when $y = 0.70$, $x = 6$. Therefore 6 liters of pure alcohol need to be added.

3. What concentration in percent of alcohol do we obtain if we add 9 liters of pure alcohol to 6 liters of a 40% solution? *Answer*: Using the TRACE feature of the graphing utility, we find that when $x = 9$, $y = 0.76$. Therefore adding 9 liters of pure alcohol will give us a 76% alcohol solution.

Concept Quiz 9.5

For Problems 1–6, answer true or false.

1. The domain of $f(x) = \dfrac{x - 4}{2x + 1}$ is all real numbers except 4 and $-\dfrac{1}{2}$.

2. If the graph of a rational function has an asymptote at $x = -3$, then -3 is not in the domain of the function.

3. Vertical asymptotes can be found by setting the denominator of the function equal to 0.

4. Horizontal asymptotes can be found by setting the numerator of the function equal to 0.

5. If the numerator of a rational function is a constant, then the horizontal asymptote of the graph of the function is always the line $f(x) = 0$.

6. The graph of a rational function always has a vertical asymptote.

Problem Set 9.5

For Problems 1–10, find the vertical and horizontal asymptotes for the graphs of the rational functions. **(Objectives 2, 3)**

1. $f(x) = \dfrac{1}{x + 3}$

2. $f(x) = \dfrac{1}{x - 4}$

3. $f(x) = \dfrac{4x}{x - 1}$

4. $f(x) = \dfrac{-2x}{x + 5}$

5. $f(x) = \dfrac{2}{(x + 3)(x - 4)}$

6. $f(x) = \dfrac{6}{x(x - 1)}$

7. $f(x) = \dfrac{x}{x^2 - 9}$

8. $f(x) = \dfrac{3x}{x^2 - x + 2}$

9. $f(x) = \dfrac{5x^2}{x^2 + 4}$

10. $f(x) = \dfrac{-2x^2}{x^2 + 1}$

For Problems 11–32, graph each of the rational functions. (Objective 3)

11. $f(x) = \dfrac{1}{x^2}$

12. $f(x) = \dfrac{-1}{x}$

13. $f(x) = \dfrac{-1}{x - 3}$

14. $f(x) = \dfrac{3}{x + 1}$

15. $f(x) = \dfrac{-3}{(x + 2)^2}$

16. $f(x) = \dfrac{2}{(x - 1)^2}$

17. $f(x) = \dfrac{2x}{x - 1}$

18. $f(x) = \dfrac{x}{x - 3}$

19. $f(x) = \dfrac{-x}{x + 1}$

20. $f(x) = \dfrac{3x}{x + 2}$

21. $f(x) = \dfrac{-2}{x^2 - 4}$

22. $f(x) = \dfrac{1}{x^2 - 1}$

23. $f(x) = \dfrac{3}{(x + 2)(x - 4)}$

24. $f(x) = \dfrac{-2}{(x + 1)(x - 2)}$

25. $f(x) = \dfrac{-1}{x^2 + x - 6}$

26. $f(x) = \dfrac{2}{x^2 + x - 2}$

27. $f(x) = \dfrac{2x - 1}{x}$

28. $f(x) = \dfrac{x + 2}{x}$

29. $f(x) = \dfrac{4x^2}{x^2 + 1}$

30. $f(x) = \dfrac{4}{x^2 + 2}$

31. $f(x) = \dfrac{x^2 - 4}{x^2}$

32. $f(x) = \dfrac{2x^4}{x^4 + 1}$

Thoughts Into Words

33. How would you explain the concept of an asymptote to an elementary algebra student?

34. Give a step-by-step description of how you would go about graphing $f(x) = \dfrac{-2}{x^2 - 9}$.

Further Investigations

35. The rational function $f(x) = \dfrac{(x - 2)(x + 3)}{x - 2}$ has a domain of all real numbers except 2 and can be simplified to $f(x) = x + 3$. Thus its graph is a straight line with a hole at $(2, 5)$. Graph each of the following functions.

(a) $f(x) = \dfrac{(x + 4)(x - 1)}{x + 4}$

(b) $f(x) = \dfrac{x^2 - 5x + 6}{x - 2}$

(c) $f(x) = \dfrac{x - 1}{x^2 - 1}$

(d) $f(x) = \dfrac{x + 2}{x^2 + 6x + 8}$

36. Graph the function $f(x) = x + 2 + \dfrac{3}{x - 2}$. It may be necessary to plot a rather large number of points. Also, defend the statement that $f(x) = x + 2$ is an **oblique asymptote**.

Graphing Calculator Activities

37. Use a graphing calculator to check your graphs for Problem 35. What feature of the graphs does not show up on the calculator?

38. Each of the following graphs is a transformation of $f(x) = \dfrac{1}{x}$. First predict the general shape and location of the graph, and then check your prediction with a graphing calculator.

(a) $f(x) = \dfrac{1}{x} - 2$

(b) $f(x) = \dfrac{1}{x + 3}$

(c) $f(x) = -\dfrac{1}{x}$

(d) $f(x) = \dfrac{1}{x - 2} + 3$

(e) $f(x) = \dfrac{2x + 1}{x}$

39. Graph $f(x) = \dfrac{1}{x^2}$. How should the graph of $f(x) = \dfrac{1}{(x - 4)^2}$, $f(x) = \dfrac{1 + 3x^2}{x^2}$, and $f(x) = \dfrac{1}{x^2}$ compare to the graph of $f(x) = \dfrac{1}{x^2}$? Graph the three functions on the same set of axes with the graph of $f(x) = \dfrac{1}{x^2}$.

40. Graph $f(x) = \dfrac{1}{x^3}$. How should the graphs of $f(x) = \dfrac{2x^3 + 1}{x^3}$, $f(x) = \dfrac{1}{(x + 2)^3}$, and $f(x) = \dfrac{-1}{x^3}$ compare to the graph of $f(x) = \dfrac{1}{x^3}$? Graph the three functions on the same set of axes with the graph of $f(x) = \dfrac{1}{x^3}$.

41. Use a graphing calculator to check your graphs for Problems 29–32.

42. Suppose that x ounces of pure acid have been added to 14 ounces of a 15% acid solution.
  (a) Set up the rational expression that represents the concentration of pure acid in the final solution.
  (b) Graph the rational function that displays the concentration.
  (c) How many ounces of pure acid need to be added to the 14 ounces of a 15% solution to raise it to a 40.5% solution? Check your answer.
  (d) How many ounces of pure acid need to be added to the 14 ounces of a 15% solution to raise it to a 50% solution? Check your answer.
  (e) What concentration of acid do we obtain if we add 12 ounces of pure acid to the 14 ounces of a 15% solution? Check your answer.

43. Solve the following problem both algebraically and graphically: One solution contains 50% alcohol, and another solution contains 80% alcohol. How many liters of each solution should be mixed to produce 10.5 liters of a 70% alcohol solution? Check your answer.

44. Graph each of the following functions. Be sure that you get a complete graph for each one. Sketch each graph on a sheet of paper, and keep them all handy as you study the next section.

  (a) $f(x) = \dfrac{x^2}{x^2 - x - 2}$ **(b)** $f(x) = \dfrac{x}{x^2 - 4}$

  (c) $f(x) = \dfrac{3x}{x^2 + 1}$ **(d)** $f(x) = \dfrac{x^2 - 1}{x - 2}$

Answers to the Concept Quiz

1. False   **2.** True   **3.** True   **4.** False   **5.** True   **6.** False

---

9.6   More on Graphing Rational Functions

OBJECTIVES

1 Find the equation for an oblique asymptote of a rational function

2 Graph rational functions with vertical, horizontal, or oblique asymptotes

The rational functions that we studied in the previous section were pretty straightforward. In fact, once we established the vertical and horizontal asymptotes, a little bit of point plotting usually determined the graph fairly easily. Such is not always the case with rational functions. In this section, we want to investigate some rational functions that behave a little differently.

Vertical asymptotes occur at values of x when the denominator is zero, so no points of a graph can be on a vertical asymptote. However, recall that horizontal asymptotes are created by the behavior of $f(x)$ as x gets infinitely large or infinitely small. This does not restrict the possibility that for some values of x, points of the graph will be on the horizontal asymptote. Let's consider some examples.

Classroom Example

Graph $f(x) = \dfrac{-x^2}{x^2 + x - 6}$.

EXAMPLE 1   Graph $f(x) = \dfrac{x^2}{x^2 - x - 2}$.

Solution

First, let's identify the vertical asymptotes by setting the denominator equal to zero and solving for x:

$$x^2 - x - 2 = 0$$
$$(x - 2)(x + 1) = 0$$
$$x - 2 = 0 \quad \text{or} \quad x + 1 = 0$$
$$x = 2 \quad\quad\quad\quad x = -1$$

Thus the lines $x = 2$ and $x = -1$ are vertical asymptotes. Next, we can divide both the numerator and the denominator of the rational expression by x^2.

$$f(x) = \frac{x^2}{x^2 - x - 2} = \frac{\dfrac{x^2}{x^2}}{\dfrac{x^2 - x - 2}{x^2}} = \frac{1}{1 - \dfrac{1}{x} - \dfrac{2}{x^2}}$$

Now we can see that as x gets larger and larger, the value of $f(x)$ approaches 1 from above. Thus the line $f(x) = 1$ is a horizontal asymptote. To determine whether any points of the graph are *on* the horizontal asymptote, we can see whether the equation

$$\frac{x^2}{x^2 - x - 2} = 1$$

has any solutions.

$$\frac{x^2}{x^2 - x - 2} = 1$$
$$x^2 = x^2 - x - 2$$
$$0 = -x - 2$$
$$x = -2$$

Therefore the point $(-2, 1)$ is on the graph. Now, by drawing the asymptotes, plotting a few points (including $(-2, 1)$), and studying the behavior of the function close to the asymptotes, we can sketch the curve shown in Figure 9.37.

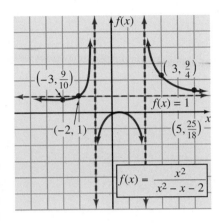

Figure 9.37

EXAMPLE 2   Graph $f(x) = \dfrac{x}{x^2 - 4}$.

Solution

First, note that $f(-x) = -f(x)$; therefore this graph is symmetric with respect to the origin. Second, let's identify the vertical asymptotes:

$$x^2 - 4 = 0$$
$$x^2 = 4$$
$$x = \pm 2$$

Thus the lines $x = -2$ and $x = 2$ are vertical asymptotes. Next, by dividing the numerator and the denominator of the rational expression by x^2, we obtain

$$f(x) = \frac{x}{x^2 - 4} = \frac{\dfrac{x}{x^2}}{\dfrac{x^2 - 4}{x^2}} = \frac{\dfrac{1}{x}}{1 - \dfrac{4}{x^2}}$$

From this form, we can see that as x gets larger and larger, the value of $f(x)$ approaches zero from above. Therefore the x axis is a horizontal asymptote. Because $f(0) = 0$, we know that the origin is a point of the graph. Finally, by concentrating our point plotting on positive values of x, we can sketch the portion of the curve to the right of the vertical axis, and then use the fact that the graph is symmetric with respect to the origin to complete the graph. Figure 9.38 shows the completed graph.

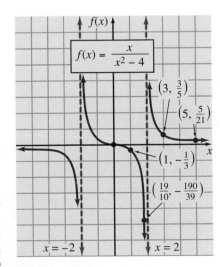

Figure 9.38

EXAMPLE 3 Graph $f(x) = \dfrac{3x}{x^2 + 1}$.

Solution

First, observe that $f(-x) = -f(x)$; therefore this graph is symmetric with respect to the origin. Second, because $x^2 + 1$ is a positive number for all real number values of x, there are no vertical asymptotes for this graph. Next, by dividing the numerator and the denominator of the rational expression by x^2, we obtain

$$f(x) = \frac{3x}{x^2 + 1} = \frac{\dfrac{3x}{x^2}}{\dfrac{x^2 + 1}{x^2}} = \frac{\dfrac{3}{x}}{1 + \dfrac{1}{x^2}}$$

From this form, we see that as x gets larger and larger, the value of $f(x)$ approaches zero from above. Thus the x axis is a horizontal asymptote. Because $f(0) = 0$, the origin is a point of the graph. Finally, by concentrating our point plotting on positive values of x, we can sketch the portion of the curve to the right of the vertical axis, and then use origin symmetry to complete the graph, as shown in Figure 9.39.

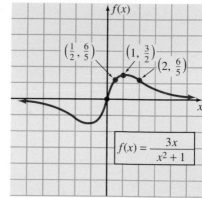

Figure 9.39

Oblique Asymptotes

Thus far we have restricted our study of rational functions to those in which the degree of the numerator is less than or equal to the degree of the denominator. As our final examples of graphing rational functions, we will consider functions in which the degree of the numerator is one greater than the degree of the denominator.

EXAMPLE 4 Graph $f(x) = \dfrac{x^2 - 1}{x - 2}$.

Solution

First, let's observe that $x = 2$ is a vertical asymptote. Second, because the degree of the numerator is greater than the degree of the denominator, we can change the form of the rational expression by division. We use synthetic division.

$$2\overline{)\begin{array}{rrr} 1 & 0 & -1 \\ & 2 & 4 \\ \hline 1 & 2 & 3 \end{array}}$$

Therefore the original function can be rewritten as

$$f(x) = \frac{x^2 - 1}{x - 2} = x + 2 + \frac{3}{x - 2}$$

Now, for very large values of $|x|$, the fraction $\dfrac{3}{x - 2}$ is close to zero. Therefore, as $|x|$ gets larger and larger, the graph of $f(x) = x + 2 + \dfrac{3}{x - 2}$ gets closer and closer to the line $f(x) = x + 2$. We call this line an **oblique asymptote** and indicate it with a dashed line in Figure 9.40. Finally, because this is a new situation, it may be necessary to plot a large number of points on both sides of the vertical asymptote, so let's make an extensive table of values. The graph of the function is shown in Figure 9.40.

x	$f(x) = \dfrac{x^2 - 1}{x - 2}$
4	7.5
3	8
2.8	8.55
2.5	10.5
2.3	14.3
2.2	19.2
2.1	34.1

x	$f(x) = \dfrac{x^2 - 1}{x - 2}$
-2	-0.75
0	0.5
1	0
1.5	-2.5
1.7	-6.3
1.8	-11.6
1.9	-26.1

These values indicate the behavior of $f(x)$ to the right of the vertical asymptote $x = 2$

These values indicate the behavior of $f(x)$ to the left of the vertical asymptote $x = 2$

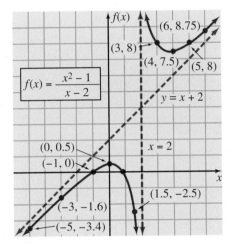

Figure 9.40

If the degree of the numerator of a rational function is *exactly one more* than the degree of its denominator, then the graph of the function has an oblique asymptote. (If the graph is a line, as is the case with $f(x) = \dfrac{(x - 2)(x + 1)}{x - 2}$, then we consider it to be its own asymptote.) As in Example 4, we find the equation of the oblique asymptote by changing the form of the function using long division. Let's consider another example.

Classroom Example

Graph $f(x) = \dfrac{x^2 + 5x - 6}{x + 2}$.

EXAMPLE 5   Graph $f(x) = \dfrac{x^2 - x - 2}{x - 1}$.

Solution

From the given form of the function, we see that $x = 1$ is a vertical asymptote. Then, by factoring the numerator, we can change the form to

$$f(x) = \frac{(x - 2)(x + 1)}{x - 1}$$

which indicates x intercepts of 2 and -1. Then, by long division, we can change the original form of the function to

$$f(x) = x - \frac{2}{x - 1}$$

which indicates an oblique asymptote $f(x) = x$. Finally, by plotting a few additional points, we can determine the graph as shown in Figure 9.41.

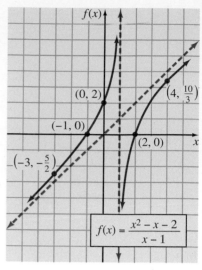

Figure 9.41

Finally, let's combine our knowledge of rational functions with the use of a graphing utility to obtain the graph of a fairly complex rational function.

Classroom Example

Graph $f(x) = \dfrac{2x^3 - 11x^2 + 12x + 9}{x^2 - 4}$.

EXAMPLE 6

Graph the rational function $f(x) = \dfrac{x^3 - 2x^2 - x - 1}{x^2 - 36}$ using a graphing utility.

Solution

Before entering this function into a graphing utility, let's analyze what we know about the graph.

1. Because $f(0) = \dfrac{1}{36}$, the point $\left(0, \dfrac{1}{36}\right)$ is on the graph.

2. Because $f(-x) \neq f(x)$ and $f(-x) \neq -f(x)$, there is no symmetry with respect to the origin or the y axis.

3. The denominator is zero at $x = \pm 6$. Thus the lines $x = 6$ and $x = -6$ are vertical asymptotes.

4. Let's change the form of the rational expression by division.

$$
\begin{array}{r}
x - 2 \\
x^2 - 36 \overline{)\, x^3 - 2x^2 - x - 1} \\
\underline{x^3 - 36x} \\
-2x^2 + 35x - 1 \\
\underline{-2x^2 + 72} \\
35x - 73
\end{array}
$$

Thus the original function can be rewritten as

$$f(x) = x - 2 + \frac{35x - 73}{x^2 - 36}$$

Therefore the line $y = x - 2$ is an oblique asymptote. Now let $Y_1 = x - 2$ and $Y_2 = \dfrac{x^3 - 2x^2 - x - 1}{x^2 - 36}$ and use a viewing rectangle in which $-15 \le x \le 15$ and $-30 \le y \le 30$ (Figure 9.42).

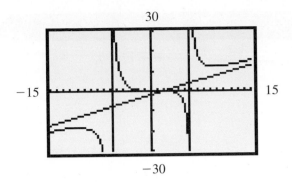

Figure 9.42

Note that the graph in Figure 9.42 is consistent with the information we had before we used the graphing calculator. Keep in mind that the oblique line and the two vertical lines are asymptotes and not part of the graph. Furthermore, the graph may appear to be symmetric about the origin, but remember that the test for origin symmetry failed. For example, the point $\left(0, \dfrac{1}{36}\right)$ is on the graph but the point $\left(0, -\dfrac{1}{36}\right)$ is not on the graph. Also note that the curve does intersect the oblique asymptote. We can use the ZOOM and TRACE features of the graphing calculator to approximate this point of intersection, or we can use an algebraic approach as follows: Because $y = \dfrac{x^3 - 2x^2 - x - 1}{x^2 - 36}$ and $y = x - 2$, we can equate the two expressions for y and solve the resulting equation for x.

$$\frac{x^3 - 2x^2 - x - 1}{x^2 - 36} = x - 2$$

$$x^3 - 2x^2 - x - 1 = (x - 2)(x^2 - 36)$$

$$x^3 - 2x^2 - x - 1 = x^3 - 2x^2 - 36x + 72$$

$$35x = 73$$

$$x = \frac{73}{35}$$

If $x = \dfrac{73}{35}$, then $y = x - 2 = \dfrac{73}{35} - 2 = \dfrac{3}{35}$. The point of intersection of the curve and the oblique asymptote is $\left(\dfrac{73}{35}, \dfrac{3}{35}\right)$.

cept Quiz 9.6

For Problems 1–6, answer true and false.

1. Every graph of a rational function has a horizontal asymptote.

2. For rational functions in which the degree of the numerator is one more than the degree of the denominator, the graph of the function will have an oblique asymptote.

3. The graph of a rational function can cross a horizontal asymptote.

4. The graph of rational function can cross a vertical asymptote.

5. If the graph of a rational function is symmetric with respect to the origin, then the line $f(x) = 0$ is a vertical asymptote.

6. For rational functions in which the degree of the numerator is less than or equal to the degree of the denominator, the graph of the function will have a horizontal asymptote.

Problem Set 9.6

For Problems 1–6, write the equation for the oblique asymptote for the graphs of the following rational functions. (Objective 1)

1. $f(x) = \dfrac{x^2 + 4}{x + 1}$

2. $f(x) = \dfrac{x^2 + 5}{x - 3}$

3. $f(x) = \dfrac{x^2 + 4x - 6}{x + 2}$

4. $f(x) = \dfrac{x^2 - x + 5}{x - 3}$

5. $f(x) = \dfrac{3x^2 + x + 2}{x + 2}$

6. $f(x) = \dfrac{x^2 + 4x - 1}{x}$

For Problems 7–26, graph each rational function. Check first for symmetry, and identify the asymptotes. (Objective 2)

7. $f(x) = \dfrac{x^2}{x^2 + x - 2}$

8. $f(x) = \dfrac{x^2}{x^2 + 2x - 3}$

9. $f(x) = \dfrac{2x^2}{x^2 - 2x - 8}$

10. $f(x) = \dfrac{-x^2}{x^2 + 3x - 4}$

11. $f(x) = \dfrac{-x}{x^2 - 1}$

12. $f(x) = \dfrac{2x}{x^2 - 9}$

13. $f(x) = \dfrac{x}{x^2 + x - 6}$

14. $f(x) = \dfrac{-x}{x^2 - 2x - 8}$

15. $f(x) = \dfrac{x^2}{x^2 - 4x + 3}$

16. $f(x) = \dfrac{1}{x^3 + x^2 - 6x}$

17. $f(x) = \dfrac{x}{x^2 + 2}$

18. $f(x) = \dfrac{6x}{x^2 + 1}$

19. $f(x) = \dfrac{-4x}{x^2 + 1}$

20. $f(x) = \dfrac{-5x}{x^2 + 2}$

21. $f(x) = \dfrac{x^2 + 2}{x - 1}$

22. $f(x) = \dfrac{x^2 - 3}{x + 1}$

23. $f(x) = \dfrac{x^2 - x - 6}{x + 1}$

24. $f(x) = \dfrac{x^2 + 4}{x + 2}$

25. $f(x) = \dfrac{x^2 + 1}{1 - x}$

26. $f(x) = \dfrac{x^3 + 8}{x^2}$

Thoughts Into Words

27. Explain the concept of an oblique asymptote.

28. Explain why it is possible for curves to intersect horizontal and oblique asymptotes but not to intersect vertical asymptotes.

29. Give a step-by-step description of how you would go about graphing $f(x) = \dfrac{x^2 - x - 12}{x - 2}$.

30. Your friend is having difficulty finding the point of intersection of a curve and the oblique asymptote. How can you help?

Graphing Calculator Activities

31. First check for symmetry and identify the asymptotes for the graphs of the following rational functions. Then use your graphing utility to graph each function.

(a) $f(x) = \dfrac{4x^2}{x^2 + x - 2}$

(b) $f(x) = \dfrac{-2x}{x^2 - 5x - 6}$

(c) $f(x) = \dfrac{x^2}{x^2 - 9}$

(d) $f(x) = \dfrac{x^2 - 4}{x^2 - 9}$

(e) $f(x) = \dfrac{x^2 - 9}{x^2 - 4}$

(f) $f(x) = \dfrac{x^2 + 2x + 1}{x^2 - 5x + 6}$

(c) $f(x) = \dfrac{2x^2 + x + 1}{x + 1}$

(d) $f(x) = \dfrac{x^2 + 4}{x - 3}$

(e) $f(x) = \dfrac{3x^2 - x - 2}{x - 2}$

(f) $f(x) = \dfrac{4x^2 + x + 1}{x + 1}$

(g) $f(x) = \dfrac{x^3 + x^2 - x - 1}{x^2 + 2x + 3}$

(h) $f(x) = \dfrac{x^3 + 2x^2 + x - 3}{x^2 - 4}$

32. For each of the following rational functions, first determine and graph any oblique asymptotes. Then, on the same set of axes, graph the function.

(a) $f(x) = \dfrac{x^2 - 1}{x - 2}$

(b) $f(x) = \dfrac{x^2 + 1}{x + 2}$

Answers to the Concept Quiz

1. False   **2.** True   **3.** True   **4.** False   **5.** False   **6.** True

OBJECTIVE	SUMMARY	EXAMPLE
Division algorithm for polynomials	The division algorithm for polynomials states that if $f(x)$ and $g(x)$ are polynomials and $d(x) \neq 0$, then there exist unique polynomials $q(x)$ and $r(x)$ such that $$f(x) = d(x)q(x) + r(x)$$ where $r(x) = 0$ or the degree of $r(x)$ is less than the degree of $d(x)$.	Given $f(x) = 6x^2 + 5x - 4$ and $g(x) = 2x + 1$, find the unique quotient and remainder polynomials. **Solution** Performing long division of polynomials yields a quotient of $3x + 1$ and a remainder of -5. Hence $$6x^2 + 5x - 4 = (2x + 1)(3x + 1) - 5$$
Use synthetic division to determine the quotient and remainder for polynomial division. (Section 9.1/Objective 1)	If the divisor is of the form $x - c$, where c is a constant, then the typical long division format for dividing polynomials can be simplified to a process called synthetic division.	Use synthetic division to find the quotient and remainder for $$(2x^3 - 3x - 6) \div (x - 2)$$ **Solution** In the division form use a placeholder for the missing x^2 term. $$\begin{array}{r} 2\,\overline{)\,2 \quad 0 \quad -3 \quad -6} \\ \quad\quad 4 \quad\; 8 \quad\; 10 \\ \hline 2 \quad 4 \quad\; 5 \quad\;\; 4 \end{array}$$ Thus the quotient is $2x^2 + 4x + 5$ and the remainder is 4.
Use the remainder theorem to evaluate a function for a given value. (Section 9.2/Objective 1)	The remainder theorem states that if a polynomial $f(x)$ is divided by $x - c$, then the remainder is equal to $f(c)$. Thus a polynomial can be evaluated for a given number by either direct substitution or by using synthetic division.	If $f(x) = 2x^3 + x^2 - 3x - 7$, find $f(-3)$ by using synthetic division and the remainder theorem. **Solution** $$\begin{array}{r} -3\,\overline{)\,2 \quad 1 \quad -3 \quad -7} \\ \quad\quad -6 \quad 15 \quad -36 \\ \hline 2 \quad -5 \quad 12 \quad -43 \end{array}$$ The remainder is -43, thus $$f(-3) = -43$$
Determine if an expression is a factor of a given polynomial. (Section 9.2/Objective 2)	The factor theorem states that a polynomial $f(x)$ has a factor $x - c$ if and only if $f(c) = 0$.	Is $x + 1$ a factor of $x^3 + 3x^2 - 2x + 1$? **Solution** Use synthetic division to determine the remainder. $$\begin{array}{r} -1\,\overline{)\,1 \quad 3 \quad -2 \quad 1} \\ \quad\quad -1 \quad -2 \quad 4 \\ \hline 1 \quad 2 \quad -4 \quad 5 \end{array}$$ Because the remainder does not equal 0, $x + 1$ is not a factor.

(continued)

OBJECTIVE	SUMMARY	EXAMPLE
Know the concept of the multiplicity of roots. (Section 9.3/Objective 1)	A polynomial equation of degree n has n solutions, where any solutions of multiplicity p is counted p times.	State the solution set for the polynomial equation $$f(x) = x^4 + 6x^3 + 8x^2 - 6x - 9$$ $$= (x + 1)(x - 1)(x + 3)(x + 3)$$ **Solution** The polynomial is fourth degree, so there are four solutions. The solutions are -1, 1, -3, and -3. So we would say the equation has solutions of -1 and 1 and a solution of -3 with a multiplicity of 2.
Use Descartes' rule of signs to determine the nature of the solutions of a polynomial equation. (Section 9.3/Objective 3)	Descartes' rule of signs: Let $$a_n x^n + a_{n-1} x^{n-1} + \cdots + a_1 x + a_0 = 0$$ be a polynomial with real coefficients. **(a)** The number of *positive real solutions* is either equal to the number of sign variations or is less then the number of sign variations by a positive even integer. **(b)** The number of *negative real solutions* either is equal to the number of sign variations in $$a_n(-x)^n + a_{n-1}(-x)^{n-1} + \cdots + a_1(-x) + a_0$$ or is less than the number of sign variations by a positive even integer.	Use Descartes' rule of signs to determine the possibilities for the nature of the solutions of $2x^4 + 3x^3 - 6x^2 + 1 = 0$. **Solution** The fact that there are two variations in sign implies that there are two or zero positive solutions. Replacing x with $-x$ produces $2x^4 - 3x^3 - 6x^2 + 1 = 0$, which has two variations in sign. Thus there are two or zero negative solutions. **Conclusion:** The given equation has either two positive and two negative solutions, two positive and two nonreal complex solutions, or two negative and two nonreal complex solutions.
Solve polynomial equations. (Section 9.3/Objective 2)	The following concepts and properties provide a basis for solving polynomial equations. **1.** Synthetic division. **2.** The factor theorem. **3.** Using the degree of the polynomial to determine the number of roots. **4.** The rational root theorem: Consider the polynomial equation $$a_n x^n + a_{n-1} x^{n-1} + \cdots + a_1 x + a_0 = 0$$ where the coefficients are *integers*. If the rational number $\dfrac{c}{d}$, reduced to lowest terms, is a solution of the equation, then c is a factor of the constant term a_0, and d is a factor of the leading coefficient a_n. **5.** Nonreal complex solutions of polynomial equations with real coefficients, if they exist, must occur in conjugate pairs. **6.** Descartes' rule of signs.	Solve $x^3 + 3x^2 - 2x - 8 = 0$. **Solution** The degree of the polynomial is 3, hence there are 3 roots. By the rational root theorem the potential rational number solutions are ± 1, ± 2, ± 4, or ± 8. Using synthetic division it can be determined that -2 is a root. $$\begin{array}{r|rrrr} -2 & 1 & 3 & -2 & -8 \\ & & -2 & -2 & 8 \\ \hline & 1 & 1 & -4 & 0 \end{array}$$ Thus the equation factors to $(x + 2)(x^2 + x - 4) = 0$. Now apply the quadratic formula to solve $x^2 + x - 4 = 0$ which yields the solutions $\dfrac{-1 + \sqrt{17}}{2}$ and $\dfrac{-1 - \sqrt{17}}{2}$. Thus the solution set is $$\left\{ -2, \frac{-1 + \sqrt{17}}{2}, \frac{-1 - \sqrt{17}}{2} \right\}$$

OBJECTIVE	SUMMARY	EXAMPLE
Know the patterns for the graphs of $f(x) = ax^n$. (Section 9.4/Objective 1)	The graph of $f(x) = ax^1$ is a straight line through the origin with a slope of a. The graph of $f(x) = ax^2$ is a parabola symmetric with respect to the y axis. The graph of $f(x) = ax^3$ for $a = 1$ is shown on page 474. The graph of $f(x) = ax^4$ is not a parabola but resembles the basic parabola, except that it is flatter at the bottom and steeper on the sides. There are two general patterns (1) for odd values of n greater than 1 and (2) for even values of n.	Graph $f(x) = -\dfrac{1}{2}x^3$. **Solution** The graph has the basic pattern of $f(x) = ax^3$. Because $a = -\dfrac{1}{2}$, the basic graph is reflected across the x axis and is not as steep.
Graph polynomial functions. (Section 9.4/Objective 2)	The following steps may be used to graph a polynomial function that is expressed in factored form: **1.** Find the x intercepts, which are also called the zeros of the polynomial function. **2.** Use a test value in each interval determined by the x intercepts to find out if the function is positive or negative over that interval. **3.** Plot any additional points that are needed to determine the graph.	Graph $f(x) = x^4 + x^3 - x^2 - x$. **Solution** The factored form is $f(x) = x(x + 1)^2(x - 1)$. The zeros are -1, 0, and 1. For the intervals $(-\infty, -1)$, $(-1, 0)$, and $(1, \infty)$, the function is positive. For the interval $(0, 1)$ the function is negative.
Find the vertical asymptote(s) for a rational function. (Section 9.5/Objective 1)	To find any vertical asymptote, set the denominator equal to zero and solve for x. See page 485 for the definition of a vertical asymptote.	Find the vertical asymptote(s) for the graph of $f(x) = \dfrac{3x^2}{x^2 - x - 6}$. **Solution** Set the denominator equal to zero and solve. $x^2 - x - 6 = 0$ $(x - 3)(x + 2) = 0$ $x = 3 \quad$ or $\quad x = -2$ The lines $x = 3$ and $x = -2$ are vertical asymptotes.

(continued)

OBJECTIVE	SUMMARY	EXAMPLE
Find the horizontal asymptote for a rational function. (Section 9.5/Objective 2)	Find any horizontal asymptotes by studying the behavior of $f(x)$ as x gets very large or very small. This may require changing the form of the original rational expression.	Find the horizontal asymptote for the graph of $f(x) = \dfrac{3x^2}{x^2 - x - 6}$. **Solution** Change the form of the expression by dividing every term by x^2. $$f(x) = \frac{\dfrac{3x^2}{x^2}}{\dfrac{x^2}{x^2} - \dfrac{x}{x^2} - \dfrac{6}{x^2}} = \frac{3}{1 - \dfrac{1}{x} - \dfrac{6}{x^2}}$$ As x gets larger and larger, the value of $f(x)$ approaches 3 from above. Therefore the line $y = 3$ is a horizontal asymptote.
Find the equation for an oblique asymptote of a rational function. (Section 9.6/Objective 1)	An oblique asymptote occurs when graphing rational functions in which the degree of the numerator is one more than the degree of the denominator. To find the equation of the oblique asymptote, change the form of the rational expression by dividing the denominator into the numerator.	Write the equation for the oblique asymptote for the graph of $f(x) = \dfrac{2x^2 - 5x + 8}{x - 3}$. **Solution** Use synthetic division to divide $(2x^2 - 5x + 8)$ by $(x - 3)$ to change the form of the original function. $$f(x) = \frac{2x^2 - 5x + 8}{x - 3} = 2x + 1 + \frac{11}{x - 3}$$ As the $|x|$ gets larger and larger, the graph approaches the line $y = 2x + 1$. Hence the line $y = 2x + 1$ is an oblique asymptote.
Graph rational functions with vertical, horizontal, or oblique asymptotes. (Section 9.6/Objective 2)	To graph a rational function, the following steps are useful: 1. Check for symmetry with respect to the vertical axis and with respect to the origin. 2. Find any vertical asymptotes by setting the denominator equal to zero. 3. Find any horizontal asymptotes by studying the behavior of $f(x)$ as x gets very large or very small. 4. If the degree of the numerator is one greater than the degree of the denominator, determine the equation of the oblique asymptote. 5. Study the behavior of the graph when it is close to the asymptotic lines. 6. Plot as many points as necessary to determine the graph.	Graph $f(x) = \dfrac{x^2 + 2}{x + 1}$. **Solution** The graph is not symmetric with respect to the y axis or the origin. The vertical asymptote is $x = -1$. The graph has an oblique asymptote with the equation of $y = x - 1$. Determining some points leads us to the following graph.

Chapter 9   **Review Problem Set**

For Problems 1–4, use synthetic division to determine the quotient and the remainder.

1. $(3x^3 - 4x^2 + 6x - 2) \div (x - 1)$

2. $(5x^3 + 7x^2 - 9x + 10) \div (x + 2)$

3. $(-2x^4 + x^3 - 2x^2 - x - 1) \div (x + 4)$

4. $(-3x^4 - 5x^2 + 9) \div (x - 3)$

For Problems 5–8, find $f(c)$ either by using synthetic division and the remainder theorem or by evaluating $f(c)$ directly.

5. $f(x) = 4x^5 - 3x^3 + x^2 - 1$ and $c = 1$

6. $f(x) = 4x^3 - 7x^2 + 6x - 8$ and $c = -3$

7. $f(x) = -x^4 + 9x^2 - x - 2$ and $c = -2$

8. $f(x) = x^4 - 9x^3 + 9x^2 - 10x + 16$ and $c = 8$

For Problems 9–12, use the factor theorem to help answer some questions about factors.

9. Is $x + 2$ a factor of $2x^3 + x^2 - 7x - 2$?

10. Is $x - 3$ a factor of $x^4 + 5x^3 - 7x^2 - x + 3$?

11. Is $x - 4$ a factor of $x^5 - 1024$?

12. Is $x + 1$ a factor of $x^5 + 1$?

For Problems 13–16, use the rational root theorem and the factor theorem to help solve each of the equations.

13. $x^3 - 3x^2 - 13x + 15 = 0$

14. $8x^3 + 26x^2 - 17x - 35 = 0$

15. $x^4 - 5x^3 + 34x^2 - 82x + 52 = 0$

16. $x^3 - 4x^2 - 10x + 4 = 0$

For Problems 17 and 18, use Descartes' rule of signs (Property 9.6) to help list the possibilities for the nature of the solutions. *Do not solve the equations.*

17. $4x^4 - 3x^3 + 2x^2 + x + 4 = 0$

18. $x^5 + 3x^3 + x + 7 = 0$

For Problems 19–22, graph each of the polynomial functions.

19. $f(x) = -(x - 2)^3 + 3$

20. $f(x) = (x + 3)(x - 1)(3 - x)$

21. $f(x) = x^4 - 4x^2$

22. $f(x) = x^3 - 4x^2 + x + 6$

For Problems 23–26, graph each of the rational functions. Be sure to identify the asymptotes.

23. $f(x) = \dfrac{2x}{x - 3}$

24. $f(x) = \dfrac{-3}{x^2 + 1}$

25. $f(x) = \dfrac{-x^2}{x^2 - x - 6}$

26. $f(x) = \dfrac{x^2 + 3}{x + 1}$

1. Divide $3x^3 + 5x^2 - 14x - 6$ by $x + 3$, and find the quotient and remainder.

2. Find the quotient and remainder when $4x^4 - 7x^2 - x + 4$ is divided by $x - 2$.

3. If $f(x) = x^5 - 8x^4 + 9x^3 - 13x^2 - 9x - 10$, find $f(7)$.

4. If $f(x) = 3x^4 + 20x^3 - 6x^2 + 9x + 19$, find $f(-7)$.

5. If $f(x) = x^5 - 35x^3 - 32x + 15$, find $f(6)$.

6. Is $x - 5$ a factor of $3x^3 - 11x^2 - 22x - 20$?

7. Is $x + 2$ a factor of $5x^3 + 9x^2 - 9x - 17$?

8. Is $x + 3$ a factor of $x^4 - 16x^2 - 17x + 12$?

9. Is $x - 6$ a factor of $x^4 - 2x^2 + 3x - 12$?

For Problems 10–14, solve each equation.

10. $x^3 - 13x + 12 = 0$

11. $2x^3 + 5x^2 - 13x - 4 = 0$

12. $x^4 - 4x^3 - 5x^2 + 38x - 30 = 0$

13. $2x^3 + 3x^2 - 17x + 12 = 0$

14. $3x^3 - 7x^2 - 8x + 20 = 0$

15. Use Descartes' rule of signs to determine the nature of the roots of $5x^4 + 3x^3 - x^2 - 9 = 0$.

16. Find the x intercepts of the graph of the function $f(x) = 3x^3 + 19x^2 - 14x$.

17. Find the equation of the vertical asymptote for the graph of the function $f(x) = \dfrac{5x}{x + 3}$.

18. Find the equation of the horizontal asymptote for the graph of the function $f(x) = \dfrac{5x^2}{x^2 - 4}$.

19. What type of symmetry does the graph of the equation $f(x) = \dfrac{x^2}{x^2 + 2}$ exhibit?

20. What type of symmetry does the graph of the equation $f(x) = \dfrac{-3x}{x^2 + 1}$ exhibit?

For Problems 21–25, graph each of the functions.

21. $f(x) = (2 - x)(x - 1)(x + 1)$

22. $f(x) = -x(x - 3)(x + 2)$

23. $f(x) = \dfrac{-x}{x - 3}$

24. $f(x) = \dfrac{-2}{x^2 - 4}$

25. $f(x) = \dfrac{4x^2 + x + 1}{x + 1}$

10 Exponential and Logarithmic Functions

10.1 Exponents and Exponential Functions

10.2 Applications of Exponential Functions

10.3 Inverse Functions

10.4 Logarithms

10.5 Logarithmic Functions

10.6 Exponential Equations, Logarithmic Equations, and Problem Solving

Because Richter numbers for reporting the intensity of an earthquake are calculated from logarithms, they are referred to as being on a logarithmic scale. Logarithmic scales are commonly used in science and mathematics to transform very large numbers to a smaller scale.

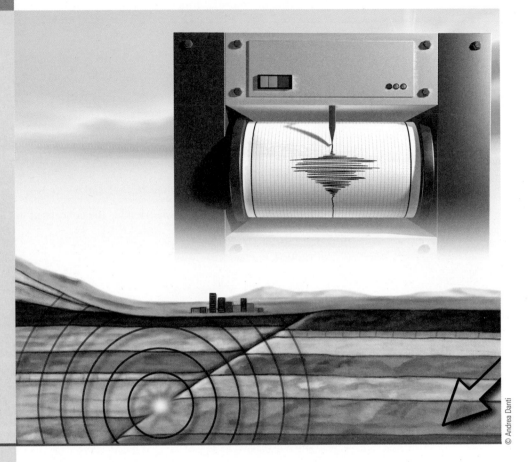

© Andrea Danti

How long will it take \$100 to triple if it is invested at 8% interest compounded continuously? We can use the formula $A = Pe^{rt}$ to generate the equation $300 = 100e^{0.08t}$, which can be solved for t using logarithms. It will take approximately 13.7 years for the money to triple.

In this chapter, we will (1) extend our understanding of exponents, (2) work with some exponential functions, (3) consider the concept of a logarithm, (4) work with some logarithmic functions, and (5) use the concepts of exponents and logarithms to expand our problem-solving skills. Your calculator will be a valuable tool throughout this chapter.

Video tutorials based on section learning objectives are available in a variety of delivery modes.

O B J E C T I V E S   1   Solve exponential equations

2   Graph exponential functions

In Chapter 1 the expression "b^n" was defined to mean n factors of b, when n is any positive integer and b is any real number. For example,

$$2^3 = 2 \cdot 2 \cdot 2 = 8 \qquad\qquad \left(\frac{1}{3}\right)^4 = \left(\frac{1}{3}\right)\left(\frac{1}{3}\right)\left(\frac{1}{3}\right)\left(\frac{1}{3}\right) = \frac{1}{81}$$

$$(-4)^2 = (-4)(-4) = 16 \qquad\qquad -(0.5)^3 = -[(0.5)(0.5)(0.5)] = -0.125$$

Then in Chapter 5, by defining "$b^0 = 1$ and $b^{-n} = \dfrac{1}{b^n}$," when n is any positive integer and b is any nonzero real number, we extended the concept of an exponent to include all integers. Examples include

$$(0.76)^0 = 1 \qquad\qquad 2^{-3} = \frac{1}{2^3} = \frac{1}{8}$$

$$\left(\frac{2}{3}\right)^{-2} = \frac{1}{\left(\frac{2}{3}\right)^2} = \frac{1}{\frac{4}{9}} = \frac{9}{4} \qquad\qquad (0.4)^{-1} = \frac{1}{(0.4)^1} = \frac{1}{0.4} = 2.5$$

In Chapter 5 we also provided for the use of all rational numbers as exponents by defining

$$b^{m/n} = \sqrt[n]{b^m} = \left(\sqrt[n]{b}\right)^m$$

where n is a positive integer greater than 1, and b is a real number such that $\sqrt[n]{b}$ exists. Some examples are

$$27^{2/3} = \left(\sqrt[3]{27}\right)^2 = 9 \qquad\qquad 16^{1/4} = \sqrt[4]{16^1} = 2$$

$$\left(\frac{1}{9}\right)^{1/2} = \sqrt{\frac{1}{9}} = \frac{1}{3} \qquad\qquad 32^{-1/5} = \frac{1}{32^{1/5}} = \frac{1}{\sqrt[5]{32}} = \frac{1}{2}$$

Formally extending the concept of an exponent to include the use of irrational numbers requires some ideas from calculus and is therefore beyond the scope of this text. However, we can take a brief glimpse at the general idea involved. Consider the number $2^{\sqrt{3}}$. By using the nonterminating and nonrepeating decimal representation 1.73205 . . . for $\sqrt{3}$, we can form the sequence of numbers 2^1, $2^{1.7}$, $2^{1.73}$, $2^{1.732}$, $2^{1.7320}$, $2^{1.73205}$, ... It seems reasonable that each successive power gets closer to $2^{\sqrt{3}}$. This is precisely what happens if b^n, when n is irrational, is properly defined using the concept of a limit. Furthermore, this will ensure that an expression such as 2^x will yield exactly one value for each value of x.

From now on, then, we can use any real number as an exponent, and we can extend the basic properties stated in Chapter 5 to include all real numbers as exponents. Let's restate those properties with the restriction that the bases a and b must be positive numbers so that we avoid expressions such as $(-4)^{1/2}$, which do not represent real numbers.

> ### Property 10.1
>
> If a and b are positive real numbers, and m and n are any real numbers, then
>
> **1.** $b^n \cdot b^m = b^{n+m}$ Product of two powers
>
> **2.** $(b^n)^m = b^{mn}$ Power of a power
>
> **3.** $(ab)^n = a^n b^n$ Power of a product
>
> **4.** $\left(\dfrac{a}{b}\right)^n = \dfrac{a^n}{b^n}$ Power of a quotient
>
> **5.** $\dfrac{b^n}{b^m} = b^{n-m}$ Quotient of two powers

Another property that we can use to solve certain types of equations that involve exponents can be stated as follows:

> ### Property 10.2
>
> If $b > 0$, $b \neq 1$, and m and n are real numbers, then $b^n = b^m$ if and only if $n = m$.

The following examples illustrate the use of Property 10.2. To use the property to solve equations, we will want both sides of the equation to have the same base number.

Classroom Example
Solve $5^x = 125$.

EXAMPLE 1   Solve $2^x = 32$.

Solution

$$2^x = 32$$
$$2^x = 2^5 \qquad\qquad 32 = 2^5$$
$$x = 5 \qquad\qquad \text{Property 10.2}$$

The solution set is $\{5\}$.

Classroom Example
Solve $5^{2x} = \dfrac{1}{25}$.

EXAMPLE 2   Solve $3^{2x} = \dfrac{1}{9}$.

Solution

$$3^{2x} = \frac{1}{9} = \frac{1}{3^2}$$

$$3^{2x} = 3^{-2}$$

$$2x = -2 \qquad\qquad \text{Property 10.2}$$
$$x = -1$$

The solution set is $\{-1\}$.

Classroom Example
Solve $\left(\dfrac{1}{2}\right)^{x+1} = \dfrac{1}{32}$.

EXAMPLE 3 Solve $\left(\dfrac{1}{5}\right)^{x-4} = \dfrac{1}{125}$.

Solution

$$\left(\frac{1}{5}\right)^{x-4} = \frac{1}{125}$$

$$\left(\frac{1}{5}\right)^{x-4} = \left(\frac{1}{5}\right)^{3}$$

$$x - 4 = 3 \qquad \text{Property 10.2}$$

$$x = 7$$

The solution set is $\{7\}$.

Classroom Example
Solve $16^{x} = 64$.

EXAMPLE 4 Solve $8^{x} = 32$.

Solution

$$8^{x} = 32$$

$$(2^{3})^{x} = 2^{5} \qquad 8 = 2^{3}$$

$$2^{3x} = 2^{5}$$

$$3x = 5 \qquad \text{Property 10.2}$$

$$x = \frac{5}{3}$$

The solution set is $\left\{\dfrac{5}{3}\right\}$.

Classroom Example
Solve $(5^{x+1})(25^{x-3}) = 5$.

EXAMPLE 5 Solve $(3^{x+1})(9^{x-2}) = 27$.

Solution

$$(3^{x+1})(9^{x-2}) = 27$$

$$(3^{x+1})(3^{2})^{x-2} = 3^{3}$$

$$(3^{x+1})(3^{2x-4}) = 3^{3}$$

$$3^{3x-3} = 3^{3}$$

$$3x - 3 = 3 \qquad \text{Property 10.2}$$

$$3x = 6$$

$$x = 2$$

The solution set is $\{2\}$.

Exponential Functions

If b is any positive number, then the expression b^{x} designates exactly one real number for every real value of x. Therefore the equation $f(x) = b^{x}$ defines a function in which the domain is the set of real numbers. Furthermore, if we include the additional restriction $b \neq 1$, then any equation of the form $f(x) = b^{x}$ describes what we will call later a one-to-one function and is known as an **exponential function**. This leads to the following definition:

> **Definition 10.1**
>
> If $b > 0$ and $b \neq 1$, then the function f defined by
>
> $$f(x) = b^x$$
>
> when x is any real number, is called the **exponential function with base b**.

Now let's consider graphing some exponential functions.

Classroom Example
Graph the function $f(x) = 5^x$.

EXAMPLE 6   Graph the function $f(x) = 2^x$.

Solution

Let's set up a table of values; keep in mind that the domain is the set of real numbers and that the equation $f(x) = 2^x$ exhibits no symmetry. Plot these points and connect them with a smooth curve to produce Figure 10.1.

x	2^x
-2	$\dfrac{1}{4}$
-1	$\dfrac{1}{2}$
0	1
1	2
2	4
3	8

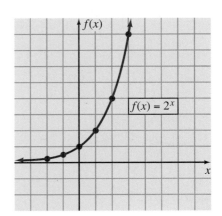

Figure 10.1

In the table for Example 6, we chose integral values for x to keep the computation simple. However, with the use of a calculator, we could easily acquire functional values by using nonintegral exponents. Consider the following additional values for $f(x) = 2^x$:

$$f(0.5) \approx 1.41 \qquad f(1.7) \approx 3.25$$

$$f(-0.5) \approx 0.71 \qquad f(-2.6) \approx 0.16$$

Use your calculator to check these results. Also note that the points generated by these values do fit the graph in Figure 10.1.

EXAMPLE 7   Graph $f(x) = \left(\dfrac{1}{2}\right)^x$.

Solution

Again, let's set up a table of values, plot the points, and connect them with a smooth curve. The graph is shown in Figure 10.2.

Classroom Example

Graph the function $f(x) = \left(\dfrac{1}{5}\right)^x$.

x	$\left(\dfrac{1}{2}\right)^x$
-3	8
-2	4
-1	2
0	1
1	$\dfrac{1}{2}$
2	$\dfrac{1}{4}$
3	$\dfrac{1}{8}$

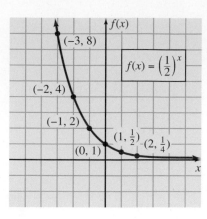

Figure 10.2

Remark: Because $\left(\dfrac{1}{2}\right)^x = \dfrac{1}{2^x} = 2^{-x}$, the graphs of $f(x) = 2^x$ and $f(x) = \left(\dfrac{1}{2}\right)^x$ are reflections of each other across the y axis. Therefore Figure 10.2 could have been drawn by reflecting Figure 10.1 across the y axis.

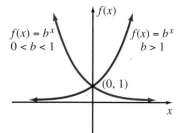

Figure 10.3

The graphs in Figures 10.1 and 10.2 illustrate a general behavior pattern of exponential functions. That is to say, if $b > 1$, then the graph of $f(x) = b^x$ *goes up to the right*, and the function is called an **increasing function**. If $0 < b < 1$, then the graph of $f(x) = b^x$ *goes down to the right*, and the function is called a **decreasing function**. These facts are illustrated in Figure 10.3. Note that $b^0 = 1$ for any $b > 0$; thus all graphs of $f(x) = b^x$ contain the point $(0, 1)$.

As you graph exponential functions, don't forget your previous graphing experiences.

1. The graph of $f(x) = 2^x - 4$ is the graph of $f(x) = 2^x$ *moved down four units*.
2. The graph of $f(x) = 2^{x+3}$ is the graph of $f(x) = 2^x$ *moved three units to the left*.
3. The graph of $f(x) = -2^x$ is the graph of $f(x) = 2^x$ *reflected across the x axis*.

We used a graphing calculator to graph these four functions on the same set of axes, as shown in Figure 10.4.

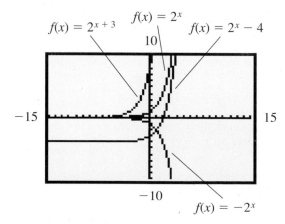

Figure 10.4

If you are faced with an exponential function that is not of the basic form $f(x) = b^x$ or a variation thereof, don't forget the graphing suggestions offered in earlier chapters. Let's consider one such example.

Classroom Example
Graph the function $f(x) = \left(\dfrac{1}{2}\right)^{x^2+1}$.

EXAMPLE 8   Graph $f(x) = 2^{-x^2}$.

Solution

Because $f(-x) = 2^{-(-x)^2} = 2^{-x^2} = f(x)$, we know that this curve is symmetric with respect to the y axis. Therefore let's set up a table of values using nonnegative values for x. Plot these points, connect them with a smooth curve, and reflect this portion of the curve across the y axis to produce the graph in Figure 10.5.

x	2^{x^2}
0	1
$\dfrac{1}{2}$	0.84
1	0.5
$\dfrac{3}{2}$	0.21
2	0.06

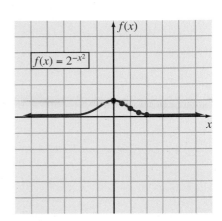

Figure 10.5

Finally, let's consider a problem in which a graphing utility gives us an approximate solution.

Classroom Example
Use a graphing utility to obtain a graph of $f(x) = 200\left(\dfrac{1}{2}\right)^x$ and find an approximate value for x when $f(x) = 54$.

EXAMPLE 9

Use a graphing utility to obtain a graph of $f(x) = 50(2^x)$ and find an approximate value for x when $f(x) = 15{,}000$.

Solution

First, we must find an appropriate viewing rectangle. Because $50(2^{10}) = 51{,}200$, let's set the boundaries so that $0 \le x \le 10$ and $0 \le y \le 50{,}000$ with a scale of $10{,}000$ on the y axis. (Certainly other boundaries could be used, but these will give us a graph that we can work with for this problem.) The graph of $f(x) = 50(2^x)$ is shown in Figure 10.6. Now we can use the TRACE and ZOOM features of the graphing utility to find that $x \approx 8.2$ at $y = 15{,}000$.

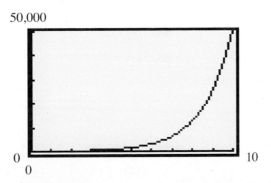

Figure 10.6

Remark: In Example 9 we used a graphical approach to solve the equation $50(2^x) = 15,000$. In Section 10.6 we will use an algebraic approach for solving that same kind of equation.

Concept Quiz 10.1

For Problems 1–10, answer true or false.

1. $2^2 \cdot 2^3 = 4^5$
2. $2^2 \cdot 2^3 = 2^6$
3. $2^{-3} = -8$
4. $-2^{-3} = 8$
5. $5^{\frac{3}{4}} = \sqrt[4]{5^3}$
6. The function $f(x) = 1^x$ is an exponential function.
7. The base, b, of an exponential function, $f(x) = b^x$, can be any number.
8. The exponential function $f(x) = b^x$ where $b > 1$ and $b \neq 1$ is an increasing function.
9. All exponential functions are increasing functions.
10. All graphs of $f(x) = b^x$ when $b > 0$ and $b \neq 1$ contain the point $(0, 1)$.

Problem Set 10.1

For Problems 1–26, solve each of the equations. **(Objective 1)**

1. $2^x = 64$
2. $3^x = 81$
3. $3^{2x} = 27$
4. $2^{2x} = 16$
5. $\left(\dfrac{1}{2}\right)^x = \dfrac{1}{128}$
6. $\left(\dfrac{1}{4}\right)^x = \dfrac{1}{256}$
7. $3^{-x} = \dfrac{1}{243}$
8. $3^{x+1} = 9$
9. $6^{3x-1} = 36$
10. $2^{2x+3} = 32$
11. $\left(\dfrac{3}{4}\right)^n = \dfrac{64}{27}$
12. $\left(\dfrac{2}{3}\right)^n = \dfrac{9}{4}$
13. $16^x = 64$
14. $4^x = 8$
15. $27^{4x} = 9^{x+1}$
16. $32^x = 16^{1-x}$
17. $9^{4x-2} = \dfrac{1}{81}$
18. $8^{3x+2} = \dfrac{1}{16}$
19. $10^x = 0.1$
20. $10^x = 0.0001$
21. $(2^{x+1})(2^x) = 64$
22. $(2^{2x-1})(2^{x+2}) = 32$
23. $(27)(3^x) = 9^x$
24. $(3^x)(3^{5x}) = 81$
25. $(4^x)(16^{3x-1}) = 8$
26. $(8^{2x})(4^{2x-1}) = 16$

For Problems 27–46, graph each of the exponential functions. **(Objective 2)**

27. $f(x) = 3^x$
28. $f(x) = 4^x$
29. $f(x) = \left(\dfrac{1}{3}\right)^x$
30. $f(x) = \left(\dfrac{1}{4}\right)^x$
31. $f(x) = \left(\dfrac{3}{2}\right)^x$
32. $f(x) = \left(\dfrac{2}{3}\right)^x$
33. $f(x) = 2^x - 3$
34. $f(x) = 2^x + 1$
35. $f(x) = 2^{x+2}$
36. $f(x) = 2^{x-1}$
37. $f(x) = -2^x$
38. $f(x) = -3^x$
39. $f(x) = 2^{-x-2}$
40. $f(x) = 2^{-x+1}$
41. $f(x) = 2^{x^2}$
42. $f(x) = 2^x + 2^{-x}$
43. $f(x) = 2^{|x|}$
44. $f(x) = 3^{1-x^2}$
45. $f(x) = 2^x - 2^{-x}$
46. $f(x) = 2^{-|x|}$

Thoughts Into Words

47. Explain how you would solve the equation $(2^{x+1})(8^{2x-3}) = 64$.

48. Why is the base of an exponential function restricted to positive numbers not including 1?

49. Explain how you would graph the function $f(x) = -\left(\dfrac{1}{3}\right)^x$.

Graphing Calculator Activities

50. Use a graphing calculator to check your graphs for Problems 27–46.

51. Graph $f(x) = 2^x$. Where should the graphs of $f(x) = 2^{x-5}$, $f(x) = 2^{x-7}$, and $f(x) = 2^{x+5}$ be located? Graph all three functions on the same set of axes with $f(x) = 2^x$.

52. Graph $f(x) = 3^x$. Where should the graphs of $f(x) = 3^x + 2$, $f(x) = 3^x - 3$, and $f(x) = 3^x - 7$ be located? Graph all three functions on the same set of axes with $f(x) = 3^x$.

53. Graph $f(x) = \left(\dfrac{1}{2}\right)^x$. Where should the graphs of $f(x) = -\left(\dfrac{1}{2}\right)^x$, $f(x) = \left(\dfrac{1}{2}\right)^{-x}$, and $f(x) = -\left(\dfrac{1}{2}\right)^{-x}$ be located? Graph all three functions on the same set of axes with $f(x) = \left(\dfrac{1}{2}\right)^x$.

54. Graph $f(x) = (1.5)^x$, $f(x) = (5.5)^x$, $f(x) = (0.3)^x$, and $f(x) = (0.7)^x$ on the same set of axes. Are these graphs consistent with Figure 10.3?

55. What is the solution for $3^x = 5$? Do you agree that it is between 1 and 2 because $3^1 = 3$ and $3^2 = 9$? Now graph $f(x) = 3^x - 5$ and use the ZOOM and TRACE features of your graphing calculator to find an approximation, to the nearest hundredth, for the x intercept. You should get an answer of 1.46. Do you see that this is an approximation for the solution of $3^x = 5$? Try it; raise 3 to the 1.46 power.

Find an approximate solution, to the nearest hundredth, for each of the following equations by graphing the appropriate function and finding the x intercept.

(a) $2^x = 19$ **(b)** $3^x = 50$ **(c)** $4^x = 47$

(d) $5^x = 120$ **(e)** $2^x = 1500$ **(f)** $3^{x-1} = 34$

Answers to the Concept Quiz

1. False   **2.** False   **3.** False   **4.** False   **5.** True   **6.** False   **7.** False   **8.** True   **9.** False   **10.** True

---

10.2   Applications of Exponential Functions

OBJECTIVES

1 Solve exponential growth and decay problems

2 Solve compound interest problems

3 Solve half-life problems

4 Solve growth problems involving the number e

5 Graph exponential functions involving a base of e

We can represent many real-world situations that involve growth or decay with equations that describe exponential functions. For example, suppose an economist predicts an annual inflation rate of 5% per year for the next 10 years. This means that an item that presently costs $8 will cost $8(105\%) = 8(1.05) = \$8.40$ a year from now. The same item will cost $[8(105\%)](105\%) = 8(1.05)^2 = \$8.82$ in 2 years. In general, the equation

$$P = P_0(1.05)^t$$

yields the predicted price P of an item in t years if the present cost is P_0 and the annual inflation rate is 5%. Using this equation, we can look at some future prices based on the prediction of a 5% inflation rate.

A $1.29 jar of mustard will cost $\$1.29(1.05)^3 = \$1.49$ in 3 years.

A $3.29 bag of potato chips will cost $\$3.29(1.05)^5 = \$4.20$ in 5 years.

A $7.69 can of coffee will cost $\$7.69(1.05)^7 = \$10.82$ in 7 years.

Compound Interest

Compound interest provides another illustration of exponential growth. Suppose that $500, called the **principal**, is invested at an interest rate of 4% compounded annually. The interest earned the first year is $500(0.04) = $20, and this amount is added to the original $500 to form a new principal of $520 for the second year. The interest earned during the second year is $520(0.04) = $20.80, and this amount is added to $520 to form a new principal of $540.80 for the third year. Each year a new principal is formed by reinvesting the interest earned during that year.

In general, suppose that a sum of money P (the principal) is invested at an interest rate of r percent compounded annually. The interest earned the first year is Pr, and the new principal for the second year is $P + Pr$, or $P(1 + r)$. Note that the new principal for the second year can be found by multiplying the original principal P by $(1 + r)$. In like fashion, the new principal for the third year can be found by multiplying the previous principal $P(1 + r)$ by $1 + r$, thus obtaining $P(1 + r)^2$. If this process is continued, after t years the total amount of money accumulated, (A), is given by

$$A = P(1 + r)^t$$

Consider the following examples of investments made at a certain rate of interest compounded annually:

1. $750 invested for 5 years at 4% compounded annually produces
   $$A = \$750(1.04)^5 = \$912.49$$

2. $1000 invested for 10 years at 7% compounded annually produces
   $$A = \$1000(1.07)^{10} = \$1967.15$$

3. $5000 invested for 20 years at 6% compounded annually produces
   $$A = \$5000(1.06)^{20} = \$16{,}035.68$$

We can use the compound interest formula to determine what rate of interest is needed to accumulate a certain amount of money based on a given initial investment. The next example illustrates this idea.

Classroom Example
What rate of interest is needed for an investment of $2500 to yield $7500 in 20 years if the interest is compounded annually?

EXAMPLE 1

What rate of interest is needed for an investment of $1000 to yield $4000 in 10 years if the interest is compounded annually?

Solution

Let's substitute $1000 for P, $4000 for A, and 10 years for t in the compound interest formula and solve for r.

$$A = P(1 + r)^t$$
$$4000 = 1000(1 + r)^{10}$$
$$4 = (1 + r)^{10}$$
$$4^{0.1} = [(1 + r)^{10}]^{0.1} \qquad \text{Raise both sides to the 0.1 power}$$
$$1.148698355 \approx 1 + r$$
$$0.148698355 \approx r$$
$$r = 14.9\% \quad \text{to the nearest tenth of a percent}$$

Therefore a rate of interest of approximately 14.9% is needed. (Perhaps you should check this answer.)

If money invested at a certain rate of interest is compounded more than once a year, then the basic formula $A = P(1 + r)^t$ can be adjusted according to the number of compounding periods in a year. For example, for *semiannual compounding*, the formula becomes $A = P\left(1 + \dfrac{r}{2}\right)^{2t}$; for *quarterly compounding*, the formula becomes $A = P\left(1 + \dfrac{r}{4}\right)^{4t}$. In general, if n represents the number of compounding periods in a year, the formula becomes

$$A = P\left(1 + \frac{r}{n}\right)^{nt}$$

The following examples illustrate the use of the formula:

1. $750 invested for 5 years at 4% compounded semiannually produces

$$A = \$750\left(1 + \frac{0.04}{2}\right)^{2(5)} = \$750(1.02)^{10} = \$914.25$$

2. $1000 invested for 10 years at 7% compounded quarterly produces

$$A = \$1000\left(1 + \frac{0.07}{4}\right)^{4(10)} = \$1000(1.0175)^{40} = \$2001.60$$

3. $5000 invested for 20 years at 6% compounded monthly produces

$$A = \$5000\left(1 + \frac{0.06}{12}\right)^{12(20)} = \$5000(1.005)^{240} = \$16,551.02$$

You may find it interesting to compare these results with those we obtained earlier for annual compounding.

Exponential Decay

Suppose that the value of a car depreciates 15% per year for the first 5 years. Therefore a car that costs $9500 will be worth $9500(100% − 15%) = $9500(85%) = $9500(0.85) = $8075 in 1 year. In 2 years the value of the car will have depreciated $9500(0.85)^2 = $6864 (to the nearest dollar). The equation

$$V = V_0(0.85)^t$$

yields the value V of a car in t years if the initial cost is V_0, and the value depreciates 15% per year. Therefore we can estimate some car values to the nearest dollar as follows:

A $13,000 car will be worth $13,000(0.85)^3 = $7984 in 3 years.
A $17,000 car will be worth $17,000(0.85)^5 = $7543 in 5 years.
A $25,000 car will be worth $25,000(0.85)^4 = $13,050 in 4 years.

Another example of exponential decay is associated with radioactive substances. The rate of decay can be described exponentially and is based on the half-life of a substance. The **half-life** of a radioactive substance is the amount of time that it takes for one-half of an initial amount of the substance to disappear as the result of decay. For example, suppose that we have 200 grams of a certain substance that has a half-life of 5 days. After 5 days, $200\left(\dfrac{1}{2}\right) = 100$ grams remain. After 10 days, $200\left(\dfrac{1}{2}\right)^2 = 50$ grams remain. After 15 days, $200\left(\dfrac{1}{2}\right)^3 = 25$ grams remain. In general, after t days, $200\left(\dfrac{1}{2}\right)^{\frac{t}{5}}$ grams remain.

The previous discussion leads to the following half-life formula. Suppose there is an initial amount (Q_0) of a radioactive substance with a half-life of h. The amount of substance remaining (Q) after a time period of t is given by the formula

$$Q = Q_0\left(\frac{1}{2}\right)^{\frac{t}{h}}$$

The units of measure for t and h must be the same.

Classroom Example
A radioactive substance has a half-life of 4 years. If there are 600 milligrams of the substance initially, how many milligrams remain after 1 year? After 20 years?

EXAMPLE 2

Barium-140 has a half-life of 13 days. If there are 500 milligrams of barium initially, how many milligrams remain after 26 days? After 100 days?

Solution

When we use $Q_0 = 500$ and $h = 13$, the half-life formula becomes

$$Q = 500\left(\frac{1}{2}\right)^{\frac{t}{13}}$$

If $t = 26$, then

$$Q = 500\left(\frac{1}{2}\right)^{\frac{26}{13}}$$

$$= 500\left(\frac{1}{2}\right)^{2}$$

$$= 500\left(\frac{1}{4}\right)$$

$$= 125$$

Thus 125 milligrams remain after 26 days. If $t = 100$, then

$$Q = 500\left(\frac{1}{2}\right)^{\frac{100}{13}}$$

$$= 500(0.5)^{\frac{100}{13}}$$

$$= 2.4 \quad \text{to the nearest tenth of a milligram}$$

Approximately 2.4 milligrams remain after 100 days.

Remark: Example 2 clearly illustrates that a calculator is useful at times but unnecessary at other times. We solved the first part of the problem very easily without a calculator, but it certainly was helpful for the second part of the problem.

Number e

An interesting situation occurs if we consider the compound interest formula for $P = \$1$, $r = 100\%$, and $t = 1$ year. The formula becomes $A = 1\left(1 + \frac{1}{n}\right)^{n}$. The following table shows some values, rounded to eight decimal places, of $\left(1 + \frac{1}{n}\right)^{n}$ for different values of n.

n	$\left(1 + \dfrac{1}{n}\right)^n$
1	2.00000000
10	2.59374246
100	2.70481383
1000	2.71692393
10,000	2.71814593
100,000	2.71826824
1,000,000	2.71828047
10,000,000	2.71828169
100,000,000	2.71828181
1,000,000,000	2.71828183

The table suggests that as n increases, the value of $\left(1 + \dfrac{1}{n}\right)^n$ gets closer and closer to some fixed number. This does happen, and the fixed number is called e. To five decimal places, $e = 2.71828$.

The function defined by the equation $f(x) = e^x$ is the **natural exponential function**. It has a great many real-world applications, some of which we will look at in a moment. First, however, let's get a picture of the natural exponential function. Because $2 < e < 3$, the graph of $f(x) = e^x$ must fall between the graphs of $f(x) = 2^x$ and $f(x) = 3^x$. To be more specific, let's use our calculator to determine a table of values. Use the $\boxed{e^x}$ key, and round the results to the nearest tenth to obtain the following table. Plot the points determined by this table, and connect them with a smooth curve to produce Figure 10.7.

x	$f(x) = e^x$
0	1.0
1	2.7
2	7.4
-1	0.4
-2	0.1

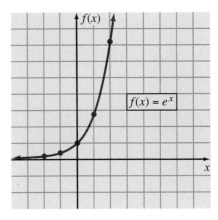

Figure 10.7

Back to Compound Interest

Let's return to the concept of compound interest. If the number of compounding periods in a year is increased indefinitely, we arrive at the concept of **compounding continuously**. Mathematically, we can accomplish this by applying the limit concept to the expression $P\left(1 + \dfrac{r}{n}\right)^{nt}$. We will not show the details here, but the following result is obtained. The formula

$$A = Pe^{rt}$$

yields the accumulated value (A) of a sum of money (P) that has been invested for t years at a rate of r percent compounded continuously. The following examples illustrate the use of the formula.

1. $750 invested for 5 years at 4% compounded continuously produces

$$A = \$750e^{(0.04)(5)} = 750e^{0.20} = \$916.05$$

2. $1000 invested for 10 years at 7% compounded continuously produces

$$A = \$1000e^{(0.07)(10)} = 1000e^{0.7} = \$2013.75$$

3. $5000 invested for 20 years at 6% compounded continuously produces

$$A = \$5000e^{(0.06)(20)} = 5000e^{1.2} = \$16,600.58$$

Again, you may find it interesting to compare these results with those you obtained earlier when you were using a different number of compounding periods.

Is it better to invest at 6% compounded quarterly or at 5.75% compounded continuously? To answer such a question, we can use the concept of *effective yield* (sometimes called effective annual rate of interest). The **effective yield** of an investment is the simple interest rate that would yield the same amount in 1 year. Thus for the investment at 6% compounded quarterly, we can calculate the effective yield as follows:

$$P(1 + r) = P\left(1 + \frac{0.06}{4}\right)^4$$

$$1 + r = \left(1 + \frac{0.06}{4}\right)^4 \qquad \text{Multiply both sides by } \frac{1}{P}$$

$$1 + r = (1.015)^4$$

$$r = (1.015)^4 - 1$$

$$r \approx 0.0613635506$$

$$r = 6.14\% \quad \text{to the nearest hundredth of a percent}$$

Likewise, for the investment at 5.75% compounded continuously, we can calculate the effective yield as follows:

$$P(1 + r) = Pe^{0.0575}$$

$$1 + r = e^{0.0575}$$

$$r = e^{0.0575} - 1$$

$$r \approx 0.0591852707$$

$$r = 5.92\% \quad \text{to the nearest hundredth of a percent}$$

Therefore, comparing the two effective yields, we see that it is better to invest at 6% compounded quarterly than to invest at 5.75% compounded continuously.

Law of Exponential Growth

The ideas behind "compounded continuously" carry over to other growth situations. We use the law of exponential growth,

$$Q(t) = Q_0 e^{kt}$$

as a mathematical model for numerous growth-and-decay applications. In this equation, $Q(t)$ represents the quantity of a given substance at any time t, Q_0 is the initial amount of the substance (when $t = 0$), and k is a constant that depends on the particular application. If $k < 0$, then $Q(t)$ decreases as t increases, and we refer to the model as the **law of decay**.

Let's consider some growth-and-decay applications.

Classroom Example
Suppose that in a certain culture, the equation $Q(t) = 2100e^{0.25t}$ expresses the number of bacteria present as a function of the time t, if t is expressed in days. Find (a) the initial number of bacteria and (b) the number of bacteria after 16 days.

EXAMPLE 3

Suppose that in a certain culture, the equation $Q(t) = 15,000e^{0.3t}$ expresses the number of bacteria present as a function of the time t, where t is expressed in hours. Find (a) the initial number of bacteria and (b) the number of bacteria after 3 hours.

Solution

(a) The initial number of bacteria is produced when $t = 0$.

$$Q(0) = 15,000e^{0.3(0)}$$
$$= 15,000e^0$$
$$= 15,000 \qquad e^0 = 1$$

(b) $Q(3) = 15,000e^{0.3(3)}$
$$= 15,000e^{0.9}$$
$$= 36,894 \quad \text{to the nearest whole number}$$

Therefore approximately 36,894 bacteria should be present after 3 hours.   ◼

Classroom Example
Suppose the number of bacteria present in a certain culture after t hours is given by the equation $Q(t) = Q_0e^{0.04t}$, if Q_0 represents the initial number of bacteria. If 9000 bacteria are present after 25 hours, how many bacteria were present initially?

EXAMPLE 4

Suppose the number of bacteria present in a certain culture after t minutes is given by the equation $Q(t) = Q_0e^{0.05t}$, where Q_0 represents the initial number of bacteria. If 5000 bacteria are present after 20 minutes, how many bacteria were present initially?

Solution

If 5000 bacteria are present after 20 minutes, then $Q(20) = 5000$.

$$5000 = Q_0e^{0.05(20)}$$
$$5000 = Q_0e^1$$
$$\frac{5000}{e} = Q_0$$
$$1839 = Q_0 \quad \text{to the nearest whole number}$$

Therefore, approximately 1839 bacteria were present initially.   ◼

Classroom Example
The number of grams Q of a certain radioactive substance present after t minutes is given by $Q(t) = 500e^{-0.2t}$. How many grams remain after 20 minutes?

EXAMPLE 5

The number of grams of a certain radioactive substance present after t seconds is given by the equation $Q(t) = 200e^{-0.3t}$. How many grams remain after 7 seconds?

Solution

Use $Q(t) = 200e^{-0.3t}$ to obtain

$$Q(7) = 200e^{(-0.3)(7)}$$
$$= 200e^{-2.1}$$
$$= 24.5 \quad \text{to the nearest tenth}$$

Thus approximately 24.5 grams remain after 7 seconds.   ◼

Finally, let's consider two examples where we use a graphing utility to produce the graph.

EXAMPLE 6

Suppose that $1000 was invested at 6.5% interest compounded continuously. How long would it take for the money to double?

Solution

Substitute $1000 for P and 0.065 for r in the formula $A = Pe^{rt}$ to produce $A = 1000e^{0.065t}$. If we let $y = A$ and $x = t$, we can graph the equation $y = 1000e^{0.065x}$. By letting $x = 20$, we obtain $y = 1000e^{0.065(20)} = 1000e^{1.3} \approx 3670$. Therefore let's set the boundaries of the viewing rectangle so that $0 \le x \le 20$ and $0 \le y \le 3700$ with a y scale of 1000. Then we obtain the graph in Figure 10.8. Now we want to find the value of x so that $y = 2000$. (The money is to double.) Using the ZOOM and TRACE features of the graphing utility, we can determine that an x value of approximately 10.7 will produce a y value of 2000. Thus it will take approximately 10.7 years for the $1000 investment to double.

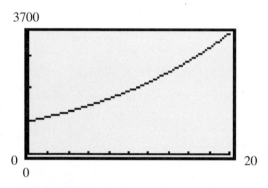

Figure 10.8

EXAMPLE 7

Graph the function $y = \dfrac{1}{\sqrt{2\pi}} e^{-x^2/2}$ and find its maximum value.

Solution

If $x = 0$, then $y = \dfrac{1}{\sqrt{2\pi}} e^0 = \dfrac{1}{\sqrt{2\pi}} \approx 0.4$, so let's set the boundaries of the viewing rectangle so that $-5 \le x \le 5$ and $0 \le y \le 1$ with a y scale of 0.1; the graph of the function is shown in Figure 10.9. From the graph, we see that the maximum value of the function occurs at $x = 0$, which we have already determined to be approximately 0.4.

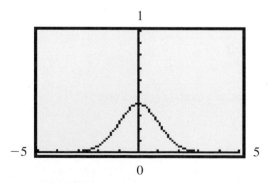

Figure 10.9

Remark: The curve in Figure 10.9 is called a **normal distribution curve**. You may want to ask your instructor to explain what it means to assign grades on the basis of the normal distribution curve.

Concept Quiz 10.2

For Problems 1–5, match each type of problem with its formula.

1. Compound continuously
2. Exponential growth or decay
3. Interest compounded annually
4. Compound interest
5. Half-life

A. $A = P\left(1 + \dfrac{r}{n}\right)^{nt}$ **B.** $Q = Q_0\left(\dfrac{1}{2}\right)^{\frac{t}{h}}$ **C.** $A = P(1 + r)^t$

D. $Q(t) = Q_0 e^{kt}$ **E.** $A = Pe^{rt}$

For Problems 6–10, answer true or false.

6. $500 invested for 2 years at 7% compounded semiannually produces $573.76.
7. $500 invested for 2 years at 7% compounded continuously produces $571.14.
8. The graph of $f(x) = e^{x-5}$ is the graph of $f(x) = e^x$ shifted 5 units to the right.
9. The graph of $f(x) = e^x - 5$ is the graph of $f(x) = e^x$ shifted 5 units downward.
10. The graph of $f(x) = -e^x$ is the graph of $f(x) = e^x$ reflected across the x axis.

Problem Set 10.2

For Problems 1–2, solve the exponential growth or decay problems. (Objective 1)

1. Assuming that the rate of inflation is 4% per year, the equation $P = P_0(1.04)^t$ yields the predicted price (P) of an item in t years that presently costs P_0. Find the predicted price of each of the following items for the indicated years ahead:
   (a) $1.38 can of soup in 3 years
   (b) $3.43 container of cocoa mix in 5 years
   (c) $1.99 jar of coffee creamer in 4 years
   (d) $1.54 can of beans and bacon in 10 years
   (e) $18,000 car in 5 years (nearest dollar)
   (f) $180,000 house in 8 years (nearest dollar)
   (g) $500 TV set in 7 years (nearest dollar)

2. Suppose it is estimated that the value of a car depreciates 30% per year for the first 5 years. The equation $A = P_0(0.7)^t$ yields the value (A) of a car after t years if the original price is P_0. Find the value (to the nearest dollar) of each of the following cars after the indicated time:
   (a) $16,500 car after 4 years
   (b) $22,000 car after 2 years
   (c) $27,000 car after 5 years
   (d) $40,000 car after 3 years

For Problems 3–14, use the formula $A = P\left(1 + \dfrac{r}{n}\right)^{nt}$ to find the total amount of money accumulated at the end of the

indicated time period for each of the following investments: (Objective 2)

3. $200 for 6 years at 6% compounded annually
4. $250 for 5 years at 7% compounded annually
5. $500 for 7 years at 4% compounded semiannually
6. $750 for 8 years at 4% compounded semiannually
7. $800 for 9 years at 5% compounded quarterly
8. $1200 for 10 years at 4% compounded quarterly
9. $1500 for 5 years at 8% compounded monthly
10. $2000 for 10 years at 3% compounded monthly
11. $5000 for 15 years at 4.5% compounded annually
12. $7500 for 20 years at 6.5% compounded semiannually
13. $8000 for 10 years at 5.5% compounded quarterly
14. $10,000 for 25 years at 4.25% compounded monthly

For Problems 15–23, use the formula $A = Pe^{rt}$ to find the total amount of money accumulated at the end of the indicated time period by compounding continuously. (Objective 4)

15. $400 for 5 years at 7%
16. $500 for 7 years at 6%
17. $750 for 8 years at 8%

18. $1000 for 10 years at 5%

19. $2000 for 15 years at 7%

20. $5000 for 20 years at 8%

21. $7500 for 10 years at 6.5%

22. $10,000 for 25 years at 4.25%

23. $15,000 for 10 years at 5.75%

24. What rate of interest, to the nearest tenth of a percent, compounded annually is needed for an investment of $200 to grow to $350 in 5 years?

25. What rate of interest, to the nearest tenth of a percent, compounded quarterly is needed for an investment of $1500 to grow to $2700 in 10 years?

26. Find the effective yield, to the nearest tenth of a percent, of an investment at 7.5% compounded monthly.

27. Find the effective yield, to the nearest hundredth of a percent, of an investment at 7.75% compounded continuously.

28. What investment yields the greater return: 7% compounded monthly or 6.85% compounded continuously?

29. What investment yields the greater return: 8.25% compounded quarterly or 8.3% compounded semi-annually?

For Problems 30–32, solve the half-life problems. (Objective 3)

30. Suppose that a certain radioactive substance has a half-life of 20 years. If there are presently 2500 milligrams of the substance, how much, to the nearest milligram, will remain after 40 years? After 50 years?

31. Strontium-90 has a half-life of 29 years. If there are 400 grams of strontium-90 initially, how much, to the nearest gram, will remain after 87 years? After 100 years?

32. The half-life of radium is approximately 1600 years. If the present amount of radium in a certain location is 500 grams, how much will remain after 800 years? Express your answer to the nearest gram.

For Problems 33–38, solve the exponential growth problems. (Objective 4)

33. Suppose that in a certain culture, the equation $Q(t) = 1000e^{0.4t}$ expresses the number of bacteria present as a function of the time t, where t is expressed in hours. How many bacteria are present at the end of 2 hours? 3 hours? 5 hours?

34. The number of bacteria present at a given time under certain conditions is given by the equation $Q = 5000e^{0.05t}$, where t is expressed in minutes. How many bacteria are present at the end of 10 minutes? 30 minutes? 1 hour?

35. The number of bacteria present in a certain culture after t hours is given by the equation $Q = Q_0e^{0.3t}$, where Q_0 represents the initial number of bacteria. If 6640 bacteria are present after 4 hours, how many bacteria were present initially?

36. The number of grams Q of a certain radioactive substance present after t seconds is given by the equation $Q = 1500e^{-0.4t}$. How many grams remain after 5 seconds? 10 seconds? 20 seconds?

37. The atmospheric pressure, measured in pounds per square inch, is a function of the altitude above sea level. The equation $P(a) = 14.7e^{-0.21a}$, where a is the altitude measured in miles, can be used to approximate atmospheric pressure. Find the atmospheric pressure at each of the following locations:
    (a) Mount McKinley in Alaska: altitude of 3.85 miles
    (b) Denver, Colorado: the "mile-high" city
    (c) Asheville, North Carolina: altitude of 1985 feet
    (d) Phoenix, Arizona: altitude of 1090 feet

38. Suppose that the present population of a city is 75,000. Using the equation $P(t) = 75,000e^{0.01t}$ to estimate future growth, estimate the population (a) 10 years from now, (b) 15 years from now, and (c) 25 years from now.

For Problems 39–44, graph each of the exponential functions. (Objective 5)

39. $f(x) = e^x + 1$

40. $f(x) = e^x - 2$

41. $f(x) = 2e^x$

42. $f(x) = -e^x$

43. $f(x) = e^{2x}$

44. $f(x) = e^{-x}$

Thoughts Into Words

45. Explain the difference between simple interest and compound interest.

46. Would it be better to invest $5000 at 6.25% interest compounded annually for 5 years or to invest $5000 at 6.25% interest compounded continuously for 5 years? Explain your answer.

47. How would you explain the concept of effective yield to someone who missed class when it was discussed?

48. How would you explain the half-life formula to someone who missed class when it was discussed?

Further Investigations

49. Complete the following chart, which illustrates what happens to $1000 invested at various rates of interest for different lengths of time but always compounded continuously. Round your answers to the nearest dollar.

$1000 Compounded continuously

	4%	5%	6%	7%
5 years				
10 years				
15 years				
20 years				
25 years				

50. Complete the following chart, which illustrates what happens to $1000 invested at 6% for different lengths of time and different numbers of compounding periods. Round all of your answers to the nearest dollar.

$1000 at 6%

	1 year	5 years	10 years	20 years
Compounded annually				
Compounded semiannually				
Compounded quarterly				
Compounded monthly				
Compounded continuously				

51. Complete the following chart, which illustrates what happens to $1000 in 10 years based on different rates of interest and different numbers of compounding periods. Round your answers to the nearest dollar.

$1000 for 10 years

	4%	5%	6%	7%
Compounded annually				
Compounded semiannually				
Compounded quarterly				
Compounded monthly				
Compounded continuously				

For Problems 52–56, graph each of the functions.

52. $f(x) = x(2^x)$

53. $f(x) = \dfrac{e^x + e^{-x}}{2}$

54. $f(x) = \dfrac{2}{e^x + e^{-x}}$

55. $f(x) = \dfrac{e^x - e^{-x}}{2}$

56. $f(x) = \dfrac{2}{e^x - e^{-x}}$

Graphing Calculator Activities

57. Use a graphing calculator to check your graphs for Problems 52–56.

58. Graph $f(x) = 2^x$, $f(x) = e^x$, and $f(x) = 3^x$ on the same set of axes. Are these graphs consistent with the discussion prior to Figure 10.7?

59. Graph $f(x) = e^x$. Where should the graphs of $f(x) = e^{x-4}$, $f(x) = e^{x-6}$, and $f(x) = e^{x+5}$ be located? Graph all three functions on the same set of axes with $f(x) = e^x$.

60. Graph $f(x) = e^x$. Now predict the graphs for $f(x) = -e^x$, $f(x) = e^{-x}$, and $f(x) = -e^{-x}$. Graph all three functions on the same set of axes with $f(x) = e^x$.

61. How do you think the graphs of $f(x) = e^x$, $f(x) = e^{2x}$, and $f(x) = 2e^x$ will compare? Graph them on the same set of axes to see if you were correct.

62. Find an approximate solution, to the nearest hundredth, for each of the following equations by graphing the appropriate function and finding the x intercept.

(a) $e^x = 7$ (b) $e^x = 21$ (c) $e^x = 53$

(d) $2e^x = 60$ (e) $e^{x+1} = 150$ (f) $e^{x-2} = 300$

63. Use a graphing approach to argue that it is better to invest money at 6% compounded quarterly than at 5.75% compounded continuously.

64. How long will it take $500 to be worth $1500 if it is invested at 7.5% interest compounded semiannually?

65. How long will it take $5000 to triple if it is invested at 6.75% interest compounded quarterly?

10.3   Inverse Functions

OBJECTIVES

1 Determine if a function is a one-to-one function

2 Verify if two functions are inverses of each other

3 Find the inverse function in terms of ordered pairs

4 Find the inverse of a function

5 Graph a function and its inverse

6 Determine the intervals for which a function is increasing (or decreasing)

Recall the vertical-line test: If each vertical line intersects a graph in no more than one point, then the graph represents a function. There is also a useful distinction between two basic types of functions. Consider the graphs of the two functions in Figure 10.10: $f(x) = 2x - 1$ and $g(x) = x^2$. In Figure 10.10(a), any *horizontal line* will intersect the graph in no more than one point. Therefore every value of $f(x)$ has only one value of x associated with it. Any function that has this property of having exactly one value of x associated with each value of $f(x)$ is called a **one-to-one function**. Thus $g(x) = x^2$ is not a one-to-one function because the horizontal line in Figure 10.10(b) intersects the parabola in two points.

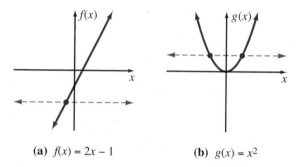

(a) $f(x) = 2x - 1$ **(b)** $g(x) = x^2$

Figure 10.10

The statement that for a function f to be a one-to-one function, every value of $f(x)$ has only one value of x associated with it can be equivalently stated: If $f(x_1) = f(x_2)$ for x_1 and x_2 in the domain of f, then $x_1 = x_2$. Let's use this last if-then statement to verify that $f(x) = 2x - 1$ is a one-to-one function. We start with the assumption that $f(x_1) = f(x_2)$:

$$2x_1 - 1 = 2x_2 - 1$$
$$2x_1 = 2x_2$$
$$x_1 = x_2$$

Thus $f(x) = 2x - 1$ is a one-to-one function.

To show that $g(x) = x^2$ is not a one-to-one function, we simply need to find two distinct real numbers in the domain of f that produce the same functional value. For example, $g(-2) = (-2)^2 = 4$ and $g(2) = 2^2 = 4$. Thus $g(x) = x^2$ is not a one-to-one function.

Now let's consider a one-to-one function f that assigns to each x in its domain D the value $f(x)$ in its range R (Figure 10.11(a)). We can define a new function g that goes from

R to D; it assigns $f(x)$ in R back to x in D, as indicated in Figure 10.11(b). The functions f and g are called *inverse functions* of each other. The following definition precisely states this concept.

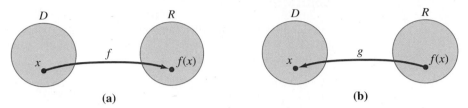

Figure 10.11

> **Definition 10.2**
>
> Let f be a one-to-one function with a domain of X and a range of Y. A function g with a domain of Y and a range of X is called the **inverse function** of f if
>
> $$(f \circ g)(x) = x \quad \text{for every } x \text{ in } Y$$
>
> and
>
> $$(g \circ f)(x) = x \quad \text{for every } x \text{ in } X$$

In Definition 10.2, note that for f and g to be inverses of each other, the domain of f must equal the range of g, and the range of f must equal the domain of g. Furthermore, g must reverse the correspondences given by f, and f must reverse the correspondences given by g. In other words, inverse functions *undo* each other. Let's use Definition 10.2 to verify that two specific functions are inverses of each other.

Classroom Example
Verify that $f(x) = 7x + 1$ and $g(x) = \dfrac{x - 1}{7}$ are inverse functions.

EXAMPLE 1

Verify that $f(x) = 4x - 5$ and $g(x) = \dfrac{x + 5}{4}$ are inverse functions.

Solution

Because the set of real numbers is the domain and range of both functions, we know that the domain of f equals the range of g and that the range of f equals the domain of g. Furthermore,

$$(f \circ g)(x) = f(g(x))$$
$$= f\left(\frac{x + 5}{4}\right)$$
$$= 4\left(\frac{x + 5}{4}\right) - 5 = x$$

and

$$(g \circ f)(x) = g(f(x))$$
$$= g(4x - 5)$$
$$= \frac{4x - 5 + 5}{4} = x$$

Therefore f and g are inverses of each other.

Classroom Example
Verify that $f(x) = x^2 - 5$ for $x \geq 0$,
and $g(x) = \sqrt{x + 5}$ for $x \geq -5$, are
inverse functions.

EXAMPLE 2

Verify that $f(x) = x^2 + 1$ for $x \geq 0$ and $g(x) = \sqrt{x - 1}$ for $x \geq 1$ are inverse functions.

Solution

First, note that the domain of f equals the range of g; namely, the set of nonnegative real numbers. Also, the range of f equals the domain of g; namely, the set of real numbers greater than or equal to 1. Furthermore,

$$(f \circ g)(x) = f(g(x))$$
$$= f\left(\sqrt{x - 1}\right)$$
$$= \left(\sqrt{x - 1}\right)^2 + 1$$
$$= x - 1 + 1 = x$$

and

$$(g \circ f)(x) = g(f(x))$$
$$= g(x^2 + 1)$$
$$= \sqrt{x^2 + 1 - 1} = \sqrt{x^2} = x \qquad \sqrt{x^2} = x \text{ because } x \geq 1$$

Therefore f and g are inverses of each other.

The inverse of a function f is commonly denoted by f^{-1} (read "f inverse" or "the inverse of f"). Do not confuse the -1 in f^{-1} with a negative exponent. The symbol f^{-1} does *not* mean $1/f^1$ but rather refers to the inverse function of function f.

Remember that a function can also be thought of as a set of ordered pairs no two of which have the same first element. Along those lines, a one-to-one function further requires that no two of the ordered pairs have the same second element. Then, if the components of each ordered pair of a given one-to-one function are interchanged, the resulting function and the given function are inverses of each other. Thus if

$$f = \{(1, 4), (2, 7), (5, 9)\}$$

then

$$f^{-1} = \{(4, 1), (7, 2), (9, 5)\}$$

Graphically, two functions that are inverses of each other are *mirror images with reference to the line $y = x$*. This is because ordered pairs (a, b) and (b, a) are reflections of each other with respect to the line $y = x$, as illustrated in Figure 10.12. (You will verify this in the next set of exercises.) Therefore, if the graph of a function f is known, as in Figure 10.13(a), then the graph of f^{-1} can be determined by reflecting f across the line $y = x$, as in Figure 10.13(b).

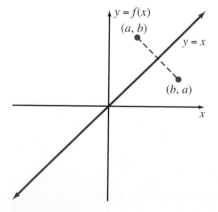

Figure 10.12

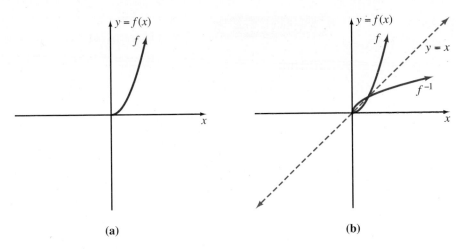

Figure 10.13

Finding Inverse Functions

The idea of inverse functions *undoing each other* provides the basis for an informal approach to finding the inverse of a function. Consider the function

$$f(x) = 2x + 1$$

To each x, this function assigns twice x plus 1. To undo this function, we can subtract 1 and divide by 2. Hence the inverse is

$$f^{-1}(x) = \frac{x-1}{2}$$

Now let's verify that f and f^{-1} are indeed inverses of each other:

$$(f \circ f^{-1})(x) = f(f^{-1}(x)) \qquad\qquad (f^{-1} \circ f)(x) = f^{-1}(f(x))$$

$$= f\left(\frac{x-1}{2}\right) \qquad\qquad\qquad = f^{-1}(2x+1)$$

$$= 2\left(\frac{x-1}{2}\right) + 1 \qquad\qquad\qquad = \frac{2x+1-1}{2}$$

$$= x - 1 + 1 \qquad\qquad\qquad\qquad = \frac{2x}{2}$$

$$= x \qquad\qquad\qquad\qquad\qquad = x$$

Thus the inverse of $f(x) = 2x + 1$ is $f^{-1}(x) = \dfrac{x-1}{2}$.

This informal approach may not work very well with more complex functions, but it does emphasize how inverse functions are related to each other. A more formal and systematic technique for finding the inverse of a function can be described as follows:

1. Replace the symbol $f(x)$ with y.
2. Interchange x and y.
3. Solve the equation for y in terms of x.
4. Replace y with the symbol $f^{-1}(x)$.

The following examples illustrate this technique.

EXAMPLE 3   Find the inverse of $f(x) = \dfrac{2}{3}x + \dfrac{3}{5}$.

Solution

When we replace $f(x)$ with y, the equation becomes $y = \dfrac{2}{3}x + \dfrac{3}{5}$. Interchanging x and y produces $x = \dfrac{2}{3}y + \dfrac{3}{5}$. Now, solving for y, we obtain

$$x = \frac{2}{3}y + \frac{3}{5}$$

$$15(x) = 15\left(\frac{2}{3}y + \frac{3}{5}\right)$$

$$15x = 10y + 9$$

$$15x - 9 = 10y$$

$$\frac{15x - 9}{10} = y$$

Finally, by replacing y with $f^{-1}(x)$, we can express the inverse function as

$$f^{-1}(x) = \frac{15x - 9}{10}$$

The domain of f is equal to the range of f^{-1} (both are the set of real numbers), and the range of f equals the domain of f^{-1} (both are the set of real numbers). Furthermore, we could show that $(f \circ f^{-1})(x) = x$ and $(f^{-1} \circ f)(x) = x$. We leave this for you to complete.

Does the function $f(x) = x^2 - 2$ have an inverse? Sometimes a graph of the function helps answer such a question. In Figure 10.14(a), it should be evident that f is not a one-to-one function and therefore cannot have an inverse. However, it should also be apparent from the graph that if we restrict the domain of f to the nonnegative real numbers, Figure 10.14(b), then it is a one-to-one function and should have an inverse function. The next example illustrates how to find the inverse function.

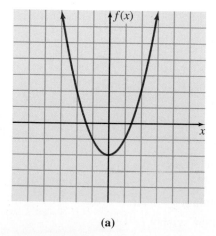
(a)

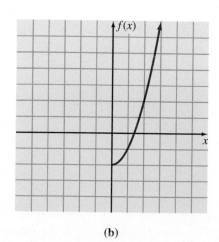
(b)

Figure 10.14

EXAMPLE 4   Find the inverse of $f(x) = x^2 - 2$, where $x \geq 0$.

Solution

When we replace $f(x)$ with y, the equation becomes

$$y = x^2 - 2, \qquad x \geq 0$$

Interchanging x and y produces

$$x = y^2 - 2, \qquad y \geq 0$$

Now let's solve for y; keep in mind that y is to be nonnegative.

$$x = y^2 - 2$$
$$x + 2 = y^2$$
$$\sqrt{x + 2} = y, \qquad x \geq -2$$

Finally, by replacing y with $f^{-1}(x)$, we can express the inverse function as

$$f^{-1}(x) = \sqrt{x + 2}, \qquad x \geq -2$$

The domain of f equals the range of f^{-1} (both are the nonnegative real numbers), and the range of f equals the domain of f^{-1} (both are the real numbers greater than or equal to -2). It can also be shown that $(f \circ f^{-1})(x) = x$ and $(f^{-1} \circ f)(x) = x$. Again, we leave this for you to complete.

Increasing and Decreasing Functions

In Section 10.1, we used exponential functions as examples of increasing and decreasing functions. In reality, one function can be both increasing and decreasing over certain intervals. For example, in Figure 10.15, the function f is said to be *increasing* on the intervals $(-\infty, x_1]$ and $[x_2, \infty)$, and f is said to be *decreasing* on the interval $[x_1, x_2]$. More specifically, increasing and decreasing functions are defined as follows:

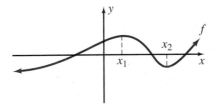

Figure 10.15

> **Definition 10.3**
>
> Let f be a function, with the interval I a subset of the domain of f. Let x_1 and x_2 be in I. Then:
>
> **1.** f is *increasing* on I if $f(x_1) < f(x_2)$ whenever $x_1 < x_2$.
> **2.** f is *decreasing* on I if $f(x_1) > f(x_2)$ whenever $x_1 < x_2$.
> **3.** f is *constant* on I if $f(x_1) = f(x_2)$ for every x_1 and x_2.

Apply Definition 10.3, and you will see that the quadratic function $f(x) = x^2$ shown in Figure 10.16 is decreasing on $(-\infty, 0]$ and increasing on $[0, \infty)$. Likewise, the linear function $f(x) = 2x$ in Figure 10.17 is increasing throughout its domain of real numbers, so we say that it is increasing on $(-\infty, \infty)$. The function $f(x) = -2x$ in Figure 10.18 is decreasing on $(-\infty, \infty)$. For our purposes in this text, we will rely on our knowledge of the graphs of the

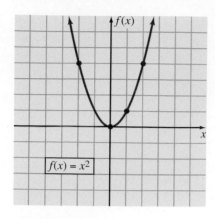

Figure 10.16

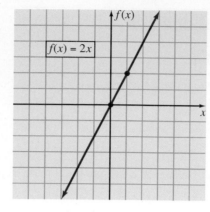

Figure 10.17

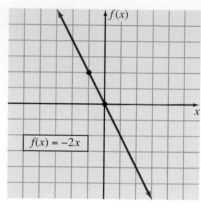

Figure 10.18

functions to determine when functions are increasing and decreasing. More formal techniques for determining when functions increase and decrease will be developed in calculus.

A function that is always increasing (or is always decreasing) over its entire domain is a one-to-one function and so has an inverse function. Furthermore, as illustrated by Example 4, even if a function is not one to one over its entire domain, it may be so over some subset of the domain. It then has an inverse function over this restricted domain. As functions become more complex, a graphing utility can be used to help with problems like those we have discussed in this section. For example, suppose that we want to know whether the function $f(x) = \dfrac{3x + 1}{x - 4}$ is a one-to-one function and therefore has an inverse function. Using a graphing utility, we can quickly get a sketch of the graph (Figure 10.19). Then, by applying the horizontal-line test to the graph, we can be fairly certain that the function is one-to-one.

A graphing utility can also be used to help determine the intervals on which a function is increasing or decreasing. For example, to determine such intervals for the function $f(x) = \sqrt{x^2 + 4}$, let's use a graphing utility to get a sketch of the curve (Figure 10.20). From this graph, we see that the function is decreasing on the interval $(-\infty, 0]$ and is increasing on the interval $[0, \infty)$.

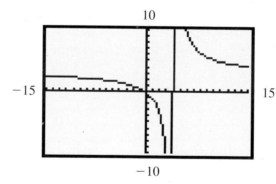

Figure 10.19

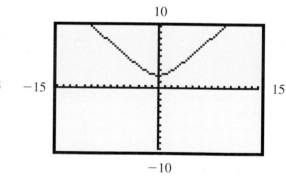

Figure 10.20

Concept Quiz 10.3

For Problems 1–10, answer true or false.

1. Over the domain of all real numbers, a quadratic function is never a one-to-one function.

2. The notation f^{-1} refers to the inverse of the function f.

3. If f and g are inverse functions, then the range of f is the domain of g.

4. If a horizontal line intersects the graph of a function in more than one point, then the function is one-to-one.

5. If $f(1) = 4$ and $f(-3) = 4$, then f is not a one-to-one function.

6. The only condition for f and g to be inverse functions is that g must reverse the correspondence given by f.

7. Given that f has an inverse function and $f(2) = -8$, then $f^{-1}(-8) = 2$.

8. The graphs of two functions that are inverses of each other are mirror images with reference to the line $y = -x$.

9. The quadratic function $f(x) = (x - 3)^2$ is decreasing on the interval $(-\infty, 0]$.

10. Any function that is increasing over its entire domain is a one-to-one function.

Problem Set 10.3

For Problems 1–6, determine whether the graph represents a one-to-one function. **(Objective 1)**

1.

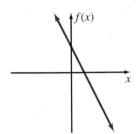

Figure 10.21

2.

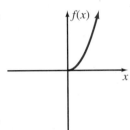

Figure 10.22

3.

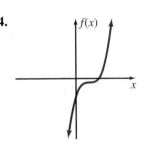

Figure 10.23

4.

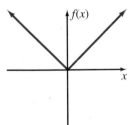

Figure 10.24

5.

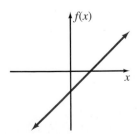

Figure 10.25

6.

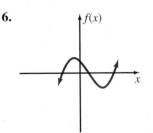

Figure 10.26

For Problems 7–14, determine whether the function f is one-to-one. **(Objective 1)**

7. $f(x) = 5x + 4$

8. $f(x) = -3x + 4$

9. $f(x) = x^3$

10. $f(x) = x^5 + 1$

11. $f(x) = |x| + 1$

12. $f(x) = -|x| - 2$

13. $f(x) = -x^4$

14. $f(x) = x^4 + 1$

For Problems 15–18, (a) list the domain and range of the function, (b) form the inverse function f^{-1}, and (c) list the domain and range of f^{-1}. **(Objective 3)**

15. $f = \{(1, 5), (2, 9), (5, 21)\}$

16. $f = \{(1, 1), (4, 2), (9, 3), (16, 4)\}$

17. $f = \{(0, 0), (2, 8), (-1, -1), (-2, -8)\}$

18. $f = \{(-1, 1), (-2, 4), (-3, 9), (-4, 16)\}$

For Problems 19–26, verify that the two given functions are inverses of each other. **(Objective 2)**

19. $f(x) = 5x - 9$ and $g(x) = \dfrac{x + 9}{5}$

20. $f(x) = -3x + 4$ and $g(x) = \dfrac{4 - x}{3}$

21. $f(x) = -\dfrac{1}{2}x + \dfrac{5}{6}$ and $g(x) = -2x + \dfrac{5}{3}$

22. $f(x) = x^3 + 1$ and $g(x) = \sqrt[3]{x - 1}$

23. $f(x) = \dfrac{1}{x-1}$ for $x > 1$, and

$g(x) = \dfrac{x+1}{x}$ for $x > 0$

24. $f(x) = x^2 + 2$ for $x \geq 0$, and

$g(x) = \sqrt{x-2}$ for $x \geq 2$

25. $f(x) = \sqrt{2x-4}$ for $x \geq 2$, and

$g(x) = \dfrac{x^2+4}{2}$ for $x \geq 0$

26. $f(x) = x^2 - 4$ for $x \geq 0$, and

$g(x) = \sqrt{x+4}$ for $x \geq -4$

For Problems 27–36, determine whether f and g are inverse functions. (Objective 2)

27. $f(x) = 3x$ and $g(x) = -\dfrac{1}{3}x$

28. $f(x) = \dfrac{3}{4}x - 2$ and $g(x) = \dfrac{4}{3}x + \dfrac{8}{3}$

29. $f(x) = x^3$ and $g(x) = \sqrt[3]{x}$

30. $f(x) = \dfrac{1}{x+1}$ and $g(x) = \dfrac{1-x}{x}$

31. $f(x) = x$ and $g(x) = \dfrac{1}{x}$

32. $f(x) = \dfrac{3}{5}x + \dfrac{1}{3}$ and $g(x) = \dfrac{5}{3}x - 3$

33. $f(x) = x^2 - 3$ for $x \geq 0$ and
$g(x) = \sqrt{x+3}$ for $x \geq -3$

34. $f(x) = |x-1|$ for $x \geq 1$ and
$g(x) = |x+1|$ for $x \geq 0$

35. $f(x) = \sqrt{x+1}$ and $g(x) = x^2 - 1$ for $x \geq 0$

36. $f(x) = \sqrt{2x-2}$ and $g(x) = \dfrac{1}{2}x^2 + 1$

For Problems 37–50, (a) find f^{-1} and (b) verify that $(f \circ f^{-1})(x) = x$ and $(f^{-1} \circ f)(x) = x$. (Objective 4)

37. $f(x) = x - 4$ **38.** $f(x) = 2x - 1$

39. $f(x) = -3x - 4$ **40.** $f(x) = -5x + 6$

41. $f(x) = \dfrac{3}{4}x - \dfrac{5}{6}$ **42.** $f(x) = \dfrac{2}{3}x - \dfrac{1}{4}$

43. $f(x) = -\dfrac{2}{3}x$ **44.** $f(x) = \dfrac{4}{3}x$

45. $f(x) = \sqrt{x}$ for $x \geq 0$

46. $f(x) = \dfrac{1}{x}$ for $x \neq 0$

47. $f(x) = x^2 + 4$ for $x \geq 0$

48. $f(x) = x^2 + 1$ for $x \leq 0$

49. $f(x) = 1 + \dfrac{1}{x}$ for $x > 0$

50. $f(x) = \dfrac{x}{x+1}$ for $x > -1$

For Problems 51–58, (a) find f^{-1} and (b) graph f and f^{-1} on the same set of axes. (Objective 5)

51. $f(x) = 3x$

52. $f(x) = -x$

53. $f(x) = 2x + 1$

54. $f(x) = -3x - 3$

55. $f(x) = \dfrac{2}{x-1}$ for $x > 1$

56. $f(x) = \dfrac{-1}{x-2}$ for $x > 2$

57. $f(x) = x^2 - 4$ for $x \geq 0$

58. $f(x) = \sqrt{x-3}$ for $x \geq 3$

For Problems 59–66, find the intervals on which the given function is increasing and the intervals on which it is decreasing. (Objective 6)

59. $f(x) = x^2 + 1$

60. $f(x) = x^3$

61. $f(x) = -3x + 1$

62. $f(x) = (x-3)^2 + 1$

63. $f(x) = -(x+2)^2 - 1$

64. $f(x) = x^2 - 2x + 6$

65. $f(x) = -2x^2 - 16x - 35$

66. $f(x) = x^2 + 3x - 1$

Thoughts Into Words

67. Does the function $f(x) = 4$ have an inverse? Explain your answer.

68. Explain why every nonconstant linear function has an inverse.

69. Are the functions $f(x) = x^4$ and $g(x) = \sqrt[4]{x}$ inverses of each other? Explain your answer.

70. What does it mean to say that 2 and -2 are additive inverses of each other? What does it mean to say that 2 and $\dfrac{1}{2}$ are multiplicative inverses of each other? What does it mean to say that the functions $f(x) = x - 2$ and $f(x) = x + 2$ are inverses of each other? Do you think that the concept of "inverse" is being used in a consistent manner? Explain your answer.

Further Investigations

71. The function notation and the operation of composition can be used to find inverses as follows: To find the inverse of $f(x) = 5x + 3$, we know that $f(f^{-1}(x))$ must produce x. Therefore

$$f(f^{-1}(x)) = 5[f^{-1}(x)] + 3 = x$$
$$5[f^{-1}(x)] = x - 3$$
$$f^{-1}(x) = \frac{x - 3}{5}$$

Use this approach to find the inverse of each of the following functions.

(a) $f(x) = 3x - 9$ **(b)** $f(x) = -2x + 6$

(c) $f(x) = -x + 1$ **(d)** $f(x) = 2x$

(e) $f(x) = -5x$ **(f)** $f(x) = x^2 + 6$ for $x \geq 0$

72. If $f(x) = 2x + 3$ and $g(x) = 3x - 5$, find
(a) $(f \circ g)^{-1}(x)$ **(b)** $(f^{-1} \circ g^{-1})(x)$
(c) $(g^{-1} \circ f^{-1})(x)$

Graphing Calculator Activities

73. For Problems 37–44, graph the given function, the inverse function that you found, and $f(x) = x$ on the same set of axes. In each case, the given function and its inverse should produce graphs that are reflections of each other through the line $f(x) = x$.

74. There is another way we can use the graphing calculator to help show that two functions are inverses of each other. Suppose we want to show that $f(x) = x^2 - 2$ for $x \geq 0$ and $g(x) = \sqrt{x + 2}$ for $x \geq -2$ are inverses of each other. Let's make the following assignments for our graphing calculator.

$$f: \ Y_1 = x^2 - 2$$
$$g: \ Y_2 = \sqrt{x + 2}$$
$$f \circ g: \ Y_3 = (Y_2)^2 - 2$$
$$g \circ f: \ Y_4 = \sqrt{Y_1 + 2}$$

Now we can proceed as follows:
a. Graph $Y_1 = x^2 - 2$, and note that for $x > 0$, the range is greater than or equal to -2.

b. Graph $Y_2 = \sqrt{x + 2}$, and note that for $x \geq -2$, the range is greater than or equal to 0.

c. Graph $Y_3 = (Y_2)^2 - 2$ for $x \geq -2$, and observe the line $y = x$ for $x \geq -2$.

d. Graph $Y_4 = \sqrt{Y_1 + 2}$ for $x \geq 0$, and observe the line $y = x$ for $x \geq 0$.

Use this approach to check your answers for Problems 45–50.

75. Use the technique demonstrated in Problem 74 to show that

$$f(x) = \frac{x}{\sqrt{x^2 + 1}}$$

and

$$g(x) = \frac{x}{\sqrt{1 - x^2}} \quad \text{for } -1 < x < 1$$

are inverses of each other.

| 10.4 | Logarithms |

O B J E C T I V E S

1 Change equations between exponential and logarithmic form

2 Evaluate a logarithmic expression

3 Apply the properties of logarithms

4 Solve logarithmic equations

In Sections 10.1 and 10.2 we discussed exponential expressions of the form b^n, where b is any positive real number and n is any real number; we used exponential expressions of the form b^n to define exponential functions; and we used exponential functions to help solve problems. In the next three sections, we will follow the same basic pattern with respect to a new concept: logarithms. Let's begin with the following definition:

Definition 10.4

If r is any positive real number, then the unique exponent t such that $b^t = r$ is called the **logarithm of r with base b** and is denoted by $\log_b r$.

According to Definition 10.4, the logarithm of 16 base 2 is the exponent t such that $2^t = 16$; thus we can write $\log_2 16 = 4$. Likewise, we can write $\log_{10} 1000 = 3$ because $10^3 = 1000$. In general, we can remember Definition 10.4 by the statement

$$\log_b r = t \quad \text{is equivalent to} \quad b^t = r$$

Therefore we can easily switch back and forth between exponential and logarithmic forms of equations, as the next examples illustrate.

$$\log_2 8 = 3 \quad \text{is equivalent to} \quad 2^3 = 8$$
$$\log_{10} 100 = 2 \quad \text{is equivalent to} \quad 10^2 = 100$$
$$\log_3 81 = 4 \quad \text{is equivalent to} \quad 3^4 = 81$$
$$\log_{10} 0.001 = -3 \quad \text{is equivalent to} \quad 10^{-3} = 0.001$$
$$\log_m n = p \quad \text{is equivalent to} \quad m^p = n$$

$$2^7 = 128 \quad \text{is equivalent to} \quad \log_2 128 = 7$$
$$5^3 = 125 \quad \text{is equivalent to} \quad \log_5 125 = 3$$
$$\left(\frac{1}{2}\right)^4 = \frac{1}{16} \quad \text{is equivalent to} \quad \log_{1/2}\left(\frac{1}{16}\right) = 4$$
$$10^{-2} = 0.01 \quad \text{is equivalent to} \quad \log_{10} 0.01 = -2$$
$$a^b = c \quad \text{is equivalent to} \quad \log_a c = b$$

Some logarithms can be determined by changing to exponential form and using the properties of exponents, as the next two examples illustrate.

Classroom Example
Evaluate $\log_{10} 0.01$.

EXAMPLE 1   Evaluate $\log_{10} 0.0001$.

Solution

Let $\log_{10} 0.0001 = x$. Then, by changing to exponential form, we have $10^x = 0.0001$, which can be solved as follows:

$$10^x = 0.0001$$

each logarithmic statement in
ple, $\log_2 8 = 3$ becomes $2^3 = 8$
ive 1)

12. $\log_2 256 = 8$

14. $\log_5 25 = 2$

16. $\log_{10} 100,000 = 5$

18. $\log_5\left(\dfrac{1}{125}\right) = -3$

20. $\log_{10} 0.000001 = -6$

e each logarithmic expression.

22. $\log_3 9$

24. $\log_2 512$

26. $\log_4 256$

28. $\log_2 \sqrt[3]{2}$

30. $\log_{10} 10$

32. $\log_{10} 0.0001$

34. $10^{\log_{10} 14}$

36. $\log_5\left(\dfrac{1}{25}\right)$

38. $\log_2(\log_4 16)$

40. $\log_2(\log_5 5)$

57. $\log_2 175$ **58.**

59. $\log_2 80$

For Problems 60–68, given th
$\log_8 11 = 1.1531$, evaluate each ex
10.5–10.7. **(Objective 3)**

60. $\log_8 55$ **61.**

62. $\log_8 25$ **63.**

64. $\log_8(5)^{2/3}$ **65.**

66. $\log_8 320$ **67.**

68. $\log_8\left(\dfrac{121}{25}\right)$

For Problems 69–80, express eac
sum or difference of simpler logari
that all variables represent positive r
For example,

$$\log_b \dfrac{x^3}{y^2} = \log_b x^3 - \log_b y^2$$
$$= 3\log_b x - 2\log_b y$$

69. $\log_b xyz$ **70.** l

71. $\log_b\left(\dfrac{y}{z}\right)$ **72.** l

73. $\log_b y^3 z^4$ **74.** l

75. $\log_b\left(\dfrac{x^{1/2}\,y^{1/3}}{z^4}\right)$ **76.** l

77. $\log_b \sqrt[3]{x^2 z}$ **78.** l

79. $\log_b\left(x\sqrt{\dfrac{x}{y}}\right)$ **80.** l

ch equation. **(Objective 4)**

42. $\log_2 x = 5$

44. $\log_{16} x = \dfrac{3}{2}$

46. $\log_8 x = -\dfrac{2}{3}$

48. $\log_9 x = -\dfrac{5}{2}$

50. $\log_x 3 = \dfrac{1}{2}$

that $\log_2 5 = 2.3219$ and
expression by using Proper-

52. $\log_2\left(\dfrac{7}{5}\right)$

54. $\log_2 49$

56. $\log_2 \sqrt[3]{5}$

For Problems 81–88, express each o
gle logarithm. (Assume that all var
real numbers.) **(Objective 3)** For exa

$$3\log_b x + 5\log_b y = \log_b x^3 y^5$$

81. $2\log_b x - 4\log_b y$

82. $\log_b x + \log_b y - \log_b z$

83. $\log_b x - (\log_b y - \log_b z)$

84. $(\log_b x - \log_b y) - \log_b z$

Classroom Example
If $\log_3 6 = 1.6309$ and
$\log_3 2 = 0.6309$, evaluate $\log_3 12$.

EXAMPLE 5   If $\log_2 5 = 2.3222$ and $\log_2 3 = 1.5850$

Solution

Because $15 = 5 \cdot 3$, we can apply Property 10.5 as follows:

$$\log_2 15 = \log_2(5 \cdot 3)$$
$$= \log_2 5 + \log_2 3$$
$$= 2.3222 + 1.5850$$
$$= 3.9072$$

Classroom Example
If $\log_{10} 232 = 2.3655$ and
$\log_{10} 73 = 1.8633$, evaluate
$\log_{10}(232 \cdot 73)$.

EXAMPLE 6

Given that $\log_{10} 178 = 2.2504$ and $\log_{10} 89 = 1.9494$, evaluate log

Solution

$$\log_{10}(178 \cdot 89) = \log_{10} 178 + \log_{10} 89$$
$$= 2.2504 + 1.9494$$
$$= 4.1998$$

Because $\dfrac{b^m}{b^n} = b^{m-n}$, we would expect a corresponding property
Property 10.6 is that property. We can verify it by using an approach s
verify Property 10.5. This verification is left for you to do as an exerc

---

Property 10.6

For positive numbers b, r, and s, where $b \neq 1$,

$$\log_b\left(\dfrac{r}{s}\right) = \log_b r - \log_b s$$

We can use Property 10.6 to change a division problem into
problem, as the next two examples illustrate.

Classroom Example
If $\log_5 39 = 2.2763$ and
$\log_5 13 = 1.5937$, evaluate $\log_5 3$.

EXAMPLE 7   If $\log_5 36 = 2.2266$ and $\log_5 4 = 0.8614$

Solution

Because $9 = \dfrac{36}{4}$, we can use Property 10.6 as follows:

$$\log_5 9 = \log_5\left(\dfrac{36}{4}\right)$$
$$= \log_5 36 - \log_5 4$$
$$= 2.2266 - 0.8614$$
$$= 1.3652$$

Classroom Example
Evaluate $\log_3 \sqrt[3]{27}$.

Classroom Example
Solve $\log_{25} x = \dfrac{3}{2}$.

Classroom Example
Solve $\log_b \dfrac{36}{121} = 2$.

$$10^x = 10^{-4} \qquad 0.0001 = \dfrac{1}{10,000} = \dfrac{1}{10^4} = 10^{-4}$$
$$x = -4$$

Thus we have $\log_{10} 0.0001 = -4$.

EXAMPLE 2   Evaluate $\log_7 \sqrt[3]{49}$.

Solution

Let $\log_7 \sqrt[3]{49} = x$. Then, by changing to exponential form, we have $7^x = \sqrt[3]{49}$, which can
be solved as follows:

$$7^x = \sqrt[3]{49}$$
$$7^x = (49)^{\frac{1}{3}}$$
$$7^x = (7^2)^{\frac{1}{3}}$$
$$7^x = 7^{\frac{2}{3}}$$
$$x = \dfrac{2}{3}$$

Therefore we have $\log_7 \sqrt[3]{49} = \dfrac{2}{3}$.

Some equations that involve logarithms can also be solved by changing to exponential
form and using our knowledge of exponents.

EXAMPLE 3   Solve $\log_8 x = \dfrac{2}{3}$.

Solution

Changing $\log_8 x = \dfrac{2}{3}$ to exponential form, we obtain

$$8^{2/3} = x$$

Therefore

$$x = \left(\sqrt[3]{8}\right)^2$$
$$= 2^2$$
$$= 4$$

The solution set is $\{4\}$.

EXAMPLE 4   Solve $\log_b\left(\dfrac{27}{64}\right) = 3$.

Solution

Change $\log_b\left(\dfrac{27}{64}\right) = 3$ to exponential form to obtain

$$b^3 = \dfrac{27}{64}$$

Therefore

$$b = \sqrt[3]{\dfrac{27}{64}}$$
$$= \dfrac{3}{4}$$

The solution set is $\left\{\dfrac{3}{4}\right\}$.

Properties of Logarithms

There are some properties of logarithms that are a direct cons[e]
the properties of exponents. For example, the following prop[]
exponential equations $b^1 = b$ and $b^0 = 1$ in logarithmic form.

Property 10.3

For $b > 0$ and $b \neq 1$,

$$\log_b b = 1 \quad \text{and} \quad \log_b 1 = 0$$

Therefore according to Property 10.3, we can write

$$\log_{10} 10 = 1 \qquad \log_4 4 = 1$$
$$\log_{10} 1 = 0 \qquad \log_5 1 = 0$$

Also, from Definition 10.2, we know that $\log_b r$ is the [ ]
Therefore, raising b to the $\log_b r$ power must produce r. This fa[ ]

Property 10.4

For $b > 0$, $b \neq 1$, and $r > 0$,

$$b^{\log_b r} = r$$

Therefore according to Property 10.4, we can write

$$10^{\log_{10} 72} = 72 \qquad 3^{\log_3 85} = 85 \qquad e^{\log_e 7} = 7$$

Because a logarithm is by definition an exponent, it seer[ ]
some properties of logarithms correspond to the basic exponenti[ ]
rate prediction; these properties provide a basis for computationa[ ]
state the first of these properties and show how we can use ou[ ]
verify it.

Property 10.5

For positive numbers b, r, and s, where $b \neq 1$,

$$\log_b rs = \log_b r + \log_b s$$

To verify Property 10.5, we can proceed as follows. Le[ ]
Change each of these equations to exponential form:

$$m = \log_b r \quad \text{becomes} \quad r = b^m$$
$$n = \log_b s \quad \text{becomes} \quad s = b^n$$

Thus the product rs becomes

$$rs = b^m \cdot b^n = b^{m+n}$$

Now, by changing $rs = b^{m+n}$ back to logarithmic form, we obtai[ ]

$$\log_b rs = m + n$$

Replace m with $\log_b r$ and replace n with $\log_b s$ to yield

$$\log_b rs = \log_b r + \log_b s$$

The following two examples illustrate the use of Property 10[ ]

Because logarithms are defined only for positive numbers,
logarithmic equations may not have any solutions. (In those cas[ ]
set.) It is also possible for a logarithmic equation to have a negat[ ]
ple illustrates.

EXAMPLE 14   Solve $\log_2 3 + \log_2(x + 4) = 3$.

Solution

$$\log_2 3 + \log_2(x + 4) = 3$$
$$\log_2 3(x + 4) = 3 \qquad \text{Property 10.5}$$
$$3(x + 4) = 2^3 \qquad \text{Change to exponential form}$$
$$3x + 12 = 8$$
$$3x = -4$$
$$x = -\frac{4}{3}$$

The only restriction is that $x + 4 > 0$ or $x > -4$. Therefore, the s[ ]

you should check this answer. —

Concept Quiz 10.4

For Problems 1–7, answer true or false.

1. For $m > 0$, the $\log_m n = q$ is equivalent to $m^q = n$.
2. The $\log_7 7$ is equal to zero.
3. A logarithm by definition is an exponent.
4. The $\log_5 9^2$ is equivalent to $2 \log_5 9$.
5. The expression $\log_2 x - \log_2 y + \log_2 z$ is equivalent to $\log_2$[ ]
6. $\log_4 4 + \log_4 1 = 1$.
7. For the equation $\log_2(x + 3) + \log_2(x + 5) = 1$, the solutio[ ]
   of x that are greater than -3.

For Problems 8–10, match each expression with its equivalent fc[ ]

8. $\log_3(2x)$ **A.** $\log_3 \frac{1}{2} + \log_3 x$

9. $\log_3\left(\frac{1}{2}x\right)$ **B.** $\frac{1}{2}\log_3 x$

10. $\log_3 \sqrt{x}$ **C.** $\log_3 2 + \log_3 x$

Problem Set 10.4

For Problems 1–10, write each exponential statement in
logarithmic form. For example, $2^5 = 32$ becomes $\log_2 32 = 5$
in logarithmic form. (Objective 1)

1. $2^7 = 128$
2. $3^3 = 27$
3. $5^3 = 125$
4. $2^6 = 64$
5. $10^3 = 1000$
6.
7. $2^{-2} = \frac{1}{4}$
8.
9. $10^{-1} = 0.1$
10.

---

85. $2\log_b x + 4\log_b y - 3\log_b z$

86. $\log_b x + \frac{1}{2}\log_b y$

87. $\frac{1}{2}\log_b x - \log_b x + 4\log_b y$

88. $2\log_b x + \frac{1}{2}\log_b(x - 1) - 4\log_b(2x + 5)$

For Problems 89–106, solve each equation. (Objective 4)

89. $\log_3 x + \log_3 4 = 2$
90. $\log_7 5 + \log_7 x = 1$
91. $\log_{10} x + \log_{10}(x - 21) = 2$
92. $\log_{10} x + \log_{10}(x - 3) = 1$
93. $\log_2 x + \log_2(x - 3) = 2$
94. $\log_3 x + \log_3(x - 2) = 1$

95. $\log_3(x + 3) + \log_3(x + 5)$

96. $\log_2(x + 2) = 1 - \log_2(x$ [ ]

97. $\log_2 3 + \log_2(x + 4) = 3$

98. $\log_4 7 + \log_4(x + 3) = 2$

99. $\log_{10}(2x - 1) - \log_{10}(x$ [ ]

100. $\log_{10}(9x - 2) = 1 + \log_{10}$[ ]

101. $\log_5(3x - 2) = 1 + \log_5($[ ]

102. $\log_6 x + \log_6(x + 5) = 2$

103. $\log_2(x - 1) - \log_2(x + 3$ [ ]

104. $\log_5 x = \log_5(x + 2) + 1$[ ]

105. $\log_8(x + 7) + \log_8 x = 1$[ ]

106. $\log_6(x + 1) + \log_6(x - 4$[ ]

107. Verify Property 10.6.

108. Verify Property 10.7.

Thoughts Into Words

109. Explain, without using Property 10.4, why $4^{\log_4 9}$
     equals 9.

110. How would you explain the concept of a logarithm to
     someone who had just completed an elementary alge-
     bra course?

111. In the next section, we w[ ]
     function $f(x) = \log_2 x$ is [ ]
     function $f(x) = 2^x$. From [ ]
     you sketch a graph of $f($[ ]

10.5   Logarithmic Functions

OBJECTIVES
1. Graph logarithmic functions
2. Evaluate common logarithms and natural logarithms
3. Solve equations for common logarithms and natural lo[ ]

We can now use the concept of a logarithm to define a logarith[ ]

Definition 10.5

If $b > 0$ and $b \neq 1$, then the function defined by

$$f(x) = \log_b x$$

where x is any positive real number, is called the **logarithm**[ ]

We can obtain the graph of a specific logarithmic function in various ways. For example, the equation $y = \log_2 x$ can be changed to the exponential equation $2^y = x$, where we can determine a table of values. In the next set of exercises you will be asked to use this approach to graph some logarithmic functions. We can also set up a table of values directly from the logarithmic equation and sketch the graph from the table. Example 1 illustrates this approach.

Classroom Example
Graph $f(x) = \log_3 x$.

EXAMPLE 1   Graph $f(x) = \log_2 x$.

Solution

Let's choose some values for x in which we can easily determine the corresponding values for $\log_2 x$. (Remember that logarithms are defined only for the positive real numbers.)

x	$f(x)$	
$\dfrac{1}{8}$	-3	$\log_2 \dfrac{1}{8} = -3$ because $2^{-3} = \dfrac{1}{2^3} = \dfrac{1}{8}$
$\dfrac{1}{4}$	-2	
$\dfrac{1}{2}$	-1	
1	0	$\log_2 1 = 0$ because $2^0 = 1$
2	1	
4	2	
8	3	

Plot these points and connect them with a smooth curve to produce Figure 10.27.

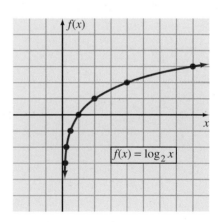

Figure 10.27

Now suppose that we consider two functions f and g as follows:

$f(x) = b^x$ Domain: all real numbers
            Range: positive real numbers

$g(x) = \log_b x$ Domain: positive real numbers
            Range: all real numbers

Furthermore, suppose that we consider the composition of f and g and the composition of g and f.

$$(f \circ g)(x) = f(g(x)) = f(\log_b x) = b^{\log_b x} = x$$
$$(g \circ f)(x) = g(f(x)) = g(b^x) = \log_b b^x = x \log_b b = x(1) = x$$

Because the domain of f is the range of g, the range of f is the domain of g, $f(g(x)) = x$, and $g(f(x)) = x$, the two functions f and g are *inverses* of each other.

Remember that the graph of a function and the graph of its inverse are reflections of each other through the line $y = x$. Thus we can determine the graph of a logarithmic function by reflecting the graph of its inverse exponential function through the line $y = x$. We demonstrate this idea in Figure 10.28, in which the graph of $y = 2^x$ has been reflected across the line $y = x$ to produce the graph of $y = \log_2 x$.

The general behavior patterns of exponential functions were illustrated back in Figure 10.3. We can now reflect each of these graphs through the line $y = x$ and observe the general behavior patterns of logarithmic functions shown in Figure 10.29.

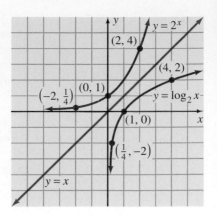

Figure 10.28

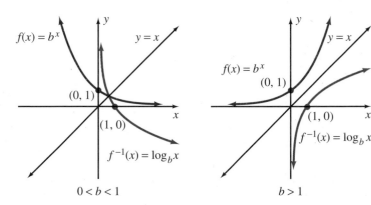

Figure 10.29

As you graph logarithmic functions, don't forget about transformations of basic curves.

1. The graph of $f(x) = 3 + \log_2 x$ is the graph of $f(x) = \log_2 x$ moved up three units. (Because $\log_2 x + 3$ is apt to be confused with $\log_2(x + 3)$, we commonly write $3 + \log_2 x$.)

2. The graph of $f(x) = \log_2(x - 4)$ is the graph of $f(x) = \log_2 x$ moved four units to the right.

3. The graph of $f(x) = -\log_2 x$ is the graph of $f(x) = \log_2 x$ reflected across the x axis.

Common Logarithms—Base 10

The properties of logarithms we discussed in Section 10.4 are true for any valid base. However, because the Hindu-Arabic numeration system that we use is a base-10 system, logarithms to base 10 have historically been used for computational purposes. Base-10 logarithms are called **common logarithms**.

Originally, common logarithms were developed to aid in complicated numerical calculations that involve products, quotients, and powers of real numbers. Today they are seldom used for that purpose, because the calculator and computer can much more effectively handle the messy computational problems. However, common logarithms do still occur in applications, so they deserve our attention.

As we know from earlier work, the definition of a logarithm provides the basis for evaluating $\log_{10} x$ for values of x that are integral powers of 10. Consider the following examples:

$\log_{10} 1000 = 3$ because $10^3 = 1000$

$\log_{10} 100 = 2$ because $10^2 = 100$

58. $\dfrac{\ln 3}{0.04}$ **59.**

Thoughts Into Word

62. Why is the number 1 excluded
logarithm?

Graphing Calculato

64. Graph $f(x) = x$, $f(x) = e^x$, and j
set of axes.

65. Graph $f(x) = x$, $f(x) = 10^x$, and f
set of axes.

66. Graph $f(x) = \ln x$. How should t
x, $f(x) = 4\ln x$, and $f(x) = 6\ln$
of $f(x) = \ln x$? Graph the three fu
of axes with $f(x) = \ln x$.

67. Graph $f(x) = \log x$. Now predict
$+ \log x$, $f(x) = -2 + \log x$, a
Graph the three functions on the
$f(x) = \log x$.

Answers to the Concept Q

1. False   **2.** False   **3.** True

10.6 Exponenti
and Proble

OBJECTIVES 1

2

3

4

5

In S
the e
if we

$\log_{10} 10 = 1$ because $10^1 = 10$

$\log_{10} 1 = 0$ because $10^0 = 1$

$\log_{10} 0.1 = -1$ because $10^{-1} = \dfrac{1}{10} = 0.1$

$\log_{10} 0.01 = -2$ because $10^{-2} = \dfrac{1}{10^2} = 0.01$

$\log_{10} 0.001 = -3$ because $10^{-3} = \dfrac{1}{10^3} = 0.001$

When working exclusively with base-10 logarithms, it is customary to omit writing the numeral 10 to designate the base. Thus the expression $\log_{10} x$ is written as $\log x$, and a statement such as $\log_{10} 1000 = 3$ becomes $\log 1000 = 3$. We will follow this practice from now on in this chapter, but don't forget that the base is understood to be 10.

$$\log_{10} x = \log x$$

To find the common logarithm of a positive number that is not an integral power of 10, we can use an appropriately equipped calculator. A calculator that has a common logarithm function (ordinarily, a key labeled $\boxed{\log}$ is used) gives us the following results rounded to four decimal places:

$\log 1.75 = 0.2430$

$\log 23.8 = 1.3766$ Be sure that you can use a calculator and obtain these results

$\log 134 = 2.1271$

$\log 0.192 = -0.7167$

$\log 0.0246 = -1.6091$

In order to use logarithms to solve problems, we sometimes need to be able to determine a number when the logarithm of the number is known. That is to say, we may need to determine x if $\log x$ is known. Let's consider an example.

Classroom Example
Find x if $\log x = 0.6805$.

EXAMPLE 2   Find x if $\log x = 0.2430$.

Solution

If $\log x = 0.2430$, then by changing to exponential form we have $10^{0.2430} = x$. Use the $\boxed{10^x}$ key to find x:

$x = 10^{0.2430} \approx 1.749846689$

Therefore $x = 1.7498$ rounded to five significant digits.

Be sure that you can use your calculator and obtain the following results. We rounded the values for x to five significant digits.

If $\log x = 0.7629$, then $x = 10^{0.7629} = 5.7930$.

If $\log x = 1.4825$, then $x = 10^{1.4825} = 30.374$.

If $\log x = 4.0214$, then $x = 10^{4.0214} = 10{,}505$.

If $\log x = -1.5162$, then $x = 10^{-1.5162} = 0.030465$.

If $\log x = -3.8921$, then $x = 10^{-3.8921} = 0.00012820$.

The **common logarithmic function** is defined by the equation $f(x) = \log x$. It should now be a simple matter to set up a table of values and sketch the function. You will do this in

Problem Set 10

For Problems 1–10, use a calc
logarithm. Express answers
(Objective 2)

1. $\log 7.24$ **2.** l

3. $\log 52.23$ **4.** l

5. $\log 3214.1$ **6.** l

7. $\log 0.729$ **8.** l

9. $\log 0.00034$ **10.** l

For Problems 11–20, use your
given $\log x$. Express answers
(Objective 3)

11. $\log x = 2.6143$ **12.** lc

13. $\log x = 4.9547$ **14.** lc

15. $\log x = 1.9006$ **16.** lc

17. $\log x = -1.3148$ **18.** lc

19. $\log x = -2.1928$ **20.** lc

For Problems 21–30, use you
natural logarithm. Express answ
(Objective 2)

21. $\ln 5$ **22.** ln

23. $\ln 32.6$ **24.** ln

25. $\ln 430$ **26.** ln

27. $\ln 0.46$ **28.** ln

29. $\ln 0.0314$ **30.** ln

For Problems 31–40, use your
given $\ln x$. Express answers to
(Objective 3)

31. $\ln x = 0.4721$ **32.**

33. $\ln x = 1.1425$ **34.**

35. $\ln x = 4.6873$ **36.**

37. $\ln x = -0.7284$ **38.**

39. $\ln x = -3.3244$ **40.**

41. (a) Complete the following
$f(x) = \log x$. Express th
nearest tenth.

x	0.1	0.5	1
$\log x$			

---

5 as a power of 3. We can solve this type of problem by using the properties of logarithms and the following property of equality:

> **Property 10.8**
>
> If $x > 0$, $y > 0$, $b > 0$, and $b \neq 1$, then $x = y$ if and only if $\log_b x = \log_b y$.

Property 10.8 is stated in terms of any valid base b; however, for most applications, we use either common logarithms or natural logarithms. Let's consider some examples.

Classroom Example
Solve $5^x = 12$ to the nearest hundredth.

EXAMPLE 1   Solve $3^x = 5$ to the nearest hundredth.

Solution

By using common logarithms, we can proceed as follows:

$$3^x = 5$$
$$\log 3^x = \log 5 \qquad \text{Property 10.8}$$
$$x \log 3 = \log 5 \qquad \log r^p = p \log r$$
$$x = \frac{\log 5}{\log 3}$$
$$x = 1.46 \quad \text{to the nearest hundredth}$$

✔ **Check**

Because $3^{1.46} \approx 4.972754647$, we say that, to the nearest hundredth, the solution set for $3^x = 5$ is $\{1.46\}$.

Classroom Example
Solve $e^{x-3} = 6$ to the nearest hundredth.

EXAMPLE 2   Solve $e^{x+1} = 5$ to the nearest hundredth.

Solution

Because base e is used in the exponential expression, let's use natural logarithms to help solve this equation.

$$e^{x+1} = 5$$
$$\ln e^{x+1} = \ln 5 \qquad \text{Property 10.8}$$
$$(x + 1) \ln e = \ln 5 \qquad \ln r^p = p \ln r$$
$$(x + 1)(1) = \ln 5 \qquad \ln e = 1$$
$$x = \ln 5 - 1$$
$$x = 0.61 \quad \text{to the nearest hundredth}$$

The solution set is $\{0.61\}$. Check it!

Classroom Example
Solve $3^{4x+3} = 4^{5x-1}$ to the nearest hundredth.

EXAMPLE 3   Solve $2^{3x-2} = 3^{2x+1}$ to the nearest hundredth.

Solution

$$2^{3x-2} = 3^{2x+1}$$
$$\log 2^{3x-2} = \log 3^{2x+1}$$
$$(3x - 2)\log 2 = (2x + 1)\log 3$$
$$3x \log 2 - 2 \log 2 = 2x \log 3 + \log 3$$
$$3x \log 2 - 2x \log 3 = \log 3 + 2 \log 2$$

$$x(3\log 2 - 2\log 3) = \log 3 + 2\log 2$$

$$x = \frac{\log 3 + 2\log 2}{3\log 2 - 2\log 3}$$

$$x = -21.10 \quad \text{to the nearest hundredth}$$

The solution set is $\{-21.10\}$. Check it!

Logarithmic Equations

In Example 11 of Section 10.4, we solved the logarithmic equation

$$\log_{10}x + \log_{10}(x + 9) = 1$$

by simplifying the left side of the equation to $\log_{10}[x(x + 9)]$ and then changing the equation to exponential form to complete the solution. Now, using Property 10.8, we can solve such a logarithmic equation another way and also expand our equation solving capabilities. Let's consider some examples.

Classroom Example
Solve $\log x + \log(x - 21) = 2$.

EXAMPLE 4   Solve $\log x + \log(x - 15) = 2$.

Solution

Because $\log 100 = 2$, the given equation becomes

$$\log x + \log(x - 15) = \log 100$$

Now simplify the left side, apply Property 10.8, and proceed as follows.

$$\log(x)(x - 15) = \log 100$$
$$x(x - 15) = 100$$
$$x^2 - 15x - 100 = 0$$
$$(x - 20)(x + 5) = 0$$
$$x - 20 = 0 \quad \text{or} \quad x + 5 = 0$$
$$x = 20 \quad \text{or} \quad x = -5$$

The domain of a logarithmic function must contain only positive numbers, so x and $x - 15$ must be positive in this problem. Therefore, we discard the solution -5; the solution set is $\{20\}$.

Classroom Example
Solve $\ln(x + 17) = \ln(x - 3) + \ln 5$.

EXAMPLE 5   Solve $\ln(x + 2) = \ln(x - 4) + \ln 3$.

Solution

$$\ln(x + 2) = \ln(x - 4) + \ln 3$$
$$\ln(x + 2) = \ln[3(x - 4)]$$
$$x + 2 = 3(x - 4)$$
$$x + 2 = 3x - 12$$
$$14 = 2x$$
$$7 = x$$

The solution set is $\{7\}$.

Classroom Example
Solve $\log_b(x - 1) + \log_b(5x + 2) = \log_b x$.

EXAMPLE 6   Solve $\log_b(x + 2) + \log_b(2x - 1) = \log_b x$.

Solution

$$\log_b(x + 2) + \log_b(2x - 1) = \log_b x$$

$$\log_b[(x + 2)(2x - 1)] = \log_b x$$
$$(x + 2)(2x - 1) = x$$
$$2x^2 + 3x - 2 = x$$
$$2x^2 + 2x - 2 = 0$$
$$x^2 + x - 1 = 0$$

Using the quadratic formula, we obtain

$$x = \frac{-1 \pm \sqrt{1 + 4}}{2}$$

$$= \frac{-1 \pm \sqrt{5}}{2}$$

Because $x + 2$, $2x - 1$, and x have to be positive, we must discard the solution $\dfrac{-1 - \sqrt{5}}{2}$;

the solution set is $\left\{ \dfrac{-1 + \sqrt{5}}{2} \right\}$. ∎

Using Logarithms to Solve Problems

In Section 10.2 we used the compound interest formula

$$A = P\left(1 + \frac{r}{n}\right)^{nt}$$

to determine the amount of money (A) accumulated at the end of t years if P dollars is invested at rate of interest r compounded n times per year. Now let's use this formula to solve other types of problems that deal with compound interest.

Classroom Example
How long will it take $6000 to double if it is invested at 3% interest compounded monthly?

EXAMPLE 7

How long will it take for $500 to double if it is invested at 12% interest compounded quarterly?

Solution

"To double" means that the $500 must grow into $1000. Thus

$$1000 = 500\left(1 + \frac{0.12}{4}\right)^{4t}$$
$$= 500(1 + 0.03)^{4t}$$
$$= 500(1.03)^{4t}$$

Multiplying both sides of $1000 = 500(1.03)^{4t}$ by $\dfrac{1}{500}$ yields

$$2 = (1.03)^{4t}$$

Therefore

$$\log 2 = \log(1.03)^{4t} \qquad\qquad \text{Property 10.8}$$
$$= 4t \log 1.03 \qquad\qquad \log r^p = p \log r$$

Now let's solve for t.

$$4t \log 1.03 = \log 2$$

$$t = \frac{\log 2}{4 \log 1.03}$$

$$t = 5.9 \quad \text{to the nearest tenth}$$

Therefore we are claiming that $500 invested at 12% interest compounded quarterly will double in approximately 5.9 years.

✔ Check

$500 invested at 12% interest compounded quarterly for 5.9 years will produce

$$A = \$500\left(1 + \frac{0.12}{4}\right)^{4(5.9)}$$

$$= \$500(1.03)^{23.6}$$

$$= \$1004.45$$

Classroom Example
For a certain virus, the equation $Q(t) = Q_0 e^{-0.2t}$, when t is the time in hours and Q_0 is the initial number of virus particles, yields the number of virus particles as a function of time. How long will it take 5000 particles to be reduced to 500 particles?

EXAMPLE 8

Suppose that the number of bacteria present in a certain culture after t minutes is given by the equation $Q(t) = Q_0 e^{0.04t}$, where Q_0 represents the initial number of bacteria. How long will it take for the bacteria count to grow from 500 to 2000?

Solution

Substituting into $Q(t) = Q_0 e^{0.04t}$ and solving for t, we obtain the following.

$$2000 = 500 e^{0.04t}$$

$$4 = e^{0.04t}$$

$$\ln 4 = \ln e^{0.04t}$$

$$\ln 4 = 0.04t \ln e$$

$$\ln 4 = 0.04t \qquad \ln e = 1$$

$$\frac{\ln 4}{0.04} = t$$

$$34.7 = t \quad \text{to the nearest tenth}$$

It should take approximately 34.7 minutes.

Richter Numbers

Seismologists use the Richter scale to measure and report the magnitude of earthquakes. The equation

$$R = \log \frac{I}{I_0} \qquad R \text{ is called a Richter number}$$

compares the intensity I of an earthquake to a minimal or reference intensity I_0. The reference intensity is the smallest earth movement that can be recorded on a seismograph. Suppose that the intensity of an earthquake was determined to be 50,000 times the reference intensity. In this case, $I = 50,000\, I_0$, and the Richter number is calculated as follows:

$$R = \log \frac{50,000\, I_0}{I_0}$$

$$= \log 50,000$$

$$\approx 4.698970004$$

Thus a Richter number of 4.7 would be reported. Let's consider two more examples that involve Richter numbers.

Classroom Example
An earthquake has a Richter number of 7.3. How did its intensity compare to the reference intensity?

EXAMPLE 9

An earthquake in the San Francisco CA, area in 1989 was reported to have a Richter number of 6.9. How did its intensity compare to the reference intensity?

Solution

$$6.9 = \log \frac{I}{I_0}$$

$$10^{6.9} = \frac{I}{I_0}$$

$$I = (10^{6.9})(I_0)$$

$$I \approx 7{,}943{,}282\, I_0$$

Its intensity was a little less than 8 million times the reference intensity.

Classroom Example
Another earthquake has a Richter number of 6.7. Compare the intensity level of this earthquake to an earthquake with a Richter number of 7.3.

EXAMPLE 10

An earthquake in Iran in 1990 had a Richter number of 7.7. Compare the intensity of this earthquake to that of the one in San Francisco referred to in Example 9.

Solution

From Example 9 we have $I = (10^{6.9})(I_0)$ for the earthquake in San Francisco. Then, using a Richter number of 7.7, we obtain $I = (10^{7.7})(I_0)$ for the earthquake in Iran. Therefore, by comparison,

$$\frac{(10^{7.7})(I_0)}{(10^{6.9})(I_0)} = 10^{7.7-6.9} = 10^{0.8} \approx 6.3$$

The earthquake in Iran was about 6 times as intense as the one in San Francisco.

Change-of-Base Formula for Logarithms with a Base Other Than 10 or *e*

The basic approach whereby we apply Property 10.8 and use either common or natural logarithms can also be used to evaluate a logarithm to some base other than 10 or *e*. Consider the following example.

Classroom Example
Evaluate $\log_7 21$.

EXAMPLE 11   Evaluate $\log_3 41$.

Solution

Let $x = \log_3 41$. Change to exponential form to obtain

$$3^x = 41$$

Now we can apply Property 10.8 and proceed as follows.

$$\log 3^x = \log 41$$

$$x \log 3 = \log 41$$

$$x = \frac{\log 41}{\log 3}$$

$$x = 3.3802 \quad \text{rounded to four decimal places}$$

Therefore we are claiming that 3 raised to the 3.3802 power will produce approximately 41. Check it!

The method of Example 11 to evaluate $\log_a r$ produces the following formula, which we often refer to as the **change-of-base formula for logarithms**.

Property 10.9

If a, b, and r are positive numbers, with $a \neq 1$ and $b \neq 1$, then

$$\log_a r = \frac{\log_b r}{\log_b a}$$

By using Property 10.9, we can easily determine a relationship between logarithms of different bases. For example, suppose that in Property 10.9 we let $a = 10$ and $b = e$. Then

$$\log_a r = \frac{\log_b r}{\log_b a}$$

becomes

$$\log_{10} r = \frac{\log_e r}{\log_e 10}$$

$$\log_e r = (\log_e 10)(\log_{10} r)$$

$$\log_e r = (2.3026)(\log_{10} r)$$

Thus the natural logarithm of any positive number is approximately equal to the common logarithm of the number times 2.3026.

Now we can use a graphing utility to graph logarithmic functions such as $f(x) = \log_2 x$. Using the change-of-base formula, we can express this function as $f(x) = \dfrac{\log x}{\log 2}$ or as $f(x) = \dfrac{\ln x}{\ln 2}$. The graph of $f(x) = \log_2 x$ is shown in Figure 10.32.

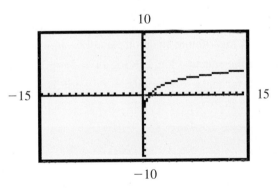

Figure 10.32

Finally, let's use a graphical approach to solve an equation that is cumbersome to solve with an algebraic approach.

Classroom Example
Solve the equation $(3^x + 3^{-x})/4 = 2$.

EXAMPLE 12   Solve the equation $(5^x - 5^{-x})/2 = 3$.

Solution

First, we need to recognize that the solutions for the equation $(5^x - 5^{-x})/2 = 3$ are the x intercepts of the graph of the equation $y = (5^x - 5^{-x})/2 - 3$. We can use a graphing utility to obtain the graph of this equation as shown in Figure 10.33. Use the ZOOM and TRACE features to determine that the graph crosses the x axis at approximately 1.13. Thus the solution set of the original expression is $\{1.13\}$.

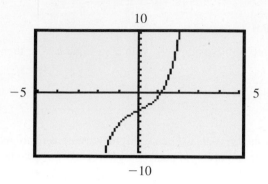

Figure 10.33

Concept Quiz 10.6

For Problems 1–10, answer true or false.

1. For $x > 0$ and $y > 0$, if $\log_2 x = \log_2 y$, then $x = y$.
2. For $x > 0$ and $y > 0$, if $x = y$, then $\ln x = \log y$.
3. The formula $Q = Q_0 e^{at}$ represents the exponential decay of a substance if $0 < a < 1$.
4. The formula $Q = Q_0 e^{at}$ represents the exponential growth of a substance if $a > 0$.
5. An earthquake with a Richter number of 7.0 is 10 times more intense than an earthquake with a Richter number of 6.0.
6. $\log_3 7 = \dfrac{\ln 7}{\ln 3}$
7. The function $f(x) = \log_4 x$ can be expressed as $f(x) = \dfrac{\log x}{\log 4}$.
8. The solution to a logarithmic equation cannot be an irrational number.
9. All solutions of the equation $\log_b x + \log_b(x + 2) = 3$ must be positive numbers.
10. The solution set for $\ln(3x - 4) - \ln(x + 1) = \ln 2$ is $\{8\}$.

Problem Set 10.6

For Problems 1–20, solve each exponential equation and express approximate solutions to the nearest hundredth. (Objective 1)

1. $3^x = 13$
2. $2^x = 21$
3. $4^n = 35$
4. $5^n = 75$
5. $2^x + 7 = 50$
6. $3^x - 6 = 25$
7. $3^{x-2} = 11$
8. $2^{x+1} = 7$
9. $5^{3t+1} = 9$
10. $7^{2t-1} = 35$
11. $e^x = 27$
12. $e^x = 86$
13. $e^{x-2} = 13.1$
14. $e^{x-1} = 8.2$
15. $3e^x - 1 = 17$
16. $2e^x = 12.4$

17. $5^{2x+1} = 7^{x+3}$
18. $3^{x-1} = 2^{x+3}$
19. $3^{2x+1} = 2^{3x+2}$
20. $5^{x-1} = 2^{2x+1}$

For Problems 21–32, solve each logarithmic equation and express irrational solutions in lowest radical form. (Objective 2)

21. $\log x + \log(x + 21) = 2$
22. $\log x + \log(x + 3) = 1$
23. $\log(3x - 1) = 1 + \log(5x - 2)$
24. $\log(2x - 1) - \log(x - 3) = 1$
25. $\log(x + 1) = \log 3 - \log(2x - 1)$

26. $\log(x - 2) = 1 - \log(x + 3)$

27. $\log(x + 2) - \log(2x + 1) = \log x$

28. $\log(x + 1) - \log(x + 2) = \log\dfrac{1}{x}$

29. $\ln(2t + 5) = \ln 3 + \ln(t - 1)$

30. $\ln(3t - 4) - \ln(t + 1) = \ln 2$

31. $\log\sqrt{x} = \sqrt{\log x}$

32. $\log x^2 = (\log x)^2$

For Problems 33–42, approximate each logarithm to three decimal places. (Example 11 and/or Property 10.9 should be of some help.) (Objective 5)

33. $\log_2 40$

34. $\log_2 93$

35. $\log_3 16$

36. $\log_3 37$

37. $\log_4 1.6$

38. $\log_4 3.2$

39. $\log_5 0.26$

40. $\log_5 0.047$

41. $\log_7 500$

42. $\log_8 750$

For Problems 43–55, solve each problem and express answers to the nearest tenth unless stated otherwise. (Objectives 3, 4)

43. How long will it take $750 to be worth $1000 if it is invested at 6% interest compounded quarterly?

44. How long will it take $1000 to double if it is invested at 6% interest compounded semiannually?

45. How long will it take $2000 to double if it is invested at 4% interest compounded continuously?

46. How long will it take $500 to triple if it is invested at 5% interest compounded continuously?

47. What rate of interest compounded continuously is needed for an investment of $500 to grow to $900 in 10 years?

48. What rate of interest compounded continuously is needed for an investment of $2500 to grow to $10,000 in 20 years?

49. For a certain strain of bacteria, the number of bacteria present after t hours is given by the equation $Q = Q_0 e^{0.34t}$,

where Q_0 represents the initial number of bacteria. How long will it take 400 bacteria to increase to 4000 bacteria?

50. A piece of machinery valued at $30,000 depreciates at a rate of 10% yearly. How long will it take for it to reach a value of $15,000?

51. The equation $P(a) = 14.7e^{-0.21a}$, in which a is the altitude above sea level measured in miles, yields the atmospheric pressure in pounds per square inch. If the atmospheric pressure at Cheyenne, Wyoming, is approximately 11.53 pounds per square inch, find that city's altitude above sea level. Express your answer to the nearest hundred feet.

52. The number of grams of a certain radioactive substance present after t hours is given by the equation $Q = Q_0 e^{-0.45t}$, where Q_0 represents the initial number of grams. How long will it take 2500 grams to be reduced to 1250 grams?

53. For a certain culture, the equation $Q(t) = Q_0 e^{0.4t}$, in which Q_0 is an initial number of bacteria, and t is the time measured in hours, yields the number of bacteria as a function of time. How long will it take 500 bacteria to increase to 2000?

54. Suppose that the equation $P(t) = P_0 e^{0.02t}$, in which P_0 represents an initial population, and t is the time in years, is used to predict population growth. How long will it take a city of 50,000 to double its population?

55. An earthquake in Los Angeles in 1971 had an intensity of approximately 5 million times the reference intensity. What was the Richter number associated with that earthquake?

56. An earthquake in San Francisco in 1906 was reported to have a Richter number of 8.3. How did its intensity compare to the reference intensity?

57. Calculate how many times more intense an earthquake with a Richter number of 7.3 is than an earthquake with a Richter number of 6.4.

58. Calculate how many times more intense an earthquake is with a Richter number of 8.9 than is an earthquake with a Richter number of 6.2.

Thoughts Into Words

59. Explain how to determine $\log_4 76$ without using Property 10.9.

60. Explain the concept of a Richter number.

61. Explain how you would solve the equation $2^x = 64$ and also how you would solve the equation $2^x = 53$.

62. How do logarithms with a base of 9 compare to logarithms with a base of 3? Explain how you reached this conclusion.

Further Investigations

63. Use the approach of Example 11 to develop Property 10.9.

64. Let $r = b$ in Property 10.9, and verify that $\log_a b = \dfrac{1}{\log_b a}$.

65. Solve the equation $\dfrac{5^x - 5^{-x}}{2} = 3$. Express your answer to the nearest hundredth.

66. Solve the equation $y = \dfrac{10^x + 10^{-x}}{2}$ for x in terms of y.

67. Solve the equation $y = \dfrac{e^x - e^{-x}}{2}$ for x in terms of y.

Graphing Calculator Activities

68. Check your answers for Problems 17–20 by graphing the appropriate function and finding the x intercept.

69. Graph $f(x) = x$, $f(x) = 2^x$, and $f(x) = \log_2 x$ on the same set of axes.

70. Graph $f(x) = x$, $f(x) = (0.5)^x$, and $f(x) = \log_{0.5} x$ on the same set of axes.

71. Graph $f(x) = \log_2 x$. Now predict the graphs for $f(x) = \log_3 x$, $f(x) = \log_4 x$, and $f(x) = \log_8 x$. Graph these three functions on the same set of axes with $f(x) = \log_2 x$.

72. Graph $f(x) = \log_5 x$. Now predict the graphs for $f(x) = 2\log_5 x$, $f(x) = -4\log_5 x$, and $f(x) = \log_5(x + 4)$. Graph these three functions on the same set of axes with $f(x) = \log_5 x$.

73. Use both a graphical and an algebraic approach to solve the equation $\dfrac{2^x - 2^{-x}}{3} = 4$.

Answers to the Concept Quiz
1. True **2.** False **3.** False **4.** True **5.** True **6.** True **7.** True **8.** False **9.** True **10.** False

OBJECTIVE	SUMMARY	EXAMPLES
Solve exponential equations (Section 10.1/Objective 1)	Some exponential equations can be solved by applying Property 11.2: If $b > 0$, $b \neq 1$, and m and n are real numbers, then $b^n = b^m$ if and only if $n = m$. This property can only be applied for equations that can be written in the form where the bases are equal.	Solve $4^{3x} = 32$. **Solution** Rewrite each side of the equation as a power of 2. Then apply property 11.2 to solve the equation. $$4^{3x} = 32$$ $$(2^2)^{3x} = 2^5$$ $$2^{6x} = 2^5$$ $$6x = 5$$ $$x = \frac{5}{6}$$ The solution set is $\left\{\frac{5}{6}\right\}$.
Graph exponential functions (Section 10.1/Objective 2)	A function defined by an equation of the form $f(x) = b^x$, for $b > 0$ and $b \neq 0$, is called an exponential function with base b.	Graph $f(x) = 4^x$. **Solution** Set up a table of values. x: -2, -1, 0, 1, 2 $f(x)$: $\frac{1}{16}$, $\frac{1}{4}$, 1, 4, 16
Solve exponential growth problems (Section 10.2/Objective 1)	In general, the equation $P = P_0(1.06)^t$ yields the predicted price P of an item in t years at the annual inflation rate of 6%, where that item presently costs P_0.	Assuming that the rate of inflation is 3% per year, find the price of a $20.00 haircut in 5 years. **Solution** Use the formula $P = P_0(1.03)^t$ and substitute $20.00 for P_0 and 5 for t. $$P = 20.00(1.03)^5 \approx 23.19$$ The haircut would cost $23.19.
Solve compound interest problems (Section 10.2/Objective 2)	A general formula for any principal, P, invested for any number of years (t) at a rate of r percent compounded n times per year is $A = P\left(1 + \dfrac{r}{n}\right)^{nt}$; where A represents the total amount of money accumulated at the end of t years.	Find the total amount of money accumulated at the end of 8 years when $4000 is invested at 6% compounded quarterly. **Solution** $$A = 4000\left(1 + \frac{0.06}{4}\right)^{4(8)}$$ $$A = 4000(1.015)^{32}$$ $$A = 6441.30$$

(continued)

OBJECTIVE	SUMMARY	EXAMPLES
Solve exponential decay half-life problems (Section 10.2/Objective 3)	For radioactive substances, the rate of decay is exponential and can be described based on the half-life of a substance. The *half-life* of a radioactive substance is the amount of time that it takes for one-half of an initial amount of the substance to disappear as the result of decay. Suppose there is an initial amount, Q_0, of a radioactive substance with a half-life of h. The amount of substance remaining, Q, after a time period of t, is given by the formula $Q = Q_0 \left(\dfrac{1}{2}\right)^{\frac{t}{h}}$. The units of measure for t and h must be the same.	Molybdenum-99 has a half-life of 66 hours. If there are 200 milligrams of Molybdenum-99 initially, how many milligrams remain after 16 hours? **Solution** $$Q = 200\left(\dfrac{1}{2}\right)^{\frac{16}{66}}$$ $Q = 169.1$ to the nearest tenth of a milligram Thus approximately 169.1 milligrams remain after 16 hours.
Solve growth problems involving the number e (Section 10.2/Objective 4)	The law of exponential growth $Q(t) = Q_0 e^{kt}$ is used as a mathematical model for growth-and-decay problems. In this equation, $Q(t)$ represents the quantity of a given substance at any time t; Q_0 is the initial amount of the substance (when $t = 0$); and k is a constant that depends on the particular application. If $k < 0$, then $Q(t)$ decreases as t increases, and we refer to the model as the **law of decay**.	The number of bacteria present in a certain culture after t hours is given by the equation $Q(t) = Q_0 e^{0.42t}$ where Q_0 represents the initial number of bacteria. How long will it take 100 bacteria to increase to 500 bacteria? **Solution** Substitute 100 for Q_0 and 500 for $Q(t)$ into $Q(t) = Q_0 e^{0.42t}$. $500 = 100e^{0.42t}$ $5 = e^{0.42t}$ $\ln 5 = \ln e^{0.42t}$ $\ln 5 = 0.42t \ln e$ $\ln 5 = 0.42t \qquad \ln e = 1$ $t = \dfrac{\ln 5}{0.42} = 3.83$ to the nearest hundredth It will take approximately 3.83 hours for 100 bacteria to increase to 500 bacteria.
Solve compound continuously problems (Section 10.2/Objective 4; Section 10.6/Objective 3)	The value of $\left(1 + \dfrac{1}{n}\right)^n$ as n gets infinitely large, approaches the number e, where $e = 2.71828$ to five decimal places. The formula $A = Pe^{rt}$ yields the accumulated value, A, of a sum of money, P, that has been invested for t years at a rate of r percent **compounded continuously**.	If \$8300 is invested at 6.5% interest compounded continuously, how much will accumulate in 10 years? **Solution** $A = 8300e^{0.065(10)}$ $= 8300e^{0.65}$ $= 15898.99$ The accumulated amount will be \$15,898.99.

OBJECTIVE	SUMMARY	EXAMPLES
Determine if a function is one to one (Section 10.3/Objective 1)	A function f is said to be one-to-one if every value of $f(x)$ has only one value of x associated with it. In terms of ordered pairs, a one-to-one function is a function such that no two ordered pairs have the same second component. In terms of a graph, the horizontal line test is used to determine if a graph is the graph of a one-to-one function. If the function is a one-to-one function, then a horizontal line will intersect the graph of the function in only one point.	Identify the graph as the graph of a one-to-one function or the graph of a function that is not one-to-one. **Solution** The graph is the graph of a one-to-one function because a horizontal line intersects the graph in only one point.
Verify if two functions are inverses of each other (Section 10.3/Objective 2)	Let f be a one-to-one function with a domain of X and a range of Y. A function g, with a domain of Y and a range of X, is called the inverse function of f if $(f \circ g)(x) = x$ for every x in Y and $(g \circ f)(x) = x$ for every x in X.	Verify that the two given functions are inverses of each other. $$f(x) = \frac{2}{3}x - \frac{5}{6}$$ and $$g(x) = \frac{3}{2}x + \frac{5}{4}$$ **Solution** $(f \circ g)(x) = f(g(x))$ $$= f\left(\frac{3}{2}x + \frac{5}{4}\right)$$ $$= \frac{2}{3}\left(\frac{3}{2}x + \frac{5}{4}\right) - \frac{5}{6}$$ $$= x + \frac{5}{6} - \frac{5}{6}$$ $$= x$$ $(g \circ f)(x) = g(f(x))$ $$= g\left(\frac{2}{3}x - \frac{5}{6}\right)$$ $$= \frac{3}{2}\left(\frac{2}{3}x - \frac{5}{6}\right) + \frac{5}{4}$$ $$= x - \frac{5}{4} + \frac{5}{4}$$ $$= x$$ Therefore the inverse of $f(x)$ is $g(x)$.
Find the inverse function in terms of ordered pairs (Section 10.3/Objective 3)	If the components of each ordered pair of a given one-to-one function are interchanged, the resulting function and the given function are **inverses** of each other. The inverse of a function f is denoted by f^{-1}.	Given $f = \{(2,4), (3,5), (7,7), (8,9)\}$, find the inverse function. **Solution** To find the inverse function, interchange the components of the ordered pairs. $f^{-1} = \{(4,2), (5,3), (7,7), (9,8)\}$

(continued)

OBJECTIVE	SUMMARY	EXAMPLES
Find the inverse of a function (Section 10.3/Objective 4)	A technique for finding the inverse of a function is as follows: **1.** Let $y = f(x)$. **2.** Interchange x and y. **3.** Solve the equation for y in terms of x. **4.** $f^{-1}(x)$ is determined by the final equation. Graphically, two functions that are inverses of each other are mirror images with reference to the line $y = x$. Don't forget the requirement that the domain of f must equal the range of f^{-1}, and the domain f^{-1} must equal the range of f for f and f^{-1} to be inverse functions.	Find the inverse of the function $$f(x) = \frac{2}{5}x - 7.$$ **Solution** **1.** Let $y = \frac{2}{5}x - 7$. **2.** Interchange x and y. $$x = \frac{2}{5}y - 7$$ **3.** Solve for y. $$x = \frac{2}{5}y - 7$$ $$5x = 2y - 35 \qquad \text{Multiply both sides by 5}$$ $$5x + 35 = 2y$$ $$y = \frac{5x + 35}{2}$$ **4.** $f^{-1}(x) = \dfrac{5x + 35}{2}$ The domain and range of f and f^{-1} is all real numbers.
Determine the intervals for which a function is increasing or decreasing. (Section 10.3/Objective 6)	Let f be a function, with the interval I a subset of the domain of f. Let x_1 and x_2 be in I. **1.** f is increasing on I if $f(x_1) < f(x_2)$ whenever $x_1 < x_2$. **2.** f is decreasing on I if $f(x_1) > f(x_2)$ whenever $x_1 < x_2$. **3.** f is constant on I if $f(x_1) = f(x_2)$ for every x_1 and x_2.	Find the intervals on which $f(x) = -(x - 2)^2 + 1$ is increasing and the intervals on which it is decreasing. **Solution** $f(x)$ is increasing on the interval $(-\infty, 2]$ and decreasing on the interval $[2, \infty)$.
Evaluate a logarithmic expression (Section 10.4/Objective 2)	Some logarithmic expressions can be evaluated by switching to exponential form and then applying Property 10.2.	Evaluate $\log_2\left(\dfrac{1}{8}\right)$. **Solution** Let $\log_2\left(\dfrac{1}{8}\right) = x$. Switching to exponential form gives $2^x = \dfrac{1}{8}$. $$2^x = \frac{1}{8}$$ $$2^x = 2^{-3}$$ $$x = -3$$ Therefore $\log_2\left(\dfrac{1}{8}\right) = -3$.

OBJECTIVE	SUMMARY	EXAMPLES
Evaluate a common logarithm (Section 10.5/Objective 2)	Base-10 logarithms are called common logarithms. When working with base-10 logarithms, it is customary to omit writing the numeral 10 to designate the base. Hence $\log_{10} x$ is written as $\log x$. A calculator with a logarithm function key, typically labeled $\boxed{\log}$ is used to evaluate a common logarithm.	Use a calculator to find $\log 245$. Express the answer to four decimal places. **Solution** Follow the instructions for your calculator. $\log 245 = 2.3892$
Evaluate a natural logarithm (Section 10.5/Objective 2)	In many practical applications of logarithms, the number e (remember that $e \approx 2.71828$) is used as a base. Logarithms with a base of e are called **natural logarithms**, and are written as $\ln x$.	Use a calculator to find $\ln 486$. Express the answer to four decimal places. **Solution** Follow the instructions for your calculator. $\ln 486 = 6.1862$
Evaluate logarithms using the change-of-base formula (Section 10.6/Objective 5)	To evaluate logarithms other than base-10 or base-e, a change-of-base formula, $$\log_a r = \frac{\log_b r}{\log_b a},$$ is used. When applying the formula, you can choose base-10 or base-e for b	Find $\log_8 724$. Round the answer to the nearest hundredth. **Solution** $$\log_8 724 = \frac{\log 724}{\log 8} = 3.17$$
Graph logarithmic functions (Section 10.5/Objective 1)	A function defined by an equation of the form $f(x) = \log_b x$, $b > 0$ *and* $b \neq 1$ is called a **logarithmic function**. The equation $y = \log_b x$ is equivalent to $x = b^y$. The two functions $f(x) = b^x$ and $g(x) = \log_b x$ are inverses of each other.	Graph $f(x) = \log_4 x$. **Solution** Change $y = \log_4 x$ to $4^y = x$ and determine a table of values. <table><tr><td>**x**</td><td>$\frac{1}{16}$</td><td>$\frac{1}{4}$</td><td>1</td><td>4</td><td>16</td></tr><tr><td>**y**</td><td>−2</td><td>−1</td><td>0</td><td>1</td><td>2</td></tr></table>
Apply the properties of logarithms (Section 10.3/Objective 3)	The following properties of logarithms are derived from the definition of a logarithm and the properties of exponents. For positive real numbers b, r, and s, where $b \neq 1$, **1.** $\log_b b = 1$ **2.** $\log_b 1 = 0$ **3.** $b^{\log_b r} = r$ **4.** $\log_b rs = \log_b r + \log_b s$ **5.** $\log_b\left(\dfrac{r}{s}\right) = \log_b r - \log_b s$ **6.** $\log_b r^p = p\log_b r$ p is any real number	Express $\log_b \dfrac{\sqrt{x}}{y^2 z}$ as the sum or difference of simpler logarithmic quantities. **Solution** $$\log_b \frac{\sqrt{x}}{y^2 z} = \log_b \sqrt{x} - \log_b(y^2 z)$$ $$= \frac{1}{2}\log_b x - [\log_b y^2 + \log_b z]$$ $$= \frac{1}{2}\log_b x - [2\log_b y + \log_b z]$$ $$= \frac{1}{2}\log_b x - 2\log_b y - \log_b z$$

(continued)

OBJECTIVE	SUMMARY	EXAMPLES
Solve logarithmic and exponential equations	The properties of equality and the properties of exponents and logarithms combine to help us solve a variety of logarithmic and exponential equations. The techniques for the various types of equations are given as follows. Note the difference in the technique depending on the form of the equation.	
Solve logarithmic equations by switching to exponential form (Section 10.6/Objective 2)	This technique is used when a single logarithmic expression is equal to a constant, such as $\log_4(3x + 5) = 2$. You may have to apply properties of logarithms to rewrite a sum or difference of logarithms as a single logarithm.	Solve $\log_3 x + \log_3(x + 8) = 2$. **Solution** Rewrite the left-hand side of the equation as a single logarithm. $\log_3 x(x + 8) = 2$ Switch to exponential form and solve the equation. $x(x + 8) = 3^2$ $x^2 + 8x = 9$ $x^2 + 8x - 9 = 0$ $(x + 9)(x - 1) = 0$ $x = -9 \quad \text{or} \quad x = 1$ **Always check your answer**. Because -9 would make the expression $\log_3 x$ undefined; the solution set is $\{1\}$.
Solve logarithmic equations of the form $\log_b x = \log_b y$ (Section 10.6/Objective 2)	The following property of equality is used for solving some logarithmic equations. If $x > 0$, and $y > 0$, and $b \neq 1$, then $x = y$ if and only if $\log_b x = \log_b y$. One application of this property is for equations in which a single logarithm equals another single logarithm.	Solve $\ln(9x + 1) - \ln(x + 4) = \ln 4$. **Solution** Write the left-hand side of the equation as a single logarithm. $\ln \dfrac{9x + 1}{x + 4} = \ln 4$ Now apply the property of equality, if $\log_b x = \log_b y$, then $x = y$. $\dfrac{9x + 1}{x + 4} = 4$ $9x + 1 = 4(x + 4)$ $9x + 1 = 4x + 16$ $5x = 15$ $x = 3$ The answer does check so the solution set is $\{3\}$.

OBJECTIVE	SUMMARY	EXAMPLES
Solve exponential equations by taking the logarithm of each side (Section 10.6/Objective 2)	Some exponential equations can be solved by applying the property of equality in the form "If $x = y$, then $\log_b x = \log_b y$ when $x > 0$, and $y > 0$, and $b \neq 1$." If the base of the exponential equation is e, then use natural logarithms and if the base is 10, then use common logarithms. Otherwise, either base can be used when taking the logarithm of both sides of the equation.	Solve $6^{3x-2} = 45$. Express the solution to the nearest hundredth. **Solution** Take the logarithm of both sides of the equation. $\log 6^{3x-2} = \log 45$ $(3x - 2)\log 6 = \log 45$ $3x(\log 6) - 2\log 6 = \log 45$ $3x(\log 6) = \log 45 + 2\log 6$ $x = \dfrac{\log 45 + 2\log 6}{3\log 6}$ $x = 1.37$ The solution set is $\{1.37\}$.
Solve problems involving Richter numbers (Section 10.6/Objective 4)	Seismologists use the Richter scale to measure and report the magnitude of earthquakes. The equation $R = \log\dfrac{I}{I_0}$ compares the intensity I of an earthquake to a minimum or reference intensity I_0.	An earthquake on the Sandwich Island (in the South Atlantic) in 2006 had an intensity about 5,011,872 times the reference intensity. Find the Richter number for that earthquake. **Solution** $R = \log\dfrac{I}{I_0}$ $R = \log\dfrac{I}{I_0} = \log\dfrac{5{,}011{,}872\ I_0}{I_0} = 6.7$ The Richter number for the earthquake is 6.7.

Chapter 10 **Review Problem Set**

For Problems 1–10, evaluate each of the following:

1. $8^{5/3}$

2. $-25^{3/2}$

3. $(-27)^{4/3}$

4. $\log_6 216$

5. $\log_7\left(\dfrac{1}{49}\right)$

6. $\log_2\sqrt[3]{2}$

7. $\log_2\left(\dfrac{\sqrt[4]{32}}{2}\right)$

8. $\log_{10} 0.00001$

9. $\ln e$

10. $7^{\log_7 12}$

For Problems 11–24, solve each equation. Express approximate solutions to the nearest hundredth.

11. $\log_{10} 2 + \log_{10} x = 1$

12. $\log_3 x = -2$

13. $4^x = 128$

14. $3^t = 42$

15. $\log_2 x = 3$

16. $\left(\dfrac{1}{27}\right)^{3x} = 3^{2x-1}$

17. $2e^x = 14$

18. $2^{2x+1} = 3^{x+1}$

19. $\ln(x + 4) - \ln(x + 2) = \ln x$

20. $\log x + \log(x - 15) = 2$

21. $\log(\log x) = 2$

22. $\log(7x - 4) - \log(x - 1) = 1$

23. $\ln(2t - 1) = \ln 4 + \ln(t - 3)$

24. $64^{2t+1} = 8^{-t+2}$

For Problems 25–28, if $\log 3 = 0.4771$ and $\log 7 = 0.8451$, evaluate each of the following:

25. $\log\left(\dfrac{7}{3}\right)$

26. $\log 21$

27. $\log 27$

28. $\log 7^{2/3}$

29. Express each of the following as the sum or difference of simpler logarithmic quantities. Assume that all variables represent positive real numbers.

(a) $\log_b\left(\dfrac{x}{y^2}\right)$

(b) $\log_b\sqrt[4]{xy^2}$

(c) $\log_b\left(\dfrac{\sqrt{x}}{y^3}\right)$

30. Express each of the following as a single logarithm. Assume that all variables represent positive real numbers.

(a) $3\log_b x + 2\log_b y$

(b) $\dfrac{1}{2}\log_b y - 4\log_b x$

(c) $\dfrac{1}{2}(\log_b x + \log_b y) - 2\log_b z$

For Problems 31–34, approximate each of the logarithms to three decimal places.

31. $\log_2 3$

32. $\log_3 2$

33. $\log_4 191$

34. $\log_2 0.23$

For Problems 35–42, graph each of the functions.

35. (a) $f(x) = \left(\dfrac{3}{4}\right)^x$

(b) $f(x) = \left(\dfrac{3}{4}\right)^x + 2$

(c) $f(x) = \left(\dfrac{3}{4}\right)^{-x}$

36. (a) $f(x) = 2^x$

(b) $f(x) = 2^{x+2}$

(c) $f(x) = -2^x$

37. (a) $f(x) = e^{x-1}$

(b) $f(x) = e^x - 1$

(c) $f(x) = e^{-x+1}$

38. (a) $f(x) = -1 + \log x$

(b) $f(x) = \log(x - 1)$

(c) $f(x) = -1 - \log x$

39. $f(x) = 3^x - 3^{-x}$

40. $f(x) = e^{-x^2/2}$

41. $f(x) = \log_2(x - 3)$

42. $f(x) = 3\log_3 x$

For Problems 43–45, use the compound interest formula $A = P\left(1 + \dfrac{r}{n}\right)^{nt}$ to find the total amount of money accumulated at the end of the indicated time period for each of the investments.

43. $7500 for 10 years at 4% compounded quarterly

44. $1250 for 15 years at 5% compounded monthly

45. $2500 for 20 years at 6.5% compounded semiannually

For Problems 46–49, determine whether f and g are inverse functions.

46. $f(x) = 7x - 1$ and $g(x) = \dfrac{x + 1}{7}$

47. $f(x) = -\dfrac{2}{3}x$ and $g(x) = \dfrac{3}{2}x$

48. $f(x) = x^2 - 6$ for $x \geq 0$ and $g(x) = \sqrt{x + 6}$ for $x \geq -6$

49. $f(x) = 2 - x^2$ for $x \geq 0$ and $g(x) = \sqrt{2 - x}$ for $x \leq 2$

For Problems 50–53, (a) find f^{-1}, and (b) verify that $(f \circ f^{-1})(x) = x$ and $(f^{-1} \circ f)(x) = x$.

50. $f(x) = 4x + 5$

51. $f(x) = -3x - 7$

52. $f(x) = \dfrac{5}{6}x - \dfrac{1}{3}$

53. $f(x) = -2 - x^2$ for $x \geq 0$

For Problems 54 and 55, find the intervals on which the function is increasing and the intervals on which it is decreasing.

54. $f(x) = -2x^2 + 16x - 35$

55. $f(x) = 2\sqrt{x - 3}$

56. How long will it take $1000 to double if it is invested at 7% interest compounded annually?

57. How long will it take $1000 to be worth $3500 if it is invested at 4.5% interest compounded quarterly?

58. What rate of interest (to the nearest tenth of a percent) compounded continuously is needed for an investment of $500 to grow to $1000 in 8 years?

59. Suppose that the present population of a city is 50,000. Use the equation $P(t) = P_0 e^{0.02t}$ (in which P_0 represents an initial population) to estimate future populations, and estimate the population of that city in 10 years, 15 years, and 20 years.

60. The number of bacteria present in a certain culture after t hours is given by the equation $Q = Q_0 e^{0.29t}$, in which Q_0 represents the initial number of bacteria. How long will it take 500 bacteria to increase to 2000 bacteria?

61. Suppose that a certain radioactive substance has a half-life of 40 days. If there are presently 750 grams of the substance, how much, to the nearest gram, will remain after 100 days?

62. An earthquake occurred in Mexico City, Mexico, in 1985 that had an intensity level about 125,000,000 times the reference intensity. Find the Richter number for that earthquake.

Chapter 10 Test

For Problems 1–4, evaluate each expression.

1. $\log_3 \sqrt{3}$

2. $\log_2(\log_2 4)$

3. $-2 + \ln e^3$

4. $\log_2(0.5)$

For Problems 5–10, solve each equation.

5. $4^x = \dfrac{1}{64}$

6. $9^x = \dfrac{1}{27}$

7. $2^{3x-1} = 128$

8. $\log_9 x = \dfrac{5}{2}$

9. $\log x + \log(x + 48) = 2$

10. $\ln x = \ln 2 + \ln(3x - 1)$

For Problems 11–13, given that $\log_3 4 = 1.2619$ and $\log_3 5 = 1.4650$, evaluate each of the following.

11. $\log_3 100$

12. $\log_3 \dfrac{5}{4}$

13. $\log_3 \sqrt{5}$

14. Find the inverse of the function $f(x) = -3x - 6$.

15. Solve $e^x = 176$ to the nearest hundredth.

16. Solve $2^{x-2} = 314$ to the nearest hundredth.

17. Determine $\log_5 632$ to four decimal places.

18. Find the inverse of the function $f(x) = \dfrac{2}{3}x - \dfrac{3}{5}$.

19. If \$3500 is invested at 7.5% interest compounded quarterly, how much money has accumulated at the end of 8 years?

20. How long will it take \$5000 to be worth \$12,500 if it is invested at 7% compounded annually? Express your answer to the nearest tenth of a year.

21. The number of bacteria present in a certain culture after t hours is given by $Q(t) = Q_0 e^{0.23t}$, in which Q_0 represents the initial number of bacteria. How long will it take 400 bacteria to increase to 2400 bacteria? Express your answer to the nearest tenth of an hour.

22. Suppose that a certain radioactive substance has a half-life of 50 years. If there are presently 7500 grams of the substance, how much will remain after 32 years? Express your answer to the nearest gram.

For Problems 23–25, graph each of the functions.

23. $f(x) = e^x - 2$

24. $f(x) = -3^{-x}$

25. $f(x) = \log_2(x - 2)$

For Problems 1–5, evaluate each algebraic expression for the given values of the variables.

1. $-5(x - 1) - 3(2x + 4) + 3(3x - 1)$ for $x = -2$

2. $\dfrac{14a^3b^2}{7a^2b}$ for $a = -1$ and $b = 4$

3. $\dfrac{2}{n} - \dfrac{3}{2n} + \dfrac{5}{3n}$ for $n = 4$

4. $4\sqrt{2x - y} + 5\sqrt{3x + y}$ for $x = 16$ and $y = 16$

5. $\dfrac{3}{x - 2} - \dfrac{5}{x + 3}$ for $x = 3$

For Problems 6–15, perform the indicated operations and express answers in simplified form.

6. $(-5\sqrt{6})(3\sqrt{12})$

7. $(2\sqrt{x} - 3)(\sqrt{x} + 4)$

8. $(3\sqrt{2} - \sqrt{6})(\sqrt{2} + 4\sqrt{6})$

9. $(2x - 1)(x^2 + 6x - 4)$

10. $\dfrac{x^2 - x}{x + 5} \cdot \dfrac{x^2 + 5x + 4}{x^4 - x^2}$

11. $\dfrac{16x^2y}{24xy^3} \div \dfrac{9xy}{8x^2y^2}$

12. $\dfrac{x + 3}{10} + \dfrac{2x + 1}{15} - \dfrac{x - 2}{18}$

13. $\dfrac{7}{12ab} - \dfrac{11}{15a^2}$

14. $\dfrac{8}{x^2 - 4x} + \dfrac{2}{x}$

15. $(8x^3 - 6x^2 - 15x + 4) \div (4x - 1)$

For Problems 16–19, simplify each of the complex fractions.

16. $\dfrac{\dfrac{5}{x^2} - \dfrac{3}{x}}{\dfrac{1}{y} + \dfrac{2}{y^2}}$

17. $\dfrac{\dfrac{2}{x} - 3}{\dfrac{3}{y} + 4}$

18. $\dfrac{2 - \dfrac{1}{n - 2}}{3 + \dfrac{4}{n + 3}}$

19. $\dfrac{3a}{2 - \dfrac{1}{a}} - 1$

For Problems 20–25, factor each of the algebraic expressions completely.

20. $20x^2 + 7x - 6$

21. $16x^3 + 54$

22. $4x^4 - 25x^2 + 36$

23. $12x^3 - 52x^2 - 40x$

24. $xy - 6x + 3y - 18$

25. $10 + 9x - 9x^2$

For Problems 26–35, evaluate each of the numerical expressions.

26. $\left(\dfrac{2}{3}\right)^{-4}$

27. $\dfrac{3}{\left(\dfrac{4}{3}\right)^{-1}}$

28. $\sqrt[3]{-\dfrac{27}{64}}$

29. $-\sqrt{0.09}$

30. $(27)^{-4/3}$

31. $4^0 + 4^{-1} + 4^{-2}$

32. $\left(\dfrac{3^{-1}}{2^{-3}}\right)^{-2}$

33. $(2^{-3} - 3^{-2})^{-1}$

34. $\log_2 64$

35. $\log_3\left(\dfrac{1}{9}\right)$

For Problems 36–38, find the indicated products and quotients; express final answers with positive integral exponents only.

36. $(-3x^{-1}y^2)(4x^{-2}y^{-3})$

37. $\dfrac{48x^{-4}y^2}{6xy}$

38. $\left(\dfrac{27a^{-4}b^{-3}}{-3a^{-1}b^{-4}}\right)^{-1}$

For Problems 39–46, express each radical expression in simplest radical form.

39. $\sqrt{80}$

40. $-2\sqrt{54}$

41. $\sqrt{\dfrac{75}{81}}$

42. $\dfrac{4\sqrt{6}}{3\sqrt{8}}$

43. $\sqrt[3]{56}$

44. $\dfrac{\sqrt[3]{3}}{\sqrt[3]{4}}$

45. $4\sqrt{52x^3y^2}$

46. $\sqrt{\dfrac{2x}{3y}}$

For Problems 47–49, use the distributive property to help simplify each of the following:

47. $-3\sqrt{24} + 6\sqrt{54} - \sqrt{6}$

48. $\dfrac{\sqrt{8}}{3} - \dfrac{3\sqrt{18}}{4} - \dfrac{5\sqrt{50}}{2}$

49. $8\sqrt[3]{3} - 6\sqrt[3]{24} - 4\sqrt[3]{81}$

For Problems 50 and 51, rationalize the denominator and simplify.

50. $\dfrac{\sqrt{3}}{\sqrt{6} - 2\sqrt{2}}$

51. $\dfrac{3\sqrt{5} - \sqrt{3}}{2\sqrt{3} + \sqrt{7}}$

For Problems 52–54, use scientific notation to help perform the indicated operations.

52. $\dfrac{(0.00016)(300)(0.028)}{0.064}$

53. $\dfrac{0.00072}{0.0000024}$

54. $\sqrt{0.00000009}$

For Problems 55–58, find each of the indicated products or quotients, and express your answers in standard form.

55. $(5 - 2i)(4 + 6i)$

56. $(-3 - i)(5 - 2i)$

57. $\dfrac{5}{4i}$

58. $\dfrac{-1 + 6i}{7 - 2i}$

59. Find the slope of the line determined by the points $(2, -3)$ and $(-1, 7)$.

60. Find the slope of the line determined by the equation $4x - 7y = 9$.

61. Find the length of the line segment with endpoints at $(4, 5)$ and $(-2, 1)$.

62. Write the equation of the line that contains the points $(3, -1)$ and $(7, 4)$.

63. Write the equation of the line that is perpendicular to the line $3x - 4y = 6$ and contains the point $(-3, -2)$.

64. Write the equation of a line that is perpendicular to the line segment between $(2, 4)$ and $(6, 10)$ and contains the midpoint of the given line segment.

65. Write the equation of a line that is parallel to the line $y = -\dfrac{3}{4}x + 1$ and contains the point $(-4, 0)$.

66. Write the equation of the line parallel to the line $x = 3$ and contains the point $(-2, 7)$.

For Problems 67–76, graph each of the functions.

67. $f(x) = -2x - 4$

68. $f(x) = -2x^2 - 2$

69. $f(x) = x^2 - 2x - 2$

70. $f(x) = \sqrt{x + 1} + 2$

71. $f(x) = 2x^2 + 8x + 9$

72. $f(x) = -|x - 2| + 1$

73. $f(x) = 2^x + 2$

74. $f(x) = \log_2(x - 2)$

75. $f(x) = -x(x + 1)(x - 2)$

76. $f(x) = \dfrac{-x}{x + 2}$

77. If $f(x) = x - 3$ and $g(x) = 2x^2 - x - 1$, find $(g \circ f)(x)$ and $(f \circ g)(x)$.

78. Find the inverse (f^{-1}) of $f(x) = 3x - 7$.

79. Find the inverse of $f(x) = -\dfrac{1}{2}x + \dfrac{2}{3}$.

80. Find the constant of variation if y varies directly as x, and $y = 2$ when $x = -\dfrac{2}{3}$.

81. If y is inversely proportional to the square of x, and $y = 4$ when $x = 3$, find y when $x = 6$.

82. The volume of gas at a constant temperature varies inversely as the pressure. What is the volume of a gas under a pressure of 25 pounds if the gas occupies 15 cubic centimeters under a pressure of 20 pounds?

For Problems 83–110, solve each equation.

83. $3(2x - 1) - 2(5x + 1) = 4(3x + 4)$

84. $n + \dfrac{3n - 1}{9} - 4 = \dfrac{3n + 1}{3}$

85. $0.92 + 0.9(x - 0.3) = 2x - 5.95$

86. $|4x - 1| = 11$

87. $3x^2 = 7x$

88. $x^3 - 36x = 0$

89. $30x^2 + 13x - 10 = 0$

90. $8x^3 + 12x^2 - 36x = 0$

91. $x^4 + 8x^2 - 9 = 0$

92. $(n + 4)(n - 6) = 11$

93. $2 - \dfrac{3x}{x - 4} = \dfrac{14}{x + 7}$

94. $\dfrac{2n}{6n^2 + 7n - 3} - \dfrac{n - 3}{3n^2 + 11n - 4} = \dfrac{5}{2n^2 + 11n + 12}$

95. $\sqrt{3y} - y = -6$

96. $\sqrt{x + 19} - \sqrt{x + 28} = -1$

97. $(3x - 1)^2 = 45$

98. $(2x + 5)^2 = -32$

99. $2x^2 - 3x + 4 = 0$

100. $3n^2 - 6n + 2 = 0$

101. $\dfrac{5}{n - 3} - \dfrac{3}{n + 3} = 1$

102. $12x^4 - 19x^2 + 5 = 0$

103. $2x^2 + 5x + 5 = 0$

104. $x^3 - 4x^2 - 25x + 28 = 0$

105. $6x^3 - 19x^2 + 9x + 10 = 0$

106. $16^x = 64$

107. $\log_3 x = 4$

108. $\log_{10} x + \log_{10} 25 = 2$

109. $\ln(3x - 4) - \ln(x + 1) = \ln 2$

110. $27^{4x} = 9^{x+1}$

For Problems 111–120, solve each inequality.

111. $-5(y - 1) + 3 > 3y - 4 - 4y$

112. $0.06x + 0.08(250 - x) \geq 19$

113. $|5x - 2| > 13$ **114.** $|6x + 2| < 8$

115. $\dfrac{x - 2}{5} - \dfrac{3x - 1}{4} \leq \dfrac{3}{10}$ **116.** $(x - 2)(x + 4) \leq 0$

117. $(3x - 1)(x - 4) > 0$ **118.** $x(x + 5) < 24$

119. $\dfrac{x - 3}{x - 7} \geq 0$ **120.** $\dfrac{2x}{x + 3} > 4$

For Problems 121–132, set up an equation or an inequality to help solve each problem.

121. Find three consecutive odd integers whose sum is 57.

122. Eric has a collection of 63 coins consisting of nickels, dimes, and quarters. The number of dimes is 6 more than the number of nickels, and the number of quarters is 1 more than twice the number of nickels. How many coins of each kind are in the collection?

123. One of two supplementary angles is 4° more than one-third of the other angle. Find the measure of each of the angles.

124. If a ring costs a jeweler $300, at what price should it be sold to make a profit of 50% on the selling price?

125. Beth invested a certain amount of money at 8% and $300 more than that amount at 9%. Her total yearly interest was $316. How much did she invest at each rate?

126. Two trains leave the same depot at the same time, one traveling east and the other traveling west. At the end of $4\dfrac{1}{2}$ hours, they are 639 miles apart. If the rate of the train traveling east is 10 miles per hour faster than the other train, find their rates.

127. A 10-quart radiator contains a 50% solution of antifreeze. How much needs to be drained out and replaced with pure antifreeze to obtain a 70% antifreeze solution?

128. Sam shot rounds of 70, 73, and 76 on the first 3 days of a golf tournament. What must he shoot on the fourth day of the tournament to average 72 or less for the 4 days?

129. The cube of a number equals nine times the same number. Find the number.

130. A strip of uniform width is to be cut off both sides and both ends of a sheet of paper that is 8 inches by 14 inches to reduce the size of the paper to an area of 72 square inches. Find the width of the strip.

131. A sum of $2450 is to be divided between two people in the ratio of 3 to 4. How much does each person receive?

132. Working together, Sue and Dean can complete a task in $1\dfrac{1}{5}$ hours. Dean can do the task by himself in 2 hours. How long would it take Sue to complete the task by herself?

11

Systems of Equations

11.1 Systems of Two Linear Equations in Two Variables

11.2 Systems of Three Linear Equations in Three Variables

11.3 Matrix Approach to Solving Linear Systems

11.4 Determinants

11.5 Cramer's Rule

11.6 Partial Fractions (Optional)

© Anyka

When mixing different solutions, a chemist could use a system of equations to determine how much of each solution is needed to produce a specific concentration.

A 10% salt solution is to be mixed with a 20% salt solution to produce 20 gallons of a 17.5% salt solution. How many gallons of the 10% solution and how many gallons of the 20% solution should be mixed? The two equations $x + y = 20$ and $0.10x + 0.20y = 0.175(20)$ algebraically represent the conditions of the problem; x represents the number of gallons of the 10% solution, and y represents the number of gallons of the 20% solution. The two equations considered together form a system of linear equations, and the problem can be solved by solving the system of equations.

Throughout most of this chapter, we consider systems of linear equations and their applications. We will discuss various techniques for solving systems of linear equations.

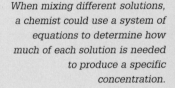 Video tutorials based on section learning objectives are available in a variety of delivery modes.

11.1 Systems of Two Linear Equations in Two Variables

OBJECTIVES

1 Solve systems of two linear equations by graphing

2 Solve systems of two linear equations by using the substitution method

3 Solve systems of two linear equations by using the elimination-by-addition method

4 Solve application problems using a system of equations

In Chapter 7 we stated that any equation of the form $Ax + By = C$, when A, B, and C are real numbers (A and B not both zero), is a **linear equation** in the two variables x and y, and its graph is a straight line. Two linear equations in two variables considered together form a **system of two linear equations in two variables**, as illustrated by the following examples:

$$\begin{pmatrix} x + y = 6 \\ x - y = 2 \end{pmatrix} \quad \begin{pmatrix} 3x + 2y = 1 \\ 5x - 2y = 23 \end{pmatrix} \quad \begin{pmatrix} 4x - 5y = 21 \\ -3x + y = -7 \end{pmatrix}$$

To *solve* such a system means to find all of the ordered pairs that simultaneously satisfy both equations in the system. For example, if we graph the two equations $x + y = 6$ and $x - y = 2$ on the same set of axes, as in Figure 11.1, then the ordered pair associated with the point of intersection of the two lines is the **solution of the system**. Thus we say that $\{(4, 2)\}$ is the solution set of the system

$$\begin{pmatrix} x + y = 6 \\ x - y = 2 \end{pmatrix}$$

To check the solution, we substitute 4 for x and 2 for y in the two equations.

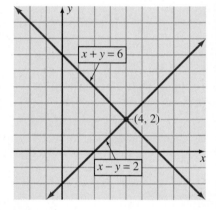

Figure 11.1

$x + y = 6$ becomes $4 + 2 = 6$, a true statement
$x - y = 2$ becomes $4 - 2 = 2$, a true statement

Because the graph of a linear equation in two variables is a straight line, three possible situations can occur when we are solving a system of two linear equations in two variables. These situations are shown in Figure 11.2.

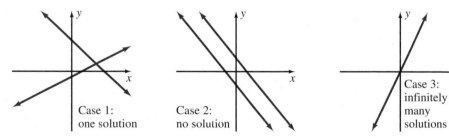

Case 1: one solution

Case 2: no solution

Case 3: infinitely many solutions

Figure 11.2

Case 1 The graphs of the two equations are two lines intersecting in one point. There is exactly one solution, and the system is called a **consistent system**.

Case 2 The graphs of the two equations are parallel lines. There is *no solution*, and the system is called an **inconsistent system**.

Case 3   The graphs of the two equations are the same line, and there are *infinitely many solutions* of the system. Any pair of real numbers that satisfies one of the equations also satisfies the other equation, and we say that the equations are dependent.

Thus, as we solve a system of two linear equations in two variables, we can expect one of three outcomes: The system will have *no* solutions, *one* ordered pair as a solution, or *infinitely many* ordered pairs as solutions.

The Substitution Method

Solving specific systems of equations by graphing requires accurate graphs. However, unless the solutions are integers, it is difficult to obtain exact solutions from a graph. Therefore we will consider some other techniques for solving systems of equations.

The **substitution method**, which works especially well with systems of two equations in two unknowns, can be described as follows.

Step 1   Solve one of the equations for one variable in terms of the other. (If possible, make a choice that will avoid fractions.)

Step 2   Substitute the expression obtained in step 1 into the other equation, producing an equation in one variable.

Step 3   Solve the equation obtained in step 2.

Step 4   Use the solution obtained in step 3, along with the expression obtained in step 1, to determine the solution of the system.

Classroom Example

Solve the system $\begin{pmatrix} 5x + y = 5 \\ 3x - 2y = 16 \end{pmatrix}$.

EXAMPLE 1   Solve the system $\begin{pmatrix} x - 3y = -25 \\ 4x + 5y = 19 \end{pmatrix}$.

Solution

Solve the first equation for x in terms of y to produce

$$x = 3y - 25$$

Substitute $3y - 25$ for x in the second equation and solve for y.

$$4x + 5y = 19$$
$$4(3y - 25) + 5y = 19$$
$$12y - 100 + 5y = 19$$
$$17y = 119$$
$$y = 7$$

Next, substitute 7 for y in the equation $x = 3y - 25$ to obtain

$$x = 3(7) - 25 = -4$$

The solution set of the given system is $\{(-4, 7)\}$. (You should check this solution in both of the original equations.)
■

Classroom Example

Solve the system:

$$\begin{pmatrix} 12x - 3y = -7 \\ 8x + 9y = -1 \end{pmatrix}$$

EXAMPLE 2   Solve the system $\begin{pmatrix} 5x + 9y = -2 \\ 2x + 4y = -1 \end{pmatrix}$.

Solution

A glance at the system should tell you that solving either equation for either variable will produce a fractional form, so let's just use the first equation and solve for x in terms of y.

$$5x + 9y = -2$$
$$5x = -9y - 2$$
$$x = \frac{-9y - 2}{5}$$

Now we can substitute this value for x into the second equation and solve for y.

$$2x + 4y = -1$$

$$2\left(\frac{-9y - 2}{5}\right) + 4y = -1$$

$$2(-9y - 2) + 20y = -5 \qquad \text{Multiplied both sides by 5}$$

$$-18y - 4 + 20y = -5$$

$$2y - 4 = -5$$

$$2y = -1$$

$$y = -\frac{1}{2}$$

Now we can substitute $-\frac{1}{2}$ for y in $x = \dfrac{-9y - 2}{5}$.

$$x = \frac{-9\left(-\dfrac{1}{2}\right) - 2}{5} = \frac{\dfrac{9}{2} - 2}{5} = \frac{1}{2}$$

The solution set is $\left\{\left(\dfrac{1}{2}, -\dfrac{1}{2}\right)\right\}$.

Classroom Example
Solve the system:
$$\begin{pmatrix} 4x + 6y = 8 \\ y = -\dfrac{2}{3}x + \dfrac{4}{3} \end{pmatrix}$$

EXAMPLE 3

Solve the system $\begin{pmatrix} 6x - 4y = 18 \\ y = \dfrac{3}{2}x - \dfrac{9}{2} \end{pmatrix}$.

Solution

The second equation is given in appropriate form for us to begin the substitution process. Substitute $\dfrac{3}{2}x - \dfrac{9}{2}$ for y in the first equation to yield

$$6x - 4y = 18$$

$$6x - 4\left(\frac{3}{2}x - \frac{9}{2}\right) = 18$$

$$6x - 6x + 18 = 18$$

$$18 = 18$$

Our obtaining a true numerical statement $(18 = 18)$ indicates that the system has infinitely many solutions. Any ordered pair that satisfies one of the equations will also satisfy the other equation. Thus in the second equation of the original system, if we let $x = k$, then $y = \dfrac{3}{2}k - \dfrac{9}{2}$. Therefore the solution set can be expressed as $\left\{\left(k, \dfrac{3}{2}k - \dfrac{9}{2}\right) \,\middle|\, k \text{ is a real number}\right\}$. If some specific solutions are needed, they can be generated by the ordered pair $\left(k, \dfrac{3}{2}k - \dfrac{9}{2}\right)$. For example, if we let $k = 1$, then we get $\dfrac{3}{2}(1) - \dfrac{9}{2} = -\dfrac{6}{2} = -3$. Thus the ordered pair $(1, -3)$ is a member of the solution set of the given system.

The Elimination-by-Addition Method

Now let's consider the **elimination-by-addition method** for solving a system of equations. This is a very important method because it is the basis for developing other techniques for solving systems that contain many equations and variables. The method involves replacing systems of equations with *simpler equivalent systems* until we obtain a system in which the solutions are obvious. **Equivalent systems** of equations are systems that have exactly the same solution set. The following operations or transformations can be applied to a system of equations to produce an equivalent system:

1. Any two equations of the system can be interchanged.

2. Both sides of any equation of the system can be multiplied by any nonzero real number.

3. Any equation of the system can be replaced by the sum of that equation and a nonzero multiple of another equation.

Classroom Example

Solve the system $\begin{pmatrix} 2x - 7y = 22 \\ 3x + 5y = 2 \end{pmatrix}$.

EXAMPLE 4   Solve the system $\begin{pmatrix} 3x + 5y = -9 \\ 2x - 3y = 13 \end{pmatrix}$.
$$\quad(1)$$
$$\quad(2)$$

Solution

We can replace the given system with an equivalent system by multiplying equation (2) by -3.

$$\begin{pmatrix} 3x + 5y = -9 \\ -6x + 9y = -39 \end{pmatrix} \qquad (3) \\ (4)$$

Now let's replace equation (4) with an equation formed by multiplying equation (3) by 2 and adding this result to equation (4).

$$\begin{pmatrix} 3x + 5y = -9 \\ 19y = -57 \end{pmatrix} \qquad (5) \\ (6)$$

From equation (6), we can easily determine that $y = -3$. Then, substituting -3 for y in equation (5) produces

$$3x + 5(-3) = -9$$
$$3x - 15 = -9$$
$$3x = 6$$
$$x = 2$$

The solution set for the given system is $\{(2, -3)\}$. ∎

Remark: We are using a format for the elimination-by-addition method that highlights the use of equivalent systems. In Section 11.3 this format will lead naturally to an approach using matrices. Thus it is beneficial to stress the use of equivalent systems at this time.

Classroom Example

Solve the system:

$$\begin{pmatrix} \frac{5}{9}x - \frac{3}{5}y = 14 \\ \frac{1}{3}x + \frac{2}{3}y = -7 \end{pmatrix}$$

EXAMPLE 5   Solve the system $\begin{pmatrix} \frac{1}{2}x + \frac{2}{3}y = -4 \\ \frac{1}{4}x - \frac{3}{2}y = 20 \end{pmatrix}$.
$$\quad(7)$$
$$\quad(8)$$

Solution

The given system can be replaced with an equivalent system by multiplying equation (7) by 6 and equation (8) by 4.

$$\begin{pmatrix} 3x + 4y = -24 \\ x - 6y = 80 \end{pmatrix} \qquad (9) \\ (10)$$

Now let's exchange equations (9) and (10).

$$\begin{pmatrix} x - 6y = 80 \\ 3x + 4y = -24 \end{pmatrix} \qquad (11) \\ (12)$$

We can replace equation (12) with an equation formed by multiplying equation (11) by -3 and adding this result to equation (12).

$$\begin{pmatrix} x - 6y = 80 \\ 22y = -264 \end{pmatrix} \qquad \begin{matrix} (13) \\ (14) \end{matrix}$$

From equation (14) we can determine that $y = -12$. Then, substituting -12 for y in equation (13) produces

$$x - 6(-12) = 80$$
$$x + 72 = 80$$
$$x = 8$$

The solution set of the given system is $\{(8, -12)\}$. (Check this!) ▪

Classroom Example
Solve the system $\begin{pmatrix} 8x - y = 5 \\ 8x - y = 9 \end{pmatrix}$.

EXAMPLE 6   Solve the system $\begin{pmatrix} x - 4y = 9 \\ x - 4y = 3 \end{pmatrix}$. $\qquad \begin{matrix} (15) \\ (16) \end{matrix}$

Solution

We can replace equation (16) with an equation formed by multiplying equation (15) by -1 and adding this result to equation (16).

$$\begin{pmatrix} x - 4y = 9 \\ 0 = -6 \end{pmatrix} \qquad \begin{matrix} (17) \\ (18) \end{matrix}$$

The statement $0 = -6$ is a contradiction, and therefore the original system is *inconsistent*; it has no solution. The solution set is $\varnothing$. ▪

Both the elimination-by-addition and the substitution methods can be used to obtain exact solutions for any system of two linear equations in two unknowns. Sometimes it is a matter of deciding which method to use on a particular system. Some systems lend themselves to one or the other of the methods by virtue of the original format of the equations. We will illustrate this idea in a moment when we solve some word problems.

Using Systems to Solve Problems

Many word problems that we solved earlier in this text with one variable and one equation can also be solved by using a system of two linear equations in two variables. In fact, in many of these problems, you may find it more natural to use two variables and two equations.

Classroom Example
A boat moving at a constant speed traveled to a destination 35 miles away, upriver. The boat was going against the current, and the trip took $2\frac{1}{3}$ hours. The return trip, going with the current, only took $1\frac{2}{3}$ hours. Find the speed of the boat and the speed of the current in miles per hour.

EXAMPLE 7

John Paul always runs his pontoon boat at full throttle, which results in the boat traveling at a constant speed. Going up the river against the current the boat traveled 72 miles in 4.5 hours. The return trip down the river with the help of the current only took three hours. Find the speed of the boat and the speed of the current.

Solution

Let x represent the speed of the boat and let y represent the speed of the current. Going up the river the rate of the boat against the current is $\dfrac{72 \text{ miles}}{4.5 \text{ hours}} = 16$ miles per hour. Going down the river the rate of the boat with the current is $\dfrac{72 \text{ miles}}{3 \text{ hours}} = 24$ miles per hour. The problem translates into the following system of equations.

$$\begin{pmatrix} x + y = 24 \\ x - y = 16 \end{pmatrix}$$

Let's use the elimination-by-addition method to solve the system. The second equation can be replaced by an equation formed by adding the two equations.

$$\begin{pmatrix} x + y = 24 \\ 2x = 40 \end{pmatrix}$$

Solving the second equation we can determine that $x = 20$. Now substituting 20 for x in the first equation produces

$$20 + y = 24$$
$$y = 4$$

Therefore, the speed of the boat is 20 miles per hour, and the speed of the current is 4 miles per hour.

Classroom Example
Lauran invested $5000, part of it at 2.5% interest and the remainder at 4.2%. Her total yearly income from the two investments was $199.80. How much did she invest at each rate?

EXAMPLE 8

Lucinda invested $950, part of it at 6% interest and the remainder at 8%. Her total yearly income from the two investments was $71.00. How much did she invest at each rate?

Solution

Let x represent the amount invested at 6% and y the amount invested at 8%. The problem translates into the following system:

$$\begin{pmatrix} x + y = 950 \\ 0.06x + 0.08y = 71.00 \end{pmatrix}$$ ← The two investments total $950
← The yearly interest from the two investments totals $71.00

Multiply the second equation by 100 to produce an equivalent system.

$$\begin{pmatrix} x + y = 950 \\ 6x + 8y = 7100 \end{pmatrix}$$

Because neither equation is solved for one variable in terms of the other, let's use the elimination-by-addition method to solve the system. The second equation can be replaced by an equation formed by multiplying the first equation by -6 and adding this result to the second equation.

$$\begin{pmatrix} x + y = 950 \\ 2y = 1400 \end{pmatrix}$$

Now we substitute 700 for y in the equation $x + y = 950$.

$$x + 700 = 950$$
$$x = 250$$

Therefore Lucinda must have invested $250 at 6% and $700 at 8%.

In our final example of this section, we will use a graphing utility to help solve a system of equations.

Classroom Example
Solve the system:
$$\begin{pmatrix} 4.31x + 8.01y = -6.79 \\ 5.79x - 9.34y = 51.18 \end{pmatrix}$$

EXAMPLE 9

Solve the system $\begin{pmatrix} 1.14x + 2.35y = -7.12 \\ 3.26x - 5.05y = 26.72 \end{pmatrix}$.

Solution

We began this section with graphing the equations in a system to find the solution. For this problem let's use a graphing utility to help find the solution of the system of equations. First, we need to solve each equation for y in terms of x. Thus the system becomes

$$\left(\begin{array}{l} y = \dfrac{-7.12 - 1.14x}{2.35} \\[2mm] y = \dfrac{3.26x - 26.72}{5.05} \end{array} \right)$$

Now we can enter both of these equations into a graphing utility and obtain Figure 11.3. From this figure it appears that the point of intersection is at approximately $x = 2$ and $y = -4$. By direct substitution into the given equations, we can verify that the point of intersection is exactly $(2, -4)$.

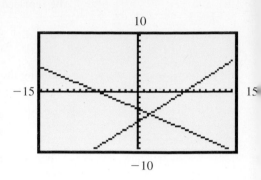

Figure 11.3

Concept Quiz 11.1

For Problems 1–8, answer true or false.

1. To *solve a system of equations* means to find all the ordered pairs that satisfy every equation in the system.

2. A consistent system of linear equations will have more than one solution.

3. If the graph of a system of two distinct linear equations results in two distinct parallel lines, then the system has no solution.

4. If the graphs of the two equations in a system are the same line, then the equations in the system are dependent.

5. Every system of equations has a solution.

6. For the system $\left(\begin{array}{r} 2x + \ \ y = 4 \\ x + 5y = 10 \end{array} \right)$, the ordered pair $(1, 2)$ is a solution.

7. Graphing a system of equations is the most accurate method for finding the solution of the system.

8. The only possibilities for the solution set of a system of two linear equations are no solutions, one solution, or two solutions.

Problem Set 11.1

For Problems 1–10, use the graphing approach to determine whether the system is consistent, the system is inconsistent, or the equations are dependent. If the system is consistent, find the solution set from the graph and check it. **(Objective 1)**

1. $\left(\begin{array}{l} x - y = 1 \\ 2x + y = 8 \end{array} \right)$

2. $\left(\begin{array}{r} 3x + \ \ y = 0 \\ x - 2y = -7 \end{array} \right)$

3. $\left(\begin{array}{l} 4x + 3y = -5 \\ 2x - 3y = -7 \end{array} \right)$

4. $\left(\begin{array}{r} 2x - \ \ y = 9 \\ 4x - 2y = 11 \end{array} \right)$

5. $\left(\begin{array}{l} \dfrac{1}{2}x + \dfrac{1}{4}y = 9 \\[2mm] 4x + 2y = 72 \end{array} \right)$

6. $\left(\begin{array}{l} 5x + 2y = -9 \\ 4x - 3y = 2 \end{array} \right)$

7. $\left(\begin{array}{l} \dfrac{1}{2}x - \dfrac{1}{3}y = 3 \\[2mm] x + 4y = -8 \end{array} \right)$

8. $\left(\begin{array}{l} 4x - 9y = -60 \\ \dfrac{1}{3}x - \dfrac{3}{4}y = -5 \end{array} \right)$

9. $\begin{pmatrix} x - \dfrac{y}{2} = -4 \\ 8x - 4y = -1 \end{pmatrix}$ **10.** $\begin{pmatrix} 3x - 2y = 7 \\ 6x + 5y = -4 \end{pmatrix}$

For Problems 11–28, solve each system by using the substitution method. (Objective 2)

11. $\begin{pmatrix} x + y = 16 \\ y = x + 2 \end{pmatrix}$ **12.** $\begin{pmatrix} 2x + 3y = -5 \\ y = 2x + 9 \end{pmatrix}$

13. $\begin{pmatrix} x = 3y - 25 \\ 4x + 5y = 19 \end{pmatrix}$ **14.** $\begin{pmatrix} 3x - 5y = 25 \\ x = y + 7 \end{pmatrix}$

15. $\begin{pmatrix} y = \dfrac{2}{3}x - 1 \\ 5x - 7y = 9 \end{pmatrix}$ **16.** $\begin{pmatrix} y = \dfrac{3}{4}x + 5 \\ 4x - 3y = -1 \end{pmatrix}$

17. $\begin{pmatrix} a = 4b + 13 \\ 3a + 6b = -33 \end{pmatrix}$ **18.** $\begin{pmatrix} 9a - 2b = 28 \\ b = -3a + 1 \end{pmatrix}$

19. $\begin{pmatrix} 2x - 3y = 4 \\ y = \dfrac{2}{3}x - \dfrac{4}{3} \end{pmatrix}$ **20.** $\begin{pmatrix} t + u = 11 \\ t = u + 7 \end{pmatrix}$

21. $\begin{pmatrix} u = t - 2 \\ t + u = 12 \end{pmatrix}$ **22.** $\begin{pmatrix} y = 5x - 9 \\ 5x - y = 9 \end{pmatrix}$

23. $\begin{pmatrix} 4x + 3y = -7 \\ 3x - 2y = 16 \end{pmatrix}$ **24.** $\begin{pmatrix} 5x - 3y = -34 \\ 2x + 7y = -30 \end{pmatrix}$

25. $\begin{pmatrix} 5x - y = 4 \\ y - 5x + 9 \end{pmatrix}$ **26.** $\begin{pmatrix} 2x + 3y = 3 \\ 4x - 9y = -4 \end{pmatrix}$

27. $\begin{pmatrix} 4x - 5y = 3 \\ 8x + 15y = -24 \end{pmatrix}$ **28.** $\begin{pmatrix} 4x + y = 9 \\ y = 15 - 4x \end{pmatrix}$

For Problems 29–44, solve each system by using the elimination-by-addition method. (Objective 3)

29. $\begin{pmatrix} 3x + 2y = 1 \\ 5x - 2y = 23 \end{pmatrix}$ **30.** $\begin{pmatrix} 4x + 3y = -22 \\ 4x - 5y = 26 \end{pmatrix}$

31. $\begin{pmatrix} x - 3y = -22 \\ 2x + 7y = 60 \end{pmatrix}$ **32.** $\begin{pmatrix} 6x - y = 3 \\ 5x + 3y = -9 \end{pmatrix}$

33. $\begin{pmatrix} 4x - 5y = 21 \\ 3x + 7y = -38 \end{pmatrix}$ **34.** $\begin{pmatrix} 5x - 3y = -34 \\ 2x + 7y = -30 \end{pmatrix}$

35. $\begin{pmatrix} 5x - 2y = 19 \\ 5x - 2y = 7 \end{pmatrix}$ **36.** $\begin{pmatrix} 4a + 2b = -4 \\ 6a - 5b = 18 \end{pmatrix}$

37. $\begin{pmatrix} 5a + 6b = 8 \\ 2a - 15b = 9 \end{pmatrix}$ **38.** $\begin{pmatrix} 7x + 2y = 11 \\ 7x + 2y = -4 \end{pmatrix}$

39. $\begin{pmatrix} \dfrac{2}{3}s + \dfrac{1}{4}t = -1 \\ \dfrac{1}{2}s - \dfrac{1}{3}t = -7 \end{pmatrix}$ **40.** $\begin{pmatrix} \dfrac{1}{4}s - \dfrac{2}{3}t = -3 \\ \dfrac{1}{3}s + \dfrac{1}{3}t = 7 \end{pmatrix}$

41. $\begin{pmatrix} \dfrac{x}{2} - \dfrac{2y}{5} = \dfrac{-23}{60} \\ \dfrac{2x}{3} + \dfrac{y}{4} = \dfrac{-1}{4} \end{pmatrix}$ **42.** $\begin{pmatrix} \dfrac{2x}{3} - \dfrac{y}{2} = \dfrac{3}{5} \\ \dfrac{x}{4} + \dfrac{y}{2} = \dfrac{7}{80} \end{pmatrix}$

43. $\begin{pmatrix} \dfrac{2}{3}x + \dfrac{1}{2}y = \dfrac{1}{6} \\ 4x + 6y = -1 \end{pmatrix}$ **44.** $\begin{pmatrix} \dfrac{1}{2}x + \dfrac{2}{3}y = -\dfrac{3}{10} \\ 5x + 4y = -1 \end{pmatrix}$

For Problems 45–60, solve each system by using either the substitution method or the elimination-by-addition method, whichever seems more appropriate.

45. $\begin{pmatrix} 5x - y = -22 \\ 2x + 3y = -2 \end{pmatrix}$ **46.** $\begin{pmatrix} 4x + 5y = -41 \\ 3x - 2y = 21 \end{pmatrix}$

47. $\begin{pmatrix} x = 3y - 10 \\ x = -2y + 15 \end{pmatrix}$ **48.** $\begin{pmatrix} y = 4x - 24 \\ 7x + y = 42 \end{pmatrix}$

49. $\begin{pmatrix} 3x - 5y = 9 \\ 6x - 10y = -1 \end{pmatrix}$ **50.** $\begin{pmatrix} y = \dfrac{2}{5}x - 3 \\ 4x - 7y = 33 \end{pmatrix}$

51. $\begin{pmatrix} \dfrac{1}{2}x - \dfrac{2}{3}y = 22 \\ \dfrac{1}{2}x + \dfrac{1}{4}y = 0 \end{pmatrix}$ **52.** $\begin{pmatrix} \dfrac{2}{5}x - \dfrac{1}{3}y = -9 \\ \dfrac{3}{4}x + \dfrac{1}{3}y = -14 \end{pmatrix}$

53. $\begin{pmatrix} t = 2u + 2 \\ 9u - 9t = -45 \end{pmatrix}$ **54.** $\begin{pmatrix} 9u - 9t = 36 \\ u = 2t + 1 \end{pmatrix}$

55. $\begin{pmatrix} x + y = 1000 \\ 0.12x + 0.14y = 136 \end{pmatrix}$ **56.** $\begin{pmatrix} x + y = 10 \\ 0.3x + 0.7y = 4 \end{pmatrix}$

57. $\begin{pmatrix} y = 2x \\ 0.09x + 0.12y = 132 \end{pmatrix}$ **58.** $\begin{pmatrix} y = 3x \\ 0.1x + 0.11y = 64.5 \end{pmatrix}$

59. $\begin{pmatrix} x + y = 10.5 \\ 0.5x + 0.8y = 7.35 \end{pmatrix}$ **60.** $\begin{pmatrix} 2x + y = 7.75 \\ 3x + 2y = 12.5 \end{pmatrix}$

For Problems 61–80, solve each problem by using a system of equations. (Objective 4)

61. The sum of two numbers is 53, and their difference is 19. Find the numbers.

62. The sum of two numbers is −3 and their difference is 25. Find the numbers.

63. The measure of the larger of two complementary angles is 15° more than four times the measure of the smaller angle. Find the measures of both angles.

64. Assume that a plane is flying at a constant speed under unvarying wind conditions. Traveling against a head wind, the plane takes 4 hours to travel 1540 miles. Traveling with a tail wind, the plane flies 1365 miles in 3 hours. Find the speed of the plane and the speed of the wind.

65. The tens digit of a two-digit number is 1 more than three times the units digit. If the sum of the digits is 9, find the number.

66. The units digit of a two-digit number is 1 less than twice the tens digit. The sum of the digits is 8. Find the number.

67. A car rental agency rents sedans at $45 a day and convertibles at $65 a day. If 32 cars were rented one day for a total of $1680, how many convertibles were rented?

68. A video store rents new release movies for $5 and favorites for $2.75. One day the number of new release movies rented was twice the number of favorites. If the total income from those rentals was $956.25, how many movies of each kind were rented?

69. A motel rents double rooms at $100 per day and single rooms at $75 per day. If 23 rooms were rented one day for a total of $2100, how many rooms of each kind were rented?

70. An apartment complex rents one-bedroom apartments for $825 per month and two-bedroom apartments for $1075 per month. One month the number of one-bedroom apartments rented was twice the number of two-bedroom apartments. If the total income for that month was $32,700, how many apartments of each kind were rented?

71. The income from a student production was $32,500. The price of a student ticket was $10, and nonstudent tickets were sold at $15 each. Three thousand tickets were sold. How many tickets of each kind were sold?

72. Michelle can enter a small business as a full partner and receive a salary of $10,000 a year and 15% of the year's profit, or she can be sales manager for a salary of $25,000 plus 5% of the year's profit. What must the year's profit be for her total earnings to be the same whether she is a full partner or a sales manager?

73. Melinda invested three times as much money at 6% yearly interest as she did at 4%. Her total yearly interest from the two investments was $110. How much did she invest at each rate?

74. Sam invested $1950, part of it at 6% and the rest at 8% yearly interest. The yearly income on the 8% investment was $6 more than twice the income from the 6% investment. How much did he invest at each rate?

75. One day last summer, Jim went kayaking on the Little Susitna River in Alaska. Paddling upstream against the current, he traveled 20 miles in 4 hours. Then he turned around and paddled twice as fast downstream and, with the help of the current, traveled 19 miles in 1 hour. Find the rate of the current.

76. One solution contains 30% alcohol and a second solution contains 70% alcohol. How many liters of each solution should be mixed to make 10 liters containing 40% alcohol?

77. Santo bought 4 gallons of green latex paint and 2 gallons of primer for a total of $116. Not having enough paint to finish the project, Santo returned to the same store and bought 3 gallons of green latex paint and 1 gallon of primer for a total of $80. What is the price of a gallon of green latex paint?

78. Four bottles of water and 2 bagels cost $10.54. At the same prices, 3 bottles of water and 5 bagels cost $11.02. Find the price per bottle of water and the price per bagel.

79. A cash drawer contains only five- and ten-dollar bills. There are 12 more five-dollar bills than ten-dollar bills. If the drawer contains $330, find the number of each kind of bill.

80. Brad has a collection of dimes and quarters totaling $47.50. The number of quarters is 10 more than twice the number of dimes. How many coins of each kind does he have?

Thoughts Into Words

81. Give a general description of how to use the substitution method to solve a system of two linear equations in two variables.

82. Give a general description of how to use the elimination-by-addition method to solve a system of two linear equations in two variables.

83. Which method would you use to solve the system $\begin{pmatrix} 9x + 4y = 7 \\ 3x + 2y = 6 \end{pmatrix}$? Why?

84. Which method would you use to solve the system $\begin{pmatrix} 5x + 3y = 12 \\ 3x - y = 10 \end{pmatrix}$? Why?

Further Investigations

A system such as

$$\left(\begin{array}{l} \dfrac{2}{x} + \dfrac{3}{y} = \dfrac{19}{15} \\[2mm] -\dfrac{2}{x} + \dfrac{1}{y} = -\dfrac{7}{15} \end{array} \right)$$

is not a linear system, but it can be solved using the elimination-by-addition method as follows. Add the first equation to the second to produce the equivalent system

$$\left(\begin{array}{l} \dfrac{2}{x} + \dfrac{3}{y} = \dfrac{19}{15} \\[2mm] \dfrac{4}{y} = \dfrac{12}{15} \end{array} \right)$$

Now solve $\dfrac{4}{y} = \dfrac{12}{15}$ to produce $y = 5$.

Substitute 5 for y in the first equation and solve for x to produce

$$\dfrac{2}{x} + \dfrac{3}{5} = \dfrac{19}{15}$$

$$\dfrac{2}{x} = \dfrac{10}{15}$$

$$10x = 30$$

$$x = 3$$

The solution set of the original system is $\{(3, 5)\}$.

For Problems 85–90, solve each system.

85. $\left(\begin{array}{l} \dfrac{1}{x} + \dfrac{2}{y} = \dfrac{7}{12} \\[2mm] \dfrac{3}{x} - \dfrac{2}{y} = \dfrac{5}{12} \end{array} \right)$

86. $\left(\begin{array}{l} \dfrac{3}{x} + \dfrac{2}{y} = 2 \\[2mm] \dfrac{2}{x} - \dfrac{3}{y} = \dfrac{1}{4} \end{array} \right)$

87. $\left(\begin{array}{l} \dfrac{3}{x} - \dfrac{2}{y} = \dfrac{13}{6} \\[2mm] \dfrac{2}{x} + \dfrac{3}{y} = 0 \end{array} \right)$

88. $\left(\begin{array}{l} \dfrac{4}{x} + \dfrac{1}{y} = 11 \\[2mm] \dfrac{3}{x} - \dfrac{5}{y} = -9 \end{array} \right)$

89. $\left(\begin{array}{l} \dfrac{5}{x} - \dfrac{2}{y} = 23 \\[2mm] \dfrac{4}{x} + \dfrac{3}{y} = \dfrac{23}{2} \end{array} \right)$

90. $\left(\begin{array}{l} \dfrac{2}{x} - \dfrac{7}{y} = \dfrac{9}{10} \\[2mm] \dfrac{5}{x} + \dfrac{4}{y} = -\dfrac{41}{20} \end{array} \right)$

91. Consider the linear system $\left(\begin{array}{l} a_1x + b_1y = c_1 \\ a_2x + b_2y = c_2 \end{array} \right)$.

    (a) Prove that this system has exactly one solution if and only if $\dfrac{a_1}{a_2} \neq \dfrac{b_1}{b_2}$.

    (b) Prove that this system has no solution if and only if $\dfrac{a_1}{a_2} = \dfrac{b_1}{b_2} \neq \dfrac{c_1}{c_2}$.

    (c) Prove that this system has infinitely many solutions if and only if $\dfrac{a_1}{a_2} = \dfrac{b_1}{b_2} = \dfrac{c_1}{c_2}$.

92. For each of the following systems, use the results from Problem 91 to determine whether the system is consistent or inconsistent or whether the equations are dependent.

    (a) $\left(\begin{array}{l} 5x + y = 9 \\ x - 5y = 4 \end{array} \right)$ **(b)** $\left(\begin{array}{l} 3x - 2y = 14 \\ 2x + 3y = 9 \end{array} \right)$

    (c) $\left(\begin{array}{l} x - 7y = 4 \\ x - 7y = 9 \end{array} \right)$ **(d)** $\left(\begin{array}{l} 3x - 5y = 10 \\ 6x - 10y = 1 \end{array} \right)$

    (e) $\left(\begin{array}{l} 3x + 6y = 2 \\ \dfrac{3}{5}x + \dfrac{6}{5}y = \dfrac{2}{5} \end{array} \right)$ **(f)** $\left(\begin{array}{l} \dfrac{2}{3}x - \dfrac{3}{4}y = 2 \\ \dfrac{1}{2}x + \dfrac{2}{5}y = 9 \end{array} \right)$

    (g) $\left(\begin{array}{l} 7x + 9y = 14 \\ 8x - 3y = 12 \end{array} \right)$ **(h)** $\left(\begin{array}{l} 4x - 5y = 3 \\ 12x - 15y = 9 \end{array} \right)$

Graphing Calculator Activities

93. For each of the systems of equations in Problem 92, use your graphing calculator to help determine whether the system is consistent or inconsistent or whether the equations are dependent.

94. Use your graphing calculator to help determine the solution set for each of the following systems. Be sure to check your answers.

    (a) $\left(\begin{array}{l} y = 3x - 1 \\ y = 9 - 2x \end{array} \right)$ **(b)** $\left(\begin{array}{l} 5x + y = -9 \\ 3x - 2y = 5 \end{array} \right)$

    (c) $\left(\begin{array}{l} 4x - 3y = 18 \\ 5x + 6y = 3 \end{array} \right)$ **(d)** $\left(\begin{array}{l} 2x - y = 20 \\ 7x + y = 79 \end{array} \right)$

    (e) $\left(\begin{array}{l} 13x - 12y = 37 \\ 15x + 13y = -11 \end{array} \right)$ **(f)** $\left(\begin{array}{l} 1.98x + 2.49y = 13.92 \\ 1.19x + 3.45y = 16.18 \end{array} \right)$

Answers to the Concept Quiz

1. True   **2.** False   **3.** True   **4.** True   **5.** False   **6.** False   **7.** False   **8.** False

11.2   Systems of Three Linear Equations in Three Variables

OBJECTIVES

1 Solve systems of three linear equations

2 Solve application problems using a system of three linear equations

Consider a linear equation in three variables x, y, and z, such as $3x - 2y + z = 7$. Any **ordered triple** (x, y, z) that makes the equation a true numerical statement is said to be a *solution* of the equation. For example, the ordered triple $(2, 1, 3)$ is a solution because $3(2) - 2(1) + 3 = 7$. However, the ordered triple $(5, 2, 4)$ is not a solution because $3(5) - 2(2) + 4 \neq 7$. There are infinitely many solutions in the solution set.

Remark: The idea of a linear equation is generalized to include equations of more than two variables. Thus an equation such as $5x - 2y + 9z = 8$ is called a linear equation in three variables; the equation $5x - 7y + 2z - 11w = 1$ is called a linear equation in four variables, and so on.

To *solve* a system of three linear equations in three variables, such as

$$\begin{pmatrix} 3x - y + 2z = 13 \\ 4x + 2y + 5z = 30 \\ 5x - 3y - z = 3 \end{pmatrix}$$

means to find all of the ordered triples that satisfy all three equations. In other words, the solution set of the system is the intersection of the solution sets of all three equations in the system.

The graph of a linear equation in three variables is a *plane*, not a line. In fact, graphing equations in three variables requires the use of a three-dimensional coordinate system. Thus using a graphing approach to solve systems of three linear equations in three variables is not at all practical. However, a simple graphical analysis does provide us with some indication of what we can expect as we begin solving such systems.

In general, because each linear equation in three variables produces a plane, a system of three such equations produces three planes. There are various ways in which three planes can be related. For example, they may be mutually parallel; or two of the planes may be parallel, with the third intersecting the other two. (You may want to analyze all of the other possibilities for the three planes!) However, for our purposes at this time, we need to realize that from a solution set viewpoint, a system of three linear equations in three variables produces one of the following possibilities:

1. There is *one ordered triple* that satisfies all three equations. The three planes have a common *point* of intersection, as indicated in Figure 11.4.

2. There are *infinitely many ordered triples* in the solution set, all of which are coordinates of points on a *line* common to the three planes. This can happen if the three planes have a common line of intersection as in Figure 11.5(a), or if two of the planes coincide and the third plane intersects them as in Figure 11.5(b).

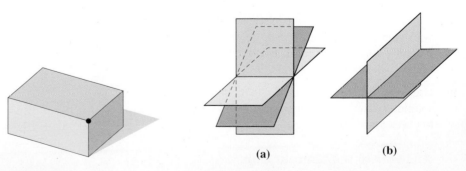

Figure 11.4   **Figure 11.5**

(a)   (b)

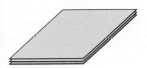

Figure 11.6

3. There are *infinitely many ordered triples* in the solution set, all of which are coordinates of points on a *plane*. This can happen if the three planes coincide, as illustrated in Figure 11.6.

4. The solution set is *empty*; thus we write ∅. This can happen in various ways, as illustrated in Figure 11.7. Note that in each situation there are no points common to all three planes.

(a) Three parallel planes

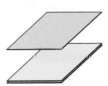

(b) Two planes coincide and the third one is parallel to the coinciding planes.

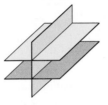

(c) Two planes are parallel and the third intersects them in parallel lines.

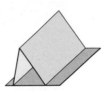

(d) No two planes are parallel, but two of them intersect in a line that is parallel to the third plane.

Figure 11.7

Now that we know what possibilities exist, let's consider finding the solution sets for some systems. Our approach will be the elimination-by-addition method, in which systems are replaced with equivalent systems until a system is obtained that allows us to easily determine the solution set. The details of this approach will become apparent as we work a few examples.

Classroom Example
Solve the system:

$$\begin{pmatrix} x + 4y - 3z = 1 \\ 3y + 4z = 4 \\ 6z = 6 \end{pmatrix}$$

EXAMPLE 1

Solve the system $\begin{pmatrix} 4x - 3y - 2z = 5 \\ 5y + z = -11 \\ 3z = 12 \end{pmatrix}$.

$\qquad\qquad(1)$
$\qquad\qquad(2)$
$\qquad\qquad(3)$

Solution

The form of this system makes it easy to solve. From equation (3), we obtain $z = 4$. Then, substituting 4 for z in equation (2), we get

$$5y + 4 = -11$$
$$5y = -15$$
$$y = -3$$

Finally, substituting 4 for z and -3 for y in equation (1) yields

$$4x - 3(-3) - 2(4) = 5$$
$$4x + 1 = 5$$
$$4x = 4$$
$$x = 1$$

Thus the solution set of the given system is $\{(1, -3, 4)\}$. ▪

Classroom Example
Solve the system:

$$\begin{pmatrix} 2x + 2y - 3z = -1 \\ 4x - 3y + 2z = 20 \\ x + 5y - z = -8 \end{pmatrix}$$

EXAMPLE 2

Solve the system $\begin{pmatrix} x - 2y + 3z = 22 \\ 2x - 3y - z = 5 \\ 3x + y - 5z = -32 \end{pmatrix}$.   (4)(5)(6)

Solution

Equation (5) can be replaced with the equation formed by multiplying equation (4) by -2 and adding this result to equation (5). Equation (6) can be replaced with the equation formed by multiplying equation (4) by -3 and adding this result to equation (6). The following equivalent system is produced, in which equations (8) and (9) contain only the two variables y and z:

$$\begin{pmatrix} x - 2y + 3z = 22 \\ y - 7z = -39 \\ 7y - 14z = -98 \end{pmatrix}$$ (7)(8)(9)

Equation (9) can be replaced with the equation formed by multiplying equation (8) by -7 and adding this result to equation (9). This produces the following equivalent system:

$$\begin{pmatrix} x - 2y + 3z = 22 \\ y - 7z = -39 \\ 35z = 175 \end{pmatrix}$$ (10)(11)(12)

From equation (12), we obtain $z = 5$. Then, substituting 5 for z in equation (11), we obtain

$$y - 7(5) = -39$$
$$y - 35 = -39$$
$$y = -4$$

Finally, substituting -4 for y and 5 for z in equation (10) produces

$$x - 2(-4) + 3(5) = 22$$
$$x + 8 + 15 = 22$$
$$x + 23 = 22$$
$$x = -1$$

The solution set of the original system is $\{(-1, -4, 5)\}$. (Perhaps you should check this ordered triple in all three of the original equations.) ▪

Classroom Example
Solve the system:

$$\begin{pmatrix} 8x - 3y + 5z = -2 \\ 3x + 7y - 2z = 12 \\ 4x - 9y + 10z = -1 \end{pmatrix}$$

EXAMPLE 3

Solve the system $\begin{pmatrix} 3x - y + 2z = 13 \\ 5x - 3y - z = 3 \\ 4x + 2y + 5z = 30 \end{pmatrix}$.   (13)(14)(15)

Solution

Equation (14) can be replaced with the equation formed by multiplying equation (13) by -3 and adding this result to equation (14). Equation (15) can be replaced with the equation formed by multiplying equation (13) by 2 and adding this result to equation (15). Thus we produce the following equivalent system, in which equations (17) and (18) contain only the two variables x and z:

$$\left(\begin{array}{rcr} 3x - y + 2z & = & 13 \\ -4x - 7z & = & -36 \\ 10x + 9z & = & 56 \end{array}\right) \qquad \begin{array}{r}(16)\\(17)\\(18)\end{array}$$

Now, if we multiply equation (17) by 5 and equation (18) by 2, we get the following equivalent system:

$$\left(\begin{array}{rcr} 3x - y + 2z & = & 13 \\ -20x - 35z & = & -180 \\ 20x + 18z & = & 112 \end{array}\right) \qquad \begin{array}{r}(19)\\(20)\\(21)\end{array}$$

Equation (21) can be replaced with the equation formed by adding equation (20) to equation (21).

$$\left(\begin{array}{rcr} 3x - y + 2z & = & 13 \\ -20x - 35z & = & -180 \\ - 17z & = & -68 \end{array}\right) \qquad \begin{array}{r}(22)\\(23)\\(24)\end{array}$$

From equation (24), we obtain $z = 4$. Then we can substitute 4 for z in equation (23).

$$-20x - 35(4) = -180$$
$$-20x - 140 = -180$$
$$-20x = -40$$
$$x = 2$$

Now we can substitute 2 for x and 4 for z in equation (22).

$$3(2) - y + 2(4) = 13$$
$$6 - y + 8 = 13$$
$$-y + 14 = 13$$
$$-y = -1$$
$$y = 1$$

The solution set of the original system is $\{(2, 1, 4)\}$.

Classroom Example
Solve the system:
$$\left(\begin{array}{rcr} 2x - 3y + z & = & -3 \\ 7x + 8y - 4z & = & -11 \\ 8x - 11y + 5z & = & -5 \end{array}\right)$$

EXAMPLE 4

Solve the system $\left(\begin{array}{rcr} 2x + 3y + z & = & 14 \\ 3x - 4y - 2z & = & -30 \\ 5x + 7y + 3z & = & 32 \end{array}\right)$. $\begin{array}{r}(25)\\(26)\\(27)\end{array}$

Solution

Equation (26) can be replaced with the equation formed by multiplying equation (25) by 2 and adding this result to equation (26). Equation (27) can be replaced with the equation formed by multiplying equation (25) by -3 and adding this result to equation (27). The following equivalent system is produced, in which equations (29) and (30) contain only the two variables x and y:

$$\left(\begin{array}{rcr} 2x + 3y + z & = & 14 \\ 7x + 2y & = & -2 \\ -x - 2y & = & -10 \end{array}\right) \qquad \begin{array}{r}(28)\\(29)\\(30)\end{array}$$

Now, equation (30) can be replaced with the equation formed by adding equation (29) to equation (30).

$$\begin{pmatrix} 2x + 3y + z = 14 \\ 7x + 2y \quad\;\; = -2 \\ 6x \qquad\quad = -12 \end{pmatrix} \qquad \begin{matrix} (31) \\ (32) \\ (33) \end{matrix}$$

From equation (33), we obtain $x = -2$. Then, substituting -2 for x in equation (32), we obtain

$$7(-2) + 2y = -2$$
$$2y = 12$$
$$y = 6$$

Finally, substituting 6 for y and -2 for x in equation (31) yields

$$2(-2) + 3(6) + z = 14$$
$$14 + z = 14$$
$$z = 0$$

The solution set of the original system is $\{(-2, 6, 0)\}$.

The ability to solve systems of three linear equations in three unknowns enhances our problem-solving capabilities. Let's conclude this section with a problem that we can solve using such a system.

Classroom Example
A small company that manufactures decorative candles produces three different styles of candles. Each style of candle requires the services of three departments, as indicated by the following table:

	Style A	Style B	Style C
Dipping	0.4 hr	0.6 hr	0.9 hr
Cutting	0.4 hr	0.4 hr	0.7 hr
Packaging	0.1 hr	0.1 hr	0.2 hr

The dipping, cutting, and packaging departments have a maximum of 539, 409, and 107 hours available per week, respectively. How many of each style of candle should be produced each week so that the company is operating at full capacity?

EXAMPLE 5

A small company that manufactures sporting equipment produces three different styles of golf shirts. Each style of shirt requires the services of three departments, as indicated by the following table:

	Style A	Style B	Style C
Cutting department	0.1 hour	0.1 hour	0.3 hour
Sewing department	0.3 hour	0.2 hour	0.4 hour
Packaging department	0.1 hour	0.2 hour	0.1 hour

The cutting, sewing, and packaging departments have available a maximum of 340, 580, and 255 work hours per week, respectively. How many of each style of golf shirt should be produced each week so that the company is operating at full capacity?

Solution

Let a represent the number of shirts of style A produced per week, b the number of style B per week, and c the number of style C per week. Then the problem translates into the following system of equations:

$$\begin{pmatrix} 0.1a + 0.1b + 0.3c = 340 \\ 0.3a + 0.2b + 0.4c = 580 \\ 0.1a + 0.2b + 0.1c = 255 \end{pmatrix} \begin{matrix} \longleftarrow \text{Cutting department} \\ \longleftarrow \text{Sewing department} \\ \longleftarrow \text{Packaging department} \end{matrix}$$

Solving this system (we will leave the details for you to carry out) produces $a = 500$, $b = 650$, and $c = 750$. Thus the company should produce 500 golf shirts of style A, 650 of style B, and 750 of style C per week.

Concept Quiz 11.2

For Problems 1–8, answer true or false.

1. For a system of three linear equations, any ordered triple that satisfies one of the equations is a solution of the system.

2. The solution set of a system of equations is the intersection of the solution sets of all the equations in the system.

3. The graph of a linear equation in three variables is a plane.

4. For a system of three linear equations, the only way for the solution set to be the empty set is if the equations represent three planes that are parallel.

5. The ordered triple (0, 0, 0) could not be a solution for a system of three linear equations.

6. The solution set for a system of three linear equations could be two ordered triples.

7. It is not possible for the solution set of a system of three linear equations to have an infinite number of solutions.

8. Graphing is a practical way to solve a system of three linear equations.

Problem Set 11.2

For Problems 1–20, solve each system. (Objective 1)

1. $\begin{pmatrix} 2x - 3y + 4z = 10 \\ 5y - 2z = -16 \\ 3z = 9 \end{pmatrix}$

2. $\begin{pmatrix} -3x + 2y + z = -9 \\ 4x - 3z = 18 \\ 4z = -8 \end{pmatrix}$

3. $\begin{pmatrix} x + 2y - 3z = 2 \\ 3y - z = 13 \\ 3y + 5z = 25 \end{pmatrix}$

4. $\begin{pmatrix} 2x + 3y - 4z = -10 \\ 2y + 3z = 16 \\ 2y - 5z = -16 \end{pmatrix}$

5. $\begin{pmatrix} 3x + 2y - 2z = 14 \\ x - 6z = 16 \\ 2x + 5z = -2 \end{pmatrix}$

6. $\begin{pmatrix} 3x + 2y - z = -11 \\ 2x - 3y = -1 \\ 4x + 5y = -13 \end{pmatrix}$

7. $\begin{pmatrix} x - 2y + 3z = 7 \\ 2x + y + 5z = 17 \\ 3x - 4y - 2z = 1 \end{pmatrix}$

8. $\begin{pmatrix} x - 2y + z = -4 \\ 2x + 4y - 3z = -1 \\ -3x - 6y + 7z = 4 \end{pmatrix}$

9. $\begin{pmatrix} 2x - y + z = 0 \\ 3x - 2y + 4z = 11 \\ 5x + y - 6z = -32 \end{pmatrix}$

10. $\begin{pmatrix} 2x - y + 3z = -14 \\ 4x + 2y - z = 12 \\ 6x - 3y + 4z = -22 \end{pmatrix}$

11. $\begin{pmatrix} 3x + 2y - z = -11 \\ 2x - 3y + 4z = 11 \\ 5x + y - 2z = -17 \end{pmatrix}$

12. $\begin{pmatrix} 9x + 4y - z = 0 \\ 3x - 2y + 4z = 6 \\ 6x - 8y - 3z = 3 \end{pmatrix}$

13. $\begin{pmatrix} 2x + 3y - 4z = -10 \\ 4x - 5y + 3z = 2 \\ 2y + z = 8 \end{pmatrix}$

14. $\begin{pmatrix} x + 2y - 3z = 2 \\ 3x - z = -8 \\ 2x - 3y + 5z = -9 \end{pmatrix}$

15. $\begin{pmatrix} 3x + 2y - 2z = 14 \\ 2x - 5y + 3z = 7 \\ 4x - 3y + 7z = 5 \end{pmatrix}$

16. $\begin{pmatrix} 4x + 3y - 2z = -11 \\ 3x - 7y + 3z = 10 \\ 9x - 8y + 5z = 9 \end{pmatrix}$

17. $\begin{pmatrix} 2x - 3y + 4z = -12 \\ 4x + 2y - 3z = -13 \\ 6x - 5y + 7z = -31 \end{pmatrix}$

18. $\begin{pmatrix} 3x + 5y - 2z = -27 \\ 5x - 2y + 4z = 27 \\ 7x + 3y - 6z = -55 \end{pmatrix}$

19. $\begin{pmatrix} 5x - 3y - 6z = 22 \\ x - y + z = -3 \\ -3x + 7y - 5z = 23 \end{pmatrix}$

20. $\begin{pmatrix} 4x + 3y - 5z = -29 \\ 3x - 7y - z = -19 \\ 2x + 5y + 2z = -10 \end{pmatrix}$

For Problems 21–30, solve each problem by setting up and solving a system of three linear equations in three variables. (Objective 2)

21. A gift store is making a mixture of almonds, pecans, and peanuts, which sells for $6.50 per pound, $8.00 per pound, and $4.00 per pound, respectively. The store-keeper wants to make 20 pounds of the mix to sell at $5.30 per pound. The number of pounds of peanuts is to be three times the number of pounds of pecans. Find the number of pounds of each to be used in the mixture.

22. The organizer for a church picnic ordered coleslaw, potato salad, and beans amounting to 50 pounds. There was to be three times as much potato salad as coleslaw. The number of pounds of beans was to be 6 less than the number of pounds of potato salad. Find the number of pounds of each.

23. A box contains $7.15 in nickels, dimes, and quarters. There are 42 coins in all, and the sum of the numbers of nickels and dimes is 2 less than the number of quarters. How many coins of each kind are there?

24. A handful of 65 coins consists of pennies, nickels, and dimes. The number of nickels is 4 less than twice the number of pennies, and there are 13 more dimes than nickels. How many coins of each kind are there?

25. The measure of the largest angle of a triangle is twice the measure of the smallest angle. The sum of the smallest angle and the largest angle is twice the other angle. Find the measure of each angle.

26. The perimeter of a triangle is 45 centimeters. The longest side is 4 centimeters less than twice the shortest side. The sum of the lengths of the shortest and longest sides is 7 centimeters less than three times the length of the remaining side. Find the lengths of all three sides of the triangle.

27. Part of $3000 is invested at 4%, another part at 5%, and the remainder at 6% yearly interest. The total yearly income from the three investments is $160. The sum of the amounts invested at 4% and 5% equals the amount invested at 6%. How much is invested at each rate?

28. Different amounts are invested at 6%, 7%, and 8% yearly interest. The amount invested at 7% is $300 more than what is invested at 6%, and the total yearly income from all three investments is $208. A total of $2900 is invested. Find the amount invested at each rate.

29. A small company makes three different types of bird houses. Each type requires the services of three different departments, as indicated by the following table.

	Type A	Type B	Type C
Cutting department	0.1 hour	0.2 hour	0.1 hour
Finishing department	0.4 hour	0.4 hour	0.3 hour
Assembly department	0.2 hour	0.1 hour	0.3 hour

The cutting, finishing, and assembly departments have available a maximum of 35, 95, and 62.5 work hours per week, respectively. How many bird houses of each type should be made per week so that the company is operating at full capacity?

30. A certain diet consists of dishes A, B, and C. Each serving of A has 1 gram of fat, 2 grams of carbohydrate, and 4 grams of protein. Each serving of B has 2 grams of fat, 1 gram of carbohydrate, and 3 grams of protein. Each serving of C has 2 grams of fat, 4 grams of carbohydrate, and 3 grams of protein. The diet allows 15 grams of fat, 24 grams of carbohydrate, and 30 grams of protein. How many servings of each dish can be eaten?

Thoughts Into Words

31. Give a general description of how to solve a system of three linear equations in three variables.

32. Give a step-by-step description of how to solve the system

$$\begin{pmatrix} x - 2y + 3z = -23 \\ 5y - 2z = 32 \\ 4z = -24 \end{pmatrix}$$

33. Give a step-by-step description of how to solve the system

$$\begin{pmatrix} 3x - 2y + 7z = 9 \\ x \quad\quad - 3z = 4 \\ 2x \quad\quad + z = 9 \end{pmatrix}$$

Answers to the Concept Quiz

1. False   **2.** True   **3.** True   **4.** False   **5.** False   **6.** False   **7.** False   **8.** False

11.3   Matrix Approach to Solving Linear Systems

OBJECTIVE   **1**   Use a matrix approach to solve a system of equations

In the first two sections of this chapter, we found that the substitution and elimination-by-addition techniques worked effectively with two equations and two unknowns, but they started to get a bit cumbersome with three equations and three unknowns. Therefore we will now begin to analyze some techniques that lend themselves to use with larger systems of equations. Some of these techniques form the basis for using a computer to solve systems. Even though these techniques are primarily designed for large systems of equations, we will study them in the context of small systems so that we won't get bogged down with the computational aspects of the techniques.

Matrices

A **matrix** is an array of numbers arranged in horizontal rows and vertical columns and enclosed in brackets. For example, the matrix

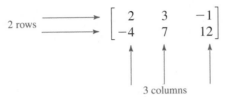

has 2 rows and 3 columns and is called a 2×3 (read "a two by three") matrix. Each number in a matrix is called an **element** of the matrix. Some additional examples of matrices (*matrices* is the plural of *matrix*) follow:

$$3 \times 2 \qquad\qquad 2 \times 2 \qquad\qquad 1 \times 2 \qquad\qquad 4 \times 1$$

$$\begin{bmatrix} 2 & 1 \\ 1 & -4 \\ 1 & 2 \\ \dfrac{1}{2} & \dfrac{2}{3} \end{bmatrix} \qquad \begin{bmatrix} 17 & 18 \\ -14 & 16 \end{bmatrix} \qquad [7 \quad 14] \qquad \begin{bmatrix} 3 \\ -2 \\ 1 \\ 19 \end{bmatrix}$$

In general, a matrix of m rows and n columns is called a matrix of **dimension** $m \times n$ or **order** $m \times n$.

With every system of linear equations, we can associate a matrix that consists of the coefficients and constant terms. For example, with the system

$$\begin{pmatrix} a_1 x + b_1 y + c_1 z = d_1 \\ a_2 x + b_2 y + c_2 z = d_2 \\ a_3 x + b_3 y + c_3 z = d_3 \end{pmatrix}$$

we can associate the matrix

$$\begin{bmatrix} a_1 & b_1 & c_1 & \vdots & d_1 \\ a_2 & b_2 & c_2 & \vdots & d_2 \\ a_3 & b_3 & c_3 & \vdots & d_3 \end{bmatrix}$$

which is commonly called the **augmented matrix** of the system of equations. The dashed line simply separates the coefficients from the constant terms and reminds us that we are working with an augmented matrix.

In Section 11.1 we listed the operations or transformations that can be applied to a system of equations to produce an equivalent system. Because augmented matrices are essentially abbreviated forms of systems of linear equations, there are analogous transformations that can be applied to augmented matrices. These transformations are usually referred to as **elementary row operations** and can be stated as follows:

For any augmented matrix of a system of linear equations, the following elementary row operations will produce a matrix of an equivalent system:

1. Any two rows of the matrix can be interchanged.
2. Any row of the matrix can be multiplied by a nonzero real number.
3. Any row of the matrix can be replaced by the sum of a nonzero multiple of another row plus that row.

Let's illustrate the use of augmented matrices and elementary row operations to solve a system of two linear equations in two variables.

Classroom Example
Solve the system:
$$\begin{pmatrix} 4x - y = -10 \\ 3x + 8y = -25 \end{pmatrix}$$

EXAMPLE 1

Solve the system $\begin{pmatrix} x - 3y = -17 \\ 2x + 7y = 31 \end{pmatrix}$.

Solution

The augmented matrix of the system is

$$\begin{bmatrix} 1 & -3 & \vdots & -17 \\ 2 & 7 & \vdots & 31 \end{bmatrix}$$

We would like to change this matrix to one of the form

$$\begin{bmatrix} 1 & 0 & \vdots & a \\ 0 & 1 & \vdots & b \end{bmatrix}$$

where we can easily determine that the solution is $x = a$ and $y = b$. Let's begin by adding -2 times row 1 to row 2 to produce a new row 2.

$$\begin{bmatrix} 1 & -3 & \vdots & -17 \\ 0 & 13 & \vdots & 65 \end{bmatrix}$$

Now we can multiply row 2 by $\dfrac{1}{13}$.

$$\begin{bmatrix} 1 & -3 & \vdots & -17 \\ 0 & 1 & \vdots & 5 \end{bmatrix}$$

Finally, we can add 3 times row 2 to row 1 to produce a new row 1.

$$\begin{bmatrix} 1 & 0 & \vdots & -2 \\ 0 & 1 & \vdots & 5 \end{bmatrix}$$

From this last matrix, we see that $x = -2$ and $y = 5$. In other words, the solution set of the original system is $\{(-2, 5)\}$.

It may seem that the matrix approach does not provide us with much extra power for solving systems of two linear equations in two unknowns. However, as the systems get larger, the compactness of the matrix approach becomes more convenient. Let's consider a system of three equations in three variables.

Classroom Example
Solve the system:
$$\begin{pmatrix} x - 3y + 2z = 21 \\ 5x + 2y - 3z = -27 \\ -3x + 4y + 5z = -17 \end{pmatrix}$$

EXAMPLE 2

Solve the system $\begin{pmatrix} x + 2y - 3z = 15 \\ -2x - 3y + z = -15 \\ 4x + 9y - 4z = 49 \end{pmatrix}$.

Solution

The augmented matrix of this system is

$$\left[\begin{array}{ccc|c} 1 & 2 & -3 & 15 \\ -2 & -3 & 1 & -15 \\ 4 & 9 & -4 & 49 \end{array}\right]$$

If the system has a unique solution, then we will be able to change the augmented matrix to the form

$$\left[\begin{array}{ccc|c} 1 & 0 & 0 & a \\ 0 & 1 & 0 & b \\ 0 & 0 & 1 & c \end{array}\right]$$

where we will be able to read the solution $x = a$, $y = b$, and $z = c$.

Add 2 times row 1 to row 2 to produce a new row 2. Likewise, add 4 times row 1 to row 3 to produce a new row 3.

$$\left[\begin{array}{ccc|c} 1 & 2 & -3 & 15 \\ 0 & 1 & -5 & 15 \\ 0 & 1 & 8 & -11 \end{array}\right]$$

Now add -2 times row 2 to row 1 to produce a new row 1. Also, add -1 times row 2 to row 3 to produce a new row 3.

$$\left[\begin{array}{ccc|c} 1 & 0 & 7 & -15 \\ 0 & 1 & -5 & 15 \\ 0 & 0 & 13 & -26 \end{array}\right]$$

Now let's multiply row 3 by $\dfrac{1}{13}$.

$$\left[\begin{array}{ccc|c} 1 & 0 & 7 & -15 \\ 0 & 1 & -5 & 15 \\ 0 & 0 & 1 & -2 \end{array}\right]$$

Finally, we can add -7 times row 3 to row 1 to produce a new row 1, and we can add 5 times row 3 to row 2 for a new row 2.

$$\left[\begin{array}{ccc|c} 1 & 0 & 0 & -1 \\ 0 & 1 & 0 & 5 \\ 0 & 0 & 1 & -2 \end{array}\right]$$

From this last matrix, we can see that the solution set of the original system is $\{(-1, 5, -2)\}$.

The final matrices of Examples 1 and 2,

$$\left[\begin{array}{cc|c} 1 & 0 & -2 \\ 0 & 1 & 5 \end{array}\right] \quad \text{and} \quad \left[\begin{array}{ccc|c} 1 & 0 & 0 & -1 \\ 0 & 1 & 0 & 5 \\ 0 & 0 & 1 & -2 \end{array}\right]$$

are said to be in *reduced echelon form*. In general, a matrix is in **reduced echelon form** if the following conditions are satisfied:

1. As we read from left to right, the first nonzero entry of each row is 1.

2. In the column containing the leftmost 1 of a row, all the other entries are zeros.

3. The leftmost 1 of any row is to the right of the leftmost 1 of the preceding row.

4. Rows containing only zeros are below all the rows containing nonzero entries.

Like the final matrices of Examples 1 and 2, the following are in reduced echelon form:

$$\begin{bmatrix} 1 & 2 & \vdots & -3 \\ 0 & 0 & \vdots & 0 \end{bmatrix} \quad \begin{bmatrix} 1 & 0 & -2 & \vdots & 5 \\ 0 & 1 & 4 & \vdots & 7 \\ 0 & 0 & 0 & \vdots & 0 \end{bmatrix} \quad \begin{bmatrix} 1 & 0 & 0 & 0 & \vdots & 8 \\ 0 & 1 & 0 & 0 & \vdots & -9 \\ 0 & 0 & 1 & 0 & \vdots & -2 \\ 0 & 0 & 0 & 1 & \vdots & 12 \end{bmatrix}$$

In contrast, the following matrices are *not* in reduced echelon form for the reason indicated below each matrix:

$$\begin{bmatrix} 1 & 0 & 0 & \vdots & 11 \\ 0 & 3 & 0 & \vdots & -1 \\ 0 & 0 & 1 & \vdots & -2 \end{bmatrix} \qquad \begin{bmatrix} 1 & 2 & -3 & \vdots & 5 \\ 0 & 1 & 7 & \vdots & 9 \\ 0 & 0 & 1 & \vdots & -6 \end{bmatrix}$$

Violates condition 1   Violates condition 2

$$\begin{bmatrix} 1 & 0 & 0 & \vdots & 7 \\ 0 & 0 & 1 & \vdots & -8 \\ 0 & 1 & 0 & \vdots & 14 \end{bmatrix} \qquad \begin{bmatrix} 1 & 0 & 0 & 0 & \vdots & -1 \\ 0 & 0 & 0 & 0 & \vdots & 0 \\ 0 & 0 & 1 & 0 & \vdots & 7 \\ 0 & 0 & 0 & 0 & \vdots & 0 \end{bmatrix}$$

Violates condition 3   Violates condition 4

Once we have an augmented matrix in reduced echelon form, it is easy to determine the solution set of the system. Furthermore, the procedure for changing a given augmented matrix to reduced echelon form can be described in a very systematic way. For example, if an augmented matrix of a system of three linear equations in three unknowns has a unique solution, then it can be changed to reduced echelon form as follows:

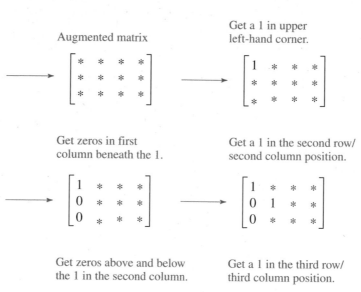

We can identify inconsistent and dependent systems while we are changing a matrix to reduced echelon form. We will show some examples of such cases in a moment, but first let's consider another example of a system of three linear equations in three unknowns for which there is a unique solution.

Classroom Example

Solve the system:

$$\begin{pmatrix} 4x - 6y + 3z = -19 \\ 3x - y + 5z = -3 \\ -x + 4y + 7z = 7 \end{pmatrix}$$

EXAMPLE 3

Solve the system $\begin{pmatrix} 2x + 4y - 5z = 37 \\ x + 3y - 4z = 29 \\ 5x - y + 3z = -20 \end{pmatrix}$.

Solution

The augmented matrix

$$\begin{bmatrix} 2 & 4 & -5 & \vdots & 37 \\ 1 & 3 & -4 & \vdots & 29 \\ 5 & -1 & 3 & \vdots & -20 \end{bmatrix}$$

does not have a 1 in the upper left-hand corner, but this can be remedied by exchanging rows 1 and 2.

$$\begin{bmatrix} 1 & 3 & -4 & \vdots & 29 \\ 2 & 4 & -5 & \vdots & 37 \\ 5 & -1 & 3 & \vdots & -20 \end{bmatrix}$$

Now we can get zeros in the first column beneath the 1 by adding -2 times row 1 to row 2 and by adding -5 times row 1 to row 3.

$$\begin{bmatrix} 1 & 3 & -4 & \vdots & 29 \\ 0 & -2 & 3 & \vdots & -21 \\ 0 & -16 & 23 & \vdots & -165 \end{bmatrix}$$

Next, we can get a 1 for the first nonzero entry of the second row by multiplying the second row by $-\dfrac{1}{2}$.

$$\begin{bmatrix} 1 & 3 & -4 & \vdots & 29 \\ 0 & 1 & -\dfrac{3}{2} & \vdots & \dfrac{21}{2} \\ 0 & -16 & 23 & \vdots & -165 \end{bmatrix}$$

Now we can get zeros above and below the 1 in the second column by adding -3 times row 2 to row 1 and by adding 16 times row 2 to row 3.

$$\begin{bmatrix} 1 & 0 & \dfrac{1}{2} & \vdots & -\dfrac{5}{2} \\ 0 & 1 & -\dfrac{3}{2} & \vdots & \dfrac{21}{2} \\ 0 & 0 & -1 & \vdots & 3 \end{bmatrix}$$

Next, we can get a 1 in the first nonzero entry of the third row by multiplying the third row by -1.

$$\begin{bmatrix} 1 & 0 & \dfrac{1}{2} & \vdots & -\dfrac{5}{2} \\ 0 & 1 & -\dfrac{3}{2} & \vdots & \dfrac{21}{2} \\ 0 & 0 & 1 & \vdots & -3 \end{bmatrix}$$

Finally, we can get zeros above the 1 in the third column by adding $-\dfrac{1}{2}$ times row 3 to row 1 and by adding $\dfrac{3}{2}$ times row 3 to row 2.

$$\left[\begin{array}{ccc|c} 1 & 0 & 0 & -1 \\ 0 & 1 & 0 & 6 \\ 0 & 0 & 1 & -3 \end{array}\right]$$

From this last matrix, we see that the solution set of the original system is $\{(-1, 6, -3)\}$.

Example 3 illustrates that even though the process of changing to reduced echelon form can be systematically described, it can involve some rather messy calculations. However, with the aid of a computer, such calculations are not troublesome. For our purposes in this text, the examples and problems involve systems that minimize messy calculations. This will allow us to concentrate on the procedures.

We want to call your attention to another issue in the solution of Example 3. Consider the matrix

$$\left[\begin{array}{ccc|c} 1 & 3 & -4 & 29 \\ 0 & 1 & -\dfrac{3}{2} & \dfrac{21}{2} \\ 0 & -16 & 23 & -165 \end{array}\right]$$

which is obtained about halfway through the solution. At this step, it seems evident that the calculations are getting a little messy. Therefore, instead of continuing toward the reduced echelon form, let's add 16 times row 2 to row 3 to produce a new row 3.

$$\left[\begin{array}{ccc|c} 1 & 3 & -4 & 29 \\ 0 & 1 & -\dfrac{3}{2} & \dfrac{21}{2} \\ 0 & 0 & -1 & 3 \end{array}\right]$$

The system represented by this matrix is

$$\left(\begin{array}{l} x + 3y - 4z = 29 \\ \quad\quad y - \dfrac{3}{2}z = \dfrac{21}{2} \\ \quad\quad\quad\quad -z = 3 \end{array}\right)$$

and it is said to be in **triangular form**. The last equation determines the value for z; then we can use the process of back-substitution to determine the values for y and x.

Finally, let's consider two examples to illustrate what happens when we use the matrix approach on inconsistent and dependent systems.

Classroom Example
Solve the system:

$$\left(\begin{array}{l} 3x - y + 2z = 3 \\ 4x + 5y - 2z = 20 \\ 6x - 2y + 4z = 5 \end{array}\right)$$

EXAMPLE 4

Solve the system $\left(\begin{array}{l} x - 2y + 3z = 3 \\ 5x - 9y + 4z = 2 \\ 2x - 4y + 6z = -1 \end{array}\right)$.

Solution

The augmented matrix of the system is

$$\left[\begin{array}{ccc|c} 1 & -2 & 3 & 3 \\ 5 & -9 & 4 & 2 \\ 2 & -4 & 6 & -1 \end{array}\right]$$

We can get zeros below the 1 in the first column by adding -5 times row 1 to row 2 and by adding -2 times row 1 to row 3.

$$\begin{bmatrix} 1 & -2 & 3 & \vdots & 3 \\ 0 & 1 & -11 & \vdots & -13 \\ 0 & 0 & 0 & \vdots & -7 \end{bmatrix}$$

At this step, we can stop because the bottom row of the matrix represents the statement $0(x) + 0(y) + 0(z) = -7$, which is obviously false for all values of x, y, and z. Thus the original system is inconsistent; its solution set is $\varnothing$.

Classroom Example

Solve the system:

$$\begin{pmatrix} -5x + 2y + 3z = 13 \\ 3x - 4y - z = -25 \\ 10x - 4y - 6z = -26 \end{pmatrix}$$

EXAMPLE 5

Solve the system $\begin{pmatrix} x + 2y + 2z = 9 \\ x + 3y - 4z = 5 \\ 2x + 5y - 2z = 14 \end{pmatrix}$.

Solution

The augmented matrix of the system is

$$\begin{bmatrix} 1 & 2 & 2 & \vdots & 9 \\ 1 & 3 & -4 & \vdots & 5 \\ 2 & 5 & -2 & \vdots & 14 \end{bmatrix}$$

We can get zeros in the first column below the 1 in the upper left-hand corner by adding -1 times row 1 to row 2 and adding -2 times row 1 to row 3.

$$\begin{bmatrix} 1 & 2 & 2 & \vdots & 9 \\ 0 & 1 & -6 & \vdots & -4 \\ 0 & 1 & -6 & \vdots & -4 \end{bmatrix}$$

Now we can get zeros in the second column above and below the 1 in the second row by adding -2 times row 2 to row 1 and adding -1 times row 2 to row 3.

$$\begin{bmatrix} 1 & 0 & 14 & \vdots & 17 \\ 0 & 1 & -6 & \vdots & -4 \\ 0 & 0 & 0 & \vdots & 0 \end{bmatrix}$$

The bottom row of zeros represents the statement $0(x) + 0(y) + 0(z) = 0$, which is true for all values of x, y, and z. The second row represents the statement $y - 6z = -4$, which can be rewritten $y = 6z - 4$. The top row represents the statement $x + 14z = 17$, which can be rewritten $x = -14z + 17$. Therefore, if we let $z = k$, when k is any real number, the solution set of infinitely many ordered triples can be represented by $\{(-14k + 17, 6k - 4, k) | k \text{ is a real number}\}$. Specific solutions can be generated by letting k take on a value. For example, if $k = 2$, then $6k - 4$ becomes $6(2) - 4 = 8$ and $-14k + 17$ becomes $-14(2) + 17 = -11$. Thus the ordered triple $(-11, 8, 2)$ is a member of the solution set.

Concept Quiz 11.3

For Problems 1–8, answer true or false.

1. A matrix with dimension $m \times n$ has m rows and n columns.

2. The augmented matrix of a system of equations consists of just the coefficients of the variables.

3. If two columns of a matrix are interchanged, the result is an equivalent matrix.

4. The matrix $\begin{bmatrix} a_1 & b_1 & c_1 \\ a_2 & b_2 & c_2 \\ a_3 & b_3 & c_3 \end{bmatrix}$ is equivalent to the matrix $\begin{bmatrix} a_1 & b_1 & c_1 \\ da_2 & db_2 & dc_2 \\ a_3 & b_3 & c_3 \end{bmatrix}$.

5. The matrix $\begin{bmatrix} 1 & 0 & 0 & -4 \\ 0 & 1 & 0 & 8 \\ 1 & 0 & 0 & 2 \end{bmatrix}$ is in reduced echelon form.

6. If the augmented matrix for a system of equations is $\begin{bmatrix} 1 & 0 & 0 & -1 \\ 0 & 1 & 0 & 5 \\ 0 & 0 & 1 & 2 \end{bmatrix}$, then the solution of the system of equations is $(-1, 5, 2)$.

7. The system of equations $\begin{pmatrix} 2x + y - z = 25 \\ 3y - 4z = 10 \\ z = 3 \end{pmatrix}$ is said to be in triangular form.

8. If the solution set of a system of equations is represented by $\{(2k + 3, k) | k$ is a real number$\}$, then $(11, 4)$ is a specific solution of the system of equations.

Problem Set 11.3

For Problems 1–10, indicate whether each matrix is in reduced echelon form.

1. $\begin{bmatrix} 1 & 0 & -4 \\ 0 & 1 & 14 \end{bmatrix}$

2. $\begin{bmatrix} 1 & 2 & 8 \\ 0 & 0 & 0 \end{bmatrix}$

3. $\begin{bmatrix} 1 & 0 & 2 & 5 \\ 0 & 1 & 3 & 7 \\ 0 & 0 & 0 & 0 \end{bmatrix}$

4. $\begin{bmatrix} 1 & 0 & 0 & 5 \\ 0 & 3 & 0 & 8 \\ 0 & 0 & 1 & -11 \end{bmatrix}$

5. $\begin{bmatrix} 1 & 0 & 0 & 17 \\ 0 & 0 & 0 & 0 \\ 0 & 1 & 0 & -14 \end{bmatrix}$

6. $\begin{bmatrix} 1 & 0 & 0 & -7 \\ 0 & 1 & 0 & 0 \\ 0 & 0 & 1 & 9 \end{bmatrix}$

7. $\begin{bmatrix} 1 & 1 & 0 & -3 \\ 0 & 1 & 2 & 5 \\ 0 & 0 & 1 & 7 \end{bmatrix}$

8. $\begin{bmatrix} 1 & 0 & 3 & 8 \\ 0 & 1 & 2 & -6 \\ 0 & 0 & 0 & 0 \end{bmatrix}$

9. $\begin{bmatrix} 1 & 0 & 0 & 3 & 4 \\ 0 & 1 & 0 & 5 & -3 \\ 0 & 0 & 1 & -1 & 7 \\ 0 & 0 & 0 & 0 & 0 \end{bmatrix}$

10. $\begin{bmatrix} 1 & 0 & 0 & 0 & 2 \\ 0 & 0 & 1 & 0 & 4 \\ 0 & 1 & 0 & 0 & -3 \\ 0 & 0 & 0 & 1 & 9 \end{bmatrix}$

For Problems 11–30, use a matrix approach to solve each system. **(Objective 1)**

11. $\begin{pmatrix} x - 3y = 14 \\ 3x + 2y = -13 \end{pmatrix}$

12. $\begin{pmatrix} x + 5y = -18 \\ -2x + 3y = -16 \end{pmatrix}$

13. $\begin{pmatrix} 3x - 4y = 33 \\ x + 7y = -39 \end{pmatrix}$

14. $\begin{pmatrix} 2x + 7y = -55 \\ x - 4y = 25 \end{pmatrix}$

15. $\begin{pmatrix} x - 6y = -2 \\ 2x - 12y = 5 \end{pmatrix}$

16. $\begin{pmatrix} 2x - 3y = -12 \\ 3x + 2y = 8 \end{pmatrix}$

17. $\begin{pmatrix} 3x - 5y = 39 \\ 2x + 7y = -67 \end{pmatrix}$

18. $\begin{pmatrix} 3x + 9y = -1 \\ x + 3y = 10 \end{pmatrix}$

19. $\begin{pmatrix} x - 2y - 3z = -6 \\ 3x - 5y - z = 4 \\ 2x + y + 2z = 2 \end{pmatrix}$

20. $\begin{pmatrix} x + 3y - 4z = 13 \\ 2x + 7y - 3z = 11 \\ -2x - y + 2z = -8 \end{pmatrix}$

21. $\begin{pmatrix} -2x - 5y + 3z = 11 \\ x + 3y - 3z = -12 \\ 3x - 2y + 5z = 31 \end{pmatrix}$

22. $\begin{pmatrix} -3x + 2y + z = 17 \\ x - y + 5z = -2 \\ 4x - 5y - 3z = -36 \end{pmatrix}$

23. $\begin{pmatrix} x - 3y - z = 2 \\ 3x + y - 4z = -18 \\ -2x + 5y + 3z = 2 \end{pmatrix}$

24. $\begin{pmatrix} x - 4y + 3z = 16 \\ 2x + 3y - 4z = -22 \\ -3x + 11y - z = -36 \end{pmatrix}$

25. $\begin{pmatrix} x - y + 2z = 1 \\ -3x + 4y - z = 4 \\ -x + 2y + 3z = 6 \end{pmatrix}$ **26.** $\begin{pmatrix} x + 2y - 5z = -1 \\ 2x + 3y - 2z = 2 \\ 3x + 5y - 7z = 4 \end{pmatrix}$

27. $\begin{pmatrix} -2x + y + 5z = -5 \\ 3x + 8y - z = -34 \\ x + 2y + z = -12 \end{pmatrix}$

28. $\begin{pmatrix} 4x - 10y + 3z = -19 \\ 2x + 5y - z = -7 \\ 2x - 13y - 2z = -2 \end{pmatrix}$

29. $\begin{pmatrix} 2x + 3y - z = 7 \\ 3x + 4y + 5z = -2 \\ 5x + y + 3z = 13 \end{pmatrix}$ **30.** $\begin{pmatrix} 4x + 3y - z = 0 \\ 3x + 2y + 5z = 6 \\ 5x - y - 3z = 3 \end{pmatrix}$

Subscript notation is frequently used for working with larger systems of equations. For Problems 31–34, use a matrix approach to solve each system. Express the solutions as 4-tuples of the form (x_1, x_2, x_3, x_4). **(Objective 1)**

31. $\begin{pmatrix} x_1 - 3x_2 - 2x_3 + x_4 = -3 \\ -2x_1 + 7x_2 + x_3 - 2x_4 = -1 \\ 3x_1 - 7x_2 - 3x_3 + 3x_4 = -5 \\ 5x_1 + x_2 + 4x_3 - 2x_4 = 18 \end{pmatrix}$

32. $\begin{pmatrix} x_1 - 2x_2 + 2x_3 - x_4 = -2 \\ -3x_1 + 5x_2 - x_3 - 3x_4 = 2 \\ 2x_1 + 3x_2 + 3x_3 + 5x_4 = -9 \\ 4x_1 - x_2 - x_3 - 2x_4 = 8 \end{pmatrix}$

33. $\begin{pmatrix} x_1 + 3x_2 - x_3 + 2x_4 = -2 \\ 2x_1 + 7x_2 + 2x_3 - x_4 = 19 \\ -3x_1 - 8x_2 + 3x_3 + x_4 = -7 \\ 4x_1 + 11x_2 - 2x_3 - 3x_4 = 19 \end{pmatrix}$

34. $\begin{pmatrix} x_1 + 2x_2 - 3x_3 + x_4 = -2 \\ -2x_1 - 3x_2 + x_3 - x_4 = 5 \\ 4x_1 + 9x_2 - 2x_3 - 2x_4 = -28 \\ -5x_1 - 9x_2 + 2x_3 - 3x_4 = 14 \end{pmatrix}$

In Problems 35–42, each matrix is the reduced echelon matrix for a system with variables x_1, x_2, x_3, and x_4. Find the solution set of each system. **(Objective 1)**

35. $\begin{bmatrix} 1 & 0 & 0 & 0 & | & -2 \\ 0 & 1 & 0 & 0 & | & 4 \\ 0 & 0 & 1 & 0 & | & -3 \\ 0 & 0 & 0 & 1 & | & 0 \end{bmatrix}$ **36.** $\begin{bmatrix} 1 & 0 & 0 & 0 & | & 0 \\ 0 & 1 & 0 & 0 & | & -5 \\ 0 & 0 & 1 & 0 & | & 0 \\ 0 & 0 & 0 & 1 & | & 4 \end{bmatrix}$

37. $\begin{bmatrix} 1 & 0 & 0 & 0 & | & -8 \\ 0 & 1 & 0 & 0 & | & 5 \\ 0 & 0 & 1 & 0 & | & -2 \\ 0 & 0 & 0 & 0 & | & 1 \end{bmatrix}$ **38.** $\begin{bmatrix} 1 & 0 & 0 & 0 & | & 2 \\ 0 & 1 & 0 & 2 & | & -3 \\ 0 & 0 & 1 & 3 & | & 4 \\ 0 & 0 & 0 & 0 & | & 0 \end{bmatrix}$

39. $\begin{bmatrix} 1 & 0 & 0 & 3 & | & 5 \\ 0 & 1 & 0 & 0 & | & -1 \\ 0 & 0 & 1 & 4 & | & 2 \\ 0 & 0 & 0 & 0 & | & 0 \end{bmatrix}$ **40.** $\begin{bmatrix} 1 & 3 & 0 & 2 & | & 0 \\ 0 & 0 & 1 & 0 & | & 0 \\ 0 & 0 & 0 & 0 & | & 1 \\ 0 & 0 & 0 & 0 & | & 0 \end{bmatrix}$

41. $\begin{bmatrix} 1 & 3 & 0 & 0 & | & 9 \\ 0 & 0 & 1 & 0 & | & 2 \\ 0 & 0 & 0 & 1 & | & -3 \\ 0 & 0 & 0 & 0 & | & 0 \end{bmatrix}$

42. $\begin{bmatrix} 1 & 0 & 0 & 0 & | & 7 \\ 0 & 1 & 0 & 0 & | & -3 \\ 0 & 0 & 1 & -2 & | & 5 \\ 0 & 0 & 0 & 0 & | & 0 \end{bmatrix}$

Thoughts Into Words

43. What is a matrix? What is an augmented matrix of a system of linear equations?

44. Describe how to use matrices to solve the system $\begin{pmatrix} x - 2y = 5 \\ 2x + 7y = 9 \end{pmatrix}$.

Further Investigations

For Problems 45–50, change each augmented matrix of the system to reduced echelon form and then indicate the solutions of the system.

45. $\begin{pmatrix} x - 2y + 3z = 4 \\ 3x - 5y - z = 7 \end{pmatrix}$

46. $\begin{pmatrix} x + 3y - 2z = -1 \\ 2x - 5y + 7z = 4 \end{pmatrix}$

47. $\begin{pmatrix} 2x - 4y + 3z = 8 \\ 3x + 5y - z = 7 \end{pmatrix}$

48. $\begin{pmatrix} 3x + 6y - z = 9 \\ 2x - 3y + 4z = 1 \end{pmatrix}$

49. $\begin{pmatrix} x - 2y + 4z = 9 \\ 2x - 4y + 8z = 3 \end{pmatrix}$

50. $\begin{pmatrix} x + y - 2z = -1 \\ 3x + 3y - 6z = -3 \end{pmatrix}$

Graphing Calculator Activities

51. If your graphing calculator has the capability of manipulating matrices, this is a good time to become familiar with those operations. Also if your calculator has a Catalog, look for a $\boxed{\text{rref}}$ key under the Catalog. The $\boxed{\text{rref}}$ stands for reduced-row-echelon form. The $\boxed{\text{rref}}$ key transforms an augmented matrix into reduced echelon form. You may need to refer to your user's manual for the key-punching instructions. To begin the familiarization process, load your calculator with the three augmented matrices in Examples 1, 2, and 3. Then, for each one, carry out the row operations as described in the text.

Answers to the Concept Quiz

1. True   **2.** False   **3.** False   **4.** True   **5.** False   **6.** True   **7.** True   **8.** True

---

11.4   Determinants

OBJECTIVES

1 Evaluate determinants

2 Apply the properties of determinants to find the determinant

Before we introduce the concept of a determinant, let's agree on some convenient new notation. A **general $m \times n$ matrix** can be represented by

$$A = \begin{bmatrix} a_{11} & a_{12} & a_{13} & \cdots & a_{1n} \\ a_{21} & a_{22} & a_{23} & \cdots & a_{2n} \\ \cdot & \cdot & \cdot & & \cdot \\ \cdot & \cdot & \cdot & & \cdot \\ \cdot & \cdot & \cdot & & \cdot \\ a_{m1} & a_{m2} & a_{m3} & \cdots & a_{mn} \end{bmatrix}$$

The double subscripts are used to identify the number of the row and the number of the column, in that order. For example, a_{23} is the entry at the intersection of the second row and the third column. In general, the entry at the intersection of row i and column j is denoted by a_{ij}.

A **square matrix** is one that has the same number of rows as columns. Each square matrix A with real number entries can be associated with a real number called the **determinant** of the matrix, denoted by $|A|$. We will first define $|A|$ for a 2×2 matrix.

> **Definition 11.1**
>
> If $A = \begin{bmatrix} a_{11} & a_{12} \\ a_{21} & a_{22} \end{bmatrix}$,   then
>
> $$|A| = \begin{vmatrix} a_{11} & a_{12} \\ a_{21} & a_{22} \end{vmatrix} = a_{11}a_{22} - a_{12}a_{21}$$

Classroom Example
Find the determinant of the matrix:

$$\begin{bmatrix} 4 & 6 \\ -3 & 7 \end{bmatrix}$$

EXAMPLE 1

If $A = \begin{bmatrix} 3 & -2 \\ 5 & 8 \end{bmatrix}$, find $|A|$.

Solution

Use Definition 11.1 to obtain

$$|A| = \begin{vmatrix} 3 & -2 \\ 5 & 8 \end{vmatrix} = 3(8) - (-2)(5)$$
$$= 24 + 10$$
$$= 34$$

Finding the determinant of a square matrix is commonly called **evaluating the determinant**, and the matrix notation is often omitted.

Classroom Example

Evaluate $\begin{vmatrix} 8 & 1 \\ 6 & -3 \end{vmatrix}$.

EXAMPLE 2   Evaluate $\begin{vmatrix} -3 & 6 \\ 2 & 8 \end{vmatrix}$.

Solution

$$\begin{vmatrix} -3 & 6 \\ 2 & 8 \end{vmatrix} = (-3)(8) - (6)(2)$$
$$= -24 - 12$$
$$= -36$$

To find the determinants of 3×3 and larger square matrices, it is convenient to introduce some additional terminology.

> **Definition 11.2**
>
> If A is a 3×3 matrix, then the **minor** (denoted by M_{ij}) of the a_{ij} element is the determinant of the 2×2 matrix obtained by deleting row i and column j of A.

Classroom Example

If $A = \begin{bmatrix} 4 & -2 & 1 \\ 2 & 1 & 3 \\ -3 & 2 & -1 \end{bmatrix}$,

find (a) M_{13} and (b) M_{22}.

EXAMPLE 3   If $A = \begin{bmatrix} 2 & 1 & 4 \\ -6 & 3 & -2 \\ 4 & 2 & 5 \end{bmatrix}$, find (a) M_{11} and (b) M_{23}.

Solution

(a) To find M_{11}, we first delete row 1 and column 1 of matrix A.

$$\begin{bmatrix} 2 & 1 & 4 \\ -6 & 3 & -2 \\ 4 & 2 & 5 \end{bmatrix}$$

Thus

$$M_{11} = \begin{vmatrix} 3 & -2 \\ 2 & 5 \end{vmatrix} = 3(5) - (-2)(2) = 19$$

(b) To find M_{23}, we first delete row 2 and column 3 of matrix A.

$$\begin{bmatrix} 2 & 1 & 4 \\ -6 & 3 & -2 \\ 4 & 2 & 5 \end{bmatrix}$$

Thus

$$M_{23} = \begin{vmatrix} 2 & 1 \\ 4 & 2 \end{vmatrix} = 2(2) - (1)(4) = 0$$

The following definition will also be used.

> ### Definition 11.3
>
> If A is a 3×3 matrix, then the **cofactor** (denoted by C_{ij}) of the element a_{ij} is defined by
>
> $$C_{ij} = (-1)^{i+j} M_{ij}$$

According to Definition 11.3, to find the cofactor of any element a_{ij} of a square matrix A, we find the minor of a_{ij} and multiply it by 1 if $i + j$ is even, or multiply it by -1 if $i + j$ is odd.

Classroom Example

If $A = \begin{bmatrix} 2 & -1 & 3 \\ 1 & 4 & -2 \\ 3 & -2 & 3 \end{bmatrix}$, find C_{13}.

EXAMPLE 4

If $A = \begin{bmatrix} 3 & 2 & -4 \\ 1 & 5 & 4 \\ 2 & -3 & 1 \end{bmatrix}$, find C_{32}.

Solution

First, let's find M_{32} by deleting row 3 and column 2 of matrix A.

$$\begin{bmatrix} 3 & 2 & -4 \\ 1 & 5 & 4 \\ 2 & 3 & 1 \end{bmatrix}$$

Thus

$$M_{32} = \begin{vmatrix} 3 & -4 \\ 1 & 4 \end{vmatrix} = 3(4) - (-4)(1) = 16$$

Therefore

$$C_{32} = (-1)^{3+2} M_{32} = (-1)^5 (16) = -16$$

The concept of a cofactor can be used to define the determinant of a 3×3 matrix as follows:

> ### Definition 11.4
>
> If $A = \begin{bmatrix} a_{11} & a_{12} & a_{13} \\ a_{21} & a_{22} & a_{23} \\ a_{31} & a_{32} & a_{33} \end{bmatrix}$, then $|A| = a_{11}C_{11} + a_{21}C_{21} + a_{31}C_{31}$.

Definition 11.4 simply states that the determinant of a 3×3 matrix can be found by multiplying each element of the first column by its corresponding cofactor and then adding the three results. Let's illustrate this procedure.

Classroom Example

Find $|A|$ if $A = \begin{bmatrix} 1 & 2 & -5 \\ 1 & 4 & 6 \\ -3 & 0 & 5 \end{bmatrix}$.

EXAMPLE 5

Find $|A|$ if $A = \begin{bmatrix} -2 & 1 & 4 \\ 3 & 0 & 5 \\ 1 & -4 & -6 \end{bmatrix}$.

Solution

$$|A| = a_{11}C_{11} + a_{21}C_{21} + a_{31}C_{31}$$

$$= (-2)(-1)^{1+1}\begin{vmatrix} 0 & 5 \\ -4 & -6 \end{vmatrix} + (3)(-1)^{2+1}\begin{vmatrix} 1 & 4 \\ -4 & -6 \end{vmatrix} + (1)(-1)^{3+1}\begin{vmatrix} 1 & 4 \\ 0 & 5 \end{vmatrix}$$

$$= (-2)(1)(20) + (3)(-1)(10) + (1)(1)(5)$$

$$= -40 - 30 + 5$$

$$= -65$$

When we use Definition 11.4, we often say that "the determinant is being expanded about the first column." It can also be shown that **any row or column can be used to expand a determinant**. For example, for matrix A in Example 5, the expansion of the determinant about the *second row* is as follows:

$$\begin{vmatrix} -2 & 1 & 4 \\ 3 & 0 & 5 \\ 1 & -4 & -6 \end{vmatrix} = (3)(-1)^{2+1}\begin{vmatrix} 1 & 4 \\ -4 & -6 \end{vmatrix} + (0)(-1)^{2+2}\begin{vmatrix} -2 & 4 \\ 1 & -6 \end{vmatrix} + (5)(-1)^{2+3}\begin{vmatrix} -2 & 1 \\ 1 & -4 \end{vmatrix}$$

$$= (3)(-1)(10) + (0)(1)(8) + (5)(-1)(7)$$

$$= -30 + 0 - 35$$

$$= -65$$

Note that when we expanded about the second row, the computation was simplified by the presence of a zero. In general, it is helpful to expand about the row or column that contains the most zeros.

The concepts of minor and cofactor have been defined in terms of 3×3 matrices. Analogous definitions can be given for any square matrix (that is, any $n \times n$ matrix with $n \geq 2$), and the determinant can then be expanded about any row or column. Certainly as the matrices become larger than 3×3, the computations get more tedious. We will concentrate most of our efforts in this text on 2×2 and 3×3 matrices.

Properties of Determinants

Determinants have several interesting properties, some of which are important primarily from a theoretical standpoint. But some of the properties are also very useful when evaluating determinants. We will state these properties for square matrices in general, but we will use 2×2 or 3×3 matrices as examples. We can demonstrate some of the proofs of these properties by evaluating the determinants involved, and some of the proofs for 3×3 matrices will be left for you to verify in the next problem set.

Property 11.1

If any row (or column) of a square matrix A contains only zeros, then $|A| = 0$.

If every element of a row (or column) of a square matrix A is zero, then it should be evident that expanding the determinant about that row (or column) of zeros will produce 0.

Property 11.2

If square matrix B is obtained from square matrix A by interchanging two rows (or two columns), then $|B| = -|A|$.

Property 11.2 states that interchanging two rows (or columns) changes the sign of the determinant. As an example of this property, suppose that

$$A = \begin{bmatrix} 2 & 5 \\ -1 & 6 \end{bmatrix}$$

and that rows 1 and 2 are interchanged to form

$$B = \begin{bmatrix} -1 & 6 \\ 2 & 5 \end{bmatrix}$$

Calculating $|A|$ and $|B|$ yields

$$|A| = \begin{vmatrix} 2 & 5 \\ -1 & 6 \end{vmatrix} = 2(6) - (5)(-1) = 17$$

and

$$|B| = \begin{vmatrix} -1 & 6 \\ 2 & 5 \end{vmatrix} = (-1)(5) - (6)(2) = -17$$

> **Property 11.3**
>
> If square matrix B is obtained from square matrix A by multiplying each element of any row (or column) of A by some real number k, then $|B| = k|A|$.

Property 11.3 states that multiplying any row (or column) by a factor of k affects the value of the determinant by a factor of k. As an example of this property, suppose that

$$A = \begin{bmatrix} 1 & -2 & 8 \\ 2 & 1 & 12 \\ 3 & 2 & -16 \end{bmatrix}$$

and that B is formed by multiplying each element of the third column by $\dfrac{1}{4}$:

$$B = \begin{bmatrix} 1 & -2 & 2 \\ 2 & 1 & 3 \\ 3 & 2 & -4 \end{bmatrix}$$

Now let's calculate $|A|$ and $|B|$ by expanding about the third column in each case.

$$|A| = \begin{vmatrix} 1 & -2 & 8 \\ 2 & 1 & 12 \\ 3 & 2 & -16 \end{vmatrix} = (8)(-1)^{1+3} \begin{vmatrix} 2 & 1 \\ 3 & 2 \end{vmatrix} + (12)(-1)^{2+3} \begin{vmatrix} 1 & -2 \\ 3 & 2 \end{vmatrix} + (-16)(-1)^{3+3} \begin{vmatrix} 1 & -2 \\ 2 & 1 \end{vmatrix}$$

$$= (8)(1)(1) + (12)(-1)(8) + (-16)(1)(5)$$

$$= -168$$

$$|B| = \begin{vmatrix} 1 & -2 & 2 \\ 2 & 1 & 3 \\ 3 & 2 & -4 \end{vmatrix} = (2)(-1)^{1+3} \begin{vmatrix} 2 & 1 \\ 3 & 2 \end{vmatrix} + (3)(-1)^{2+3} \begin{vmatrix} 1 & -2 \\ 3 & 2 \end{vmatrix} + (-4)(-1)^{3+3} \begin{vmatrix} 1 & -2 \\ 2 & 1 \end{vmatrix}$$

$$= (2)(1)(1) + (3)(-1)(8) + (-4)(1)(5)$$

$$= -42$$

We see that $|B| = \dfrac{1}{4}|A|$. This example also illustrates the usual computational use of Property 11.3: We can factor out a common factor from a row or column and then adjust the value of the determinant by that factor. For example,

$$\begin{vmatrix} 2 & 6 & 8 \\ -1 & 2 & 7 \\ 5 & 2 & 1 \end{vmatrix} = 2 \begin{vmatrix} 1 & 3 & 4 \\ -1 & 2 & 7 \\ 5 & 2 & 1 \end{vmatrix}$$

Factor a 2 from
the top row

Property 11.4

If square matrix B is obtained from square matrix A by adding k times a row (or column) of A to another row (or column) of A, then $|B| = |A|$.

Property 11.4 states that adding the product of k times a row (or column) to another row (or column) does not affect the value of the determinant. As an example of this property, suppose that

$$A = \begin{bmatrix} 1 & 2 & 4 \\ 2 & 4 & 7 \\ -1 & 3 & 5 \end{bmatrix}$$

Now let's form B by replacing row 2 with the result of adding -2 times row 1 to row 2.

$$B = \begin{bmatrix} 1 & 2 & 4 \\ 0 & 0 & -1 \\ -1 & 3 & 5 \end{bmatrix}$$

Next, let's evaluate $|A|$ and $|B|$ by expanding about the second row in each case.

$$|A| = \begin{vmatrix} 1 & 2 & 4 \\ 2 & 4 & 7 \\ -1 & 3 & 5 \end{vmatrix} = (2)(-1)^{2+1}\begin{vmatrix} 2 & 4 \\ 3 & 5 \end{vmatrix} + (4)(-1)^{2+2}\begin{vmatrix} 1 & 4 \\ -1 & 5 \end{vmatrix} + (7)(-1)^{2+3}\begin{vmatrix} 1 & 2 \\ -1 & 3 \end{vmatrix}$$

$$= 2(-1)(-2) + (4)(1)(9) + (7)(-1)(5)$$

$$= 5$$

$$|B| = \begin{vmatrix} 1 & 2 & 4 \\ 0 & 0 & -1 \\ -1 & 3 & 5 \end{vmatrix} = (0)(-1)^{2+1}\begin{vmatrix} 2 & 4 \\ 3 & 5 \end{vmatrix} + (0)(-1)^{2+2}\begin{vmatrix} 1 & 4 \\ -1 & 5 \end{vmatrix} + (-1)(-1)^{2+3}\begin{vmatrix} 1 & 2 \\ -1 & 3 \end{vmatrix}$$

$$= 0 + 0 + (-1)(-1)(5)$$

$$= 5$$

Note that $|B| = |A|$. Furthermore, note that because of the zeros in the second row, evaluating $|B|$ is much easier than evaluating $|A|$. Property 11.4 can often be used to obtain some zeros before we evaluate a determinant.

A word of caution is in order at this time. Be careful not to confuse Properties 11.2, 11.3, and 11.4 with the three elementary row transformations of augmented matrices that were used in Section 11.3. The statements of the two sets of properties do resemble each other, but the properties pertain to *two different concepts*, so be sure you understand the distinction between them.

One final property of determinants should be mentioned.

Property 11.5

If two rows (or columns) of a square matrix A are identical, then $|A| = 0$.

Property 11.5 is a direct consequence of Property 11.2. Suppose that A is a square matrix (any size) with two identical rows. Square matrix B can be formed from A by interchanging the two identical rows. Because identical rows were interchanged, $|B| = |A|$. *But* by Property 11.2, $|B| = -|A|$. For both of these statements to hold, $|A| = 0$.

Let's conclude this section by evaluating a 4×4 determinant, using Properties 11.3 and 11.4 to facilitate the computation.

Classroom Example

Evaluate $\begin{vmatrix} 5 & -2 & 0 & 4 \\ 3 & 1 & -1 & 2 \\ 2 & -4 & 0 & 1 \\ -1 & 11 & -3 & 8 \end{vmatrix}$.

EXAMPLE 6

Evaluate $\begin{vmatrix} 6 & 2 & 1 & -2 \\ 9 & -1 & 4 & 1 \\ 12 & -2 & 3 & -1 \\ 0 & 0 & 9 & 3 \end{vmatrix}$.

Solution

First, let's add -3 times the fourth column to the third column.

$$\begin{vmatrix} 6 & 2 & 7 & -2 \\ 9 & -1 & 1 & 1 \\ 12 & -2 & 6 & -1 \\ 0 & 0 & 0 & 3 \end{vmatrix}$$

Now, if we expand about the fourth row, we get only one nonzero product.

$$(3)(-1)^{4+4}\begin{vmatrix} 6 & 2 & 7 \\ 9 & -1 & 1 \\ 12 & -2 & 6 \end{vmatrix}$$

Factoring a 3 out of the first column of the 3×3 determinant yields

$$(3)(-1)^{8}(3)\begin{vmatrix} 2 & 2 & 7 \\ 3 & -1 & 1 \\ 4 & -2 & 6 \end{vmatrix}$$

Next, working with the 3×3 determinant, we can first add column 3 to column 2 and then add -3 times column 3 to column 1.

$$(3)(-1)^{8}(3)\begin{vmatrix} -19 & 9 & 7 \\ 0 & 0 & 1 \\ -14 & 4 & 6 \end{vmatrix}$$

Finally, by expanding this 3×3 determinant about the second row, we obtain

$$(3)(-1)^{8}(3)(1)(-1)^{2+3}\begin{vmatrix} -19 & 9 \\ -14 & 4 \end{vmatrix}$$

Our final result is

$$(3)(-1)^{8}(3)(1)(-1)^{5}(50) = -450$$

Concept Quiz 11.4

For Problems 1–8, answer true or false.

1. The element of a matrix a_{15} is located at the intersection of the first row and 5th column.

2. If $A = \begin{vmatrix} a_{11} & a_{12} \\ a_{12} & a_{22} \end{vmatrix}$, then $|A| = a_{11}a_{12} - a_{21}a_{22}$.

3. The determinant of a matrix is never a negative value.

4. If $A = \begin{vmatrix} 2 & -1 & 4 \\ 7 & 0 & 0 \\ 8 & -3 & 9 \end{vmatrix}$, the easiest way to find the determinant would be to expand about the second row.

5. The only way for a determinant to be equal to zero is if a row (or column) contains all zeros.

6. If $A = \begin{vmatrix} 3 & -4 \\ 2 & 6 \end{vmatrix}$ and $B = \begin{vmatrix} 2 & 6 \\ 3 & -4 \end{vmatrix}$, then $-|A| = |B|$.

7. Multiplying a row of a matrix by 3 affects the determinant by a factor of $\dfrac{1}{3}$.

8. Interchanging two columns of a matrix has no effect on the determinant.

Problem Set 11.4

For Problems 1–12, evaluate each 2×2 determinant by using Definition 11.1. (Objective 1)

1. $\begin{vmatrix} 4 & 3 \\ 2 & 7 \end{vmatrix}$

2. $\begin{vmatrix} 3 & 5 \\ 6 & 4 \end{vmatrix}$

3. $\begin{vmatrix} -3 & 2 \\ 7 & 5 \end{vmatrix}$

4. $\begin{vmatrix} 5 & 3 \\ 6 & -1 \end{vmatrix}$

5. $\begin{vmatrix} 2 & -3 \\ 8 & -2 \end{vmatrix}$

6. $\begin{vmatrix} -5 & 5 \\ -6 & 2 \end{vmatrix}$

7. $\begin{vmatrix} -2 & -3 \\ -1 & -4 \end{vmatrix}$

8. $\begin{vmatrix} -4 & -3 \\ -5 & -7 \end{vmatrix}$

9. $\begin{vmatrix} \dfrac{1}{2} & \dfrac{1}{3} \\ -3 & -6 \end{vmatrix}$

10. $\begin{vmatrix} \dfrac{2}{3} & \dfrac{3}{4} \\ 8 & 6 \end{vmatrix}$

11. $\begin{vmatrix} \dfrac{1}{2} & \dfrac{2}{3} \\ \dfrac{3}{4} & -\dfrac{1}{3} \end{vmatrix}$

12. $\begin{vmatrix} \dfrac{2}{3} & \dfrac{1}{5} \\ -\dfrac{1}{4} & \dfrac{3}{2} \end{vmatrix}$

For Problems 13–28, evaluate each 3×3 determinant. Use the properties of determinants to your advantage. (Objective 2)

13. $\begin{vmatrix} 1 & 2 & -1 \\ 3 & 1 & 2 \\ 2 & 4 & 3 \end{vmatrix}$

14. $\begin{vmatrix} 1 & -2 & 1 \\ 2 & 1 & -1 \\ 3 & 2 & 4 \end{vmatrix}$

15. $\begin{vmatrix} 1 & -4 & 1 \\ 2 & 5 & -1 \\ 3 & 3 & 4 \end{vmatrix}$

16. $\begin{vmatrix} 3 & -2 & 1 \\ 2 & 1 & 4 \\ -1 & 3 & 5 \end{vmatrix}$

17. $\begin{vmatrix} 6 & 12 & 3 \\ -1 & 5 & 1 \\ -3 & 6 & 2 \end{vmatrix}$

18. $\begin{vmatrix} 2 & 35 & 5 \\ 1 & -5 & 1 \\ -4 & 15 & 2 \end{vmatrix}$

19. $\begin{vmatrix} 2 & -1 & 3 \\ 0 & 3 & 1 \\ 1 & -2 & -1 \end{vmatrix}$

20. $\begin{vmatrix} 2 & -17 & 3 \\ 0 & 5 & 1 \\ 1 & -3 & -1 \end{vmatrix}$

21. $\begin{vmatrix} -3 & -2 & 1 \\ 5 & 0 & 6 \\ 2 & 1 & -4 \end{vmatrix}$

22. $\begin{vmatrix} -5 & 1 & -1 \\ 3 & 4 & 2 \\ 0 & 2 & -3 \end{vmatrix}$

23. $\begin{vmatrix} 3 & -4 & -2 \\ 5 & -2 & 1 \\ 1 & 0 & 0 \end{vmatrix}$

24. $\begin{vmatrix} -6 & 5 & 3 \\ 2 & 0 & -1 \\ 4 & 0 & 7 \end{vmatrix}$

25. $\begin{vmatrix} 24 & -1 & 4 \\ 40 & 2 & 0 \\ -16 & 6 & 0 \end{vmatrix}$

26. $\begin{vmatrix} 2 & -1 & 3 \\ 0 & 3 & 1 \\ 4 & -8 & -4 \end{vmatrix}$

27. $\begin{vmatrix} 2 & 3 & -4 \\ 4 & 6 & -1 \\ -6 & 1 & -2 \end{vmatrix}$

28. $\begin{vmatrix} 1 & 2 & -3 \\ -3 & -1 & 1 \\ 4 & 5 & 4 \end{vmatrix}$

For Problems 29–32, evaluate each 4×4 determinant. Use the properties of determinants to your advantage. (Objective 2)

29. $\begin{vmatrix} 1 & -2 & 3 & 2 \\ 2 & -1 & 0 & 4 \\ -3 & 4 & 0 & -2 \\ -1 & 1 & 1 & 5 \end{vmatrix}$

30. $\begin{vmatrix} 1 & 2 & 5 & 7 \\ -6 & 3 & 0 & 9 \\ -3 & 5 & 2 & 7 \\ 2 & 1 & 4 & 3 \end{vmatrix}$

31. $\begin{vmatrix} 3 & -1 & 2 & 3 \\ 1 & 0 & 2 & 1 \\ 2 & 3 & 0 & 1 \\ 5 & 2 & 4 & -5 \end{vmatrix}$

32. $\begin{vmatrix} 1 & 2 & 0 & 0 \\ 3 & -1 & 4 & 5 \\ -2 & 4 & 1 & 6 \\ 2 & -1 & -2 & -3 \end{vmatrix}$

For Problems 33–42, use the appropriate property of determinants from this section to justify each true statement. *Do not* evaluate the determinants.

33. $(-4)\begin{vmatrix} 2 & 1 & -1 \\ 3 & 2 & 1 \\ 2 & 1 & 3 \end{vmatrix} = \begin{vmatrix} 2 & -4 & -1 \\ 3 & -8 & 1 \\ 2 & -4 & 3 \end{vmatrix}$

34. $\begin{vmatrix} 1 & -2 & 3 \\ 4 & -6 & -8 \\ 0 & 2 & 7 \end{vmatrix} = (-2)\begin{vmatrix} 1 & -2 & 3 \\ -2 & 3 & 4 \\ 0 & 2 & 7 \end{vmatrix}$

35. $\begin{vmatrix} 4 & 7 & 9 \\ 6 & -8 & 2 \\ 4 & 3 & -1 \end{vmatrix} = -\begin{vmatrix} 4 & 9 & 7 \\ 6 & 2 & -8 \\ 4 & -1 & 3 \end{vmatrix}$

36. $\begin{vmatrix} 3 & -1 & 4 \\ 5 & 2 & 7 \\ 3 & -1 & 4 \end{vmatrix} = 0$

37. $\begin{vmatrix} 1 & 3 & 4 \\ -2 & 5 & 7 \\ -3 & -1 & 2 \end{vmatrix} = \begin{vmatrix} 1 & 3 & 4 \\ -2 & 5 & 7 \\ 0 & 8 & 14 \end{vmatrix}$

38. $\begin{vmatrix} 3 & 2 & 0 \\ 1 & 4 & 1 \\ -4 & 9 & 2 \end{vmatrix} = \begin{vmatrix} 3 & 2 & -3 \\ 1 & 4 & 0 \\ -4 & 9 & 6 \end{vmatrix}$

39. $\begin{vmatrix} 6 & 2 & 2 \\ 3 & -1 & 4 \\ 9 & -3 & 6 \end{vmatrix} = 6\begin{vmatrix} 2 & 2 & 1 \\ 1 & -1 & 2 \\ 3 & -3 & 3 \end{vmatrix} = 18\begin{vmatrix} 2 & 2 & 1 \\ 1 & -1 & 2 \\ 1 & -1 & 1 \end{vmatrix}$

40. $\begin{vmatrix} 2 & 1 & -3 \\ 0 & 2 & -4 \\ -5 & 1 & 3 \end{vmatrix} = -\begin{vmatrix} 2 & 1 & -3 \\ -5 & 1 & 3 \\ 0 & 2 & -4 \end{vmatrix}$

42. $\begin{vmatrix} 3 & 1 & 2 \\ -4 & 5 & -1 \\ 2 & -2 & -4 \end{vmatrix} = \begin{vmatrix} 3 & 1 & 0 \\ -4 & 5 & -11 \\ 2 & -2 & 0 \end{vmatrix}$

41. $\begin{vmatrix} 2 & -3 & 2 \\ 1 & -4 & 1 \\ 7 & 8 & 7 \end{vmatrix} = 0$

Thoughts Into Words

43. Explain the difference between a matrix and a determinant.

44. Explain the concept of a cofactor and how it is used to help expand a determinant.

45. What does it mean to say that any row or column can be used to expand a determinant?

46. Give a step-by-step explanation of how to evaluate the determinant

$$\begin{vmatrix} 3 & 0 & 2 \\ 1 & -2 & 5 \\ 6 & 0 & 9 \end{vmatrix}$$

Further Investigations

For Problems 47–50, use

$$A = \begin{bmatrix} a_{11} & a_{12} & a_{13} \\ a_{21} & a_{22} & a_{23} \\ a_{31} & a_{32} & a_{33} \end{bmatrix}$$

as a general representation for any 3×3 matrix.

47. Verify Property 11.2 for 3×3 matrices.

48. Verify Property 11.3 for 3×3 matrices.

49. Verify Property 11.4 for 3×3 matrices.

50. Show that $|A| = a_{11}a_{22}a_{33}a_{44}$ if

$$A = \begin{bmatrix} a_{11} & a_{12} & a_{13} & a_{14} \\ 0 & a_{22} & a_{23} & a_{24} \\ 0 & 0 & a_{33} & a_{34} \\ 0 & 0 & 0 & a_{44} \end{bmatrix}$$

Graphing Calculator Activities

51. Use a calculator to check your answers for Problems 29–32.

52. Consider the following matrix:

$$A = \begin{bmatrix} 2 & 5 & 7 & 9 \\ -4 & 6 & 2 & 4 \\ 6 & 9 & 12 & 3 \\ 5 & 4 & -2 & 8 \end{bmatrix}$$

Form matrix B by interchanging rows 1 and 3 of matrix A. Now use your calculator to show that $|B| = -|A|$.

53. Consider the following matrix:

$$A = \begin{bmatrix} 2 & 1 & 7 & 6 & 8 \\ 3 & -2 & 4 & 5 & -1 \\ 6 & 7 & 9 & 12 & 13 \\ -4 & -7 & 6 & 2 & 1 \\ 9 & 8 & 12 & 14 & 17 \end{bmatrix}$$

Form matrix B by multiplying each element of the second row of matrix A by 3. Now use your calculator to show that $|B| = 3|A|$.

54. Consider the following matrix:

$$A = \begin{bmatrix} 4 & 3 & 2 & 1 & 5 & -3 \\ 5 & 2 & 7 & 8 & 6 & 3 \\ 0 & 9 & 1 & 4 & 7 & 2 \\ 4 & 3 & 2 & 1 & 5 & -3 \\ -4 & -6 & 7 & 12 & 11 & 9 \\ 5 & 8 & 6 & -3 & 2 & -1 \end{bmatrix}$$

Use your calculator to show that $|A| = 0$.

11.5   Cramer's Rule

OBJECTIVE   **1** Use Cramer's Rule to solve 2×2 and 3×3 systems of equations

Determinants provide the basis for another method of solving linear systems. Consider the following linear system of two equations and two unknowns:

$$\begin{pmatrix} a_1x + b_1y = c_1 \\ a_2x + b_2y = c_2 \end{pmatrix}$$

The augmented matrix of this system is

$$\begin{bmatrix} a_1 & b_1 & \vdots & c_1 \\ a_2 & b_2 & \vdots & c_2 \end{bmatrix}$$

Using the elementary row transformation of augmented matrices, we can change this matrix to the following reduced echelon form. (The details are left for you to do as an exercise.)

$$\begin{bmatrix} 1 & 0 & \vdots & \dfrac{c_1b_2 - c_2b_1}{a_1b_2 - a_2b_1} \\ 0 & 1 & \vdots & \dfrac{a_1c_2 - a_2c_1}{a_1b_2 - a_2b_1} \end{bmatrix}, \qquad a_1b_2 - a_2b_1 \neq 0$$

The solution for x and y can be expressed in determinant form as follows:

$$x = \frac{c_1b_2 - c_2b_1}{a_1b_2 - a_2b_1} = \frac{\begin{vmatrix} c_1 & b_1 \\ c_2 & b_2 \end{vmatrix}}{\begin{vmatrix} a_1 & b_1 \\ a_2 & b_2 \end{vmatrix}} \qquad y = \frac{a_1c_2 - a_2c_1}{a_1b_2 - a_2b_1} = \frac{\begin{vmatrix} a_1 & c_1 \\ a_2 & c_2 \end{vmatrix}}{\begin{vmatrix} a_1 & b_1 \\ a_2 & b_2 \end{vmatrix}}$$

This method of using determinants to solve a system of two linear equations in two variables is called **Cramer's rule** and can be stated as follows:

Cramer's Rule (2×2 case)

Given the system

$$\begin{pmatrix} a_1x + b_1y = c_1 \\ a_2x + b_2y = c_2 \end{pmatrix}$$

with

$$D = \begin{vmatrix} a_1 & b_1 \\ a_2 & b_2 \end{vmatrix} \neq 0 \qquad D_x = \begin{vmatrix} c_1 & b_1 \\ c_2 & b_2 \end{vmatrix} \qquad \text{and} \qquad D_y = \begin{vmatrix} a_1 & c_1 \\ a_2 & c_2 \end{vmatrix}$$

then the solution for this system is given by

$$x = \frac{D_x}{D} \qquad \text{and} \qquad y = \frac{D_y}{D}$$

Note that the elements of D are the coefficients of the variables in the given system. In D_x, the coefficients of x are replaced by the corresponding constants, and in D_y, the coefficients of y are replaced by the corresponding constants. Let's illustrate the use of Cramer's rule to solve some systems.

Classroom Example
Solve the system:

$$\begin{pmatrix} 5x - 2y = -12 \\ 3x + 7y = 1 \end{pmatrix}$$

EXAMPLE 1 Solve the system $\begin{pmatrix} 6x + 3y = 2 \\ 3x + 2y = -4 \end{pmatrix}$.

Solution

The system is in the proper form for us to apply Cramer's rule, so let's determine D, D_x, and D_y.

$$D = \begin{vmatrix} 6 & 3 \\ 3 & 2 \end{vmatrix} = 12 - 9 = 3$$

$$D_x = \begin{vmatrix} 2 & 3 \\ -4 & 2 \end{vmatrix} = 4 + 12 = 16$$

$$D_y = \begin{vmatrix} 6 & 2 \\ 3 & -4 \end{vmatrix} = -24 - 6 = -30$$

Therefore

$$x = \frac{D_x}{D} = \frac{16}{3}$$

and

$$y = \frac{D_y}{D} = \frac{-30}{3} = -10$$

The solution set is $\left\{ \left(\dfrac{16}{3}, -10 \right) \right\}$.

Classroom Example
Solve the system:

$$\begin{pmatrix} y = -8x - 4 \\ 4x + 7y = 11 \end{pmatrix}$$

EXAMPLE 2 Solve the system $\begin{pmatrix} y = -2x - 2 \\ 4x - 5y = 17 \end{pmatrix}$.

Solution

To begin, we must change the form of the first equation so that the system fits the form given in Cramer's rule. The equation $y = -2x - 2$ can be rewritten $2x + y = -2$. The system now becomes

$$\begin{pmatrix} 2x + y = -2 \\ 4x - 5y = 17 \end{pmatrix}$$

and we can proceed to determine D, D_x, and D_y.

$$D = \begin{vmatrix} 2 & 1 \\ 4 & -5 \end{vmatrix} = -10 - 4 = -14$$

$$D_x = \begin{vmatrix} -2 & 1 \\ 17 & -5 \end{vmatrix} = 10 - 17 = -7$$

$$D_y = \begin{vmatrix} 2 & -2 \\ 4 & 17 \end{vmatrix} = 34 - (-8) = 42$$

Thus

$$x = \frac{D_x}{D} = \frac{-7}{-14} = \frac{1}{2} \quad \text{and} \quad y = \frac{D_y}{D} = \frac{42}{-14} = -3$$

The solution set is $\left\{ \left(\dfrac{1}{2}, -3 \right) \right\}$, which can be verified, as always, by substituting back into the original equations.

Classroom Example
Solve the system:

$$\begin{pmatrix} \dfrac{3}{4}x - \dfrac{1}{2}y = -17 \\ \dfrac{5}{6}x + \dfrac{7}{8}y = 4 \end{pmatrix}$$

EXAMPLE 3

Solve the system $\begin{pmatrix} \dfrac{1}{2}x + \dfrac{2}{3}y = -4 \\ \dfrac{1}{4}x - \dfrac{3}{2}y = 20 \end{pmatrix}$.

Solution

With such a system, either we can first produce an equivalent system with integral coefficients and then apply Cramer's rule, or we can apply the rule immediately. Let's avoid some work with fractions by multiplying the first equation by 6 and the second equation by 4 to produce the following equivalent system:

$$\begin{pmatrix} 3x + 4y = -24 \\ x - 6y = 80 \end{pmatrix}$$

Now we can proceed as before.

$$D = \begin{vmatrix} 3 & 4 \\ 1 & -6 \end{vmatrix} = -18 - 4 = -22$$

$$D_x = \begin{vmatrix} -24 & 4 \\ 80 & -6 \end{vmatrix} = 144 - 320 = -176$$

$$D_y = \begin{vmatrix} 3 & -24 \\ 1 & 80 \end{vmatrix} = 240 - (-24) = 264$$

Therefore

$$x = \frac{D_x}{D} = \frac{-176}{-22} = 8 \quad \text{and} \quad y = \frac{D_y}{D} = \frac{264}{-22} = -12$$

The solution set is $\{(8, -12)\}$.

In the statement of Cramer's rule, the condition that $D \neq 0$ was imposed. If $D = 0$ and either D_x or D_y (or both) is nonzero, then the system is inconsistent and has no solution. If $D = 0$, $D_x = 0$, and $D_y = 0$, then the equations are dependent and there are infinitely many solutions.

Cramer's Rule Extended

Without showing the details, we will simply state that Cramer's rule also applies to solving systems of three linear equations in three variables. It can be stated as follows:

Cramer's Rule (3 × 3 case)

Given the system

$$\begin{pmatrix} a_1x + b_1y + c_1z = d_1 \\ a_2x + b_2y + c_2z = d_2 \\ a_3x + b_3y + c_3z = d_3 \end{pmatrix}$$

with

$$D = \begin{vmatrix} a_1 & b_1 & c_1 \\ a_2 & b_2 & c_2 \\ a_3 & b_3 & c_3 \end{vmatrix} \neq 0 \qquad D_x = \begin{vmatrix} d_1 & b_1 & c_1 \\ d_2 & b_2 & c_2 \\ d_3 & b_3 & c_3 \end{vmatrix}$$

$$D_y = \begin{vmatrix} a_1 & d_1 & c_1 \\ a_2 & d_2 & c_2 \\ a_3 & d_3 & c_3 \end{vmatrix} \qquad D_z = \begin{vmatrix} a_1 & b_1 & d_1 \\ a_2 & b_2 & d_2 \\ a_3 & b_3 & d_3 \end{vmatrix}$$

then $x = \dfrac{D_x}{D}$, $y = \dfrac{D_y}{D}$, and $z = \dfrac{D_z}{D}$.

Again, note the restriction that $D \neq 0$. If $D = 0$ and at least one of D_x, D_y, and D_z is not zero, then the system is inconsistent. If D, D_x, D_y, and D_z are all zero, then the equations are dependent, and there are infinitely many solutions.

Classroom Example
Solve the system:

$$\begin{pmatrix} 2x - y + 3z = 1 \\ x + 4y - 2z = 3 \\ 3x - 2y + 3z = 5 \end{pmatrix}$$

EXAMPLE 4

Solve the system $\begin{pmatrix} x - 2y + z = -4 \\ 2x + y - z = 5 \\ 3x + 2y + 4z = 3 \end{pmatrix}$.

Solution

We will simply indicate the values of D, D_x, D_y, and D_z and leave the computations for you to check.

$$D = \begin{vmatrix} 1 & -2 & 1 \\ 2 & 1 & -1 \\ 3 & 2 & 4 \end{vmatrix} = 29 \qquad D_x = \begin{vmatrix} -4 & -2 & 1 \\ 5 & 1 & -1 \\ 3 & 2 & 4 \end{vmatrix} = 29$$

$$D_y = \begin{vmatrix} 1 & -4 & 1 \\ 2 & 5 & -1 \\ 3 & 3 & 4 \end{vmatrix} = 58 \qquad D_z = \begin{vmatrix} 1 & -2 & -4 \\ 2 & 1 & 5 \\ 3 & 2 & 3 \end{vmatrix} = -29$$

Therefore

$$x = \frac{D_x}{D} = \frac{29}{29} = 1$$

$$y = \frac{D_y}{D} = \frac{58}{29} = 2$$

$$z = \frac{D_z}{D} = \frac{-29}{29} = -1$$

The solution set is $\{(1, 2, -1)\}$. (Be sure to check it!)

Classroom Example
Solve the system:

$$\begin{pmatrix} 4x - 10y + 6z = 10 \\ 7x + 3y - 2z = 10 \\ 2x - 5y + 3z = 6 \end{pmatrix}$$

EXAMPLE 5

Solve the system $\begin{pmatrix} x + 3y - z = 4 \\ 3x - 2y + z = 7 \\ 2x + 6y - 2z = 1 \end{pmatrix}$.

Solution

$$D = \begin{vmatrix} 1 & 3 & -1 \\ 3 & -2 & 1 \\ 2 & 6 & -2 \end{vmatrix} = 2\begin{vmatrix} 1 & 3 & -1 \\ 3 & -2 & 1 \\ 1 & 3 & -1 \end{vmatrix} = 2(0) = 0$$

$$D_x = \begin{vmatrix} 4 & 3 & -1 \\ 7 & -2 & 1 \\ 1 & 6 & -2 \end{vmatrix} = -7$$

Therefore, because $D = 0$ and at least one of D_x, D_y, and D_z is not zero, the system is inconsistent. The solution set is $\varnothing$.

Example 5 illustrates why D should be determined first. Once we found that $D = 0$ and $D_x \neq 0$, we knew that the system was inconsistent, and there was no need to find D_y and D_z.

Finally, it should be noted that Cramer's rule can be extended to systems of n linear equations in n variables; however, that method is not considered to be a very efficient way of solving a large system of linear equations.

Concept Quiz 11.5

For Problems 1–8, answer true or false.

1. When using Cramer's rule the elements of D are the coefficients of the variables in the given sytem.

2. The system $\begin{pmatrix} 2x - y + 3z = 9 \\ -x + z - 4y = 2 \\ 5x + 2y - z = 8 \end{pmatrix}$ is in the proper form to apply Cramer's rule.

3. When using Cramer's rule for D_y the coefficients of y are replaced by the corresponding constants from the system of equations.

4. Applying Cramer's rule to the system $\begin{pmatrix} \dfrac{1}{4}x + \dfrac{5}{12}y = -1 \\ \dfrac{1}{3}x - \dfrac{2}{3}y = 7 \end{pmatrix}$ produces the same solution set as applying Cramer's rule to the system $\begin{pmatrix} 3x + 5y = -12 \\ x - 2y = 21 \end{pmatrix}$.

5. When using Cramer's rule, if $D = 0$ then the system either has no solution or an infinite number of solutions.

6. When using Cramer's rule, if $D = 0$ and $D_y = 4$, then the system is inconsistent.

7. When using Cramer's rule, if $D_x \neq 0$ then the system of equations always has a solution.

8. Cramer's rule can be extended to solve systems of n linear equations in n variables.

Problem Set 11.5

For Problems 1–32, use Cramer's rule to find the solution set for each system. If the equations are dependent, simply indicate that there are infinitely many solutions. (Objective 1)

1. $\begin{pmatrix} 2x - y = -2 \\ 3x + 2y = 11 \end{pmatrix}$

2. $\begin{pmatrix} 3x + y = -9 \\ 4x - 3y = 1 \end{pmatrix}$

3. $\begin{pmatrix} 5x + 2y = 5 \\ 3x - 4y = 29 \end{pmatrix}$

4. $\begin{pmatrix} 4x - 7y = -23 \\ 2x + 5y = -3 \end{pmatrix}$

5. $\begin{pmatrix} 5x - 4y = 14 \\ -x + 2y = -4 \end{pmatrix}$

6. $\begin{pmatrix} -x + 2y = 10 \\ 3x - y = -10 \end{pmatrix}$

7. $\begin{pmatrix} y = 2x - 4 \\ 6x - 3y = 1 \end{pmatrix}$

8. $\begin{pmatrix} -3x - 4y = 14 \\ -2x + 3y = -19 \end{pmatrix}$

9. $\begin{pmatrix} -4x + 3y = 3 \\ 4x - 6y = -5 \end{pmatrix}$

10. $\begin{pmatrix} x = 4y - 1 \\ 2x - 8y = -2 \end{pmatrix}$

11. $\begin{pmatrix} 9x - y = -2 \\ 8x + y = 4 \end{pmatrix}$

12. $\begin{pmatrix} 6x - 5y = 1 \\ 4x - 7y = 2 \end{pmatrix}$

13. $\begin{pmatrix} -\dfrac{2}{3}x + \dfrac{1}{2}y = -7 \\ \dfrac{1}{3}x - \dfrac{3}{2}y = 6 \end{pmatrix}$

14. $\begin{pmatrix} \dfrac{1}{2}x + \dfrac{2}{3}y = -6 \\ \dfrac{1}{4}x - \dfrac{1}{3}y = -1 \end{pmatrix}$

15. $\begin{pmatrix} 2x + 7y = -1 \\ x = 2 \end{pmatrix}$

16. $\begin{pmatrix} 5x - 3y = 2 \\ y = 4 \end{pmatrix}$

17. $\begin{pmatrix} x - y + 2z = -8 \\ 2x + 3y - 4z = 18 \\ -x + 2y - z = 7 \end{pmatrix}$

18. $\begin{pmatrix} x - 2y + z = 3 \\ 3x + 2y + z = -3 \\ 2x - 3y - 3z = -5 \end{pmatrix}$

19. $\begin{pmatrix} 2x - 3y + z = -7 \\ -3x + y - z = -7 \\ x - 2y - 5z = -45 \end{pmatrix}$

20. $\begin{pmatrix} 3x - y - z = 18 \\ 4x + 3y - 2z = 10 \\ -5x - 2y + 3z = -22 \end{pmatrix}$

21. $\begin{pmatrix} 4x + 5y - 2z = -14 \\ 7x - y + 2z = 42 \\ 3x + y + 4z = 28 \end{pmatrix}$

22. $\begin{pmatrix} -5x + 6y + 4z = -4 \\ -7x - 8y + 2z = -2 \\ 2x + 9y - z = 1 \end{pmatrix}$

23. $\begin{pmatrix} 2x - y + 3z = -17 \\ 3y + z = 5 \\ x - 2y - z = -3 \end{pmatrix}$

24. $\begin{pmatrix} 2x - y + 3z = -5 \\ 3x + 4y - 2z = -25 \\ -x + z = 6 \end{pmatrix}$

25. $\begin{pmatrix} x + 3y - 4z = -1 \\ 2x - y + z = 2 \\ 4x + 5y - 7z = 0 \end{pmatrix}$

26. $\begin{pmatrix} x - 2y + z = 1 \\ 3x + y - z = 2 \\ 2x - 4y + 2z = -1 \end{pmatrix}$

27. $\begin{pmatrix} 3x - 2y - 3z = -5 \\ x + 2y + 3z = -3 \\ -x + 4y - 6z = 8 \end{pmatrix}$

28. $\begin{pmatrix} 3x - 2y + z = 11 \\ 5x + 3y = 17 \\ x + y - 2z = 6 \end{pmatrix}$

29. $\begin{pmatrix} x - 2y + 3z = 1 \\ -2x + 4y - 3z = -3 \\ 5x - 6y + 6z = 10 \end{pmatrix}$

30. $\begin{pmatrix} 2x - y + 2z = -1 \\ 4x + 3y - 4z = 2 \\ x + 5y - z = 9 \end{pmatrix}$

31. $\begin{pmatrix} -x - y + 3z = -2 \\ -2x + y + 7z = 14 \\ 3x + 4y - 5z = 12 \end{pmatrix}$

32. $\begin{pmatrix} -2x + y - 3z = -4 \\ x + 5y - 4z = 13 \\ 7x - 2y - z = 37 \end{pmatrix}$

Thoughts Into Words

33. Give a step-by-step description of how you would solve the system

$$\begin{pmatrix} 2x - y + 3z = 31 \\ x - 2y - z = 8 \\ 3x + 5y + 8z = 35 \end{pmatrix}$$

34. Give a step-by-step description of how you would find the value of x in the solution for the system

$$\begin{pmatrix} x + 5y - z = -9 \\ 2x - y + z = 11 \\ -3x - 2y + 4z = 20 \end{pmatrix}$$

Further Investigations

35. A linear system in which the constant terms are all zero is called a **homogeneous system**.

(a) Verify that for a 3×3 homogeneous system, if $D \neq 0$, then $(0, 0, 0)$ is the only solution for the system.

(b) Verify that for a 3×3 homogeneous system, if $D = 0$, then the equations are dependent.

For Problems 36–39, solve each of the homogeneous systems (see the text above). If the equations are dependent, indicate that the system has infinitely many solutions.

36. $\begin{pmatrix} x - 2y + 5z = 0 \\ 3x + y - 2z = 0 \\ 4x - y + 3z = 0 \end{pmatrix}$

37. $\begin{pmatrix} 2x - y + z = 0 \\ 3x + 2y + 5z = 0 \\ 4x - 7y + z = 0 \end{pmatrix}$

38. $\begin{pmatrix} 3x + y - z = 0 \\ x - y + 2z = 0 \\ 4x - 5y - 2z = 0 \end{pmatrix}$

39. $\begin{pmatrix} 2x - y + 2z = 0 \\ x + 2y + z = 0 \\ x - 3y + z = 0 \end{pmatrix}$

Graphing Calculator Activities

40. Use determinants and your calculator to solve each of the following systems:

(a) $\begin{pmatrix} 4x - 3y + z = 10 \\ 8x + 5y - 2z = -6 \\ -12x - 2y + 3z = -2 \end{pmatrix}$

(b) $\begin{pmatrix} 2x + y - z + w = -4 \\ x + 2y + 2z - 3w = 6 \\ 3x - y - z + 2w = 0 \\ 2x + 3y + z + 4w = -5 \end{pmatrix}$

(c) $\begin{pmatrix} x - 2y + z - 3w = 4 \\ 2x + 3y - z - 2w = -4 \\ 3x - 4y + 2z - 4w = 12 \\ 2x - y - 3z + 2w = -2 \end{pmatrix}$

(d) $\begin{pmatrix} 1.98x + 2.49y + 3.45z = 80.10 \\ 2.15x + 3.20y + 4.19z = 97.16 \\ 1.49x + 4.49y + 2.79z = 83.92 \end{pmatrix}$

Answers to the Concept Quiz

1. True   **2.** False   **3.** True   **4.** True   **5.** True   **6.** True   **7.** False   **8.** True

---

11.6   Partial Fractions (Optional)

OBJECTIVE   **1** Find partial fraction decompositions for rational expressions

In Chapter 4, we reviewed the process of adding rational expressions. For example,

$$\frac{3}{x - 2} + \frac{2}{x + 3} = \frac{3(x + 3) + 2(x - 2)}{(x - 2)(x + 3)} = \frac{3x + 9 + 2x - 4}{(x - 2)(x + 3)} = \frac{5x + 5}{(x - 2)(x + 3)}$$

Now suppose that we want to reverse the process. That is, suppose we are given the rational expression

$$\frac{5x + 5}{(x - 2)(x + 3)}$$

and we want to express it as the sum of two simpler rational expressions called **partial fractions**. This process, called **partial fraction decomposition**, has several applications in calculus and differential equations. The following property provides the basis for partial fraction decomposition.

Property 11.6

Let $f(x)$ and $g(x)$ be polynomials with real coefficients, such that the degree of $f(x)$ is less than the degree of $g(x)$. The indicated quotient $f(x)/g(x)$ can be decomposed into partial fractions as follows.

1. If $g(x)$ has a linear factor of the form $ax + b$, then the partial fraction decomposition will contain a term of the form

$$\frac{A}{ax + b} \quad \text{where } A \text{ is a constant}$$

2. If $g(x)$ has a linear factor of the form $ax + b$ raised to the kth power, then the partial fraction decomposition will contain terms of the form

$$\frac{A_1}{ax + b} + \frac{A_2}{(ax + b)^2} + \cdots + \frac{A_k}{(ax + b)^k}$$

where $A_1, A_2, \ldots, A_k$ are constants.

(Continued)

> **3.** If $g(x)$ has a quadratic factor of the form $ax^2 + bx + c$, where $b^2 - 4ac < 0$, then the partial fraction decomposition will contain a term of the form
>
> $$\frac{Ax + B}{ax^2 + bx + c} \quad \text{where } A \text{ and } B \text{ are constants.}$$
>
> **4.** If $g(x)$ has a quadratic factor of the form $ax^2 + bx + c$ raised to the kth power, where $b^2 - 4ac < 0$, then the partial fraction decomposition will contain terms of the form
>
> $$\frac{A_1 x + B_1}{ax^2 + bx + c} + \frac{A_2 x + B_2}{(ax^2 + bx + c)^2} + \cdots + \frac{A_k x + B_k x}{(ax^2 + bx + c)^k}$$
>
> where $A_1, A_2, \ldots, A_k$, and $B_1, B_2, \ldots, B_k$ are constants.

Note that Property 11.6 applies only to **proper fractions**—that is, fractions in which the degree of the numerator is less than the degree of the denominator. If the numerator is not of lower degree, we can divide and then apply Property 11.6 to the remainder, which will be a proper fraction. For example,

$$\frac{x^3 - 3x^2 - 3x - 5}{x^2 - 4} = x - 3 + \frac{x - 17}{x^2 - 4}$$

and the proper fraction $\dfrac{x - 17}{x^2 - 4}$ can be decomposed into partial fractions by applying Property 11.6. Now let's consider some examples to illustrate the four cases in Property 11.6.

Classroom Example
Find the partial fraction decomposition of $\dfrac{13x - 5}{5x^2 - 13x - 6}$.

EXAMPLE 1

Find the partial fraction decomposition of $\dfrac{11x + 2}{2x^2 + x - 1}$.

Solution

The denominator can be expressed as $(x + 1)(2x - 1)$. Therefore, according to part 1 of Property 11.6, each of the linear factors produces a partial fraction of the form *constant over linear factor*. In other words, we can write

$$\frac{11x + 2}{(x + 1)(2x - 1)} = \frac{A}{x + 1} + \frac{B}{2x - 1} \tag{1}$$

for some constants A and B. To find A and B, we multiply both sides of equation (1) by the least common denominator $(x + 1)(2x - 1)$:

$$11x + 2 = A(2x - 1) + B(x + 1) \tag{2}$$

Equation (2) is an **identity**: *It is true for all values of x.* Therefore, let's choose some convenient values for x that will determine the values for A and B. If we let $x = -1$, then equation (2) becomes an equation in only A.

$$11(-1) + 2 = A[2(-1) - 1] + B(-1 + 1)$$
$$-9 = -3A$$
$$3 = A$$

If we let $x = \dfrac{1}{2}$, then equation (2) becomes an equation only in B.

$$11\left(\frac{1}{2}\right) + 2 = A\left[2\left(\frac{1}{2}\right) - 1\right] + B\left(\frac{1}{2} + 1\right)$$
$$\frac{15}{2} = \frac{3}{2}B$$
$$5 = B$$

Therefore, the given rational expression can now be written

$$\frac{11x + 2}{2x^2 + x - 1} = \frac{3}{x + 1} + \frac{5}{2x - 1}$$

∎

The key idea in Example 1 is the statement that equation (2) is true for all values of x. If we had chosen *any* two values for x, we still would have been able to determine the values for A and B. For example, letting $x = 1$ and then $x = 2$ produces the equations $13 = A + 2B$ and $24 = 3A + 3B$. Solving this system of two equations in two unknowns produces $A = 3$ and $B = 5$. In Example 1, our choices of letting $x = -1$ and then $x = \frac{1}{2}$ simply eliminated the need for solving a system of equations to find A and B.

Classroom Example
Find the partial fraction decomposition
of $\dfrac{6x^2 + 25x + 36}{x(x + 3)^2}$.

EXAMPLE 2

Find the partial fraction decomposition of $\dfrac{-2x^2 + 7x + 2}{x(x - 1)^2}$.

Solution

Apply part 1 of Property 11.6 to determine that there is a partial fraction of the form A/x corresponding to the factor of x. Next, applying part 2 of Property 11.6 and the squared factor $(x - 1)^2$ gives rise to a sum of partial fractions of the form

$$\frac{B}{x - 1} + \frac{C}{(x - 1)^2}$$

Therefore, the complete partial fraction decomposition is of the form

$$\frac{-2x^2 + 7x + 2}{x(x - 1)^2} = \frac{A}{x} + \frac{B}{x - 1} + \frac{C}{(x - 1)^2} \qquad (1)$$

Multiply both sides of equation (1) by $x(x - 1)^2$ to produce

$$-2x^2 + 7x + 2 = A(x - 1)^2 + Bx(x - 1) + Cx \qquad (2)$$

which is true for all values of x. If we let $x = 1$, then equation (2) becomes an equation in only C.

$$-2(1)^2 + 7(1) + 2 = A(1 - 1)^2 + B(1)(1 - 1) + C(1)$$
$$7 = C$$

If we let $x = 0$, then equation (2) becomes an equation in just A.

$$-2(0)^2 + 7(0) + 2 = A(0 - 1)^2 + B(0)(0 - 1) + C(0)$$
$$2 = A$$

If we let $x = 2$, then equation (2) becomes an equation in A, B, and C.

$$-2(2)^2 + 7(2) + 2 = A(2 - 1)^2 + B(2)(2 - 1) + C(2)$$
$$8 = A + 2B + 2C$$

But we already know that $A = 2$ and $C = 7$, so we can easily determine B.

$$8 = 2 + 2B + 14$$
$$-8 = 2B$$
$$-4 = B$$

Therefore, the original rational expression can be written

$$\frac{-2x^2 + 7x + 2}{x(x - 1)^2} = \frac{2}{x} - \frac{4}{x - 1} + \frac{7}{(x - 1)^2}$$

∎

Classroom Example
Find the partial fraction decomposition

of $\dfrac{5x^2 + 21x + 4}{(x + 2)(x^2 + 6x + 2)}$.

EXAMPLE 3

Find the partial fraction decomposition of $\dfrac{4x^2 + 6x - 10}{(x + 3)(x^2 + x + 2)}$.

Solution

Apply part 1 of Property 11.6 to determine that there is a partial fraction of the form $A/(x + 3)$ that corresponds to the factor $x + 3$. Apply part 3 of Property 11.6 to determine that there is also a partial fraction of the form

$$\frac{Bx + C}{x^2 + x + 2}$$

Thus the complete partial fraction decomposition is of the form

$$\frac{4x^2 + 6x - 10}{(x + 3)(x^2 + x + 2)} = \frac{A}{x + 3} + \frac{Bx + C}{x^2 + x + 2} \tag{1}$$

Multiply both sides of equation (1) by $(x + 3)(x^2 + x + 2)$ to produce

$$4x^2 + 6x - 10 = A(x^2 + x + 2) + (Bx + C)(x + 3) \tag{2}$$

which is true for all values of x. If we let $x = -3$, then equation (2) becomes an equation in A alone.

$$4(-3)^2 + 6(-3) - 10 = A[(-3)^2 + (-3) + 2] + [B(-3) + C][(-3) + 3]$$
$$8 = 8A$$
$$1 = A$$

If we let $x = 0$, then equation (2) becomes an equation in A and C.

$$4(0)^2 + 6(0) - 10 = A(0^2 + 0 + 2) + [B(0) + C](0 + 3)$$
$$-10 = 2A + 3C$$

Because $A = 1$, we obtain the value of C.

$$-10 = 2 + 3C$$
$$-12 = 3C$$
$$-4 = C$$

If we let $x = 1$, then equation (2) becomes an equation in A, B, and C.

$$4(1)^2 + 6(1) - 10 = A(1^2 + 1 + 2) + [B(1) + C](1 + 3)$$
$$0 = 4A + 4B + 4C$$
$$0 = A + B + C$$

But because $A = 1$ and $C = -4$, we obtain the value of B.

$$0 = A + B + C$$
$$0 = 1 + B + (-4)$$
$$3 = B$$

Therefore, the original rational expression can now be written

$$\frac{4x^2 + 6x - 10}{(x + 3)(x^2 + x + 2)} = \frac{1}{x + 3} + \frac{3x - 4}{x^2 + x + 2}$$

Classroom Example
Find the partial fraction decomposition
of $\dfrac{x^3 + 2x^2 + 3x + 9}{(x^2 + 3)^2}$.

EXAMPLE 4   Find the partial fraction decomposition of $\dfrac{x^3 + x^2 + x + 3}{(x^2 + 1)^2}$.

Solution

Apply part 4 of Property 11.6 to determine that the partial fraction decomposition of this fraction is of the form

$$\frac{x^3 + x^2 + x + 3}{(x^2 + 1)^2} = \frac{Ax + B}{x^2 + 1} + \frac{Cx + D}{(x^2 + 1)^2} \tag{1}$$

Multiply both sides of equation (1) by $(x^2 + 1)^2$ to produce

$$x^3 + x^2 + x + 3 = (Ax + B)(x^2 + 1) + Cx + D \tag{2}$$

which is true for all values of x. Equation (2) is an identity, so we know that the coefficients of similar terms on both sides of the equation must be equal. Therefore, let's collect similar terms on the right side of equation (2).

$$x^3 + x^2 + x + 3 = Ax^3 + Ax + Bx^2 + B + Cx + D$$
$$= Ax^3 + Bx^2 + (A + C)x + B + D$$

Now we can equate coefficients from both sides:

$$1 = A \qquad 1 = B \qquad 1 = A + C \qquad \text{and} \qquad 3 = B + D$$

From these equations, we can determine that $A = 1$, $B = 1$, $C = 0$, and $D = 2$. Therefore, the original rational expression can be written

$$\frac{x^3 + x^2 + x + 3}{(x^2 + 1)^2} = \frac{x + 1}{x^2 + 1} + \frac{2}{(x^2 + 1)^2}$$

Concept Quiz 11.6

For Problems 1–8, answer true or false.

1. The process of partial fraction decomposition expresses a rational expression as the sum of two or more simpler rational expressions.

2. A rational expression is considered a proper fraction if the degree of the numerator is equal to or less than the degree of the denominator.

3. The process of partial fraction decomposition applies only to proper fractions.

4. To apply partial fraction decomposition to a rational expression that is not a proper fraction, use long division to obtain a remainder that is a proper fraction.

5. If an equation is an identity, any value of x substituted into the equation produces an equivalent equation.

6. A quadratic expression such as $ax^2 + bx + c$ is not factorable over the real numbers if $b^2 - 4ac < 0$.

7. Given that $5x + 3 = A(x - 4) + B(x + 7)$ is an identity, the value of A can be determined by substituting any value of x into the identity.

8. Given that $3x - 1 = A(x - 2) + B(x + 5)$ is an identity, the value of B can be determined by substituting -5 for x into the identity.

Problem Set 11.6

For Problems 1–22, find the partial fraction decomposition for each rational expression. **(Objective 1)**

1. $\dfrac{11x - 10}{(x - 2)(x + 1)}$

2. $\dfrac{11x - 2}{(x + 3)(x - 4)}$

3. $\dfrac{-2x - 8}{x^2 - 1}$

4. $\dfrac{-2x + 32}{x^2 - 4}$

5. $\dfrac{20x - 3}{6x^2 + 7x - 3}$

6. $\dfrac{-2x - 8}{10x^2 - x - 2}$

7. $\dfrac{x^2 - 18x + 5}{(x - 1)(x + 2)(x - 3)}$

8. $\dfrac{-9x^2 + 7x - 4}{x^3 - 3x^2 - 4x}$

9. $\dfrac{-6x^2 + 7x + 1}{x(2x - 1)(4x + 1)}$

10. $\dfrac{15x^2 + 20x + 30}{(x + 3)(3x + 2)(2x + 3)}$

11. $\dfrac{2x + 1}{(x - 2)^2}$

12. $\dfrac{-3x + 1}{(x + 1)^2}$

13. $\dfrac{-6x^2 + 19x + 21}{x^2(x + 3)}$

14. $\dfrac{10x^2 - 73x + 144}{x(x - 4)^2}$

15. $\dfrac{-2x^2 - 3x + 10}{(x^2 + 1)(x - 4)}$

16. $\dfrac{8x^2 + 15x + 12}{(x^2 + 4)(3x - 4)}$

17. $\dfrac{3x^2 + 10x + 9}{(x + 2)^3}$

18. $\dfrac{2x^3 + 8x^2 + 2x + 4}{(x + 1)^2(x^2 + 3)}$

19. $\dfrac{5x^2 + 3x + 6}{x(x^2 - x + 3)}$

20. $\dfrac{x^3 + x^2 + 2}{(x^2 + 2)^2}$

21. $\dfrac{2x^3 + x + 3}{(x^2 + 1)^2}$

22. $\dfrac{4x^2 + 3x + 14}{x^3 - 8}$

Thoughts Into Words

23. Give a general description of partial fraction decomposition for someone who missed class the day it was discussed.

24. Give a step-by-step explanation of how to find the partial fraction decomposition of $\dfrac{11x + 5}{2x^2 + 5x - 3}$.

Answers to the Concept Quiz

1. True   **2.** False   **3.** True   **4.** True   **5.** True   **6.** True   **7.** False   **8.** False

OBJECTIVE	SUMMARY	EXAMPLE
Solve systems of two linear equations by graphing. (Section 11.1/Objective 1)	Graphing a **system of two linear equations in two variables** produces one of the following results. 1. The graphs of the two equations are two intersecting lines, which indicates that there is *one unique solution* of the system. Such a system is called a *consistent system*. 2. The graphs of the two equations are two parallel lines, which indicates that there is *no solution* for the system. It is called an *inconsistent system*. 3. The graphs of the two equations are the same line, which indicates *infinitely many solutions* for the system. The equations are called *dependent* equations.	Solve $\begin{pmatrix} x - 3y = 6 \\ 2x + 3y = 3 \end{pmatrix}$ by graphing. **Solution** Graph the lines by determining the x and y intercepts and a check point. $x - 3y = 6$ 	x	y	 |---|---| 	0	-2	 	6	0	 	-3	-3	 $2x + 3y = 3$ 	x	y	 |---|---| 	0	1	 	$\frac{3}{2}$	0	 	-1	$\frac{5}{3}$	 It appears that $(3, -1)$ is the solution. Checking these values in the equations, we can determine that the solution set is $\{(3, -1)\}$.
Solve systems of two linear equations by substitution. (Section 11.1/Objective 2)	We can describe the **substitution method** of solving a system of equations as follows: **Step 1** Solve one of the equations for one variable in terms of the other variable if neither equation is in such a form. (If possible, make a choice that will avoid fractions.) **Step 2** Substitute the expression obtained in step 1 into the other equation to produce an equation with one variable. **Step 3** Solve the equation obtained in step 2. **Step 4** Use the solution obtained in step 3, along with the expression obtained in step 1, to determine the solution of the system.	Solve the system $\begin{pmatrix} 3x + y = -9 \\ 2x + 3y = 8 \end{pmatrix}$. **Solution** Solving the first equation for y gives the equation $y = -3x - 9$. In the second equation, substitute $-3x - 9$ for y and solve. $2x + 3(-3x - 9) = 8$ $2x - 9x - 27 = 8$ $-7x = 35$ $x = -5$ Now to find the value of y, substitute -5 for x in the equation $y = -3x - 9$. $y = -3(-5) - 9 = 6$ The solution set of the system is $\{(-5, 6)\}$.

(continued)

OBJECTIVE	SUMMARY	EXAMPLE
Solve systems of equations by using the elimination-by-addition method. (Section 11.1/Objective 3)	The **elimination-by-addition method** involves the replacement of a system of equations with equivalent systems until a system is obtained whereby the solutions can be easily determined. The following operations or transformations can be performed on a system to produce an equivalent system. 1. Any two equations of the system can be interchanged. 2. Both sides of any equation of the system can be multiplied by any nonzero real number. 3. Any equation of the system can be replaced by the *sum* of that equation and a nonzero multiple of another equation.	Solve the system $\begin{pmatrix} 2x - 5y = 31 \\ 4x + 3y = 23 \end{pmatrix}$. **Solution** Let's multiply the first equation by -2 and add the result to the second equation to eliminate the x variable. Then the equivalent system is $\begin{pmatrix} 2x - 5y = 31 \\ 13y = -39 \end{pmatrix}$. Now solving the second equation for y, we obtain $y = -3$. Substitute -3 for y in either of the original equations and solve for x. $2x - 5(-3) = 31$ $2x + 15 = 31$ $2x = 16$ $x = 8$ The solution set of the system is $\{(8, -3)\}$.
Solve application problems using a system of equations. (Section 11.1/Objective 4)	Many problems that were solved earlier using only one variable may seem easier to solve by using two variables and a system of equations.	A car dealership has 220 vehicles on the lot. The number of cars on the lot is five less than twice the number of trucks. Find the number of cars and the number of trucks on the lot. **Solution** Letting x represent the number of cars and y represent the number of trucks, we obtain the following system: $\begin{pmatrix} x + y = 220 \\ x = 2y - 5 \end{pmatrix}$ Solving the system we can determine that the dealership has 145 cars and 75 trucks on the lot.
Solve systems of three linear equations. (Section 11.2/Objective 1)	Solving **a system of three linear equations in three variables** produces one of the following results. 1. There is *one ordered triple* that satisfies all three equations. 2. There are *infinitely many ordered triples* in the solution set, all of which are coordinates of points on a line common to the planes. 3. There are *infinitely many ordered triples* in the solution set, all of which are coordinates of points on a plane. 4. The solution set is empty; it is $\varnothing$.	Solve $\begin{pmatrix} 4x + 3y - 2z = -5 \\ 2y + 3z = -7 \\ y - 3z = -8 \end{pmatrix}$. **Solution** Replacing the third equation with the sum of the second equation and the third equation yields $3y = -15$. Therefore we can determine that $y = -5$. Substituting -5 for y in the third equation gives $-5 - 3z = -8$. Solving this equation yields $z = 1$. Substituting -5 for y and 1 for z in the first equation gives $4x + 3(-5) - 2(1) = -5$. Solving this equation gives $x = 3$. The solution set for the system is $\{(3, -5, 1)\}$.

OBJECTIVE	SUMMARY	EXAMPLE
Solve application problems using a system of three linear equations. (Section 11.2/Objective 2)	Many word problems involving three variables can be solved using a system of three linear equations.	The sum of the measures of the angles in a triangle is 180°. The largest angle is 8 times the smallest angle. The sum of the smallest and the largest angle is three times the other angle. Find the measure of each angle. **Solution** Let x represent the measure of the largest angle, let y represent the measure of the middle angle, and let z represent the measure of the smallest angle. From the information in the problem we can write the following system of equations: $$\begin{pmatrix} x + y + z = 180 \\ x = 8z \\ x + z = 3y \end{pmatrix}$$ By solving this system, we can determine that the measure of the angles of the triangle are 15°, 45°, and 120°.
Use a matrix approach to solve a system of equations. (Section 11.3/Objective 1)	The following elementary row operations provide the basis for transforming matrices. 1. Any two rows of an augmented matrix can be interchanged. 2. Any row can be multiplied by a nonzero constant. 3. Any row can be replaced by adding a nonzero multiple of another row to that row. Transforming an augmented matrix to triangular form and then using back substitution provides a systematic technique for solving systems of linear equations.	Solve $\begin{pmatrix} x + 3y = 1 \\ 3x + 4y = 8 \end{pmatrix}$. **Solution** The augmented matrix is $\begin{bmatrix} 1 & 3 & 1 \\ 3 & 4 & 8 \end{bmatrix}$. Multiply row one by -3 and add this result to row 2 to produce a new row 2. $\begin{bmatrix} 1 & 3 & 1 \\ 0 & -5 & 5 \end{bmatrix}$. This matrix represents the system $\begin{pmatrix} x + 3y = 1 \\ -5y = 5 \end{pmatrix}$. From the last equation we can determine that $y = -1$. Now substitute -1 for y in the equation $x + 3y = 1$ to determine that $x = 4$. The solution set is $\{(4, -1)\}$.
Evaluate the determinant of a 2×2 matrix. (Section 11.4/Objective 1)	A rectangular array of numbers is called a matrix. A square matrix has the same number of rows as columns. For a 2×2 matrix $\begin{bmatrix} a_1 & b_1 \\ a_2 & b_2 \end{bmatrix}$ the determinant of the matrix is written as $\begin{vmatrix} a_1 & b_1 \\ a_2 & b_2 \end{vmatrix}$ and defined by $\begin{vmatrix} a_1 & b_1 \\ a_2 & b_2 \end{vmatrix} = a_1b_2 - a_2b_1$	Find the determinant of the matrix $\begin{bmatrix} 8 & -3 \\ 5 & 2 \end{bmatrix}$ **Solution** $\begin{vmatrix} 8 & -3 \\ 5 & 2 \end{vmatrix}$ $= 8(2) - (5)(-3) = 16 + 15 = 31$

(continued)

OBJECTIVE	SUMMARY	EXAMPLE
Evaluate the determinant for a 3×3 matrix by expansion. (Section 11.4/Objective 2)	A 3×3 determinant is defined by $$\begin{vmatrix} a_1 & b_1 & c_1 \\ a_2 & b_2 & c_2 \\ a_3 & b_3 & c_3 \end{vmatrix}$$ $$= a_1 \begin{vmatrix} b_2 & c_2 \\ b_3 & c_3 \end{vmatrix} - a_2 \begin{vmatrix} b_1 & c_1 \\ b_3 & c_3 \end{vmatrix} + a_3 \begin{vmatrix} b_1 & c_1 \\ b_2 & c_2 \end{vmatrix}$$ and this is called the expansion of the determinant by minors about the first column.	Evaluate $\begin{vmatrix} 2 & -1 & 3 \\ 0 & 5 & 4 \\ -3 & 6 & 1 \end{vmatrix}$ by expanding about the first column. **Solution** $$\begin{vmatrix} 2 & -1 & 3 \\ 0 & 5 & 4 \\ -3 & 6 & 1 \end{vmatrix}$$ $$= 2 \begin{vmatrix} 5 & 4 \\ 6 & 1 \end{vmatrix} - 0 \begin{vmatrix} -1 & 3 \\ 6 & 1 \end{vmatrix}$$ $$+ (-3) \begin{vmatrix} -1 & 3 \\ 5 & 4 \end{vmatrix}$$ $$= 2(-19) - 0 - 3(-19)$$ $$= 19$$
Use Cramer's rule to solve a 2×2 system of equations. (Section 11.5/Objective 1)	Cramer's rule for solving a system of two linear equations in two variables is stated as follows: Given the system $\begin{pmatrix} a_1 x + b_1 y = c_1 \\ a_2 x + b_2 y = c_2 \end{pmatrix}$ with $$D = \begin{vmatrix} a_1 & b_1 \\ a_2 & b_2 \end{vmatrix} \neq 0$$ $$D_x = \begin{vmatrix} c_1 & b_1 \\ c_2 & b_2 \end{vmatrix}$$ $$D_y = \begin{vmatrix} a_1 & c_1 \\ a_2 & c_2 \end{vmatrix}$$ then $x = \dfrac{D_x}{D}$, and $y = \dfrac{D_y}{D}$.	Use Cramer's rule to solve $$\begin{pmatrix} 2x + 3y = -10 \\ x + 4y = -5 \end{pmatrix}$$ **Solution** $$D = \begin{vmatrix} 2 & 3 \\ 1 & 4 \end{vmatrix} = 2(4) - 1(3) = 5$$ $$D_x = \begin{vmatrix} -10 & 3 \\ -5 & 4 \end{vmatrix} = -10(4) - (-5)(3)$$ $$= -25$$ $$D_y = \begin{vmatrix} 2 & -10 \\ 1 & -5 \end{vmatrix} = 2(-5) - 1(-10) = 0$$ $$x = \frac{D_x}{D} = \frac{-25}{5} = -5$$ and $$y = \frac{D_y}{D} = \frac{0}{5} = 0$$ The solution set is $\{(-5, 0)\}$.

OBJECTIVE	SUMMARY	EXAMPLE
Use Cramer's rule to solve a 3×3 system of equations. (Section 11.5/Objective 1)	Cramer's rule for solving a system of three linear equations in two variables is stated as follows: Given the system $$\begin{pmatrix} a_1 x + b_1 y + c_1 z = d_1 \\ a_2 x + b_2 y + c_2 z = d_2 \\ a_3 x + b_3 y + c_3 z = d_3 \end{pmatrix} \text{ with}$$ $$D = \begin{vmatrix} a_1 & b_1 & c_1 \\ a_2 & b_2 & c_2 \\ a_3 & b_3 & c_3 \end{vmatrix} \neq 0$$ $$D_x = \begin{vmatrix} d_1 & b_1 & c_1 \\ d_2 & b_2 & c_2 \\ d_3 & b_3 & c_3 \end{vmatrix} \quad D_y = \begin{vmatrix} a_1 & d_1 & c_1 \\ a_2 & d_2 & c_2 \\ a_3 & d_3 & c_3 \end{vmatrix}$$ $$D_z = \begin{vmatrix} a_1 & b_1 & d_1 \\ a_2 & b_2 & d_2 \\ a_3 & b_3 & d_3 \end{vmatrix}$$ then $x = \dfrac{D_x}{D}, y = \dfrac{D_y}{D}$, and $z = \dfrac{D_z}{D}$.	Use Cramer's rule to solve $$\begin{pmatrix} 2x - y + z = 8 \\ x - 2y - 3z = -5 \\ 3x + y - 2z = -1 \end{pmatrix}$$ **Solution** Setting up and expanding the appropriate determinants we can determine that $D = 28, D_x = 56, D_y = -28$, and $D_z = 84$. Therefore, $$x = \frac{D_x}{D} = \frac{56}{28} = 2$$ $$y = \frac{D_y}{D} = \frac{-28}{28} = -1 \quad \text{and}$$ $$z = \frac{D_z}{D} = \frac{84}{28} = 3$$ The solution set is $\{(2, -1, 3)\}$.

Chapter 11 Review Problem Set

For Problems 1–4, solve each system by using the *substitution* method.

1. $\begin{pmatrix} 3x - y = 16 \\ 5x + 7y = -34 \end{pmatrix}$

2. $\begin{pmatrix} 6x + 5y = -21 \\ x - 4y = 11 \end{pmatrix}$

3. $\begin{pmatrix} 2x - 3y = 12 \\ 3x + 5y = -20 \end{pmatrix}$

4. $\begin{pmatrix} 5x + 8y = 1 \\ 4x + 7y = -2 \end{pmatrix}$

For Problems 5–8, solve each system by using the *elimination-by-addition* method.

5. $\begin{pmatrix} 4x - 3y = 34 \\ 3x + 2y = 0 \end{pmatrix}$

6. $\begin{pmatrix} \dfrac{1}{2}x - \dfrac{2}{3}y = 1 \\ \dfrac{3}{4}x + \dfrac{1}{6}y = -1 \end{pmatrix}$

7. $\begin{pmatrix} 2x - y + 3z = -19 \\ 3x + 2y - 4z = 21 \\ 5x - 4y - z = -8 \end{pmatrix}$

8. $\begin{pmatrix} 3x + 2y - 4z = 4 \\ 5x + 3y - z = 2 \\ 4x - 2y + 3z = 11 \end{pmatrix}$

For Problems 9–12, solve each system by *changing the augmented matrix to reduced echelon form*.

9. $\begin{pmatrix} x - 3y = 17 \\ -3x + 2y = -23 \end{pmatrix}$

10. $\begin{pmatrix} 2x + 3y = 25 \\ 3x - 5y = -29 \end{pmatrix}$

11. $\begin{pmatrix} x - 2y + z = -7 \\ 2x - 3y + 4z = -14 \\ -3x + y - 2z = 10 \end{pmatrix}$

12. $\begin{pmatrix} -2x - 7y + z = 9 \\ x + 3y - 4z = -11 \\ 4x + 5y - 3z = -11 \end{pmatrix}$

For Problems 13–16, solve each system by using *Cramer's rule*.

13. $\begin{pmatrix} 5x + 3y = -18 \\ 4x - 9y = -3 \end{pmatrix}$

14. $\begin{pmatrix} 0.2x + 0.3y = 2.6 \\ 0.5x - 0.1y = 1.4 \end{pmatrix}$

15. $\begin{pmatrix} 2x - 3y - 3z = 25 \\ 3x + y + 2z = -5 \\ 5x - 2y - 4z = 32 \end{pmatrix}$

16. $\begin{pmatrix} 3x - y + z = -10 \\ 6x - 2y + 5z = -35 \\ 7x + 3y - 4z = 19 \end{pmatrix}$

For Problems 17–24, solve each system by using the method you think is most appropriate.

17. $\begin{pmatrix} 4x + 7y = -15 \\ 3x - 2y = 25 \end{pmatrix}$

18. $\begin{pmatrix} \dfrac{3}{4}x - \dfrac{1}{2}y = -15 \\ \dfrac{2}{3}x + \dfrac{1}{4}y = -5 \end{pmatrix}$

19. $\begin{pmatrix} x + 4y = 3 \\ 3x - 2y = 1 \end{pmatrix}$

20. $\begin{pmatrix} 7x - 3y = -49 \\ y = \dfrac{3}{5}x - 1 \end{pmatrix}$

21. $\begin{pmatrix} x - y - z = 4 \\ -3x + 2y + 5z = -21 \\ 5x - 3y - 7z = 30 \end{pmatrix}$

22. $\begin{pmatrix} 2x - y + z = -7 \\ -5x + 2y - 3z = 17 \\ 3x + y + 7z = -5 \end{pmatrix}$

23. $\begin{pmatrix} 3x - 2y - 5z = 2 \\ -4x + 3y + 11z = 3 \\ 2x - y + z = -1 \end{pmatrix}$

24. $\begin{pmatrix} 7x - y + z = -4 \\ -2x + 9y - 3z = -50 \\ x - 5y + 4z = 42 \end{pmatrix}$

For Problems 25–30, evaluate each determinant.

25. $\begin{vmatrix} -2 & 6 \\ 3 & 8 \end{vmatrix}$

26. $\begin{vmatrix} 5 & -4 \\ 7 & -3 \end{vmatrix}$

27. $\begin{vmatrix} 2 & 3 & -1 \\ 3 & 4 & -5 \\ 6 & 4 & 2 \end{vmatrix}$

28. $\begin{vmatrix} 3 & -2 & 4 \\ 1 & 0 & 6 \\ 3 & -3 & 5 \end{vmatrix}$

29. $\begin{vmatrix} 5 & 4 & 3 \\ 2 & -7 & 0 \\ 3 & -2 & 0 \end{vmatrix}$

30. $\begin{vmatrix} 5 & -4 & 2 & 1 \\ 3 & 7 & 6 & -2 \\ 2 & 1 & -5 & 0 \\ 3 & -2 & 4 & 0 \end{vmatrix}$

For Problems 31–34, solve each problem by setting up and solving a system of linear equations.

31. How many quarts of 1% milk must be mixed with 4% milk to obtain 10 quarts of 2% milk?

32. The perimeter of a rectangle is 56 centimeters. The length of the rectangle is three times the width. Find the dimensions of the rectangle.

33. Antonio had a total of $4200 debt on two credit cards. One of the cards charged 1% interest per month, and the other card charged 1.5% interest per month. Find the amount of debt on each card if he paid $57 in interest charges for the month.

34. After working her shift as a waitress, Kelly had collected 30 bills consisting of one-dollar bills and five-dollar bills. If her tips amounted to $50, how many bills of each type did she have?

35. In an ideal textbook, every problem set had a fixed number of review problems and a fixed number of problems on the new material. Professor Kelly always assigned 80% of the review problems and 40% of the problems on the new material, which amounted to 56 problems. Professor Edward always assigned 100% of the review problems and 60% of the problems on the new material, which amounted to 78 problems. How many problems of each type are in the problem sets?

36. Sara invested $2500, part of it at 4% and the rest at 6% yearly interest. The yearly income on the 6% investment was $60 more than the income on the 4% investment. How much money did she invest at each rate?

37. A box contains $17.70 in nickels, dimes, and quarters. The number of dimes is 8 less than twice the number of nickels. The number of quarters is 2 more than the sum of the numbers of nickels and dimes. How many coins of each kind are there in the box?

38. After an evening of selling flowers, a vendor had collected 64 bills consisting of five-dollar bills, ten-dollar bills, and twenty-dollar bills, which amounted to $620. The number of ten-dollar bills was three times the number of twenty-dollar bills. Find the number of each type of bill.

39. The measure of the largest angle of a triangle is twice the measure of the smallest angle of the triangle. The sum of the measures of the largest angle and the smallest angle of a triangle is twice the measure of the remaining angle of the triangle. Find the measure of each angle of the triangle.

40. The measure of the largest angle of a triangle is 10° more than four times the smallest angle. The sum of the smallest and largest angles is three times the measure of the other angle. Find the measure of each angle of the triangle.

41. Kenisha has a Bank of US credit card that charges 1% interest per month, a Community Bank credit card that charges 1.5% interest per month, and a First National credit card that charges 2% interest per month. In total she has $6400 charged between the three credit cards. The total interest for the month for all three cards is $99. The amount charged on the Community Bank card is $500 less than the amount charged on the Bank of US card. Find the amount charged on each card.

42. The perimeter of a triangle is 33 inches. The longest side is 3 inches more than twice the shortest side. The sum of the lengths of the shortest side and the longest side is 9 more than the remaining side. Find the length of each side of the triangle.

For Problems 1–4, refer to the following systems of equations:

I. $\begin{pmatrix} 3x - 2y = 4 \\ 9x - 6y = 12 \end{pmatrix}$ **II.** $\begin{pmatrix} 5x - y = 4 \\ 3x + 7y = 9 \end{pmatrix}$

III. $\begin{pmatrix} 2x - y = 4 \\ 2x - y = -6 \end{pmatrix}$

1. For which system are the graphs parallel lines?

2. For which system are the equations dependent?

3. For which system is the solution set $\varnothing$?

4. Which system is consistent?

For Problems 5–8, evaluate each determinant.

5. $\begin{vmatrix} -2 & 4 \\ -5 & 6 \end{vmatrix}$

6. $\begin{vmatrix} \dfrac{1}{2} & \dfrac{1}{3} \\ \dfrac{3}{4} & -\dfrac{2}{3} \end{vmatrix}$

7. $\begin{vmatrix} -1 & 2 & 1 \\ 3 & 1 & -2 \\ 2 & -1 & 1 \end{vmatrix}$

8. $\begin{vmatrix} 2 & 4 & -5 \\ -4 & 3 & 0 \\ -2 & 6 & 1 \end{vmatrix}$

9. How many ordered pairs of real numbers are in the solution set for the system $\begin{pmatrix} y = 3x - 4 \\ 9x - 3y = 12 \end{pmatrix}$?

10. Solve the system $\begin{pmatrix} 3x - 2y = -14 \\ 7x + 2y = -6 \end{pmatrix}$

11. Solve the system $\begin{pmatrix} 4x - 5y = 17 \\ y = -3x + 8 \end{pmatrix}$

12. Find the value of x in the solution for the system

$$\begin{pmatrix} \dfrac{3}{4}x - \dfrac{1}{2}y = -21 \\ \dfrac{2}{3}x + \dfrac{1}{6}y = -4 \end{pmatrix}$$

13. Find the value of y in the solution for the system

$$\begin{pmatrix} 4x - y = 7 \\ 3x + 2y = 2 \end{pmatrix}.$$

14. Suppose that the augmented matrix of a system of three linear equations in the three variables x, y, and z can be changed to the matrix

$$\begin{bmatrix} 1 & 1 & -4 & | & 3 \\ 0 & 1 & 4 & | & 5 \\ 0 & 0 & 3 & | & 6 \end{bmatrix}$$

Find the value of x in the solution for the system.

15. Suppose that the augmented matrix of a system of three linear equations in the three variables x, y, and z can be changed to the matrix

$$\begin{bmatrix} 1 & 2 & -3 & | & 4 \\ 0 & 1 & 2 & | & 5 \\ 0 & 0 & 2 & | & -8 \end{bmatrix}$$

Find the value of y in the solution for the system.

16. How many ordered triples are there in the solution set for the following system?

$$\begin{pmatrix} x + 3y - z = 5 \\ 2x - y - z = 7 \\ 5x + 8y - 4z = 22 \end{pmatrix}$$

17. How many ordered triples are there in the solution set for the following system?

$$\begin{pmatrix} 3x - y - 2z = 1 \\ 4x + 2y + z = 5 \\ 6x - 2y - 4z = 9 \end{pmatrix}$$

18. Solve the following system:

$$\begin{pmatrix} 5x - 3y - 2z = -1 \\ 4y + 7z = 3 \\ 4z = -12 \end{pmatrix}$$

19. Solve the following system:

$$\begin{pmatrix} x - 2y + z = 0 \\ y - 3z = -1 \\ 2y + 5z = -2 \end{pmatrix}$$

20. Find the value of x in the solution for the system

$$\begin{pmatrix} x - 4y + z = 12 \\ -2x + 3y - z = -11 \\ 5x - 3y + 2z = 17 \end{pmatrix}$$

21. Find the value of y in the solution for the system

$$\begin{pmatrix} x - 3y + z = -13 \\ 3x + 5y - z = 17 \\ 5x - 2y + 2z = -13 \end{pmatrix}$$

22. One solution is 30% alcohol and another solution is 70% alcohol. Some of each of the two solutions is mixed to produce 8 liters of a 40% solution. How many liters of the 70% solution should be used?

23. A car wash charges $5.00 for an express wash and $15.00 for a full wash. On a recent day there were 75 car washes of these two types, which brought in $825.00. Find the number of express washes.

24. A catering company makes batches of three different types of pastries to serve at brunches. Each batch requires the services of three different operations, as indicated by the following table:

	Cream puffs	Eclairs	Danish rolls
Dough	0.2 hour	0.5 hour	0.4 hour
Baking	0.3 hour	0.1 hour	0.2 hour
Frosting	0.1 hour	0.5 hour	0.3 hour

The dough, baking, and frosting operations have available a maximum of 7.0, 3.9, and 5.5 hours, respectively. How many batches of each type should be made so that the company is operating at full capacity?

25. The measure of the largest angle of a triangle is 20° more than the sum of the measures of the other two angles. The difference in the measures of the largest and smallest angles is 65°. Find the measure of each angle.

12

Algebra of Matrices

12.1 Algebra of 2 × 2 Matrices

12.2 Multiplicative Inverses

12.3 $m \times n$ Matrices

12.4 Systems of Linear Inequalities: Linear Programming

© arenacreative

A financial planner might use the techniques of linear programming when developing a plan for clients.

In Section 11.3, we used matrices strictly as a device to help solve systems of linear equations. Our primary objective was to develop techniques for solving systems of equations, not to study matrices. However, matrices can be studied from an algebraic viewpoint, much as we study the set of real numbers. That is, we can define certain operations on matrices and verify properties of those operations. This algebraic approach to matrices is the focal point of this chapter. In order to get a simplified view of the algebra of matrices, we will begin by studying 2 × 2 matrices, and then later we will enlarge our discussion to include $m \times n$ matrices. As a bonus, another technique for solving systems of equations will emerge from our study. In the final section of this chapter, we expand our problem-solving capabilities by studying systems of linear inequalities.

Video tutorials based on section learning objectives are available in a variety of delivery modes.

12.1   Algebra of 2 × 2 Matrices

OBJECTIVES

1. Add and subtract matrices

2. Multiply a matrix by a scalar

3. Multiply 2 × 2 matrices

Throughout these next two sections, we will be working primarily with 2×2 matrices; therefore any reference to matrices means 2×2 matrices unless stated otherwise. The following 2×2 matrix notation will be used frequently.

$$A = \begin{bmatrix} a_{11} & a_{12} \\ a_{21} & a_{22} \end{bmatrix} \qquad B = \begin{bmatrix} b_{11} & b_{12} \\ b_{21} & b_{22} \end{bmatrix} \qquad C = \begin{bmatrix} c_{11} & c_{12} \\ c_{21} & c_{22} \end{bmatrix}$$

Two matrices are **equal** if and only if all elements in corresponding positions are equal. Thus $A = B$ if and only if $a_{11} = b_{11}$, $a_{12} = b_{12}$, $a_{21} = b_{21}$, and $a_{22} = b_{22}$.

Addition of Matrices

To **add** two matrices, we add the elements that appear in corresponding positions. Therefore the sum of matrix A and matrix B is defined as follows:

Definition 12.1

$$A + B = \begin{bmatrix} a_{11} & a_{12} \\ a_{21} & a_{22} \end{bmatrix} + \begin{bmatrix} b_{11} & b_{12} \\ b_{21} & b_{22} \end{bmatrix}$$

$$= \begin{bmatrix} a_{11} + b_{11} & a_{12} + b_{12} \\ a_{21} + b_{21} & a_{22} + b_{22} \end{bmatrix}$$

For example,

$$\begin{bmatrix} 2 & -1 \\ -3 & 4 \end{bmatrix} + \begin{bmatrix} -5 & 4 \\ -1 & 7 \end{bmatrix} = \begin{bmatrix} -3 & 3 \\ -4 & 11 \end{bmatrix}$$

It is not difficult to show that the **commutative** and **associative properties** are valid for the addition of matrices. Thus we can state that

$$A + B = B + A \qquad \text{and} \qquad (A + B) + C = A + (B + C)$$

Because

$$\begin{bmatrix} a_{11} & a_{12} \\ a_{21} & a_{22} \end{bmatrix} + \begin{bmatrix} 0 & 0 \\ 0 & 0 \end{bmatrix} = \begin{bmatrix} a_{11} & a_{12} \\ a_{21} & a_{22} \end{bmatrix}$$

we see that $\begin{bmatrix} 0 & 0 \\ 0 & 0 \end{bmatrix}$, which is called the **zero matrix**, represented by O, is the **additive identity element**. Thus we can state that

$$A + O = O + A = A$$

Because every real number has an additive inverse, it follows that any matrix A has an **additive inverse**, $-A$, which is formed by taking the additive inverse of each element of A. For example, if

$$A = \begin{bmatrix} 4 & -2 \\ -1 & 0 \end{bmatrix} \quad \text{then} \quad -A = \begin{bmatrix} -4 & 2 \\ 1 & 0 \end{bmatrix}$$

and

$$A + (-A) = \begin{bmatrix} 4 & -2 \\ -1 & 0 \end{bmatrix} + \begin{bmatrix} -4 & 2 \\ 1 & 0 \end{bmatrix} = \begin{bmatrix} 0 & 0 \\ 0 & 0 \end{bmatrix}$$

In general, we can state that every matrix A has an additive inverse $-A$ such that

$$A + (-A) = (-A) + A = O$$

Subtraction of Matrices

Like the algebra of real numbers, **subtraction** of matrices can be defined in terms of *adding the additive inverse*. Therefore we can define subtraction as follows:

Definition 12.2

$$A - B = A + (-B)$$

For example,

$$\begin{bmatrix} 2 & -7 \\ -6 & 5 \end{bmatrix} - \begin{bmatrix} 3 & 4 \\ -2 & -1 \end{bmatrix} = \begin{bmatrix} 2 & -7 \\ -6 & 5 \end{bmatrix} + \begin{bmatrix} -3 & -4 \\ 2 & 1 \end{bmatrix}$$

$$= \begin{bmatrix} -1 & -11 \\ -4 & 6 \end{bmatrix}$$

Scalar Multiplication

When we work with matrices, we commonly refer to a single real number as a **scalar** to distinguish it from a matrix. So, to get the **product** of a scalar and a matrix (often referred to as **scalar multiplication**) we would multiply each element of the matrix by the scalar. For example,

$$3 \begin{bmatrix} -4 & -6 \\ 1 & -2 \end{bmatrix} = \begin{bmatrix} 3(-4) & 3(-6) \\ 3(1) & 3(-2) \end{bmatrix} = \begin{bmatrix} -12 & -18 \\ 3 & -6 \end{bmatrix}$$

In general, scalar multiplication can be defined as follows:

Definition 12.3

$$kA = k \begin{bmatrix} a_{11} & a_{12} \\ a_{21} & a_{22} \end{bmatrix} = \begin{bmatrix} ka_{11} & ka_{12} \\ ka_{21} & ka_{22} \end{bmatrix}$$

where k is any real number.

EXAMPLE 1

If $A = \begin{bmatrix} -4 & 3 \\ 2 & -5 \end{bmatrix}$ and $B = \begin{bmatrix} 2 & -3 \\ 7 & -6 \end{bmatrix}$, find (a) $-2A$, (b) $3A + 2B$, and (c) $A - 4B$.

Solutions

(a) $-2A = -2\begin{bmatrix} -4 & 3 \\ 2 & -5 \end{bmatrix} = \begin{bmatrix} 8 & -6 \\ -4 & 10 \end{bmatrix}$

(b) $3A + 2B = 3\begin{bmatrix} -4 & 3 \\ 2 & -5 \end{bmatrix} + 2\begin{bmatrix} 2 & -3 \\ 7 & -6 \end{bmatrix}$

$= \begin{bmatrix} -12 & 9 \\ 6 & -15 \end{bmatrix} + \begin{bmatrix} 4 & -6 \\ 14 & -12 \end{bmatrix}$

$= \begin{bmatrix} -8 & 3 \\ 20 & -27 \end{bmatrix}$

(c) $A - 4B = \begin{bmatrix} -4 & 3 \\ 2 & -5 \end{bmatrix} - 4\begin{bmatrix} 2 & -3 \\ 7 & -6 \end{bmatrix}$

$= \begin{bmatrix} -4 & 3 \\ 2 & -5 \end{bmatrix} - \begin{bmatrix} 8 & -12 \\ 28 & -24 \end{bmatrix}$

$= \begin{bmatrix} -4 & 3 \\ 2 & -5 \end{bmatrix} + \begin{bmatrix} -8 & 12 \\ -28 & 24 \end{bmatrix}$

$= \begin{bmatrix} -12 & 15 \\ -26 & 19 \end{bmatrix}$

The following properties, which are easy to check, pertain to scalar multiplication and matrix addition (where k and l represent any real numbers):

$$k(A + B) = kA + kB$$
$$(k + l)A = kA + lA$$
$$(kl)A = k(lA)$$

Multiplication of Matrices

At this time, it probably would seem quite natural to define matrix multiplication by multiplying corresponding elements of two matrices. However, such a definition does not have many worthwhile applications. Instead, we use a special type of **matrix multiplication**, sometimes referred to as a "row-by-column multiplication." We state the definition below, paraphrase what it says, and then give some examples.

Definition 12.4

$$AB = \begin{bmatrix} a_{11} & a_{12} \\ a_{21} & a_{22} \end{bmatrix}\begin{bmatrix} b_{11} & b_{12} \\ b_{21} & b_{22} \end{bmatrix}$$

$$= \begin{bmatrix} a_{11}b_{11} + a_{12}b_{21} & a_{11}b_{12} + a_{12}b_{22} \\ a_{21}b_{11} + a_{22}b_{21} & a_{21}b_{12} + a_{22}b_{22} \end{bmatrix}$$

Note the row-by-column pattern of Definition 12.4. We multiply the rows of A times the columns of B in a pairwise entry fashion, adding the results. For example, the element in the first row and second column of the product is obtained by multiplying the elements of the first row of A times the elements of the second column of B and adding the results.

$$\begin{bmatrix} a_{11} & a_{12} \\ a_{21} & a_{22} \end{bmatrix}\begin{bmatrix} b_{11} & b_{12} \\ b_{21} & b_{22} \end{bmatrix} = \begin{bmatrix} & a_{11}b_{12} + a_{12}b_{22} \end{bmatrix}$$

Now let's look at some specific examples.

Classroom Example

If $A = \begin{bmatrix} 3 & -2 \\ 1 & 6 \end{bmatrix}$ and $B = \begin{bmatrix} -2 & 3 \\ -5 & 1 \end{bmatrix}$,

find (a) AB and (b) BA.

EXAMPLE 2   If $A = \begin{bmatrix} -2 & 1 \\ 4 & 5 \end{bmatrix}$ and $B = \begin{bmatrix} 3 & -2 \\ -1 & 7 \end{bmatrix}$, find (a) AB and (b) BA.

Solutions

(a) $AB = \begin{bmatrix} -2 & 1 \\ 4 & 5 \end{bmatrix}\begin{bmatrix} 3 & -2 \\ -1 & 7 \end{bmatrix}$

$= \begin{bmatrix} (-2)(3) + (1)(-1) & (-2)(-2) + (1)(7) \\ (4)(3) + (5)(-1) & (4)(-2) + (5)(7) \end{bmatrix}$

$= \begin{bmatrix} -7 & 11 \\ 7 & 27 \end{bmatrix}$

(b) $BA = \begin{bmatrix} 3 & -2 \\ -1 & 7 \end{bmatrix}\begin{bmatrix} -2 & 1 \\ 4 & 5 \end{bmatrix}$

$= \begin{bmatrix} (3)(-2) + (-2)(4) & (3)(1) + (-2)(5) \\ (-1)(-2) + (7)(4) & (-1)(1) + (7)(5) \end{bmatrix}$

$= \begin{bmatrix} -14 & -7 \\ 30 & 34 \end{bmatrix}$

Example 2 makes it immediately apparent that matrix multiplication is *not* a **commutative** operation.

Classroom Example

If $A = \begin{bmatrix} 4 & 8 \\ 1 & 2 \end{bmatrix}$ and $B = \begin{bmatrix} -2 & -4 \\ 1 & 2 \end{bmatrix}$,

find AB.

EXAMPLE 3   If $A = \begin{bmatrix} 2 & -6 \\ -3 & 9 \end{bmatrix}$ and $B = \begin{bmatrix} -3 & 6 \\ -1 & 2 \end{bmatrix}$, find AB.

Solution

Once you feel comfortable with Definition 12.4, you can do the addition mentally.

$$AB = \begin{bmatrix} 2 & -6 \\ -3 & 9 \end{bmatrix}\begin{bmatrix} -3 & 6 \\ -1 & 2 \end{bmatrix} = \begin{bmatrix} 0 & 0 \\ 0 & 0 \end{bmatrix}$$

Example 3 illustrates that the product of two matrices can be the zero matrix, even though neither of the two matrices is the zero matrix. This is different from the property of real numbers that states $ab = 0$ if and only if $a = 0$ or $b = 0$.

As we illustrated and stated earlier, matrix multiplication is *not* a commutative operation. However, it is an **associative** operation and it does exhibit two **distributive properties**. These properties can be stated as follows:

$$(AB)C = A(BC)$$
$$A(B + C) = AB + AC$$
$$(B + C)A = BA + CA$$

We will ask you to verify these properties in the next set of problems.

Concept Quiz 12.1

For the following problems, given that A, B, and C are 2×2 matrices and k and l are real numbers, answer true or false.

1. The matrix $\begin{bmatrix} 0 & 0 \\ 0 & 0 \end{bmatrix}$ is the additive identity element.

2. If $A + B = \begin{bmatrix} 0 & 0 \\ 0 & 0 \end{bmatrix}$, then A and B are additive inverses.

3. $A + B = B + A$.

4. $AB = BA$.

5. If $AB = \begin{bmatrix} 0 & 0 \\ 0 & 0 \end{bmatrix}$, then either $A = \begin{bmatrix} 0 & 0 \\ 0 & 0 \end{bmatrix}$ or $B = \begin{bmatrix} 0 & 0 \\ 0 & 0 \end{bmatrix}$.

6. The product of A times B can never equal $\begin{bmatrix} 0 & 0 \\ 0 & 0 \end{bmatrix}$.

7. To perform the scalar multiplication kA, only the elements in the first row of A are multiplied by k.

8. If $A = \begin{bmatrix} 1 & 2 \\ 3 & 4 \end{bmatrix}$, then $A^2 = AA = \begin{bmatrix} 1 & 4 \\ 9 & 16 \end{bmatrix}$.

Problem Set 12.1

For Problems 1–12, compute the indicated matrix by using the following matrices: (Objectives 1 and 2)

$$A = \begin{bmatrix} 1 & -2 \\ 3 & 4 \end{bmatrix} \qquad B = \begin{bmatrix} 2 & -3 \\ 5 & -1 \end{bmatrix}$$

$$C = \begin{bmatrix} 0 & 6 \\ -4 & 2 \end{bmatrix} \qquad D = \begin{bmatrix} -2 & 3 \\ 5 & -4 \end{bmatrix}$$

$$E = \begin{bmatrix} 2 & 5 \\ 7 & 3 \end{bmatrix}$$

1. $A + B$

2. $B - C$

3. $3C + D$

4. $2D - E$

5. $4A - 3B$

6. $2B + 3D$

7. $(A - B) - C$

8. $B - (D - E)$

9. $2D - 4E$

10. $3A - 4E$

11. $B - (D + E)$

12. $A - (B + C)$

For Problems 13–26, compute AB and BA. (Objective 3)

13. $A = \begin{bmatrix} 1 & -1 \\ 2 & -2 \end{bmatrix}$, $B = \begin{bmatrix} 3 & -4 \\ -1 & 2 \end{bmatrix}$

14. $A = \begin{bmatrix} -3 & 4 \\ 2 & 1 \end{bmatrix}$, $B = \begin{bmatrix} -2 & 5 \\ 6 & -1 \end{bmatrix}$

15. $A = \begin{bmatrix} 1 & -3 \\ -4 & 6 \end{bmatrix}$, $B = \begin{bmatrix} 7 & -3 \\ 4 & 5 \end{bmatrix}$

16. $A = \begin{bmatrix} 5 & 0 \\ -2 & 3 \end{bmatrix}$, $B = \begin{bmatrix} -3 & 6 \\ 4 & 1 \end{bmatrix}$

17. $A = \begin{bmatrix} 2 & -4 \\ 1 & -2 \end{bmatrix}$, $B = \begin{bmatrix} 1 & -2 \\ -3 & 6 \end{bmatrix}$

18. $A = \begin{bmatrix} 1 & 2 \\ 1 & 2 \end{bmatrix}$, $B = \begin{bmatrix} 2 & 2 \\ -1 & -1 \end{bmatrix}$

19. $A = \begin{bmatrix} -3 & -2 \\ -4 & -1 \end{bmatrix}$, $B = \begin{bmatrix} 2 & -1 \\ 4 & 5 \end{bmatrix}$

20. $A = \begin{bmatrix} -2 & 3 \\ -1 & 7 \end{bmatrix}$, $B = \begin{bmatrix} -1 & -3 \\ -5 & -7 \end{bmatrix}$

21. $A = \begin{bmatrix} 2 & -1 \\ -5 & 3 \end{bmatrix}$, $B = \begin{bmatrix} 3 & 1 \\ 5 & 2 \end{bmatrix}$

22. $A = \begin{bmatrix} -8 & -5 \\ 3 & 2 \end{bmatrix}$, $B = \begin{bmatrix} -2 & -5 \\ 3 & 8 \end{bmatrix}$

23. $\begin{bmatrix} \dfrac{1}{2} & -\dfrac{1}{3} \\ \dfrac{1}{3} & \dfrac{1}{4} \end{bmatrix}$, $B = \begin{bmatrix} 4 & -6 \\ 6 & -4 \end{bmatrix}$

24. $A = \begin{bmatrix} \dfrac{1}{3} & -\dfrac{1}{2} \\ \dfrac{3}{2} & \dfrac{2}{3} \end{bmatrix}$, $B = \begin{bmatrix} -6 & -18 \\ 12 & -12 \end{bmatrix}$

25. $A = \begin{bmatrix} 5 & 6 \\ 2 & 3 \end{bmatrix}$, $B = \begin{bmatrix} 1 & -2 \\ -\dfrac{2}{3} & \dfrac{5}{3} \end{bmatrix}$

26. $A = \begin{bmatrix} -3 & -5 \\ 2 & 4 \end{bmatrix}$, $B = \begin{bmatrix} 2 & -\dfrac{5}{2} \\ 1 & \dfrac{3}{2} \end{bmatrix}$

For Problems 27–30, use the following matrices.
(Objective 3)

$A = \begin{bmatrix} -2 & 3 \\ 5 & 4 \end{bmatrix}$ $B = \begin{bmatrix} 0 & 1 \\ 1 & 0 \end{bmatrix}$

$C = \begin{bmatrix} 1 & 0 \\ 1 & 0 \end{bmatrix}$ $D = \begin{bmatrix} 1 & 1 \\ 1 & 1 \end{bmatrix}$

$I = \begin{bmatrix} 1 & 0 \\ 0 & 1 \end{bmatrix}$

27. Compute AB and BA.

28. Compute AC and CA.

29. Compute AD and DA.

30. Compute AI and IA.

For Problems 31–34, use the following matrices.
(Objective 3)

$A = \begin{bmatrix} 2 & 4 \\ 5 & -3 \end{bmatrix}$ $B = \begin{bmatrix} -2 & 3 \\ -1 & 2 \end{bmatrix}$

$C = \begin{bmatrix} 2 & 1 \\ 3 & 7 \end{bmatrix}$

31. Show that $(AB)C = A(BC)$.

32. Show that $A(B + C) = AB + AC$.

33. Show that $(A + B)C = AC + BC$.

34. Show that $(3 + 2)A = 3A + 2A$.

For Problems 35–43, use the following matrices.

$A = \begin{bmatrix} a_{11} & a_{12} \\ a_{21} & a_{22} \end{bmatrix}$ $B = \begin{bmatrix} b_{11} & b_{12} \\ b_{21} & b_{22} \end{bmatrix}$

$C = \begin{bmatrix} c_{11} & c_{12} \\ c_{21} & c_{22} \end{bmatrix}$ $O = \begin{bmatrix} 0 & 0 \\ 0 & 0 \end{bmatrix}$

35. Show that $A + B = B + A$.

36. Show that $(A + B) + C = A + (B + C)$.

37. Show that $A + (-A) = O$.

38. Show that $k(A + B) = kA + kB$ for any real number k.

39. Show that $(k + l)A = kA + lA$ for any real numbers k and l.

40. Show that $(kl)A = k(lA)$ for any real numbers k and l.

41. Show that $(AB)C = A(BC)$.

42. Show that $A(B + C) = AB + AC$.

43. Show that $(A + B)C = AC + BC$.

Thoughts Into Words

44. How would you show that addition of 2 × 2 matrices is a commutative operation?

45. How would you show that subtraction of 2 × 2 matrices is not a commutative operation?

46. How would you explain matrix multiplication to someone who missed class the day it was discussed?

47. Your friend says that because multiplication of real numbers is a commutative operation, it seems reasonable that multiplication of matrices should also be a commutative operation. How would you react to that statement?

Further Investigations

48. If $A = \begin{bmatrix} 2 & 0 \\ 0 & 3 \end{bmatrix}$, calculate A^2 and A^3, where A^2 means AA, and A^3 means AAA.

49. If $A = \begin{bmatrix} 1 & -1 \\ 2 & 3 \end{bmatrix}$, calculate A^2 and A^3.

50. Does $(A + B)(A - B) = A^2 - B^2$ for all 2 × 2 matrices? Defend your answer.

Graphing Calculator Activities

51. Use a calculator to check the answers to all three parts of Example 1.

52. Use a calculator to check your answers for Problems 21–26.

53. Use the following matrices:

$$A = \begin{bmatrix} 7 & -4 \\ 6 & 9 \end{bmatrix} \quad B = \begin{bmatrix} -3 & 8 \\ -5 & 7 \end{bmatrix} \quad C = \begin{bmatrix} 8 & -2 \\ 4 & -7 \end{bmatrix}$$

(a) Show that $(AB)C = A(BC)$.
(b) Show that $A(B + C) = AB + AC$.
(c) Show that $(B + C)A = BA + CA$.

Answers to the Concept Quiz

1. True   **2.** True   **3.** True   **4.** False   **5.** False   **6.** False   **7.** False   **8.** False

---

12.2   Multiplicative Inverses

OBJECTIVES

1. Find the multiplicative inverse of a 2 × 2 matrix

2. Find the product of a 2 × 2 and a 2 × 1 matrix

3. Solve a system of two linear equations by using matrices

We know that 1 is a multiplicative identity element for the set of real numbers. That is, $a(1) = 1(a) = a$ for any real number a. Is there a multiplicative identity element for 2 × 2 matrices? Yes. The matrix

$$I = \begin{bmatrix} 1 & 0 \\ 0 & 1 \end{bmatrix}$$

is the **multiplicative identity element** because

$$\begin{bmatrix} 1 & 0 \\ 0 & 1 \end{bmatrix}\begin{bmatrix} a_{11} & a_{12} \\ a_{21} & a_{22} \end{bmatrix} = \begin{bmatrix} a_{11} & a_{12} \\ a_{21} & a_{22} \end{bmatrix}$$

and

$$\begin{bmatrix} a_{11} & a_{12} \\ a_{21} & a_{22} \end{bmatrix}\begin{bmatrix} 1 & 0 \\ 0 & 1 \end{bmatrix} = \begin{bmatrix} a_{11} & a_{12} \\ a_{21} & a_{22} \end{bmatrix}$$

Therefore we can state that

$$AI = IA = A$$

for all 2 × 2 matrices.

Again, refer to the set of real numbers, in which every nonzero real number a has a multiplicative inverse $1/a$ such that $a(1/a) = (1/a)\,a = 1$. Does every 2 × 2 matrix have a multiplicative inverse? To help answer this question, let's think about finding the multiplicative inverse (if one exists) for a specific matrix. This should give us some clues about a general approach.

Classroom Example
Find the multiplicative inverse of

$$A = \begin{bmatrix} 9 & 3 \\ 4 & 2 \end{bmatrix}.$$

EXAMPLE 1

Find the multiplicative inverse of $A = \begin{bmatrix} 3 & 5 \\ 2 & 4 \end{bmatrix}$.

Solution

We are looking for a matrix A^{-1} such that $AA^{-1} = A^{-1}A = I$. In other words, we want to solve the following matrix equation:

$$\begin{bmatrix} 3 & 5 \\ 2 & 4 \end{bmatrix}\begin{bmatrix} x & y \\ z & w \end{bmatrix} = \begin{bmatrix} 1 & 0 \\ 0 & 1 \end{bmatrix}$$

We need to multiply the two matrices on the left side of this equation and then set the elements of the product matrix equal to the corresponding elements of the identity matrix. We obtain the following system of equations:

$$\begin{pmatrix} 3x + 5z = 1 \\ 3y + 5w = 0 \\ 2x + 4z = 0 \\ 2y + 4w = 1 \end{pmatrix} \qquad \begin{matrix} (1) \\ (2) \\ (3) \\ (4) \end{matrix}$$

Solving equations (1) and (3) simultaneously produces values for x and z.

$$x = \frac{\begin{vmatrix} 1 & 5 \\ 0 & 4 \end{vmatrix}}{\begin{vmatrix} 3 & 5 \\ 2 & 4 \end{vmatrix}} = \frac{1(4) - 5(0)}{3(4) - 5(2)} = \frac{4}{2} = 2$$

$$z = \frac{\begin{vmatrix} 3 & 1 \\ 2 & 0 \end{vmatrix}}{\begin{vmatrix} 3 & 5 \\ 2 & 4 \end{vmatrix}} = \frac{3(0) - 1(2)}{3(4) - 5(2)} = \frac{-2}{2} = -1$$

Likewise, solving equations (2) and (4) simultaneously produces values for y and w.

$$y = \frac{\begin{vmatrix} 0 & 5 \\ 1 & 4 \end{vmatrix}}{\begin{vmatrix} 3 & 5 \\ 2 & 4 \end{vmatrix}} = \frac{0(4) - 5(1)}{3(4) - 5(2)} = \frac{-5}{2} = -\frac{5}{2}$$

$$w = \frac{\begin{vmatrix} 3 & 0 \\ 2 & 1 \end{vmatrix}}{\begin{vmatrix} 3 & 5 \\ 2 & 4 \end{vmatrix}} = \frac{3(1) - 0(2)}{3(4) - 5(2)} = \frac{3}{2}$$

Therefore

$$A^{-1} = \begin{bmatrix} x & y \\ z & w \end{bmatrix} = \begin{bmatrix} 2 & -\dfrac{5}{2} \\ -1 & \dfrac{3}{2} \end{bmatrix}$$

To check this, we perform the following multiplication:

$$\begin{bmatrix} 3 & 5 \\ 2 & 4 \end{bmatrix} \begin{bmatrix} 2 & -\dfrac{5}{2} \\ -1 & \dfrac{3}{2} \end{bmatrix} = \begin{bmatrix} 2 & -\dfrac{5}{2} \\ -1 & \dfrac{3}{2} \end{bmatrix} \begin{bmatrix} 3 & 5 \\ 2 & 4 \end{bmatrix} = \begin{bmatrix} 1 & 0 \\ 0 & 1 \end{bmatrix}$$

Now let's use the approach in Example 1 on the general matrix

$$A = \begin{bmatrix} a_{11} & a_{12} \\ a_{21} & a_{22} \end{bmatrix}$$

We want to find

$$A^{-1} = \begin{bmatrix} x & y \\ z & w \end{bmatrix}$$

such that $AA^{-1} = I$. Therefore we need to solve the matrix equation

$$\begin{bmatrix} a_{11} & a_{12} \\ a_{21} & a_{22} \end{bmatrix} \begin{bmatrix} x & y \\ z & w \end{bmatrix} = \begin{bmatrix} 1 & 0 \\ 0 & 1 \end{bmatrix}$$

for x, y, z, and w. Once again, we multiply the two matrices on the left side of the equation and set the elements of this product matrix equal to the corresponding elements of the identity matrix. We then obtain the following system of equations:

$$\begin{pmatrix} a_{11}x + a_{12}z = 1 \\ a_{11}y + a_{12}w = 0 \\ a_{21}x + a_{22}z = 0 \\ a_{21}y + a_{22}w = 1 \end{pmatrix}$$

Solving this system produces

$$x = \frac{a_{22}}{a_{11}a_{22} - a_{12}a_{21}} \qquad y = \frac{-a_{12}}{a_{11}a_{22} - a_{12}a_{21}}$$

$$z = \frac{-a_{21}}{a_{11}a_{22} - a_{12}a_{21}} \qquad w = \frac{a_{11}}{a_{11}a_{22} - a_{12}a_{21}}$$

Note that the number in each denominator, $a_{11}a_{22} - a_{12}a_{21}$, is the determinant of the matrix A. Thus, if $|A| \neq 0$, then

$$A^{-1} = \frac{1}{|A|} \begin{bmatrix} a_{22} & -a_{12} \\ -a_{21} & a_{11} \end{bmatrix}$$

Matrix multiplication will show that $AA^{-1} = A^{-1}A = I$. If $|A| = 0$, then the matrix A has *no* multiplicative inverse.

Classroom Example
Find A^{-1} if $A = \begin{bmatrix} -1 & -3 \\ 2 & 5 \end{bmatrix}$.

EXAMPLE 2   Find A^{-1} if $A = \begin{bmatrix} 3 & 5 \\ -2 & -4 \end{bmatrix}$.

Solution

First let's find $|A|$.

$$|A| = (3)(-4) - (5)(-2) = -2$$

Therefore

$$A^{-1} = \frac{1}{-2} \begin{bmatrix} -4 & -5 \\ 2 & 3 \end{bmatrix} = -\frac{1}{2} \begin{bmatrix} -4 & -5 \\ 2 & 3 \end{bmatrix} = \begin{bmatrix} 2 & \frac{5}{2} \\ -1 & -\frac{3}{2} \end{bmatrix}$$

It is easy to check that $AA^{-1} = A^{-1}A = I$.

Classroom Example
Find A^{-1} if $A = \begin{bmatrix} -2 & -3 \\ 6 & 9 \end{bmatrix}$.

EXAMPLE 3   Find A^{-1} if $A = \begin{bmatrix} 8 & -2 \\ -12 & 3 \end{bmatrix}$.

Solution

$$|A| = (8)(3) - (-2)(-12) = 0$$

Therefore A has no multiplicative inverse.

More about the Multiplication of Matrices

Thus far we have found the products of only 2×2 matrices. The row-by-column multiplication pattern can be applied to many different kinds of matrices, which we shall see in the next section. For now, let's find the product of a 2×2 matrix and a 2×1 matrix, with the 2×2 matrix on the left, as follows:

$$\begin{bmatrix} a_{11} & a_{12} \\ a_{21} & a_{22} \end{bmatrix} \begin{bmatrix} b_{11} \\ b_{21} \end{bmatrix} = \begin{bmatrix} a_{11}b_{11} + a_{12}b_{21} \\ a_{21}b_{11} + a_{22}b_{21} \end{bmatrix}$$

Note that the product matrix is a 2×1 matrix. The following example illustrates this pattern:

$$\begin{bmatrix} -2 & 3 \\ 1 & -4 \end{bmatrix} \begin{bmatrix} 5 \\ 7 \end{bmatrix} = \begin{bmatrix} (-2)(5) + (3)(7) \\ (1)(5) + (-4)(7) \end{bmatrix} = \begin{bmatrix} 11 \\ -23 \end{bmatrix}$$

Back to Solving Systems of Equations

The linear system of equations

$$\begin{pmatrix} a_{11}x + a_{12}y = d_1 \\ a_{21}x + a_{22}y = d_2 \end{pmatrix}$$

can be represented by the matrix equation

$$\begin{bmatrix} a_{11} & a_{12} \\ a_{21} & a_{22} \end{bmatrix} \begin{bmatrix} x \\ y \end{bmatrix} = \begin{bmatrix} d_1 \\ d_2 \end{bmatrix}$$

If we let

$$A = \begin{bmatrix} a_{11} & a_{12} \\ a_{21} & a_{22} \end{bmatrix} \qquad X = \begin{bmatrix} x \\ y \end{bmatrix} \qquad \text{and} \qquad B = \begin{bmatrix} d_1 \\ d_2 \end{bmatrix}$$

then the previous matrix equation can be written $AX = B$.

If A^{-1} exists, then we can multiply both sides of $AX = B$ by A^{-1} (on the left) and simplify as follows:

$$AX = B$$

$$A^{-1}(AX) = A^{-1}(B)$$

$$(A^{-1}A)X = A^{-1}B$$

$$IX = A^{-1}B$$

$$X = A^{-1}B$$

Therefore the product $A^{-1}B$ is the solution of the system.

Classroom Example
Solve the system $\begin{pmatrix} 8x + 3y = 12 \\ 5x + 7y = -13 \end{pmatrix}$.

EXAMPLE 4 Solve the system $\begin{pmatrix} 5x + 4y = 10 \\ 6x + 5y = 13 \end{pmatrix}$.

Solution

If we let

$$A = \begin{bmatrix} 5 & 4 \\ 6 & 5 \end{bmatrix} \qquad X = \begin{bmatrix} x \\ y \end{bmatrix} \qquad \text{and} \qquad B = \begin{bmatrix} 10 \\ 13 \end{bmatrix}$$

then the given system can be represented by the matrix equation $AX = B$. From our previous discussion, we know that the solution of this equation is $X = A^{-1}B$, so we need to find A^{-1} and the product $A^{-1}B$.

$$A^{-1} = \frac{1}{|A|} \begin{bmatrix} 5 & -4 \\ -6 & 5 \end{bmatrix} = \frac{1}{1} \begin{bmatrix} 5 & -4 \\ -6 & 5 \end{bmatrix} = \begin{bmatrix} 5 & -4 \\ -6 & 5 \end{bmatrix}$$

Therefore

$$A^{-1}B = \begin{bmatrix} 5 & -4 \\ -6 & 5 \end{bmatrix} \begin{bmatrix} 10 \\ 13 \end{bmatrix} = \begin{bmatrix} -2 \\ 5 \end{bmatrix}$$

The solution set of the given system is $\{(-2, 5)\}$.

Classroom Example

Solve the system $\begin{pmatrix} -2x - 3y = 2 \\ 2x - 5y = -18 \end{pmatrix}$.

EXAMPLE 5   Solve the system $\begin{pmatrix} 3x - 2y = 9 \\ 4x + 7y = -17 \end{pmatrix}$.

Solution

If we let

$$A = \begin{bmatrix} 3 & -2 \\ 4 & 7 \end{bmatrix} \qquad X = \begin{bmatrix} x \\ y \end{bmatrix} \qquad \text{and} \qquad B = \begin{bmatrix} 9 \\ -17 \end{bmatrix}$$

then the system is represented by $AX = B$, where $X = A^{-1}B$ and

$$A^{-1} = \frac{1}{|A|} \begin{bmatrix} 7 & 2 \\ -4 & 3 \end{bmatrix} = \frac{1}{29} \begin{bmatrix} 7 & 2 \\ -4 & 3 \end{bmatrix} = \begin{bmatrix} \dfrac{7}{29} & \dfrac{2}{29} \\ -\dfrac{4}{29} & \dfrac{3}{29} \end{bmatrix}$$

Therefore

$$A^{-1}B = \begin{bmatrix} \dfrac{7}{29} & \dfrac{2}{29} \\ -\dfrac{4}{29} & \dfrac{3}{29} \end{bmatrix} \begin{bmatrix} 9 \\ -17 \end{bmatrix} = \begin{bmatrix} 1 \\ -3 \end{bmatrix}$$

The solution set of the given system is $\{(1, -3)\}$.

This technique of using matrix inverses to solve systems of linear equations is especially useful when there are many systems to be solved that have the same coefficients but different constant terms.

Concept Quiz 12.2

For the following problems, answer true or false.

1. Every 2×2 matrix has a multiplicative inverse.

2. If $A = \begin{bmatrix} 4 & 7 \\ 2 & 5 \end{bmatrix}$, then $A^{-1} = \begin{bmatrix} \dfrac{1}{4} & \dfrac{1}{7} \\ \dfrac{1}{2} & \dfrac{1}{5} \end{bmatrix}$.

3. If $|A| = 0$, then A does not have a multiplicative inverse.

4. If $|A| = 1$, then A does have a multiplicative inverse.

5. The multiplicative identity element for 2×2 matrices is $\begin{bmatrix} 1 & 1 \\ 1 & 1 \end{bmatrix}$.

6. If A has an inverse A^{-1}, then $AA^{-1} = \begin{bmatrix} 0 & 1 \\ 1 & 0 \end{bmatrix}$.

7. The commutative property holds for the multiplication of a matrix and its inverse.

8. The commutative property holds for the multiplication of a matrix and the multiplicative identity element.

Problem Set 12.2

For Problems 1–18, find the multiplicative inverse (if one exists) of each matrix. **(Objective 1)**

1. $\begin{bmatrix} 5 & 7 \\ 2 & 3 \end{bmatrix}$

2. $\begin{bmatrix} 3 & 4 \\ 2 & 3 \end{bmatrix}$

3. $\begin{bmatrix} 3 & 8 \\ 2 & 5 \end{bmatrix}$

4. $\begin{bmatrix} 2 & 9 \\ 3 & 13 \end{bmatrix}$

5. $\begin{bmatrix} -1 & 2 \\ 3 & 4 \end{bmatrix}$

6. $\begin{bmatrix} 1 & -2 \\ 4 & -3 \end{bmatrix}$

7. $\begin{bmatrix} -2 & -3 \\ 4 & 6 \end{bmatrix}$

8. $\begin{bmatrix} 5 & -1 \\ 3 & 4 \end{bmatrix}$

9. $\begin{bmatrix} -3 & 2 \\ -4 & 5 \end{bmatrix}$

10. $\begin{bmatrix} 3 & -4 \\ 6 & -8 \end{bmatrix}$

11. $\begin{bmatrix} 0 & 1 \\ 5 & 3 \end{bmatrix}$

12. $\begin{bmatrix} -2 & 0 \\ -3 & 5 \end{bmatrix}$

13. $\begin{bmatrix} -2 & -3 \\ -1 & -4 \end{bmatrix}$

14. $\begin{bmatrix} -2 & -5 \\ -3 & -6 \end{bmatrix}$

15. $\begin{bmatrix} -2 & 5 \\ -3 & 6 \end{bmatrix}$

16. $\begin{bmatrix} -3 & 4 \\ 1 & -2 \end{bmatrix}$

17. $\begin{bmatrix} 1 & 1 \\ 1 & -1 \end{bmatrix}$

18. $\begin{bmatrix} 1 & -1 \\ 1 & 1 \end{bmatrix}$

For Problems 19–26, compute AB. **(Objective 2)**

19. $A = \begin{bmatrix} 4 & 3 \\ 2 & 5 \end{bmatrix}$, $\quad B = \begin{bmatrix} 3 \\ 6 \end{bmatrix}$

20. $A = \begin{bmatrix} 5 & -2 \\ 3 & 1 \end{bmatrix}$, $\quad B = \begin{bmatrix} 5 \\ 8 \end{bmatrix}$

21. $A = \begin{bmatrix} -3 & -4 \\ 2 & 1 \end{bmatrix}$, $\quad B = \begin{bmatrix} 4 \\ -3 \end{bmatrix}$

22. $A = \begin{bmatrix} 5 & 2 \\ -1 & -3 \end{bmatrix}$, $\quad B = \begin{bmatrix} 3 \\ -5 \end{bmatrix}$

23. $A = \begin{bmatrix} -4 & 2 \\ 7 & -5 \end{bmatrix}$, $\quad B = \begin{bmatrix} -1 \\ -4 \end{bmatrix}$

24. $A = \begin{bmatrix} 0 & -3 \\ 2 & 9 \end{bmatrix}$, $\quad B = \begin{bmatrix} -3 \\ -6 \end{bmatrix}$

25. $A = \begin{bmatrix} -2 & -3 \\ -5 & -6 \end{bmatrix}$, $\quad B = \begin{bmatrix} 5 \\ -2 \end{bmatrix}$

26. $A = \begin{bmatrix} -3 & -5 \\ 4 & 7 \end{bmatrix}$, $\quad B = \begin{bmatrix} -3 \\ -10 \end{bmatrix}$

For Problems 27–40, use the method of matrix inverses to solve each system. **(Objective 3)**

27. $\left(\begin{array}{l} 2x + 3y = 13 \\ x + 2y = 8 \end{array} \right)$

28. $\left(\begin{array}{l} 3x + 2y = 10 \\ 7x + 5y = 23 \end{array} \right)$

29. $\left(\begin{array}{l} 4x - 3y = -23 \\ -3x + 2y = 16 \end{array} \right)$

30. $\left(\begin{array}{l} 6x - y = -14 \\ 3x + 2y = -17 \end{array} \right)$

31. $\left(\begin{array}{l} x - 7y = 7 \\ 6x + 5y = -5 \end{array} \right)$

32. $\left(\begin{array}{l} x + 9y = -5 \\ 4x - 7y = -20 \end{array} \right)$

33. $\left(\begin{array}{l} 3x - 5y = 2 \\ 4x - 3y = -1 \end{array} \right)$

34. $\left(\begin{array}{l} 5x - 2y = 6 \\ 7x - 3y = 8 \end{array} \right)$

35. $\left(\begin{array}{l} y = 19 - 3x \\ 9x - 5y = 1 \end{array} \right)$

36. $\left(\begin{array}{l} 4x + 3y = 31 \\ x = 5y + 2 \end{array} \right)$

37. $\left(\begin{array}{l} 3x + 2y = 0 \\ 30x - 18y = -19 \end{array} \right)$

38. $\left(\begin{array}{l} 12x + 30y = 23 \\ 12x - 24y = -13 \end{array} \right)$

39. $\left(\begin{array}{l} \dfrac{1}{3}x + \dfrac{3}{4}y = 12 \\ \dfrac{2}{3}x + \dfrac{1}{5}y = -2 \end{array} \right)$

40. $\left(\begin{array}{l} \dfrac{3}{2}x + \dfrac{1}{6}y = 11 \\ \dfrac{2}{3}x - \dfrac{1}{4}y = 1 \end{array} \right)$

Thoughts Into Words

41. Describe how to solve the system $\left(\begin{array}{l} x - 2y = -10 \\ 3x + 5y = 14 \end{array} \right)$

using each of the following techniques.
(a) substitution method
(b) elimination-by-addition method
(c) reduced echelon form of the augmented matrix
(d) determinants
(e) the method of matrix inverses

Graphing Calculator Activities

42. Use your calculator to find the multiplicative inverse (if one exists) of each of the following matrices. Be sure to check your answers by showing that $A^{-1}A = I$.

(a) $\begin{bmatrix} 7 & 6 \\ 8 & 7 \end{bmatrix}$

(b) $\begin{bmatrix} -12 & 5 \\ -19 & 8 \end{bmatrix}$

(c) $\begin{bmatrix} -7 & 9 \\ 6 & -8 \end{bmatrix}$

(d) $\begin{bmatrix} -6 & -11 \\ -4 & -8 \end{bmatrix}$

(e) $\begin{bmatrix} 13 & 12 \\ 4 & 4 \end{bmatrix}$

(f) $\begin{bmatrix} 15 & -8 \\ 9 & 5 \end{bmatrix}$

(g) $\begin{bmatrix} 9 & 36 \\ 3 & 12 \end{bmatrix}$

(h) $\begin{bmatrix} 1.2 & 1.5 \\ 7.6 & 4.5 \end{bmatrix}$

43. Use your calculator to find the multiplicative inverse of
$\begin{bmatrix} 1 & 2 \\ 2 & 5 \\ \frac{3}{4} & \frac{1}{4} \end{bmatrix}$ What difficulty did you encounter?

44. Use your calculator and the method of matrix inverses to solve each of the following systems. Be sure to check your solutions.

(a) $\begin{pmatrix} 5x + 7y = 82 \\ 7x + 10y = 116 \end{pmatrix}$ **(b)** $\begin{pmatrix} 9x - 8y = -150 \\ -10x + 9y = 168 \end{pmatrix}$

(c) $\begin{pmatrix} 15x - 8y = -15 \\ -9x + 5y = 12 \end{pmatrix}$ **(d)** $\begin{pmatrix} 1.2x + 1.5y = 5.85 \\ 7.6x + 4.5y = 19.55 \end{pmatrix}$

(e) $\begin{pmatrix} 12x - 7y = -34.5 \\ 8x + 9y = 79.5 \end{pmatrix}$ **(f)** $\begin{pmatrix} \frac{3x}{2} + \frac{y}{6} = 11 \\ \frac{2x}{3} - \frac{y}{4} = 1 \end{pmatrix}$

(g) $\begin{pmatrix} 114x + 129y = 2832 \\ 127x + 214y = 4139 \end{pmatrix}$

(h) $\begin{pmatrix} \frac{x}{2} + \frac{2y}{5} = 14 \\ \frac{3x}{4} + \frac{y}{4} = 14 \end{pmatrix}$

12.3 $m \times n$ Matrices

OBJECTIVES

1 Add and subtract general $m \times n$ matrices

2 Multiply an $m \times n$ matrix by a scalar

3 Multiply an $m \times n$ matrix by an $n \times p$ matrix

4 Find the inverse of a square $m \times m$ matrix

5 Solve systems of linear equations using matrices

Now let's see how much of the algebra of 2×2 matrices extends to $m \times n$ matrices—that is, to matrices of any dimension. In Section 11.4 we represented a general $m \times n$ matrix by

$$A = \begin{bmatrix} a_{11} & a_{12} & a_{13} & \dots & a_{1n} \\ a_{21} & a_{22} & a_{23} & \dots & a_{2n} \\ \cdot & \cdot & \cdot & & \cdot \\ \cdot & \cdot & \cdot & & \cdot \\ \cdot & \cdot & \cdot & & \cdot \\ a_{m1} & a_{m2} & a_{m3} & \dots & a_{mn} \end{bmatrix}$$

We denote the element at the intersection of row i and column j by a_{ij}. It is also customary to denote a matrix A with the abbreviated notation (a_{ij}).

Addition of matrices can be extended to matrices of any dimension by the following definition:

Definition 12.5

Let $A = (a_{ij})$ and $B = (b_{ij})$ be two matrices of the *same dimension*. Then

$$A + B = (a_{ij}) + (b_{ij}) = (a_{ij} + b_{ij})$$

Definition 12.5 states that to add two matrices, we add the elements that appear in corresponding positions in the matrices. For this to work, the matrices must be of the same dimension. An example of the sum of two 3×2 matrices is

$$\begin{bmatrix} 3 & 2 \\ 4 & -1 \\ -3 & 8 \end{bmatrix} + \begin{bmatrix} -2 & 1 \\ -3 & -7 \\ 5 & 9 \end{bmatrix} = \begin{bmatrix} 1 & 3 \\ 1 & -8 \\ 2 & 17 \end{bmatrix}$$

The **commutative** and **associative properties** hold for any matrices that can be added. The $m \times n$ **zero matrix**, denoted by O, is the matrix that contains all zeros. It is the **identity element for addition**. For example,

$$\begin{bmatrix} 2 & 3 & -1 & -5 \\ -7 & 6 & 2 & 8 \end{bmatrix} + \begin{bmatrix} 0 & 0 & 0 & 0 \\ 0 & 0 & 0 & 0 \end{bmatrix} = \begin{bmatrix} 2 & 3 & -1 & -5 \\ -7 & 6 & 2 & 8 \end{bmatrix}$$

Every matrix A has an **additive inverse**, $-A$, that can be found by changing the sign of each element of A. For example, if

$$A = \begin{bmatrix} 2 & -3 & 0 & 4 & -7 \end{bmatrix}$$

then

$$-A = \begin{bmatrix} -2 & 3 & 0 & -4 & 7 \end{bmatrix}$$

Furthermore, $A + (-A) = O$ for all matrices.

The definition we gave earlier for subtraction, $A - B = A + (-B)$, can be extended to any two matrices of the same dimension. For example,

$$\begin{bmatrix} -4 & 3 & -5 \end{bmatrix} - \begin{bmatrix} 7 & -4 & -1 \end{bmatrix} = \begin{bmatrix} -4 & 3 & -5 \end{bmatrix} + \begin{bmatrix} -7 & 4 & 1 \end{bmatrix}$$
$$= \begin{bmatrix} -11 & 7 & -4 \end{bmatrix}$$

The **scalar product** of any real number k and any $m \times n$ matrix $A = (a_{ij})$ is defined by

$$kA = (ka_{ij})$$

In other words, to find kA, we simply multiply each element of A by k. For example,

$$(-4)\begin{bmatrix} 1 & -1 \\ -2 & 3 \\ 4 & 5 \\ 0 & -8 \end{bmatrix} = \begin{bmatrix} -4 & 4 \\ 8 & -12 \\ -16 & -20 \\ 0 & 32 \end{bmatrix}$$

The properties $k(A + B) = kA + kB$, $(k + l)A = kA + lA$, and $(kl)A = k(lA)$ hold for all matrices. The matrices A and B must be of the same dimension to be added.

The row-by-column definition for multiplying two matrices can be extended, but we must take care. In order for us to define the product AB of two matrices A and B, **the number of columns of A must equal the number of rows of B.** Suppose $A = (a_{ij})$ is $m \times n$, and $B = (b_{ij})$ is $n \times p$. Then

$$AB = \begin{bmatrix} a_{11} & a_{12} & \cdots & a_{1n} \\ \cdot & \cdot & & \cdot \\ \cdot & \cdot & & \cdot \\ \cdot & \cdot & & \cdot \\ a_{i1} & a_{i2} & \cdots & a_{in} \\ \cdot & \cdot & & \cdot \\ \cdot & \cdot & & \cdot \\ \cdot & \cdot & & \cdot \\ a_{m1} & a_{m2} & \cdots & a_{mn} \end{bmatrix} \begin{bmatrix} b_{11} & \cdots & b_{1j} & \cdots & b_{1p} \\ b_{21} & \cdots & b_{2j} & \cdots & b_{2p} \\ \cdot & & \cdot & & \cdot \\ \cdot & & \cdot & & \cdot \\ \cdot & & \cdot & & \cdot \\ b_{n1} & \cdots & b_{nj} & \cdots & b_{np} \end{bmatrix} = C$$

The product matrix C is of the dimension $m \times p$, and the general element, c_{ij}, is determined as follows:

$$c_{ij} = a_{i1}b_{1j} + a_{i2}b_{2j} + \cdots + a_{in}b_{nj}$$

A specific element of the product matrix, such as c_{23}, is the result of multiplying the elements in row 2 of matrix A by the elements in column 3 of matrix B and adding the results. Therefore

$$c_{23} = a_{21}b_{13} + a_{22}b_{23} + \cdots + a_{2n}b_{n3}$$

The following example illustrates the product of a 2×3 matrix and a 3×2 matrix:

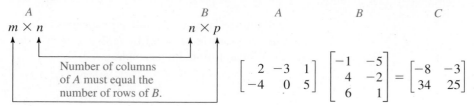

$$c_{11} = (2)(-1) + (-3)(4) + (1)(6) = -8$$

$$c_{12} = (2)(-5) + (-3)(-2) + (1)(1) = -3$$

$$c_{21} = (-4)(-1) + (0)(4) + (5)(6) = 34$$

$$c_{22} = (-4)(-5) + (0)(-2) + (5)(1) = 25$$

Recall that matrix multiplication is *not* commutative. In fact, it may be that AB is defined and BA is not defined. For example, if A is a 2×3 matrix and B is a 3×4 matrix, then the product AB is a 2×4 matrix, but the product BA is not defined because the number of columns of B does not equal the number of rows of A.

The **associative property for multiplication** and the two **distributive properties** hold if the matrices have the proper number of rows and columns for the operations to be defined. In that case, we have $(AB)C = A(BC)$, $A(B + C) = AB + AC$, and $(A + B)C = AC + BC$.

Square Matrices

Now let's extend some of the algebra of 2×2 matrices to all square matrices (where the number of rows equals the number of columns). For example, the general **multiplicative identity element** for square matrices contains 1s in the main diagonal from the upper left-hand corner to the lower right-hand corner and 0s elsewhere. Therefore, for 3×3 and 4×4 matrices, the multiplicative identity elements are as follows:

$$I_3 = \begin{bmatrix} 1 & 0 & 0 \\ 0 & 1 & 0 \\ 0 & 0 & 1 \end{bmatrix} \qquad I_4 = \begin{bmatrix} 1 & 0 & 0 & 0 \\ 0 & 1 & 0 & 0 \\ 0 & 0 & 1 & 0 \\ 0 & 0 & 0 & 1 \end{bmatrix}$$

We saw in Section 12.2 that some, but not all, 2×2 matrices have multiplicative inverses. In general, some, but not all, square matrices of a particular dimension have multiplicative inverses. If an $n \times n$ square matrix A does have a multiplicative inverse A^{-1}, then

$$AA^{-1} = A^{-1}A = I_n$$

The technique used in Section 12.2 for finding multiplicative inverses of 2×2 matrices does generalize, but it becomes quite complicated. Therefore, we shall now describe another technique that works for all square matrices. Given an $n \times n$ matrix A, we begin by forming the $n \times 2n$ matrix

$$\left[\begin{array}{cccc|ccccc} a_{11} & a_{12} & \cdots & a_{1n} & 1 & 0 & 0 & \cdots & 0 \\ a_{21} & a_{22} & \cdots & a_{2n} & 0 & 1 & 0 & \cdots & 0 \\ \cdot & \cdot & & \cdot & \cdot & \cdot & \cdot & & \cdot \\ \cdot & \cdot & & \cdot & \cdot & \cdot & \cdot & & \cdot \\ \cdot & \cdot & & \cdot & \cdot & \cdot & \cdot & & \cdot \\ a_{n1} & a_{n2} & \cdots & a_{nn} & 0 & 0 & 0 & \cdots & 1 \end{array} \right]$$

where the identity matrix I_n appears to the right of A. Now we apply a succession of elementary row transformations to this double matrix until we obtain a matrix of the form

$$\left[\begin{array}{ccccc:cccc} 1 & 0 & 0 & \dots & 0 & b_{11} & b_{12} & \dots & b_{1n} \\ 0 & 1 & 0 & \dots & 0 & b_{21} & b_{22} & \dots & b_{2n} \\ . & . & . & & . & . & . & & . \\ . & . & . & & . & . & . & & . \\ . & . & . & & . & . & . & & . \\ 0 & 0 & 0 & \dots & 1 & b_{n1} & b_{n2} & \dots & b_{nn} \end{array}\right]$$

The B matrix in this matrix is the desired inverse A^{-1}. If A does not have an inverse, then it is impossible to change the original matrix to this final form.

Classroom Example

Find A^{-1} if $A = \begin{bmatrix} 3 & 1 \\ 1 & 2 \end{bmatrix}$.

EXAMPLE 1 Find A^{-1} if $A = \begin{bmatrix} 2 & 4 \\ 3 & 5 \end{bmatrix}$.

Solution

First form the matrix

$$\left[\begin{array}{cc:cc} 2 & 4 & 1 & 0 \\ 3 & 5 & 0 & 1 \end{array}\right]$$

Now multiply row 1 by $\dfrac{1}{2}$.

$$\left[\begin{array}{cc:cc} 1 & 2 & \dfrac{1}{2} & 0 \\ 3 & 5 & 0 & 1 \end{array}\right]$$

Next, add -3 times row 1 to row 2 to form a new row 2.

$$\left[\begin{array}{cc:cc} 1 & 2 & \dfrac{1}{2} & 0 \\ 0 & -1 & -\dfrac{3}{2} & 1 \end{array}\right]$$

Then multiply row 2 by -1.

$$\left[\begin{array}{cc:cc} 1 & 2 & \dfrac{1}{2} & 0 \\ 0 & 1 & \dfrac{3}{2} & -1 \end{array}\right]$$

Finally, add -2 times row 2 to row 1 to form a new row 1.

$$\left[\begin{array}{cc:cc} 1 & 0 & -\dfrac{5}{2} & 2 \\ 0 & 1 & \dfrac{3}{2} & -1 \end{array}\right]$$

The matrix inside the box is A^{-1}; that is,

$$A^{-1} = \begin{bmatrix} -\dfrac{5}{2} & 2 \\ \dfrac{3}{2} & -1 \end{bmatrix}$$

This can be checked, as always, by showing that $AA^{-1} = A^{-1}A = I_2$.

Classroom Example

Find A^{-1} if $A = \begin{bmatrix} -2 & 5 & 3 \\ -3 & 1 & -1 \\ 1 & 4 & 5 \end{bmatrix}$.

EXAMPLE 2

Find A^{-1} if $A = \begin{bmatrix} 1 & 1 & 2 \\ 2 & 3 & -1 \\ -3 & 1 & -2 \end{bmatrix}$.

Solution

Form the matrix $\left[\begin{array}{ccc|ccc} 1 & 1 & 2 & 1 & 0 & 0 \\ 2 & 3 & -1 & 0 & 1 & 0 \\ -3 & 1 & -2 & 0 & 0 & 1 \end{array}\right]$.

Add -2 times row 1 to row 2, and add 3 times row 1 to row 3.

$$\left[\begin{array}{ccc|ccc} 1 & 1 & 2 & 1 & 0 & 0 \\ 0 & 1 & -5 & -2 & 1 & 0 \\ 0 & 4 & 4 & 3 & 0 & 1 \end{array}\right]$$

Add -1 times row 2 to row 1, and add -4 times row 2 to row 3.

$$\left[\begin{array}{ccc|ccc} 1 & 0 & 7 & 3 & -1 & 0 \\ 0 & 1 & -5 & -2 & 1 & 0 \\ 0 & 0 & 24 & 11 & -4 & 1 \end{array}\right]$$

Multiply row 3 by $\dfrac{1}{24}$.

$$\left[\begin{array}{ccc|ccc} 1 & 0 & 7 & 3 & -1 & 0 \\ 0 & 1 & -5 & -2 & 1 & 0 \\ 0 & 0 & 1 & \dfrac{11}{24} & -\dfrac{1}{6} & \dfrac{1}{24} \end{array}\right]$$

Add -7 times row 3 to row 1, and add 5 times row 3 to row 2.

$$\left[\begin{array}{ccc|ccc} 1 & 0 & 0 & -\dfrac{5}{24} & \dfrac{1}{6} & -\dfrac{7}{24} \\ 0 & 1 & 0 & \dfrac{7}{24} & \dfrac{1}{6} & \dfrac{5}{24} \\ 0 & 0 & 1 & \dfrac{11}{24} & -\dfrac{1}{6} & \dfrac{1}{24} \end{array}\right]$$

Therefore

$$A^{-1} = \begin{bmatrix} -\dfrac{5}{24} & \dfrac{1}{6} & -\dfrac{7}{24} \\ \dfrac{7}{24} & \dfrac{1}{6} & \dfrac{5}{24} \\ \dfrac{11}{24} & -\dfrac{1}{6} & \dfrac{1}{24} \end{bmatrix}$$ Be sure to check this!

Systems of Equations

In Section 12.2 we used the concept of the multiplicative inverse to solve systems of two linear equations in two variables. This same technique can be applied to general systems of n linear equations in n variables. Let's consider one such example involving three equations in three variables.

Classroom Example
Solve the system

$$\begin{pmatrix} x - y + 4z = 11 \\ 4x - 2y + 3z = 3 \\ 2x + y + 4z = 7 \end{pmatrix}, \text{ given that}$$

the inverse of the coefficient matrix
is

$$\begin{bmatrix} -\dfrac{11}{31} & \dfrac{8}{31} & \dfrac{5}{31} \\[2mm] -\dfrac{10}{31} & -\dfrac{4}{31} & \dfrac{13}{31} \\[2mm] \dfrac{8}{31} & -\dfrac{3}{31} & \dfrac{2}{31} \end{bmatrix}.$$

EXAMPLE 3

Solve the system $\begin{pmatrix} x + y + 2z = -8 \\ 2x + 3y - z = 3 \\ -3x + y - 2z = 4 \end{pmatrix}$.

Solution

If we let

$$A = \begin{bmatrix} 1 & 1 & 2 \\ 2 & 3 & -1 \\ -3 & 1 & -2 \end{bmatrix} \qquad X = \begin{bmatrix} x \\ y \\ z \end{bmatrix} \qquad \text{and} \qquad B = \begin{bmatrix} -8 \\ 3 \\ 4 \end{bmatrix}$$

then the given system can be represented by the matrix equation $AX = B$. Therefore, we know that $X = A^{-1}B$, so we need to find A^{-1} and the product $A^{-1}B$. The matrix A^{-1} was found in Example 2, so let's use that result and find $A^{-1}B$.

$$X = A^{-1}B = \begin{bmatrix} -\dfrac{5}{24} & \dfrac{1}{6} & -\dfrac{7}{24} \\[2mm] \dfrac{7}{24} & \dfrac{1}{6} & \dfrac{5}{24} \\[2mm] \dfrac{11}{24} & -\dfrac{1}{6} & \dfrac{1}{24} \end{bmatrix} \begin{bmatrix} -8 \\ 3 \\ 4 \end{bmatrix} = \begin{bmatrix} 1 \\ -1 \\ -4 \end{bmatrix}$$

The solution set of the given system is $\{(1, -1, -4)\}$.

Concept Quiz 12.3

For the following problems, answer true or false.

1. If A is a 5×2 matrix, then it has 5 rows and 2 columns of elements.

2. If $B = \begin{bmatrix} 3 & 2 & 5 & 7 \\ 4 & 0 & 8 & -1 \end{bmatrix}$, then B is a 4×2 matrix.

3. Only square matrices have an additive inverse.

4. For matrices that can be added, the commutative property holds.

5. If A is a 3×3 matrix, then $AA^{-1} = \begin{bmatrix} 1 & 1 & 1 \\ 1 & 1 & 1 \\ 1 & 1 & 1 \end{bmatrix}$.

6. Every square matrix has a multiplicative inverse matrix.

7. Given that a_{14} is an element of matrix A, then the element is in the first row and fourth column.

8. If $A = \begin{bmatrix} 2 & -4 & 5 \\ -1 & 0 & 3 \end{bmatrix}$, then $3A = \begin{bmatrix} 6 & -4 & 5 \\ -3 & 0 & 3 \end{bmatrix}$.

Problem Set 12.3

For Problems 1–8, find $A + B$, $A - B$, $2A + 3B$, and $4A - 2B$. (Objectives 1 and 2)

1. $A = \begin{bmatrix} 2 & -1 & 4 \\ -2 & 0 & 5 \end{bmatrix}$, $\qquad B = \begin{bmatrix} -1 & 4 & -7 \\ 5 & -6 & 2 \end{bmatrix}$

2. $A = \begin{bmatrix} 3 & -6 \\ 2 & -1 \\ -4 & 5 \end{bmatrix}$, $\qquad B = \begin{bmatrix} 1 & 0 \\ 5 & -7 \\ -6 & 9 \end{bmatrix}$

3. $A = \begin{bmatrix} 2 & -1 & 4 & 12 \end{bmatrix}$, $B = \begin{bmatrix} -3 & -6 & 9 & -5 \end{bmatrix}$

4. $A = \begin{bmatrix} 3 \\ -9 \\ 7 \end{bmatrix}$, $B = \begin{bmatrix} -6 \\ 12 \\ 9 \end{bmatrix}$

5. $A = \begin{bmatrix} 3 & -2 & 1 \\ -1 & 4 & -7 \\ 0 & 5 & 9 \end{bmatrix}$, $B = \begin{bmatrix} 5 & -1 & -3 \\ 10 & -2 & 4 \\ 7 & 0 & 12 \end{bmatrix}$

6. $A = \begin{bmatrix} 7 & -4 \\ -5 & 9 \\ -1 & 2 \end{bmatrix}$, $B = \begin{bmatrix} 12 & 3 \\ -2 & -4 \\ -6 & 7 \end{bmatrix}$

7. $A = \begin{bmatrix} -1 & 0 \\ 2 & 3 \\ -5 & -4 \\ -7 & 11 \end{bmatrix}$, $B = \begin{bmatrix} 1 & 2 \\ -3 & 7 \\ 6 & -5 \\ 9 & -2 \end{bmatrix}$

8. $A = \begin{bmatrix} 0 & -1 & -2 \\ 3 & -4 & 6 \\ 5 & 4 & -9 \end{bmatrix}$, $B = \begin{bmatrix} 2 & 1 & -7 \\ -6 & 4 & 5 \\ 3 & -2 & -1 \end{bmatrix}$

For Problems 9–20, find AB and BA, whenever they exist. (Objective 3)

9. $A = \begin{bmatrix} 2 & -1 \\ 0 & -4 \\ -5 & 3 \end{bmatrix}$, $B = \begin{bmatrix} 5 & -2 & 6 \\ -1 & 4 & -2 \end{bmatrix}$

10. $A = \begin{bmatrix} -2 & 3 & -1 \\ 7 & -4 & 5 \end{bmatrix}$, $B = \begin{bmatrix} 1 & -1 \\ -2 & 3 \\ -5 & -6 \end{bmatrix}$

11. $A = \begin{bmatrix} 2 & -1 & -3 \\ 0 & -4 & 7 \end{bmatrix}$, $B = \begin{bmatrix} 2 & 1 & -1 & 4 \\ 0 & -2 & 3 & 5 \\ -6 & 4 & -2 & 0 \end{bmatrix}$

12. $A = \begin{bmatrix} 3 & -1 & -4 \\ -5 & 2 & 2 \end{bmatrix}$, $B = \begin{bmatrix} 3 & -2 \\ -4 & -1 \end{bmatrix}$

13. $A = \begin{bmatrix} 1 & -1 & 2 \\ 0 & 1 & -2 \\ 3 & 1 & 4 \end{bmatrix}$, $B = \begin{bmatrix} 2 & 3 & -1 \\ 4 & 0 & 2 \\ -5 & 1 & -1 \end{bmatrix}$

14. $A = \begin{bmatrix} 1 & 0 & 1 \\ 0 & 1 & 1 \\ -1 & 2 & 3 \end{bmatrix}$, $B = \begin{bmatrix} -1 & -1 & 1 \\ 0 & 1 & 0 \\ 2 & -3 & 1 \end{bmatrix}$

15. $A = \begin{bmatrix} 2 & -1 & 3 & 4 \end{bmatrix}$, $B = \begin{bmatrix} -1 \\ -3 \\ 2 \\ -4 \end{bmatrix}$

16. $A = \begin{bmatrix} -2 \\ 3 \\ -5 \end{bmatrix}$, $B = \begin{bmatrix} 3 & -4 & -5 \end{bmatrix}$

17. $A = \begin{bmatrix} 2 \\ -7 \end{bmatrix}$, $B = \begin{bmatrix} 3 & -2 \\ 1 & 0 \\ -1 & 4 \end{bmatrix}$

18. $A = \begin{bmatrix} 3 & -2 & 2 & -4 \\ 1 & 0 & -1 & 2 \end{bmatrix}$, $B = \begin{bmatrix} 3 & -2 & 1 \\ -3 & 1 & 4 \\ 5 & 2 & 0 \\ -4 & -1 & -2 \end{bmatrix}$

19. $A = \begin{bmatrix} 3 \\ -4 \\ 2 \end{bmatrix}$, $B = \begin{bmatrix} 3 & -4 \end{bmatrix}$

20. $A = \begin{bmatrix} 3 & -7 \end{bmatrix}$, $B = \begin{bmatrix} 8 \\ -9 \end{bmatrix}$

For Problems 21–36, use the technique discussed in this section to find the multiplicative inverse (if one exists) of each matrix. (Objective 4)

21. $\begin{bmatrix} 1 & 3 \\ 4 & 2 \end{bmatrix}$

22. $\begin{bmatrix} 1 & 2 \\ 2 & -3 \end{bmatrix}$

23. $\begin{bmatrix} 2 & 1 \\ 7 & 4 \end{bmatrix}$

24. $\begin{bmatrix} 3 & 7 \\ 2 & 5 \end{bmatrix}$

25. $\begin{bmatrix} -2 & 1 \\ 3 & -4 \end{bmatrix}$

26. $\begin{bmatrix} -3 & 1 \\ 3 & -2 \end{bmatrix}$

27. $\begin{bmatrix} 1 & 2 & 3 \\ 1 & 3 & 4 \\ 1 & 4 & 3 \end{bmatrix}$

28. $\begin{bmatrix} 1 & 3 & -2 \\ 1 & 4 & -1 \\ -2 & -7 & 5 \end{bmatrix}$

29. $\begin{bmatrix} 1 & -2 & 1 \\ -2 & 5 & 3 \\ 3 & -5 & 7 \end{bmatrix}$

30. $\begin{bmatrix} 1 & 4 & -2 \\ -3 & -11 & 1 \\ 2 & 7 & 3 \end{bmatrix}$

31. $\begin{bmatrix} 2 & 3 & -4 \\ 3 & -1 & -2 \\ 1 & -4 & 2 \end{bmatrix}$

32. $\begin{bmatrix} -2 & 2 & 3 \\ 1 & -1 & 0 \\ 0 & 1 & 4 \end{bmatrix}$

33. $\begin{bmatrix} 1 & 2 & 3 \\ -3 & -4 & 3 \\ 2 & 4 & -1 \end{bmatrix}$

34. $\begin{bmatrix} 1 & -2 & 3 \\ -1 & 3 & -2 \\ -2 & 6 & 1 \end{bmatrix}$

35. $\begin{bmatrix} 2 & 0 & 0 \\ 0 & 4 & 0 \\ 0 & 0 & 10 \end{bmatrix}$

36. $\begin{bmatrix} 1 & -3 & 5 \\ 0 & 1 & 2 \\ 0 & 0 & 1 \end{bmatrix}$

For Problems 37–46, use the method of matrix inverses to solve each system. The required multiplicative inverses were found in Problems 21–36. (Objective 5)

37. $\begin{pmatrix} 2x + y = -4 \\ 7x + 4y = -13 \end{pmatrix}$

38. $\begin{pmatrix} 3x + 7y = -38 \\ 2x + 5y = -27 \end{pmatrix}$

39. $\begin{pmatrix} -2x + y = 1 \\ 3x - 4y = -14 \end{pmatrix}$

40. $\begin{pmatrix} -3x + y = -18 \\ 3x - 2y = 15 \end{pmatrix}$

41. $\begin{pmatrix} x + 2y + 3z = -2 \\ x + 3y + 4z = -3 \\ x + 4y + 3z = -6 \end{pmatrix}$

42. $\begin{pmatrix} x + 3y - 2z = 5 \\ x + 4y - z = 3 \\ -2x - 7y + 5z = -12 \end{pmatrix}$

43. $\begin{pmatrix} x - 2y + z = -3 \\ -2x + 5y + 3z = 34 \\ 3x - 5y + 7z = 14 \end{pmatrix}$

44. $\begin{pmatrix} x + 4y - 2z = 2 \\ -3x - 11y + z = -2 \\ 2x + 7y + 3z = -2 \end{pmatrix}$

45. $\begin{pmatrix} x + 2y + 3z = 2 \\ -3x - 4y + 3z = 0 \\ 2x + 4y - z = 4 \end{pmatrix}$

46. $\begin{pmatrix} x - 2y + 3z = -39 \\ -x + 3y - 2z = 40 \\ -2x + 6y + z = 45 \end{pmatrix}$

47. We can generate five systems of linear equations from the system

$$\begin{pmatrix} x + y + 2z = a \\ 2x + 3y - z = b \\ -3x + y - 2z = c \end{pmatrix}$$

by letting *a*, *b*, and *c* assume five different sets of values. Solve the system for each set of values. The inverse of the coefficient matrix of these systems is given in Example 2 of this section.

(a) $a = 7$, $b = 1$, and $c = -1$

(b) $a = -7$, $b = 5$, and $c = 1$

(c) $a = -9$, $b = -8$, and $c = 19$

(d) $a = -1$, $b = -13$, and $c = -17$

(e) $a = -2$, $b = 0$, and $c = -2$

Thoughts Into Words

48. How would you describe row-by-column multiplication of matrices?

49. Give a step-by-step explanation of how to find the multiplicative inverse of the matrix $\begin{bmatrix} 1 & 3 \\ -2 & 4 \end{bmatrix}$ by using the technique of Section 12.3.

50. Explain how to find the multiplicative inverse of the matrix in Problem 49 by using the technique discussed in Section 12.2.

Further Investigations

51. Matrices can be used to code and decode messages. For example, suppose that we set up a one-to-one correspondence between the letters of the alphabet and the first 26 counting numbers, as follows:

A B C   Z
↕ ↕ ↕ ... ↕
1 2 3   26

Now suppose that we want to code the message PLAY IT BY EAR. We can partition the letters of the message into groups of two. Because the last group will contain only one letter, let's arbitrarily stick in a Z to form a group of two. Let's also assign a number to each letter on the basis of the letter/number association we exhibited.

P L A Y I T B Y E A R Z
↕ ↕ ↕ ↕ ↕ ↕ ↕ ↕ ↕ ↕ ↕ ↕
16 12 1 25 9 20 2 25 5 1 18 26

Each pair of numbers can be recorded as columns in a 2 × 6 matrix *B*.

$$B = \begin{bmatrix} 16 & 1 & 9 & 2 & 5 & 18 \\ 12 & 25 & 20 & 25 & 1 & 26 \end{bmatrix}$$

Now let's choose a 2 × 2 matrix such that the matrix contains only integers, and its inverse also contains only integers. For example, we can use $A = \begin{bmatrix} 3 & 1 \\ 5 & 2 \end{bmatrix}$; then

$$A^{-1} = \begin{bmatrix} 2 & -1 \\ -5 & 3 \end{bmatrix}.$$

Next, let's find the product AB.

$$AB = \begin{bmatrix} 3 & 1 \\ 5 & 2 \end{bmatrix} \begin{bmatrix} 16 & 1 & 9 & 2 & 5 & 18 \\ 12 & 25 & 20 & 25 & 1 & 26 \end{bmatrix}$$

$$= \begin{bmatrix} 60 & 28 & 47 & 31 & 16 & 80 \\ 104 & 55 & 85 & 60 & 27 & 142 \end{bmatrix}$$

Now we have our coded message:

60   104   28   55   47   85   31   60   16   27   80   142

A person decoding the message would put the numbers back into a 2×6 matrix, multiply it on the left by A^{-1}, and convert the numbers back to letters.

Each of the following coded messages was formed by using the matrix $A = \begin{bmatrix} 2 & 3 \\ 1 & 2 \end{bmatrix}$. Decode each of the messages.

(a) 53 34 48 25   39 22 35 20 78 47
56 37 83 54

(b) 62 40 78 47 64 36 19 11 93 57
93 56 88 57

(c) 64 36 58 37 63 36 21 13 75 47
63 36 38 23 118 72

(d) 29 15 96 58 60 37 75 47 19 10
37 21 70 42 90 55 98 59 72 45
51 28 86 56

52. Suppose that the ordered pair (x, y) of a rectangular coordinate system is recorded as a 2×1 matrix and then multiplied on the left by the matrix $\begin{bmatrix} 1 & 0 \\ 0 & -1 \end{bmatrix}$. We would obtain

$$\begin{bmatrix} 1 & 0 \\ 0 & -1 \end{bmatrix} \begin{bmatrix} x \\ y \end{bmatrix} = \begin{bmatrix} x \\ -y \end{bmatrix}$$

The point $(x, -y)$ is an x-axis reflection of the point (x, y). Therefore the matrix $\begin{bmatrix} 1 & 0 \\ 0 & -1 \end{bmatrix}$ performs an x-axis reflection. What type of geometric transformation is performed by each of the following matrices?

(a) $\begin{bmatrix} -1 & 0 \\ 0 & 1 \end{bmatrix}$ **(b)** $\begin{bmatrix} -1 & 0 \\ 0 & -1 \end{bmatrix}$

(c) $\begin{bmatrix} 0 & -1 \\ 1 & 0 \end{bmatrix}$

(d) $\begin{bmatrix} 0 & 1 \\ -1 & 0 \end{bmatrix}$

Graphing Calculator Activities

53. Use your calculator to check your answers for Problems 14, 18, 28, 30, 32, 34, 36, 42, 44, 46, and 47.

54. Use your calculator and the method of matrix inverses to solve each of the following systems. Be sure to check your solutions.

(a) $\begin{pmatrix} 2x - 3y + 4z = 54 \\ 3x + y - z = 32 \\ 5x - 4y + 3z = 58 \end{pmatrix}$

(b) $\begin{pmatrix} 17x + 15y - 19z = 10 \\ 18x - 14y + 16z = 94 \\ 13x + 19y - 14z = -23 \end{pmatrix}$

(c) $\begin{pmatrix} 1.98x + 2.49y + 3.15z = 45.72 \\ 2.29x + 1.95y + 2.75z = 42.05 \\ 3.15x + 3.20y + 1.85z = 42 \end{pmatrix}$

(d) $\begin{pmatrix} x_1 + 2x_2 - 4x_3 + 7x_4 = -23 \\ 2x_1 - 3x_2 + 5x_3 - x_4 = -22 \\ 5x_1 + 4x_2 - 2x_3 - 8x_4 = 59 \\ 3x_1 - 7x_2 + 8x_3 + 9x_4 = -103 \end{pmatrix}$

(e) $\begin{pmatrix} 2x_1 - x_2 + 3x_3 - 4x_4 + 12x_5 = 98 \\ x_1 + 2x_2 - x_3 - 7x_4 + 5x_5 = 41 \\ 3x_1 + 4x_2 - 7x_3 + 6x_4 - 9x_5 = -41 \\ 4x_1 - 3x_2 + x_3 - x_4 + x_5 = 4 \\ 7x_1 + 8x_2 - 4x_3 - 6x_4 - 6x_5 = 12 \end{pmatrix}$

Answers to the Concept Quiz

1. True   **2.** False   **3.** False   **4.** True   **5.** False   **6.** False   **7.** True   **8.** False

12.4   Systems of Linear Inequalities: Linear Programming

OBJECTIVES

1 Solve a system of linear inequalities

2 Find the minimum and maximum value of linear functions for a specified region

3 Solve linear programming problems

Finding solution sets for **systems of linear inequalities** relies heavily on the graphing approach. (Recall that we discussed graphing of linear inequalities in Section 7.3.) The solution set of the system

$$\begin{pmatrix} x + y > 2 \\ x - y < 2 \end{pmatrix}$$

is the intersection of the solution sets of the individual inequalities. In Figure 12.1(a), we indicate the solution set for $x + y > 2$, and in Figure 12.1(b), we indicate the solution set for $x - y < 2$. The shaded region in Figure 12.1(c) represents the intersection of the two solution sets; therefore it is the graph of the system. Remember that dashed lines are used to indicate that the points on the lines are not included in the solution set. In the following examples, we indicate only the final solution set for the system.

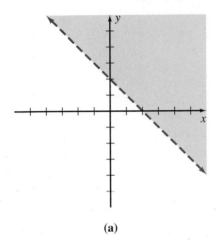   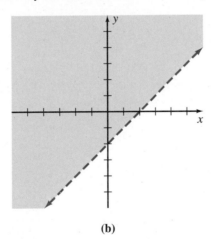   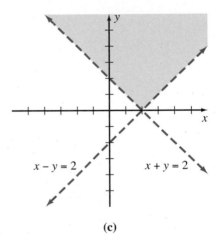

(a)   (b)   (c)

Figure 12.1

EXAMPLE 1   Solve the following system by graphing:

$$\begin{pmatrix} 2x - y \ge 4 \\ x + 2y < 2 \end{pmatrix}$$

Solution

The graph of $2x - y \ge 4$ consists of all points *on or below* the line $2x - y = 4$. The graph of $x + 2y < 2$ consists of all points *below* the line $x + 2y = 2$. The graph of the system is indicated by the shaded region in Figure 12.2. Note that all points in the shaded region are on or below the line $2x - y = 4$ and below the line $x + 2y = 2$.

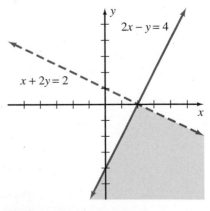

Figure 12.2

EXAMPLE 2   Solve the following system by graphing:

$$\begin{pmatrix} x \leq 2 \\ y \geq -1 \end{pmatrix}$$

Solution

Remember that even though each inequality contains only one variable, we are working in a rectangular coordinate system involving ordered pairs. That is, the system could also be written

$$\begin{pmatrix} x + 0(y) \leq 2 \\ 0(x) + y \geq -1 \end{pmatrix}$$

The graph of this system is the shaded region in Figure 12.3. Note that all points in the shaded region are *on or to the left* of the line $x = 2$ and *on or above* the line $y = -1$.

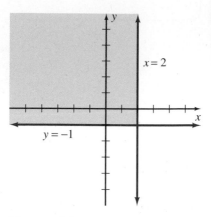

Figure 12.3

A system may contain more than two inequalities, as the next example illustrates.

EXAMPLE 3   Solve the following system by graphing:

$$\begin{pmatrix} x \geq 0 \\ y \geq 0 \\ 2x + 3y \leq 12 \\ 3x + y \leq 6 \end{pmatrix}$$

Solution

The solution set for the system is the intersection of the solution sets of the four inequalities. The shaded region in Figure 12.4 indicates the solution set for the system. Note that all points in the shaded region are *on or to the right* of the y axis, *on or above* the x axis, *on or below* the line $2x + 3y = 12$, and *on or below* the line $3x + y = 6$.

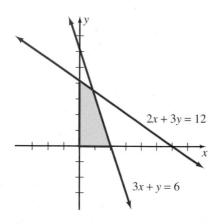

Figure 12.4

Linear Programming: Another Look at Problem Solving

Throughout this text problem solving has been a unifying theme. Therefore it seems appropriate at this time to give you a brief glimpse of an area of mathematics that was developed in the 1940s specifically as a problem-solving tool. Many applied problems involve the idea of *maximizing* or *minimizing* a certain function that is subject to various constraints; these can be expressed as linear inequalities. **Linear programming** was developed as one method for solving such problems.

Remark: The term "programming" refers to the distribution of limited resources in order to maximize or minimize a certain function, such as cost, profit, distance, and so on. Thus it does not mean the same thing that it means in computer programming. The constraints that govern the distribution of resources determine the linear inequalities and equations; thus the term "linear programming" is used.

Before we introduce a linear programming type of problem, we need to extend one mathematical concept a bit. A **linear function in two variables**, x and y, is a function of the form $f(x, y) = ax + by + c$, where a, b, and c are real numbers. In other words, with each ordered pair (x, y) we associate a third number by the rule $ax + by + c$. For example, suppose the function f is described by $f(x, y) = 4x + 3y + 5$. Then $f(2, 1) = 4(2) + 3(1) + 5 = 16$.

First, let's take a look at some mathematical ideas that form the basis for solving a linear programming problem. Consider the shaded region in Figure 12.5 and the following linear functions in two variables:

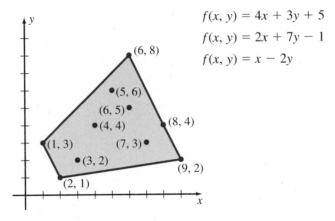

$$f(x, y) = 4x + 3y + 5$$
$$f(x, y) = 2x + 7y - 1$$
$$f(x, y) = x - 2y$$

Figure 12.5

Suppose that we need to find the maximum value and the minimum value achieved by each of the functions in the indicated region. The following chart summarizes the values for the ordered pairs indicated in Figure 12.5. Note that for each function, the maximum and minimum values are obtained at vertices of the region.

	Ordered pairs	Value of $f(x, y) = 4x + 3y + 5$	Value of $f(x, y) = 2x + 7y - 1$	Value of $f(x, y) = x - 2y$
Vertex	(2, 1)	16 (*minimum*)	10 (*minimum*)	0
	(3, 2)	23	19	−1
Vertex	(9, 2)	47	31	5 (*maximum*)
Vertex	(1, 3)	18	22	−5
	(7, 3)	42	34	1
	(4, 4)	33	35	−4
	(8, 4)	49	43	0
	(6, 5)	44	46	−4
	(5, 6)	43	51	−7
Vertex	(6, 8)	53 (*maximum*)	67 (*maximum*)	−10 (*minimum*)

We claim that for linear functions, maximum and minimum functional values are *always* obtained at vertices of the region. To substantiate this, let's consider the family of lines

$x - 2y = k$, in which k is an arbitrary constant. (We are now working only with the function $f(x, y) = x - 2y$.) In slope-intercept form, $x - 2y = k$ becomes $y = \frac{1}{2}x - \frac{1}{2}k$, so we have a family of parallel lines each having a slope of $\frac{1}{2}$. In Figure 12.6, we sketched some of these lines so that each line has at least one point in common with the given region. Note that $x - 2y$ reaches a minimum value of -10 at the vertex $(6, 8)$ and a maximum value of 5 at the vertex $(9, 2)$.

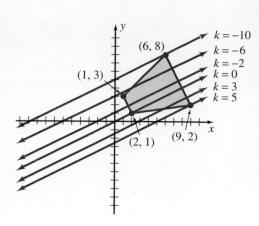

Figure 12.6

In general, suppose that f is a linear function in two variables x and y and that S is a region of the xy plane. If f attains a maximum (minimum) value in S, then that maximum (minimum) value is obtained at a vertex of S.

Remark: A subset of the xy plane is said to be **bounded** if there is a circle that contains all of its points; otherwise, the subset is said to be **unbounded**. A bounded set will contain maximum and minimum values for a function, but an unbounded set may not contain such values.

Now we will consider two examples that illustrate a general graphing approach to solving a linear programming problem in two variables. The first example gives us the general makeup of such a problem; the second example will illustrate the type of setting from which the function and inequalities evolve.

Classroom Example
Find the maximum value and the minimum value of the function $f(x, y) = 20x + 35y$ in the region determined by the following system of inequalities:

$$\begin{pmatrix} x \ge 0 \\ y \ge 0 \\ x + 2y \le 8 \\ 4x + 5y \le 26 \end{pmatrix}$$

EXAMPLE 4

Find the maximum value and the minimum value of the function $f(x, y) = 9x + 13y$ in the region determined by the following system of inequalities:

$$\begin{pmatrix} x \ge 0 \\ y \ge 0 \\ 2x + 3y \le 18 \\ 2x + y \le 10 \end{pmatrix}$$

Solution

First, let's graph the inequalities to determine the region, as indicated in Figure 12.7. (Such a region is called the **set of feasible solutions**, and the inequalities are referred to as **constraints**.) The point $(3, 4)$ is determined by solving the system

$$\begin{pmatrix} 2x + 3y = 18 \\ 2x + y = 10 \end{pmatrix}$$

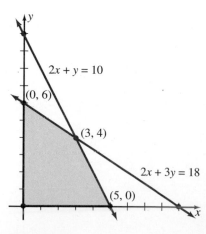

Figure 12.7

Next, we can determine the values of the given function at the vertices of the region. (Such a function to be maximized or minimized is called the **objective function**.)

Vertices	Value of $f(x, y) = 9x + 13y$
$(0, 0)$	0 (*minimum*)
$(5, 0)$	45
$(3, 4)$	79 (*maximum*)
$(0, 6)$	78

A minimum value of 0 is obtained at $(0, 0)$, and a maximum value of 79 is obtained at $(3, 4)$.

Classroom Example
A company that manufactures gidgets and gadgets has the following production information available:

1. To produce a gidget requires 2 hours of time on machine A and 5 hours on machine B.
2. To produce a gadget requires 3 hours on machine A and 1 hour on machine B.
3. Machine A is available for no more than 145 hours per week, and machine B is available for no more than 135 hours per week.
4. Gidgets can be sold at a profit of $12.50 each, and a profit of $9.75 can be realized on a gadget.

How many gidgets and how many gadgets should the company produce each week to maximize its profit? What would the maximum profit be?

EXAMPLE 5

A company that manufactures gidgets and gadgets has the following production information available:

1. To produce a gidget requires 3 hours of working time on machine A and 1 hour on machine B.
2. To produce a gadget requires 2 hours on machine A and 1 hour on machine B.
3. Machine A is available for no more than 120 hours per week, and machine B is available for no more than 50 hours per week.
4. Gidgets can be sold at a profit of $3.75 each, and a profit of $3 can be realized on a gadget.

How many gidgets and how many gadgets should the company produce each week to maximize its profit? What would the maximum profit be?

Solution

Let x be the number of gidgets and y be the number of gadgets. Thus the profit function is $P(x, y) = 3.75x + 3y$. The constraints for the problem can be represented by the following inequalities:

$$3x + 2y \le 120 \qquad \text{Machine A is available for no more than 120 hours}$$
$$x + y \le 50 \qquad \text{Machine B is available for no more than 50 hours}$$
$$x \ge 0 \qquad \text{The number of gidgets and gadgets must be}$$
$$y \ge 0 \qquad \text{represented by a nonnegative number}$$

When we graph these inequalities, we obtain the set of feasible solutions indicated by the shaded region in Figure 12.8. Next, we find the value of the profit function at the vertices; this produces the following chart.

Vertices	Value of $P(x, y) = 3.75x + 3y$
$(0, 0)$	0
$(40, 0)$	150
$(20, 30)$	165 (*maximum*)
$(0, 50)$	150

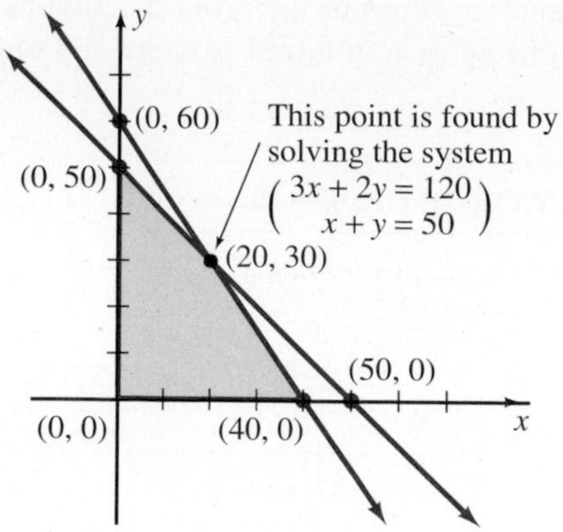

Figure 12.8

Thus a maximum profit of $165 is realized by producing 20 gidgets and 30 gadgets.

Concept Quiz 12.4

1. Write a system of a two linear inequalities that has the empty set as the solution.

For the following problems, answer true or false.

2. The point $(2, -5)$ is a solution of the system of inequalities $\begin{pmatrix} 2x - y > 9 \\ x + 3y < 0 \end{pmatrix}$.

3. The coordinates of every point in the rectangular coordinate plane satisfy the system of inequalities $\begin{pmatrix} 2x - y > 4 \\ 2x - y < 4 \end{pmatrix}$.

4. Given $f(x, y) = 2x - y + 3$, then $f(4, -1) = 12$.

5. A subset of the rectangular coordinate plane is bounded if there can be a circle drawn that contains all of its points.

6. The region determined by the system of inequalities $\begin{pmatrix} x \geq 0 \\ y \geq 0 \end{pmatrix}$ is a bounded region.

7. For linear programming, maximum and minimum function values are always obtained at the vertices of a bounded region.

8. For linear programming problems, the region determined by the system of inequalities is called the set of feasible solutions.

Problem Set 12.4

For Problems 1–24, indicate the solution set for each system of inequalities by graphing the system and shading the appropriate region. **(Objective 1)**

1. $\begin{pmatrix} x + y > 3 \\ x - y > 1 \end{pmatrix}$

2. $\begin{pmatrix} x - y < 2 \\ x + y < 1 \end{pmatrix}$

3. $\begin{pmatrix} x - 2y \leq 4 \\ x + 2y > 4 \end{pmatrix}$

4. $\begin{pmatrix} 3x - y > 6 \\ 2x + y \leq 4 \end{pmatrix}$

5. $\begin{pmatrix} 2x + 3y \leq 6 \\ 3x - 2y \leq 6 \end{pmatrix}$

6. $\begin{pmatrix} 4x + 3y \geq 12 \\ 3x - 4y \geq 12 \end{pmatrix}$

7. $\begin{pmatrix} 2x - y \geq 4 \\ x + 3y < 3 \end{pmatrix}$

8. $\begin{pmatrix} 3x - y < 3 \\ x + y \geq 1 \end{pmatrix}$

9. $\begin{pmatrix} x + 2y > -2 \\ x - y < -3 \end{pmatrix}$

10. $\begin{pmatrix} x - 3y < -3 \\ 2x - 3y > -6 \end{pmatrix}$

11. $\begin{pmatrix} y > x - 4 \\ y < x \end{pmatrix}$

12. $\begin{pmatrix} y \leq x + 2 \\ y \geq x \end{pmatrix}$

13. $\begin{pmatrix} x - y > 2 \\ x - y > -1 \end{pmatrix}$

14. $\begin{pmatrix} x + y > 1 \\ x + y > 3 \end{pmatrix}$

15. $\begin{pmatrix} y \geq x \\ x > -1 \end{pmatrix}$

16. $\begin{pmatrix} y < x \\ y \leq 2 \end{pmatrix}$

17. $\begin{pmatrix} y < x \\ y > x + 3 \end{pmatrix}$

18. $\begin{pmatrix} x \leq 3 \\ y \leq -1 \end{pmatrix}$

19. $\begin{pmatrix} y > -2 \\ x > 1 \end{pmatrix}$

20. $\begin{pmatrix} x + 2y > 4 \\ x + 2y < 2 \end{pmatrix}$

21. $\begin{pmatrix} x \geq 0 \\ y \geq 0 \\ x + y \leq 4 \\ 2x + y \leq 6 \end{pmatrix}$

22. $\begin{pmatrix} x \geq 0 \\ y \geq 0 \\ x - y \leq 5 \\ 4x + 7y \leq 28 \end{pmatrix}$

23. $\begin{pmatrix} x \geq 0 \\ y \geq 0 \\ 2x + y \leq 4 \\ 2x - 3y \leq 6 \end{pmatrix}$

24. $\begin{pmatrix} x \geq 0 \\ y \geq 0 \\ 3x + 5y \geq 15 \\ 5x + 3y \geq 15 \end{pmatrix}$

For Problems 25–28, find the maximum value and the minimum value of the given function in the indicated region. (Objective 2)

25. $f(x, y) = 3x + 5y$

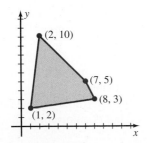

Figure 12.9

26. $f(x, y) = 8x + 3y$

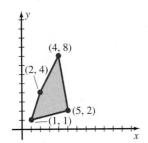

Figure 12.10

27. $f(x, y) = x + 4y$

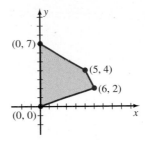

Figure 12.11

28. $f(x, y) = 2.5x + 3.5y$

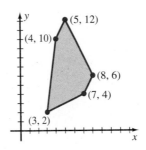

Figure 12.12

29. Maximize the function $f(x, y) = 3x + 7y$ in the region determined by the following constraints:

$$3x + 2y \leq 18$$
$$3x + 4y \geq 12$$
$$x \geq 0$$
$$y \geq 0$$

30. Maximize the function $f(x, y) = 1.5x + 2y$ in the region determined by the following constraints:

$$3x + 2y \leq 36$$
$$3x + 10y \leq 60$$
$$x \geq 0$$
$$y \geq 0$$

31. Maximize the function $f(x, y) = 40x + 55y$ in the region determined by the following constraints:

$$2x + y \leq 10$$
$$x + y \leq 7$$
$$2x + 3y \leq 18$$
$$x \geq 0$$
$$y \geq 0$$

32. Maximize the function $f(x, y) = 0.08x + 0.09y$ in the region determined by the following constraints:

$$x + y \leq 8000$$
$$y \leq \frac{1}{3}x$$
$$y \geq 500$$
$$x \leq 7000$$
$$x \geq 0$$

33. Minimize the function $f(x, y) = 0.2x + 0.5y$ in the region determined by the following constraints:

$$2x + y \geq 12$$
$$2x + 5y \geq 20$$
$$x \geq 0$$
$$y \geq 0$$

34. Minimize the function $f(x, y) = 3x + 7y$ in the region determined by the following constraints:

$$x + y \geq 9$$
$$6x + 11y \geq 84$$
$$x \geq 0$$
$$y \geq 0$$

35. Maximize the function $f(x, y) = 9x + 2y$ in the region determined by the following constraints:

$$5y - 4x \leq 20$$
$$4x + 5y \leq 60$$
$$x \geq 0$$
$$x \leq 10$$
$$y \geq 0$$

36. Maximize the function $f(x, y) = 3x + 4y$ in the region determined by the following constraints:

$$2y - x \leq 6$$
$$x + y \leq 12$$
$$x \geq 2$$
$$x \leq 8$$
$$y \geq 0$$

For Problems 37–42, solve each linear programming problem by using the graphing method illustrated in Example 5 on page 653. (Objective 3)

37. Suppose that an investor wants to invest up to $10,000. She plans to buy one speculative type of stock and one conservative type. The speculative stock is paying a 12% return, and the conservative stock is paying a 9% return. She has decided to invest at least $2000 in the conservative stock and no more than $6000 in the speculative stock. Furthermore, she does not want the speculative investment to exceed the conservative one. How much should she invest at each rate to maximize her return?

38. A manufacturer of golf clubs makes a profit of $50 per set on a model A set and $45 per set on a model B set. Daily production of the model A clubs is between 30 and 50 sets, inclusive, and that of the model B clubs is between 10 and 20 sets, inclusive. The total daily production is not to exceed 50 sets. How many sets of each model should be manufactured per day to maximize the profit?

39. A company makes two types of calculators. Type A sells for $12, and type B sells for $10. It costs the company $9 to produce one type A calculator and $8 to produce one type B calculator. In one month, the company is equipped to produce between 200 and 300, inclusive, of the type A calculator and between 100 and 250, inclusive, of the type B calculator, but not more than 300 altogether. How many calculators of each type should be produced per month to maximize the difference between the total selling price and the total cost of production?

40. A manufacturer of small copiers makes a profit of $200 on a deluxe model and $250 on a standard model. The company wants to produce at least 50 deluxe models per week and at least 75 standard models per week. However, the weekly production is not to exceed 150 copiers. How many copiers of each kind should be produced in order to maximize the profit?

41. Products A and B are produced by a company according to the following production information.
   (a) To produce one unit of product A requires 1 hour of working time on machine I, 2 hours on machine II, and 1 hour on machine III.
   (b) To produce one unit of product B requires 1 hour of working time on machine I, 1 hour on machine II, and 3 hours on machine III.
   (c) Machine I is available for no more than 40 hours per week, machine II for no more than 40 hours per week, and machine III for no more than 60 hours per week.
   (d) Product A can be sold at a profit of $2.75 per unit and product B at a profit of $3.50 per unit.

How many units each of product A and product B should be produced per week to maximize profit?

42. Suppose that the company we refer to in Example 5 also manufactures widgets and wadgets and has the following production information available:
   (a) To produce a widget requires 4 hours of working time on machine A and 2 hours on machine B.

(b) To produce a wadget requires 5 hours of working time on machine A and 5 hours on machine B.

(c) Machine A is available for no more than 200 hours per month, and machine B is available for no more than 150 hours per month.

(d) Widgets can be sold at a profit of $7 each and wadgets at a profit of $8 each.

How many widgets and how many wadgets should be produced per month in order to maximize profit?

Thoughts Into Words

43. Describe in your own words the process of solving a system of inequalities.

44. What is linear programming? Write a paragraph or two answering this question in a way that elementary algebra students could understand.

Answers to the Concept Quiz

1. $\begin{pmatrix} x + y > 5 \\ x + y < -2 \end{pmatrix}$ Answers may vary.   **2.** False   **3.** False   **4.** True   **5.** True   **6.** False   **7.** True   **8.** True

OBJECTIVE	SUMMARY	EXAMPLE
Add and subtract matrices. (Section 12.1/Objective 1; Section 12.3/Objective 1)	Matrices of the same dimensions are added by combining the elements in corresponding positions. Matrix addition is a commutative and an associative operation. Matrices of the same dimension can be subtracted by the definition $A - B = A + (-B)$	If $A = \begin{bmatrix} -3 & 9 \\ 5 & 7 \end{bmatrix}$ and $B = \begin{bmatrix} -2 & -6 \\ -8 & 4 \end{bmatrix}$, find $A + B$. **Solution** $\begin{bmatrix} -3 & 9 \\ 5 & 7 \end{bmatrix} + \begin{bmatrix} -2 & -6 \\ -8 & 4 \end{bmatrix} = \begin{bmatrix} -5 & 3 \\ -3 & 11 \end{bmatrix}$
Multiply a matrix by a scalar. (Section 12.1/Objective 2; Section 12.3/Objective 2)	The scalar product of a real number k and a matrix A can be found by multiplying each element of A by k. The following properties hold for scalar multiplication and matrix addition: $k(A + B) = kA + kB$ $(k + l)A = kA + lA$ $(kl)A = k(lA)$	If $A = \begin{bmatrix} -1 & 9 \\ 4 & -7 \end{bmatrix}$, find $-3A$. **Solution** $-3\begin{bmatrix} -1 & 9 \\ 4 & -7 \end{bmatrix} = \begin{bmatrix} 3 & -27 \\ -12 & 21 \end{bmatrix}$
Multiply matrices. (Section 12.1/Objective 3; Section 12.2/Objective 2; Section 12.3/Objective 3)	If A is an $m \times n$ matrix and B is an $n \times p$ matrix, then the product AB is an $m \times p$ matrix. See page 648 for the procedure to multiply two matrices. Matrix multiplication is *not* a commutative operation, but it is an associative operation. Matrix multiplication has two distributive properties: $A(B + C) = AB + AC$ and $(A + B)C = AC + BC$	If $A = \begin{bmatrix} -2 & 3 \\ 1 & 5 \end{bmatrix}$ and $B = \begin{bmatrix} -6 & 7 \\ 9 & 4 \end{bmatrix}$, find AB. **Solution** $\begin{bmatrix} -2 & 3 \\ 1 & 5 \end{bmatrix}\begin{bmatrix} -6 & 7 \\ 9 & 4 \end{bmatrix}$ $= \begin{bmatrix} (-2)(-6) + (3)(9) & (-2)(7) + (3)(4) \\ (1)(-6) + (5)(9) & (1)(7) + (5)(4) \end{bmatrix}$ $= \begin{bmatrix} 39 & -2 \\ 39 & 27 \end{bmatrix}$
Find the multiplicative inverse of a matrix. (Section 12.2/Objective 1; Section 12.3/Objective 4)	The multiplicative inverse of the 2×2 matrix $A = \begin{bmatrix} a_{11} & a_{12} \\ a_{21} & a_{22} \end{bmatrix}$ is $A^{-1} = \frac{1}{\|A\|}\begin{bmatrix} a_{22} & -a_{12} \\ -a_{21} & a_{11} \end{bmatrix}$ for $\|A\| \neq 0$. If $\|A\| = 0$, then the matrix A has no inverse. A general technique for finding the inverse of a square matrix, when one exists, is described on page 642.	If $A = \begin{bmatrix} 5 & -4 \\ 1 & -2 \end{bmatrix}$, find A^{-1}. **Solution** Find $\|A\|$. $\|A\| = (5)(-2) - (1)(-4) = -6$ $A^{-1} = \frac{1}{-6}\begin{bmatrix} -2 & 4 \\ -1 & 5 \end{bmatrix}$ $= \begin{bmatrix} \frac{1}{3} & -\frac{2}{3} \\ \frac{1}{6} & -\frac{5}{6} \end{bmatrix}$

OBJECTIVE	SUMMARY	EXAMPLE
Solve systems of linear equations using matrices. (Section 12.2/Objective 3; Section 12.3/Objective 5)	The solution set of n linear equations in n variables can be found by multiplying the inverse of the coefficient matrix by the column matrix, which consists of constant terms. For example, the solution set of the system $$\begin{cases} 2x + 3y - z = 4 \\ 3x - y + 2z = 5 \\ 5x - 7y - 4z = -1 \end{cases}$$ can be found by the product $$\begin{bmatrix} 2 & 3 & -1 \\ 3 & -1 & 2 \\ 5 & -7 & -4 \end{bmatrix}^{-1} \begin{bmatrix} 4 \\ 5 \\ -1 \end{bmatrix}$$	Solve the system $\begin{bmatrix} x + 2y - z = -1 \\ 2x + 3y + z = 3 \\ 3x - y + 2z = 0 \end{bmatrix}$. **Solution** $$A = \begin{bmatrix} 1 & 2 & -1 \\ 2 & 3 & 1 \\ 3 & -1 & 2 \end{bmatrix}, X = \begin{bmatrix} x \\ y \\ z \end{bmatrix},$$ $$B = \begin{bmatrix} -1 \\ 3 \\ 0 \end{bmatrix}$$ $$A^{-1} = \begin{bmatrix} \dfrac{7}{16} & \dfrac{-3}{16} & \dfrac{5}{16} \\ \dfrac{-1}{16} & \dfrac{5}{16} & \dfrac{-3}{16} \\ \dfrac{-11}{16} & \dfrac{7}{16} & \dfrac{-1}{16} \end{bmatrix}.$$ $$X = A^{-1}B$$ $$= \begin{bmatrix} \dfrac{7}{16} & \dfrac{-3}{16} & \dfrac{5}{16} \\ \dfrac{-1}{16} & \dfrac{5}{16} & \dfrac{-3}{16} \\ \dfrac{-11}{16} & \dfrac{7}{16} & \dfrac{-1}{16} \end{bmatrix} \begin{bmatrix} -1 \\ 3 \\ 0 \end{bmatrix}$$ $$= \begin{bmatrix} -1 \\ 1 \\ 2 \end{bmatrix}$$ The solution set is $\{(-1, 1, 2)\}$.

(continued)

OBJECTIVE	SUMMARY	EXAMPLE
Solve a system of linear inequalities. (Section 12.4/Objective 1)	The solution set of a set of linear inequalities is the intersection of the solution sets of the individual inequalities. Such solution sets are determined by the graphing approach.	Solve the system by graphing: $$\begin{pmatrix} 3x - y \le 6 \\ y \le x - 2 \end{pmatrix}$$ **Solution**
Find the minimum and maximum value of linear functions for a specified region. (Section 12.4/Objective 2)	Linear programming problems deal with the idea of maximizing or minimizing a certain linear function that is subject to various constraints. The constraints are expressed as linear inequalities. See Section 12.4, Example 4, for a summary of the general approach to a linear programming problem.	Find the minimum value and the maximum value of the function $f(x, y) = 13x + 5y$ in the region determined by the following system of inequalities. **Solution** $$\begin{pmatrix} x \ge 0 \\ y \ge 0 \\ 3x + 4y \le 24 \\ 3x + y \le 15 \end{pmatrix}$$

Vertices	$f(x, y) = 13x + 5y$
$(0, 0)$	$f(0, 0) = 13(0) + 5(0)$ $= 0$ *minimum*
$(5, 0)$	$f(5, 0) = 13(5) + 5(0) = 65$
$(4, 3)$	$f(4, 3) = 13(4) + 5(3)$ $= 67$ *maximum*
$(0, 6)$	$f(0, 6) = 13(0) + 5(6) = 30$

OBJECTIVE	SUMMARY	EXAMPLE
Solve linear programming problems. (Section 12.4/Objective 3)	Many applied problems involve the idea of maximizing or minimizing a certain function. The term "programming" refers to the distribution of limited resources. See Section 12.4 Example 5 for a summary of an application problem solved by linear programming.	A credit union is offering two different types of savings account products for its customers, one at 3.5% interest and the other at 4.5% interest. Certain conditions have been imposed on the investments: the total amount invested has to be between \$0 and \$4000 inclusive; the amount invested at 4.5% must be less than the amount invested at 3.5%; the amount invested at 4.5% must be between \$0 and \$2000 inclusive and the amount invested at 3.5% must be between \$0 and \$3000 inclusive. How much should a customer invest at each rate to maximize his return?

Solution

Let x represent the amount invested at 3.5% and y represent the amount invested at 4.5%.

Use the following system of inequalities to solve the problem.

$$\begin{pmatrix} x + y \le 4000 \\ 0 \le y \le 2000 \\ 0 \le x \le 3000 \\ y \le x \end{pmatrix}$$

To maximize the interest evaluate the function $f(x, y) = 0.035x + 0.045y$ for the vertices of the identified region.

Vertices	$f(x, y) = 0.035x + 0.045y$
$(0, 0)$	$f(0, 0) = 0.035(0)$ $+ 0.045(0) = 0$
$(3000, 0)$	$f(3000, 0) = 0.035(3000)$ $+ 0.045(0) = 105$
$(3000, 1000)$	$f(3000, 1000) = 0.035(3000)$ $+ 0.045(1000) = 150$
$(2000, 2000)$	$f(2000, 2000) = 0.035(2000)$ $+ 0.045(2000) = 160$

The customer should invest \$2000 at 3.5% and \$2000 at 4.5% to maximize the return.

Chapter 12 Review Problem Set

For Problems 1–10, compute the indicated matrix, if it exists, using the following matrices:

$$A = \begin{bmatrix} 2 & -4 \\ -3 & 8 \end{bmatrix} \qquad B = \begin{bmatrix} 5 & -1 \\ 0 & 2 \end{bmatrix}$$

$$C = \begin{bmatrix} 3 & -1 \\ -2 & 4 \\ 5 & -6 \end{bmatrix} \qquad D = \begin{bmatrix} -2 & -1 & 4 \\ 5 & 0 & -3 \end{bmatrix},$$

$$E = \begin{bmatrix} 1 \\ -3 \\ -7 \end{bmatrix} \qquad F = \begin{bmatrix} 1 & -2 \\ 4 & -4 \\ 7 & -8 \end{bmatrix}$$

1. $A + B$

2. $B - A$

3. $C - F$

4. $2A + 3B$

5. $3C - 2F$

6. CD

7. DC

8. $DC + AB$

9. DE

10. EF

11. Use A and B from the preceding problems and show that $AB \neq BA$.

12. Use C, D, and F from the preceding problems and show that $D(C + F) = DC + DF$.

13. Use C, D, and F from the preceding problems and show that $(C + F)D = CD + FD$.

For each matrix in Problems 14–23, find the multiplicative inverse, if it exists.

14. $\begin{bmatrix} 9 & 5 \\ 7 & 4 \end{bmatrix}$

15. $\begin{bmatrix} 9 & 4 \\ 7 & 3 \end{bmatrix}$

16. $\begin{bmatrix} -2 & 1 \\ 2 & 3 \end{bmatrix}$

17. $\begin{bmatrix} 4 & -6 \\ 2 & -3 \end{bmatrix}$

18. $\begin{bmatrix} -1 & -3 \\ -4 & -5 \end{bmatrix}$

19. $\begin{bmatrix} 0 & -3 \\ 7 & 6 \end{bmatrix}$

20. $\begin{bmatrix} 1 & -2 & 1 \\ 2 & -5 & 2 \\ -3 & 7 & 5 \end{bmatrix}$

21. $\begin{bmatrix} 1 & 3 & -2 \\ 4 & 13 & -7 \\ 5 & 16 & -8 \end{bmatrix}$

22. $\begin{bmatrix} -2 & 4 & 7 \\ 1 & -3 & 5 \\ 1 & -5 & 22 \end{bmatrix}$

23. $\begin{bmatrix} -1 & 2 & 3 \\ 2 & -5 & -7 \\ -3 & 5 & 11 \end{bmatrix}$

For Problems 24–28, use the multiplicative inverse matrix approach to solve each system. The required inverses were found in Problems 14–23.

24. $\begin{pmatrix} 9x + 5y = 12 \\ 7x + 4y = 10 \end{pmatrix}$

25. $\begin{pmatrix} -2x + y = -9 \\ 2x + 3y = 5 \end{pmatrix}$

26. $\begin{pmatrix} x - 2y + z = 7 \\ 2x - 5y + 2z = 17 \\ -3x + 7y + 5z = -32 \end{pmatrix}$

27. $\begin{pmatrix} x + 3y - 2z = -7 \\ 4x + 13y - 7z = -21 \\ 5x + 16y - 8z = -23 \end{pmatrix}$

28. $\begin{pmatrix} -x + 2y + 3z = 22 \\ 2x - 5y - 7z = -51 \\ -3x + 5y + 11z = 71 \end{pmatrix}$

For Problems 29–32, indicate the solution set for each system of linear inequalities by graphing the system and shading the appropriate region.

29. $\begin{pmatrix} 3x - 4y \geq 0 \\ 2x + 3y \leq 0 \end{pmatrix}$

30. $\begin{pmatrix} 3x - 2y < 6 \\ 2x - 3y < 6 \end{pmatrix}$

31. $\begin{pmatrix} x - 4y < 4 \\ 2x + y \geq 2 \end{pmatrix}$

32. $\begin{pmatrix} x \geq 0 \\ y \geq 0 \\ x + 2y \leq 4 \\ 2x - y \leq 4 \end{pmatrix}$

33. Maximize the function $f(x, y) = 8x + 5y$ in the region determined by the following constraints:

$$y \leq 4x$$
$$x + y \leq 5$$
$$x \geq 0$$
$$y \geq 0$$
$$x \leq 4$$

34. Maximize the function $f(x, y) = 2x + 7y$ in the region determined by the following constraints:

$$x \geq 0$$
$$y \geq 0$$
$$x + 2y \leq 16$$
$$x + y \leq 9$$
$$3x + 2y \leq 24$$

35. Maximize the function $f(x, y) = 7x + 5y$ in the region determined by the constraints of Problem 34.

36. Maximize the function $f(x, y) = 150x + 200y$ in the region determined by the constraints of Problem 34.

37. A manufacturer of electric ice cream freezers makes a profit of \$4.50 on a one-gallon freezer and a profit of \$5.25 on a two-gallon freezer. The company wants to produce at least 75 one-gallon and at least 100 two-gallon freezers per week. However, the weekly production is not to exceed a total of 250 freezers. How many freezers of each type should be produced per week in order to maximize the profit?

For Problems 1–10, compute the indicated matrix, if it exists, using the following matrices:

$$A = \begin{bmatrix} -1 & 3 \\ 4 & -2 \end{bmatrix} \quad B = \begin{bmatrix} 3 & -2 \\ 4 & -1 \end{bmatrix} \quad C = \begin{bmatrix} -3 \\ 5 \\ -6 \end{bmatrix}$$

$$D = \begin{bmatrix} 2 & -1 \\ 3 & -2 \\ 6 & 5 \end{bmatrix} \quad E = \begin{bmatrix} 2 & -1 & 4 \\ 5 & 1 & -3 \end{bmatrix}$$

$$F = \begin{bmatrix} -1 & 6 \\ 2 & -5 \\ 3 & 4 \end{bmatrix}$$

1. AB

2. BA

3. DE

4. BC

5. EC

6. $2A - B$

7. $3D + 2F$

8. $-3A - 2B$

9. EF

10. $AB - EF$

For Problems 11–16, find the multiplicative inverse, if it exists.

11. $\begin{bmatrix} 3 & -2 \\ 5 & -3 \end{bmatrix}$ **12.** $\begin{bmatrix} -2 & 5 \\ 3 & -7 \end{bmatrix}$ **13.** $\begin{bmatrix} 1 & -3 \\ -2 & 8 \end{bmatrix}$

14. $\begin{bmatrix} 3 & 5 \\ 1 & 4 \end{bmatrix}$ **15.** $\begin{bmatrix} -2 & 2 & 3 \\ 1 & -1 & 0 \\ 0 & 1 & 4 \end{bmatrix}$ **16.** $\begin{bmatrix} 1 & -2 & 4 \\ 0 & 1 & 3 \\ 0 & 0 & 1 \end{bmatrix}$

For Problems 17–19, use the multiplicative inverse matrix approach to solve each system.

17. $\begin{pmatrix} 3x - 2y = 48 \\ 5x - 3y = 76 \end{pmatrix}$ **18.** $\begin{pmatrix} x - 3y = 36 \\ -2x + 8y = -100 \end{pmatrix}$

19. $\begin{pmatrix} 3x + 5y = 92 \\ x + 4y = 61 \end{pmatrix}$

20. Solve the system

$$\begin{pmatrix} -x + 3y + z = 1 \\ 2x + 5y = 3 \\ 3x + y - 2z = -2 \end{pmatrix}$$

where the inverse of the coefficient matrix is

$$\begin{bmatrix} -\dfrac{10}{9} & \dfrac{7}{9} & -\dfrac{5}{9} \\ \dfrac{4}{9} & -\dfrac{1}{9} & \dfrac{2}{9} \\ -\dfrac{13}{9} & \dfrac{10}{9} & -\dfrac{11}{9} \end{bmatrix}$$

21. Solve the system

$$\begin{pmatrix} x + y + 2z = 3 \\ 2x + 3y - z = 3 \\ -3x + y - 2z = 3 \end{pmatrix}$$

where the inverse of the coefficient matrix is

$$\begin{bmatrix} -\dfrac{5}{24} & \dfrac{1}{6} & -\dfrac{7}{24} \\ \dfrac{7}{24} & \dfrac{1}{6} & \dfrac{5}{24} \\ \dfrac{11}{24} & -\dfrac{1}{6} & \dfrac{1}{24} \end{bmatrix}$$

For Problems 22–24, indicate the solution set for each system of inequalities by graphing the system and shading the appropriate region.

22. $\begin{pmatrix} 2x - y > 4 \\ x + 3y < 3 \end{pmatrix}$ **23.** $\begin{pmatrix} 2x - 3y \leq 6 \\ x + 4y > 4 \end{pmatrix}$

24. $\begin{pmatrix} y \leq 2x - 2 \\ y \geq x + 1 \end{pmatrix}$

25. Maximize the function $f(x, y) = 500x + 350y$ in the region determined by the following constraints:

$$3x + 2y \leq 24$$

$$x + 2y \leq 16$$

$$x + y \leq 9$$

$$x \geq 0$$

$$y \geq 0$$

For Problems 1–4, state the property of equality or the property of real numbers that justifies each of the statements.

1. $\left(\frac{1}{2}\right)2 = 1$

2. $(bc)d = b(cd)$

3. $3 + (b + 4) = (b + 4) + 3$

4. $\frac{x}{y} + 0 = \frac{x}{y}$

For Problems 5–8, simplify each numerical expression.

5. $4(-3)^2 - 2^3 \div 4\left(\frac{1}{2}\right)$

6. $\frac{1}{2} \div \frac{3}{4}(-2)^3$

7. $\frac{4}{3} - \left(\frac{7}{6}\right)\left(\frac{1}{3}\right) \div \frac{1}{6}$

8. $\frac{10}{9} - \frac{4}{3} - 3\left(\frac{3}{4}\right)\left(\frac{1}{6}\right)$

For Problems 9–12, evaluate each algebraic expression for the given values of the variables.

9. $\frac{4x^2 - 3y}{2xy}$ for $x = 3$ and $y = -6$

10. $\sqrt{3a + b} - 5\sqrt{2a - b}$ for $a = 5$ and $b = 1$

11. $\frac{c - d}{\frac{1}{c} - \frac{1}{d}}$ for $c = 1$ and $d = -1$

12. $\frac{1}{x + 1} + \frac{y}{x - y}$ for $x = -\frac{1}{2}$ and $y = \frac{1}{2}$

For Problems 13–16, compute the indicated matrix.

$A = \begin{bmatrix} -4 & 3 \\ -1 & -3 \end{bmatrix}$　　　　$B = \begin{bmatrix} 0 & -7 \\ 6 & 1 \end{bmatrix}$

13. $A + B$

14. $2A - B$

15. AB

16. BA

For Problems 17 and 18, evaluate each determinant.

17. $\begin{vmatrix} -5 & -3 \\ 4 & 7 \end{vmatrix}$

18. $\begin{vmatrix} 1 & -6 & 7 \\ 0 & 2 & 3 \\ 4 & 5 & 2 \end{vmatrix}$

For Problems 19–22, write an equation of a line that satisfies the given conditions. Write each equation in standard form.

19. Contains the points $(-5, 6)$ and $(2, -3)$

20. Has an x intercept of 1 and a slope of $-\frac{2}{3}$

21. Contains the point $(5, -4)$ and is perpendicular to the line with equation $2x - 5y = 7$

22. Contains the point $(-2, 1)$ and is perpendicular to the line with equation $y = \quad x$

For Problems 23 and 24, find the indicated products and quotients. Express answers with positive integral exponents.

23. $(4a^{-1}b^2)^{-3}(3^{-1}a^2b^{-3})^{-2}$

24. $\left(\frac{-6m^3n^{-4}}{4m^{-2}n^{-1}}\right)^{-2}$

For Problems 25–32, express each radical expression in simplest radical form.

25. $\sqrt{68}$

26. $\sqrt[3]{81}$

27. $\sqrt{\frac{16}{5}}$

28. $\sqrt{\frac{7}{18a^3}}$

29. $\frac{3}{10}\sqrt{75x^2y}$

30. $\frac{\sqrt{16a^3b^2}}{\sqrt{2ab}}$

31. $\sqrt[3]{\frac{3}{4}}$

32. $\sqrt[3]{128c^5d^7}$

For Problems 33 and 34, rationalize the denominator and simplify.

33. $\frac{6}{\sqrt{5} - 1}$

34. $\frac{8}{3\sqrt{6} + 4\sqrt{2}}$

For Problems 35–38, solve for x.

35. $2(x - 3y) = 4$

36. $4y - 9x = 13$

37. $\frac{ax + b}{x} = \frac{c - d}{y}$

38. $\frac{4}{3}x + \frac{1}{2}a = c$

For Problems 39 and 40, simplify each of the complex fractions.

39. $2 - \dfrac{c}{\dfrac{1}{c} - 1}$

40. $\dfrac{\dfrac{1}{a + 1} - 4}{3 + \dfrac{4}{a - 2}}$

For Problems 41–42, use synthetic division to find $f(c)$.

41. $f(x) = 2x^3 - 7x^2 + 4x - 1$ and $c = -1$

42. $f(x) = x^4 - x^2 + 4x + 3$ and $c = -2$

For Problems 43 and 44, find the values of the given functions.

43. If $f(x) = -2x^2 + x - 9$, find $f(0), f(-1), f(a)$.

44. If $f(x) = \begin{cases} 2x & \text{for } x \geq 0 \\ -x^2 & \text{for } x < 0 \end{cases}$, find $f(0), f(3), f(-1), f(-3)$.

For Problems 45 and 46, find $\dfrac{f(a+h)-f(a)}{h}$.

45. $f(x) = -2x + 7$

46. $f(x) = 3x^2 - x + 4$

For Problems 47 and 48, determine the domain of each function.

47. $g(x) = \dfrac{2}{3x^2 + x - 2}$

48. $f(x) = \dfrac{x-4}{x^2-1}$

For Problems 49–51, determine the domain and range.

49. $f(x) = \sqrt{3x+2}$

50. $f(x) = |x-5|$

51. $f(x) = -2x^2 - 1$

For Problems 52–54, write the domain of the given function using interval notation.

52. $f(x) = \sqrt{x^2 - 25}$

53. $f(x) = \sqrt{x^2 + 9}$

54. $f(x) = \sqrt{4x^2 - 11x - 3}$

For Problems 55 and 56, find $(f \circ g)(x)$ and $(g \circ f)(x)$. Find the domain of each.

55. $f(x) = 3x - 1;\ g(x) = x^2 + 3x - 4$

56. $f(x) = \dfrac{2}{x};\ g(x) = \dfrac{1}{x-1}$

For Problems 57–84, solve the equation.

57. $-3(2a - 7) - 6(a + 4) = 8(-3a - 1)$

58. $\dfrac{2x+9}{3} - \dfrac{7x-3}{4} = \dfrac{11}{2}$

59. $|4 - 3x| = 16$

60. $|-4x + 3| = |-4x - 7|$

61. $x(2x + 5) = 7$

62. $9x - 4x^3 = 0$

63. $12x^2 - x - 63 = 0$

64. $\dfrac{3}{x-2} + \dfrac{4}{x+3} = \dfrac{3}{2}$

65. $\dfrac{5x}{2x^2 + 3x - 2} - \dfrac{x+1}{x^2 - 3x - 10} = \dfrac{-10}{2x^2 - 11x + 5}$

66. $\sqrt{3x - 11} = 8$

67. $\sqrt{2x + 3} = -7$

68. $\sqrt[3]{x^2 - 8} = 2$

69. $5 - \sqrt{x - 4} = \sqrt{x + 1}$

70. $4\sqrt{x} = x - 5$

71. $0 = 3n^2 - 7n$

72. $12x^2 = 15$

73. $x^2 + 11x = 1$

74. $2x^2 + x + 7 = 0$

75. $x^4 + 15x^2 - 54 = 0$

76. $\dfrac{5}{x-3} + \dfrac{1}{x} = 2$

77. $x^3 - 19x + 30 = 0$

78. $x^4 - 6x^3 + 10x^2 + 2x - 15 = 0$

79. $\log_x\left(\dfrac{9}{4}\right) = 2$

80. $\log_9 x = -\dfrac{1}{2}$

81. $\log_5 x + \log_5 4 = -1$

82. $\log_5(4x - 3) = 1 + \log_5(x - 2)$

83. $\log_6(3x + 9) + \log_6(x + 4) = 1$

84. $16^x = 8^{2x+1}$

For Problems 85–88, solve and round each solution to the nearest hundredth.

85. $5^x = 9$

86. $5^{x+1} = 3^{2x-1}$

87. $2e^{x+3} = 7$

88. $e^{2x-1} = 12.3$

For Problems 89–94, solve each inequality, and express the solution set using interval notation.

89. $\dfrac{2}{3}x - \dfrac{6}{7}x > \dfrac{2}{21}$

90. $-3 \le 9 - x \le 3$

91. $\left|\dfrac{3x-2}{5}\right| + 2 < 6$

92. $|5x - 8| > 0$

93. $2x^2 + 7x \ge 0$

94. $\dfrac{3x-1}{x+1} < 2$

For Problems 95–97, solve each system using the substitution method or the elimination-by-addition method.

95. $\begin{pmatrix} 3x - 2y = -4 \\ \dfrac{1}{2}x - 5y = -24 \end{pmatrix}$

96. $\begin{pmatrix} x = 4y - 7 \\ x = 7y + 8 \end{pmatrix}$

97. $\begin{pmatrix} 2x + 6y + 5z = 13 \\ 4x + 5y - z = -7 \\ x + 2y + 2z = 5 \end{pmatrix}$

For Problems 98–99, indicate the solution set for each system of linear inequalities by graphing the system and shading the appropriate region.

98. $\begin{pmatrix} 2x + y \le 6 \\ 3x - 2y < 12 \end{pmatrix}$ **99.** $\begin{pmatrix} -x + 4y \le 4 \\ 5x + 3y \ge 15 \end{pmatrix}$

For Problems 100–102, graph the functions.

100. $f(x) = |x - 1| - 1$

101. $f(x) = \sqrt{2x + 3}$

102. $f(x) = x(x + 2)(x - 3)$

103. On a bicycle trail map, 0.8 inches represents 30 miles. If two rest stations are 1.2 inches apart on the map, find the number of miles between the rest stations.

104. The sum of two numbers is 10, and their product is 8. Find both numbers.

105. The length of the radius of a circle is three times the length of the side of a square. If the perimeter of the square is equal to the area of the circle, find the length of the side of the square and the length of the radius of the circle.

106. On a 195-mile trip from Pensacola to Tallahassee, Florida, Shanna drove 10 miles per hour slower than she did on her 100-mile trip from Ocala to Orlando, Florida. The Tallahassee trip took 1 hour 40 minutes longer than the Orlando trip. How fast did Shanna drive on her Tallahassee trip?

107. How long will it take $5000 to double if it is invested at 5.5% interest compounded monthly?

108. How many cups of pure orange juice should be added to 6 cups of pineapple-orange juice (which is 20% orange juice) to obtain a pineapple-orange juice mix that is 40% orange juice?

109. Use the formula $A = P\left(1 + \dfrac{r}{n}\right)^{nt}$ to calculate the amount of money accumulated when investing $1000 for 5 years at 4% interest compounded:

(a) Annually   (b) Semi-annually

(c) Quarterly   (d) Monthly

(e) Continuously (Hint: Use $A = Pe^{rt}$)

110. The measure of the smallest angle in a triangle is 5° less than the measure of the middle angle. Three times the measure of the middle angle is 15° more than twice the measure of the largest angle. Find the measure of each angle of the triangle.

111. A pharmacist makes eye drops with saline solution. A 10% saline solution mixed with an 80% saline solution makes 7 cups of a 60% saline solution. How many cups of the 80% solution should be used?

112. A dog breeder makes her own dog food. She uses the chart below, which lists the necessary amounts of the three ingredients (dry food, wet food, and vitamins) for each meal.

	Dry	Wet	Vitamins
Breakfast	0.3 oz.	0.8 oz.	0.1 oz.
Lunch	0.7 oz.	0.2 oz.	0.3 oz.
Dinner	0.5 oz.	0.6 oz.	0.2 oz.

The total amount of food for breakfast is 6 ounces; the total amount of food for lunch is 5.8 ounces; and the total amount of food for dinner is 6.4 ounces. How many servings of dry food, wet food, and vitamins are needed?

113. Tianna puts her leftover cash into a special container as a way to save money for gifts. The last time she emptied the container she had one-dollar bills, five-dollar bills, and twenty-dollar bills. She had a total of 18 bills, and the number of one-dollar bills was 1 more than the number of twenty-dollar bills. The sum of the number of one-dollar bills and twenty-dollar bills was 5 times the number of five-dollar bills. How many of each bill had she saved?

114. Sophie leaves Camp Tesomas paddling a kayak downriver, with the current, at the same time that Finn leaves the camp paddling a canoe upstream, against the current. Finn paddles for 1 hour at half Sophie's rate for 1 mile, and Sophie paddles for 3 hours for 15 miles. Find the rate of the current, Sophie's rate, and Finn's rate.

115. Action Toy Company makes action figures once a month. Producing the cricket action figure requires 3 hours of time on Machine I and 9 hours on Machine II. Producing the beetle action figure requires 8 hours of time on Machine I and 4 hours on Machine II. Machine I is only available for 240 hours per month, but Machine II is available for 360 hours per month. The cricket action figure can be sold at a profit of $2.90, and the beetle action figure can be sold at a profit of $3.50. How many of each action figure should the company produce each month to maximize its profit?

Conic Sections

13.1 Circles

13.2 Parabolas

13.3 Ellipses

13.4 Hyperbolas

13.5 Systems Involving Nonlinear Equations

Examples of conic sections, in particular, parabolas and ellipses, can be found in corporate logos throughout the world.

© Jim Lopes

Circles, ellipses, parabolas, and hyperbolas can be formed by intersecting a plane and a right-circular conical surface as shown in Figure 13.1. These figures are often referred to as **conic sections**. In this chapter we will define each conic section as a set of points satisfying a set of conditions. Then we will use the definitions to develop standard forms for the equations of the conic sections. Next we will use the standard forms of the equations to (1) determine specific equations for specific conics, (2) determine graphs of specific equations, and (3) solve problems. Finally, we will consider some systems of equations involving the conic sections.

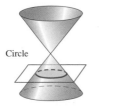
Circle

Ellipse

Parabola

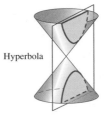
Hyperbola

Figure 13.1

Video tutorials based on section learning objectives are available in a variety of delivery modes.

13.1   Circles

OBJECTIVES   1 Write the equation of a circle

2 Given the equation of a circle, find the center and the length of a radius

The distance formula $d = \sqrt{(x_2 - x_1)^2 + (y_2 - y_1)^2}$, developed in Section 7.4 and applied to the definition of a circle, produces what is known as the *standard form of the equation of a circle*. We start with a precise definition of a circle.

> **Definition 13.1**
>
> A **circle** is the set of all points in a plane equidistant from a given fixed point called the **center**. A line segment determined by the center and any point on the circle is called a **radius**.

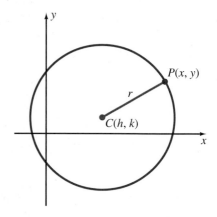

Figure 13.2

Now let's consider a circle with a radius of length r and a center at (h, k) on a coordinate system, as shown in Figure 13.2. For any point P on the circle with coordinates (x, y), the length of a radius, denoted by r, can be expressed as $r = \sqrt{(x - h)^2 + (y - k)^2}$. Thus squaring both sides of the equation, we obtain the **standard form of the equation of a circle**:

$$(x - h)^2 + (y - k)^2 = r^2$$

The standard form of the equation of a circle can be used to solve two basic kinds of problems; namely, (1) given the coordinates of the center and the length of a radius of a circle, find its equation, and (2) given the equation of a circle, determine its graph. Let's illustrate each of these types of problems.

EXAMPLE 1

Find the equation of a circle with its center at $(-3, 5)$ and a radius of length 4 units.

Solution

Substituting -3 for h, 5 for k, and 4 for r in the standard form and simplifying, we obtain

$$(x - h)^2 + (y - k)^2 = r^2$$
$$(x - (-3))^2 + (y - 5)^2 = 4^2$$
$$(x + 3)^2 + (y - 5)^2 = 4^2$$
$$x^2 + 6x + 9 + y^2 - 10y + 25 = 16$$
$$x^2 + y^2 + 6x - 10y + 18 = 0$$

Note in Example 1 that we simplified the equation to the form $x^2 + y^2 + Dx + Ey + F = 0$, where D, E, and F are constants. This is another form that we commonly use when working with circles.

Classroom Example
Find the equation of a circle with a center at $(-3, -8)$ and a radius of length $2\sqrt{5}$ units. Express the final equation in the form $x^2 + y^2 + Dx + Ey + F = 0$.

EXAMPLE 2

Find the equation of a circle with its center at $(-5, -9)$ and a radius of length $2\sqrt{3}$ units. Express the final equation in the form $x^2 + y^2 + Dx + Ey + F = 0$.

Solution

In the standard form, substitute -5 for h, -9 for k, and $2\sqrt{3}$ for r.

$$(x - h)^2 + (y - k)^2 = r^2$$
$$(x - (-5))^2 + (y - (-9))^2 = (2\sqrt{3})^2$$
$$(x + 5)^2 + (y + 9)^2 = (2\sqrt{3})^2$$
$$x^2 + 10x + 25 + y^2 + 18y + 81 = 12$$
$$x^2 + y^2 + 10x + 18y + 94 = 0$$

Classroom Example
Find the equation of a circle with a center at the origin and a radius of length 4 units.

EXAMPLE 3

Find the equation of a circle with its center at the origin and a radius of length r units.

Solution

Substitute 0 for h, 0 for k, and r for r in the standard form of the equation of a circle.

$$(x - h)^2 + (y - k)^2 = r^2$$
$$(x - 0)^2 + (y - 0)^2 = r^2$$
$$x^2 + y^2 = r^2$$

Note in Example 3 that

$$x^2 + y^2 = r^2$$

is the standard form of the equation of a circle that has its **center at the origin**. Therefore, by inspection, we can recognize that $x^2 + y^2 = 9$ is a circle with its center at the origin and radius of length 3 units. Likewise, the equation $5x^2 + 5y^2 = 10$ is equivalent to $x^2 + y^2 = 2$, and therefore its graph is a circle with its center at the origin and a radius of length $\sqrt{2}$ units. Furthermore, we can easily determine that the equation of the circle with its center at the origin and a radius of 8 units is $x^2 + y^2 = 64$.

Classroom Example
Find the center and the length of a radius of the circle
$x^2 + y^2 + 4x - 10y + 1 = 0$.

EXAMPLE 4

Find the center of the circle $x^2 + y^2 - 6x + 12y - 2 = 0$ and the length of its radius.

Solution

We can change the given equation into the standard form of the equation of a circle by completing the square on x and y as follows:

$$x^2 + y^2 - 6x + 12y - 2 = 0$$
$$(x^2 - 6x + \underline{\quad}) + (y^2 + 12y + \underline{\quad}) = 2$$
$$(x^2 - 6x + 9) + (y^2 + 12y + 36) = 2 + 9 + 36$$

| Add 9 to complete the square on x | Add 36 to complete the square on y | Add 9 and 36 to compensate for the 9 and 36 added on the left side |

$$(x - 3)^2 + (y + 6)^2 = 47 \qquad \text{Factor}$$
$$(x - 3)^2 + (y - (-6))^2 = \left(\sqrt{47}\right)^2$$

$$\uparrow \qquad\qquad \uparrow \qquad\qquad \uparrow$$
$$h \qquad\qquad k \qquad\qquad r$$

The center is at $(3, -6)$, and the length of a radius is $\sqrt{47}$ units.

Classroom Example
Graph $x^2 + y^2 + 8x + 14y + 56 = 0$.

EXAMPLE 5   Graph $x^2 + y^2 - 6x + 4y + 9 = 0$.

Solution

We can change the given equation into the standard form of the equation of a circle by completing the square on x and y as follows:

$$x^2 + y^2 - 6x + 4y + 9 = 0$$
$$(x^2 - 6x + \underline{\quad}) + (y^2 + 4y + \underline{\quad}) = -9$$
$$(x^2 - 6x + 9) + (y^2 + 4y + 4) = -9 + 9 + 4$$

$$\uparrow \qquad\qquad\qquad \uparrow \qquad\qquad\quad \swarrow\uparrow$$

Add 9 to	Add 4 to	Add 9 and 4 to
complete	complete	compensate for
the square	the square	the 9 and 4 added
on x	on y	on the left side

$$(x - 3)^2 + (y + 2)^2 = 2^2$$
$$(x - 3)^2 + (y - (-2))^2 = 2^2$$

$$\uparrow \qquad\qquad \uparrow \qquad \uparrow$$
$$h \qquad\qquad k \qquad r$$

The center is at $(3, -2)$, and the length of a radius is 2 units. Thus the circle can be drawn as shown in Figure 13.3.

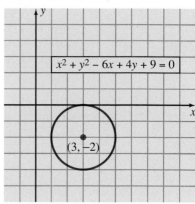

Figure 13.3

It should be evident that to determine the equation of a specific circle, we need the values of h, k, and r. To determine these values from a given set of conditions often requires the use of some of the following concepts from elementary geometry.

1. A tangent to a circle is a line that has one and only one point in common with the circle. This common point is called a *point of tangency*.

2. A radius drawn to the point of tangency is perpendicular to the tangent line.

3. Three noncollinear points in a plane determine a circle.

4. A chord of a circle is a line segment with endpoints that lie on the circle.

5. The perpendicular bisector of a chord contains the center of a circle.

Now let's consider two problems that use some of these concepts. We will offer an analysis of these problems but will leave the details for you to complete.

EXAMPLE 6

Find the equation of the circle that has its center at $(2, 1)$ and is tangent to the line $x - 3y = 9$.

Analysis

Let's sketch a figure to help with the analysis of the problem (Figure 13.4). The point of tangency (a, b) is on the line $x - 3y = 9$, so we have $a - 3b = 9$. Also, the line determined by $(2, 1)$ and (a, b) is perpendicular to the line $x - 3y = 9$, so their slopes are negative reciprocals of each other. This relationship produces another equation with the variables a and b. (This equation is $3a + b = 7$.) Solving the system

$$\begin{pmatrix} a - 3b = 9 \\ 3a + b = 7 \end{pmatrix}$$

will produce the values for (a, b), and this point, along with the center of the circle, determines the length of a radius. Then the center, along with the length of a radius, determines the equation of the circle. (The equation is $x^2 + y^2 - 4x - 2y - 5 = 0$.)

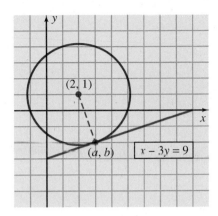

Figure 13.4

EXAMPLE 7

Find the equation of the circle that passes through the three points $(2, -4)$, $(-6, 4)$, and $(-2, -8)$.

Analysis

Three chords of the circle are determined by the three given points. (The points are noncollinear.) The center of the circle can be found at the intersection of the perpendicular bisectors of any two chords. Then the center and one of the given points can be used to find the length of a radius. From the center and the length of a radius, the equation of the circle can be determined. (The equation is $x^2 + y^2 + 8x + 4y - 20 = 0$.)

OR

Because three noncollinear points in a plane determine a circle, we could substitute the coordinates of the three given points into the general equation $x^2 + y^2 + Dx + Ey + F = 0$. This will produce a system of three linear equations in the three unknowns D, E, and F. (Perhaps you should do this and check your answer from the first method.)

When using a graphing utility to graph circles, we need to solve the given equation for y in terms of x and then graph these two equations. Furthermore, it may be necessary to change the boundaries of the viewing rectangle so that a complete graph is shown. Let's consider an example.

EXAMPLE 8   Use a graphing utility to graph $x^2 - 40x + y^2 + 351 = 0$.

Solution

First we need to solve for y in terms of x.

$$x^2 - 40x + y^2 + 351 = 0$$
$$y^2 = -x^2 + 40x - 351$$
$$y = \pm\sqrt{-x^2 + 40x - 351}$$

Now we can make the following assignments:

$$Y_1 = \sqrt{-x^2 + 40x - 351}$$
$$Y_2 = -Y_1$$

(Note that we assigned Y_2 in terms of Y_1. By doing this, we avoid repetitive key strokes and thus reduce the chance for errors. You may need to consult your user's manual for instructions on how to keystroke $-Y_1$.) Figure 13.5 shows the graph.

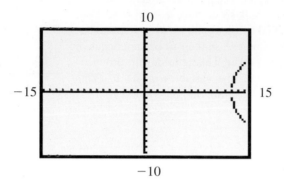

Figure 13.5

We know from the original equation that this graph is a circle, so we need to make some adjustments on the boundaries of the viewing rectangle in order to get a complete graph. This can be done by completing the square on the original equation to change its form to $(x - 20)^2 + y^2 = 49$, or simply by a trial-and-error process. By changing the boundaries on x so that $-15 \leq x \leq 30$, we obtain Figure 13.6.

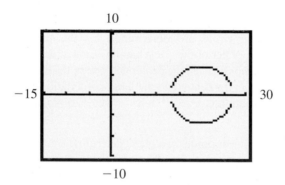

Figure 13.6

Concept Quiz 13.1

For Problems 1–8, answer true or false.

1. A circle is the set of all points in a plane that are equidistant from a fixed point.

2. A line segment determined by the center and any point on the circle is called the diameter.

3. The circle $(x - 2)^2 + (y + 4)^2 = 20$ has its center at $(2, 4)$.

4. The circle $(x - 2)^2 + (y + 4)^2 = 20$ has a radius of length 20 units.

5. The circle $x^2 + y^2 = 36$ has its center at the origin.

6. A tangent to the circle is a line that intersects the circle in two points.

7. A circle can only have one chord.

8. The center of the circle will lie on the perpendicular bisector of any chord of the circle.

Problem Set 13.1

For Problems 1–14, write the equation of each of the circles that satisfies the stated conditions. In some cases there may be more than one circle that satisfies the conditions. Express the final equations in the form $x^2 + y^2 + Dx + Ey + F = 0$. (Objective 1)

1. Center at (2, 3) and $r = 5$

2. Center at (−3, 4) and $r = 2$

3. Center at (−1, −5) and $r = 3$

4. Center at (4, −2) and $r = 1$

5. Center at (3, 0) and $r = 3$

6. Center at (0, −4) and $r = 6$

7. Center at the origin and $r = 7$

8. Center at the origin and $r = 1$

9. Tangent to the x axis, a radius of length 4, and abscissa of center is −3

10. Tangent to the y axis, a radius of length 5, and ordinate of center is 3

11. Tangent to both axes, a radius of 6, and the center in the third quadrant

12. x intercept of 6, y intercept of −4, and passes through the origin

13. Tangent to the y axis, x intercepts of 2 and 6

14. Tangent to the x axis, y intercepts of 1 and 5

For Problems 15–32, find the center and the length of a radius of each of the circles. (Objective 2)

15. $(x - 5)^2 + (y - 7)^2 = 25$

16. $(x + 6)^2 + (y - 9)^2 = 49$

17. $(x + 1)^2 + (y + 8)^2 = 12$

18. $(x - 7)^2 + (y + 2)^2 = 24$

19. $3(x - 10)^2 + 3(y + 5)^2 = 9$

20. $5(x - 3)^2 + 5(y - 3)^2 = 30$

21. $x^2 + y^2 - 6x - 10y + 30 = 0$

22. $x^2 + y^2 + 8x - 12y + 43 - 0$

23. $x^2 + y^2 + 10x + 14y + 73 = 0$

24. $x^2 + y^2 + 6y - 7 = 0$

25. $x^2 + y^2 - 10x = 0$

26. $x^2 + y^2 + 7x - 2 = 0$

27. $x^2 + y^2 - 5y - 1 = 0$

28. $x^2 + y^2 - 4x + 2y = 0$

29. $x^2 + y^2 = 8$

30. $4x^2 + 4y^2 = 1$

31. $4x^2 + 4y^2 - 4x - 8y - 11 = 0$

32. $36x^2 + 36y^2 + 48x - 36y - 11 = 0$

33. Find the equation of the line that is tangent to the circle $x^2 + y^2 - 2x + 3y - 12 = 0$ at the point (4, 1).

34. Find the equation of the line that is tangent to the circle $x^2 + y^2 + 4x - 6y - 4 = 0$ at the point (−1, −1).

35. Find the equation of the circle that passes through the origin and has its center at (−3, −4).

36. Find the equation of the circle for which the line segment determined by (−4, 9) and (10, −3) is a diameter.

37. Find the equations of the circles that have their centers on the line $2x + 3y = 10$ and are tangent to both axes.

38. Find the equation of the circle that has its center at (−2, −3) and is tangent to the line $x + y = -3$.

39. The point (−1, 4) is the midpoint of a chord of a circle whose equation is $x^2 + y^2 + 8x + 4y - 30 = 0$. Find the equation of the chord.

40. Find the equation of the circle that is tangent to the line $3x - 4y = -26$ at the point (−2, 5) and passes through the point (5, −2).

41. Find the equation of the circle that passes through the three points (1, 2), (−3, −8), and (−9, 6).

42. Find the equation of the circle that passes through the three points (3, 0), (6, −9), and (10, −1).

Thoughts Into Words

43. What is the graph of the equation $x^2 + y^2 = 0$? Explain your answer.

44. What is the graph of the equation $x^2 + y^2 = -4$? Explain your answer.

45. Your friend claims that the graph of an equation of the form $x^2 + y^2 + Dx + Ey + F = 0$, where $F = 0$, is a circle that passes through the origin. Is she correct? Explain why or why not.

Further Investigations

46. Use a coordinate geometry approach to prove that an angle inscribed in a semicircle is a right angle. (See Figure 13.7.)

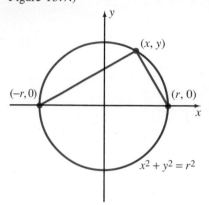

Figure 13.7

47. Use a coordinate geometry approach to prove that a line segment from the center of a circle bisecting a chord is perpendicular to the chord. [*Hint:* Let the ends of the chord be $(r, 0)$ and (a, b).]

48. By expanding $(x - h)^2 + (y - k)^2 = r^2$, we obtain $x^2 - 2hx + h^2 + y^2 - 2ky + k^2 - r^2 = 0$. When we compare this result to the form $x^2 + y^2 + Dx + Ey + F = 0$, we see that $D = -2h$, $E = -2k$, and $F = h^2 + k^2 - r^2$. Therefore, solving those equations respectively for h, k, and r, we can find the center and the length of a radius of a circle by using $h = \dfrac{D}{-2}$, $k = \dfrac{E}{-2}$, and $r = \sqrt{h^2 + k^2 - F}$. Use these relationships to find the center and the length of a radius of each of the following circles:

(a) $x^2 + y^2 - 2x - 8y + 8 = 0$
(b) $x^2 + y^2 + 4x - 14y + 49 = 0$
(c) $x^2 + y^2 + 12x + 8y - 12 = 0$
(d) $x^2 + y^2 - 16x + 20y + 115 = 0$
(e) $x^2 + y^2 - 12x - 45 = 0$
(f) $x^2 + y^2 + 14x = 0$

Graphing Calculator Activities

49. For each circle in Problems 15–32, you were asked to find the center and the length of a radius. Now use your graphing calculator and graph each of those circles. Be sure that your graph is consistent with the information you obtained earlier.

50. For each of the following, graph the two circles on the same set of axes and determine the coordinates of the points of intersection. Express the coordinates to the nearest tenth. If the circles do not intersect, so indicate.

(a) $x^2 + 4x + y^2 = 0$ and $x^2 - 2x + y^2 - 3 = 0$
(b) $x^2 + y^2 - 12y + 27 = 0$ and $x^2 + y^2 - 6y + 5 = 0$
(c) $x^2 - 4x + y^2 - 5 = 0$ and $x^2 - 14x + y^2 + 45.4 = 0$
(d) $x^2 - 6x + y^2 - 2y + 1 = 0$ and $x^2 - 6x + y^2 + 4y + 4 = 0$
(e) $x^2 - 4x + y^2 - 6y - 3 = 0$ and $x^2 - 8x + y^2 + 2y - 8 = 0$

Answers to the Concept Quiz

1. True   **2.** False   **3.** False   **4.** False   **5.** True   **6.** False   **7.** False   **8.** True

---

13.2   Parabolas

OBJECTIVES

1 Find the vertex, focus, and directrix of a parabola

2 Sketch the graph of a parabola

3 Determine the equation of a parabola

4 Solve application problems involving parabolas

We discussed parabolas as the graphs of quadratic functions in Sections 8.3 and 8.4. All parabolas in those sections had vertical lines as axes of symmetry. Furthermore, we did not state the definition for a parabola at that time. We shall now define a parabola and derive standard forms of equations for those that have either vertical or horizontal axes of symmetry.

> **Definition 13.2**
>
> A **parabola** is the set of all points in a plane such that the distance of each point from a fixed point F (the **focus**) is equal to its distance from a fixed line d (the **directrix**) in the plane.

Using Definition 13.2, we can sketch a parabola by starting with a fixed line d (directrix) and a fixed point F (focus) not on d. Then a point P is on the parabola if and only if $PF = PP'$, where $\overline{PP'}$ is perpendicular to the directrix d (Figure 13.8). The dashed curved line in Figure 13.8 indicates the possible positions of P; it is the parabola. The line l, through F and perpendicular to the directrix, is called the **axis of symmetry**. The point V, on the axis of symmetry halfway from F to the directrix d, is the **vertex** of the parabola.

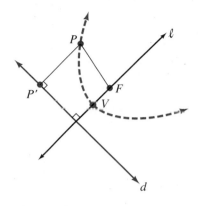

Figure 13.8

We can derive a standard form for the equation of a parabola by superimposing coordinates on the plane such that the origin is at the vertex of the parabola and the y axis is the axis of symmetry (Figure 13.9). If the focus is at $(0, p)$, where $p \neq 0$, then the equation of the directrix is $y = -p$. Therefore, for any point P on the parabola, $PF = PP'$, and using the distance formula yields

$$\sqrt{(x - 0)^2 + (y - p)^2} = \sqrt{(x - x)^2 + (y + p)^2}$$

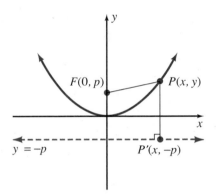

Squaring both sides and simplifying, we obtain

$$(x - 0)^2 + (y - p)^2 = (x - x)^2 + (y + p)^2$$
$$x^2 + y^2 - 2py + p^2 = y^2 + 2py + p^2$$
$$x^2 = 4py$$

Figure 13.9

Thus the **standard form for the equation of a parabola** with its vertex at the origin and the y axis as its axis of symmetry is

> $$x^2 = 4py$$

If $p > 0$, the parabola opens upward; if $p < 0$, the parabola opens downward.

A line segment that contains the focus and has endpoints on the parabola is called a **focal chord**. The specific focal chord that is parallel to the directrix we shall call the **primary focal chord**; this is line segment $\overline{QP}$ in Figure 13.10. Because $FP = PP' = |2p|$, the entire length of the primary focal chord is $|4p|$ units. You will see in a moment how we can use this fact when graphing parabolas.

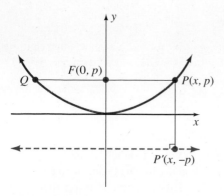

Figure 13.10

In a similar fashion, we can develop the standard form for the equation of a parabola with its vertex at the origin and the x axis as its axis of symmetry. By choosing a focus at $F(p, 0)$ and a directrix with an equation of $x = -p$ (see Figure 13.11), and by applying the definition of a parabola, we obtain the standard form for the equation:

$$y^2 = 4px$$

If $p > 0$, the parabola opens to the right, as in Figure 13.11; if $p < 0$, it opens to the left.

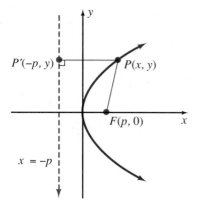

Figure 13.11

The concept of symmetry can be used to decide which of the two equations, $x^2 = 4py$ or $y^2 = 4px$, is to be used. The graph of $x^2 = 4py$ is symmetric with respect to the y axis because replacing x with $-x$ does not change the equation. Likewise, the graph of $y^2 = 4px$ is symmetric with respect to the x axis because replacing y with $-y$ leaves the equation unchanged. Let's summarize these ideas.

Standard Equations: Parabolas with Vertices at the Origin

The graph of each of the following equations is a parabola that has its vertex at the origin and has the indicated focus, directrix, and symmetry.

1. $x^2 = 4py$ focus $(0, p)$, directrix $y = -p$, y-axis symmetry

2. $y^2 = 4px$ focus $(p, 0)$, directrix $x = -p$, x-axis symmetry

Now let's illustrate some uses of the equations $x^2 = 4py$ and $y^2 = 4px$.

EXAMPLE 1

Find the focus and directrix of the parabola $x^2 = -8y$, and sketch its graph.

Solution

Compare $x^2 = -8y$ to the standard form $x^2 = 4py$, and we have $4p = -8$. Therefore $p = -2$, and the parabola opens downward. The focus is at $(0, -2)$, and the equation of the directrix is $y = -(-2) = 2$. The primary focal chord is $|4p| = |-8| = 8$ units long. Therefore the endpoints of the primary focal chord are at $(4, -2)$ and $(-4, -2)$. The graph is sketched in Figure 13.12.

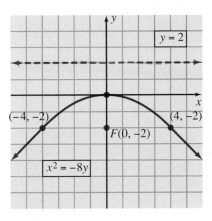

Figure 13.12

EXAMPLE 2

Write the equation of the parabola that is symmetric with respect to the y axis, has its vertex at the origin, and contains the point $P(6, 3)$.

Solution

The standard form of the parabola is $x^2 = 4py$. Because P is on the parabola, the ordered pair $(6, 3)$ must satisfy the equation. Therefore

$$6^2 = 4p(3)$$
$$36 = 12p$$
$$3 = p$$

If $p = 3$, the equation becomes

$$x^2 = 4(3)y$$
$$x^2 = 12y$$

EXAMPLE 3

Find the focus and directrix of the parabola $y^2 = 6x$ and sketch its graph.

Solution

Compare $y^2 = 6x$ to the standard form $y^2 = 4px$; we see that $4p = 6$ and therefore $p = \dfrac{3}{2}$. Thus the focus is at $\left(\dfrac{3}{2}, 0\right)$, and the equation of the directrix is $x = -\dfrac{3}{2}$. Because $p > 0$, the parabola opens to the right. The primary focal chord is $|4p| = |6| = 6$ units long. Therefore the endpoints of the primary focal chord are at $\left(\dfrac{3}{2}, 3\right)$ and $\left(\dfrac{3}{2}, -3\right)$. The graph is sketched in Figure 13.13.

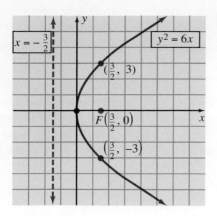

Figure 13.13

Other Parabolas

Using these skills, we can develop the standard form for the equation of a parabola that is symmetric with respect to a line parallel to a coordinate axis. In Figure 13.14 we have taken the vertex V at (h, k) and the focus F at $(h, k + p)$; the equation of the directrix is $y = k - p$. By the definition of a parabola, we know that $FP = PP'$. Therefore we can apply the distance formula as follows:

$$\sqrt{(x - h)^2 + (y - (k + p))^2} = \sqrt{(x - x)^2 + [y - (k - p)]^2}$$

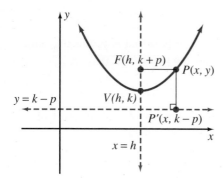

Figure 13.14

We leave it to the reader to show that this equation simplifies to

$$(x - h)^2 = 4p(y - k)$$

which is called the standard form of the equation of a parabola that has its vertex at (h, k) and is symmetric with respect to the line $x = h$. If $p > 0$, the parabola opens upward; if $p < 0$, the parabola opens downward.

In a similar fashion, we can show that the standard form of the equation of a parabola that has its vertex at (h, k) and is symmetric with respect to the line $y = k$ is

$$(y - k)^2 = 4p(x - h)$$

If $p > 0$, the parabola opens to the right; if $p < 0$, it opens to the left.

Let's summarize our discussion of parabolas that have lines of symmetry parallel to the x axis or to the y axis.

Standard Equations: Parabolas with Vertices Not at the Origin

The graph of each of the following equations is a parabola that has its vertex at (h, k) and has the indicated focus, directrix, and symmetry.

1. $(x - h)^2 = 4p(y - k)$ focus $(h, k + p)$, directrix $y = k - p$,
   line of symmetry $x = h$

2. $(y - k)^2 = 4p(x - h)$ focus $(h + p, k)$, directrix $x = h - p$,
   line of symmetry $y = k$

Classroom Example
Find the vertex, focus, and directrix of the parabola $y^2 + 2y - 8x + 25 = 0$, and sketch its graph.

EXAMPLE 4

Find the vertex, focus, and directrix of the parabola $y^2 + 4y - 4x + 16 = 0$, and sketch its graph.

Solution

Write the equation as $y^2 + 4y = 4x - 16$, and we can complete the square on the left side by adding 4 to both sides.

$$y^2 + 4y + 4 = 4x - 16 + 4$$
$$(y + 2)^2 = 4x - 12$$
$$(y + 2)^2 = 4(x - 3)$$

Now let's compare this final equation to the form $(y - k)^2 = 4p(x - h)$:

$$[y - (-2)]^2 = 4(x - 3)$$

$$k = -2 \qquad 4p = 4 \qquad h = 3$$
$$p = 1$$

The vertex is at $(3, -2)$, and because $p > 0$, the parabola opens to the right and the focus is at $(4, -2)$. The equation of the directrix is $x = 2$. The primary focal chord is $|4p| = |4| = 4$ units long, and its endpoints are at $(4, 0)$ and $(4, -4)$. The graph is sketched in Figure 13.15.

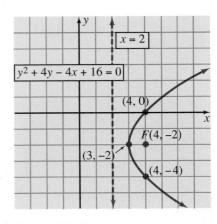

Figure 13.15

Remark: If we were using a graphing calculator to graph the parabola in Example 4, then after the step $(y + 2)^2 = 4x - 12$, we would solve for y to obtain $y = -2 \pm \sqrt{4x - 12}$. Then we could enter the two functions $Y_1 = -2 + \sqrt{4x - 12}$ and $Y_2 = -2 - \sqrt{4x - 12}$ and obtain a figure that closely resembles Figure 13.15. (You are asked to do this in the Graphing Calculator Activities.) Some graphing utilities can graph the equation in Example 4 without changing its form.

Classroom Example
Write the equation of the parabola if its focus is at $(2, 5)$, and the equation of its directrix is $y = -1$.

EXAMPLE 5

Write the equation of the parabola if its focus is at $(-4, 1)$, and the equation of its directrix is $y = 5$.

Solution

Because the directrix is a horizontal line, we know that the equation of the parabola is of the form $(x - h)^2 = 4p(y - k)$. The vertex is halfway between the focus and the directrix, so the vertex is at $(-4, 3)$. This means that $h = -4$ and $k = 3$. The parabola opens downward because the focus is below the directrix, and the distance between the focus and the vertex is 2 units; thus, $p = -2$. Substitute -4 for h, 3 for k, and -2 for p in the equation $(x - h)^2 = 4p(y - k)$ to obtain

$$(x - (-4))^2 = 4(-2)(y - 3)$$

which simplifies to

$$(x + 4)^2 = -8(y - 3)$$
$$x^2 + 8x + 16 = -8y + 24$$
$$x^2 + 8x + 8y - 8 = 0$$

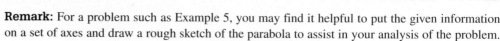

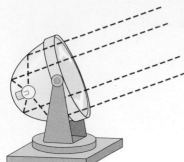

Figure 13.16

Remark: For a problem such as Example 5, you may find it helpful to put the given information on a set of axes and draw a rough sketch of the parabola to assist in your analysis of the problem.

Parabolas possess various properties that make them very useful. For example, if a parabola is rotated about its axis, a parabolic surface is formed. The rays from a source of light placed at the focus of this surface reflect from the surface parallel to the axis. It is for this reason that parabolic reflectors are used on searchlights, as in Figure 13.16. Likewise, rays of light coming into a parabolic surface parallel to the axis are reflected through the focus. This property of parabolas is useful in the design of mirrors for telescopes (see Figure 13.17) and in the construction of radar antennas.

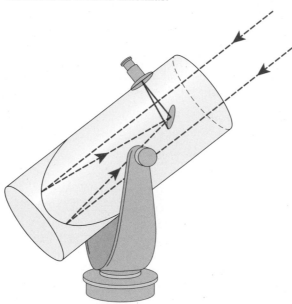

Figure 13.17

Concept Quiz 13.2

For Problems 1–8, answer true or false.

1. For a parabola, the axis of symmetry is parallel to the directrix.

2. For the parabola with an equation of $x^2 = 8y$, the length of the primary focal chord is 8 units

3. The graph of $y^2 = -4x$ is symmetric with respect to the x axis.

4. For the parabola with an equation of $y^2 = 3x$, the directrix is the point $\left(\dfrac{4}{3}, 0\right)$.

5. The parabola with an equation of $x^2 = -6y$ opens downward.

6. For the graph of a parabola with an equation of $(x - 4)^2 = 8(y - 1)$, the vertex is located at $(-4, 1)$.

7. The vertex of a parabola always lies on the axis of symmetry.

8. A parabola has an infinite number of focal chords but only one primary focal chord.

Problem Set 13.2

For Problems 1–30, find the vertex, focus, and directrix of the given parabola and sketch its graph. **(Objectives 1 and 2)**

1. $y^2 = 8x$

2. $y^2 = -4x$

3. $x^2 = -12y$

4. $x^2 = 8y$

5. $y^2 = -2x$

6. $y^2 = 6x$

7. $x^2 = 6y$

8. $x^2 = -7y$

9. $x^2 - 12(y + 1)$

10. $x^2 = -12(y - 2)$

11. $y^2 = -8(x - 3)$

12. $y^2 = 4(x + 1)$

13. $x^2 - 4y + 8 = 0$

14. $x^2 - 8y - 24 = 0$

15. $x^2 + 8y + 16 = 0$

16. $x^2 + 4y - 4 = 0$

17. $y^2 - 12x + 24 = 0$

18. $y^2 + 8x - 24 = 0$

19. $(x - 2)^2 = -4(y + 2)$

20. $(x + 3)^2 = 4(y - 4)$

21. $(y + 4)^2 = -8(x + 2)$

22. $(y - 3)^2 = 8(x - 1)$

23. $x^2 - 2x - 4y + 9 = 0$

24. $x^2 + 4x - 8y - 4 = 0$

25. $x^2 + 6x + 8y + 1 = 0$

26. $x^2 - 4x + 4y - 4 = 0$

27. $y^2 - 2y + 12x - 35 = 0$

28. $y^2 + 4y + 8x - 4 = 0$

29. $y^2 + 6y - 4x + 1 = 0$

30. $y^2 - 6y - 12x + 21 = 0$

For Problems 31–50, find an equation of the parabola that satisfies the given conditions. **(Objective 3)**

31. Focus $(0, 3)$, directrix $y = -3$

32. Focus $\left(0, -\dfrac{1}{2}\right)$, directrix $y = \dfrac{1}{2}$

33. Focus $(-1, 0)$, directrix $x = 1$

34. Focus $(5, 0)$, directrix $x = 1$

35. Focus $(0, 1)$, directrix $y = 7$

36. Focus $(0, -2)$, directrix $y = -10$

37. Focus $(3, 4)$, directrix $y = -2$

38. Focus $(-3, -1)$, directrix $y = 7$

39. Focus $(-4, 5)$, directrix $x = 0$

40. Focus $(5, -2)$, directrix $x = -1$

41. Vertex $(0, 0)$, symmetric with respect to the x axis, and contains the point $(-3, 5)$

42. Vertex $(0, 0)$, symmetric with respect to the y axis, and contains the point $(-2, -4)$

43. Vertex $(0, 0)$, focus $\left(\dfrac{5}{2}, 0\right)$

44. Vertex $(0, 0)$, focus $\left(0, -\dfrac{7}{2}\right)$

45. Vertex $(7, 3)$, focus $(7, 5)$, and symmetric with respect to the line $x = 7$

46. Vertex $(-4, -6)$, focus $(-7, -6)$, and symmetric with respect to the line $y = -6$

47. Vertex $(8, -3)$, focus $(11, -3)$, and symmetric with respect to the line $y = -3$

48. Vertex $(-2, 9)$, focus $(-2, 5)$, and symmetric with respect to the line $x = -2$

49. Vertex $(-9, 1)$, symmetric with respect to the line $x = -9$, and contains the point $(-8, 0)$

50. Vertex $(6, -4)$, symmetric with respect to the line $y = -4$, and contains the point $(8, -3)$

For Problems 51–55, solve each problem. **(Objective 4)**

51. One section of a suspension bridge hangs between two towers that are 40 feet above the surface and 300 feet apart, as shown in Figure 13.18. A cable strung between the tops of the two towers is in the shape of a parabola with its vertex 10 feet above the surface. With axes drawn as indicated in the figure, find the equation of the parabola.

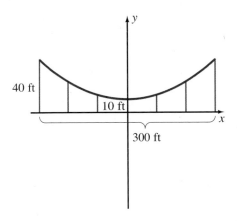

Figure 13.18

52. Suppose that five equally spaced vertical cables are used to support the bridge in Figure 13.18. Find the total length of these supports.

53. Suppose that an arch is shaped like a parabola. It is 20 feet wide at the base and 100 feet high. How wide is the arch 50 feet above the ground?

54. A parabolic arch 27 feet high spans a parkway. How wide is the arch if the center section of the parkway, a section that is 50 feet wide, has a minimum clearance of 15 feet?

55. A parabolic arch spans a stream 200 feet wide. How high above the stream must the arch be to give a minimum clearance of 40 feet over a channel in the center that is 120 feet wide?

Thoughts Into Words

56. Give a step-by-step description of how you would go about graphing the parabola $x^2 - 2x - 4y - 7 = 0$.

57. Suppose that someone graphed the equation $y^2 - 6y - 2x + 11 = 0$ and obtained the graph in Figure 13.19. How do you know by looking at the equation that this graph is incorrect?

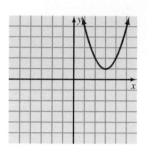

Figure 13.19

Graphing Calculator Activities

58. The parabola determined by the equation $x^2 + 4x - 8y - 4 = 0$ (Problem 24) is easy to graph using a graphing calculator because it can be expressed as a function of x without much computation. Let's solve the equation for y.

$$8y = x^2 + 4x - 4$$

$$y = \frac{x^2 + 4x - 4}{8}$$

Use your graphing calculator to graph this function.

As noted in the Remark that follows Example 4, solving the equation $y^2 + 4y - 4x + 16 = 0$ for y produces two functions: $Y_1 = -2 + \sqrt{4x - 12}$ and $Y_2 = -2 - \sqrt{4x - 12}$. Graph these two functions on the same set of axes. Your result should resemble Figure 13.15.

Use your graphing calculator to check your graphs for Problems 1–30.

Answers to the Concept Quiz

1. False   **2.** True   **3.** True   **4.** False   **5.** True   **6.** False   **7.** True   **8.** True

---

13.3   Ellipses

OBJECTIVES

1 Find the vertices, endpoints of the minor axis, and the foci of an ellipse

2 Sketch the graph of an ellipse

3 Determine the equation of an ellipse

4 Solve application problems involving ellipses

Let's begin by defining an ellipse.

> ### Definition 13.3
>
> An **ellipse** is the set of all points in a plane such that the sum of the distances of each point from two fixed points F and F' (the **foci**) in the plane is constant.

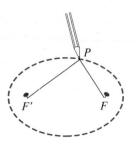

Figure 13.20

With two thumbtacks, a piece of string, and a pencil, it is easy to draw an ellipse by satisfying the conditions of Definition 13.3. First, insert two thumbtacks into a piece of cardboard at points F and F', and fasten the ends of the piece of string to the thumbtacks, as in Figure 13.20. Then loop the string around the point of a pencil and hold the pencil so that the string is taut. Finally, move the pencil around the tacks, always keeping the string taut. You will draw an ellipse. The two points F and F' are the foci referred to in Definition 13.3, and the sum of the distances FP and $F'P$ is constant because it represents the length of the piece of string. With the same piece of string, you can vary the shape of the ellipse by changing the positions of the foci. Moving F and F' farther apart will make the ellipse flatter. Likewise, moving F and F' closer together will cause the ellipse to resemble a circle. In fact, if $F = F'$, you will obtain a circle.

We can derive a standard form for the equation of an ellipse by superimposing coordinates on the plane such that the foci are on the x axis, equidistant from the origin (Figure 13.21). If F has coordinates $(c, 0)$, where $c > 0$, then F' has coordinates $(-c, 0)$, and the distance between F and F' is $2c$ units. We will let $2a$ represent the constant sum of $FP + F'P$. Note that $2a > 2c$ and therefore $a > c$. For any point P on the ellipse,

$$FP + F'P = 2a$$

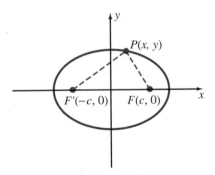

Figure 13.21

Use the distance formula to write this as

$$\sqrt{(x - c)^2 + (y - 0)^2} + \sqrt{(x + c)^2 + (y - 0)^2} = 2a$$

Let's change the form of this equation to

$$\sqrt{(x - c)^2 + y^2} = 2a - \sqrt{(x + c)^2 + y^2}$$

and square both sides:

$$(x - c)^2 + y^2 = 4a^2 - 4a\sqrt{(x + c)^2 + y^2} + (x + c)^2 + y^2$$

This can be simplified to

$$a^2 + cx = a\sqrt{(x + c)^2 + y^2}$$

Again, square both sides to produce

$$a^4 + 2a^2cx + c^2x^2 = a^2[(x + c)^2 + y^2]$$

which can be written in the form

$$x^2(a^2 - c^2) + a^2y^2 = a^2(a^2 - c^2)$$

Divide both sides by $a^2(a^2 - c^2)$, which yields the form

$$\frac{x^2}{a^2} + \frac{y^2}{a^2 - c^2} = 1$$

Letting $b^2 = a^2 - c^2$, where $b > 0$, produces the equation

$$\frac{x^2}{a^2} + \frac{y^2}{b^2} = 1 \qquad\qquad (1)$$

Because $c > 0$, $a > c$, and $b^2 = a^2 - c^2$, it follows that $a^2 > b^2$ and hence $a > b$. This equation that we have derived is called the **standard form of the equation of an ellipse** with its foci on the x axis and its center at the origin.

The x intercepts of equation (1) can be found by letting $y = 0$. Doing this produces $x^2/a^2 = 1$, or $x^2 = a^2$; consequently, the x intercepts are a and $-a$. The corresponding points on the graph (see Figure 13.22) are $A(a, 0)$ and $A'(-a, 0)$, and the line segment $\overline{A'A}$, which is of length $2a$, is called the **major axis** of the ellipse. The endpoints of the major axis are also referred to as the **vertices** of the ellipse. Similarly, letting $x = 0$ produces $y^2/b^2 = 1$ or $y^2 = b^2$; consequently the y intercepts are b and $-b$. The corresponding points on the graph are $B(0, b)$ and $B'(0, -b)$, and the line segment $\overline{BB'}$, which is of length $2b$, is called the **minor axis**. Because $a > b$, *the major axis is always longer than the minor axis.* The point of intersection of the major and minor axes is called the **center** of the ellipse.

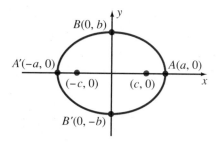

Figure 13.22

Standard Equation: Ellipse with Major Axis on the x Axis

The standard equation of an ellipse with its center at $(0, 0)$ and its major axis on the x axis is

$$\frac{x^2}{a^2} + \frac{y^2}{b^2} = 1 \quad \text{where } a > b$$

The vertices are $(-a, 0)$ and $(a, 0)$, and the length of the major axis is $2a$. The endpoints of the minor axis are $(0, -b)$ and $(0, b)$, and the length of the minor axis is $2b$. The foci are at $(-c, 0)$ and $(c, 0)$, where $c^2 = a^2 - b^2$.

Note that replacing y with $-y$, or x with $-x$, or both x and y with $-x$ and $-y$ leaves the equation unchanged. Thus the graph of

$$\frac{x^2}{a^2} + \frac{y^2}{b^2} = 1$$

is symmetric with respect to the x axis, the y axis, and the origin.

Classroom Example
Find the vertices, the endpoints of the minor axis, and the foci of the ellipse $4x^2 + 9y^2 = 144$, and sketch the ellipse.

EXAMPLE 1

Find the vertices, the endpoints of the minor axis, and the foci of the ellipse $4x^2 + 9y^2 = 36$, and sketch the ellipse.

Solution

The given equation can be changed to standard form by dividing both sides by 36.

$$\frac{4x^2}{36} + \frac{9y^2}{36} = \frac{36}{36}$$

$$\frac{x^2}{9} + \frac{y^2}{4} = 1$$

Therefore $a^2 = 9$ and $b^2 = 4$; hence the vertices are at $(3, 0)$ and $(-3, 0)$, and the endpoints of the minor axis are at $(0, 2)$ and $(0, -2)$. Because $c^2 = a^2 - b^2$, we have

$$c^2 = 9 - 4 = 5$$

Thus the foci are at $\left(\sqrt{5}, 0\right)$ and $\left(-\sqrt{5}, 0\right)$. The ellipse is sketched in Figure 13.23.

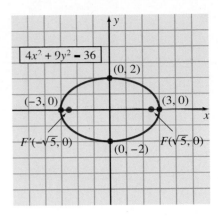

Figure 13.23

Classroom Example
Find the equation of the ellipse with vertices at $(\pm 5, 0)$ and foci at $(\pm 3, 0)$.

EXAMPLE 2

Find the equation of the ellipse with vertices at $(\pm 6, 0)$ and foci at $(\pm 4, 0)$.

Solution

From the given information, we know that $a = 6$ and $c = 4$. Therefore

$$b^2 = a^2 - c^2 = 36 - 16 = 20$$

Substitute 36 for a^2 and 20 for b^2 in the standard form to produce

$$\frac{x^2}{36} + \frac{y^2}{20} = 1$$

Multiply both sides by 180 to get

$$5x^2 + 9y^2 = 180$$

Ellipses with Foci on the *y* Axis

An ellipse with its center at the origin can also have its major axis on the y axis, as shown in Figure 13.24. In this case, the sum of the distances from any point P on the ellipse to the foci is set equal to the constant $2b$.

$$\sqrt{(x - 0)^2 + (y - c)^2} + \sqrt{(x - 0)^2 + (y + c)^2} = 2b$$

With the conditions this time that $b > a$ and $c^2 = b^2 - a^2$, the equation simplifies to the same standard equation, $\frac{x^2}{a^2} + \frac{y^2}{b^2} = 1$. Let's summarize these ideas.

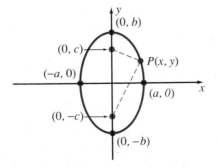

Figure 13.24

> **Standard Equation: Ellipse with Major Axis on the *y* Axis**
>
> The standard equation of an ellipse with its center at $(0, 0)$ and its major axis on the *y* axis is
>
> $$\frac{x^2}{a^2} + \frac{y^2}{b^2} = 1 \quad \text{where } b > a$$
>
> The vertices are $(0, -b)$ and $(0, b)$, and the length of the major axis is $2b$. The endpoints of the minor axis are $(-a, 0)$ and $(a, 0)$, and the length of the minor axis is $2a$. The foci are at $(0, -c)$ and $(c, 0)$, where $c^2 = b^2 - a^2$.

Classroom Example
Find the vertices, the endpoints of the minor axis, and the foci of the ellipse $12x^2 + 4y^2 = 48$, and sketch the ellipse.

EXAMPLE 3

Find the vertices, the endpoints of the minor axis, and the foci of the ellipse $18x^2 + 4y^2 = 36$, and sketch the ellipse.

Solution

The given equation can be changed to standard form by dividing both sides by 36:

$$\frac{18x^2}{36} + \frac{4y^2}{36} = \frac{36}{36}$$

$$\frac{x^2}{2} + \frac{y^2}{9} = 1$$

Therefore $a^2 = 2$ and $b^2 = 9$; hence the vertices are at $(0, 3)$ and $(0, -3)$, and the endpoints of the minor axis are at $\left(\sqrt{2}, 0\right)$ and $\left(-\sqrt{2}, 0\right)$. From the relationship $c^2 = b^2 - a^2$, we obtain $c^2 = 9 - 2 = 7$; hence the foci are at $\left(0, \sqrt{7}\right)$ and $\left(0, -\sqrt{7}\right)$. The ellipse is sketched in Figure 13.25.

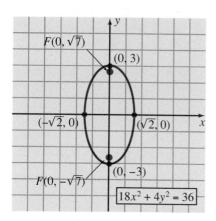

Figure 13.25

Other Ellipses

By applying the definition of an ellipse, we could also develop the standard equation of an ellipse whose center is not at the origin but whose major and minor axes are either on the coordinate axes or on lines parallel to the coordinate axes. In other words, we want to consider ellipses that are horizontal and vertical translations of the two basic ellipses. We will not show these developments in this text but will use Figures 13.26 (a) and (b) to indicate the basic facts needed to develop the standard equation. Note that in each figure, the center of the ellipse is at a point (h, k). Furthermore, the physical significance of a, b, and c is the same as before, but these values are used relative to the new center (h, k) to find the foci, vertices, and endpoints of the minor axis. Let's see how this works in a specific example.

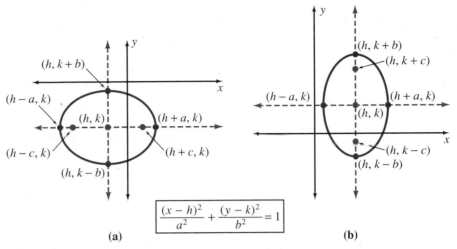

$$\frac{(x - h)^2}{a^2} + \frac{(y - k)^2}{b^2} = 1$$

(a)   (b)

Figure 13.26

Classroom Example
Find the vertices, the endpoints of the minor axis, and the foci of the ellipse $49x^2 - 196x + 16y^2 + 32y - 572 = 0$, and sketch the ellipse.

EXAMPLE 4

Find the vertices, the endpoints of the minor axis, and the foci of the ellipse $9x^2 + 54x + 4y^2 - 8y + 49 = 0$, and sketch the ellipse.

Solution

First, we need to change to standard form by completing the square on both x and y.

$$9(x^2 + 6x + \underline{\quad}) + 4(y^2 - 2y + \underline{\quad}) = -49$$

$$9(x^2 + 6x + 9) + 4(y^2 - 2y + 1) = -49 + 9(9) + 4(1)$$

$$9(x + 3)^2 + 4(y - 1)^2 = 36$$

$$\frac{(x + 3)^2}{4} + \frac{(y - 1)^2}{9} = 1$$

From this equation, we can determine that $h = -3$, $k = 1$, $a = \sqrt{4} = 2$, and $b = \sqrt{9} = 3$. Because $b > a$, the foci and vertices are on the vertical line $x = -3$. The vertices are three units up and three units down from the center $(-3, 1)$, so they are at $(-3, 4)$ and $(-3, -2)$. The endpoints of the minor axis are two units to the right and two units to the left of the center, so they are at $(-1, 1)$ and $(-5, 1)$. From the relationship $c^2 = b^2 - a^2$, we obtain $c^2 = 9 - 4 = 5$. Thus the foci are at $\left(-3, 1 + \sqrt{5}\right)$ and $\left(-3, 1 - \sqrt{5}\right)$. The ellipse is sketched in Figure 13.27.

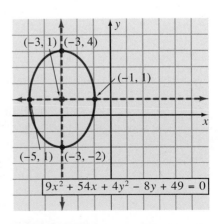

Figure 13.27

EXAMPLE 5

Write the equation of the ellipse that has vertices at $(-3, -5)$ and $(7, -5)$ and foci at $(-1, -5)$ and $(5, -5)$.

Solution

Because the vertices and foci are on the same horizontal line ($y = -5$), the equation of this ellipse is of the form

$$\frac{(x - h)^2}{a^2} + \frac{(y - k)^2}{b^2} = 1$$

where $a > b$. The center of the ellipse is at the midpoint of the major axis:

$$h = \frac{-3 + 7}{2} = 2 \qquad \text{and} \qquad k = \frac{-5 + (-5)}{2} = -5$$

The distance between the center $(2, -5)$ and a vertex $(7, -5)$ is 5 units; thus $a = 5$. The distance between the center $(2, -5)$ and a focus $(5, -5)$ is 3 units; thus $c = 3$. Using the relationship $c^2 = a^2 - b^2$, we obtain

$$b^2 = a^2 - c^2 = 25 - 9 = 16$$

Now let's substitute 2 for h, -5 for k, 25 for a^2, and 16 for b^2 in the standard form, and then we can simplify.

$$\frac{(x - 2)^2}{25} + \frac{(y + 5)^2}{16} = 1$$
$$16(x - 2)^2 + 25(y + 5)^2 = 400$$
$$16(x^2 - 4x + 4) + 25(y^2 + 10y + 25) = 400$$
$$16x^2 - 64x + 64 + 25y^2 + 250y + 625 = 400$$
$$16x^2 - 64x + 25y^2 + 250y + 289 = 0$$

Remark: Again, for a problem such as Example 5, it might be helpful to start by recording the given information on a set of axes and drawing a rough sketch of the figure.

Like parabolas, ellipses possess properties that make them very useful. For example, the elliptical surface formed by rotating an ellipse about its major axis has the following property: Light or sound waves emitted at one focus reflect off the surface and converge at the other focus. This is the principle behind "whispering galleries," such as the Rotunda of the Capitol Building in Washington, D.C. In such buildings, two people standing at two specific spots that are the foci of the elliptical ceiling can whisper and yet hear each other clearly, even though they may be quite far apart.

One very important use of an elliptical surface is in the construction of a medical device called a lithotriptor. This device is used to break up kidney stones. A source that emits ultra-high-frequency shock waves is placed at one focus, and the kidney stone is placed at the other.

Ellipses also play an important role in astronomy. Johannes Kepler (1571–1630) showed that the orbit of a planet is an ellipse with the sun at one focus. For example, the orbit of Earth is elliptical but nearly circular; at the same time, the moon moves about the earth in an elliptical path (see Figure 13.28).

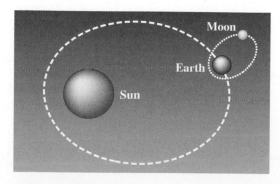

Figure 13.28

The arches for concrete bridges are sometimes elliptical. (One example is shown in Figure 13.30 in the next set of problems.) Also, elliptical gears are used in certain kinds of machinery that require a slow but powerful force at impact, such as a heavy-duty punch (see Figure 13.29).

Figure 13.29

Concept Quiz 13.3

For Problems 1–8, answer true or false.

1. For an ellipse, the endpoints of its major axis are called the vertices.

2. For an ellipse, the major axis is always longer than the minor axis.

3. The foci of an ellipse always lie on the major axis.

4. The point of intersection of the axes of an ellipse is called the vertex.

5. The graph of an ellipse whose equation is $\dfrac{x^2}{25} + \dfrac{y^2}{9} = 1$, is symmetric to both the x and y axis.

6. For the ellipse whose equation is $\dfrac{x^2}{16} + \dfrac{y^2}{49} = 1$, the endpoints of the minor axis are at $(4, 0)$ and $(-4, 0)$.

7. For the ellipse whose equation is $\dfrac{x^2}{16} + \dfrac{y^2}{25} = 1$, the foci are at $(3, 0)$ and $(-3, 0)$.

8. For the ellipse whose equation is $\dfrac{x^2}{49} + \dfrac{y^2}{36} = 1$, the length of the major axis is 7 units.

Problem Set 13.3

For Problems 1–26, find the vertices, the endpoints of the minor axis, and the foci of the given ellipse, and sketch its graph. **(Objectives 1 and 2)**

1. $\dfrac{x^2}{4} + \dfrac{y^2}{1} = 1$

2. $\dfrac{x^2}{16} + \dfrac{y^2}{1} = 1$

3. $\dfrac{x^2}{4} + \dfrac{y^2}{9} = 1$

4. $\dfrac{x^2}{4} + \dfrac{y^2}{16} = 1$

5. $9x^2 + 3y^2 = 27$

6. $4x^2 + 3y^2 = 36$

7. $2x^2 + 5y^2 = 50$

8. $5x^2 + 36y^2 = 180$

9. $12x^2 + y^2 = 36$

10. $8x^2 + y^2 = 16$

11. $7x^2 + 11y^2 = 77$

12. $4x^2 + y^2 = 12$

13. $\dfrac{(x - 2)^2}{9} + \dfrac{(y - 1)^2}{4} = 1$

14. $\dfrac{(x + 3)^2}{16} + \dfrac{(y - 2)^2}{4} = 1$

15. $\dfrac{(x + 1)^2}{9} + \dfrac{(y + 2)^2}{16} = 1$

16. $\dfrac{(x - 4)^2}{4} + \dfrac{(y + 2)^2}{25} = 1$

17. $4x^2 - 8x + 9y^2 - 36y + 4 = 0$

18. $x^2 + 6x + 9y^2 - 36y + 36 = 0$

19. $4x^2 + 16x + y^2 + 2y + 1 = 0$

20. $9x^2 - 36x + 4y^2 + 16y + 16 = 0$

21. $x^2 - 6x + 4y^2 + 5 = 0$

22. $16x^2 + 9y^2 + 36y - 108 = 0$

23. $9x^2 - 72x + 2y^2 + 4y + 128 = 0$

24. $5x^2 + 10x + 16y^2 + 160y + 325 = 0$

25. $2x^2 + 12x + 11y^2 - 88y + 172 = 0$

26. $9x^2 + 72x + y^2 + 6y + 135 = 0$

For Problems 27–40, find an equation of the ellipse that satisfies the given conditions. (Objective 3)

27. Vertices $(\pm 5, 0)$, foci $(\pm 3, 0)$

28. Vertices $(\pm 4, 0)$, foci $(\pm 2, 0)$

29. Vertices $(0, \pm 6)$, foci $(0, \pm 5)$

30. Vertices $(0, \pm 3)$, foci $(0, \pm 2)$

31. Vertices $(\pm 3, 0)$, length of minor axis is 2

32. Vertices $(0, \pm 5)$, length of minor axis is 4

33. Foci $(0, \pm 2)$, length of minor axis is 3

34. Foci $(\pm 1, 0)$, length of minor axis is 2

35. Vertices $(0, \pm 5)$, contains the point $(3, 2)$

36. Vertices $(\pm 6, 0)$, contains the point $(5, 1)$

37. Vertices $(5, 1)$ and $(-3, 1)$, foci $(3, 1)$ and $(-1, 1)$

38. Vertices $(2, 4)$ and $(2, -6)$, foci $(2, 3)$ and $(2, -5)$

39. Center $(0, 1)$, one focus at $(-4, 1)$, length of minor axis is 6

40. Center $(3, 0)$, one focus at $(3, 2)$, length of minor axis is 4

For Problems 41–44, solve each problem. (Objective 4)

41. Find an equation of the set of points in a plane such that the sum of the distances between each point of the set and the points $(2, 0)$ and $(-2, 0)$ is 8 units.

42. Find an equation of the set of points in a plane such that the sum of the distances between each point of the set and the points $(0, 3)$ and $(0, -3)$ is 10 units.

43. An arch of the bridge shown in Figure 13.30 is semi-elliptical, and the major axis is horizontal. The arch is 30 feet wide and 10 feet high. Find the height of the arch 10 feet from the center of the base.

44. In Figure 13.30, how much clearance is there 10 feet from the bank?

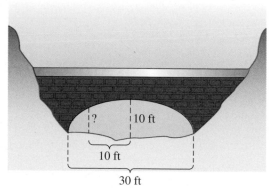

Figure 13.30

Thoughts Into Words

45. What type of figure is the graph of the equation $x^2 + 6x + 2y^2 - 20y + 59 = 0$? Explain your answer.

46. Suppose that someone graphed the equation $4x^2 - 16x + 9y^2 + 18y - 11 = 0$ and obtained the graph shown in Figure 13.31. How do you know by looking at the equation that this is an incorrect graph?

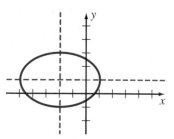

Figure 13.31

Graphing Calculator Activities

47. Use your graphing calculator to check your graphs for Problems 17–26.

48. Use your graphing calculator to graph each of the following ellipses:

(a) $2x^2 - 40x + y^2 + 2y + 185 = 0$
(b) $x^2 - 4x + 2y^2 - 48y + 272 = 0$
(c) $4x^2 - 8x + y^2 - 4y - 136 = 0$
(d) $x^2 + 6x + 2y^2 + 56y + 301 = 0$

Answers to the Concept Quiz

1. True **2.** True **3.** True **4.** False **5.** True **6.** True **7.** False **8.** False

13.4   Hyperbolas

OBJECTIVES

1 Find the vertices, the foci, and the equations of the asymptotes for a hyperbola

2 Sketch the graph of a hyperbola

3 Determine the equation of a hyperbola

A hyperbola and an ellipse are similar by definition; however, an ellipse involves the *sum* of distances, and a hyperbola involves the *difference* of distances.

Definition 13.4

A **hyperbola** is the set of all points in a plane such that the difference of the distances of each point from two fixed points F and F' (the **foci**) in the plane is a positive constant.

Using Definition 13.4, we can sketch a hyperbola by starting with two fixed points F and F' as shown in Figure 13.32. Then we locate all points P such that $PF' - PF$ is a positive constant. Likewise, as shown in Figure 13.32, all points Q are located such that $QF - QF'$ is the same positive constant. The two dashed curved lines in Figure 13.32 make up the hyperbola. The two curves are sometimes referred to as the *branches* of the hyperbola.

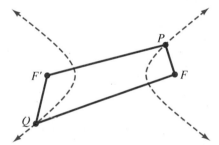

Figure 13.32

To develop a standard form for the equation of a hyperbola, let's superimpose coordinates on the plane such that the foci are located at $F(c, 0)$ and $F'(-c, 0)$, as indicated in Figure 13.33. Using the distance formula and setting $2a$ equal to the difference of the distances from any point P on the hyperbola to the foci, we have the following equation:

$$\left| \sqrt{(x - c)^2 + (y - 0)^2} - \sqrt{(x + c)^2 + (y - 0)^2} \right| = 2a$$

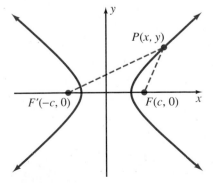

Figure 13.33

(The absolute-value sign is used to allow the point P to be on either branch of the hyperbola.) Using the same type of simplification procedure that we used for deriving the standard form for the equation of an ellipse, we find that this equation simplifies to

$$\frac{x^2}{a^2} - \frac{y^2}{c^2 - a^2} = 1$$

Letting $b^2 = c^2 - a^2$, where $b > 0$, we obtain the standard form

$$\frac{x^2}{a^2} - \frac{y^2}{b^2} = 1 \qquad\qquad\qquad (1)$$

Equation (1) indicates that this hyperbola is symmetric with respect to both axes and the origin. Furthermore, by letting $y = 0$, we obtain $x^2/a^2 = 1$, or $x^2 = a^2$, so the x intercepts are a and $-a$. The corresponding points $A(a, 0)$ and $A'(-a, 0)$ are the **vertices** of the hyperbola, and the line segment $\overline{AA'}$ is called the **transverse axis**; it is of length $2a$ (see Figure 13.34). The midpoint of the transverse axis is called the **center** of the hyperbola; it is located at the origin. By letting $x = 0$ in equation (1), we obtain $-y^2/b^2 = 1$, or $y^2 = -b^2$. This implies that there are no y intercepts, as indicated in Figure 13.34.

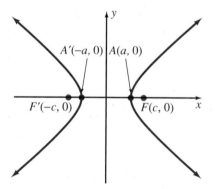

Figure 13.34

Standard Equation: Hyperbola with Transverse Axis on the _x_ Axis

The standard equation of a hyperbola with its center at $(0, 0)$ and its transverse axis on the x axis is

$$\frac{x^2}{a^2} - \frac{y^2}{b^2} = 1$$

where the foci are at $(-c, 0)$ and $(c, 0)$, the vertices are at $(-a, 0)$ and $(a, 0)$, and $c^2 = a^2 + b^2$.

In conjunction with every hyperbola, there are two intersecting lines that pass through the center of the hyperbola. These lines, referred to as **asymptotes**, are very helpful when we are sketching a hyperbola. Their equations are easily determined by using the following type of reasoning. Solving the equation

$$\frac{x^2}{a^2} - \frac{y^2}{b^2} = 1$$

for y produces $y = \pm\dfrac{b}{a}\sqrt{x^2 - a^2}$. From this form, it is evident that there are no points on the graph for $x^2 - a^2 < 0$; that is, if $-a < x < a$. However, there are points on the graph if $x \geq a$ or $x \leq -a$. If $x \geq a$, then $y = \pm\dfrac{b}{a}\sqrt{x^2 - a^2}$ can be written

$$y = \pm\frac{b}{a}\sqrt{x^2\left(1 - \frac{a^2}{x^2}\right)}$$

$$= \pm\frac{b}{a}\sqrt{x^2}\sqrt{1 - \frac{a^2}{x^2}}$$

$$= \pm\frac{b}{a}x\sqrt{\left(1 - \frac{a^2}{x^2}\right)}$$

Now suppose that we are going to determine some y values for very large values of x. (Remember that a and b are arbitrary constants; they have specific values for a particular hyperbola.) When x is very large, a^2/x^2 will be close to zero, so the radicand will be close to 1. Therefore the y value will be close to either $(b/a)x$ or $-(b/a)x$. In other words, as x becomes larger and larger, the point $P(x, y)$ gets closer and closer to either the line $y = (b/a)x$ or the line $y = -(b/a)x$. A corresponding situation occurs when $x \leq a$. The lines with equations

$$y = \pm\frac{b}{a}x$$

are the **asymptotes** of the hyperbola.

As we mentioned earlier, the asymptotes are very helpful for sketching hyperbolas. An easy way to sketch the asymptotes is first to plot the vertices $A(a, 0)$ and $A'(-a, 0)$ and the points $B(0, b)$ and $B'(0, -b)$, as in Figure 13.35. The line segment $\overline{BB'}$ is of length $2b$ and is called the **conjugate axis** of the hyperbola. The horizontal line segments drawn through B and B', together with the vertical line segments drawn through A and A', form a rectangle. The diagonals of this rectangle have slopes b/a and $-(b/a)$. Therefore, by extending the diagonals, we obtain the asymptotes $y = (b/a)x$ and $y = -(b/a)x$. The two branches of the hyperbola can be sketched by using the asymptotes as guidelines, as shown in Figure 13.35.

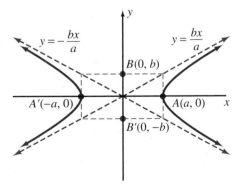

Figure 13.35

Classroom Example
Find the vertices, the foci, and the equations of the asymptotes of the hyperbola $16x^2 - 25y^2 = 400$, and sketch the hyperbola.

EXAMPLE 1

Find the vertices, the foci, and the equations of the asymptotes of the hyperbola $9x^2 - 4y^2 = 36$, and sketch the hyperbola.

Solution

Dividing both sides of the given equation by 36 and simplifying, we change the equation to the standard form

$$\frac{x^2}{4} - \frac{y^2}{9} = 1$$

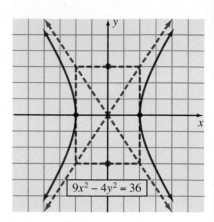

where $a^2 = 4$ and $b^2 = 9$. Hence $a = 2$ and $b = 3$. The vertices are $(\pm 2, 0)$, and the endpoints of the conjugate axis are $(0, \pm 3)$; these points determine the rectangle whose diagonals extend to become the asymptotes. With $a = 2$ and $b = 3$, the equations of the asymptotes are $y = \frac{3}{2}x$ and $y = -\frac{3}{2}x$. Then, using the relationship $c^2 = a^2 + b^2$, we obtain $c^2 = 4 + 9 = 13$. Thus the foci are at $\left(\sqrt{13}, 0\right)$ and $\left(-\sqrt{13}, 0\right)$. (The foci are not shown in Figure 13.36.) Using the vertices and the asymptotes, we have sketched the hyperbola in Figure 13.36.

Figure 13.36

$9x^2 - 4y^2 = 36$

Classroom Example
Find the equation of the hyperbola with vertices at $(\pm 3, 0)$ and foci at $\left(\pm\sqrt{58}, 0\right)$.

EXAMPLE 2

Find the equation of the hyperbola with vertices at $(\pm 4, 0)$ and foci at $\left(\pm 2\sqrt{5}, 0\right)$.

Solution

From the given information, we know that $a = 4$ and $c = 2\sqrt{5}$. Then, using the relationship $b^2 = c^2 - a^2$, we obtain

$$b^2 = \left(2\sqrt{5}\right)^2 - 4^2 = 20 - 16 = 4$$

Substituting 16 for a^2 and 4 for b^2 in the standard form produces

$$\frac{x^2}{16} - \frac{y^2}{4} = 1$$

Multiplying both sides of this equation by 16 yields

$$x^2 - 4y^2 = 16$$

Hyperbolas with Foci on the *y* Axis

In a similar fashion, we could develop a standard form for the equation of a hyperbola whose foci are on the *y* axis. The following statement summarizes the results of such a development.

> ### Standard Equation: Hyperbola with Transverse Axis on the *y* Axis
>
> The standard equation of a hyperbola with its center at $(0, 0)$ and its transverse axis on the *y* axis is
>
> $$\frac{y^2}{b^2} - \frac{x^2}{a^2} = 1$$
>
> where the foci are at $(0, -c)$ and $(0, c)$, the vertices are at $(0, -b)$ and $(0, b)$, and $c^2 = a^2 + b^2$.

The endpoints of the conjugate axis are at $(-a, 0)$ and $(a, 0)$. Again, we can determine the asymptotes by extending the diagonals of the rectangle formed by the horizontal lines through the vertices and the vertical lines through the endpoints of the conjugate axis. The equations of the asymptotes are again $y = \pm\dfrac{b}{a}x$. Let's summarize these ideas with Figure 13.37.

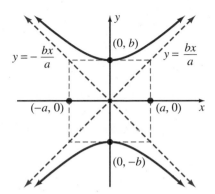

Figure 13.37

Classroom Example
Find the vertices, the foci, and the equations of the asymptotes of the hyperbola $y^2 - 5x^2 = 20$, and sketch the hyperbola.

EXAMPLE 3

Find the vertices, the foci, and the equations of the asymptotes of the hyperbola $4y^2 - x^2 = 12$, and sketch the hyperbola.

Solution

Divide both sides of the given equation by 12 to change the equation to the standard form:

$$\frac{y^2}{3} - \frac{x^2}{12} = 1$$

where $b^2 = 3$ and $a^2 = 12$. Hence $b = \sqrt{3}$ and $a = 2\sqrt{3}$. The vertices, $(0, \pm\sqrt{3})$, and the endpoints of the conjugate axis, $(\pm 2\sqrt{3}, 0)$, determine the rectangle with diagonals that extend to become the asymptotes. With $b = \sqrt{3}$ and $a = 2\sqrt{3}$, the equations of the asymptotes are $y = \dfrac{\sqrt{3}}{2\sqrt{3}}x = \dfrac{1}{2}x$ and $y = -\dfrac{1}{2}x$. Then, using the relationship $c^2 = a^2 + b^2$, we obtain $c^2 = 12 + 3 = 15$. Thus the foci are at $(0, \sqrt{15})$ and $(0, -\sqrt{15})$. The hyperbola is sketched in Figure 13.38.

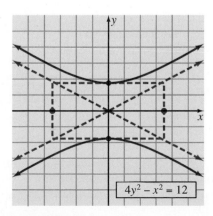

$$4y^2 - x^2 = 12$$

Figure 13.38

Other Hyperbolas

With these skills, we can develop the standard form for the equation of a hyperbola that is symmetric with respect to a line parallel to a coordinate axis. We will not show such developments in this text but will simply state and use the results.

$$\frac{(x - h)^2}{a^2} - \frac{(y - k)^2}{b^2} = 1$$ A hyperbola with center at (h, k) and transverse axis on the horizontal line $y = k$

$$\frac{(y - k)^2}{b^2} - \frac{(x - h)^2}{a^2} = 1$$ A hyperbola with center at (h, k) and transverse axis on the vertical line $x = h$

The relationship $c^2 = a^2 + b^2$ still holds, and the physical significance of a, b, and c remains the same. However, these values are used relative to the center (h, k) to find the endpoints of the transverse and conjugate axes and to find the foci. Furthermore, the slopes of the asymptotes are as before, but these lines now contain the new center, (h, k). Let's see how all of this works in a specific example.

Classroom Example
Find the vertices, the foci, and
the equations of the asymptotes
of the hyperbola
$4x^2 + 8x - 9y^2 + 54y - 113 = 0$,
and sketch the hyperbola.

EXAMPLE 4

Find the vertices, the foci, and the equations of the asymptotes of the hyperbola, and sketch the hyperbola $9x^2 - 36x - 16y^2 + 96y - 252 = 0$.

Solution

First, we need to change to the standard form by completing the square on both x and y.

$$9(x^2 - 4x + \underline{\quad}) - 16(y^2 - 6y + \underline{\quad}) = 252$$

$$9(x^2 - 4x + 4) - 16(y^2 - 6y + 9) = 252 + 9(4) - 16(9)$$

$$9(x - 2)^2 - 16(y - 3)^2 = 144$$

$$\frac{(x - 2)^2}{16} - \frac{(y - 3)^2}{9} = 1$$

The center is at $(2, 3)$, and the transverse axis is on the line $y = 3$. Because $a^2 = 16$, we know that $a = 4$. Therefore the vertices are four units to the right and four units to the left of the center, $(2, 3)$, so they are at $(6, 3)$ and $(-2, 3)$. Likewise, because $b^2 = 9$, or $b = 3$, the endpoints of the conjugate axis are three units up and three units down from the center, so they are at $(2, 6)$ and $(2, 0)$. With $a = 4$ and $b = 3$, the slopes of the asymptotes are $\frac{3}{4}$ and $-\frac{3}{4}$.

Then, using the slopes, the center $(2, 3)$, and the point-slope form for writing the equation of a line, we can determine the equations of the asymptotes to be $3x - 4y = -6$ and $3x + 4y = 18$. From the relationship $c^2 = a^2 + b^2$, we obtain $c^2 = 16 + 9 = 25$. Thus the foci are at $(7, 3)$ and $(-3, 3)$. The hyperbola is sketched in Figure 13.39.

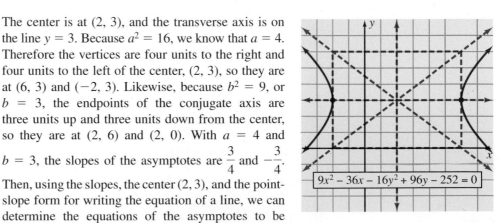

$$9x^2 - 36x - 16y^2 + 96y - 252 = 0$$

Figure 13.39

Classroom Example
Find the equation of the hyperbola with vertices at $(2, 8)$ and $(2, -2)$ and with foci at $(2, 9)$ and $(2, -3)$.

EXAMPLE 5

Find the equation of the hyperbola with vertices at $(-4, 2)$ and $(-4, -4)$ and with foci at $(-4, 3)$ and $(-4, -5)$.

Solution

Because the vertices and foci are on the same vertical line $(x = -4)$, this hyperbola has an equation of the form

$$\frac{(y - k)^2}{b^2} - \frac{(x - h)^2}{a^2} = 1$$

The center of the hyperbola is at the midpoint of the transverse axis. Therefore

$$h = \frac{-4 + (-4)}{2} = -4 \quad \text{and} \quad k = \frac{2 + (-4)}{2} = -1$$

The distance between the center, $(-4, -1)$, and a vertex, $(-4, 2)$, is three units, so $b = 3$. The distance between the center, $(-4, -1)$, and a focus, $(-4, 3)$, is four units, so $c = 4$. Then, using the relationship $c^2 = a^2 + b^2$, we obtain

$$a^2 = c^2 - b^2 = 16 - 9 = 7$$

Now we can substitute -4 for h, -1 for k, 9 for b^2, and 7 for a^2 in the general form and simplify:

$$\frac{(y + 1)^2}{9} - \frac{(x + 4)^2}{7} = 1$$
$$7(y + 1)^2 - 9(x + 4)^2 = 63$$
$$7(y^2 + 2y + 1) - 9(x^2 + 8x + 16) = 63$$
$$7y^2 + 14y + 7 - 9x^2 - 72x - 144 = 63$$
$$7y^2 + 14y - 9x^2 - 72x - 200 = 0$$

■

The hyperbola also has numerous applications, including many you may not be aware of. For example, one method of artillery range-finding is based on the concept of a hyperbola. If each of two listening posts, P_1 and P_2 in Figure 13.40, records the time that an artillery blast is heard, then the difference between the times multiplied by the speed of sound gives the difference of the distances of the gun from the two fixed points. Thus the gun is located somewhere on the hyperbola whose foci are the two listening posts. By bringing in a third listening post, P_3, we can form another hyperbola with foci at P_2 and P_3. Then the location of the gun must be at one of the intersections of the two hyperbolas.

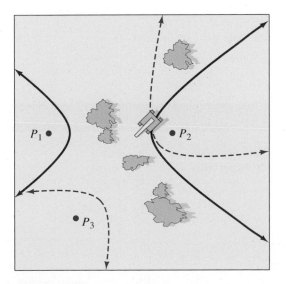

Figure 13.40

This same principle of intersecting hyperbolas is used in a long-range navigation system known as LORAN. Radar stations serve as the foci of the hyperbolas, and, of course, computers are used for the many calculations that are necessary to fix the location of a plane or ship. At the present time, LORAN is probably used mostly for coastal navigation in connection with small pleasure boats.

Some unique architectural creations have used the concept of a hyperbolic paraboloid, pictured in Figure 13.41. For example, the original TWA Flight Center at New York's John F. Kennedy Airport (currently under renovation) is so designed. Some comets, upon entering the sun's gravitational field, follow a hyperbolic path, with the sun as one of the foci (see Figure 13.42).

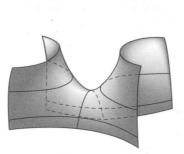

Figure 13.41

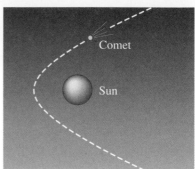

Figure 13.42

Concept Quiz 13.4

For Problems 1–8, answer true or false.

1. The graph of a hyperbola consists of two curves called the branches of the hyperbola.
2. The asymptotes of a hyperbola are always straight lines.
3. The graph of a hyperbola with a center at the origin is symmetric with both the x and y axes.
4. The slopes of the asymptotes of a hyperbola are negative reciprocals.
5. A hyperbola has both a transverse axis and a conjugate axis.
6. For a hyperbola's asymptote, which has a positive slope, the slope of that asymptote is the ratio of the length of the conjugate axis to the length of the transverse axis.
7. The foci of the hyperbola with an equation of $\dfrac{x^2}{9} - \dfrac{y^2}{16} = 1$ are located at the points $(0, 5)$ and $(0, -5)$.
8. For the hyperbola with an equation of $\dfrac{y^2}{36} - \dfrac{x^2}{49} = 1$, the equations of the asymptotes are $y = \pm\dfrac{6}{7}x$.

Problem Set 13.4

For Problems 1–26, find the vertices, the foci, and the equations of the asymptotes, and sketch each hyperbola. (Objectives 1 and 2)

1. $\dfrac{x^2}{9} - \dfrac{y^2}{4} = 1$

2. $\dfrac{x^2}{4} - \dfrac{y^2}{16} = 1$

3. $\dfrac{y^2}{4} - \dfrac{x^2}{9} = 1$

4. $\dfrac{y^2}{16} - \dfrac{x^2}{4} = 1$

5. $9y^2 - 16x^2 = 144$

6. $4y^2 - x^2 = 4$

7. $x^2 - y^2 = 9$

8. $x^2 - y^2 = 1$

9. $5y^2 - x^2 = 25$

10. $y^2 - 2x^2 = 8$

11. $y^2 - 9x^2 = -9$

12. $16y^2 - x^2 = -16$

13. $\dfrac{(x - 1)^2}{9} - \dfrac{(y + 1)^2}{4} = 1$

14. $\dfrac{(x + 2)^2}{9} - \dfrac{(y + 3)^2}{16} = 1$

15. $\dfrac{(y-2)^2}{9} - \dfrac{(x-1)^2}{16} = 1$

16. $\dfrac{(y+1)^2}{1} - \dfrac{(x+2)^2}{4} = 1$

17. $4x^2 - 24x - 9y^2 - 18y - 9 = 0$

18. $9x^2 + 72x - 4y^2 - 16y + 92 = 0$

19. $y^2 - 4y - 4x^2 - 24x - 36 = 0$

20. $9y^2 + 54y - x^2 + 6x + 63 = 0$

21. $2x^2 - 8x - y^2 + 4 = 0$

22. $x^2 + 6x - 3y^2 = 0$

23. $y^2 + 10y - 9x^2 + 16 = 0$

24. $4y^2 - 16y - x^2 + 12 = 0$

25. $x^2 + 4x - y^2 - 4y - 1 = 0$

26. $y^2 + 8y - x^2 + 2x + 14 = 0$

For Problems 27–42, find an equation of the hyperbola that satisfies the given conditions. (Objective 3)

27. Vertices $(\pm 2, 0)$, foci $(\pm 3, 0)$

28. Vertices $(\pm 1, 0)$, foci $(\pm 4, 0)$

29. Vertices $(0, \pm 3)$, foci $(0, \pm 5)$

30. Vertices $(0, \pm 2)$, foci $(0, \pm 6)$

31. Vertices $(\pm 1, 0)$, contains the point $(2, 3)$

32. Vertices $(0, \pm 1)$, contains the point $(-3, 5)$

33. Vertices $\left(0, \pm\sqrt{3}\right)$, length of conjugate axis is 4

34. Vertices $\left(\pm\sqrt{5}, 0\right)$, length of conjugate axis is 6

35. Foci $\left(\pm\sqrt{23}, 0\right)$, length of transverse axis is 8

36. Foci $\left(0, \pm 3\sqrt{2}\right)$, length of conjugate axis is 4

37. Vertices $(6, -3)$ and $(2, -3)$, foci $(7, -3)$ and $(1, -3)$

38. Vertices $(-7, -4)$ and $(-5, -4)$, foci $(-8, -4)$ and $(-4, -4)$

39. Vertices $(-3, 7)$ and $(-3, 3)$, foci $(-3, 9)$ and $(-3, 1)$

40. Vertices $(7, 5)$ and $(7, -1)$, foci $(7, 7)$ and $(7, -3)$

41. Vertices $(0, 0)$ and $(4, 0)$, foci $(5, 0)$ and $(-1, 0)$

42. Vertices $(0, 0)$ and $(0, -6)$, foci $(0, 2)$ and $(0, -8)$

For Problems 43–52, identify the graph of each of the equations as a straight line, a circle, a parabola, an ellipse, or a hyperbola. Do not sketch the graphs.

43. $x^2 - 7x + y^2 + 8y - 2 = 0$

44. $x^2 - 7x - y^2 + 8y - 2 = 0$

45. $5x - 7y = 9$

46. $4x^2 - x + y^2 + 2y - 3 = 0$

47. $10x^2 + y^2 = 8$

48. $-3x - 2y = 9$

49. $5x^2 + 3x - 2y^2 - 3y - 1 = 0$

50. $x^2 + y^2 - 3y - 6 = 0$

51. $x^2 - 3x + y - 4 = 0$

52. $5x + y^2 - 2y - 1 = 0$

Thoughts Into Words

53. What is the difference between the graphs of the equations $x^2 + y^2 = 0$ and $x^2 - y^2 = 0$?

54. What is the difference between the graphs of the equations $4x^2 + 9y^2 = 0$ and $9x^2 + 4y^2 = 0$?

55. A flashlight produces a "cone of light" that can be cut by the plane of a wall to illustrate the conic sections. Try shining a flashlight against a wall (stand within a couple of feet of the wall) at different angles to produce a circle, an ellipse, a parabola, and one branch of a hyperbola. (You may find it difficult to distinguish between a parabola and a branch of a hyperbola.) Write a paragraph to someone else explaining this experiment.

Graphing Calculator Activities

56. Use a graphing calculator to check your graphs for Problems 17–26. Be sure to graph the asymptotes for each hyperbola.

57. Use a graphing calculator to check your answers for Problems 43–52.

Answers to the Concept Quiz

1. True   **2.** True   **3.** True   **4.** False   **5.** True   **6.** True   **7.** False   **8.** True

13.5   Systems Involving Nonlinear Equations

OBJECTIVES

1 Sketch the graphs of nonlinear systems of equations and approximate the real number solutions

2 Solve nonlinear system of equations using the substitution method

3 Solve nonlinear system of equations using the elimination method

In Chapters 11 and 12, we used several techniques to solve systems of linear equations. We will use two of those techniques in this section to solve some systems that contain at least one nonlinear equation. We will also use our knowledge of graphing lines, circles, parabolas, ellipses, and hyperbolas to get a pictorial view of the systems. That will give us a basis for predicting approximate real number solutions if there are any. In other words, we have once again arrived at a topic that vividly illustrates the merging of mathematical ideas. Let's begin by considering a system that contains one linear and one nonlinear equation.

Classroom Example

Solve the system $\begin{pmatrix} x^2 + y^2 = 17 \\ 4x - y = 0 \end{pmatrix}$.

EXAMPLE 1   Solve the system $\begin{pmatrix} x^2 + y^2 = 13 \\ 3x + 2y = 0 \end{pmatrix}$.

Solution

From our previous graphing experiences, we should recognize that $x^2 + y^2 = 13$ is a circle, and $3x + 2y = 0$ is a straight line. Thus the system can be pictured as in Figure 13.43. The graph indicates that the solution set of this system should consist of two ordered pairs of real numbers that represent the points of intersection in the second and fourth quadrants.

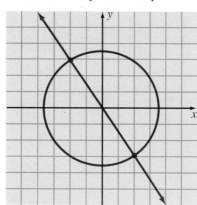

Figure 13.43

Now let's solve the system analytically by using the *substitution method*. Change the form of $3x + 2y = 0$ to $y = -3x/2$, and then substitute $-3x/2$ for y in the other equation to produce

$$x^2 + \left(-\frac{3x}{2}\right)^2 = 13$$

This equation can now be solved for x.

$$x^2 + \frac{9x^2}{4} = 13$$

$$4x^2 + 9x^2 = 52$$

$$13x^2 = 52$$

$$x^2 = 4$$

$$x = \pm 2$$

Substitute 2 for x and then -2 for x in the second equation of the system to produce two values for y.

$$3x + 2y = 0 \qquad\qquad 3x + 2y = 0$$
$$3(2) + 2y = 0 \qquad\qquad 3(-2) + 2y = 0$$
$$2y = -6 \qquad\qquad 2y = 6$$
$$y = -3 \qquad\qquad y = 3$$

Therefore the solution set of the system is $\{(2, -3), (-2, 3)\}$. _____ ■

Remark: Don't forget that, as always, you can check the solutions by substituting them back into the original equations. Graphing the system permits you to approximate any possible real number solutions before solving the system. Then, after solving the system, you can use the graph again to check that the answers are reasonable.

Classroom Example

Solve the system $\begin{pmatrix} x^2 + y^2 = 25 \\ x^2 - y^2 = 9 \end{pmatrix}$.

EXAMPLE 2   Solve the system $\begin{pmatrix} x^2 + y^2 = 16 \\ y^2 - x^2 = 4 \end{pmatrix}$.

Solution

Graphing the system produces Figure 13.44. This figure indicates that there should be four ordered pairs of real numbers in the solution set of the system. Solving the system by using the *elimination method* works nicely. We can simply add the two equations, which eliminates the x's.

$$\begin{array}{r} x^2 + y^2 = 16 \\ -x^2 + y^2 = 4 \\ \hline 2y^2 = 20 \\ y^2 = 10 \\ y = \pm\sqrt{10} \end{array}$$

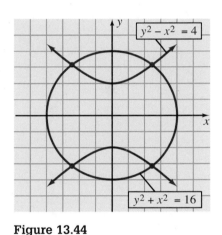

Figure 13.44

Substituting $\sqrt{10}$ for y in the first equation yields

$$x^2 + y^2 = 16$$
$$x^2 + (\sqrt{10})^2 = 16$$
$$x^2 + 10 = 16$$
$$x^2 = 6$$
$$x = \pm\sqrt{6}$$

Thus $(\sqrt{6}, \sqrt{10})$ and $(-\sqrt{6}, \sqrt{10})$ are solutions. Substituting $-\sqrt{10}$ for y in the first equation yields

$$x^2 + y^2 = 16$$
$$x^2 + (-\sqrt{10})^2 = 16$$
$$x^2 + 10 = 16$$
$$x^2 = 6$$
$$x = \pm\sqrt{6}$$

Thus $(\sqrt{6}, -\sqrt{10})$ and $(-\sqrt{6}, -\sqrt{10})$ are also solutions. The solution set is $\{(-\sqrt{6}, \sqrt{10}), (-\sqrt{6}, -\sqrt{10}), (\sqrt{6}, \sqrt{10}), (\sqrt{6}, -\sqrt{10})\}$. _____ ■

Sometimes a sketch of the graph of a system may not clearly indicate whether the system contains any real number solutions. The next example illustrates such a situation.

EXAMPLE 3

Solve the system $\begin{pmatrix} y = x^2 + 2 \\ 6x - 4y = -5 \end{pmatrix}$.

Solution

From our previous graphing experiences, we recognize that $y = x^2 + 2$ is the basic parabola shifted upward two units and that $6x - 4y = -5$ is a straight line (see Figure 13.45). Because of the close proximity of the curves, it is difficult to tell whether they intersect. In other words, the graph does not definitely indicate any real number solutions for the system.

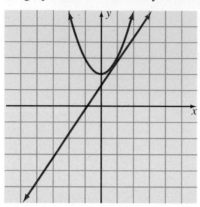

Figure 13.45

Let's solve the system by using the substitution method. We can substitute $x^2 + 2$ for y in the second equation, which produces two values for x:

$$6x - 4(x^2 + 2) = -5$$
$$6x - 4x^2 - 8 = -5$$
$$-4x^2 + 6x - 3 = 0$$
$$4x^2 - 6x + 3 = 0$$
$$x = \frac{6 \pm \sqrt{36 - 48}}{8}$$
$$= \frac{6 \pm \sqrt{-12}}{8}$$
$$= \frac{6 \pm 2i\sqrt{3}}{8}$$
$$= \frac{3 \pm i\sqrt{3}}{4}$$

It is now obvious that the system has no real number solutions. That is, the line and the parabola do not intersect in the real number plane. However, there will be two pairs of complex numbers in the solution set. We can substitute $(3 + i\sqrt{3})/4$ for x in the first equation:

$$y = \left(\frac{3 + i\sqrt{3}}{4}\right)^2 + 2$$
$$= \frac{6 + 6i\sqrt{3}}{16} + 2$$
$$= \frac{6 + 6i\sqrt{3} + 32}{16}$$
$$= \frac{38 + 6i\sqrt{3}}{16}$$
$$= \frac{19 + 3i\sqrt{3}}{8}$$

Likewise, we can substitute $\left(3 - i\sqrt{3}\right)/4$ for x in the first equation:

$$y = \left(\frac{3 - i\sqrt{3}}{4}\right)^2 + 2$$

$$= \frac{6 - 6i\sqrt{3}}{16} + 2$$

$$= \frac{6 - 6i\sqrt{3} + 32}{16}$$

$$= \frac{38 - 6i\sqrt{3}}{16}$$

$$= \frac{19 - 3i\sqrt{3}}{8}$$

The solution set is $\left\{\left(\dfrac{3 + i\sqrt{3}}{4}, \dfrac{19 + 3i\sqrt{3}}{8}\right), \left(\dfrac{3 - i\sqrt{3}}{4}, \dfrac{19 - 3i\sqrt{3}}{8}\right)\right\}$.

In Example 3 the use of a graphing utility may not, at first, indicate whether the system has any real number solutions. Suppose that we graph the system using a viewing rectangle such that $-15 \le x \le 15$ and $-10 \le y \le 10$. As shown in the display in Figure 13.46, we cannot tell whether the line and the parabola intersect. However, if we change the viewing rectangle so that $0 \le x \le 2$ and $0 \le y \le 4$, as shown in Figure 13.47, it becomes apparent that the two graphs do not intersect.

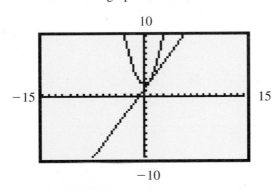

Figure 13.46   **Figure 13.47**

EXAMPLE 4

Find the real number solutions for the system $\left(\begin{array}{l} y = \log_2(x - 3) - 2 \\ y = -\log_2 x \end{array}\right)$.

Solution

First, let's use a graphing calculator to obtain a graph of the system as shown in Figure 13.48. The two curves appear to intersect at approximately $x = 4$ and $y = -2$.

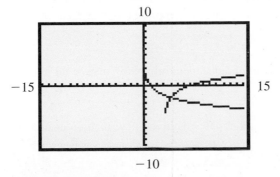

Figure 13.48

To solve the system algebraically, we can equate the two expressions for y and solve the resulting equation for x:

$$\log_2(x - 3) - 2 \doteq -\log_2 x$$
$$\log_2 x + \log_2(x - 3) = 2$$
$$\log_2 x(x - 3) = 2$$

At this step, we can either change to exponential form or rewrite 2 as $\log_2 4$:

$$\log_2 x(x - 3) = \log_2 4$$
$$x(x - 3) = 4$$
$$x^2 - 3x - 4 = 0$$
$$(x - 4)(x + 1) = 0$$
$$x - 4 = 0 \quad \text{or} \quad x + 1 = 0$$
$$x = 4 \quad \text{or} \quad x = -1$$

Because logarithms are not defined for negative numbers, -1 is discarded. Therefore, if $x = 4$, then

$$y = -\log_2 x$$

becomes

$$y = -\log_2 4$$
$$= -2$$

Therefore the solution set is $\{(4, -2)\}$.

Concept Quiz 13.5

For Problems 1–5, answer true or false.

1. A system of nonlinear equations could have a solution set that consists of one ordered pair of real numbers.

2. A graph can be used to approximate both real number and complex number solutions for non-linear systems.

3. Every nonlinear system will have at least one real number ordered pair solution.

4. The elimination method for solving nonlinear equations can be used to solve any nonlinear system of equations.

5. The substitution method for solving nonlinear equations can be used to solve any nonlinear system of equations.

6. By visualizing the graphs, determine how many real number solutions there are for the system of equations $\begin{pmatrix} x^2 + y^2 = 4 \\ x^2 + y^2 = 9 \end{pmatrix}$.

7. By visualizing the graphs, determine how many real number solutions there are for the system of equations $\begin{pmatrix} y = x^2 + 3 \\ y = -x^2 + 3 \end{pmatrix}$.

8. By visualizing the graphs, determine how many real number solutions there are for the system of equations $\begin{pmatrix} y = 2x \\ x^2 + y^2 = 9 \end{pmatrix}$.

Problem Set 13.5

For Problems 1–30, (a) graph the system so that approximate real number solutions (if there are any) can be predicted, and (b) solve the system by the substitution or elimination method. (Objectives 1, 2, and 3)

1. $\begin{pmatrix} x^2 + y^2 = 5 \\ x + 2y = 5 \end{pmatrix}$

2. $\begin{pmatrix} x^2 + y^2 = 13 \\ 2x + 3y = 13 \end{pmatrix}$

3. $\begin{pmatrix} x^2 + y^2 = 26 \\ x + y = -4 \end{pmatrix}$

4. $\begin{pmatrix} x^2 + y^2 = 10 \\ x + y = -2 \end{pmatrix}$

5. $\begin{pmatrix} x^2 + y^2 = 2 \\ x - y = 4 \end{pmatrix}$

6. $\begin{pmatrix} x^2 + y^2 = 3 \\ x - y = -5 \end{pmatrix}$

7. $\begin{pmatrix} y = x^2 + 6x + 7 \\ 2x + y = -5 \end{pmatrix}$

8. $\begin{pmatrix} y = x^2 - 4x + 5 \\ y - x = 1 \end{pmatrix}$

9. $\begin{pmatrix} 2x + y = -2 \\ y = x^2 + 4x + 7 \end{pmatrix}$

10. $\begin{pmatrix} 2x + y = 0 \\ y = -x^2 + 2x - 4 \end{pmatrix}$

11. $\begin{pmatrix} y = x^2 - 3 \\ x + y = -4 \end{pmatrix}$

12. $\begin{pmatrix} y = -x^2 + 1 \\ x + y = 2 \end{pmatrix}$

13. $\begin{pmatrix} x^2 + 2y^2 = 9 \\ x - 4y = -9 \end{pmatrix}$

14. $\begin{pmatrix} 2x - y = 7 \\ 3x^2 + y^2 = 21 \end{pmatrix}$

15. $\begin{pmatrix} x + y = -3 \\ x^2 + 2y^2 - 12y - 18 = 0 \end{pmatrix}$

16. $\begin{pmatrix} 4x^2 + 9y^2 = 25 \\ 2x + 3y = 7 \end{pmatrix}$

17. $\begin{pmatrix} x - y = 2 \\ x^2 - y^2 = 16 \end{pmatrix}$

18. $\begin{pmatrix} x^2 - 4y^2 = 16 \\ 2y - x = 2 \end{pmatrix}$

19. $\begin{pmatrix} y = -x^2 + 3 \\ y = x^2 + 1 \end{pmatrix}$

20. $\begin{pmatrix} y = x^2 \\ y = x^2 - 4x + 4 \end{pmatrix}$

21. $\begin{pmatrix} y = x^2 + 2x - 1 \\ y = x^2 + 4x + 5 \end{pmatrix}$

22. $\begin{pmatrix} y = -x^2 + 1 \\ y = x^2 - 2 \end{pmatrix}$

23. $\begin{pmatrix} x^2 - y^2 = 4 \\ x^2 + y^2 = 4 \end{pmatrix}$

24. $\begin{pmatrix} 2x^2 + y^2 = 8 \\ x^2 + y^2 = 4 \end{pmatrix}$

25. $\begin{pmatrix} 8y^2 - 9x^2 = 6 \\ 8x^2 - 3y^2 = 7 \end{pmatrix}$

26. $\begin{pmatrix} 2x^2 + y^2 = 11 \\ x^2 - y^2 = 4 \end{pmatrix}$

27. $\begin{pmatrix} 2x^2 - 3y^2 = -1 \\ 2x^2 + 3y^2 = 5 \end{pmatrix}$

28. $\begin{pmatrix} 4x^2 + 3y^2 = 9 \\ y^2 - 4x^2 = 7 \end{pmatrix}$

29. $\begin{pmatrix} xy = 3 \\ 2x + 2y = 7 \end{pmatrix}$

30. $\begin{pmatrix} x^2 + 4y^2 = 25 \\ xy = 6 \end{pmatrix}$

For Problems 31–36, solve each system for all real number solutions.

31. $\begin{pmatrix} y = \log_3(x - 6) - 3 \\ y = -\log_3 x \end{pmatrix}$

32. $\begin{pmatrix} y = \log_{10}(x - 9) - 1 \\ y = -\log_{10} x \end{pmatrix}$

33. $\begin{pmatrix} y = e^x - 1 \\ y = 2e^{-x} \end{pmatrix}$

34. $\begin{pmatrix} y = 28 - 11e^x \\ y = -e^{2x} \end{pmatrix}$

35. $\begin{pmatrix} y = x^3 \\ y = x^3 + 2x^2 + 5x - 3 \end{pmatrix}$

36. $\begin{pmatrix} y = 3(4^x) - 8 \\ y = 4^{2x} - 2(4^x) - 4 \end{pmatrix}$

Thoughts Into Words

37. What happens if you try to graph the system

$$\begin{pmatrix} 7x^2 + 8y^2 = 36 \\ 11x^2 + 5y^2 = -4 \end{pmatrix}$$

38. For what value(s) of k will the line $x + y = k$ touch the ellipse $x^2 + 2y^2 = 6$ in one and only one point? Defend your answer.

39. The system

$$\begin{pmatrix} x^2 - 6x + y^2 - 4y + 4 = 0 \\ x^2 - 4x + y^2 + 8y - 5 = 0 \end{pmatrix}$$

represents two circles that intersect in two points. An equivalent system can be formed by replacing the second equation with the result of adding -1 times the first equation to the second equation. Thus we obtain the system

$$\begin{pmatrix} x^2 - 6x + y^2 - 4y + 4 = 0 \\ 2x + 12y - 9 = 0 \end{pmatrix}$$

Explain why the linear equation in this system is the equation of the common chord of the original two intersecting circles.

Graphing Calculator Activities

40. Graph the system of equations $\begin{pmatrix} y = x^2 + 2 \\ 6x - 4y = -5 \end{pmatrix}$, and use the TRACE and ZOOM features of your calculator to show that this system has no real number solutions.

41. Use a graphing calculator to graph the systems in Problems 31–36, and check the reasonableness of your answers to those problems.

For Problems 42–47, use a graphing calculator to approximate, to the nearest tenth, the real number solutions for each system of equations.

42. $\begin{pmatrix} y = e^x + 1 \\ y = x^3 + x^2 - 2x - 1 \end{pmatrix}$

43. $\begin{pmatrix} y = x^3 + 2x^2 - 3x + 2 \\ y = -x^3 - x^2 + 1 \end{pmatrix}$

44. $\begin{pmatrix} y = 2^x + 1 \\ y = 2^{-x} + 2 \end{pmatrix}$

45. $\begin{pmatrix} y = \ln(x - 1) \\ y = x^2 - 16x + 64 \end{pmatrix}$

46. $\begin{pmatrix} x = y^2 - 2y + 3 \\ x^2 + y^2 = 25 \end{pmatrix}$

47. $\begin{pmatrix} y^2 - x^2 = 16 \\ 2y^2 - x^2 = 8 \end{pmatrix}$

Answers to the Concept Quiz

1. True **2.** False **3.** False **4.** False **5.** True **6.** No solution **7.** 1 **8.** 2

Chapter 13 Summary

CONIC SECTIONS	STANDARD FORM OF THE EQUATION
Circle with the center at the origin	$x^2 + y^2 = r^2$ Center at $(0, 0)$ and a radius of length r
Circle with the center at (h, k)	$(x - h)^2 + (y - k)^2 = r^2$ Center at (h, k) and a radius of length r
Parabola with the y axis as its axis of symmetry and vertex at the origin	$x^2 = 4py$ Focus $(0, p)$, directrix $y = -p$, y-axis symmetry
Parabola with a vertical axis of symmetry and vertex at (h, k)	$(x - h)^2 = 4p(y - k)$ Focus $(h, k + p)$, directrix $y = k - p$, symmetric to the line $x = h$ The graphs of these parabolas open upward or downward.
Parabola with the x axis as its axis of symmetry and vertex at the origin	$y^2 = 4px$ Focus $(p, 0)$, directrix $x = -p$, x-axis symmetry
Parabola with a horizontal axis of symmetry and vertex at (h, k)	$(y - k)^2 = 4p(x - h)$ Focus $(h + p, k)$, directrix $x = h - p$, symmetric to the line $y = k$ The graphs of these parabolas open to the right or to the left.
Ellipse with the major axis on the x axis and center at $(0, 0)$	$\dfrac{x^2}{a^2} + \dfrac{y^2}{b^2} = 1, \qquad a^2 > b^2$ Center $(0, 0)$, vertices $(\pm a, 0)$, endpoints of the minor axis $(0, \pm b)$, foci $(\pm c, 0)$, $c^2 = a^2 - b^2$
Ellipse with the major axis parallel to the x axis and center at (h, k)	$\dfrac{(x - h)^2}{a^2} + \dfrac{(y - k)^2}{b^2} = 1, \qquad a^2 > b^2$ Center (h, k), vertices $(h \pm a, k)$, endpoints of the minor axis $(h, k \pm b)$, foci $(h \pm c, k)$, $c^2 = a^2 - b^2$
Ellipse with the major axis on the y axis and center at $(0, 0)$	$\dfrac{x^2}{a^2} + \dfrac{y^2}{b^2} = 1, \qquad b^2 > a^2$ Center $(0, 0)$, vertices $(0, \pm b)$, endpoints of the minor axis $(\pm a, 0)$, foci $(0, \pm c)$, $c^2 = b^2 - a^2$
Ellipse with the major axis parallel to the y axis and center at (h, k)	$\dfrac{(x - h)^2}{a^2} + \dfrac{(y - k)^2}{b^2} = 1, \qquad b^2 > a^2$ Center (h, k), vertices $(h, k \pm b)$, endpoints of the minor axis $(h \pm a, k)$, foci $(h, k \pm c)$, $c^2 = b^2 - a^2$
Hyperbola with the transverse axis on the x axis and center at $(0, 0)$	$\dfrac{x^2}{a^2} - \dfrac{y^2}{b^2} = 1$ Center $(0, 0)$, vertices $(\pm a, 0)$, endpoints of the conjugate axis $(0, \pm b)$, foci $(\pm c, 0)$, $c^2 = a^2 + b^2$, asymptotes $y = \pm\dfrac{b}{a}x$
Hyperbola with the transverse axis on the horizontal line $y = k$ and center at (h, k)	$\dfrac{(x - h)^2}{a^2} - \dfrac{(y - k)^2}{b^2} = 1$ Center (h, k), vertices $(h \pm a, k)$, endpoints of the conjugate axis $(h, k \pm b)$, foci $(h \pm c, k)$, $c^2 = a^2 + b^2$, asymptotes $y - k = \pm\dfrac{b}{a}(x - h)$

(continued)

CONIC SECTIONS	STANDARD FORM OF THE EQUATION
Hyperbola with the transverse axis on the y axis and center at $(0, 0)$	$\dfrac{y^2}{b^2} - \dfrac{x^2}{a^2} = 1$ Center $(0, 0)$, vertices $(0, \pm b)$, endpoints of the conjugate axis $(\pm a, 0)$, foci $(0, \pm c)$, $c^2 = b^2 + a^2$, asymptotes $y = \pm \dfrac{b}{a}x$
Hyperbola with the transverse axis on the vertical line $x = h$ and center at (h, k)	$\dfrac{(y - k)^2}{b^2} - \dfrac{(x - h)^2}{a^2} = 1$ Center (h, k), vertices $(h, k \pm b)$, endpoints of the conjugate axis $(h \pm a, k)$, foci $(h, k \pm c)$, $c^2 = b^2 + a^2$, asymptotes $y - k = \pm \dfrac{b}{a}(x - h)$

OBJECTIVE	SUMMARY	EXAMPLE
Write the equation of a circle. (Section 13.1/Objective 1)	The standard form of the equation of a circle is $(x - h)^2 + (y - k)^2 = r^2$. We can use the standard form of the equation of a circle to solve two basic kinds of circle problems: 1. Given the coordinates of the center, and the length of a radius of a circle, find its equation. 2. Given the equation of a circle, find its center and the length of a radius.	Write the equation of the circle that has its center at $(-7, 3)$ and a radius of length 4 units. **Solution** Substitute -7 for h, 3 for k, and 4 for r in $(x - h)^2 + (y - k)^2 = r^2$ $(x - (-7))^2 + (y - 3)^2 = 4^2$ $(x + 7)^2 + (y - 3)^2 = 16$
Given the equation of a circle, find the center and the length of a radius. (Section 13.1/Objective 2)	Given an equation of a circle in standard form, $(x - h)^2 + (y - k)^2 = r^2$, the center of the circle is located at (h, k) and a radius has a length of r.	Find the center and the length of a radius of the circle with an equation of $(x - 4)^2 + (y + 1)^2 = 72$. **Solution** The center is located at $(4, -1)$ and the length of a radius is $\sqrt{72} = 6\sqrt{2}$.
Find the vertex, focus, and directrix of a parabola. (Section 13.2/Objective 1)	For parabolas with graphs that open upward or downward, the equations are of the form $(x - h)^2 = 4p(y - k)$ and the vertex is located at (h, k), the focus is located at $(h, k + p)$, and the equation of the directrix is $y = k - p$. For parabolas with graphs that open left or right, the equations are of the form $(y - k)^2 = 4p(x - h)$, and the vertex is located at (h, k), the focus is located at $(h + p, k)$, and the equation of the directrix is $x = h - p$.	Find the vertex, focus, and directrix of a parabola $x^2 + 6x - 4y + 13 = 0$. **Solution** Write the equation as $x^2 + 6x = 4y - 13$ and complete the square by adding 9 to each side. $x^2 + 6x + 9 = 4y - 13 + 9$ $(x + 3)^2 = 4y - 4$ $(x + 3)^2 = 4(y - 1)$ $h = -3 \qquad 4p = 4 \qquad k = 1$ $h = -3 \qquad p = 1 \qquad k = 1$ The vertex is located at $(-3, 1)$. The focus is located at $(-3, 1 + 1) = (-3, 2)$ The equation of the directrix is $y = 1 - 1 = 0$

OBJECTIVE	SUMMARY	EXAMPLE
Determine the equation of a parabola. (Section 13.2/Objective 3)	The standard form $(x - h)^2 = 4p (y - k)$ will be used if the directrix is a horizontal line. The standard form $$(y - k)^2 = 4p(x - h)$$ will be used if the equation of the directrix is a vertical line.	Write the equation of a parabola if its focus is at $(2, 3)$, and the equation of the directrix is $x = 6$. **Solution** Because the directrix is a vertical line, the equation will be in the form $(y - k)^2 = 4p(x - h)$. The vertex is halfway between the focus and the directrix, so the vertex is at $(4, 3)$. This means that $h = 4$ and $k = 3$. Because the focus is to the left of the directrix, the parabola opens to the left, and the directed distance from the vertex to the focus is -2 units; thus $p = -2$. The equation is $(y - 3)^2 = -8(x - 4)$.
Find the vertices, endpoints of the minor axis, and the foci of an ellipse. (Section 13.3/Objective 1)	When the equation is of the form $\dfrac{(x - h)^2}{a^2} + \dfrac{(y - k)^2}{b^2} = 1$, and $a^2 > b^2$, the major axis is a horizontal line. When the equation is of the form $\dfrac{(x - h)^2}{a^2} + \dfrac{(y - k)^2}{b^2} = 1$, and $b^2 > a^2$, the major axis is a vertical line.	Find the vertices, endpoints of the minor axis, and the foci of the ellipse $$\dfrac{(x + 2)^2}{25} + \dfrac{(y - 1)^2}{16} = 1$$ **Solution** From the equation we can determine that $h = -2, k = 1, a = \sqrt{25} = 5$, $b = \sqrt{16} = 4$, and $c = \sqrt{25 - 16} = 3$. Because $a > b$, the foci and the vertices are on the horizontal line $y = 1$. The vertices are 5 units to the left and right of the center $(-2, 1)$, so the vertices are at $(-7, 1)$ and $(3, 1)$. The endpoints of the minor axis are 4 units up and down from the center, so they are located at $(-2, 5)$ and $(-2, -3)$. The foci are 3 units to the left and right of the center, so the foci are at $(-5, 1)$ and $(1, 1)$.
Determine the equation of an ellipse. (Section 13.3/Objective 3)	First determine if the vertices and foci are on a horizontal line or a vertical line. Then use the appropriate form of the equation of an ellipse.	Write the equation of the ellipse that has vertices at $(3, 4)$ and $(3, -4)$ and foci at $(3, 3)$ and $(3, -3)$. **Solution** Because the vertices are on the same vertical line, the equation of the ellipse is of the form $\dfrac{(x - h)^2}{a^2} + \dfrac{(y - k)^2}{b^2} = 1$, where $b > a$. The center is at the midpoint of the major axis $(3, 0)$. The distance between the center and a vertex is 4 units; thus $b = 4$. The distance between the center and a focus is 3 units; thus $c = 3$. Therefore $a = \sqrt{16 - 9} = \sqrt{7}$. The equation is $\dfrac{(x - 3)^2}{7} + \dfrac{y^2}{16} = 1$.

(continued)

OBJECTIVE	SUMMARY	EXAMPLE
For a hyperbola, find the vertices, foci, and equations of the asymptotes. (Section 13.4/Objective 1)	A hyperbola with the transverse axis on the horizontal line $y = k$ and center at (h, k) has an equation of the form $$\frac{(x - h)^2}{a^2} - \frac{(y - k)^2}{b^2} = 1$$ A hyperbola with the transverse axis on the vertical line $x = h$, and center at (h, k), has an equation of the form $$\frac{(y - k)^2}{b^2} - \frac{(x - h)^2}{a^2} = 1.$$	Find the vertices, foci, and equations of the asymptotes for the hyperbola $$\frac{(y - 1)^2}{9} - \frac{(x + 2)^2}{16} = 1$$ **Solution** The center is at $(-2, 1)$, and the transverse axis is on the line $x = -2$. Because $a = 4$ the vertices are 4 units above and below the center so the vertices are located at $(-2, 5)$ and $(-2, -3)$. Because $c = \sqrt{9 + 16} = \sqrt{25} = 5$, the foci are located 5 units above and below the center at $(-2, 6)$ and $(-2, -4)$. With $a = 4$ and $b = 3$, the slopes of the asymptotes are $\pm\frac{3}{4}$. Using the slope and the center $(-2, 1)$ the equations for the asymptotes are $$y - 1 = \frac{3}{4}(x + 2)$$ and $$y - 1 = -\frac{3}{4}(x + 2)$$ Simplifying these equations yields $3x - 4y = -10$ and $3x + 4y = -2$.
Determine the equation of a hyperbola. (Section 13.4/Objective 3)	First determine if the transverse axis is a horizontal or vertical line. Then use the appropriate formula for a hyperbola.	Find the equation of the hyperbola with vertices at $(2, -3)$ and $(6, -3)$ and with foci at $(1, -3)$ and $(7, -3)$. **Solution** Because the vertices and foci are on the same horizontal line, the hyperbola has an equation of the form $\frac{(x - h)^2}{a^2} - \frac{(y - k)^2}{b^2} = 1$. The center is the midpoint of the vertices, therefore the center is at $(4, -3)$. The distance between the center and a vertex is 2 units, so $a = 2$. The distance between the center and a focus is 3 units, so $c = 3$. We obtain b by $b = \sqrt{9 - 4} = \sqrt{5}$. The equation of the hyperbola in general form is $\frac{(x - 4)^2}{4} - \frac{(y + 3)^2}{5} = 1$.

OBJECTIVE	SUMMARY	EXAMPLE
Solve systems of equations involving nonlinear equations using the substitution method. (Section 13.5/Objective 2)	Graphing the equations of the system will provide a basis for approximating the real number solutions if there are any. To solve by substitution, solve one equation for x or y and substitute for that variable in the other equation.	Solve the system $\begin{pmatrix} y = x^2 - 6x - 10 \\ y = -x + 6 \end{pmatrix}$. **Solution** The first equation is already solved for y, so substitute for y in the second equation. $$-x + 6 = x^2 - 6x + 10$$ Now solve for x. $$0 = x^2 - 5x + 4$$ $$0 = (x - 4)(x - 1)$$ $$x = 4 \quad \text{or} \quad x = 1$$ Now substitute 4 for x in the second equation to find the value of y. $$y = -x + 6 = -4 + 6 = 2$$ Now substitute 1 for x in the second equation to find the value of y. $$y = -x + 6 = -1 + 6 = 5$$ The solutions are $(4, 2)$ and $(1, 5)$.
Solve systems of equations involving nonlinear equations using the elimination method. (Section 13.5/Objective 3)	Certain systems of equations can be solved by using the elimination method. In order to solve by elimination, the addition of the equation has to eliminate one variable. Sometimes the equations have to be multiplied by a nonzero constant before a variable can be eliminated.	Solve the system $\begin{pmatrix} x^2 + 2y^2 = 5 \\ x^2 + y^2 = 4 \end{pmatrix}$. **Solution** Multiply the second equation by -1 and add the equations. $$x^2 + 2y^2 = 5$$ $$\underline{-x^2 - y^2 = -4}$$ $$y^2 = 1$$ $$y = 1 \quad \text{or} \quad y = -1$$ Now substitute 1 for y in the second equation and determine the value for x. $$x^2 + 1^2 = 4$$ $$x^2 = 3$$ $$x = \pm\sqrt{3}$$ Now substitute -1 for y in the second equation and determine the value for x. $$x^2 + (-1)^2 = 4$$ $$x^2 = 3$$ $$x = \pm\sqrt{3}$$ The solutions are $\left(\sqrt{3}, 1\right), \left(-\sqrt{3}, 1\right), \left(\sqrt{3}, -1\right)$, and $\left(-\sqrt{3}, -1\right)$.

Chapter 13 Review Problem Set

For Problems 1–14, (a) identify the conic section as a circle, a parabola, an ellipse, or a hyperbola. (b) If it is a circle, find its center and the length of a radius; if it is a parabola, find its vertex, focus, and directrix; if it is an ellipse, find its vertices, the endpoints of its minor axis, and its foci; if it is a hyperbola, find its vertices, the endpoints of its conjugate axis, its foci, and its asymptotes. (c) Sketch each of the curves.

1. $x^2 + 2y^2 = 32$ **2.** $y^2 = -12x$

3. $3y^2 - x^2 = 9$ **4.** $2x^2 - 3y^2 = 18$

5. $5x^2 + 2y^2 = 20$ **6.** $x^2 = 2y$

7. $x^2 + y^2 = 10$

8. $x^2 - 8x - 2y^2 + 4y + 10 = 0$

9. $9x^2 - 54x + 2y^2 + 8y + 71 = 0$

10. $y^2 - 2y + 4x + 9 = 0$

11. $x^2 + 2x + 8y + 25 = 0$

12. $x^2 + 10x + 4y^2 - 16y + 25 = 0$

13. $3y^2 + 12y - 2x^2 - 8x - 8 = 0$

14. $x^2 - 6x + y^2 + 4y - 3 = 0$

For Problems 15–28, find the equation of the indicated conic section that satisfies the given conditions.

15. Circle with center at $(-8, 3)$ and a radius of length $\sqrt{5}$ units

16. Parabola with vertex $(0, 0)$, focus $(-5, 0)$, directrix $x = 5$

17. Ellipse with vertices $(0, \pm 4)$, foci $\left(0, \pm\sqrt{15}\right)$

18. Hyperbola with vertices $\left(\pm\sqrt{2}, 0\right)$, length of conjugate axis 10

19. Circle with center at $(5, -12)$, passes through the origin

20. Ellipse with vertices $(\pm 2, 0)$, contains the point $(1, -2)$

21. Parabola with vertex $(0, 0)$, symmetric with respect to the y axis, contains the point $(2, 6)$

22. Hyperbola with vertices $(0, \pm 1)$, foci $\left(0, \pm\sqrt{10}\right)$

23. Ellipse with vertices $(6, 1)$ and $(6, 7)$, length of minor axis 2 units

24. Parabola with vertex $(4, -2)$, focus $(6, -2)$

25. Hyperbola with vertices $(-5, -3)$ and $(-5, -5)$, foci $(-5, -2)$ and $(-5, -6)$

26. Parabola with vertex $(-6, -3)$, symmetric with respect to the line $x = -6$, contains the point $(-5, -2)$

27. Ellipse with endpoints of minor axis $(-5, 2)$ and $(-5, -2)$, length of major axis 10 units

28. Hyperbola with vertices $(2, 0)$ and $(6, 0)$, length of conjugate axis 8 units

For Problems 29–34, (a) graph the system, and (b) solve the system by using the substitution or elimination method.

29. $\begin{pmatrix} x^2 + y^2 = 17 \\ x - 4y = -17 \end{pmatrix}$ **30.** $\begin{pmatrix} x^2 - y^2 = 8 \\ 3x - y = 8 \end{pmatrix}$

31. $\begin{pmatrix} x - y = 1 \\ y = x^2 + 4x + 1 \end{pmatrix}$ **32.** $\begin{pmatrix} 4x^2 - y^2 = 16 \\ 9x^2 + 9y^2 = 16 \end{pmatrix}$

33. $\begin{pmatrix} x^2 + 2y^2 = 8 \\ 2x^2 + 3y^2 = 12 \end{pmatrix}$ **34.** $\begin{pmatrix} y^2 - x^2 = 1 \\ 4x^2 + y^2 = 4 \end{pmatrix}$

Chapter 13   Test

1. Find the focus of the parabola $x^2 = -20y$.

2. Find the vertex of the parabola $y^2 - 4y - 8x - 20 = 0$.

3. Find the equation of the directrix for the parabola $2y^2 = 24x$.

4. Find the focus of the parabola $y^2 = 24x$.

5. Find the vertex of the parabola $x^2 + 4x - 12y - 8 = 0$.

6. Find the center of the circle $x^2 + 6x + y^2 + 18y + 87 = 0$.

7. Find the equation of the parabola that has its vertex at the origin, is symmetric with respect to the x axis, and contains the point $(-2, 4)$.

8. Find the equation of the parabola that has its vertex at $(3, 4)$ and its focus at $(3, 1)$.

9. Find the equation of the circle that has its center at $(-1, 6)$ and has a radius of length 5 units.

10. Find the length of the major axis of the ellipse $x^2 - 4x + 9y^2 - 18y + 4 = 0$.

11. Find the endpoints of the minor axis of the ellipse $9x^2 + 90x + 4y^2 - 8y + 193 = 0$.

12. Find the foci of the ellipse $x^2 + 4y^2 = 16$.

13. Find the center of the ellipse $3x^2 + 30x + y^2 - 16y + 79 = 0$.

14. Find the equation of the ellipse that has the endpoints of its major axis at $(0, \pm10)$ and its foci at $(0, \pm8)$.

15. Find the equation of the ellipse that has the endpoints of its major axis at $(2, -2)$ and $(10, -2)$ and the endpoints of its minor axis at $(6, 0)$ and $(6, -4)$.

16. Find the equations of the asymptotes of the hyperbola $4y^2 - 9x^2 = 32$.

17. Find the vertices of the hyperbola $y^2 - 6y - 3x^2 - 6x - 3 = 0$.

18. Find the foci of the hyperbola $5x^2 - 4y^2 = 20$.

19. Find the equation of the hyperbola that has its vertices at $(\pm6, 0)$ and its foci at $\left(\pm4\sqrt{3}, 0\right)$.

20. Find the equation of the hyperbola that has its vertices at $(0, 4)$ and $(-2, 4)$ and its foci at $(2, 4)$ and $(-4, 4)$.

21. How many real number solutions are there for the system $\begin{pmatrix} x^2 + y^2 = 16 \\ x^2 - 4y = 8 \end{pmatrix}$?

22. Solve the system $\begin{pmatrix} x^2 + 4y^2 = 25 \\ xy = 6 \end{pmatrix}$

For Problems 23–25, graph each conic section.

23. $y^2 + 4y + 8x - 4 = 0$

24. $9x^2 - 36x + 4y^2 + 16y + 16 = 0$

25. $4x_2 + 24x - 9y_2 = 0$

14

Sequences and Mathematical Induction

14.1 Arithmetic Sequences

14.2 Geometric Sequences

14.3 Another Look at Problem Solving

14.4 Mathematical Induction

©Royalty-Free/CORBIS

When objects are arranged in a sequence, the total number of objects is the sum of the terms of the sequence.

Suppose that an auditorium has 35 seats in the first row, 40 seats in the second row, 45 seats in the third row, and so on, for ten rows. The numbers 35, 40, 45, 50, . . . , 80 represent the number of seats per row from row 1 through row 10. This list of numbers has a constant difference of 5 between any two successive numbers in the list; such a list is called an *arithmetic sequence*. (Used in this sense, the word arithmetic is pronounced with the accent on the syllable *met*.)

Suppose that a fungus culture growing under controlled conditions doubles in size each day. If today the size of the culture is 6 units, then the numbers 12, 24, 48, 96, 192 represent the size of the culture for the next 5 days. In this list of numbers, each number after the first is twice the previous number; such a list is called a *geometric sequence*. Arithmetic sequences and geometric sequences will be the center of our attention in this chapter.

Video tutorials based on section learning objectives are available in a variety of delivery modes.

14.1   Arithmetic Sequences

OBJECTIVES

1. Write the terms of a sequence
2. Find the general term for an arithmetic sequence
3. Find a specific term for an arithmetic sequence
4. Find the sum of the terms of an arithmetic sequence
5. Determine the sum indicated by summation notation

An **infinite sequence** is a function with a domain that is the set of positive integers. For example, consider the function defined by the equation

$$f(n) = 5n + 1$$

in which the domain is the set of positive integers. If we substitute the numbers of the domain in order, starting with 1, we can list the resulting ordered pairs:

$$(1, 6) \quad (2, 11) \quad (3, 16) \quad (4, 21) \quad (5, 26)$$

and so on. However, because we know we are using the domain of positive integers in order, starting with 1, there is no need to use ordered pairs. We can simply express the infinite sequence as

$$6, 11, 16, 21, 26, \ldots$$

Often the letter a is used to represent sequential functions, and the functional value of a at n is written a_n (this is read "a sub n") instead of $a(n)$. The sequence is then expressed as

$$a_1, a_2, a_3, a_4, \ldots$$

where a_1 is the *first term*, a_2 is the *second term*, a_3 is the *third term,* and so on. The expression a_n, which defines the sequence, is called the *general term* of the sequence. Knowing the general term of a sequence enables us to find as many terms of the sequence as needed and also to find any specific terms. Consider the following example.

Classroom Example
Find the first five terms of the sequence in which $a_n = 3n^3 + 1$, and then find the 10th term.

EXAMPLE 1

Find the first five terms of the sequence when $a_n = 2n^2 - 3$; find the 20th term.

Solution

The first five terms are generated by replacing n with 1, 2, 3, 4, and 5:

$$a_1 = 2(1)^2 - 3 = -1 \qquad a_2 = 2(2)^2 - 3 = 5$$
$$a_3 = 2(3)^2 - 3 = 15 \qquad a_4 = 2(4)^2 - 3 = 29$$
$$a_5 = 2(5)^2 - 3 = 47$$

The first five terms are thus $-1, 5, 15, 29,$ and 47. The 20th term is

$$a_{20} = 2(20)^2 - 3 = 797$$

Arithmetic Sequences

An **arithmetic sequence** (also called an **arithmetic progression**) is a sequence that has a common difference between successive terms. The following are examples of arithmetic sequences:

$$1, 8, 15, 22, 29, \ldots$$
$$4, 7, 10, 13, 16, \ldots$$

$$4, 1, -2, -5, -8, \ldots$$
$$-1, -6, -11, -16, -21, \ldots$$

The common difference in the first sequence is 7. That is, $8 - 1 = 7$, $15 - 8 = 7$, $22 - 15 = 7$, $29 - 22 = 7$, and so on. The common differences for the next three sequences are 3, -3, and -5, respectively.

In a more general setting, we say that the sequence

$$a_1, a_2, a_3, a_4, \ldots, a_n, \ldots$$

is an arithmetic sequence if and only if there is a real number d such that

$$a_{k+1} - a_k = d$$

for every positive integer k. The number d is called the **common difference**.

From the definition, we see that $a_{k+1} = a_k + d$. In other words, we can generate an arithmetic sequence that has a common difference of d by starting with a first term a_1 and then simply adding d to each successive term.

First term:	a_1
Second term:	$a_1 + d$
Third term:	$a_1 + 2d$ $(a_1 + d) + d = a_1 + 2d$
Fourth term:	$a_1 + 3d$
.	
.	
.	
nth term:	$a_1 + (n - 1)d$

Thus the **general term** of an arithmetic sequence is given by

$$a_n = a_1 + (n - 1)d$$

where a_1 is the first term, and d is the common difference. This formula for the general term can be used to solve a variety of problems involving arithmetic sequences.

Classroom Example
Find the general term of the arithmetic sequence $-4, 3, 10, 17, \ldots$.

EXAMPLE 2   Find the general term of the arithmetic sequence $6, 2, -2, -6, \ldots$.

Solution

The common difference, d, is $2 - 6 = -4$, and the first term, a_1, is 6. Substitute these values into $a_n = a_1 + (n - 1)d$ and simplify to obtain

$$\begin{aligned} a_n &= a_1 + (n - 1)d \\ &= 6 + (n - 1)(-4) \\ &= 6 - 4n + 4 \\ &= -4n + 10 \end{aligned}$$

Classroom Example
Find the 15th term of the arithmetic sequence $11, 8, 5, 2, \ldots$.

EXAMPLE 3   Find the 40th term of the arithmetic sequence $1, 5, 9, 13, \ldots$.

Solution

Using $a_n = a_1 + (n - 1)d$, we obtain

$$\begin{aligned} a_{40} &= 1 + (40 - 1)4 \\ &= 1 + (39)(4) \\ &= 157 \end{aligned}$$

Classroom Example
Find the first term of the arithmetic
sequence if the fifth term is 28 and
the twelfth term is 63.

EXAMPLE 4

Find the first term of the arithmetic sequence if the fourth term is 26 and the ninth term is 61.

Solution

Using $a_n = a_1 + (n-1)d$ with $a_4 = 26$ (the fourth term is 26) and $a_9 = 61$ (the ninth term is 61), we have

$$26 = a_1 + (4-1)d = a_1 + 3d$$
$$61 = a_1 + (9-1)d = a_1 + 8d$$

Solving the system of equations

$$\begin{pmatrix} a_1 + 3d = 26 \\ a_1 + 8d = 61 \end{pmatrix}$$

yields $a_1 = 5$ and $d = 7$. Thus the first term is 5. ∎

Sums of Arithmetic Sequences

We often use sequences to solve problems, so we need to be able to find the sum of a certain number of terms of the sequence. Before we develop a general-sum formula for arithmetic sequences, let's consider an approach to a specific problem that we can then use in a general setting.

Classroom Example
Find the sum of the first 25 positive
integers.

EXAMPLE 5   Find the sum of the first 100 positive integers.

Solution

We are being asked to find the sum of $1 + 2 + 3 + 4 + \cdots + 100$. Rather than adding in the usual way, we will find the sum in the following manner: Let's simply write the indicated sum forward and backward, and then add in columns:

$$
\begin{array}{ccccccccccc}
1 & + & 2 & + & 3 & + & 4 & + \cdots + & 100 \\
100 & + & 99 & + & 98 & + & 97 & + \cdots + & 1 \\
\hline
101 & + & 101 & + & 101 & + & 101 & + \cdots + & 101
\end{array}
$$

We have produced 100 sums of 101. However, this result is double the amount we want because we wrote the sum twice. To find the sum of just the numbers 1 to 100, we need to multiply 100 by 101 and then divide by 2:

$$\frac{100(101)}{2} = \frac{\overset{50}{\cancel{100}}(101)}{\cancel{2}} = 5050$$

Thus the sum of the first 100 positive integers is 5050. ∎

The *forward–backward* approach we used in Example 5 can be used to develop a formula for finding the sum of the first n terms of any arithmetic sequence. Consider an arithmetic sequence $a_1, a_2, a_3, a_4, \ldots, a_n$ with a common difference of d. Use S_n to represent the sum of the first n terms, and proceed as follows:

$$S_n = a_1 + (a_1 + d) + (a_1 + 2d) + \cdots + (a_n - 2d) + (a_n - d) + a_n$$

Now write this sum in reverse:

$$S_n = a_n + (a_n - d) + (a_n - 2d) + \cdots + (a_1 + 2d) + (a_1 + d) + a_1$$

Add the two equations to produce

$$2S_n = (a_1 + a_n) + (a_1 + a_n) + (a_1 + a_n) + \cdots + (a_1 + a_n) + (a_1 + a_n) + (a_1 + a_n)$$

That is, we have n sums $a_1 + a_n$, so

$$2S_n = n(a_1 + a_n)$$

from which we obtain a **sum formula**:

$$S_n = \frac{n(a_1 + a_n)}{2}$$

Using the nth-term formula and/or the sum formula, we can solve a variety of problems involving arithmetic sequences.

Classroom Example
Find the sum of the first 20 terms of the arithmetic sequence 2, 7, 12, 17, ...

EXAMPLE 6

Find the sum of the first 30 terms of the arithmetic sequence $3, 7, 11, 15, \ldots$.

Solution

To use the formula $S_n = \dfrac{n(a_1 + a_n)}{2}$, we need to know the number of terms (n), the first term (a_1), and the last term (a_n). We are given the number of terms and the first term, so we need to find the last term. Using $a_n = a_1 + (n - 1)d$, we can find the 30th term.

$$a_{30} = 3 + (30 - 1)4 = 3 + 29(4) = 119$$

Now we can use the sum formula.

$$S_{30} = \frac{30(3 + 119)}{2} = 1830$$

Classroom Example
Find the sum
$3 + 11 + 19 + \cdots + 283$.

EXAMPLE 7   Find the sum $7 + 10 + 13 + \cdots + 157$.

Solution

To use the sum formula, we need to know the number of terms. Applying the nth-term formula will give us that information:

$$a_n = a_1 + (n - 1)d$$
$$157 = 7 + (n - 1)3$$
$$157 = 7 + 3n - 3$$
$$157 = 3n + 4$$
$$153 = 3n$$
$$51 = n$$

Now we can use the sum formula:

$$S_{51} = \frac{51(7 + 157)}{2} = 4182$$

Keep in mind that we developed the sum formula for an arithmetic sequence by using the forward–backward technique, which we had previously used on a specific problem. Now that we have the sum formula, we have two choices when solving problems. We can either memorize the formula and use it or simply use the forward–backward technique. If you choose to use the formula and some day you forget it, don't panic. Just use the forward–backward technique. In other words, understanding the development of a formula often enables you to do problems even when you forget the formula itself.

Summation Notation

Sometimes a special notation is used to indicate the sum of a certain number of terms of a sequence. The capital Greek letter *sigma*, Σ, is used as a **summation symbol**. For example,

$$\sum_{i=1}^{5} a_i$$

represents the sum $a_1 + a_2 + a_3 + a_4 + a_5$. The letter i is frequently used as the **index of summation**; the letter i takes on all integer values from the lower limit to the upper limit, inclusive. Thus

$$\sum_{i=1}^{4} b_i = b_1 + b_2 + b_3 + b_4$$

$$\sum_{i=3}^{7} a_i = a_3 + a_4 + a_5 + a_6 + a_7$$

$$\sum_{i=1}^{15} i^2 = 1^2 + 2^2 + 3^2 + \cdots + 15^2$$

$$\sum_{i=1}^{n} a_i = a_1 + a_2 + a_3 + \cdots + a_n$$

If $a_1, a_2, a_3, \ldots$ represents an arithmetic sequence, we can now write the sum formula

$$\sum_{i=1}^{n} a_i = \frac{n}{2}(a_1 + a_n)$$

Classroom Example
Find the sum $\sum_{i=1}^{28} (5i - 3)$.

EXAMPLE 8

Find the sum $\sum_{i=1}^{50} (3i + 4)$.

Solution

This indicated sum means

$$\sum_{i=1}^{50} (3i + 4) = [3(1) + 4] + [3(2) + 4] + [3(3) + 4] + \cdots + [3(50) + 4]$$

$$= 7 + 10 + 13 + \cdots + 154$$

Because this is an indicated sum of an arithmetic sequence, we can use our sum formula:

$$S_{50} = \frac{50}{2}(7 + 154) = 4025$$

Classroom Example
Find the sum $\sum_{i=4}^{9} 3i^2$.

EXAMPLE 9

Find the sum $\sum_{i=2}^{7} 2i^2$.

Solution

This indicated sum means

$$\sum_{i=2}^{7} 2i^2 = 2(2)^2 + 2(3)^2 + 2(4)^2 + 2(5)^2 + 2(6)^2 + 2(7)^2$$

$$= 8 + 18 + 32 + 50 + 72 + 98$$

This is not the indicated sum of an *arithmetic* sequence; therefore let's simply add the numbers in the usual way. The sum is 278.

Example 9 suggests a word of caution. Be sure to analyze the sequence of numbers that is represented by the summation symbol. You may or may not be able to use a formula for adding the numbers.

Concept Quiz 14.1

For Problems 1–8, answer true or false.

1. An infinite sequence is a function whose domain is the set of all real numbers.

2. An arithmetic sequence is a sequence that has a common difference between successive terms.

3. The sequence 2, 4, 8, 16, . . . is an arithmetic sequence.

4. The odd whole numbers form an arithmetic sequence.

5. The terms of an arithmetic sequence are always positive.

6. The 6th term of an arithmetic sequence is equal to the first term plus 6 times the common difference.

7. The sum formula for n terms of an arithmetic sequence is n times the average of the first and last terms.

8. The indicated sum $\displaystyle\sum_{i=1}^{4} (2i - 7)^2$ is the sum of the first four terms of an arithmetic sequence.

Problem Set 14.1

For Problems 1–10, write the first five terms of the sequence that has the indicated general term. (Objective 1)

1. $a_n = 3n - 7$

2. $a_n = 5n - 2$

3. $a_n = -2n + 4$

4. $a_n = -4n + 7$

5. $a_n = 3n^2 - 1$

6. $a_n = 2n^2 - 6$

7. $a_n = n(n - 1)$

8. $a_n = (n + 1)(n + 2)$

9. $a_n = 2^{n+1}$

10. $a_n = 3^{n-1}$

11. Find the 15th and 30th terms of the sequence when $a_n = -5n - 4$.

12. Find the 20th and 50th terms of the sequence when $a_n = -n - 3$.

13. Find the 25th and 50th terms of the sequence when $a_n = (-1)^{n+1}$.

14. Find the 10th and 15th terms of the sequence when $a_n = -n^2 - 10$.

For Problems 15–24, find the general term (the nth term) for each arithmetic sequence. (Objective 2)

15. 11, 13, 15, 17, 19, . . .

16. 7, 10, 13, 16, 19, . . .

17. 2, −1, −4, −7, −10, . . .

18. 4, 2, 0, −2, −4, . . .

19. $\dfrac{3}{2}, 2, \dfrac{5}{2}, 3, \dfrac{7}{2}, \ldots$

20. $0, \dfrac{1}{2}, 1, \dfrac{3}{2}, 2, \ldots$

21. 2, 6, 10, 14, 18, . . .

22. 2, 7, 12, 17, 22, . . .

23. −3, −6, −9, −12, −15, . . .

24. −4, −8, −12, −16, −20, . . .

For Problems 25–30, find the required term for each arithmetic sequence. (Objective 3)

25. The 15th term of 3, 8, 13, 18, . . .

26. The 20th term of 4, 11, 18, 25, . . .

27. The 30th term of 15, 26, 37, 48, . . .

28. The 35th term of 9, 17, 25, 33, . . .

29. The 52nd term of $1, \dfrac{5}{3}, \dfrac{7}{3}, 3, \ldots$

30. The 47th term of $\dfrac{1}{2}, \dfrac{5}{4}, 2, \dfrac{11}{4}, \ldots$

For Problems 31–42, solve each problem.

31. If the 6th term of an arithmetic sequence is 12 and the 10th term is 16, find the first term.

32. If the 5th term of an arithmetic sequence is 14 and the 12th term is 42, find the first term.

33. If the 3rd term of an arithmetic sequence is 20 and the 7th term is 32, find the 25th term.

34. If the 5th term of an arithmetic sequence is −5 and the 15th term is −25, find the 50th term.

35. Find the sum of the first 50 terms of the arithmetic sequence 5, 7, 9, 11, 13, ...

36. Find the sum of the first 30 terms of the arithmetic sequence $0, 2, 4, 6, 8, \ldots$.

37. Find the sum of the first 40 terms of the arithmetic sequence $2, 6, 10, 14, 18, \ldots$.

38. Find the sum of the first 60 terms of the arithmetic sequence $-2, 3, 8, 13, 18, \ldots$.

39. Find the sum of the first 75 terms of the arithmetic sequence $5, 2, -1, -4, -7, \ldots$.

40. Find the sum of the first 80 terms of the arithmetic sequence $7, 3, -1, -5, -9, \ldots$.

41. Find the sum of the first 50 terms of the arithmetic sequence $\dfrac{1}{2}, 1, \dfrac{3}{2}, 2, \dfrac{5}{2}, \ldots$.

42. Find the sum of the first 100 terms of the arithmetic sequence $-\dfrac{1}{3}, \dfrac{1}{3}, 1, \dfrac{5}{3}, \dfrac{7}{3}, \ldots$.

For Problems 43–50, find the indicated sum. **(Objective 4)**

43. $1 + 5 + 9 + 13 + \cdots + 197$

44. $3 + 8 + 13 + 18 + \cdots + 398$

45. $2 + 8 + 14 + 20 + \cdots + 146$

46. $6 + 9 + 12 + 15 + \cdots + 93$

47. $(-7) + (-10) + (-13) + (-16) + \cdots + (-109)$

48. $(-5) + (-9) + (-13) + (-17) + \cdots + (-169)$

49. $(-5) + (-3) + (-1) + 1 + \cdots + 119$

50. $(-7) + (-4) + (-1) + 2 + \cdots + 131$

For Problems 51–58, solve each problem.

51. Find the sum of the first 200 odd whole numbers.

52. Find the sum of the first 175 positive even whole numbers.

53. Find the sum of all even numbers between 18 and 482, inclusive.

54. Find the sum of all odd numbers between 17 and 379, inclusive.

55. Find the sum of the first 30 terms of the arithmetic sequence with the general term $a_n = 5n - 4$.

56. Find the sum of the first 40 terms of the arithmetic sequence with the general term $a_n = 4n - 7$.

57. Find the sum of the first 25 terms of the arithmetic sequence with the general term $a_n = -4n - 1$.

58. Find the sum of the first 35 terms of the arithmetic sequence with the general term $a_n = -5n - 3$.

For Problems 59–70, find each sum. **(Objective 5)**

59. $\displaystyle\sum_{i=1}^{45} (5i + 2)$

60. $\displaystyle\sum_{i=1}^{38} (3i + 6)$

61. $\displaystyle\sum_{i=1}^{30} (-2i + 4)$

62. $\displaystyle\sum_{i=1}^{40} (-3i + 3)$

63. $\displaystyle\sum_{i=4}^{32} (3i - 10)$

64. $\displaystyle\sum_{i=6}^{47} (4i - 9)$

65. $\displaystyle\sum_{i=10}^{20} 4i$

66. $\displaystyle\sum_{i=15}^{30} (-5i)$

67. $\displaystyle\sum_{i=1}^{5} i^2$

68. $\displaystyle\sum_{i=1}^{6} (i^2 + 1)$

69. $\displaystyle\sum_{i=3}^{8} (2i^2 + i)$

70. $\displaystyle\sum_{i=4}^{7} (3i^2 - 2)$

Thoughts Into Words

71. Before developing the formula $a_n = a_1 + (n - 1)d$, we stated the equation $a_{k+1} - a_k = d$. In your own words, explain what this equation says.

72. Explain how to find the sum $1 + 2 + 3 + 4 + \cdots + 175$ without using the sum formula.

73. Explain in words how to find the sum of the first n terms of an arithmetic sequence.

74. Explain how one can tell that a particular sequence is an arithmetic sequence.

Further Investigations

The general term of a sequence can consist of one expression for certain values of n and another expression (or expressions) for other values of n. That is, a *multiple description* of the sequence can be given. For example,

$$a_n = \begin{cases} 2n + 3 & \text{for } n \text{ odd} \\ 3n - 2 & \text{for } n \text{ even} \end{cases}$$

means that we use $a_n = 2n + 3$ for $n = 1, 3, 5, 7, \ldots$, and we use $a_n = 3n - 2$ for $n = 2, 4, 6, 8, \ldots$. The first six terms of this sequence are 5, 4, 9, 10, 13, and 16.

For Problems 75–78, write the first six terms of each sequence.

75. $a_n = \begin{cases} 2n + 1 & \text{for } n \text{ odd} \\ 2n - 1 & \text{for } n \text{ even} \end{cases}$

76. $a_n = \begin{cases} \dfrac{1}{n} & \text{for } n \text{ odd} \\[2mm] n^2 & \text{for } n \text{ even} \end{cases}$

77. $a_n = \begin{cases} 3n + 1 & \text{for } n \leq 3 \\ 4n - 3 & \text{for } n > 3 \end{cases}$

78. $a_n = \begin{cases} 5n - 1 & \text{for } n \text{ a multiple of 3} \\ 2n & \text{otherwise} \end{cases}$

The multiple-description approach can also be used to give a *recursive description* for a sequence. A sequence is said to be *described recursively* if the first n terms are stated, and then each succeeding term is defined as a function of one or more of the preceding terms. For example,

$\begin{cases} a_1 = 2 \\ a_n = 2a_{n-1} & \text{for } n \geq 2 \end{cases}$

means that the first term, a_1, is 2 and each succeeding term is 2 times the previous term. Thus the first six terms are 2, 4, 8, 16, 32, and 64.

For Problems 79–84, write the first six terms of each sequence.

79. $\begin{cases} a_1 = 4 \\ a_n = 3a_{n-1} & \text{for } n \geq 2 \end{cases}$

80. $\begin{cases} a_1 = 3 \\ a_n = a_{n-1} + 2 & \text{for } n \geq 2 \end{cases}$

81. $\begin{cases} a_1 = 1 \\ a_2 = 1 \\ a_n = a_{n-2} + a_{n-1} & \text{for } n \geq 3 \end{cases}$

82. $\begin{cases} a_1 = 2 \\ a_2 = 3 \\ a_n = 2a_{n-2} + 3a_{n-1} & \text{for } n \geq 3 \end{cases}$

83. $\begin{cases} a_1 = 3 \\ a_2 = 1 \\ a_n = (a_{n-1} - a_{n-2})^2 & \text{for } n \geq 3 \end{cases}$

84. $\begin{cases} a_1 = 1 \\ a_2 = 2 \\ a_3 = 3 \\ a_n = a_{n-1} + a_{n-2} + a_{n-3} & \text{for } n \geq 4 \end{cases}$

Answers to the Concept Quiz

1. False **2.** True **3.** False **4.** True **5.** False **6.** False **7.** True **8.** False

14.2 Geometric Sequences

OBJECTIVES
1. Find the general term for a geometric sequence
2. Find a specific term for a geometric sequence
3. Determine the sum of the terms of a geometric sequence
4. Determine the sum of an infinite geometric sequence
5. Change a repeating decimal into $\dfrac{a}{b}$ form

A **geometric sequence** (or **geometric progression**) is a sequence in which we obtain each term after the first by multiplying the preceding term by a common multiplier, which is called the *common ratio* of the sequence. We can find the **common ratio** of a geometric sequence by dividing any term (other than the first) by the preceding term. The following geometric sequences have common ratios of 3, 2, $\dfrac{1}{2}$, and -4, respectively:

$1, 3, 9, 27, 81, \ldots$

$3, 6, 12, 24, 48, \ldots$

$16, 8, 4, 2, 1, \ldots$

$-1, 4, -16, 64, -256, \ldots$

In a more general setting, we say that the sequence $a_1, a_2, a_3, \ldots, a_n, \ldots$ is a geometric sequence if and only if there is a nonzero real number r such that

$$a_{k+1} = ra_k$$

for every positive integer k. The nonzero real number r is called the common ratio of the sequence.

The previous equation can be used to generate a general geometric sequence that has a_1 as a first term and r as a common ratio. We can proceed as follows:

First term:	a_1	
Second term:	a_1r	
Third term:	a_1r^2	$(a_1r)(r) = a_1r^2$
Fourth term:	a_1r^3	
⋮		
nth term:	a_1r^{n-1}	

Thus the **general term** of a geometric sequence is given by

$$a_n = a_1r^{n-1}$$

where a_1 is the first term and r is the common ratio.

Classroom Example
Find the general term for the geometric sequence 3, 9, 27, 81, ...

EXAMPLE 1   Find the general term for the geometric sequence 8, 16, 32, 64, ...

Solution

The common ratio (r) is $\dfrac{16}{8} = 2$, and the first term (a_1) is 8. Substitute these values into $a_n = a_1r^{n-1}$ and simplify to obtain

$$a_n = 8(2)^{n-1} = (2^3)(2)^{n-1} = 2^{n+2}$$

Classroom Example
Find the sixth term of the geometric sequence 32, 8, 2, $\dfrac{1}{2}$, ...

EXAMPLE 2   Find the ninth term of the geometric sequence 27, 9, 3, 1, ...

Solution

The common ratio (r) is $\dfrac{9}{27} = \dfrac{1}{3}$, and the first term ($a_1$) is 27. Using $a_n = a_1r^{n-1}$, we obtain

$$a_9 = 27\left(\frac{1}{3}\right)^{9-1} = 27\left(\frac{1}{3}\right)^8$$

$$= \frac{3^3}{3^8}$$

$$= \frac{1}{3^5}$$

$$= \frac{1}{243}$$

Sums of Geometric Sequences

As with arithmetic sequences, we often need to find the sum of a certain number of terms of a geometric sequence. Before we develop a general-sum formula for geometric sequences, let's consider an approach to a specific problem that we can then use in a general setting.

Classroom Example
Find the sum of
$1 + 4 + 16 + 64 + \cdots + 16{,}384.$

EXAMPLE 3   Find the sum of $1 + 3 + 9 + 27 + \cdots + 6561.$

Solution

Let S represent the sum and proceed as follows:

$$S = 1 + 3 + 9 + 27 + \cdots + 6561 \tag{1}$$

$$3S = \quad 3 + 9 + 27 + \cdots + 6561 + 19{,}683 \tag{2}$$

Equation (2) is the result of multiplying equation (1) by the common ratio 3. Subtracting equation (1) from equation (2) produces

$$2S = 19{,}683 - 1 = 19{,}682$$
$$S = 9841$$

Now let's consider a general geometric sequence $a_1, a_1r, a_1r^2, \ldots, a_1r^{n-1}$. By applying a procedure similar to the one we used in Example 3, we can develop a formula for finding the sum of the first n terms of any geometric sequence. We let S_n represent the sum of the first n terms.

$$S_n = a_1 + a_1r + a_1r^2 + \cdots + a_1r^{n-1} \tag{3}$$

Next, we multiply both sides of equation (3) by the common ratio r.

$$rS_n = a_1r + a_1r^2 + a_1r^3 + \cdots + a_1r^n \tag{4}$$

We then subtract equation (3) from equation (4).

$$rS_n - S_n = a_1r^n - a_1$$

When we apply the distributive property to the left side and then solve for S_n, we obtain

$$S_n(r - 1) = a_1r^n - a_1$$
$$S_n = \frac{a_1r^n - a_1}{r - 1}, \qquad r \neq 1$$

Therefore the sum of the first n terms of a geometric sequence with a first term a_1 and a common ratio r is given by

$$S_n = \frac{a_1r^n - a_1}{r - 1}, \qquad r \neq 1$$

Classroom Example
Find the sum of the first ten terms of the geometric sequence 1, 3, 9, 27, ...

EXAMPLE 4

Find the sum of the first eight terms of the geometric sequence $1, 2, 4, 8, \ldots .$

Solution

To use the sum formula $S_n = \dfrac{a_1r^n - a_1}{r - 1}$, we need to know the number of terms (n), the first term (a_1), and the common ratio (r). We are given the number of terms and the first term, and we can determine that $r = \dfrac{2}{1} = 2$. Using the sum formula, we obtain

$$S_8 = \frac{1(2)^8 - 1}{2 - 1} = \frac{2^8 - 1}{1} = 255$$

If the common ratio of a geometric sequence is less than 1, it may be more convenient to change the form of the sum formula. That is, the fraction

$$\frac{a_1r^n - a_1}{r - 1}$$

can be changed to

$$\frac{a_1 - a_1r^n}{1 - r}$$

by multiplying both the numerator and the denominator by -1. Thus by using

$$S_n = \frac{a_1 - a_1r^n}{1 - r}$$

we can sometimes avoid unnecessary work with negative numbers when $r < 1$, as the next example illustrates.

Classroom Example
Find the sum
$$1 + \frac{1}{3} + \frac{1}{9} + \cdots + \frac{1}{729}.$$

EXAMPLE 5   Find the sum $1 + \dfrac{1}{2} + \dfrac{1}{4} + \cdots + \dfrac{1}{256}$.

Solution A

To use the sum formula, we need to know the number of terms, which can be found by counting them or by applying the nth-term formula, as follows:

$$a_n = a_1r^{n-1}$$

$$\frac{1}{256} = 1\left(\frac{1}{2}\right)^{n-1}$$

$$\left(\frac{1}{2}\right)^8 = \left(\frac{1}{2}\right)^{n-1}$$

$$8 = n - 1 \qquad \text{If } b^n = b^m, \text{ then } n = m$$
$$9 = n$$

Now we use $n = 9$, $a_1 = 1$, and $r = \dfrac{1}{2}$ in the sum formula of the form

$$S_n = \frac{a_1 - a_1r^n}{1 - r}$$

$$S_9 = \frac{1 - 1\left(\frac{1}{2}\right)^9}{1 - \frac{1}{2}} = \frac{1 - \frac{1}{512}}{\frac{1}{2}} = \frac{\frac{511}{512}}{\frac{1}{2}} = 1\frac{255}{256}$$

We can also do a problem like Example 5 without finding the number of terms; we use the general approach illustrated in Example 3. Solution B demonstrates this idea.

Solution B

Let S represent the desired sum.

$$S = 1 + \frac{1}{2} + \frac{1}{4} + \cdots + \frac{1}{256}$$

Multiply both sides by the common ratio $\dfrac{1}{2}$.

$$\frac{1}{2}S = \frac{1}{2} + \frac{1}{4} + \frac{1}{8} + \cdots + \frac{1}{256} + \frac{1}{512}$$

Subtract the second equation from the first, and solve for S.

$$\frac{1}{2}S = 1 - \frac{1}{512} = \frac{511}{512}$$

$$S = \frac{511}{256} = 1\frac{255}{256}$$

Summation notation can also be used to indicate the sum of a certain number of terms of a geometric sequence.

Classroom Example

Find the sum $\displaystyle\sum_{i=1}^{8} 3^i$.

| **EXAMPLE 6** | Find the sum $\displaystyle\sum_{i=1}^{10} 2^i$. |

Solution

This indicated sum means

$$\sum_{i=1}^{10} 2^i = 2^1 + 2^2 + 2^3 + \cdots + 2^{10}$$

$$= 2 + 4 + 8 + \cdots + 1024$$

This is the indicated sum of a geometric sequence, so we can use the sum formula with $a_1 = 2$, $r = 2$, and $n = 10$.

$$S_{10} = \frac{2(2)^{10} - 2}{2 - 1} = \frac{2(2^{10} - 1)}{1} = 2046$$

The Sum of an Infinite Geometric Sequence

Let's take the formula

$$S_n = \frac{a_1 - a_1 r^n}{1 - r}$$

and rewrite the right-hand side by applying the property

$$\frac{a - b}{c} = \frac{a}{c} - \frac{b}{c}$$

Thus we obtain

$$S_n = \frac{a_1}{1 - r} - \frac{a_1 r^n}{1 - r}$$

Now let's examine the behavior of r^n for $|r| < 1$, that is, for $-1 < r < 1$. For example, suppose that $r = \dfrac{1}{2}$. Then

$$r^2 = \left(\frac{1}{2}\right)^2 = \frac{1}{4} \qquad r^3 = \left(\frac{1}{2}\right)^3 = \frac{1}{8}$$

$$r^4 = \left(\frac{1}{2}\right)^4 = \frac{1}{16} \qquad r^5 = \left(\frac{1}{2}\right)^5 = \frac{1}{32}$$

and so on. We can make $\left(\dfrac{1}{2}\right)^n$ as close to zero as we please by choosing sufficiently large values for n. In general, for values of r such that $|r| < 1$, the expression r^n approaches zero as n gets larger and larger. Therefore the fraction $a_1 r^n/(1 - r)$ in equation (1) approaches zero as n increases. We say that the **sum of the infinite geometric sequence** is given by

$$S_\infty = \frac{a_1}{1 - r}, \qquad |r| < 1$$

Classroom Example

Find the sum of the infinite geometric sequence:

$1, \dfrac{1}{4}, \dfrac{1}{16}, \dfrac{1}{64}, \cdots$

| **EXAMPLE 7** | Find the sum of the infinite geometric sequence $1, \dfrac{1}{2}, \dfrac{1}{4}, \dfrac{1}{8}, \ldots$. |

Solution

Because $a_1 = 1$ and $r = \dfrac{1}{2}$, we obtain

$$S_\infty = \dfrac{1}{1 - \dfrac{1}{2}} = \dfrac{1}{\dfrac{1}{2}} = 2$$

When we state that $S_\infty = 2$ in Example 7, we mean that as we add more and more terms, the sum approaches 2. Observe what happens when we calculate the sum up to five terms.

First term:	1
Sum of first two terms:	$1 + \dfrac{1}{2} = 1\dfrac{1}{2}$
Sum of first three terms:	$1 + \dfrac{1}{2} + \dfrac{1}{4} = 1\dfrac{3}{4}$
Sum of first four terms:	$1 + \dfrac{1}{2} + \dfrac{1}{4} + \dfrac{1}{8} = 1\dfrac{7}{8}$
Sum of first five terms:	$1 + \dfrac{1}{2} + \dfrac{1}{4} + \dfrac{1}{8} + \dfrac{1}{16} = 1\dfrac{15}{16}$

If $|r| > 1$, the absolute value of r^n increases without bound as n increases. In the next table, note the unbounded growth of the absolute value of r^n.

Let $r = 3$	Let $r = -2$	
$r^2 = 3^2 = 9$	$r^2 = (-2)^2 = 4$	
$r^3 = 3^3 = 27$	$r^3 = (-2)^3 = -8$	$|-8| = 8$
$r^4 = 3^4 = 81$	$r^4 = (-2)^4 = 16$	
$r^5 = 3^5 = 243$	$r^5 = (-2)^5 = -32$	$|-32| = 32$

If $r = 1$, then $S_n = na_1$, and as n increases without bound, $|S_n|$ also increases without bound. If $r = -1$, then S_n will be either a_1 or 0. Therefore we say that the sum of any infinite geometric sequence where $|r| \geq 1$ *does not exist*.

Repeating Decimals as Sums of Infinite Geometric Sequences

In Section 1.1, we defined rational numbers to be numbers that have either a terminating or a repeating decimal representation. For example,

$$2.23 \qquad 0.147 \qquad 0.\overline{3} \qquad 0.\overline{14} \qquad \text{and} \qquad 0.\overline{56}$$

are rational numbers. (Remember that $0.\overline{3}$ means 0.3333 . . . .) Place value provides the basis for changing terminating decimals such as 2.23 and 0.147 to a/b form, where a and b are integers and $b \neq 0$.

$$2.23 = \dfrac{223}{100} \qquad \text{and} \qquad 0.147 = \dfrac{147}{1000}$$

However, changing repeating decimals to a/b form requires a different technique, and our work with sums of infinite geometric sequences provides the basis for one such approach. Consider the following examples.

Classroom Example

Change $0.\overline{261}$ to $\dfrac{a}{b}$ form; a and b are

integers and $b \neq 0$.

EXAMPLE 8   Change $0.\overline{14}$ to a/b form, where a and b are integers and $b \neq 0$.

Solution

The repeating decimal $0.\overline{14}$ can be written as the indicated sum of an infinite geometric sequence with first term 0.14 and common ratio 0.01.

$$0.14 + 0.0014 + 0.000014 + \cdots$$

Using $S_\infty = a_1/(1 - r)$, we obtain

$$S_\infty = \frac{0.14}{1 - 0.01} = \frac{0.14}{0.99} = \frac{14}{99}$$

Thus $0.\overline{14} = \dfrac{14}{99}$.

If the repeating block of digits does not begin immediately after the decimal point, as in $0.5\overline{6}$, we can make an adjustment in the technique we used in Example 8.

Classroom Example

Change $0.3\overline{7}$ to $\dfrac{a}{b}$ form; a and b are

integers and $b \neq 0$.

EXAMPLE 9   Change $0.5\overline{6}$ to a/b form, where a and b are integers and $b \neq 0$.

Solution

The repeating decimal $0.5\overline{6}$ can be written

$$(0.5) + (0.06 + 0.006 + 0.0006 + \cdots)$$

where

$$0.06 + 0.006 + 0.0006 + \cdots$$

is the indicated sum of the infinite geometric sequence with $a_1 = 0.06$ and $r = 0.1$. Therefore

$$S_\infty = \frac{0.06}{1 - 0.1} = \frac{0.06}{0.9} = \frac{6}{90} = \frac{1}{15}$$

Now we can add 0.5 and $\dfrac{1}{15}$.

$$0.5\overline{6} = 0.5 + \frac{1}{15} = \frac{1}{2} + \frac{1}{15} = \frac{15}{30} + \frac{2}{30} = \frac{17}{30}$$

Concept Quiz 14.2

For Problems 1–8, answer true or false.

1. The common ratio for a geometric sequence is found by dividing any term by the next successive term.

2. The 5th term of a geometric sequence is equal to the first term multiplied by the common ratio raised to the fourth power.

3. The common ratio of a geometric sequence could be zero.

4. The common ratio of a geometric sequence can be negative.

5. S_∞ denotes the sum of an infinite geometric sequence.

6. If the common ratio of an infinite geometric sequence is greater than 1, then the sum of the sequence does not exist.

7. For the sequence, $2, -2, 2, -2, 2, \ldots, S_9 = 2$.

8. Every repeating decimal can be changed into $\dfrac{a}{b}$ form in which a and b are integers, and $b \neq 0$.

Problem Set 14.2

For Problems 1–12, find the general term (the *n*th term) for each geometric sequence. (Objective 1)

1. 3, 6, 12, 24, . . .

2. 2, 6, 18, 54, . . .

3. 3, 9, 27, 81, . . .

4. 2, 6, 18, 54, . . .

5. $\dfrac{1}{4}, \dfrac{1}{8}, \dfrac{1}{16}, \dfrac{1}{32}, \cdots$

6. 8, 4, 2, 1, . . .

7. 4, 16, 64, 256, . . .

8. $6, 2, \dfrac{2}{3}, \dfrac{2}{9}, \cdots$

9. 1, 0.3, 0.09, 0.027, . . .

10. 0.2, 0.04, 0.008, 0.0016, . . .

11. 1, −2, 4, −8, . . .

12. −3, 9, −27, 81, . . .

For Problems 13–20, find the required term for each geometric sequence. (Objective 2)

13. The 8th term of $\dfrac{1}{2}$, 1, 2, 4, . . .

14. The 7th term of 2, 6, 18, 54, . . .

15. The 9th term of 729, 243, 81, 27, . . .

16. The 11th term of 768, 384, 192, 96, . . .

17. The 10th term of 1, −2, 4, −8, . . .

18. The 8th term of $-1, -\dfrac{3}{2}, -\dfrac{9}{4}, -\dfrac{27}{8}, \cdots$

19. The 8th term of $\dfrac{1}{2}, \dfrac{1}{6}, \dfrac{1}{18}, \dfrac{1}{54}, \cdots$

20. The 9th term of $\dfrac{16}{81}, \dfrac{8}{27}, \dfrac{4}{9}, \dfrac{2}{3}, \cdots$

For Problems 21–32, solve each problem.

21. Find the first term of the geometric sequence with 5th term $\dfrac{32}{3}$ and common ratio 2.

22. Find the first term of the geometric sequence with 4th term $\dfrac{27}{128}$ and common ratio $\dfrac{3}{4}$.

23. Find the common ratio of the geometric sequence with 3rd term 12 and 6th term 96.

24. Find the common ratio of the geometric sequence with 2nd term $\dfrac{8}{3}$ and 5th term $\dfrac{64}{81}$.

25. Find the sum of the first ten terms of the geometric sequence 1, 2, 4, 8, ...

26. Find the sum of the first seven terms of the geometric sequence 3, 9, 27, 81, ...

27. Find the sum of the first nine terms of the geometric sequence 2, 6, 18, 54, ...

28. Find the sum of the first ten terms of the geometric sequence 5, 10, 20, 40, ...

29. Find the sum of the first eight terms of the geometric sequence 8, 12, 18, 27, ...

30. Find the sum of the first eight terms of the geometric sequence $9, 12, 16, \dfrac{64}{3}, \cdots$.

31. Find the sum of the first ten terms of the geometric sequence −4, 8, −16, 32, ...

32. Find the sum of the first nine terms of the geometric sequence −2, 6, −18, 54, ...

For Problems 33–38, find each indicated sum. (Objective 3)

33. $9 + 27 + 81 + \cdots + 729$

34. $2 + 8 + 32 + \cdots + 8192$

35. $4 + 2 + 1 + \cdots + \dfrac{1}{512}$

36. $1 + (-2) + 4 + \cdots + 256$

37. $(-1) + 3 + (-9) + \cdots + (-729)$

38. $16 + 8 + 4 + \cdots + \dfrac{1}{32}$

For Problems 39–44, find each indicated sum. (Objective 3)

39. $\displaystyle\sum_{i=1}^{9} 2^{i-3}$

40. $\displaystyle\sum_{i=1}^{6} 3^{i}$

41. $\displaystyle\sum_{i=2}^{5} (-3)^{i+1}$

42. $\displaystyle\sum_{i=3}^{8} (-2)^{i-1}$

43. $\displaystyle\sum_{i=1}^{6} 3\left(\dfrac{1}{2}\right)^{i}$

44. $\displaystyle\sum_{i=1}^{5} 2\left(\dfrac{1}{3}\right)^{i}$

For Problems 45–56, find the sum of each infinite geometric sequence. If the sequence has no sum, so state. (Objective 4)

45. $2, 1, \dfrac{1}{2}, \dfrac{1}{4}, \cdots$

46. $9, 3, 1, \dfrac{1}{3}, \cdots$

47. $1, \dfrac{2}{3}, \dfrac{4}{9}, \dfrac{8}{27}, \cdots$

48. $5, 3, \dfrac{9}{5}, \dfrac{27}{25}, \cdots$

49. 4, 8, 16, 32, . . .

50. 32, 16, 8, 4, . . .

51. $9, -3, 1, -\dfrac{1}{3}, \cdots$

52. 2, −6, 18, −54, . . .

53. $\dfrac{1}{2}, \dfrac{3}{8}, \dfrac{9}{32}, \dfrac{27}{128}, \cdots$

54. $4, -\dfrac{4}{3}, \dfrac{4}{9}, -\dfrac{4}{27}, \cdots$

55. $8, -4, 2, -1, \ldots$ **56.** $7, \dfrac{14}{5}, \dfrac{28}{25}, \dfrac{56}{125}, \ldots$

60. $0.\overline{18}$ **61.** $0.\overline{123}$ **62.** $0.2\overline{73}$

For Problems 57–68, change each repeating decimal to a/b form, in which a and b are integers and $b \neq 0$. Express a/b in reduced form. (Objective 5)

63. $0.2\overline{6}$ **64.** $0.4\overline{3}$ **65.** $0.2\overline{14}$

66. $0.3\overline{71}$ **67.** $2.\overline{3}$ **68.** $3.\overline{7}$

57. $0.\overline{3}$ **58.** $0.\overline{4}$ **59.** $0.\overline{26}$

Thoughts Into Words

69. Explain the difference between an arithmetic sequence and a geometric sequence.

70. What does it mean to say that the sum of the infinite geometric sequence $1, \dfrac{1}{2}, \dfrac{1}{4}, \dfrac{1}{8}, \ldots$ is 2?

71. What do we mean when we say that the infinite geometric sequence $1, 2, 4, 8, \ldots$ has no sum?

72. Why don't we discuss the sum of an infinite arithmetic sequence?

Answers to the Concept Quiz
1. False   **2.** True   **3.** False   **4.** True   **5.** True   **6.** True   **7.** True   **8.** True

---

14.3   Another Look at Problem Solving

OBJECTIVES   **1** Solve application problems involving arithmetic sequences

2 Solve application problems involving geometric sequences

In the previous two sections, many of the exercises fell into one of the following four categories:

1. Find the nth term of an arithmetic sequence:

$$a_n = a_1 + (n - 1)d$$

2. Find the sum of the first n terms of an arithmetic sequence:

$$S_n = \frac{n(a_1 + a_n)}{2}$$

3. Find the nth term of a geometric sequence:

$$a_n = a_1 r^{n-1}$$

4. Find the sum of the first n terms of a geometric sequence:

$$S_n = \frac{a_1 r^n - a_1}{r - 1}$$

In this section we want to use this knowledge of arithmetic sequences and geometric sequences to expand our problem-solving capabilities. Let's begin by restating some old problem-solving suggestions that continue to apply here; we will also consider some other suggestions that are directly related to problems that involve sequences of numbers. (We will indicate the new suggestions with an asterisk.)

Suggestions for Solving Word Problems

1. Read the problem carefully and make certain that you understand the meanings of all the words. Be especially alert for any technical terms used in the statement of the problem.

2. Read the problem a second time (perhaps even a third time) to get an overview of the situation being described and to determine the known facts, as well as what you are to find.

3. Sketch a figure, diagram, or chart that might be helpful in analyzing the problem.

*4. Write down the first few terms of the sequence to describe what is taking place in the problem. Be sure that you understand, term by term, what the sequence represents in the problem.

*5. Determine whether the sequence is arithmetic or geometric.

*6. Determine whether the problem is asking for a specific term of the sequence or for the sum of a certain number of terms.

7. Carry out the necessary calculations and check your answer for reasonableness.

As we work out some examples, these suggestions will become more meaningful.

Classroom Example
Don started to work in 2000 at an annual salary of $43,600. He received a $1744 raise each year. What was his annual salary in 2009?

EXAMPLE 1

Domenica started to work in 2001 at an annual salary of $32,500. She received a $1200 raise each year. What was her annual salary in 2010?

Solution

The following sequence represents her annual salary beginning in 2001:

32,500,   33,700,   34,900,   36,100,   . . .

This is an arithmetic sequence, with $a_1 = 32,500$ and $d = 1200$. Her salary in 2001 is the first term of the sequence, and her salary in 2010 is the tenth term of the sequence. So, using $a_n = a_1 + (n - 1)d$, we obtain the tenth term of the arithmetic sequence:

$$a_{10} = 32,500 + (10 - 1)1200 = 32,500 + 9(1200) = 43,300$$

Her annual salary in 2010 was $43,300.

Classroom Example
An auditorium has 10 seats in the front row, 15 seats in the second row, 20 seats in the third row, and so on, for 18 rows. How many seats are there in the auditorium?

EXAMPLE 2

An auditorium has 20 seats in the front row, 24 seats in the second row, 28 seats in the third row, and so on, for 15 rows. How many seats are there in the auditorium?

Solution

The following sequence represents the number of seats per row, starting with the first row:

20, 24, 28, 32, . . .

This is an arithmetic sequence, with $a_1 = 20$ and $d = 4$. Therefore the 15th term, which represents the number of seats in the 15th row, is given by

$$a_{15} = 20 + (15 - 1)4 = 20 + 14(4) = 76$$

The total number of seats in the auditorium is represented by

$$20 + 24 + 28 + \cdots + 76$$

Use the sum formula for an arithmetic sequence to obtain

$$S_{15} = \frac{15}{2}(20 + 76) = 720$$

There are 720 seats in the auditorium.   ∎

Classroom Example

Suppose you are given 10 cents the first day of a week, 30 cents the second day, and 90 cents the third day, and then that amount triples each day. How much will you be given on the seventh day? What will the total amount be for the week?

EXAMPLE 3

Suppose that you save 25 cents the first day of a week, 50 cents the second day, and one dollar the third day, and then you continue to double your savings each day. How much will you save on the seventh day? What will be your total savings for the week?

Solution

The following sequence represents your savings per day, expressed in cents:

$$25, 50, 100, \ldots$$

This is a geometric sequence, with $a_1 = 25$ and $r = 2$. Your savings on the seventh day is the seventh term of this sequence. Therefore, using $a_n = a_1 r^{n-1}$, we obtain

$$a_7 = 25(2)^6 = 1600$$

You will save \$16 on the seventh day. Your total savings for the seven days is given by

$$25 + 50 + 100 + \cdots + 1600$$

Use the sum formula for a geometric sequence to obtain

$$S_7 = \frac{25(2)^7 - 25}{2 - 1} = \frac{25(2^7 - 1)}{1} = 3175$$

Thus you will save a total of \$31.75 for the week.   ∎

Classroom Example

A pump is attached to a container for the purpose of creating a vacuum. For each stroke of the pump, $\frac{1}{3}$ of the air that remains in the container is removed. To the nearest tenth of a percent, how much of the air remains in the container after five strokes?

EXAMPLE 4

A pump is attached to a container for the purpose of creating a vacuum. For each stroke of the pump, $\frac{1}{4}$ of the air that remains in the container is removed. To the nearest tenth of a percent, how much of the air remains in the container after six strokes?

Solution

Let's draw a chart to help with the analysis of this problem.

First stroke:	$\frac{1}{4}$ of the air is removed	$1 - \frac{1}{4} = \frac{3}{4}$ of the air remains
Second stroke:	$\frac{1}{4}\left(\frac{3}{4}\right) = \frac{3}{16}$ of the air is removed	$\frac{3}{4} - \frac{3}{16} = \frac{9}{16}$ of the air remains
Third stroke:	$\frac{1}{4}\left(\frac{9}{16}\right) = \frac{9}{64}$ of the air is removed	$\frac{9}{16} - \frac{9}{64} = \frac{27}{64}$ of the air remains

The diagram suggests two approaches to the problem.

Approach A   The sequence $\dfrac{1}{4}, \dfrac{3}{16}, \dfrac{9}{64}, \dots$ represents, term by term, the fractional amount of air that is removed with each successive stroke. Therefore, we can find the total amount removed and subtract it from 100%. The sequence is geometric with $a_1 = \dfrac{1}{4}$ and $r = \dfrac{\frac{3}{16}}{\frac{1}{4}} = \dfrac{3}{16} \cdot \dfrac{4}{1} = \dfrac{3}{4}$. Using the sum formula $S_n = \dfrac{a_1 - a_1 r^n}{1 - r}$, we obtain

$$S_6 = \frac{\dfrac{1}{4} - \dfrac{1}{4}\left(\dfrac{3}{4}\right)^6}{1 - \dfrac{3}{4}} = \frac{\dfrac{1}{4}\left[1 - \left(\dfrac{3}{4}\right)^6\right]}{\dfrac{1}{4}}$$

$$= 1 - \frac{729}{4096} = \frac{3367}{4096} = 82.2\%$$

Therefore $100\% - 82.2\% = 17.8\%$ of the air remains after six strokes.

Approach B   The sequence

$$\frac{3}{4}, \frac{9}{16}, \frac{27}{64}, \dots$$

represents, term by term, the amount of air that remains in the container after each stroke. Therefore when we find the sixth term of this geometric sequence, we will have the answer to the problem. Because $a_1 = \dfrac{3}{4}$ and $r = \dfrac{3}{4}$, we obtain

$$a_6 = \frac{3}{4}\left(\frac{3}{4}\right)^5 = \left(\frac{3}{4}\right)^6 = \frac{729}{4096} = 17.8\%$$

Therefore 17.8% of the air remains after six strokes.

It will be helpful for you to take another look at the two approaches we used to solve Problem 4. Note that in Approach B, finding the sixth term of the sequence produced the answer to the problem without any further calculations. In Approach A, we had to find the sum of six terms of the sequence and then subtract that amount from 100%. As we solve problems that involve sequences, we must understand what each particular sequence represents on a term-by-term basis.

Problem Set 14.3

Use your knowledge of arithmetic sequences and geometric sequences to help solve Problems 1–28. **(Objectives 1 and 2)**

1. A man started to work in 1990 at an annual salary of $19,500. He received a $1700 raise each year. How much was his annual salary in 2010?

2. A woman started to work in 1995 at an annual salary of $23,400. She received a $1200 raise each year. How much was her annual salary in 2010?

3. State University had an enrollment of 15,600 students in 1994. Each year the enrollment increased by 1050 students. What was the enrollment in 2009?

4. Math University had an enrollment of 12,800 students in 2003. Each year the enrollment decreased by 75 students. What was the enrollment in 2010?

5. The enrollment at Online University is predicted to increase at the rate of 10% per year. If the enrollment for

2006 was 5000 students, find the predicted enrollment for 2010. Express your answer to the nearest whole number.

6. If you pay $22,000 for a car and it depreciates 20% per year, how much will it be worth in 5 years? Express your answer to the nearest dollar.

7. A tank contains 16,000 liters of water. Each day one-half of the water in the tank is removed and not replaced. How much water remains in the tank at the end of 7 days?

8. If the price of a pound of coffee is $6.20, and the projected rate of inflation is 5% per year, how much per pound will coffee cost in 5 years? Express your answer to the nearest cent.

9. A tank contains 5832 gallons of water. Each day one-third of the water in the tank is removed and not replaced. How much water remains in the tank at the end of 6 days?

10. A fungus culture growing under controlled conditions doubles in size each day. How many units will the culture contain after 7 days if it originally contains 4 units?

11. Sue is saving quarters. She saves 1 quarter the first day, 2 quarters the second day, 3 quarters the third day, and so on for 30 days. How much money will she have saved in 30 days?

12. Suppose you save a penny the first day of a month, 2 cents the second day, 3 cents the third day, and so on for 31 days. What will be your total savings for the 31 days?

13. Suppose you save a penny the first day of a month, 2 cents the second day, 4 cents the third day, and continue to double your savings each day. How much will you save on the 15th day of the month? How much will your total savings be for the 15 days?

14. Eric saved a nickel the first day of a month, a dime the second day, and 20 cents the third day and then continued to double his daily savings each day for 14 days. What were his daily savings on the 14th day? What were his total savings for the 14 days?

15. Ms. Bryan invested $1500 at 6% simple interest at the beginning of each year for a period of 10 years. Find the total accumulated value of all the investments at the end of the 10-year period.

16. Mr. Woodley invested $1200 at 5% simple interest at the beginning of each year for a period of 8 years. Find the total accumulated value of all the investments at the end of the 8-year period.

17. An object falling from rest in a vacuum falls approximately 16 feet the first second, 48 feet the second second, 80 feet the third second, 112 feet the fourth second, and so on. How far will it fall in 11 seconds?

18. A raffle is organized so that the amount paid for each ticket is determined by the number on the ticket. The tickets are numbered with the consecutive odd whole numbers 1, 3, 5, 7, ... Each contestant pays as many cents as the number on the ticket drawn. How much money will the raffle take in if 1000 tickets are sold?

19. Suppose an element has a half-life of 4 hours. This means that if n grams of it exist at a specific time, then only $\frac{1}{2}n$ grams remain 4 hours later. If at a particular moment we have 60 grams of the element, how many grams of it will remain 24 hours later?

20. Suppose an element has a half-life of 3 hours. (See Problem 19 for a definition of half-life.) If at a particular moment we have 768 grams of the element, how many grams of it will remain 24 hours later?

21. A rubber ball is dropped from a height of 1458 feet, and at each bounce it rebounds one-third of the height from which it last fell. How far has the ball traveled by the time it strikes the ground for the sixth time?

22. A rubber ball is dropped from a height of 100 feet, and at each bounce it rebounds one-half of the height from which it last fell. What distance has the ball traveled up to the instant it hits the ground for the eighth time?

23. A pile of logs has 25 logs in the bottom layer, 24 logs in the next layer, 23 logs in the next layer, and so on, until the top layer has 1 log. How many logs are in the pile?

24. A well driller charges $9.00 per foot for the first 10 feet, $9.10 per foot for the next 10 feet, $9.20 per foot for the next 10 feet, and so on, at a price increase of $0.10 per foot for succeeding intervals of 10 feet. How much does it cost to drill a well to a depth of 150 feet?

25. A pump is attached to a container for the purpose of creating a vacuum. For each stroke of the pump, one-third of the air remaining in the container is removed. To the nearest tenth of a percent, how much of the air remains in the container after seven strokes?

26. Suppose that in Problem 25, each stroke of the pump removes one-half of the air remaining in the container. What fractional part of the air has been removed after six strokes?

27. A tank contains 20 gallons of water. One-half of the water is removed and replaced with antifreeze. Then one-half of this mixture is removed and replaced with antifreeze. This process is continued eight times. How much water remains in the tank after the eighth replacement process?

28. The radiator of a truck contains 10 gallons of water. Suppose we remove 1 gallon of water and replace it with antifreeze. Then we remove 1 gallon of this mixture and replace it with antifreeze. This process is carried out seven times. To the nearest tenth of a gallon, how much antifreeze is in the final mixture?

Thoughts Into Words

29. Your friend solves Problem 6 as follows: If the car depreciates 20% per year, then at the end of 5 years it will have depreciated 100% and be worth zero dollars. How would you convince him that his reasoning is incorrect?

30. A contractor wants you to clear some land for a housing project. He anticipates that it will take 20 working days to do the job. He offers to pay you one of two ways: (1) a fixed amount of $3000 or (2) a penny the first day, 2 cents the second day, 4 cents the third day, and so on, doubling your daily wages each day for the 20 days. Which offer should you take and why?

14.4   Mathematical Induction

OBJECTIVE   **1** Use mathematical induction to prove mathematical statements

Is $2^n > n$ for all positive integer values of n? In an attempt to answer this question, we might proceed as follows:

If $n = 1$, then $2^n > n$ becomes $2^1 > 1$, a true statement.

If $n = 2$, then $2^n > n$ becomes $2^2 > 2$, a true statement.

If $n = 3$, then $2^n > n$ becomes $2^3 > 3$, a true statement.

We can continue in this way as long as we want, but obviously we can never show in this manner that $2^n > n$ for *every* positive integer n. However, we do have a form of proof, called **proof by mathematical induction**, that can be used to verify the truth of many mathematical statements involving positive integers. This form of proof is based on the following principle.

> **Principle of Mathematical Induction**
>
> Let P_n be a statement in terms of n, where n is a positive integer. If
>
> **1.** P_1 is true, and
> **2.** the truth of P_k implies the truth of P_{k+1} for every positive integer k,
>
> then P_n is true for every positive integer n.

The principle of mathematical induction, a proof that some statement is true for all positive integers, consists of two parts. First, we must show that the statement is true for the positive integer 1. Second, we must show that if the statement is true for some positive integer, then it follows that it is also true for the next positive integer. Let's illustrate what this means.

EXAMPLE 1   Prove that $2^n > n$ for all positive integer values of n.

Proof

Part 1   If $n = 1$, then $2^n > n$ becomes $2^1 > 1$, which is a true statement.

Part 2   We must prove that if $2^k > k$, then $2^{k+1} > k + 1$ for all positive integer values of k. In other words, we should be able to start with $2^k > k$ and from that deduce $2^{k+1} > k + 1$. This can be done as follows:

$$2^k > k$$

$$2(2^k) > 2(k) \qquad \text{Multiply both sides by 2}$$

$$2^{k+1} > 2k$$

We know that $k \geq 1$ because we are working with positive integers. Therefore

$$k + k \geq k + 1 \qquad \text{Add } k \text{ to both sides}$$

$$2k \geq k + 1$$

Because $2^{k+1} > 2k$ and $2k \geq k + 1$, by the transitive property we conclude that

$$2^{k+1} > k + 1$$

Therefore, using parts 1 and 2, we proved that $2^n > n$ for *all* positive integers.   ◼

It will be helpful for you to look back over the proof in Example 1. Note that in part 1, we established that $2^n > n$ is true for $n = 1$. Then, in part 2, we established that if $2^n > n$ is true for any positive integer, then it must be true for the next consecutive positive integer. Therefore, because $2^n > n$ is true for $n = 1$, it must be true for $n = 2$. Likewise, if $2^n > n$ is true for $n = 2$, then it must be true for $n = 3$, and so on, for *all* positive integers.

We can depict proof by mathematical induction with dominoes. Suppose that in Figure 14.1, we have infinitely many dominoes lined up. If we can push the first domino over (part 1 of a mathematical induction proof), and if the dominoes are spaced so that each time one falls over, it causes the next one to fall over (part 2 of a mathematical induction proof), then by pushing the first one over we will cause a chain reaction that will topple all of the dominoes (Figure 14.2).

Figure 14.1

Figure 14.2

Recall that in the first three sections of this chapter, we used a_n to represent the nth term of a sequence and S_n to represent the sum of the first n terms of a sequence. For example, if $a_n = 2n$, then the first three terms of the sequence are $a_1 = 2(1) = 2$, $a_2 = 2(2) = 4$, and $a_3 = 2(3) = 6$. Furthermore, the kth term is $a_k = 2(k) = 2k$, and the $(k + 1)$ term is $a_{k+1} = 2(k + 1) = 2k + 2$. Relative to this same sequence, we can state that $S_1 = 2$, $S_2 = 2 + 4 = 6$, and $S_3 = 2 + 4 + 6 = 12$.

There are numerous sum formulas for sequences that can be verified by mathematical induction. For such proofs, the following property of sequences is used:

$$S_{k+1} = S_k + a_{k+1}$$

This property states that *the sum of the first $k + 1$ terms is equal to the sum of the first k terms plus the $(k + 1)$ term.* Let's see how this can be used in a specific example.

Classroom Example
Prove $S_n = 2n(n + 1)$ for the sequence $a_n = 4n$, if n is any positive integer.

EXAMPLE 2

Prove that $S_n = n(n + 1)$ for the sequence $a_n = 2n$, when n is any positive integer.

Proof

Part 1 If $n = 1$, then $S_1 = 1(1 + 1) = 2$, and 2 is the first term of the sequence $a_n = 2n$, so $S_1 = a_1 = 2$.

Part 2 Now we need to prove that if $S_k = k(k + 1)$, then $S_{k+1} = (k + 1)(k + 2)$. Using the property $S_{k+1} = S_k + a_{k+1}$, we can proceed as follows:

$$S_{k+1} = S_k + a_{k+1}$$
$$= k(k + 1) + 2(k + 1)$$
$$= (k + 1)(k + 2)$$

Therefore, using parts 1 and 2, we proved that $S_n = n(n + 1)$ will yield the correct sum for any number of terms of the sequence $a_n = 2n$. ∎

Classroom Example
Prove that $S_n = \dfrac{n(3n + 5)}{2}$ for the sequence $a_n = 3n + 1$, if n is any positive integer.

EXAMPLE 3

Prove that $S_n = 5n(n + 1)/2$ for the sequence $a_n = 5n$, when n is any positive integer.

Proof

Part 1 Because $S_1 = 5(1)(1 + 1)/2 = 5$, and 5 is the first term of the sequence $a_n = 5n$, we have $S_1 = a_1 = 5$.

Part 2 We need to prove that if $S_k = 5k(k + 1)/2$, then $S_{k+1} = \dfrac{5(k + 1)(k + 2)}{2}$.

$$S_{k+1} = S_k + a_{k+1}$$
$$= \frac{5k(k + 1)}{2} + 5(k + 1)$$
$$= \frac{5k(k + 1)}{2} + 5k + 5$$
$$= \frac{5k(k + 1) + 2(5k + 5)}{2}$$
$$= \frac{5k^2 + 5k + 10k + 10}{2}$$
$$= \frac{5k^2 + 15k + 10}{2}$$
$$= \frac{5(k^2 + 3k + 2)}{2}$$
$$= \frac{5(k + 1)(k + 2)}{2}$$

Therefore, using parts 1 and 2, we proved that $S_n = 5n(n + 1)/2$ yields the correct sum for any number of terms of the sequence $a_n = 5n$. ∎

Classroom Example
Prove that $S_n - \dfrac{3^n - 1}{2}$ for the sequence $a_n = 3^{n-1}$, if n is any positive integer.

EXAMPLE 4

Prove that $S_n = (4^n - 1)/3$ for the sequence $a_n = 4^{n-1}$, where n is any positive integer.

Proof

Part 1 Because $S_1 = (4^1 - 1)/3 = 1$, and 1 is the first term of the sequence $a_n = 4^{n-1}$, we have $S_1 = a_1 = 1$.

Part 2 We need to prove that if $S_k = (4^k - 1)/3$, then $S_{k+1} = (4^{k+1} - 1)/3$:

$$S_{k+1} = S_k + a_{k+1}$$
$$= \frac{4^k - 1}{3} + 4^k$$
$$= \frac{4^k - 1 + 3(4^k)}{3}$$
$$= \frac{4^k + 3(4^k) - 1}{3}$$
$$= \frac{4^k(1 + 3) - 1}{3}$$
$$= \frac{4^k(4) - 1}{3}$$
$$= \frac{4^{k+1} - 1}{3}$$

Therefore, using parts 1 and 2, we proved that $S_n = (4^n - 1)/3$ yields the correct sum for any number of terms of the sequence $a_n = 4^{n-1}$. ■

As our final example of this section, let's consider a proof by mathematical induction involving the concept of divisibility.

Classroom Example
Prove that for all positive integers n, the number $3^n - 1$ is divisible by 2.

EXAMPLE 5

Prove that for all positive integers n, the number $3^{2n} - 1$ is divisible by 8.

Proof

Part 1 If $n = 1$, then $3^{2n} - 1$ becomes $3^{2(1)} - 1 = 3^2 - 1 = 8$, and of course 8 is divisible by 8.

Part 2 We need to prove that if $3^{2k} - 1$ is divisible by 8, then $3^{2k+2} - 1$ is divisible by 8 for all integer values of k. This can be verified as follows. If $3^{2k} - 1$ is divisible by 8, then for some integer x, we have $3^{2k} - 1 = 8x$. Therefore

$$3^{2k} - 1 = 8x$$
$$3^{2k} = 1 + 8x$$
$$3^2(3^{2k}) = 3^2(1 + 8x) \qquad \text{Multiply both sides by } 3^2$$
$$3^{2k+2} = 9(1 + 8x)$$
$$3^{2k+2} = 9 + 9(8x)$$
$$3^{2k+2} = 1 + 8 + 9(8x) \qquad 9 = 1 + 8$$
$$3^{2k+2} = 1 + 8(1 + 9x)$$
$$3^{2k+2} - 1 = 8(1 + 9x) \qquad \begin{array}{l}\text{Apply distributive} \\ \text{property to } 8 + 9(8x)\end{array}$$

Therefore $3^{2k+2} - 1$ is divisible by 8.

Thus using parts 1 and 2, we proved that $3^{2n} - 1$ is divisible by 8 for all positive integers n.

∎

We conclude this section with a few final comments about proof by mathematical induction. Every mathematical induction proof is a two-part proof, and both parts are absolutely necessary. There can be mathematical statements that hold for one or the other of the two parts but not for both. For example, $(a + b)^n = a^n + b^n$ is true for $n = 1$, but it is false for every positive integer greater than 1. Therefore, if we were to attempt a mathematical induction proof for $(a + b)^n = a^n + b^n$, we could establish part 1 but not part 2. Another example of this type is the statement that $n^2 - n + 41$ produces a prime number for all positive integer values of n. This statement is true for $n = 1, 2, 3, 4, \ldots, 40$, but it is false when $n = 41$ (because $41^2 - 41 + 41 = 41^2$, which is not a prime number).

It is also possible that part 2 of a mathematical induction proof can be established but not part 1. For example, consider the sequence $a_n = n$ and the sum formula $S_n = (n + 3)(n - 2)/2$. If $n = 1$, then $a_1 = 1$ but $S_1 = (4)(-1)/2 = -2$, so part 1 does not hold. However, it is possible to show that $S_k = (k + 3)(k - 2)/2$ implies $S_{k+1} = (k + 4)(k - 1)/2$. We will leave the details of this for you to do.

Finally, it is important to realize that some mathematical statements are true for all positive integers greater than some fixed positive integer other than 1. (In Figure 14.1, this implies that we cannot knock down the first four dominoes; however, we can knock down the fifth domino and every one thereafter.) For example, we can prove by mathematical induction that $2^n > n^2$ for all positive integers $n > 4$. It requires a slight variation in the statement of the principle of mathematical induction. We will not concern ourselves with such problems in this text, but we want you to be aware of their existence.

Concept Quiz 14.4

For Problems 1–4, answer true or false.

1. Mathematical induction is used to prove mathematical statements involving positive integers.
2. A proof by mathematical induction consists of two parts.
3. Because $(a + b)^n = a^n + b^n$ is true for $n = 1$, it is true for all positive integer values of n.
4. To prove a mathematical statement involving positive integers by mathematical induction, the statement must be true for $n = 1$.

Problem Set 14.4

For Problems 1–10, use mathematical induction to prove each of the sum formulas for the indicated sequences. They are to hold for all positive integers n. (Objective 1)

1. $S_n = \dfrac{n(n + 1)}{2}$ for $a_n = n$

2. $S_n = n^2$ for $a_n = 2n - 1$

3. $S_n = \dfrac{n(3n + 1)}{2}$ for $a_n = 3n - 1$

4. $S_n = \dfrac{n(5n + 9)}{2}$ for $a_n = 5n + 2$

5. $S_n = 2(2^n - 1)$ for $a_n = 2^n$

6. $S_n = \dfrac{3(3^n - 1)}{2}$ for $a_n = 3^n$

7. $S_n = \dfrac{n(n + 1)(2n + 1)}{6}$ for $a_n = n^2$

8. $S_n = \dfrac{n^2(n + 1)^2}{4}$ for $a_n = n^3$

9. $S_n = \dfrac{n}{n + 1}$ for $a_n = \dfrac{1}{n(n + 1)}$

10. $S_n = \dfrac{n(n + 1)(n + 2)}{3}$ for $a_n = n(n + 1)$

In Problems 11–20, use mathematical induction to prove that each statement is true for all positive integers n.

11. $3^n \geq 2n + 1$

12. $4^n \geq 4n$

13. $n^2 \geq n$

14. $2^n \geq n + 1$

15. $4^n - 1$ is divisible by 3

16. $5^n - 1$ is divisible by 4

17. $6^n - 1$ is divisible by 5

18. $9^n - 1$ is divisible by 4

19. $n^2 + n$ is divisible by 2

20. $n^2 - n$ is divisible by 2

Thoughts Into Words

21. How would you describe proof by mathematical induction?

22. Compare inductive reasoning to prove by mathematical induction.

Answers to the Concept Quiz

1. True   **2.** True   **3.** False   **4.** False

OBJECTIVE	SUMMARY	EXAMPLE
Write the terms of a sequence. (Section 14.1/Objective 1)	An infinite sequence is a function with a domain that is the set of positive integers. When the letter a represents the function, the functional value of a at n is written as a_n. The expression a_n, which defines the function, is called the general term.	Find the first four terms of the sequence when $a_n = 2n + 7$. **Solution** $a_1 = 2(1) + 7 = 9$ $a_2 = 2(2) + 7 = 11$ $a_3 = 2(3) + 7 = 13$ $a_4 = 2(4) + 7 = 15$ The first four terms are 9, 11, 13, and 15.
Find the general term for an arithmetic sequence. (Section 14.1/Objective 2)	An arithmetic sequence is a sequence that has a common difference between successive terms. The general term of an arithmetic sequence is given by the formula $a_n = a_1 + (n-1)d$ in which a_1 is the first term, n is the number of terms, and d is the common difference.	Find the general term of the arithmetic sequence 8, 11, 14, 17, ... **Solution** The common difference is $11 - 8 = 3$ and the first term is 8. Substitute these values into $a_n = a_1 + (n-1)d$ and simplify: $a_n = 8 + (n-1)(3)$ $= 8 + 3n - 3$ $= 3n + 5$
Find a specific term for an arithmetic sequence. (Section 14.1/Objective 3)	The formula $a_n = a_1 + (n-1)d$ can be used to find specific terms of an arithmetic sequence.	Find the 13th term of the arithmetic sequence 56, 52, 48, 44, ... **Solution** The common difference is $52 - 56 = -4$, the first term is 56 and $n = 13$. Substitute these values into $a_n = a_1 + (n-1)d$ and simplify: $a_{13} = 56 + (13-1)(-4)$ $= 8$
Determine the sum of the terms of an arithmetic sequence. (Section 14.1/Objective 4)	The sum of the first n terms of an arithmetic sequence is given by the formula $S_n = \dfrac{n(a_1 + a_n)}{2}$. The formula can be interpreted as the average of the first and last terms times the number of terms.	Find the sum of the first 60 terms of the sequence when $a_n = 3n - 2$. **Solution** To use the sum formula we need to know the value of the first term, the last term, and the number of terms. The number of terms is 60, $a_1 = 1$, and $a_n = 178$. $S_{60} = \dfrac{60(1 + 178)}{2} = 5370$
Determine the sum indicated by summation notation. (Section 14.1/Objective 5)	The capital Greek letter sigma, $\sum$, is used as a summation symbol. The letter i is usually used as the index of summation; the letter i takes on all integer values from the lower limit to the upper limit, inclusively.	Find the sum $\displaystyle\sum_{i=3}^{7} i^2$. **Solution** The indicated sum means $\displaystyle\sum_{i=3}^{7} i^2 = 3^2 + 4^2 + 5^2 + 6^2 + 7^2 = 135$

OBJECTIVE	SUMMARY	EXAMPLE
Find the general term for a geometric sequence. (Section 14.2/Objective 1)	A geometric sequence has a common ratio between successive terms *after the first term*. The common ratio can be found by dividing any term (other than the first term) by the preceding term. The general term of a geometric sequence is given by the formula $a_n = a_1 r^{n-1}$ where a_1 is the first term, n is the number of terms, and r is the common ratio.	Find the general term for the geometric sequence $-2, 4, -8, 16, \ldots$. **Solution** The common ratio, r, is $\dfrac{4}{-2} = -2,$ and the first term, a_1, is -2. Substituting these values into $a_n = a_1 r^{n-1}$, we obtain $a_n = -2(-2)^{n-1} = (-2)^n$.
Find a specific term for a geometric sequence. (Section 14.2/Objective 2)	The formula $a_n = a_1 r^{n-1}$ can be used to find specific terms of a geometric sequence.	Find the sixth term of the geometric sequence $24, 36, 54, 81, \ldots$. **Solution** The common ratio is $\dfrac{36}{24} = \dfrac{3}{2}$. Using $a_n = a_1 r^{n-1}$, we obtain $$a_6 = 24\left(\frac{3}{2}\right)^{6-1}$$ $$= 24\left(\frac{3}{2}\right)^{5}$$ $$= 182\frac{1}{4}$$ $$= \frac{729}{4}$$
Determine the sum of the terms of a geometric sequence. (Section 14.2/Objective 3)	The sum of the first n terms of a geometric sequence with a first term a_1 and a common ratio of r is given by $$S_n = \frac{a_1 r^n - a_1}{r - 1}, r \neq 1$$	Find the sum of the first ten terms of the geometric sequence $-10, 30, -90, 270, \ldots$. **Solution** From the given we can determine that $n = 10$, $r = -3$, and $a_1 = -10$. Substituting these values into the sum formula yields $$S_{10} = \frac{(-10)(-3)^{10} - (-10)}{(-3) - 1} = 147{,}620$$
Determine the sum of an infinite geometric sequence. (Section 14.2/Objective 4)	For values of r such that $-1 < r < 1$, the sum of an infinite geometric sequence can be determined.	Find the sum of the infinite geometric sequence $-9, 6, -4, \dfrac{8}{3}, -\dfrac{16}{9}, \ldots$. **Solution** $a_1 = -9$ and $r = \dfrac{6}{-9} = -\dfrac{2}{3}$ $$S_\infty = \frac{a_1}{1 - r}$$ $$= \frac{-9}{1 - \left(-\dfrac{2}{3}\right)}$$ $$= \frac{-9}{\dfrac{5}{3}} = \frac{27}{5}$$

(continued)

OBJECTIVE	SUMMARY	EXAMPLE
Change a repeating decimal into $\dfrac{a}{b}$ form. (Section 14.2/Objective 5)	Repeating decimals (such as $0.\overline{4}$) can be changed to $\dfrac{a}{b}$ form, where a and b are integers and $b \neq 0$, by treating them as the sum of an infinite geometric sequence. For example, the repeating decimal $0.\overline{4}$ can be written $0.4 + 0.04 + 0.004 + 0.0004 + \cdots\cdot$.	Change $0.\overline{09}$ to reduced $\dfrac{a}{b}$ form, in which a and b are integers and $b \neq 0$. **Solution** Write $0.\overline{09}$ as the indicated sum of an infinite geometric sequence: $0.09 + 0.0009 + 0.000009 + \cdots$ Using $$S_\infty = \frac{a_1}{1-r} = \frac{0.09}{1-0.01} = \frac{0.09}{0.99} = \frac{1}{11}$$
Solve application problem sequences. (Section 14.3/Objectives 1 and 2)	Many of the problem-solving suggestions offered earlier in this text are still appropriate when we are solving problems that deal with sequences. However, there are also some special suggestions pertaining to sequence problems. 1. Write down the first few terms of the sequence to describe what is taking place in the problem. Drawing a picture or diagram may help with this step. 2. Be sure that you understand, term by term, what the sequence represents in the problem. 3. Determine whether the sequence is arithmetic or geometric. 4. Determine whether the problem is asking for a specific term or for the sum of a certain number of terms.	Mary Ann received an email message about a computer virus requesting her to forward the email to three people. Assuming Mary Ann and all the recipients did forward the message, how many emails in total were sent if the emails were forwarded ten times? **Solution** This problem can be represented by the sequence 3, 9, 27, 81, ... where $a_1 = 3$ and $r = 3$. The sequence is a geometric sequence. Use the formula $S_n = \dfrac{a_1 r^n - a_1}{r-1}$ to find the sum of the first ten terms: $$S_{10} = \frac{3(3)^{10} - 3}{3-1} = \frac{177{,}144}{2} = 88{,}572$$ A total of 88,572 emails were sent.
Use mathematical induction to prove mathematical statements. (Section 14.4/Objective 1)	Proof by mathematical induction relies on the following principle of induction: Let P_n be a statement in terms of n, where n is a positive integer. If 1. P_1 is true, and 2. the truth of P_k implies the truth of P_{k+1} for every positive integer k, then P_n is true for every positive integer n.	See Section 14.4 for examples of proof by induction.

Chapter 14 Review Problem Set

For Problems 1–10, find the general term (the nth term) for each sequence. These problems include both arithmetic sequences and geometric sequences.

1. $3, 9, 15, 21, \ldots$

2. $\dfrac{1}{3}, 1, 3, 9, \ldots$

3. $10, 20, 40, 80, \ldots$

4. $5, 2, -1, -4, \ldots$

5. $-5, -3, -1, 1, \ldots$

6. $9, 3, 1, \dfrac{1}{3}, \ldots$

7. $-1, 2, -4, 8, \ldots$

8. $12, 15, 18, 21, \ldots$

9. $\dfrac{2}{3}, 1, \dfrac{4}{3}, \dfrac{5}{3}, \ldots$

10. $1, 4, 16, 64, \ldots$

For Problems 11–16, find the required term of each of the sequences.

11. The 19th term of $1, 5, 9, 13, \ldots$

12. The 28th term of $-2, 2, 6, 10, \ldots$

13. The 9th term of $8, 4, 2, 1, \ldots$

14. The 8th term of $\dfrac{243}{32}, \dfrac{81}{16}, \dfrac{27}{8}, \dfrac{9}{4}, \ldots$

15. The 34th term of $7, 4, 1, -2, \ldots$

16. The 10th term of $-32, 16, -8, 4, \ldots$

For Problems 17–29, solve each problem.

17. If the 5th term of an arithmetic sequence is -19 and the 8th term is -34, find the common difference of the sequence.

18. If the 8th term of an arithmetic sequence is 37 and the 13th term is 57, find the 20th term.

19. Find the first term of a geometric sequence if the third term is 5 and the sixth term is 135.

20. Find the common ratio of a geometric sequence if the second term is $\dfrac{1}{2}$ and the sixth term is 8.

21. Find the sum of the first nine terms of the sequence $81, 27, 9, 3, \ldots$.

22. Find the sum of the first 70 terms of the sequence $-3, 0, 3, 6, \ldots$.

23. Find the sum of the first 75 terms of the sequence $5, 1, -3, -7, \ldots$.

24. Find the sum of the first ten terms of the sequence if $a_n = 2^{5-n}$.

25. Find the sum of the first 95 terms of the sequence if $a_n = 7n + 1$.

26. Find the sum $5 + 7 + 9 + \cdots + 137$.

27. Find the sum $64 + 16 + 4 + \cdots + \dfrac{1}{64}$.

28. Find the sum of all even numbers between 8 and 384, inclusive.

29. Find the sum of all multiples of 3 between 27 and 276, inclusive.

For Problems 30–33, find each indicated sum.

30. $\displaystyle\sum_{i=1}^{45} (-2i + 5)$

31. $\displaystyle\sum_{i=1}^{5} i^3$

32. $\displaystyle\sum_{i=1}^{8} 2^{8-i}$

33. $\displaystyle\sum_{i=4}^{75} (3i - 4)$

For Problems 34–36, solve each problem.

34. Find the sum of the infinite geometric sequence $64, 16, 4, 1, \ldots$.

35. Change $0.\overline{36}$ to reduced a/b form, when a and b are integers and $b \neq 0$.

36. Change $0.4\overline{5}$ to reduced a/b form, when a and b are integers and $b \neq 0$.

Solve each of Problems 37–40 by using your knowledge of arithmetic sequences and geometric sequences.

37. Suppose that your savings account contains \$3750 at the beginning of a year. If you withdraw \$250 per month from the account, how much will it contain at the end of the year?

38. Sonya decides to start saving dimes. She plans to save one dime the first day of April, two dimes the second day, three dimes the third day, four dimes the fourth day, and so on for the 30 days of April. How much money will she save in April?

39. Nancy decides to start saving dimes. She plans to save one dime the first day of April, two dimes the second day, four dimes the third day, eight dimes the fourth day, and so on for the first 15 days of April. How much will she save in 15 days?

40. A tank contains 61,440 gallons of water. Each day one-fourth of the water is drained out. How much water remains in the tank at the end of 6 days?

For Problems 41–43, show a mathematical induction proof.

41. Prove that $5^n > 5n - 1$ for all positive integer values of n.

42. Prove that $n^3 - n + 3$ is divisible by 3 for all positive integer values of n.

43. Prove that

$$S_n = \frac{n(n + 3)}{4(n + 1)(n + 2)}$$

is the sum formula for the sequence

$$a_n = \frac{1}{n(n + 1)(n + 2)}$$

where n is any positive integer.

1. Find the 15th term of the sequence for which $a_n = -n^2 - 1$.

2. Find the fifth term of the sequence for which $a_n = 3(2)^{n-1}$.

3. Find the general term of the sequence $-3, -8, -13, -18, \ldots$.

4. Find the general term of the sequence $5, \dfrac{5}{2}, \dfrac{5}{4}, \dfrac{5}{8}, \ldots$.

5. Find the general term of the sequence $10, 16, 22, 28, \ldots$.

6. Find the seventh term of the sequence $8, 12, 18, 27, \ldots$.

7. Find the 75th term of the sequence $1, 4, 7, 10, \ldots$.

8. Find the number of terms in the sequence $7, 11, 15, \ldots, 243$.

9. Find the sum of the first 40 terms of the sequence $1, 4, 7, 10, \ldots$.

10. Find the sum of the first eight terms of the sequence $3, 6, 12, 24, \ldots$.

11. Find the sum of the first 45 terms of the sequence for which $a_n = 7n - 2$.

12. Find the sum of the first ten terms of the sequence for which $a_n = 3(2)^n$.

13. Find the sum of the first 150 positive even whole numbers.

14. Find the sum of the odd whole numbers between 11 and 193, inclusive.

15. Find the indicated sum $\displaystyle\sum_{i=1}^{50} (3i + 5)$.

16. Find the indicated sum $\displaystyle\sum_{i=1}^{10} (-2)^{i-1}$.

17. Find the sum of the infinite geometric sequence $3, \dfrac{3}{2}, \dfrac{3}{4}, \dfrac{3}{8}, \ldots$.

18. Find the sum of the infinite geometric sequence for which $a_n = 2\left(\dfrac{1}{3}\right)^{n+1}$.

19. Change $0.\overline{18}$ to reduced a/b form, if a and b are integers and $b \neq 0$.

20. Change $0.2\overline{6}$ to reduced a/b form, if a and b are integers and $b \neq 0$.

For Problems 21–23, solve each problem.

21. A tank contains 49,152 liters of gasoline. Each day, three-fourths of the gasoline remaining in the tank is pumped out and not replaced. How much gasoline remains in the tank at the end of 7 days?

22. Suppose that you save a dime the first day of a month, $0.20 the second day, and $0.40 the third day and that you continue to double your savings each day for 14 days. Find the total amount that you will save at the end of 14 days.

23. A woman invests $350 at 6% simple interest at the beginning of each year for a period of 10 years. Find the total accumulated value of all the investments at the end of the 10-year period.

For Problems 24 and 25, show a mathematical induction proof.

24. $S_n = \dfrac{n(3n - 1)}{2}$ for $a_n = 3n - 2$

25. $9^n - 1$ is divisible by 8 for all positive integer values for n.

Appendixes

A   Prime Numbers and Operations with Fractions

This appendix reviews the operations with rational numbers in common fractional form. Throughout this section, we will refer to "multiplying fractions." Be aware that this phrase means multiplying rational numbers in common fractional form. A strong foundation here will simplify your later work in rational expressions. Because prime numbers and prime factorization play an important role in the operations with fractions, let's begin by considering two special kinds of whole numbers, prime numbers and composite numbers.

> **Definition A.1**
>
> A **prime number** is a whole number greater than 1 that has no factors (divisors) other than itself and 1. Whole numbers greater than 1 that are not prime numbers are called **composite numbers**.

The prime numbers less than 50 are 2, 3, 5, 7, 11, 13, 17, 19, 23, 29, 31, 37, 41, 43, and 47. Note that each of these has no factors other than itself and 1. We can express every composite number as the indicated product of prime numbers. Consider the following examples:

$$4 = 2 \cdot 2 \qquad 6 = 2 \cdot 3 \qquad 8 = 2 \cdot 2 \cdot 2 \qquad 10 = 2 \cdot 5 \qquad 12 = 2 \cdot 2 \cdot 3$$

In each case we express a composite number as the indicated product of prime numbers. The indicated-product form is called the prime-factored form of the number. There are various procedures to find the prime factors of a given composite number. For our purposes, the simplest technique is to factor the given composite number into any two easily recognized factors and then continue to factor each of these until we obtain only prime factors. Consider these examples:

$$18 = 2 \cdot 9 = 2 \cdot 3 \cdot 3 \qquad\qquad 27 = 3 \cdot 9 = 3 \cdot 3 \cdot 3$$
$$24 = 4 \cdot 6 = 2 \cdot 2 \cdot 2 \cdot 3 \qquad 150 = 10 \cdot 15 = 2 \cdot 5 \cdot 3 \cdot 5$$

It does not matter which two factors we choose first. For example, we might start by expressing 18 as $3 \cdot 6$ and then factor 6 into $2 \cdot 3$, which produces a final result of $18 = 3 \cdot 2 \cdot 3$. Either way, 18 contains two prime factors of 3 and one prime factor of 2. The order in which we write the prime factors is not important.

Least Common Multiple

It is sometimes necessary to determine the smallest common nonzero multiple of two or more whole numbers. We call this nonzero number the **least common multiple**. In our work with fractions, there will be problems for which it will be necessary to find the least common multiple of some numbers, usually the denominators of fractions. So let's review the concepts of multiples. We know that 35 is a multiple of 5 because $5 \cdot 7 = 35$. The set of all whole numbers that are multiples of 5 consists of 0, 5, 10, 15, 20, 25, and so on. In other words, 5 times each successive whole number ($5 \cdot 0 = 0, 5 \cdot 1 = 5, 5 \cdot 2 = 10, 5 \cdot 3 = 15$, and so on) produces the multiples of 5. In a like manner, the set of multiples of 4 consists of 0, 4, 8, 12, 16, and so on. We can illustrate the concept of the least common multiple and find the least common multiple of 5 and 4 by using a simple listing of the multiples of 5 and the multiples of 4.

Multiples of 5 are 0, 5, 10, 15, 20, 25, 30, 35, 40, 45, . . .

Multiples of 4 are 0, 4, 8, 12, 16, 20, 24, 28, 32, 36, 40, 44, 48, . . .

The nonzero numbers in common on the lists are 20 and 40. The least of these, 20, is the least common multiple. Stated another way, 20 is the smallest nonzero whole number that is divisible by both 4 and 5.

Drawing on your knowledge of arithmetic, you will often be able to determine the least common multiple by inspection. For instance, the least common multiple of 6 and 8 is 24. Therefore, 24 is the smallest nonzero whole number that is divisible by both 6 and 8. If we cannot determine the least common multiple by inspection, then using the prime-factorized form of composite numbers is helpful. The procedure is as follows.

Step 1   Express each number as a product of prime factors.

Step 2   The least common multiple contains each different prime factor as many times as the most times it appears in any one of the factorizations from step 1.

The following examples illustrate this technique for finding the least common multiple of two or more numbers.

EXAMPLE 1   Find the least common multiple of 24 and 36.

Solution

Let's first express each number as a product of prime factors.

$$24 = 2 \cdot 2 \cdot 2 \cdot 3$$
$$36 = 2 \cdot 2 \cdot 3 \cdot 3$$

The prime factor 2 occurs the most times (three times) in the factorization of 24. Because the factorization of 24 contains three 2s, the least common multiple must have three 2s. The prime factor 3 occurs the most times (two times) in the factorization of 36. Because the factorization of 36 contains two 3s, the least common multiple must have two 3s. The least common multiple of 24 and 36 is therefore $2 \cdot 2 \cdot 2 \cdot 3 \cdot 3 = 72$. ∎

EXAMPLE 2   Find the least common multiple of 48 and 84.

Solution

$$48 = 2 \cdot 2 \cdot 2 \cdot 2 \cdot 3$$
$$84 = 2 \cdot 2 \cdot 3 \cdot 7$$

We need four 2s in the least common multiple because of the four 2s in 48. We need one 3 because of the 3 in each of the numbers, and we need one 7 because of the 7 in 84. The least common multiple of 48 and 84 is $2 \cdot 2 \cdot 2 \cdot 2 \cdot 3 \cdot 7 = 336$. ∎

EXAMPLE 3   Find the least common multiple of 12, 18, and 28.

Solution

$$28 = 2 \cdot 2 \cdot 7$$
$$18 = 2 \cdot 3 \cdot 3$$
$$12 = 2 \cdot 2 \cdot 3$$

The least common multiple is $2 \cdot 2 \cdot 3 \cdot 3 \cdot 7 = 252$. ∎

EXAMPLE 4   Find the least common multiple of 8 and 9.

Solution

$$9 = 3 \cdot 3$$
$$8 = 2 \cdot 2 \cdot 2$$

The least common multiple is $2 \cdot 2 \cdot 2 \cdot 3 \cdot 3 = 72$. ∎

Multiplying Fractions

We can define the multiplication of fractions in common fractional form as follows:

> **Multiplying Fractions**
>
> If a, b, c, and d are integers, with b and d not equal to zero, then $\dfrac{a}{b} \cdot \dfrac{c}{d} = \dfrac{a \cdot c}{b \cdot d}$.

To multiply fractions in common fractional form, we simply multiply numerators and multiply denominators. The following examples illustrate the multiplication of fractions:

$$\frac{1}{3} \cdot \frac{2}{5} = \frac{1 \cdot 2}{3 \cdot 5} = \frac{2}{15}$$

$$\frac{3}{4} \cdot \frac{5}{7} = \frac{3 \cdot 5}{4 \cdot 7} = \frac{15}{28}$$

$$\frac{3}{5} \cdot \frac{5}{3} = \frac{15}{15} = 1$$

The last of these examples is a very special case. If the product of two numbers is 1, then the numbers are said to be reciprocals of each other.

Before we proceed too far with multiplying fractions, we need to learn about reducing fractions. The following property is applied throughout our work with fractions. We call this property the *fundamental property of fractions*.

> **Fundamental Property of Fractions**
>
> If b and k are nonzero integers, and a is any integer, then $\dfrac{a \cdot k}{b \cdot k} = \dfrac{a}{b}$.

The fundamental property of fractions provides the basis for what is often called reducing fractions to lowest terms, or expressing fractions in simplest or reduced form. Let's apply the property to a few examples.

EXAMPLE 5   Reduce $\dfrac{12}{18}$ to lowest terms.

Solution

$$\frac{12}{18} = \frac{2 \cdot 6}{3 \cdot 6} = \frac{2}{3}$$

A common factor of 6 has been divided out of both numerator and denominator

EXAMPLE 6   Change $\dfrac{14}{35}$ to simplest form.

Solution

$$\frac{14}{35} = \frac{2 \cdot 7}{5 \cdot 7} = \frac{2}{5}$$

A common factor of 7 has been divided out of both numerator and denominator

EXAMPLE 7   Reduce $\dfrac{72}{90}$.

Solution

$$\frac{72}{90} = \frac{2 \cdot 2 \cdot 2 \cdot 3 \cdot 3}{2 \cdot 3 \cdot 3 \cdot 5} = \frac{4}{5}$$

The prime-factored forms of the numerator and denominator may be used to find common factors

We are now ready to consider multiplication problems with the understanding that the final answer should be expressed in reduced form. Study the following examples carefully; we use different methods to simplify the problems.

EXAMPLE 8   Multiply $\left(\dfrac{9}{4}\right)\left(\dfrac{14}{15}\right)$.

Solution

$$\left(\frac{9}{4}\right)\left(\frac{14}{15}\right) = \frac{3 \cdot 3 \cdot 2 \cdot 7}{2 \cdot 2 \cdot 3 \cdot 5} = \frac{21}{10}$$

EXAMPLE 9   Find the product of $\dfrac{8}{9}$ and $\dfrac{18}{24}$.

Solution

$$\frac{\overset{1}{8}}{\underset{1}{9}} \cdot \frac{\overset{2}{18}}{\underset{3}{24}} = \frac{2}{3}$$ A common factor of 8 has been divided out of 8 and 24, and a common factor of 9 has been divided out of 9 and 18

Dividing Fractions

The next example motivates a definition for the division of rational numbers in fractional form:

$$\frac{\frac{3}{4}}{\frac{2}{3}} = \left(\frac{\frac{3}{4}}{\frac{2}{3}}\right)\left(\frac{\frac{3}{2}}{\frac{3}{2}}\right) = \frac{\left(\frac{3}{4}\right)\left(\frac{3}{2}\right)}{1} = \left(\frac{3}{4}\right)\left(\frac{3}{2}\right) = \frac{9}{8}$$

Note that $\left(\dfrac{\frac{3}{2}}{\frac{3}{2}}\right)$ is a form of 1, and $\dfrac{3}{2}$ is the reciprocal of $\dfrac{2}{3}$. In other words, $\dfrac{3}{4}$ divided by $\dfrac{2}{3}$ is equivalent to $\dfrac{3}{4}$ times $\dfrac{3}{2}$. The following definition for division now should seem reasonable.

> **Division of Fractions**
>
> If b, c, and d are nonzero integers, and a is any integer, then $\dfrac{a}{b} \div \dfrac{c}{d} = \dfrac{a}{b} \cdot \dfrac{d}{c}$.

Note that to divide $\dfrac{a}{b}$ by $\dfrac{c}{d}$, we multiply $\dfrac{a}{b}$ times the reciprocal of $\dfrac{c}{d}$, which is $\dfrac{d}{c}$. The next examples demonstrate the important steps of a division problem:

$$\frac{2}{3} \div \frac{1}{2} = \frac{2}{3} \cdot \frac{2}{1} = \frac{4}{3}$$

$$\frac{5}{6} \div \frac{3}{4} = \frac{5}{6} \cdot \frac{4}{3} = \frac{5 \cdot 4}{6 \cdot 3} = \frac{5 \cdot 2 \cdot 2}{2 \cdot 3 \cdot 3} = \frac{10}{9}$$

$$\frac{\frac{6}{7}}{\frac{2}{1}} = \frac{\overset{3}{6}}{7} \cdot \frac{1}{\underset{1}{2}} = \frac{3}{7}$$

Adding and Subtracting Fractions

Suppose that it is one-fifth of a mile between your dorm and the union and two-fifths of a mile between the union and the library along a straight line as indicated in Figure A.1. The total distance between your dorm and the library is three-fifths of a mile, and we write $\frac{1}{5} + \frac{2}{5} = \frac{3}{5}$.

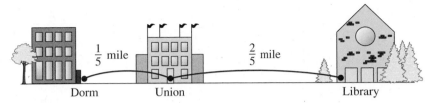

$\frac{1}{5}$ mile $\frac{2}{5}$ mile

Dorm   Union   Library

Figure A.1

A pizza is cut into seven equal pieces and you eat two of the pieces (see Figure A.2). How much of the pizza remains? We represent the whole pizza by $\frac{7}{7}$ and conclude that $\frac{7}{7} - \frac{2}{7} = \frac{5}{7}$ of the pizza remains.

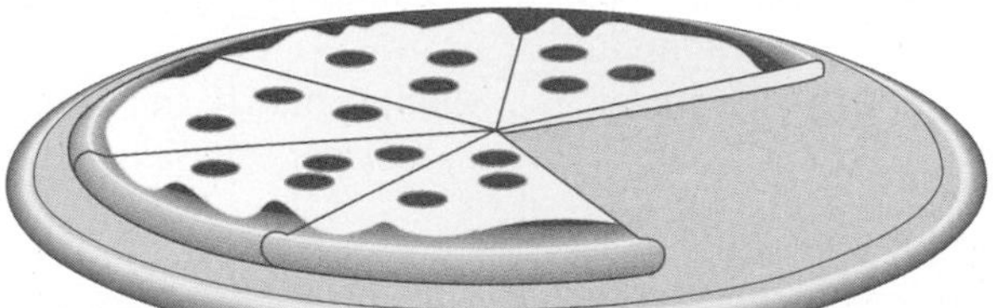

Figure A.2

These examples motivate the following definition for addition and subtraction of rational numbers in $\frac{a}{b}$ form.

> ### Addition and Subtraction of Fractions
>
> If a, b, and c are integers, and b is not zero, then
>
> $$\frac{a}{b} + \frac{c}{b} = \frac{a + c}{b} \qquad \text{Addition}$$
>
> $$\frac{a}{b} - \frac{c}{b} = \frac{a - c}{b} \qquad \text{Subtraction}$$

We say that fractions with common denominators can be added or subtracted by adding or subtracting the numerators and placing the results over the common denominator. Consider the following examples:

$$\frac{3}{7} + \frac{2}{7} = \frac{3 + 2}{7} = \frac{5}{7}$$

$$\frac{7}{8} - \frac{2}{8} = \frac{7 - 2}{8} = \frac{5}{8}$$

$$\frac{5}{6} - \frac{1}{6} = \frac{5 - 1}{6} = \frac{4}{6} = \frac{2}{3} \qquad \text{We agree to reduce the final answer}$$

How do we add or subtract if the fractions do not have a common denominator? We use the fundamental principle of fractions, $\dfrac{a \cdot k}{b \cdot k} = \dfrac{a}{b}$, to get equivalent fractions that have a common denominator. **Equivalent fractions** are fractions that name the same number. Consider the next example, which shows the details.

EXAMPLE 10   Add $\dfrac{1}{4} + \dfrac{2}{5}$.

Solution

$$\dfrac{1}{4} = \dfrac{1 \cdot 5}{4 \cdot 5} = \dfrac{5}{20} \qquad \dfrac{1}{4} \text{ and } \dfrac{5}{20} \text{ are equivalent fractions}$$

$$\dfrac{2}{5} = \dfrac{2 \cdot 4}{5 \cdot 4} = \dfrac{8}{20} \qquad \dfrac{2}{5} \text{ and } \dfrac{8}{20} \text{ are equivalent fractions}$$

$$\dfrac{5}{20} + \dfrac{8}{20} = \dfrac{13}{20}$$

Note that in Example 10 we chose 20 as the common denominator, and 20 is the least common multiple of the original denominators 4 and 5. (Recall that the least common multiple is the smallest nonzero whole number divisible by the given numbers.) In general, we use the least common multiple of the denominators of the fractions to be added or subtracted as a **least common denominator** (LCD).

Recall that the least common multiple may be found either by inspection or by using prime factorization forms of the numbers. Consider some examples involving these procedures.

EXAMPLE 11   Subtract $\dfrac{5}{8} - \dfrac{7}{12}$.

Solution

By inspection the LCD is 24.

$$\dfrac{5}{8} - \dfrac{7}{12} = \dfrac{5 \cdot 3}{8 \cdot 3} - \dfrac{7 \cdot 2}{12 \cdot 2} = \dfrac{15}{24} - \dfrac{14}{24} = \dfrac{1}{24}$$

If the LCD is not obvious by inspection, then we can use the technique of prime factorization to find the least common multiple.

EXAMPLE 12   Add $\dfrac{5}{18} + \dfrac{7}{24}$.

Solution

If we cannot find the LCD by inspection, then we can use the prime-factorized forms.

$$\left. \begin{array}{l} 18 = 2 \cdot 3 \cdot 3 \\ 24 = 2 \cdot 2 \cdot 2 \cdot 3 \end{array} \right\} \longrightarrow \text{LCD} = 2 \cdot 2 \cdot 2 \cdot 3 \cdot 3 = 72$$

$$\dfrac{5}{18} + \dfrac{7}{24} = \dfrac{5 \cdot 4}{18 \cdot 4} + \dfrac{7 \cdot 3}{24 \cdot 3} = \dfrac{20}{72} + \dfrac{21}{72} = \dfrac{41}{72}$$

EXAMPLE 13

Marcey put $\dfrac{5}{8}$ of a pound of chemicals in the spa to adjust the water quality. Michael, not realizing that Marcey had already put in chemicals, put $\dfrac{3}{14}$ of a pound of chemicals in the spa.

The chemical manufacturer states that you should never add more than 1 pound of chemicals. Have Marcey and Michael together put in more than 1 pound of chemicals?

Solution

Add $\dfrac{5}{8} + \dfrac{3}{14}$.

$$\left.\begin{array}{l} 8 = 2 \cdot 2 \cdot 2 \\ 14 = 2 \cdot 7 \end{array}\right\} \longrightarrow \text{LCD} = 2 \cdot 2 \cdot 2 \cdot 7 = 56$$

$$\frac{5}{8} + \frac{3}{14} = \frac{5 \cdot 7}{8 \cdot 7} + \frac{3 \cdot 4}{14 \cdot 4} = \frac{35}{56} + \frac{12}{56} = \frac{47}{56}$$

No, Marcey and Michael have not added more than 1 pound of chemicals. ∎

Simplifying Numerical Expressions

Let's now consider simplifying numerical expressions that contain fractions. In agreement with the order of operations, first perform multiplications and divisions as they appear from left to right, and then perform additions and subtractions as they appear from left to right. In these next examples, we show only the major steps. Be sure you can fill in all the details.

EXAMPLE 14   Simplify $\dfrac{3}{4} + \dfrac{2}{3} \cdot \dfrac{3}{5} - \dfrac{1}{2} \cdot \dfrac{1}{5}$.

Solution

$$\frac{3}{4} + \frac{2}{3} \cdot \frac{3}{5} - \frac{1}{2} \cdot \frac{1}{5} = \frac{3}{4} + \frac{2}{5} - \frac{1}{10}$$

$$= \frac{15}{20} + \frac{8}{20} - \frac{2}{20} = \frac{15 + 8 - 2}{20} = \frac{21}{20}$$

∎

EXAMPLE 15   Simplify $\dfrac{5}{8}\left(\dfrac{1}{2} + \dfrac{1}{3}\right)$.

Solution

$$\frac{5}{8}\left(\frac{1}{2} + \frac{1}{3}\right) = \frac{5}{8}\left(\frac{3}{6} + \frac{2}{6}\right) = \frac{5}{8}\left(\frac{5}{6}\right) = \frac{25}{48}$$

∎

Practice Exercises

For Problems 1–12, factor each composite number into a product of prime numbers; for example, $18 = 2 \cdot 3 \cdot 3$.

1. 26

2. 16

3. 36

4. 80

5. 49

6. 92

7. 56

8. 144

9. 120

10. 84

11. 135

12. 98

For Problems 13–24, find the least common multiple of the given numbers.

13. 6 and 8

14. 8 and 12

15. 12 and 16

16. 9 and 12

17. 28 and 35

18. 42 and 66

19. 49 and 56

20. 18 and 24

21. 8, 12, and 28

22. 6, 10, and 12

23. 9, 15, and 18

24. 8, 14, and 24

For Problems 25–30, reduce each fraction to lowest terms.

25. $\dfrac{8}{12}$

26. $\dfrac{12}{16}$

27. $\dfrac{16}{24}$

28. $\dfrac{18}{32}$

29. $\dfrac{15}{9}$

30. $\dfrac{48}{36}$

For Problems 31–36, multiply or divide as indicated, and express answers in reduced form.

31. $\dfrac{3}{4} \cdot \dfrac{5}{7}$

32. $\dfrac{4}{5} \cdot \dfrac{3}{11}$

33. $\dfrac{2}{7} \div \dfrac{3}{5}$

34. $\dfrac{5}{6} \div \dfrac{11}{13}$

35. $\dfrac{3}{8} \cdot \dfrac{12}{15}$

36. $\dfrac{4}{9} \cdot \dfrac{3}{2}$

37. A certain recipe calls for $\dfrac{3}{4}$ cup of milk. To make half of the recipe, how much milk is needed?

38. John is adding a diesel fuel additive to his fuel tank, which is half full. The directions say to add $\dfrac{1}{3}$ of the bottle to a full fuel tank. What portion of the bottle should he add to his fuel tank?

39. Mark shares a backup hard drive with his roommates. He has partitioned the hard drive in such a way that he gets $\dfrac{1}{3}$ of the disk space. His part of the hard drive is currently $\dfrac{2}{3}$ full. What portion of the computer's hard drive space is he currently using?

40. Angelina teaches $\dfrac{2}{3}$ of the deaf children in her local school. Her local school educates $\dfrac{1}{2}$ of the deaf children in the school district. What portion of the school district's deaf children is Angelina teaching?

For Problems 41–57, add or subtract as indicated and express answers in lowest terms.

41. $\dfrac{2}{7} + \dfrac{3}{7}$

42. $\dfrac{3}{11} + \dfrac{5}{11}$

43. $\dfrac{7}{9} - \dfrac{2}{9}$

44. $\dfrac{11}{13} - \dfrac{6}{13}$

45. $\dfrac{3}{4} + \dfrac{9}{4}$

46. $\dfrac{5}{6} + \dfrac{7}{6}$

47. $\dfrac{11}{12} - \dfrac{3}{12}$

48. $\dfrac{13}{16} - \dfrac{7}{16}$

49. $\dfrac{5}{24} + \dfrac{11}{24}$

50. $\dfrac{7}{36} + \dfrac{13}{36}$

51. $\dfrac{1}{3} + \dfrac{1}{5}$

52. $\dfrac{1}{6} + \dfrac{1}{8}$

53. $\dfrac{15}{16} - \dfrac{3}{8}$

54. $\dfrac{13}{12} - \dfrac{1}{6}$

55. $\dfrac{7}{10} + \dfrac{8}{15}$

56. $\dfrac{7}{12} + \dfrac{5}{8}$

57. $\dfrac{11}{24} + \dfrac{5}{32}$

58. Alicia and her brother Jeff shared a pizza. Alicia ate $\dfrac{1}{8}$ of the pizza, while Jeff ate $\dfrac{2}{3}$ of the pizza. How much of the pizza has been eaten?

59. Rosa has $\dfrac{1}{3}$ pound of blueberries, $\dfrac{1}{4}$ pound of strawberries, and $\dfrac{1}{2}$ pound of raspberries. If she combines these for a fruit salad, how many pounds of berries will be in the salad?

60. A chemist has $\dfrac{11}{16}$ of an ounce of dirt residue on which to perform crime lab tests. He needs $\dfrac{3}{8}$ of an ounce to perform a test for iron content. How much of the dirt residue will be left for the chemist to use for other testing?

For Problems 61–68, simplify each numerical expression, and express answers in reduced form.

61. $\dfrac{1}{4} - \dfrac{3}{8} + \dfrac{5}{12} - \dfrac{1}{24}$

62. $\dfrac{3}{4} + \dfrac{2}{3} - \dfrac{1}{6} + \dfrac{5}{12}$

63. $\dfrac{5}{6} + \dfrac{2}{3} \cdot \dfrac{3}{4} - \dfrac{1}{4} \cdot \dfrac{2}{5}$

64. $\dfrac{2}{3} + \dfrac{1}{2} \cdot \dfrac{2}{5} - \dfrac{1}{3} \cdot \dfrac{1}{5}$

65. $\dfrac{3}{4} \cdot \dfrac{6}{9} - \dfrac{5}{6} \cdot \dfrac{8}{10} + \dfrac{2}{3} \cdot \dfrac{6}{8}$

66. $\dfrac{3}{5} \cdot \dfrac{5}{7} + \dfrac{2}{3} \cdot \dfrac{3}{5} - \dfrac{1}{7} \cdot \dfrac{2}{5}$

67. $\dfrac{7}{13}\left(\dfrac{2}{3} - \dfrac{1}{6}\right)$

68. $48\left(\dfrac{5}{12} - \dfrac{1}{6} + \dfrac{3}{8}\right)$

69. Blake Scott leaves $\dfrac{1}{4}$ of his estate to the Boy Scouts, $\dfrac{2}{5}$ to the local cancer fund, and the rest to his church. What fractional part of the estate does the church receive?

70. Franco has $\dfrac{7}{8}$ of an ounce of gold. He wants to give $\dfrac{3}{16}$ of an ounce to his friend Julie. He plans to divide the remaining amount of his gold in half to make two rings. How much gold will he have for each ring?

B   Binomial Theorem

In Chapter 4, when multiplying polynomials, we developed patterns for squaring and cubing binomials. Now we want to develop a general pattern that can be used to raise a binomial to any positive integral power. Let's begin by looking at some specific expansions that can be verified by direct multiplication. (Note that the patterns for squaring and cubing a binomial are a part of this list.)

$$(x + y)^0 = 1$$
$$(x + y)^1 = x + y$$
$$(x + y)^2 = x^2 + 2xy + y^2$$
$$(x + y)^3 = x^3 + 3x^2y + 3xy^2 + y^3$$
$$(x + y)^4 = x^4 + 4x^3y + 6x^2y^2 + 4xy^3 + y^4$$
$$(x + y)^5 = x^5 + 5x^4y + 10x^3y^2 + 10x^2y^3 + 5xy^4 + y^5$$

First, note the pattern of the exponents for x and y on a term-by-term basis. The exponents of x begin with the exponent of the binomial and decrease by 1, term by term, until the last term has x^0, which is 1. The exponents of y begin with zero ($y^0 = 1$) and increase by 1, term by term, until the last term contains y to the power of the binomial. In other words, the variables in the expansion of $(x + y)^n$ have the following pattern.

$$x^n, \quad x^{n-1}y, \quad x^{n-2}y^2, \quad x^{n-3}y^3, \quad \ldots, \quad xy^{n-1}, \quad y^n$$

Note that for each term, the sum of the exponents of x and y is n.

Now let's look for a pattern for the coefficients by examining specifically the expansion of $(x + y)^5$.

$$(x + y)^5 = x^5 + 5x^4y^1 + 10x^3y^2 + 10x^2y^3 + 5x^1y^4 + 1y^5$$

$$C(5, 1) \quad C(5, 2) \quad C(5, 3) \quad C(5, 4) \quad C(5, 5)$$

As indicated by the arrows, the coefficients are numbers that arise as different-sized combinations of five things. To see why this happens, consider the coefficient for the term containing x^3y^2. The two y's (for y^2) come from two of the factors of $(x + y)$, and therefore the three x's (for x^3) must come from the other three factors of $(x + y)$. In other words, the coefficient is $C(5, 2)$.

We can now state a general expansion formula for $(x + y)^n$; this formula is often called the **binomial theorem**. But before stating it, let's make a small switch in notation. Instead of $C(n, r)$, we shall write $\binom{n}{r}$, which will prove to be a little more convenient at this time. The symbol $\binom{n}{r}$, still refers to the number of combinations of n things taken r at a time, but in this context, it is called a **binomial coefficient**.

> ### Binomial Theorem
>
> For any binomial $(x + y)$ and any natural number n,
>
> $$(x + y)^n = x^n + \binom{n}{1}x^{n-1}y + \binom{n}{2}x^{n-2}y^2 + \cdots + \binom{n}{n}y^n$$

The binomial theorem can be proved by mathematical induction, but we will not do that in this text. Instead, we'll consider a few examples that put the binomial theorem to work.

EXAMPLE 1   Expand $(x + y)^7$.

Solution

$$(x + y)^7 = x^7 + \binom{7}{1}x^6y + \binom{7}{2}x^5y^2 + \binom{7}{3}x^4y^3 + \binom{7}{4}x^3y^4$$

$$+ \binom{7}{5}x^2y^5 + \binom{7}{6}xy^6 + \binom{7}{7}y^7$$

$$= x^7 + 7x^6y + 21x^5y^2 + 35x^4y^3 + 35x^3y^4 + 21x^2y^5 + 7xy^6 + y^7$$

EXAMPLE 2   Expand $(x - y)^5$.

Solution

We shall treat $(x - y)^5$ as $[x + (-y)]^5$:

$$[x + (-y)]^5 = x^5 + \binom{5}{1}x^4(-y) + \binom{5}{2}x^3(-y)^2 + \binom{5}{3}x^2(-y)^3$$

$$+ \binom{5}{4}x(-y)^4 + \binom{5}{5}(-y)^5$$

$$= x^5 - 5x^4y + 10x^3y^2 - 10x^2y^3 + 5xy^4 - y^5$$

EXAMPLE 3   Expand $(2a + 3b)^4$.

Solution

Let $x = 2a$ and $y = 3b$ in the binomial theorem:

$$(2a + 3b)^4 = (2a)^4 + \binom{4}{1}(2a)^3(3b) + \binom{4}{2}(2a)^2(3b)^2$$

$$+ \binom{4}{3}(2a)(3b)^3 + \binom{4}{4}(3b)^4$$

$$= 16a^4 + 96a^3b + 216a^2b^2 + 216ab^3 + 81b^4$$

EXAMPLE 4   Expand $\left(a + \dfrac{1}{n}\right)^5$.

Solution

$$\left(a + \frac{1}{n}\right)^5 = a^5 + \binom{5}{1}a^4\left(\frac{1}{n}\right) + \binom{5}{2}a^3\left(\frac{1}{n}\right)^2 + \binom{5}{3}a^2\left(\frac{1}{n}\right)^3 + \binom{5}{4}a\left(\frac{1}{n}\right)^4 + \binom{5}{5}\left(\frac{1}{n}\right)^5$$

$$= a^5 + \frac{5a^4}{n} + \frac{10a^3}{n^2} + \frac{10a^2}{n^3} + \frac{5a}{n^4} + \frac{1}{n^5}$$

EXAMPLE 5 Expand $(x^2 - 2y^3)^6$.

Solution

$$[x^2 + (-2y^3)]^6 = (x^2)^6 + \binom{6}{1}(x^2)^5(-2y^3) + \binom{6}{2}(x^2)^4(-2y^3)^2$$
$$+ \binom{6}{3}(x^2)^3(-2y^3)^3 + \binom{6}{4}(x^2)^2(-2y^3)^4$$
$$+ \binom{6}{5}(x^2)(-2y^3)^5 + \binom{6}{6}(-2y^3)^6$$
$$= x^{12} - 12x^{10}y^3 + 60x^8y^6 - 160x^6y^9 + 240x^4y^{12} - 192x^2y^{15} + 64y^{18}$$

Finding Specific Terms

Sometimes it is convenient to be able to write down the specific term of a binomial expansion without writing out the entire expansion. For example, suppose that we want the sixth term of the expansion $(x + y)^{12}$. We can proceed as follows: The sixth term will contain y^5. (Note in the binomial theorem that the *exponent of y is always one less than the number of the term*.) Because the sum of the exponents for x and y must be 12 (the exponent of the binomial), the sixth term will also contain x^7. The coefficient is $\binom{12}{5}$, and the 5 agrees with the exponent of y^5. Therefore the sixth term of $(x + y)^{12}$ is

$$\binom{12}{5}x^7y^5 = 792x^7y^5$$

EXAMPLE 6 Find the fourth term of $(3a + 2b)^7$.

Solution

The fourth term will contain $(2b)^3$, and therefore it will also contain $(3a)^4$. The coefficient is $\binom{7}{3}$. Thus the fourth term is

$$\binom{7}{3}(3a)^4(2b)^3 = (35)(81a^4)(8b^3) = 22{,}680a^4b^3$$

EXAMPLE 7 Find the sixth term of $(4x - y)^9$.

Solution

The sixth term will contain $(-y)^5$, and therefore it will also contain $(4x)^4$. The coefficient is $\binom{9}{5}$. Thus the sixth term is

$$\binom{9}{5}(4x)^4(-y)^5 = (126)(256x^4)(-y^5) = -32{,}256x^4y^5$$

Practice Exercises

For Problems 1–26, expand and simplify each binomial.

1. $(x + y)^8$

2. $(x + y)^9$

3. $(x - y)^6$

4. $(x - y)^4$

5. $(a + 2b)^4$

6. $(3a + b)^4$

7. $(x - 3y)^5$

8. $(2x - y)^6$

9. $(2a - 3b)^4$

10. $(3a - 2b)^5$

11. $(x^2 + y)^5$

12. $(x + y^3)^6$

13. $(2x^2 - y^2)^4$

14. $(3x^2 - 2y^2)^5$

15. $(x + 3)^6$

16. $(x + 2)^7$

17. $(x - 1)^9$

18. $(x - 3)^4$

19. $\left(1 + \dfrac{1}{n}\right)^4$

20. $\left(2 + \dfrac{1}{n}\right)^5$

21. $\left(a - \dfrac{1}{n}\right)^6$

22. $\left(2a - \dfrac{1}{n}\right)^5$

23. $\left(1 + \sqrt{2}\right)^4$

24. $\left(2 + \sqrt{3}\right)^3$

25. $\left(3 - \sqrt{2}\right)^5$

26. $\left(1 - \sqrt{3}\right)^4$

For Problems 27–36, write the first four terms of each expansion.

27. $(x + y)^{12}$

28. $(x + y)^{15}$

29. $(x - y)^{20}$

30. $(a - 2b)^{13}$

31. $(x^2 - 2y^3)^{14}$

32. $(x^3 - 3y^2)^{11}$

33. $\left(a + \dfrac{1}{n}\right)^9$

34. $\left(2 - \dfrac{1}{n}\right)^6$

35. $(-x + 2y)^{10}$

36. $(-a - b)^{14}$

For Problems 37–46, find the specified term for each binomial expansion.

37. The fourth term of $(x + y)^8$

38. The seventh term of $(x + y)^{11}$

39. The fifth term of $(x - y)^9$

40. The fourth term of $(x - 2y)^6$

41. The sixth term of $(3a + b)^7$

42. The third term of $(2x - 5y)^5$

43. The eighth term of $(x^2 + y^3)^{10}$

44. The ninth term of $(a + b^3)^{12}$

45. The seventh term of $\left(1 - \dfrac{1}{n}\right)^{15}$

46. The eighth term of $\left(1 - \dfrac{1}{n}\right)^{13}$

Chapter 1

Problem Set 1.1 (page 8)

1. True 3. False 5. True 7. False 9. True
11. 0 and 14 13. $0, 14, \frac{2}{3}, -\frac{11}{14}, 2.34, 3.2\bar{1}, \frac{55}{8}, -19$, and -2.6
15. 0 and 14 17. All of them 19. $\not\subseteq$ 21. $\subseteq$ 23. $\not\subseteq$
25. $\subseteq$ 27. $\not\subseteq$ 29. Real, rational, an integer, and negative
31. Real, irrational, and negative
33. $\{1, 2\}$ 35. $\{0, 1, 2, 3, 4, 5\}$ 37. $\{\ldots, -1, 0, 1, 2\}$
39. $\varnothing$ 41. $\{0, 1, 2, 3, 4\}$ 43. -6 45. 2 47. $3x + 1$
49. $5x$ 51. 26 53. 84 55. 23 57. 65 59. 60 61. 33
63. 1320 65. 20 67. 119 69. 18 71. 4 73. 31

Problem Set 1.2 (page 18)

1.

3. (a) 7 (b) 0 (c) 15 5. -7 7. -19 9. -22 11. -7
13. 108 15. -70 17. 14 19. -7 21. $3\frac{1}{2}$ 23. $5\frac{1}{2}$
25. $-\frac{2}{15}$ 27. -4 29. 0 31. Undefined 33. -60
35. -4.8 37. 14.13 39. -6.5 41. -38.88 43. 0.2
45. $-\frac{13}{12}$ 47. $-\frac{3}{4}$ 49. $-\frac{13}{9}$ 51. $-\frac{3}{5}$ 53. $-\frac{3}{2}$ 55. -12
57. -24 59. $\frac{35}{4}$ 61. 15 63. -17 65. $\frac{47}{12}$ 67. 5 69. 0
71. 26 73. 6 75. 25 77. 78 79. -10 81. 5 83. -5
85. 10.5 87. -3.3 89. 19.5 91. $\frac{3}{4}$ 93. $\frac{5}{2}$
97. 10 over par 99. Lost \$16.50 101. A gain of 0.88 dollar
103. No; they made it 49.1 pounds lighter

Problem Set 1.3 (page 26)

1. Associative property of addition
3. Commutative property of addition
5. Additive inverse property
7. Multiplication property of negative one
9. Commutative property of multiplication
11. Distributive property
13. Associative property of multiplication
15. 18 17. 2 19. -1300 21. 1700 23. -47 25. 3200
27. -19 29. -41 31. -17 33. -39 35. 24 37. 20
39. 55 41. 16 43. 49 45. -216 47. -14 49. -8
51. $\frac{3}{16}$ 53. $-\frac{10}{9}$ 57. 2187 59. -2048 61. $-15{,}625$
63. 3.9525416

Problem Set 1.4 (page 34)

1. $4x$ 3. $-a^2$ 5. $-6n$ 7. $-5x + 2y$ 9. $6a^2 + 5b^2$
11. $21x - 13$ 13. $-2a^2b - ab^2$ 15. $8x + 21$
17. $-5a + 2$ 19. $-5n^2 + 11$ 21. $-7x^2 + 32$
23. $22x - 3$ 25. $-14x - 7$ 27. $-10n^2 + 4$
29. $4x - 30y$ 31. $-13x - 31$ 33. $-21x - 9$ 35. -17

37. 12 39. 4 41. 3 43. -38 45. -14 47. 64
49. 104 51. 5 53. 4 55. $-\frac{22}{3}$ 57. $\frac{29}{4}$
59. 221.6 61. 1092.4 63. 1420.5 65. $n + 12$
67. $n - 5$ 69. $50n$ 71. $\frac{1}{2}n - 4$ 73. $\frac{n}{8}$ 75. $2n - 9$
77. $10(n - 6)$ 79. $n + 20$ 81. $2t - 3$ 83. $n + 47$
85. $8y$ 87. 25 cm 89. $\frac{c}{25}$ 91. $n + 2$ 93. $\frac{c}{5}$
95. $12d$ 97. $3y + f$ 99. $5280m$

Chapter 1 Review Problem Set (page 38)

1. (a) 67 (b) 0, -8, and 67 (c) 0 and 67
   (d) $0, \frac{3}{4}, -\frac{5}{6}, \frac{25}{3}, -8, 0.34, 0.2\bar{3}, 67$, and $\frac{9}{7}$
   (e) $\sqrt{2}$ and $-\sqrt{3}$
2. Associative property of addition
3. Substitution property of equality
4. Multiplication property of negative one
5. Distributive property
6. Associative property of multiplication
7. Commutative property of addition
8. Distributive property
9. Multiplicative inverse property
10. Symmetric property of equality
11. 6.2 12. $\frac{7}{3}$ 13. $\sqrt{15}$ 14. 8 15. $-6\frac{1}{2}$ 16. $-6\frac{1}{6}$
17. -8 18. -15 19. 20 20. 49 21. -56 22. 8
23. -24 24. 6 25. 4 26. 100 27. $-4a^2 - 5b^2$
28. $3x - 2$ 29. ab^2 30. $-\frac{7}{3}x^2y$ 31. $10n^2 - 17$
32. $-13a + 4$ 33. $-2n + 2$ 34. $-7x - 29y$ 35. $-7a - 9$
36. $-9x^2 + 7$ 37. $-6\frac{1}{2}$ 38. $-\frac{5}{16}$ 39. -55 40. 144
41. -16 42. -44 43. 19.4 44. 59.6 45. $-\frac{59}{3}$ 46. $\frac{9}{2}$
47. $4 + 2n$ 48. $3n - 50$ 49. $\frac{2}{3}n - 6$ 50. $10(n - 14)$
51. $5n - 8$ 52. $\frac{n}{n - 3}$ 53. $5(n + 2) - 3$ 54. $\frac{3}{4}(n + 12)$
55. $37 - n$ 56. $\frac{w}{60}$ 57. $2y - 7$ 58. $n + 3$
59. $p + 5n + 25q$ 60. $\frac{i}{48}$ 61. $24f + 72y$ 62. $10d$
63. $12f + i$ 64. $25 - c$ 65. 1 minute 66. Loss of \$0.03
67. 0.2 ounces 68. 32 pounds

Chapter 1 Test (page 40)

1. Symmetric property 2. Distributive property 3. -3
4. -23 5. $-\frac{23}{6}$ 6. 11 7. 8 8. -94 9. -4 10. 960

11. -32 **12.** $-x^2 - 8x - 2$ **13.** $-19n - 20$ **14.** 27

15. $\dfrac{11}{16}$ **16.** $\dfrac{2}{3}$ **17.** 77 **18.** -22.5 **19.** 93 **20.** -5

21. $6n - 30$ **22.** $3n + 28$ or $3(n + 8) + 4$ **23.** $\dfrac{72}{n}$

24. $5n + 10d + 25q$ **25.** $6x + 2y$

Chapter 2

Problem Set 2.1 (page 47)

1. $\{4\}$ **3.** $\{-3\}$ **5.** $\{-14\}$ **7.** $\{6\}$ **9.** $\left\{\dfrac{19}{3}\right\}$ **11.** $\{1\}$

13. $\left\{-\dfrac{10}{3}\right\}$ **15.** $\{4\}$ **17.** $\left\{-\dfrac{13}{3}\right\}$ **19.** $\{3\}$ **21.** $\{8\}$

23. $\{-9\}$ **25.** $\{-3\}$ **27.** $\{0\}$ **29.** $\left\{-\dfrac{7}{2}\right\}$ **31.** $\{-2\}$

33. $\left\{-\dfrac{5}{3}\right\}$ **35.** $\left\{\dfrac{33}{2}\right\}$ **37.** $\{-35\}$ **39.** $\left\{\dfrac{11}{2}\right\}$ **41.** $\left\{\dfrac{1}{6}\right\}$

43. $\{5\}$ **45.** $\{-1\}$ **47.** $\left\{-\dfrac{21}{16}\right\}$ **49.** $\left\{\dfrac{12}{7}\right\}$ **51.** 14

53. 13, 14, and 15 **55.** 9, 11, and 13 **57.** 14 and 81
59. $11 per hour **61.** 30 pennies, 50 nickels, and 70 dimes
63. $300 **65.** 20 three-bedroom, 70 two-bedroom, and 140
one-bedroom **73. (a)** $\varnothing$ **(c)** $\{0\}$ **(e)** $\varnothing$

Problem Set 2.2 (page 55)

1. $\{12\}$ **3.** $\left\{-\dfrac{3}{5}\right\}$ **5.** $\{3\}$ **7.** $\{-2\}$ **9.** $\{-36\}$ **11.** $\left\{\dfrac{20}{9}\right\}$

13. $\{3\}$ **15.** $\{3\}$ **17.** $\{-2\}$ **19.** $\left\{\dfrac{8}{5}\right\}$ **21.** $\{-3\}$

23. $\left\{\dfrac{48}{17}\right\}$ **25.** $\left\{\dfrac{103}{6}\right\}$ **27.** $\{3\}$ **29.** $\left\{\dfrac{40}{3}\right\}$ **31.** $\left\{-\dfrac{20}{7}\right\}$

33. $\left\{\dfrac{24}{5}\right\}$ **35.** $\{-10\}$ **37.** $\left\{-\dfrac{25}{4}\right\}$ **39.** $\{0\}$ **41.** 18

43. 16 inches long and 5 inches wide **45.** 14, 15, and 16
47. 8 feet **49.** Angie is 22 and her mother is 42.
51. Sydney is 18 and Marcus is 36. **53.** 80, 90, and 94
55. $48°$ and $132°$ **57.** $78°$

Problem Set 2.3 (page 62)

1. $\{20\}$ **3.** $\{50\}$ **5.** $\{40\}$ **7.** $\{12\}$ **9.** $\{6\}$ **11.** $\{400\}$
13. $\{400\}$ **15.** $\{38\}$ **17.** $\{6\}$ **19.** $\{3000\}$ **21.** $\{3000\}$
23. $\{400\}$ **25.** $\{14\}$ **27.** $\{15\}$ **29.** $90 **31.** $54.40
33. $48 **35.** $2400 **37.** 65% **39.** 62.5% **41.** $42,000
43. $3000 at 4% and $4500 at 6% **45.** $53,000
47. 8 pennies, 15 nickels, and 18 dimes
49. 15 dimes, 45 quarters, and 10 half-dollars **55.** $\{7.5\}$
57. $\{-4775\}$ **59.** $\{8.7\}$ **61.** $\{17.1\}$ **63.** $\{13.5\}$
65. Yes, based on the selling price

Problem Set 2.4 (page 71)

1. $600 **3.** 3 years **5.** 6% **7.** $800 **9.** $1350 **11.** 8%

13. $200 **15.** $b_2 = \dfrac{2A - hb_1}{h}$; 6 feet; 14 feet; 10 feet; 20 feet;

7 feet; 2 feet **17.** $h = \dfrac{V}{B}$ **19.** $h = \dfrac{V}{\pi r^2}$ **21.** $r = \dfrac{C}{2\pi}$

23. $C = \dfrac{100M}{I}$ **25.** $C = \dfrac{5}{9}(F - 32)$ or $C = \dfrac{5F - 160}{9}$

27. $x = \dfrac{y - b}{m}$ **29.** $x = \dfrac{y - y_1 + mx_1}{m}$ **31.** $x = \dfrac{ab + bc}{b - a}$

33. $x = a + bc$ **35.** $x = \dfrac{3b - 6a}{2}$ **37.** $x = \dfrac{5y + 7}{2}$

39. $y = -7x - 4$ **41.** $x = \dfrac{6y + 4}{3}$ **43.** $x = \dfrac{cy - ac - b^2}{b}$

45. $y = \dfrac{x - a + 1}{a - 3}$ **47.** 22 meters long and 6 meters wide

49. $16\dfrac{2}{3}$ years **51.** $16\dfrac{2}{3}$ years **53.** 4 hours **55.** 3 hours

57. 40 miles **59.** 8 ounces of 6% solution and 8 ounces
of 14% solution **61.** 25 milliliters **67.** $281.25
69. 1.5 years **71.** 8% **73.** $1850

Problem Set 2.5 (page 80)

1. $(1, \infty)$

3. $[-1, \infty)$

5. $(-\infty, -2)$

7. $(-\infty, 2]$

9. $x < 4$ **11.** $x \leq -7$ **13.** $x > 8$ **15.** $x \geq -7$

17. $(1, \infty)$

19. $(-\infty, -4]$

21. $(-\infty, -2]$

23. $(-\infty, 2)$

25. $(-1, \infty)$

27. $[-1, \infty)$

29. $(-2, \infty)$

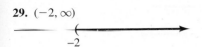

31. $(-2, \infty)$

33. $(-\infty, -2)$

35. $[-3, \infty)$

37. $(0, \infty)$

39. $[4, \infty)$

41. $\left(\dfrac{7}{2}, \infty\right)$ **43.** $\left(\dfrac{12}{5}, \infty\right)$ **45.** $\left(-\infty, -\dfrac{5}{2}\right]$ **47.** $\left[\dfrac{5}{12}, \infty\right)$

49. $(-6, \infty)$ **51.** $(-5, \infty)$ **53.** $\left(-\infty, \dfrac{5}{3}\right]$ **55.** $(-36, \infty)$

57. $\left(-\infty, -\dfrac{8}{17}\right]$ **59.** $\left(-\dfrac{11}{2}, \infty\right)$ **61.** $(23, \infty)$ **63.** $(-\infty, 3)$

65. $\left(-\infty, -\dfrac{1}{7}\right]$ **67.** $(-22, \infty)$ **69.** $\left(-\infty, \dfrac{6}{5}\right)$

Problem Set 2.6 (page 88)

1. $(4, \infty)$ **3.** $\left(-\infty, \dfrac{23}{3}\right)$ **5.** $[5, \infty)$ **7.** $[-9, \infty)$

9. $\left(-\infty, -\dfrac{37}{3}\right]$ **11.** $\left(-\infty, -\dfrac{19}{6}\right)$ **13.** $(-\infty, 50]$

15. $(300, \infty)$ **17.** $[4, \infty)$

19. $(-1, 2)$

21. $(-1, 2]$

23. $(-\infty, -1) \cup (2, \infty)$

25. $(-\infty, 1] \cup (3, \infty)$

27. $(0, \infty)$

29. $\varnothing$

31. $(-\infty, \infty)$

33. $(-1, \infty)$

35. $(1, 3)$

37. $(-\infty, -5) \cup (1, \infty)$

39. $[3, \infty)$

41. $\left(\dfrac{1}{3}, \dfrac{2}{5}\right)$

43. $(-\infty, -1) \cup \left(-\dfrac{1}{3}, \infty\right)$

45. $(-2, 2)$ **47.** $[-5, 4]$ **49.** $\left(-\dfrac{1}{2}, \dfrac{3}{2}\right)$

51. $\left(-\dfrac{1}{4}, \dfrac{11}{4}\right)$ **53.** $[-11, 13]$ **55.** $(-1, 5)$

57. More than 7.5% **59.** 5 feet and 10 inches or better
61. 168 or better **63.** 77 or less **65.** $163° \le C \le 218°$
67. $6.3 \le M \le 11.25$

Problem Set 2.7 (page 95)

1. $\{-7, 9\}$ **3.** $\{-1, 5\}$ **5.** $\left\{-5, \dfrac{7}{3}\right\}$ **7.** $\{-1, 5\}$

9. $\left\{\dfrac{1}{12}, \dfrac{7}{12}\right\}$ **11.** $\{0, 3\}$ **13.** $\{-6, 2\}$ **15.** $\left\{\dfrac{3}{4}\right\}$

17. $(-5, 5)$

19. $[-2, 2]$

21. $(-\infty, -2) \cup (2, \infty)$

23. $(-1, 3)$

25. $[-6, 2]$

27. $(-\infty, -3) \cup (-1, \infty)$

$$-3 \quad -1$$

29. $(-\infty, 1] \cup [5, \infty)$

$$1 \qquad 5$$

31. $(-\infty, -4) \cup (8, \infty)$ **33.** $(-8, 2)$ **35.** $[-4, 5]$

37. $\left(-\infty, -\dfrac{7}{2}\right] \cup \left[\dfrac{5}{2}, \infty\right)$ **39.** $(-\infty, -2) \cup (6, \infty)$

41. $\left(-\dfrac{1}{2}, \dfrac{3}{2}\right)$ **43.** $\left[-5, \dfrac{7}{5}\right]$ **45.** $[-3, 10]$ **47.** $(-5, 11)$

49. $\left(-\infty, -\dfrac{3}{2}\right) \cup \left(\dfrac{1}{2}, \infty\right)$ **51.** $(-\infty, -14] \cup [0, \infty)$

53. $[-2, 3]$ **55.** $\varnothing$ **57.** $(-\infty, \infty)$ **59.** $\left\{\dfrac{2}{5}\right\}$ **61.** $\varnothing$

63. $\varnothing$ **69.** $\left\{-2, -\dfrac{4}{3}\right\}$ **71.** $\{-2\}$ **73.** $\{0\}$

Chapter 2 Review Problem Set (page 101)

1. $\{18\}$ **2.** $\{-14\}$ **3.** $\{0\}$ **4.** $\left\{\dfrac{1}{2}\right\}$ **5.** $\{10\}$ **6.** $\left\{\dfrac{7}{3}\right\}$

7. $\left\{\dfrac{28}{17}\right\}$ **8.** $\left\{-\dfrac{1}{38}\right\}$ **9.** $\left\{\dfrac{27}{17}\right\}$ **10.** $\left\{-\dfrac{21}{13}\right\}$ **11.** $\{50\}$

12. $\left\{-\dfrac{39}{2}\right\}$ **13.** $\{200\}$ **14.** $\{-8\}$ **15.** The length is 15 m and the width is 7 m **16.** 4, 5, and 6 **17.** $10.50 per hour

18. 20 nickels, 50 dimes, 75 quarters **19.** $80°$

20. $200 invested at 7%, $300 invested at 8% **21.** $45.60

22. $300.00 **23.** 60% **24.** $64.00 **25.** $8000 **26.** 4.5%

27. 11 m **28.** $-20°$ **29.** $x = \dfrac{2b + 2}{a}$ **30.** $x = \dfrac{c}{a - b}$

31. $x = \dfrac{pb - ma}{m - p}$ **32.** $x = \dfrac{11 + 7y}{5}$ **33.** $x = \dfrac{by + b + ac}{c}$

34. $s = \dfrac{A - \pi r^2}{\pi r}$ **35.** $b_2 = \dfrac{2A - hb_1}{h}$ **36.** $n = \dfrac{2S_n}{a_1 + a_2}$

37. $R = \dfrac{R_1 R_2}{R_1 + R_2}$ **38.** $y = \dfrac{c - ax}{b}$ **39.** $6\dfrac{2}{3}$ pints **40.** 55 mph

41. Sonya for $3\dfrac{1}{4}$ hr, Rita for $4\dfrac{1}{2}$ hr **42.** $6\dfrac{1}{4}$ cups of orange juice

43. $[-2, \infty)$ **44.** $(6, \infty)$ **45.** $(-\infty, -1)$ **46.** $(-\infty, 0]$

47. $[-5, \infty)$ **48.** $(4, \infty)$ **49.** $\left(-\dfrac{7}{3}, \infty\right)$ **50.** $\left[\dfrac{17}{2}, \infty\right)$

51. $(-\infty, -17)$ **52.** $\left(-\infty, \dfrac{1}{3}\right)$ **53.** $\left(\dfrac{53}{11}, \infty\right)$

54. $\left(-\infty, -\dfrac{15}{4}\right)$ **55.** $[6, \infty)$ **56.** $(-\infty, 100]$

57.

$$-1 \quad 1$$

58.

$$-3 \qquad 2$$

59.

$$3$$

60.

61.

$$-2 \qquad 1$$

62.

$$-2 \qquad 1$$

63.

$$\dfrac{1}{2} \quad 3$$

64. $\varnothing$ **65.** 88 or better **66.** More than $4000

67. $\left\{-\dfrac{10}{3}, 4\right\}$ **68.** $\left\{-\dfrac{7}{2}, \dfrac{1}{2}\right\}$ **69.** $\left\{-\dfrac{11}{3}, 3\right\}$ **70.** $\{-18, 6\}$

71. $(-5, 6)$ **72.** $\left(-\infty, -\dfrac{11}{3}\right) \cup (3, \infty)$

73. $\left(-\infty, -\dfrac{4}{5}\right] \cup \left[\dfrac{12}{5}, \infty\right)$ **74.** $[-28, 20]$

Chapter 2 Test (page 104)

1. $\{-3\}$ **2.** $\{5\}$ **3.** $\left\{\dfrac{1}{2}\right\}$ **4.** $\left\{\dfrac{16}{5}\right\}$ **5.** $\left\{-\dfrac{14}{5}\right\}$ **6.** $\{-1\}$

7. $\left\{-\dfrac{3}{2}, 3\right\}$ **8.** $\{3\}$ **9.** $\left\{\dfrac{31}{3}\right\}$ **10.** $\{650\}$ **11.** $y = \dfrac{8x - 24}{9}$

12. $h = \dfrac{S - 2\pi r^2}{2\pi r}$ **13.** $(-2, \infty)$ **14.** $[-4, \infty)$

15. $(-\infty, -35]$ **16.** $(-\infty, 10)$ **17.** $(3, \infty)$ **18.** $(-\infty, 200]$

19. $\left(-1, \dfrac{7}{3}\right)$ **20.** $\left(-\infty, -\dfrac{11}{4}\right] \cup \left[\dfrac{1}{4}, \infty\right)$ **21.** $72

22. 19 centimeters **23.** $\dfrac{2}{3}$ of a cup **24.** 97 or better **25.** $70°$

Chapters 1–2 Cumulative Test (page 105)

1.

	Natural numbers	Whole numbers	Integers	Rational numbers	Irrational numbers	Real numbers
9	x	x	x	x		x
$-\dfrac{1}{2}$				x		x
$-\sqrt{7}$					x	x
$0.\overline{3}$				x		x
$\dfrac{8}{3}$				x		x
-2			x	x		x
0		x	x	x		x

2. (a) Commutative Property of Multiplication
(b) Distributive Property **(c)** Symmetric Property of Equality

3. 3 **4.** 24 **5.** 84 **6.** 1 **7.** $-\dfrac{67}{15}$ **8.** -20 **9.** -2

10. $-6c^2 + 1$ **11.** $25a + 9$ **12.** $\dfrac{5}{6}cd^2$ **13.** -1 **14.** 7.4

15. $\dfrac{19}{18}$ **16.** $\dfrac{2x}{3x - 2}$ **17.** $\left\{\dfrac{50}{11}\right\}$ **18.** $\left\{-\dfrac{9}{2}\right\}$ **19.** $\{1200\}$

20. $x = \dfrac{3y + 6z}{4}$ **21.** $\left\{ -\dfrac{25}{3}, 11 \right\}$ **22.** $\varnothing$ **23.** $\left\{ \dfrac{2}{3} \right\}$

24. $[-2, \infty)$ **25.** $(-\infty, 4)$ **26.** $\left[-\dfrac{1}{3}, 3 \right]$

27. $(-\infty, 0) \cup (5, \infty)$ **28.** $\varnothing$ **29.** $18

30. 25 leashes, 9 collars   **31.** 4 tens, 3 fifties, 12 twenties; $430

32. $2625   **33.** $84°$ **34.** 6.5 hours   **35.** $6000   **36.** $26,518.50

Chapter 3

Problem Set 3.1 (page 112)

1. 2   **3.** 3   **5.** 2   **7.** 6   **9.** 0   **11.** $10x - 3$ **13.** $-11t + 5$

15. $-x^2 + 2x - 2$ **17.** $17a^2b^2 - 5ab$ **19.** $-9x + 7$

21. $-2x + 6$ **23.** $10a + 7$ **25.** $4x^2 + 10x + 6$

27. $-6a^2 + 12a + 14$ **29.** $3x^3 + x^2 + 13x - 11$ **31.** $7x + 8$

33. $-3x - 16$ **35.** $2x^2 - 2x - 8$ **37.** $-3x^3 + 5x^2 - 2x + 9$

39. $5x^2 - 4x + 11$ **41.** $-6x^2 + 9x + 7$ **43.** $-2x^2 + 9x + 4$

45. $-10n^2 + n + 9$ **47.** $8x - 2$ **49.** $8x - 14$

51. $-9x^2 - 12x + 4$ **53.** $10x^2 + 13x - 18$

55. $-n^2 - 4n - 4$ **57.** $-x + 6$ **59.** $6x^2 - 4$

61. $-7n^2 + n + 6$ **63.** $t^2 - 4t + 8$ **65.** $4n^2 - n - 12$

67. $-4x - 2y$ **69.** $-x^3 - x^2 + 3x$ **71.** (a) $8x + 4$

(c) $12x + 6$ **73.** $8\pi h + 32\pi$ (a) 226.1   (c) 452.2

Problem Set 3.2 (page 118)

1. $36x^4$ **3.** $-12x^5$ **5.** $4a^3b^4$ **7.** $-3x^3y^2z^6$ **9.** $-30xy^4$

11. $27a^4b^5$ **13.** $-m^3n^3$ **15.** $\dfrac{3}{10}x^3y^6$ **17.** $-\dfrac{3}{20}a^3b^4$

19. $-\dfrac{1}{6}x^3y^4$ **21.** $30x^6$ **23.** $-18x^9$ **25.** $-3x^6y^6$ **27.** $-24y^9$

29. $-56a^4b^2$ **31.** $-18a^3b^3$ **33.** $-10x^7y^7$ **35.** $50x^5y^2$

37. $27x^3y^6$ **39.** $-32x^{10}y^5$ **41.** $x^{16}y^{20}$ **43.** $a^6b^{12}c^{18}$

45. $64a^{12}b^{18}$ **47.** $81x^2y^8$ **49.** $81a^4b^{12}$ **51.** $-16a^4b^4$

53. $-x^6y^{12}z^{18}$ **55.** $-125a^6b^6c^3$ **57.** $-x^7y^{28}z^{14}$ **59.** $3x^3y^3$

61. $-5x^3y^2$ **63.** $9bc^2$ **65.** $-18xyz^4$ **67.** $-a^2b^3c^2$ **69.** 9

71. $-b^2$ **73.** $-18x^3$ **75.** $6x^{3n}$ **77.** a^{5n+3} **79.** x^{4n}

81. a^{5n+1} **83.** $-10x^{2n}$ **85.** $12a^{n+4}$ **87.** $6x^{3n+2}$ **89.** $12x^{n+2}$

91. $22x^2$; $6x^3$ **93.** $\pi r^2 - 36\pi$

Problem Set 3.3 (page 125)

1. $10x^2y^3 + 6x^3y^4$ **3.** $-12a^3b^3 + 15a^5b$

5. $24a^4b^5 - 16a^4b^6 + 32a^5b^6$ **7.** $-6x^3y^3 - 3x^4y^4 + x^5y^2$

9. $ax + ay + 2bx + 2by$ **11.** $ac + 4ad - 3bc - 12bd$

13. $x^2 + 16x + 60$ **15.** $y^2 + 6y - 55$ **17.** $n^2 - 5n - 14$

19. $x^2 - 36$ **21.** $x^2 - 12x + 36$ **23.** $x^2 - 14x + 48$

25. $x^3 - 4x^2 + x + 6$ **27.** $x^3 - x^2 - 9x + 9$

29. $t^2 + 18t + 81$ **31.** $y^2 - 14y + 49$ **33.** $4x^2 + 33x + 35$

35. $9y^2 - 1$ **37.** $14x^2 + 3x - 2$ **39.** $5 + 3t - 2t^2$

41. $9t^2 + 42t + 49$ **43.** $4 - 25x^2$ **45.** $49x^2 - 56x + 16$

47. $18x^2 - 39x - 70$ **49.** $2x^2 + xy - 15y^2$ **51.** $25x^2 - 4a^2$

53. $t^3 - 14t - 15$ **55.** $x^3 + x^2 - 24x + 16$

57. $2x^3 + 9x^2 + 2x - 30$ **59.** $12x^3 - 7x^2 + 25x - 6$

61. $x^4 + 5x^3 + 11x^2 + 11x + 4$ **63.** $2x^4 - x^3 - 12x^2 + 5x + 4$

65. $x^3 + 6x^2 + 12x + 8$ **67.** $x^3 - 12x^2 + 48x - 64$

69. $8x^3 + 36x^2 + 54x + 27$ **71.** $64x^3 - 48x^2 + 12x - 1$

73. $125x^3 + 150x^2 + 60x + 8$ **75.** $x^{2n} - 16$

77. $x^{2a} + 4x^a - 12$ **79.** $6x^{2n} + x^n - 35$

81. $x^{4a} - 10x^{2a} + 21$ **83.** $4x^{2n} + 20x^n + 25$

87. $2x^2 + 6$ **89.** $4x^3 - 64x^2 + 256x$; $256 - 4x^2$

93. (a) $a^6 + 6a^5b + 15a^4b^2 + 20a^3b^3 + 15a^2b^4 + 6ab^5 + b^6$

(c) $a^8 + 8a^7b + 28a^6b^2 + 56a^5b^3 + 70a^4b^4 + 56a^3b^5 + 28a^2b^6 + 8ab^7 + b^8$

Problem Set 3.4 (page 133)

1. Composite   **3.** Prime   **5.** Composite   **7.** Composite

9. Prime   **11.** $2 \cdot 2 \cdot 7$ **13.** $2 \cdot 2 \cdot 11$ **15.** $2 \cdot 2 \cdot 2 \cdot 7$

17. $2 \cdot 2 \cdot 2 \cdot 3 \cdot 3$ **19.** $3 \cdot 29$ **21.** No   **23.** No

25. $3(2x + y)$ **27.** $2x(3x + 7)$ **29.** $4y(7y - 1)$

31. $5x(4y - 3)$ **33.** $x^2(7x + 10)$ **35.** $9ab(2a + 3b)$

37. $3x^3y^3(4y - 13x)$ **39.** $4x^2(2x^2 + 3x - 6)$

41. $x(5 + 7x + 9x^3)$ **43.** $5xy^2(3xy + 4 + 7x^2y^2)$

45. $(y + 2)(x + 3)$ **47.** $(2a + b)(3x - 2y)$ **49.** $(x + 2)(x + 5)$

51. $(a + 4)(x + y)$ **53.** $(a - 2b)(x + y)$ **55.** $(a - b)(3x - y)$

57. $(a + 1)(2x + y)$ **59.** $(a - 1)(x^2 + 2)$ **61.** $(a + b)(2c + 3d)$

63. $(a + b)(x - y)$ **65.** $(x + 9)(x + 6)$ **67.** $(x + 4)(2x + 1)$

69. $\{-7, 0\}$ **71.** $\{0, 1\}$ **73.** $\{0, 5\}$ **75.** $\left\{ -\dfrac{1}{2}, 0 \right\}$

77. $\left\{ -\dfrac{7}{3}, 0 \right\}$ **79.** $\left\{ 0, \dfrac{5}{4} \right\}$ **81.** $\left\{ 0, \dfrac{1}{4} \right\}$ **83.** $\{-12, 0\}$

85. $\left\{ 0, \dfrac{3a}{5b} \right\}$ **87.** $\left\{ -\dfrac{3a}{2b}, 0 \right\}$ **89.** $\{a, -2b\}$ **91.** 0 or 7

93. 6 units   **95.** $\dfrac{4}{\pi}$ units

97. The square is 100 feet by 100 feet, and the rectangle is 50 feet by 100 feet.

99. 6 units   **105.** $x^a(2x^a - 3)$ **107.** $y^{2m}(y^m + 5)$

109. $x^{4a}(2x^{2a} - 3x^a + 7)$

Problem Set 3.5 (page 140)

1. $(x + 1)(x - 1)$ **3.** $(4x + 5)(4x - 5)$

5. $(3x + 5y)(3x - 5y)$ **7.** $(5xy + 6)(5xy - 6)$

9. $(2x + y^2)(2x - y^2)$ **11.** $(1 + 12n)(1 - 12n)$

13. $(x + 2 + y)(x + 2 - y)$ **15.** $(2x + y + 1)(2x - y - 1)$

17. $(3a + 2b + 3)(3a - 2b - 3)$ **19.** $-5(2x + 9)$

21. $9(x + 2)(x - 2)$ **23.** $5(x^2 + 1)$ **25.** $8(y + 2)(y - 2)$

27. $ab(a + 3)(a - 3)$ **29.** Not factorable

31. $(n + 3)(n - 3)(n^2 + 9)$ **33.** $3x(x^2 + 9)$

35. $4xy(x + 4y)(x - 4y)$ **37.** $6x(1 + x)(1 - x)$

39. $(1 + xy)(1 - xy)(1 + x^2y^2)$ **41.** $4(x + 4y)(x - 4y)$

43. $3(x + 2)(x - 2)(x^2 + 4)$ **45.** $(a - 4)(a^2 + 4a + 16)$

47. $(x + 1)(x^2 - x + 1)$ **49.** $(3x + 4y)(9x^2 - 12xy + 16y^2)$

51. $(1 - 3a)(1 + 3a + 9a^2)$ **53.** $(xy - 1)(x^2y^2 + xy + 1)$

55. $(x + y)(x - y)(x^2 - xy + y^2)(x^2 + xy + y^2)$

57. $\{-5, 5\}$ **59.** $\left\{-\dfrac{7}{3}, \dfrac{7}{3}\right\}$ **61.** $\{-2, 2\}$ **63.** $\{-1, 0, 1\}$

65. $\{-2, 2\}$ **67.** $\{-3, 3\}$ **69.** $\{0\}$ **71.** $-3, 0,$ or 3

73. 4 centimeters and 8 centimeters **75.** 10 meters long and
5 meters wide **77.** 6 inches **79.** 8 yards

Problem Set 3.6 (page 147)

1. $(x + 5)(x + 4)$ **3.** $(x - 4)(x - 7)$ **5.** $(a + 9)(a - 4)$

7. $(y + 6)(y + 14)$ **9.** $(x - 7)(x + 2)$ **11.** Not factorable

13. $(6 - x)(1 + x)$ **15.** $(x + 3y)(x + 12y)$

17. $(a - 8b)(a + 7b)$ **19.** $(x + 10)(x + 15)$

21. $(n - 16)(n - 20)$ **23.** $(t + 15)(t - 12)$

25. $(t^2 - 3)(t^2 - 2)$ **27.** $(x + 1)(x - 1)(x^2 - 8)$

29. $(x + 1)(x - 1)(x + 4)(x - 4)$ **31.** $(3x + 1)(5x + 6)$

33. $(4x - 3)(3x + 2)$ **35.** $(a + 3)(4a - 9)$

37. $(n - 4)(3n + 5)$ **39.** Not factorable **41.** $(2n - 7)(5n + 3)$

43. $(4x - 5)(2x + 9)$ **45.** $(1 - 6x)(6 + x)$

47. $(5y + 9)(4y - 1)$ **49.** $(12n + 5)(2n - 1)$

51. $(5n + 3)(n + 6)$ **53.** $(2x^2 - 1)(5x^2 + 4)$

55. $(3n + 1)(3n - 1)(2n^2 + 3)$ **57.** $(y - 8)^2$ **59.** $(2x + 3y)^2$

61. $2(2y - 1)^2$ **63.** $2(t + 2)(t - 2)$ **65.** $(4x + 5y)(3x - 2y)$

67. $3n(2n + 5)(3n - 1)$ **69.** $(n - 12)(n - 5)$ **71.** $(6a - 1)^2$

73. $6(x^2 + 9)$ **75.** Not factorable **77.** $(x + y - 7)(x - y + 7)$

79. $(1 + 4x^2)(1 + 2x)(1 - 2x)$ **81.** $(4n + 9)(n + 4)$

83. $n(n + 7)(n - 7)$ **85.** $(x - 8)(x + 1)$

87. $3x(x - 3)(x^2 + 3x + 9)$ **89.** $(x^2 + 3)^2$

91. $(x + 3)(x - 3)(x^2 + 4)$ **93.** $(2w - 7)(3w + 5)$

95. Not factorable **97.** $2n(n^2 + 7n - 10)$

99. $(2x + 1)(y + 3)$ **105.** $(x^a + 3)(x^a + 7)$ **107.** $(2x^a + 5)^2$

109. $(5x^n - 1)(4x^n + 5)$ **111.** $(x - 2)(x - 4)$

113. $(3x - 11)(3x + 2)$ **115.** $(5x + 9)(3x + 4)$

Problem Set 3.7 (page 153)

1. $\{-3, -1\}$ **3.** $\{-12, -6\}$ **5.** $\{4, 9\}$ **7.** $\{-6, 2\}$

9. $\{-1, 5\}$ **11.** $\{-13, -12\}$ **13.** $\left\{-5, \dfrac{1}{3}\right\}$ **15.** $\left\{-\dfrac{7}{2}, -\dfrac{2}{3}\right\}$

17. $\{0, 4\}$ **19.** $\left\{\dfrac{1}{6}, 2\right\}$ **21.** $\{-6, 0, 6\}$ **23.** $\{-4, 6\}$

25. $\{-4, 4\}$ **27.** $\{-11, 4\}$ **29.** $\{-5, 5\}$ **31.** $\left\{-\dfrac{5}{3}, -\dfrac{3}{5}\right\}$

33. $\left\{-\dfrac{1}{8}, 6\right\}$ **35.** $\left\{\dfrac{3}{7}, \dfrac{5}{4}\right\}$ **37.** $\left\{-\dfrac{2}{7}, \dfrac{4}{5}\right\}$ **39.** $\left\{-7, \dfrac{2}{3}\right\}$

41. $\{-20, 18\}$ **43.** $\left\{-2, -\dfrac{1}{3}, \dfrac{1}{3}, 2\right\}$ **45.** $\left\{-\dfrac{2}{3}, 16\right\}$

47. $\left\{-\dfrac{3}{2}, 1\right\}$ **49.** $\left\{-\dfrac{5}{2}, -\dfrac{4}{3}, 0\right\}$ **51.** $\left\{-1, \dfrac{5}{3}\right\}$ **53.** $\left\{-\dfrac{3}{2}, \dfrac{1}{2}\right\}$

55. 8 and 9 or -9 and -8 **57.** 7 and 15

59. 10 inches by 6 inches **61.** -7 and -6 or 6 and 7

63. 4 centimeters by 4 centimeters and 6 centimeters by
8 centimeters **65.** 3, 4, and 5 units **67.** 9 inches and 12 inches

69. An altitude of 4 inches and a side 14 inches long

Chapter 3 Review Problem Set (page 158)

1. Third degree **2.** Fourth degree **3.** Sixth degree

4. Fifth degree **5.** $5x - 3$ **6.** $3x^2 + 12x - 2$

7. $12x^2 - x + 5$ **8.** $11x^2 + 2x + 4$ **9.** $2x + y - 2$

10. $5x + 5y - 2$ **11.** $-20x^5y^7$ **12.** $-6a^5b^5$

13. $-8a^7b^3$ **14.** $27x^5y^8$ **15.** $256x^8y^{12}$ **16.** $-8x^6y^9z^3$

17. $-12a^5b^7$ **18.** $6x^{4n}$ **19.** $-13x^2y$ **20.** $2x^3y^3$ **21.** $-4b^2$

22. $4a^3b^3$ **23.** $15a^4 - 10a^3 - 5a^2$ **24.** $-8x^5 + 6x^4 + 10x^3$

25. $3x^3 + 7x^2 - 21x - 4$ **26.** $6x^3 - 11x^2 - 7x + 2$

27. $x^4 + x^3 - 18x^2 - x + 35$

28. $3x^4 + 5x^3 - 21x^2 - 3x + 20$

29. $24x^2 + 2xy - 15y^2$ **30.** $7x^2 + 19x - 36$

31. $21 + 26x - 15x^2$ **32.** $x^4 + 5x^2 - 24$ **33.** $4x^2 - 12x + 9$

34. $25x^2 - 10x + 1$ **35.** $16x^2 + 24xy + 9y^2$

36. $4x^2 + 20xy + 25y^2$ **37.** $4x^2 - 49$ **38.** $9x^2 - 1$

39. $x^3 - 6x^2 + 12x - 8$ **40.** $8x^3 + 60x^2 + 150x + 125$

41. $2x^2 + 7x - 2$ **42.** $2x^3 + 2x^2$ **43.** $5ab(2a - b^2 - 3a^2b)$

44. $xy(3 - 5xy - 15x^2y^2)$ **45.** $(x + 4)(a + b)$

46. $(3x - 1)(y + 7)$ **47.** $(2x + y)(3x^2 + z^2)$

48. $(m + 5n)(n - 4)$ **49.** $(7a - 5b)(7a + 5b)$

50. $(6x - y)(6x + y)$ **51.** $(5a - 2)(25a^2 + 10a + 4)$

52. $(3x + 4y)(9x^2 - 12xy + 16y^2)$ **53.** $(x - 3)(x - 6)$

54. $(x + 4)(x + 7)$ **55.** $(x - 7)(x + 3)$ **56.** $(x + 8)(x - 2)$

57. $(2x + 1)(x + 4)$ **58.** $(3x - 4)(2x - 1)$

59. $(3x - 2)(4x + 1)$ **60.** $(4x + 1)(2x - 3)$ **61.** $(2x - 3y)^2$

62. $(x + 8y)^2$ **63.** $(x + 7)(x - 4)$ **64.** $2(t + 3)(t - 3)$

65. Not factorable **66.** $(4n - 1)(3n - 1)$

67. $x^2(x^2 + 1)(x + 1)(x - 1)$ **68.** $x(x - 12)(x + 6)$

69. $2a^2b(3a + 2b - c)$ **70.** $(x - y + 1)(x + y - 1)$

71. $4(2x^2 + 3)$ **72.** $(4x + 7)(3x - 5)$ **73.** $(4n - 5)^2$

74. $4n(n - 2)$ **75.** $3w(w^2 + 6w - 8)$ **76.** $(5x + 2y)(4x - y)$

77. $16a(a - 4)$ **78.** $3x(x + 1)(x - 6)$ **79.** $(n + 8)(n - 16)$

80. $(t + 5)(t - 5)(t^2 + 3)$ **81.** $(5x - 3)(7x + 2)$

82. $(3 - x)(5 - 3x)$ **83.** $(4n - 3)(16n^2 + 12n + 9)$

84. $2(2x + 5)(4x^2 - 10x + 25)$ **85.** $\{-3, 3\}$ **86.** $\{-6, 1\}$

87. $\left\{\dfrac{2}{7}\right\}$ **88.** $\left\{-\dfrac{2}{5}, \dfrac{1}{3}\right\}$ **89.** $\left\{-\dfrac{1}{3}, 3\right\}$ **90.** $\{-3, 0, 3\}$

91. $\{-1, 0, 1\}$ **92.** $\{-7, 9\}$ **93.** $\left\{-\dfrac{4}{7}, \dfrac{2}{7}\right\}$ **94.** $\left\{-\dfrac{4}{5}, \dfrac{5}{6}\right\}$

95. $\{-2, 2\}$ **96.** $\left\{\dfrac{5}{3}\right\}$ **97.** $\{-8, 6\}$ **98.** $\left\{-5, \dfrac{2}{7}\right\}$

99. $\{-8, 5\}$ **100.** $\{-12, 1\}$ **101.** $\varnothing$ **102.** $\left\{-5, \dfrac{6}{5}\right\}$

103. $\{0, 1, 8\}$ **104.** $\left\{-10, \dfrac{1}{4}\right\}$

105. 8, 9, and 10 or -1, 0, and 1 **106.** -6 and 8

107. 13 and 15 **108.** 12 miles and 16 miles **109.** 4 m by 12 m

110. 9 rows and 16 chairs per row

111. The side is 13 ft long and the altitude is 6 ft.

112. 3 ft **113.** 5 cm by 5 cm and 8 cm by 8 cm **114.** 6 in.

Chapter 3 Test (page 161)

1. $2x - 11$ **2.** $-48x^4y^4$ **3.** $-27x^6y^{12}$

4. $20x^2 + 17x - 63$ **5.** $6n^2 - 13n + 6$

6. $x^3 - 12x^2y + 48xy^2 - 64y^3$ **7.** $2x^3 + 11x^2 - 11x - 30$

8. $-14x^3y$ **9.** $(6x - 5)(x + 4)$ **10.** $3(2x + 1)(2x - 1)$

11. $(4 + t)(16 - 4t + t^2)$ **12.** $2x(3 - 2x)(5 + 4x)$

13. $(x - y)(x + 4)$ **14.** $(3n + 8)(8n - 3)$ **15.** $\{-12, 4\}$

16. $\left\{0, \dfrac{1}{4}\right\}$ **17.** $\left\{\dfrac{3}{2}\right\}$ **18.** $\{-4, -1\}$ **19.** $\{-9, 0, 2\}$

20. $\left\{-\dfrac{3}{7}, \dfrac{4}{5}\right\}$ **21.** $\left\{-\dfrac{1}{3}, 2\right\}$ **22.** $\{-2, 2\}$ **23.** 9 inches

24. 15 rows **25.** 8 feet

Chapter 4

Problem Set 4.1 (page 168)

1. $\dfrac{3}{4}$ **3.** $\dfrac{5}{6}$ **5.** $-\dfrac{2}{5}$ **7.** $\dfrac{2}{7}$ **9.** $\dfrac{2x}{7}$ **11.** $\dfrac{2a}{5b}$ **13.** $-\dfrac{y}{4x}$

15. $-\dfrac{9c}{13d}$ **17.** $\dfrac{5x^2}{3y^3}$ **19.** $\dfrac{x-2}{x}$ **21.** $\dfrac{3x+2}{2x-1}$ **23.** $\dfrac{a+5}{a-9}$

25. $\dfrac{n-3}{5n-1}$ **27.** $\dfrac{5x^2+7}{10x}$ **29.** $\dfrac{3x+5}{4x+1}$

31. $\dfrac{3x}{x^2+4x+16}$ **33.** $\dfrac{x+6}{3x-1}$ **35.** $\dfrac{x(2x+7)}{y(x+9)}$

37. $\dfrac{y+4}{5y-2}$ **39.** $\dfrac{3x(x-1)}{x^2+1}$ **41.** $\dfrac{2(x+3y)}{3x(3x+y)}$

43. $\dfrac{3n-2}{7n+2}$ **45.** $\dfrac{4-x}{5+3x}$ **47.** $\dfrac{9x^2+3x+1}{2(x+2)}$

49. $\dfrac{-2(x-1)}{x+1}$ **51.** $\dfrac{y+b}{y+c}$ **53.** $\dfrac{x+2y}{2x+y}$ **55.** $\dfrac{x+1}{x-6}$

57. $\dfrac{2s+5}{3s+1}$ **59.** -1 **61.** $-n-7$ **63.** $-\dfrac{2}{x+1}$

65. -2 **67.** $-\dfrac{n+3}{n+5}$

Problem Set 4.2 (page 173)

1. $\dfrac{1}{10}$ **3.** $-\dfrac{4}{15}$ **5.** $\dfrac{3}{16}$ **7.** $-\dfrac{5}{6}$ **9.** $-\dfrac{2}{3}$

11. $\dfrac{10}{11}$ **13.** $-\dfrac{5x^3}{12y^2}$ **15.** $\dfrac{2a^3}{3b}$ **17.** $\dfrac{3x^3}{4}$

19. $\dfrac{25x^3}{108y^2}$ **21.** $\dfrac{ac^2}{2b^2}$ **23.** $\dfrac{3x}{4y}$ **25.** $\dfrac{3(x^2+4)}{5y(x+8)}$

27. $\dfrac{5(a+3)}{a(a-2)}$ **29.** $\dfrac{3}{2}$ **31.** $\dfrac{3xy}{4(x+6)}$

33. $\dfrac{5(x-2y)}{7y}$ **35.** $\dfrac{5+n}{3-n}$ **37.** $\dfrac{x^2+1}{x^2-10}$

39. $\dfrac{6x+5}{3x+4}$ **41.** $\dfrac{2t^2+5}{2(t^2+1)(t+1)}$ **43.** $\dfrac{t(t+6)}{4t+5}$

45. $\dfrac{n+3}{n(n-2)}$ **47.** $\dfrac{25x^3y^3}{4(x+1)}$ **49.** $\dfrac{2(a-2b)}{a(3a-2b)}$

Problem Set 4.3 (page 180)

1. $\dfrac{13}{12}$ **3.** $\dfrac{11}{40}$ **5.** $\dfrac{19}{20}$ **7.** $\dfrac{49}{75}$ **9.** $\dfrac{17}{30}$ **11.** $-\dfrac{11}{84}$

13. $\dfrac{2x+4}{x-1}$ **15.** 4 **17.** $\dfrac{7y-10}{7y}$ **19.** $\dfrac{5x+3}{6}$

21. $\dfrac{12a+1}{12}$ **23.** $\dfrac{n+14}{18}$ **25.** $-\dfrac{11}{15}$ **27.** $\dfrac{3x-25}{30}$

29. $\dfrac{43}{40x}$ **31.** $\dfrac{20y-77x}{28xy}$ **33.** $\dfrac{16y+15x-12xy}{12xy}$

35. $\dfrac{21+22x}{30x^2}$ **37.** $\dfrac{10n-21}{7n^2}$ **39.** $\dfrac{45-6n+20n^2}{15n^2}$

41. $\dfrac{11x-10}{6x^2}$ **43.** $\dfrac{42t+43}{35t^3}$ **45.** $\dfrac{20b^2-33a^3}{96a^2b}$

47. $\dfrac{14-24y^3+45xy}{18xy^3}$ **49.** $\dfrac{2x^2+3x-3}{x(x-1)}$

51. $\dfrac{a^2-a-8}{a(a+4)}$ **53.** $\dfrac{-41n-55}{(4n+5)(3n+5)}$

Problem Set 4.4 (page 188)

55. $\dfrac{-3x+17}{(x+4)(7x-1)}$ **57.** $\dfrac{-x+74}{(3x-5)(2x+7)}$

59. $\dfrac{38x+13}{(3x-2)(4x+5)}$ **61.** $\dfrac{5x+5}{2x+5}$ **63.** $\dfrac{x-}{x-}$

65. $\dfrac{-2x-4}{2x+1}$ **67.** (a) -1 (c) 0

1. $\dfrac{7x+20}{x(x+4)}$ **3.** $\dfrac{-x-3}{x(x+7)}$ **5.** $\dfrac{6x-5}{(x+1)(x-1)}$

7. $\dfrac{1}{a+1}$ **9.** $\dfrac{5n+15}{4(n+5)(n-5)}$ **11.** $\dfrac{x^2+60}{x(x+6)}$

13. $\dfrac{11x+13}{(x+2)(x+7)(2x+1)}$ **15.** $\dfrac{-3a+1}{(a-5)(a+2)(a+9)}$

17. $\dfrac{3a^2+14a+1}{(4a-3)(2a+1)(a+4)}$ **19.** $\dfrac{3x^2+20x-111}{(x^2+3)(x+7)(x-3)}$

21. $\dfrac{x+6}{(x-3)^2}$ **23.** $\dfrac{14x-4}{(x-1)(x+1)^2}$

25. $\dfrac{-7y-14}{(y+8)(y-2)}$ **27.** $\dfrac{-2x^2-4x+3}{(x+2)(x-2)}$

29. $\dfrac{2x^2+14x-19}{(x+10)(x-2)}$ **31.** $\dfrac{2n+1}{n-6}$

33. $\dfrac{2x^2-32x+16}{(x+1)(2x-1)(3x-2)}$ **35.** $\dfrac{1}{(n^2+1)(n+1)}$

37. $\dfrac{-16x}{(5x-2)(x-1)}$ **39.** $\dfrac{t+1}{t-2}$ **41.** $\dfrac{2}{11}$ **43.** $-\dfrac{7}{27}$ **45.** $\dfrac{x}{4}$

47. $\dfrac{3y-2x}{4x-7}$ **49.** $\dfrac{6ab^2-5a^2}{12b^2+2a^2b}$ **51.** $\dfrac{2y-3xy}{3x+4xy}$ **53.** $\dfrac{3n+14}{5n+19}$

55. $\dfrac{5n-17}{4n-13}$ **57.** $\dfrac{-x+5y-10}{3y-10}$ **59.** $\dfrac{-x+15}{-2x-1}$

61. $\dfrac{3a^2-2a+1}{2a-1}$ **63.** $\dfrac{-x^2+6x-4}{3x-2}$

Problem Set 4.5 (page 195)

1. $3x^3+6x^2$ **3.** $-6x^4+9x^6$ **5.** $3a^2-5a-8$

7. $-13x^2+17x-28$ **9.** $-3xy+4x^2y-8xy^2$

11. $x-13$ **13.** $x+20$ **15.** $2x+1-\dfrac{3}{x-1}$

17. $5x-1$ **19.** $3x^2-2x-7$ **21.** x^2+5x-6

23. $4x^2+7x+12+\dfrac{30}{x-2}$ **25.** x^3-4x^2-5x+3

27. $x^2+5x+25$ **29.** $x^2-x+1+\dfrac{63}{x+1}$

31. $2x^2-4x+7-\dfrac{20}{x+2}$ **33.** $4a-4b$

35. $4x+7+\dfrac{23x-6}{x^2-3x}$ **37.** $8y-9+\dfrac{8y+5}{y^2+y}$

39. $2x-1$ **41.** $x-3$ **43.** $5a-8+\dfrac{42a-41}{a^2+3a-4}$

45. $2n^2+3n-4$ **47.** $x^4+x^3+x^2+x+1$

49. x^3-x^2+x-1 **51.** $3x^2+x+1+\dfrac{7}{x^2-1}$

53. $x-6$ **55.** $x+6$, R $=14$ **57.** x^2-1

59. x^2-2x-3 **61.** $2x^2-x-6$, R $=-6$

63. $x^3+7x^2+21x+56$, R $=167$

Set 4.6 (page 201)

$\{2\}$ **3.** $\{-3\}$ **5.** $\{6\}$ **7.** $\left\{-\dfrac{85}{18}\right\}$ **9.** $\left\{\dfrac{7}{10}\right\}$

11. $\{5\}$ **13.** $\{58\}$ **15.** $\left\{\dfrac{1}{4}, 4\right\}$ **17.** $\left\{-\dfrac{2}{5}, 5\right\}$ **19.** $\{-16\}$

21. $\left\{-\dfrac{13}{3}\right\}$ **23.** $\{-3, 1\}$ **25.** $\left\{-\dfrac{5}{2}\right\}$ **27.** $\{-51\}$

29. $\left\{-\dfrac{5}{3}, 4\right\}$ **31.** $\varnothing$ **33.** $\left\{-\dfrac{11}{8}, 2\right\}$ **35.** $\{-29, 0\}$

37. $\{-9, 3\}$ **39.** $\left\{-2, \dfrac{23}{8}\right\}$ **41.** $\left\{\dfrac{11}{23}\right\}$ **43.** $\left\{3, \dfrac{7}{2}\right\}$

45. $750 and $1000 **47.** $48°$ and $72°$
49. $3500 **51.** $69 for Tammy and $51.75 for Laura
53. 14 feet and 6 feet **55.** 690 females and 460 males

Problem Set 4.7 (page 208)

1. $\{-21\}$ **3.** $\{-1, 2\}$ **5.** $\{2\}$ **7.** $\left\{\dfrac{37}{15}\right\}$ **9.** $\{-1\}$

11. $\{-1\}$ **13.** $\left\{0, \dfrac{13}{2}\right\}$ **15.** $\left\{-2, \dfrac{19}{2}\right\}$ **17.** $\{-2\}$

19. $\left\{-\dfrac{1}{5}\right\}$ **21.** $\varnothing$ **23.** $\left\{\dfrac{7}{2}\right\}$ **25.** $\{-3\}$ **27.** $\left\{-\dfrac{7}{9}\right\}$

29. $\left\{-\dfrac{7}{6}\right\}$ **31.** $x = \dfrac{18y - 4}{15}$ **33.** $y = \dfrac{-5x + 22}{2}$

35. $M = \dfrac{IC}{100}$ **37.** $R = \dfrac{ST}{S + T}$ **39.** $y = \dfrac{bx - x - 3b + a}{a - 3}$

41. $y = \dfrac{ab - bx}{a}$ **43.** $y = \dfrac{-2x - 9}{3}$

45. 50 miles per hour for Dave and 54 miles per hour for Kent
47. 60 minutes
49. 60 words per minute for Connie and 40 words per minute for Katie
51. Plane B could travel at 400 miles per hour for 5 hours and plane A at 350 miles per hour for 4 hours, or plane B could travel at 250 miles per hour for 8 hours and plane A at 200 miles per hour for 7 hours.
53. 60 minutes for Nancy and 120 minutes for Amy
55. 3 hours
57. 16 miles per hour on the way out and 12 miles per hour on the way back, or 12 miles per hour out and 8 miles per hour back

Chapter 4 Review Problem Set (page 216)

1. $\dfrac{2y}{3x^2}$ **2.** $\dfrac{a - 3}{a}$ **3.** $\dfrac{n - 5}{n - 1}$ **4.** $\dfrac{x^2 + 1}{x}$ **5.** $\dfrac{2x + 1}{3}$

6. $\dfrac{x^2 - 10}{2x^2 + 1}$ **7.** $\dfrac{3}{22}$ **8.** $\dfrac{18y + 20x}{48y - 9x}$ **9.** $\dfrac{3x + 2}{3x - 2}$ **10.** $\dfrac{x - 1}{2x - 1}$

11. $\dfrac{2x}{7y^2}$ **12.** $3b$ **13.** $\dfrac{n(n + 5)}{n - 1}$ **14.** $\dfrac{x(x - 3y)}{x^2 + 9y^2}$

15. $\dfrac{23x - 6}{20}$ **16.** $\dfrac{57 - 2n}{18n}$ **17.** $\dfrac{3x^2 - 2x - 14}{x(x + 7)}$ **18.** $\dfrac{2}{x - 5}$

19. $\dfrac{5n - 21}{(n - 9)(n + 4)(n - 1)}$ **20.** $\dfrac{6y - 23}{(2y + 3)(y - 6)}$

21. xy^4 **22.** $\dfrac{3x^2 y^5}{4}$ **23.** $\dfrac{4(x + 1)}{x + 4}$ **24.** $-\dfrac{5}{3(x + 2)(x + 1)}$

25. $6x - 1$ **26.** $3x^2 - 7x + 22 - \dfrac{90}{x + 4}$

27. $3x^3 - 2x^2 - x + 2$

28. $2x^3 - 2x^2 + 3x - 4 + \dfrac{7}{x + 1}$ **29.** $\left\{\dfrac{4}{13}\right\}$ **30.** $\left\{\dfrac{3}{16}\right\}$

31. $\varnothing$ **32.** $\{-17\}$ **33.** $\left\{\dfrac{2}{7}, \dfrac{7}{2}\right\}$ **34.** $\{22\}$ **35.** $\left\{-\dfrac{6}{7}, 3\right\}$

36. $\left\{\dfrac{3}{4}, \dfrac{5}{2}\right\}$ **37.** $\left\{\dfrac{9}{7}\right\}$ **38.** $\left\{-\dfrac{5}{4}\right\}$ **39.** $y = \dfrac{3x + 27}{4}$

40. $y = \dfrac{bx - ab}{a}$ **41.** $525 and $875
42. Busboy $36; Waiter $126
43. 20 minutes for Julio and 30 minutes for Dan
44. 50 miles per hour and 55 miles per hour or $8\frac{1}{3}$ miles per hour and $13\frac{1}{3}$ miles per hour
45. 9 hours **46.** 80 hours **47.** 13 miles per hour

Chapter 4 Test (page 218)

1. $\dfrac{13y^2}{24x}$ **2.** $\dfrac{3x - 1}{x(x - 6)}$ **3.** $\dfrac{2n - 3}{n + 4}$ **4.** $-\dfrac{2x}{x + 1}$ **5.** $\dfrac{3y^2}{8}$

6. $\dfrac{a - b}{4(2a + b)}$ **7.** $\dfrac{x + 4}{5x - 1}$ **8.** $\dfrac{13x + 7}{12}$ **9.** $\dfrac{3x}{2}$

10. $\dfrac{10n - 26}{15n}$ **11.** $\dfrac{3x^2 + 2x - 12}{x(x - 6)}$ **12.** $\dfrac{11 - 2x}{x(x - 1)}$

13. $\dfrac{13n + 46}{(2n + 5)(n - 2)(n + 7)}$ **14.** $3x^2 - 2x - 1$

15. $\dfrac{18 - 2x}{8 + 9x}$ **16.** $y = \dfrac{4x + 20}{3}$ **17.** $\{1\}$ **18.** $\left\{\dfrac{1}{10}\right\}$

19. $\{-35\}$ **20.** $\{-1, 5\}$ **21.** $\left\{\dfrac{5}{3}\right\}$ **22.** $\left\{-\dfrac{9}{13}\right\}$ **23.** $\dfrac{27}{72}$

24. 60 minutes **25.** 15 miles per hour

Chapters 1–4 Cumulative Review Problem Set (page 219)

1. 16 **2.** -13 **3.** 104 **4.** $\dfrac{5}{2}$ **5.** $7a^2 + 11a + 1$

6. $-2x^2 + 9x - 4$ **7.** $-2x^3 y^5$ **8.** $16x^2 y^6$ **9.** $36a^7 b^2$
10. $-24a^6 b^4$ **11.** $-18x^4 + 3x^3 - 12x^2$ **12.** $10x^2 + xy - 3y^2$
13. $x^2 + 8xy + 16y^2$ **14.** $a^3 - a^2 b - 11ab^2 + 3b^3$
15. $(x - 2)(x - 3)$ **16.** $(2x + 1)(3x - 4)$
17. $2(x - 1)(x - 3)$ **18.** $3(x + 8)(x - 2)$
19. $(3m - 4n)(3m + 4n)$ **20.** $(3a + 2)(9a^2 - 6a + 4)$

21. $-\dfrac{7y^4}{x^2}$ **22.** $-x$ **23.** $\dfrac{x(x - 5)}{x - 1}$ **24.** $\dfrac{x + 7}{x + 3}$ **25.** $\dfrac{9n - 26}{10}$

26. $\dfrac{8x - 19}{(x - 2)(x + 3)(x - 3)}$ **27.** $\dfrac{2y + 3x}{6xy}$ **28.** $\dfrac{m - n}{mn}$

29. $3x^2 - x + 4$ **30.** $2x^2 + 5x - 3 + \dfrac{2}{x - 4}$ **31.** $\{6\}$

32. $\{24\}$ **33.** $\left\{\dfrac{15}{7}\right\}$ **34.** $\{6\}$ **35.** $\left\{-2, \dfrac{10}{3}\right\}$

36. $\{-28, 12\}$ **37.** $\{-8, 1\}$ **38.** $\left\{-5, -\dfrac{3}{2}\right\}$

39. $\left\{-\dfrac{1}{3}, 9\right\}$ **40.** $\varnothing$ **41.** $P = \dfrac{A}{1 + rt}$ **42.** $B = \dfrac{3V}{h}$

43. $(-\infty, 2]$ **44.** $(-4, 2)$ **45.** $\left(-\dfrac{9}{3}, 3\right)$

46. $(-\infty, -13] \cup [7, \infty)$ **47.** $(-\infty, -10] \cup (2, \infty)$
48. $5.76 **49.** $690 **50.** Width is 23 in., length is 38 in.
51. 4 hr **52.** $13,600 and $54,400 **53.** 12 min

54. 5 in., 12 in., and 13 in. **55.** $16\frac{2}{3}$ yr **56.** 27 dimes and 13 quarters.

Chapter 5

Problem Set 5.1 (page 227)

1. $\dfrac{1}{27}$ **3.** $-\dfrac{1}{100}$ **5.** 81 **7.** -27 **9.** -8 **11.** 1 **13.** $\dfrac{9}{49}$

15. 16 **17.** $\dfrac{1}{1000}$ **19.** $\dfrac{1}{1000}$ **21.** 27 **23.** $\dfrac{1}{125}$ **25.** $\dfrac{9}{8}$

27. $\dfrac{256}{25}$ **29.** $\dfrac{2}{25}$ **31.** $\dfrac{81}{4}$ **33.** 81 **35.** $\dfrac{1}{10,000}$ **37.** $\dfrac{13}{36}$

39. $\dfrac{1}{2}$ **41.** $\dfrac{72}{17}$ **43.** $\dfrac{1}{x^6}$ **45.** $\dfrac{1}{a^3}$ **47.** $\dfrac{1}{a^8}$ **49.** $\dfrac{y^6}{x^2}$

51. $\dfrac{c^8}{a^4 b^{12}}$ **53.** $\dfrac{y^{12}}{8x^9}$ **55.** $\dfrac{x^3}{y^{12}}$ **57.** $\dfrac{4a^4}{9b^2}$ **59.** $\dfrac{1}{x^2}$ **61.** $a^5 b^2$

63. $\dfrac{6y^3}{x}$ **65.** $7b^2$ **67.** $\dfrac{7x}{y^2}$ **69.** $-\dfrac{12b^3}{a}$ **71.** $\dfrac{x^5 y^5}{5}$

73. $\dfrac{b^{20}}{81}$ **75.** $\dfrac{x+1}{x^3}$ **77.** $\dfrac{y-x^3}{x^3 y}$ **79.** $\dfrac{3b+4a^2}{a^2 b}$

81. $\dfrac{1-x^2 y}{xy^2}$ **83.** $\dfrac{2x-3}{x^2}$

Problem Set 5.2 (page 236)

1. 8 **3.** -10 **5.** 3 **7.** -4 **9.** 3 **11.** $\dfrac{4}{5}$ **13.** $-\dfrac{6}{7}$

15. $\dfrac{1}{2}$ **17.** $\dfrac{3}{4}$ **19.** 8 **21.** $3\sqrt{3}$ **23.** $4\sqrt{2}$ **25.** $4\sqrt{5}$

27. $4\sqrt{10}$ **29.** $12\sqrt{2}$ **31.** $-12\sqrt{5}$ **33.** $2\sqrt{3}$

35. $3\sqrt{6}$ **37.** $-\dfrac{5}{3}\sqrt{7}$ **39.** $\dfrac{\sqrt{19}}{2}$ **41.** $\dfrac{3\sqrt{3}}{4}$ **43.** $\dfrac{5\sqrt{3}}{9}$

45. $\dfrac{\sqrt{14}}{7}$ **47.** $\dfrac{\sqrt{6}}{3}$ **49.** $\dfrac{\sqrt{15}}{6}$ **51.** $\dfrac{\sqrt{66}}{12}$ **53.** $\dfrac{\sqrt{6}}{3}$

55. $\sqrt{5}$ **57.** $\dfrac{2\sqrt{21}}{7}$ **59.** $-\dfrac{8\sqrt{15}}{5}$ **61.** $\dfrac{\sqrt{6}}{4}$ **63.** $-\dfrac{12}{25}$

65. $2\sqrt[3]{2}$ **67.** $6\sqrt[3]{3}$ **69.** $\dfrac{2\sqrt[3]{3}}{3}$ **71.** $\dfrac{3\sqrt[3]{2}}{2}$ **73.** $\dfrac{\sqrt[3]{12}}{2}$

75. 42 miles per hour; 49 miles per hour; 65 miles per hour
77. 107 square centimeters **79.** 140 square inches
85. **(a)** 1.414 **(c)** 12.490 **(e)** 57.000 **(g)** 0.374 **(i)** 0.930

Problem Set 5.3 (page 241)

1. $13\sqrt{2}$ **3.** $54\sqrt{3}$ **5.** $-30\sqrt{2}$ **7.** $-\sqrt{5}$ **9.** $-21\sqrt{6}$

11. $-\dfrac{7\sqrt{7}}{12}$ **13.** $\dfrac{37\sqrt{10}}{10}$ **15.** $\dfrac{41\sqrt{2}}{20}$ **17.** $-9\sqrt[3]{3}$

19. $10\sqrt[3]{2}$ **21.** $4\sqrt{2x}$ **23.** $5x\sqrt{3}$ **25.** $2x\sqrt{5y}$

27. $8xy^3\sqrt{xy}$ **29.** $3a^2 b\sqrt{6b}$ **31.** $3x^3 y^4\sqrt{7}$

33. $4a\sqrt{10a}$ **35.** $\dfrac{8y}{3}\sqrt{6xy}$ **37.** $\dfrac{\sqrt{10xy}}{5y}$ **39.** $\dfrac{\sqrt{15}}{6x^2}$

41. $\dfrac{5\sqrt{2y}}{6y}$ **43.** $\dfrac{\sqrt{14xy}}{4y^3}$ **45.** $\dfrac{3y\sqrt{2xy}}{4x}$ **47.** $\dfrac{2\sqrt{42ab}}{7b^2}$

49. $2\sqrt[3]{3y}$ **51.** $2x\sqrt[3]{2x}$ **53.** $2x^2 y^2\sqrt[3]{7y^2}$ **55.** $\dfrac{\sqrt[3]{21x}}{3x}$

57. $\dfrac{\sqrt[3]{12x^2 y}}{4x^2}$ **59.** $\dfrac{\sqrt[3]{4x^2 y^2}}{xy^2}$ **61.** $2\sqrt{2x+3y}$

63. $4\sqrt{x+3y}$ **65.** $33\sqrt{x}$ **67.** $-30\sqrt{2x}$ **69.** $7\sqrt{3n}$

71. $-40\sqrt{ab}$ **73.** $-7x\sqrt{2x}$ **79.** **(a)** $5|x|\sqrt{5}$ **(b)** $4x^2$
  (c) $2b\sqrt{2b}$ **(d)** $y^2\sqrt{3y}$ **(e)** $12|x^3|\sqrt{2}$ **(f)** $2m^4\sqrt{7}$

(g) $8|c^5|\sqrt{2}$ **(h)** $3d^3\sqrt{2d}$ **(i)** $7|x|$
(j) $4n^{10}\sqrt{5}$ **(k)** $9h\sqrt{h}$

Problem Set 5.4 (page 247)

1. $6\sqrt{2}$ **3.** $18\sqrt{2}$ **5.** $-24\sqrt{10}$ **7.** $24\sqrt{6}$ **9.** 120

11. 24 **13.** $56\sqrt[3]{3}$ **15.** $\sqrt{6}+\sqrt{10}$

17. $6\sqrt{10}-3\sqrt{35}$ **19.** $24\sqrt{3}-60\sqrt{2}$

21. $-40-32\sqrt{15}$ **23.** $15\sqrt{2x}+3\sqrt{xy}$

25. $5xy-6x\sqrt{y}$ **27.** $2\sqrt{10xy}+2y\sqrt{15y}$

29. $-25\sqrt{6}$ **31.** $-25-3\sqrt{3}$ **33.** $23-9\sqrt{5}$

35. $6\sqrt{35}+3\sqrt{10}-4\sqrt{21}-2\sqrt{6}$

37. $8\sqrt{3}-36\sqrt{2}+6\sqrt{10}-18\sqrt{15}$

39. $11+13\sqrt{30}$ **41.** $141-51\sqrt{6}$ **43.** -10 **45.** -8

47. $2x-3y$ **49.** $10\sqrt[3]{12}+2\sqrt[3]{18}$ **51.** $12-36\sqrt[3]{2}$

53. $\dfrac{\sqrt{7}-1}{3}$ **55.** $\dfrac{-3\sqrt{2}-15}{23}$ **57.** $\dfrac{\sqrt{7}-\sqrt{2}}{5}$

59. $\dfrac{2\sqrt{5}+\sqrt{6}}{7}$ **61.** $\dfrac{\sqrt{15}-2\sqrt{3}}{2}$ **63.** $\dfrac{6\sqrt{7}+4\sqrt{6}}{13}$

65. $\sqrt{3}-\sqrt{2}$ **67.** $\dfrac{2\sqrt{x}-8}{x-16}$ **69.** $\dfrac{x+5\sqrt{x}}{x-25}$

71. $\dfrac{x-8\sqrt{x}+12}{x-36}$ **73.** $\dfrac{x-2\sqrt{xy}}{x-4y}$ **75.** $\dfrac{6\sqrt{xy}+9y}{4x-9y}$

Problem Set 5.5 (page 253)

1. $\{20\}$ **3.** $\varnothing$ **5.** $\left\{\dfrac{25}{4}\right\}$ **7.** $\left\{\dfrac{4}{9}\right\}$ **9.** $\{5\}$ **11.** $\left\{\dfrac{39}{4}\right\}$

13. $\left\{\dfrac{10}{3}\right\}$ **15.** $\{-1\}$ **17.** $\varnothing$ **19.** $\{1\}$ **21.** $\left\{\dfrac{3}{2}\right\}$ **23.** $\{3\}$

25. $\left\{\dfrac{61}{25}\right\}$ **27.** $\{-3,3\}$ **29.** $\{-9,-4\}$ **31.** $\{0\}$ **33.** $\{3\}$

35. $\{4\}$ **37.** $\{-4,-3\}$ **39.** $\{12\}$ **41.** $\{25\}$ **43.** $\{29\}$

45. $\{-15\}$ **47.** $\left\{-\dfrac{1}{3}\right\}$ **49.** $\{-3\}$ **51.** $\{0\}$ **53.** $\{5\}$

55. $\{2,6\}$ **57.** 56 feet; 106 feet; 148 feet
59. 3.2 feet; 5.1 feet; 7.3 feet

Problem Set 5.6 (page 258)

1. 9 **3.** 3 **5.** -2 **7.** -5 **9.** $\dfrac{1}{6}$ **11.** 3 **13.** 8 **15.** 81

17. -1 **19.** -32 **21.** $\dfrac{81}{16}$ **23.** 4 **25.** $\dfrac{1}{128}$ **27.** -125

29. 625 **31.** $\sqrt[3]{x^4}$ **33.** $3\sqrt{x}$ **35.** $\sqrt[3]{2y}$ **37.** $\sqrt{2x-3y}$

39. $\sqrt[3]{(2a-3b)^2}$ **41.** $\sqrt[3]{x^2 y}$ **43.** $-3\sqrt[5]{xy^2}$ **45.** $5^{\frac{1}{2}}y^2$

47. $3y^{\frac{1}{2}}$ **49.** $x^{\frac{1}{3}}y^{\frac{2}{3}}$ **51.** $a^{\frac{1}{2}}b^{\frac{3}{4}}$ **53.** $(2x-y)^{\frac{3}{5}}$ **55.** $5xy^{\frac{1}{2}}$

57. $-(x+y)^{\frac{1}{3}}$ **59.** $12x^{\frac{13}{20}}$ **61.** $y^{\frac{5}{12}}$ **63.** $\dfrac{4}{x^{\frac{1}{10}}}$ **65.** $16xy^2$

67. $2x^2 y$ **69.** $4x^{\frac{4}{15}}$ **71.** $\dfrac{4}{b^{\frac{5}{12}}}$ **73.** $\dfrac{36x^{\frac{4}{5}}}{49y^{\frac{4}{3}}}$ **75.** $\dfrac{y^{\frac{3}{2}}}{x}$ **77.** $4x^{\frac{1}{6}}$

79. $\dfrac{16}{a^{\frac{11}{10}}}$ **81.** $\sqrt[6]{243}$ **83.** $\sqrt[4]{216}$ **85.** $\sqrt[12]{3}$ **87.** $\sqrt{2}$

89. $\sqrt[4]{3}$ **93.** **(a)** 12 **(c)** 7 **(e)** 11 **95.** **(a)** 1024
  (c) 512 **(e)** 49

Problem Set 5.7 (page 263)

1. $(8.9)(10^1)$ 3. $(4.29)(10^3)$ 5. $(6.12)(10^6)$ 7. $(4)(10^7)$
9. $(3.764)(10^2)$ 11. $(3.47)(10^{-1})$ 13. $(2.14)(10^{-2})$
15. $(5)(10^{-5})$ 17. $(1.94)(10^{-9})$ 19. 23 21. 4190
23. 500,000,000 25. 31,400,000,000 27. 0.43
29. 0.000914 31. 0.00000005123 33. 0.000000074
35. 0.77 37. 300,000,000,000 39. 0.000000004
41. 1000 43. 1000 45. 3000 47. 20 49. 27,000,000
51. $(6.02)(10^{23})$ 53. 831 55. $(3.5)(10^4)$ dollars
57. 0.000137 in^2 59. 1833 63. (a) 7000 (c) 120 (e) 30
65. (a) $(4.385)(10^{14})$ (c) $(2.322)(10^{17})$ (e) $(3.052)(10^{12})$

Chapter 5 Review Problem Set (page 269)

1. $\dfrac{1}{64}$ 2. $\dfrac{9}{4}$ 3. 3 4. 1 5. 27 6. $\dfrac{1}{125}$ 7. $\dfrac{x^6}{y^8}$ 8. $\dfrac{27a^3b^{12}}{8}$
9. $\dfrac{9a^4}{16b^4}$ 10. $\dfrac{y^6}{125x^9}$ 11. $\dfrac{x^{12}}{9}$ 12. $\dfrac{1}{4y^3}$ 13. $-10x^3$ 14. $\dfrac{3b^5}{a^3}$
15. $\dfrac{b^3}{a^5}$ 16. $\dfrac{x^4}{y}$ 17. $-\dfrac{2}{x^2}$ 18. $-\dfrac{2a}{b}$ 19. $\dfrac{y+x^2}{x^2y}$
20. $\dfrac{b-2a}{a^2b}$ 21. $\dfrac{2y^2+3x}{xy^2}$ 22. $\dfrac{y^2+6x}{2xy^2}$ 23. $3\sqrt{6}$
24. $4x\sqrt{3xy}$ 25. $2\sqrt[3]{7}$ 26. $3xy^2\sqrt[3]{4xy^2}$ 27. $\dfrac{15\sqrt{6}}{4}$
28. $2y\sqrt{5xy}$ 29. $2\sqrt{2}$ 30. $\dfrac{\sqrt{15x}}{6x^2}$ 31. $\dfrac{\sqrt[3]{6}}{3}$ 32. $\dfrac{3\sqrt{5}}{5}$
33. $\dfrac{x\sqrt{21x}}{7}$ 34. $2\sqrt{x}$ 35. $\sqrt{5}$ 36. $5\sqrt[3]{3}$ 37. $\dfrac{29\sqrt{6}}{5}$
38. $-15\sqrt{3x}$ 39. $24\sqrt{10}$ 40. 60 41. $2x\sqrt{15y}$
42. $-18y^2\sqrt{x}$ 43. $24\sqrt{3}-6\sqrt{14}$ 44. $x-2\sqrt{x}-15$
45. 17 46. $12-8\sqrt{3}$ 47. $6a-5\sqrt{ab}-4b$ 48. 70

49. $\dfrac{2(\sqrt{7}+1)}{3}$ 50. $\dfrac{2\sqrt{6}-\sqrt{15}}{3}$ 51. $\dfrac{3\sqrt{5}-2\sqrt{3}}{11}$
52. $\dfrac{6\sqrt{3}+3\sqrt{5}}{7}$ 53. $\left\{\dfrac{19}{7}\right\}$ 54. $\{4\}$ 55. $\{8\}$ 56. $\varnothing$
57. $\{14\}$ 58. $\{-10,1\}$ 59. $\{2\}$ 60. $\{8\}$ 61. 493 ft
62. 4.7 ft 63. 32 64. 1 65. $\dfrac{4}{9}$ 66. -64 67. $\dfrac{1}{9}$ 68. $\dfrac{1}{4}$
69. 27 70. 8 71. $\sqrt[3]{xy^2}$ 72. $\sqrt[4]{a^3}$ 73. $4\sqrt{y}$
74. $\sqrt[3]{(x+5y)^2}$ 75. $x^{\frac{3}{5}}y^{\frac{1}{5}}$ 76. $4^{\frac{1}{3}}a^{\frac{2}{3}}$ 77. $6y^{\frac{1}{2}}$
78. $(3a+b)^{\frac{5}{3}}$ 79. $20x^{\frac{7}{10}}$ 80. $7a^{\frac{5}{12}}$ 81. $\dfrac{y^{\frac{4}{3}}}{x}$ 82. $-\dfrac{6}{a^{\frac{1}{4}}}$
83. $\dfrac{1}{x^{\frac{2}{5}}}$ 84. $-6y^{\frac{5}{12}}$ 85. $\sqrt[4]{3^3}$ 86. $3\sqrt[6]{3}$ 87. $\sqrt[12]{5}$
88. $\sqrt[6]{2^5}$ 89. $(5.4)(10^8)$ 90. $(8.4)(10^4)$ 91. $(3.2)(10^{-8})$
92. $(7.68)(10^{-4})$ 93. 0.0000014 94. 0.000638
95. 41,200,000 96. 125,000 97. 0.000000006
98. 36,000,000,000 99. 6 100. 0.15 101. 0.000028
102. 0.002 103. 0.002 104. 8,000,000,000

Chapter 5 Test (page 271)

1. $\dfrac{1}{32}$ 2. -32 3. $\dfrac{81}{16}$ 4. $\dfrac{1}{4}$ 5. $3\sqrt{7}$ 6. $3\sqrt[3]{4}$
7. $2x^2y\sqrt{13y}$ 8. $\dfrac{5\sqrt{6}}{6}$ 9. $\dfrac{\sqrt{42x}}{12x^2}$ 10. $72\sqrt{2}$ 11. $-5\sqrt{6}$
12. $-38\sqrt{2}$ 13. $\dfrac{3\sqrt{6}+3}{10}$ 14. $\dfrac{9x^2y^2}{4}$ 15. $-\dfrac{12}{a^{\frac{3}{10}}}$
16. $\dfrac{y^3+x}{xy^3}$ 17. $-12x^{\frac{1}{4}}$ 18. 33 19. 600 20. 0.003
21. $\left\{\dfrac{8}{3}\right\}$ 22. $\{2\}$ 23. $\{4\}$ 24. $\{5\}$ 25. $\{4,6\}$

Chapter 6

Problem Set 6.1 (page 280)

1. False 3. True 5. True 7. True 9. $10+8i$
11. $-6+10i$ 13. $-2-5i$ 15. $-12+5i$ 17. $-1-23i$
19. $-4-5i$ 21. $1+3i$ 23. $\dfrac{5}{3}-\dfrac{5}{12}i$ 25. $-\dfrac{17}{9}+\dfrac{23}{30}i$
27. $9i$ 29. $i\sqrt{14}$ 31. $\dfrac{4}{5}i$ 33. $3i\sqrt{2}$ 35. $5i\sqrt{3}$
37. $6i\sqrt{7}$ 39. $-8i\sqrt{5}$ 41. $36i\sqrt{10}$ 43. -8
45. $-\sqrt{15}$ 47. $-3\sqrt{6}$ 49. $-5\sqrt{3}$ 51. $-3\sqrt{6}$
53. $4i\sqrt{3}$ 55. $\dfrac{5}{2}$ 57. $2\sqrt{2}$ 59. $2i$ 61. $-20+0i$
63. $42+0i$ 65. $15+6i$ 67. $-42+12i$ 69. $7+22i$
71. $40-20i$ 73. $-3-28i$ 75. $-3-15i$
77. $-9+40i$ 79. $-12+16i$ 81. $85+0i$
83. $5+0i$ 85. $\dfrac{3}{5}+\dfrac{3}{10}i$ 87. $\dfrac{5}{17}-\dfrac{3}{17}i$ 89. $2+\dfrac{2}{3}i$
91. $0-\dfrac{2}{7}i$ 93. $\dfrac{22}{25}-\dfrac{4}{25}i$ 95. $-\dfrac{18}{41}+\dfrac{39}{41}i$ 97. $\dfrac{9}{2}-\dfrac{5}{2}i$

99. $\dfrac{4}{13}-\dfrac{1}{26}i$ 101. (a) $-2-i\sqrt{3}$ (c) $\dfrac{-1-3i\sqrt{2}}{2}$
(e) $\dfrac{10+3i\sqrt{5}}{4}$

Problem Set 6.2 (page 286)

1. $\{0,9\}$ 3. $\{-3,0\}$ 5. $\{-4,0\}$ 7. $\left\{0,\dfrac{9}{5}\right\}$ 9. $\{-6,5\}$
11. $\{7,12\}$ 13. $\left\{-8,-\dfrac{3}{2}\right\}$ 15. $\left\{-\dfrac{7}{3},\dfrac{2}{5}\right\}$ 17. $\left\{\dfrac{3}{5}\right\}$
19. $\left\{-\dfrac{3}{2},\dfrac{7}{3}\right\}$ 21. $\{1,4\}$ 23. $\{8\}$ 25. $\{12\}$ 27. $\{\pm1\}$
29. $\{\pm6i\}$ 31. $\{\pm\sqrt{14}\}$ 33. $\{\pm2\sqrt{7}\}$ 35. $\{\pm3\sqrt{2}\}$
37. $\left\{\pm\dfrac{\sqrt{14}}{2}\right\}$ 39. $\left\{\pm\dfrac{2\sqrt{3}}{3}\right\}$ 41. $\left\{\pm\dfrac{2i\sqrt{30}}{5}\right\}$
43. $\left\{\pm\dfrac{\sqrt{6}}{2}\right\}$ 45. $\{-1,5\}$ 47. $\{-8,2\}$ 49. $\{-6\pm2i\}$

51. $\{1, 2\}$ **53.** $\{4 \pm \sqrt{5}\}$ **55.** $\{-5 \pm 2\sqrt{3}\}$

57. $\left\{\dfrac{2 \pm 3i\sqrt{3}}{3}\right\}$ **59.** $\{-12, -2\}$ **61.** $\left\{\dfrac{2 \pm \sqrt{10}}{5}\right\}$

63. $2\sqrt{13}$ centimeters   **65.** $4\sqrt{5}$ inches   **67.** 8 yards

69. $6\sqrt{2}$ inches   **71.** $a = b = 4\sqrt{2}$ meters

73. $b = 3\sqrt{3}$ inches and $c = 6$ inches

75. $a = 7$ centimeters and $b = 7\sqrt{3}$ centimeters

77. $a = \dfrac{10\sqrt{3}}{3}$ feet and $c = \dfrac{20\sqrt{3}}{3}$ feet   **79.** 17.9 feet

81. 38 meters   **83.** 53 meters   **87.** 10.8 centimeters

89. $h = s\sqrt{2}$

Problem Set 6.3 (page 292)

1. $\{-6, 10\}$ **3.** $\{4, 10\}$ **5.** $\{-5, 10\}$ **7.** $\{-8, 1\}$

9. $\left\{-\dfrac{5}{2}, 3\right\}$ **11.** $\left\{-3, \dfrac{2}{3}\right\}$ **13.** $\{-16, 10\}$

15. $\{-2 \pm \sqrt{6}\}$ **17.** $\{-3 \pm 2\sqrt{3}\}$ **19.** $\{5 \pm \sqrt{26}\}$

21. $\{4 \pm i\}$ **23.** $\{-6 \pm 3\sqrt{3}\}$ **25.** $\{-1 \pm i\sqrt{5}\}$

27. $\left\{\dfrac{-3 \pm \sqrt{17}}{2}\right\}$ **29.** $\left\{\dfrac{-5 \pm \sqrt{21}}{2}\right\}$ **31.** $\left\{\dfrac{7 \pm \sqrt{37}}{2}\right\}$

33. $\left\{\dfrac{-2 \pm \sqrt{10}}{2}\right\}$ **35.** $\left\{\dfrac{3 \pm i\sqrt{6}}{3}\right\}$ **37.** $\left\{\dfrac{-5 \pm \sqrt{37}}{6}\right\}$

39. $\{-12, 4\}$ **41.** $\left\{\dfrac{4 \pm \sqrt{10}}{2}\right\}$ **43.** $\left\{-\dfrac{9}{2}, \dfrac{1}{3}\right\}$

45. $\{-3, 8\}$ **47.** $\{3 \pm 2\sqrt{3}\}$ **49.** $\left\{\dfrac{3 \pm i\sqrt{3}}{3}\right\}$

51. $\{-20, 12\}$ **53.** $\left\{-1, -\dfrac{2}{3}\right\}$ **55.** $\left\{\dfrac{1}{2}, \dfrac{3}{2}\right\}$

57. $\{-6 \pm 2\sqrt{10}\}$ **59.** $\left\{\dfrac{-1 \pm \sqrt{3}}{2}\right\}$

61. $\left\{\dfrac{-b \pm \sqrt{b^2 - 4ac}}{2a}\right\}$ **65.** $x = \dfrac{a\sqrt{b^2 - y^2}}{b}$

67. $r = \dfrac{\sqrt{A\pi}}{\pi}$ **69.** $\{2a, 3a\}$ **71.** $\left\{\dfrac{a}{2}, -\dfrac{2a}{3}\right\}$

73. $\left\{\dfrac{2b}{3}\right\}$

Problem Set 6.4 (page 299)

1. $\dfrac{1 \pm \sqrt{5}}{2}$ **3.** $-2 \pm \sqrt{3}$ **5.** $\dfrac{2 \pm \sqrt{2}}{3}$

7. $\dfrac{-2 \pm \sqrt{3}}{2}$ **9.** $\dfrac{-3 \pm 2\sqrt{3}}{2}$ **11.** $\{-1 \pm \sqrt{2}\}$

13. $\left\{\dfrac{-5 \pm \sqrt{37}}{2}\right\}$ **15.** $\{4 \pm 2\sqrt{5}\}$ **17.** $\left\{\dfrac{-5 \pm i\sqrt{7}}{2}\right\}$

19. $\{8, 10\}$ **21.** $\left\{\dfrac{9 \pm \sqrt{61}}{2}\right\}$ **23.** $\left\{\dfrac{-1 \pm \sqrt{33}}{4}\right\}$

25. $\left\{\dfrac{-1 \pm i\sqrt{3}}{4}\right\}$ **27.** $\left\{\dfrac{4 \pm \sqrt{10}}{3}\right\}$ **29.** $\left\{-1, \dfrac{5}{2}\right\}$

31. $\left\{-5, -\dfrac{4}{3}\right\}$ **33.** $\left\{\dfrac{5}{6}\right\}$ **35.** $\left\{\dfrac{1 \pm \sqrt{13}}{4}\right\}$

37. $\left\{0, \dfrac{13}{5}\right\}$ **39.** $\left\{\pm\dfrac{\sqrt{15}}{3}\right\}$ **41.** $\left\{\dfrac{-1 \pm \sqrt{73}}{12}\right\}$

43. $\{-18, -14\}$ **45.** $\left\{\dfrac{11}{4}, \dfrac{10}{3}\right\}$ **47.** $\left\{\dfrac{2 \pm i\sqrt{2}}{2}\right\}$

49. $\left\{\dfrac{1 \pm \sqrt{7}}{6}\right\}$

51. Two real solutions; $\{-7, 3\}$ **53.** One real solution; $\left\{\dfrac{1}{3}\right\}$

55. Two complex solutions; $\left\{\dfrac{7 \pm i\sqrt{3}}{2}\right\}$

57. Two real solutions; $\left\{-\dfrac{4}{3}, \dfrac{1}{5}\right\}$

59. Two real solutions; $\left\{\dfrac{-2 \pm \sqrt{10}}{3}\right\}$

65. $\{-1.381, 17.381\}$ **67.** $\{-13.426, 3.426\}$

69. $\{-0.347, -8.653\}$ **71.** $\{0.119, 1.681\}$

73. $\{-0.708, 4.708\}$ **75.** $k = 4$ or $k = -4$

Problem Set 6.5 (page 305)

1. $\{2 \pm \sqrt{10}\}$ **3.** $\left\{-9, \dfrac{4}{3}\right\}$ **5.** $\{9 \pm 3\sqrt{10}\}$

7. $\left\{\dfrac{3 \pm i\sqrt{23}}{4}\right\}$ **9.** $\{-15, -9\}$ **11.** $\{-8, 1\}$

13. $\left\{\dfrac{2 \pm i\sqrt{10}}{2}\right\}$ **15.** $\{9 \pm \sqrt{66}\}$ **17.** $\left\{-\dfrac{5}{4}, \dfrac{2}{5}\right\}$

19. $\left\{\dfrac{-1 \pm \sqrt{2}}{2}\right\}$ **21.** $\left\{\dfrac{3}{4}, 4\right\}$ **23.** $\left\{\dfrac{11 \pm \sqrt{109}}{2}\right\}$

25. $\left\{\dfrac{3}{7}, 4\right\}$ **27.** $\left\{\dfrac{7 \pm \sqrt{129}}{10}\right\}$ **29.** $\left\{-\dfrac{10}{7}, 3\right\}$

31. $\{1 \pm \sqrt{34}\}$ **33.** $\{\pm\sqrt{6}, \pm 2\sqrt{3}\}$

35. $\left\{\pm 3, \pm\dfrac{2\sqrt{6}}{3}\right\}$ **37.** $\left\{\pm\dfrac{i\sqrt{15}}{3}, \pm 2i\right\}$

39. $\left\{\pm\dfrac{\sqrt{14}}{2}, \pm\dfrac{2\sqrt{3}}{3}\right\}$ **41.** 8 and 9   **43.** 9 and 12

45. $5 + \sqrt{3}$ and $5 - \sqrt{3}$ **47.** 3 and 6

49. 9 inches and 12 inches   **51.** 1 meter

53. 8 inches by 14 inches   **55.** 20 miles per hour for Lorraine and 25 miles per hour for Charlotte, or 45 miles per hour for Lorraine and 50 miles per hour for Charlotte

57. 55 miles per hour   **59.** 6 hours for Tom and 8 hours for Terry

61. 2 hours   **63.** 8 students   **65.** 50 numbers   **67.** 9%

73. $\{9, 36\}$ **75.** $\{1\}$ **77.** $\left\{-\dfrac{8}{27}, \dfrac{27}{8}\right\}$ **79.** $\left\{-4, \dfrac{3}{5}\right\}$

81. $\{4\}$ **83.** $\{\pm 4\sqrt{2}\}$ **85.** $\left\{\dfrac{3}{2}, \dfrac{5}{2}\right\}$ **87.** $\{-1, 3\}$

Problem Set 6.6 (page 312)

1. $(-\infty, -2) \cup (1, \infty)$

3. $(-4, -1)$

5. $\left(-\infty, -\dfrac{7}{3}\right] \cup \left[\dfrac{1}{2}, \infty\right)$

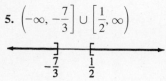

7. $\left[-2, \dfrac{3}{4}\right]$

9. $(-1, 1) \cup (3, \infty)$

11. $(-\infty, -2] \cup [0, 4]$

13. $(-7, 5)$ **15.** $(-\infty, 4) \cup (7, \infty)$ **17.** $\left[-5, \dfrac{2}{3}\right]$

19. $\left(-\infty, -\dfrac{5}{2}\right] \cup \left[-\dfrac{1}{4}, \infty\right)$ **21.** $\left(-\infty, -\dfrac{4}{5}\right) \cup (8, \infty)$

23. $(-\infty, \infty)$ **25.** $\left\{-\dfrac{5}{2}\right\}$ **27.** $(-1, 3) \cup (3, \infty)$

29. $(-\infty, -2) \cup (2, \infty)$ **31.** $(-6, 6)$ **33.** $(-\infty, \infty)$
35. $(-\infty, 0] \cup [2, \infty)$ **37.** $(-4, 0) \cup (0, \infty)$

39. $(-\infty, -1) \cup (2, \infty)$ **41.** $(-2, 3)$ **43.** $(-\infty, 0) \cup \left[\dfrac{1}{2}, \infty\right)$

45. $(-\infty, 1) \cup [2, \infty)$ **47.** $(-6, -3)$

49. $(-\infty, 5) \cup [9, \infty)$ **51.** $\left(-\infty, \dfrac{4}{3}\right) \cup (3, \infty)$

53. $(-4, 6]$ **55.** $(-\infty, 2)$

Chapter 6 Review Problem Set (page 318)

1. $2 - 2i$ **2.** $-3 - i$ **3.** $8 - 8i$ **4.** $-2 + 4i$ **5.** $2i\sqrt{2}$
6. $5i$ **7.** $12i$ **8.** $6i\sqrt{2}$ **9.** $-2\sqrt{3}$ **10.** $6i$ **11.** $\sqrt{7}$
12. $i\sqrt{3}$ **13.** $30 + 15i$ **14.** $86 - 2i$ **15.** $-32 + 4i$
16. $25 + 0i$ **17.** $\dfrac{9}{20} + \dfrac{13}{20}i$ **18.** $-\dfrac{3}{29} + \dfrac{7}{29}i$ **19.** $2 - \dfrac{3}{2}i$
20. $-5 - 6i$ **21.** $\{-8, 0\}$ **22.** $\{0, 6\}$ **23.** $\{-4, 7\}$
24. $\left\{-\dfrac{3}{2}, 1\right\}$ **25.** $\{\pm 3\sqrt{5}\}$ **26.** $3 \pm 3i\sqrt{2}$
27. $\left\{\dfrac{-3 \pm 2\sqrt{6}}{2}\right\}$ **28.** $\{\pm 3\sqrt{3}\}$ **29.** $\{-9 \pm \sqrt{91}\}$
30. $\{-3 \pm i\sqrt{11}\}$ **31.** $\{5 \pm 2\sqrt{6}\}$ **32.** $\left\{\dfrac{-5 \pm \sqrt{33}}{2}\right\}$
33. $\{-3 \pm \sqrt{5}\}$ **34.** $\{-2 \pm i\sqrt{2}\}$
35. $\left\{\dfrac{1 \pm i\sqrt{11}}{3}\right\}$ **36.** $\left\{\dfrac{1 \pm \sqrt{61}}{10}\right\}$
37. One real solution with a multiplicity of 2
38. Two nonreal complex solutions
39. Two unequal real solutions
40. Two unequal real solutions **41.** $\{0, 17\}$ **42.** $\{-4, 8\}$
43. $\left\{\dfrac{1 \pm 8i}{2}\right\}$ **44.** $\{-3, 7\}$ **45.** $\{-1 \pm \sqrt{10}\}$
46. $\{3 \pm 5i\}$ **47.** $\{25\}$ **48.** $\left\{-4, \dfrac{2}{3}\right\}$ **49.** $\{-10, 20\}$

50. $\left\{\dfrac{-1 \pm \sqrt{61}}{6}\right\}$ **51.** $\left\{\dfrac{1 \pm i\sqrt{11}}{2}\right\}$
52. $\left\{\dfrac{5 \pm i\sqrt{23}}{4}\right\}$ **53.** $\left\{\dfrac{-2 \pm \sqrt{14}}{2}\right\}$ **54.** $\{-9, 4\}$
55. $\{-2 \pm i\sqrt{5}\}$ **56.** $\{-6, 12\}$ **57.** $\{1 \pm \sqrt{10}\}$
58. $\left\{\pm\dfrac{\sqrt{14}}{2}, \pm 2\sqrt{2}\right\}$ **59.** $\left\{\dfrac{-3 \pm \sqrt{97}}{2}\right\}$
60. 34.6 ft and 40.0 ft **61.** 47.2 m **62.** $4\sqrt{2}$ in.
63. $3 + \sqrt{7}$ and $3 - \sqrt{7}$ **64.** 8 hr
65. Andre: 45 mph and Sandy: 52 mph
66. 8 units **67.** 8 and 10 **68.** 7 in. by 12 in.
69. 4 hr for Reena and 6 hr for Billy **70.** 10 m
71. $(-\infty, -5) \cup (2, \infty)$ **72.** $\left[-\dfrac{7}{2}, 3\right]$ **73.** $\left[-\dfrac{1}{2}, \dfrac{1}{2}\right]$
74. $(-\infty, 2) \cup (5, \infty)$ **75.** $(-\infty, -6) \cup [4, \infty)$
76. $\left(-\dfrac{5}{2}, -1\right)$ **77.** $(-9, 4)$ **78.** $\left[-\dfrac{1}{3}, 1\right)$

Chapter 6 Test (page 320)

1. $39 - 2i$ **2.** $-\dfrac{6}{25} - \dfrac{17}{25}i$ **3.** $\{0, 7\}$ **4.** $\{-1, 7\}$
5. $\{-6, 3\}$ **6.** $\{1 - \sqrt{2}, 1 + \sqrt{2}\}$ **7.** $\left\{\dfrac{1 - 2i}{5}, \dfrac{1 + 2i}{5}\right\}$
8. $\{-16, -14\}$ **9.** $\left\{\dfrac{1 - 6i}{3}, \dfrac{1 + 6i}{3}\right\}$ **10.** $\left\{-\dfrac{7}{4}, \dfrac{6}{5}\right\}$
11. $\left\{-3, \dfrac{19}{6}\right\}$ **12.** $\left\{-\dfrac{10}{3}, 4\right\}$ **13.** $\{-2, 2, -4i, 4i\}$
14. $\left\{-\dfrac{3}{4}, 1\right\}$ **15.** $\left\{\dfrac{1 - \sqrt{10}}{3}, \dfrac{1 + \sqrt{10}}{3}\right\}$
16. Two equal real solutions
17. Two nonreal complex solutions
18. $[-6, 9]$ **19.** $(-\infty, -2) \cup \left(\dfrac{1}{3}, \infty\right)$
20. $[-10, -6)$ **21.** 20.8 ft **22.** 29 m **23.** 3 hr
24. $6\dfrac{1}{2}$ in. **25.** $3 + \sqrt{5}$

Chapters 1–6 Cumulative Review Problem Set (page 321)

1. $\dfrac{8}{27}$ **2.** $\dfrac{1}{4}$ **3.** 2 **4.** $\dfrac{1}{2}$ **5.** $\dfrac{1}{9}$ **6.** 16 **7.** $\dfrac{5}{6}$ **8.** $-\dfrac{6}{11}$
9. 6 **10.** -3 **11.** 64 **12.** $\dfrac{1}{2}$ **13.** $\dfrac{19}{45}$ **14.** 0.864
15. $-12a^6b^6$ **16.** $\dfrac{1}{3}c^4d^3$ **17.** $81m^4n^{12}$ **18.** $3a^3 - 7a^2 + 9a - 14$
19. $-5tk^2$ **20.** $12x^2 - 11xy - 5y^2$ **21.** $49m^2 - 84mn + 36n^2$
22. $\dfrac{a^3b}{2}$ **23.** $\dfrac{x - 3}{2(x + 7)}$ **24.** $\dfrac{21x - 19}{6}$
25. $3x^2 - x - 1 + \dfrac{-8}{x - 2}$ **26.** $\dfrac{7x - 2}{4x - 1}$ **27.** $\dfrac{27 + 28x}{3x - 60}$
28. $(x - y)(2a + 3c)$ **29.** $9(3m + n)(3m - n)$
30. $(2x + 1)(x - 7)$ **31.** $(2y + 5)(6y - 1)$
32. $2(3t - 4)(t + 7)$ **33.** $(c + y^3)(c - y^3)$
34. $(4h + 3)(2h - 5)$ **35.** $(a + 2b)(a^2 - 2ab + 4b^2)$
36. $\{-2\}$ **37.** $\varnothing$ **38.** $\{2\}$ **39.** $\left\{\dfrac{41}{13}\right\}$ **40.** $\{1500\}$
41. $t = \dfrac{A - P}{Pr}$ **42.** $\left\{\dfrac{20}{3}\right\}$ **43.** $\{3\}$ **44.** $\left\{-\dfrac{\sqrt{3}}{3}, \dfrac{\sqrt{3}}{3}\right\}$

45. {1}   **46.** $\left\{-\dfrac{5}{3}, 5\right\}$ **47.** {25}   **48.** $\left\{-\dfrac{1}{2}, 2\right\}$

49. $\left\{-\dfrac{5}{2}, \dfrac{4}{3}\right\}$ **50.** $\left\{-\dfrac{3}{2}, 4\right\}$ **51.** $w = \dfrac{P - 2l}{2}$ **52.** $\left\{\dfrac{2}{9}\right\}$

53. $\left\{-\dfrac{11}{2}, 2\right\}$ **54.** $\left\{-\dfrac{2}{3}\right\}$ **55.** $\left\{-\dfrac{6}{17}\right\}$ **56.** {−6, 2}

57. {−3, −1}   **58.** {−2, 0}   **59.** $\left(-\infty, -\dfrac{5}{2}\right)$ **60.** $\left[\dfrac{19}{20}, \infty\right)$

61. $(-\infty, \infty)$ **62.** $[6, \infty)$ **63.** $x \geq 1000$ or $[1000, \infty)$

64. $\left(-\dfrac{4}{3}, 4\right)$ **65.** $\varnothing$ **66.** $(-\infty, -4)$

67. $(-\infty, -3] \cup \left[\dfrac{5}{2}, \infty\right)$ **68.** $(-10, 5)$

69. $(-\infty, -5] \cup (1, \infty)$ **70.** $[-2, 4]$ **71.** At 2:20 p.m.

72. $1,600   **73.** 25°, 50°, 105°   **74.** 8 hours   **75.** 142.1 feet

76. 4%   **77.** $12\dfrac{1}{2}$ hours   **78.** 8 feet and 15 feet

79. Canoe: $1\dfrac{3}{5}$ miles per hour; Kayak: 4 miles per hour

80. 0.32 units

Chapter 7

Problem Set 7.1 (page 334)

1. (2, 4), (−1, −5)   **3.** (−2, 10), (3, 0)

5. 5, 4, 3, −1   **7.** −10, −6, −2, 2

9.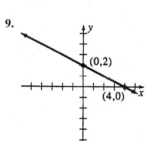

11.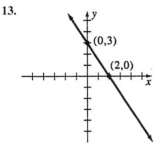

13.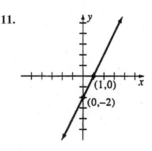

15.

17.

19.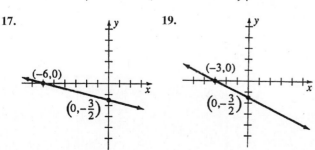

21.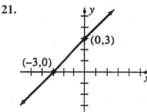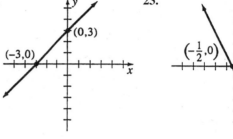

23.

25.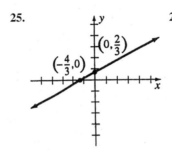

27.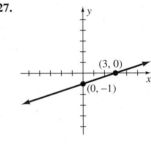

29.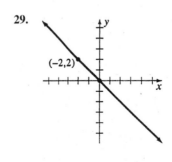

31.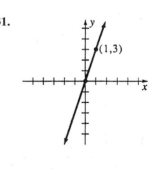

33.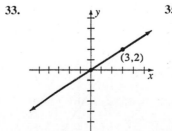

35.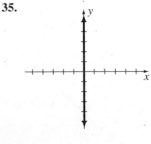

37.

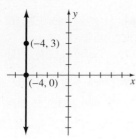

39.

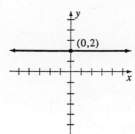

41. (a)

m	5	10	15	20	30	60
c	11.25	12.50	13.75	15.00	17.50	25.00

(b)

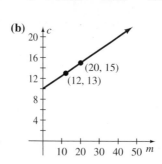

(d) 16.25, 20.00, 21.25

43. (a)

h	6.0	6.5	7.0	8.0	8.5	9.0	10.0
G	120	135	150	180	195	210	240

(b)

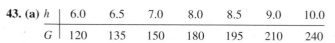

(d) 105, 165

45.

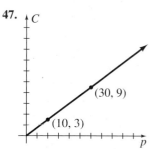

47.

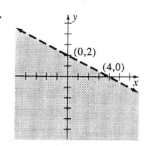

53.

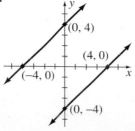

55.

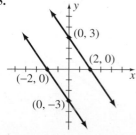

Problem Set 7.2 (page 341)

1.

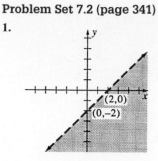

3.

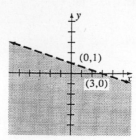

5.

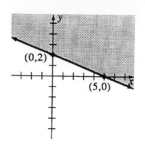

7.

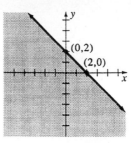

9.

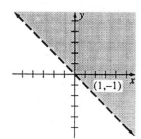

11.

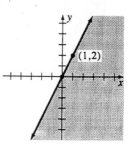

13.

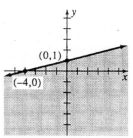

15.

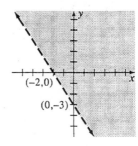

17.

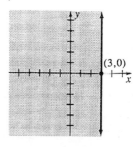

19.

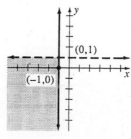

21.

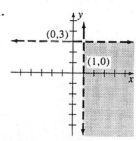

23.

27.

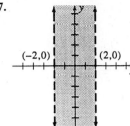

29.

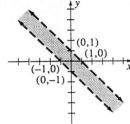

43. $4x - 7y = 0$ **45.** $x + 2y = 5$ **47.** $3x + 2y = 0$

49. $m = -3$ and $b = 7$ **51.** $m = -\dfrac{3}{2}$ and $b = \dfrac{9}{2}$

53. $m = \dfrac{1}{5}$ and $b = -\dfrac{12}{5}$

Problem Set 7.3 (page 350)

1. 15   **3.** $\sqrt{13}$ **5.** $3\sqrt{2}$ **7.** $3\sqrt{5}$ **9.** 6   **11.** $3\sqrt{10}$

13. The lengths of the sides are 10, $5\sqrt{5}$, and 5. Because $10^2 + 5^2 = (5\sqrt{5})^2$, it is a right triangle.

15. The distances between (3, 6), and (7, 12), between (7, 12) and (11, 18), and between (11, 18) and (15, 24) are all $2\sqrt{13}$ units.

17. $\dfrac{4}{3}$ **19.** $-\dfrac{7}{3}$ **21.** -2 **23.** $\dfrac{3}{5}$ **25.** 0   **27.** $\dfrac{1}{2}$

29. 7   **31.** -2 **33–39.** Answers will vary.

41. $-\dfrac{2}{3}$ **43.** $\dfrac{1}{2}$ **45.** $\dfrac{4}{7}$ **47.** 0   **49.** -5

55.

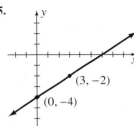

57.

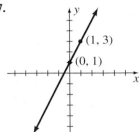

59.

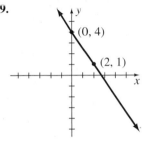

61.

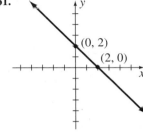

51.

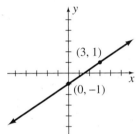

53.

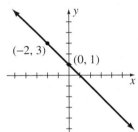

63.

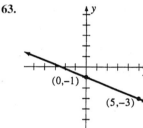

65.

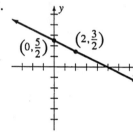

55.

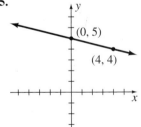

57.

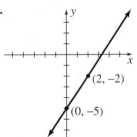

67.

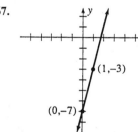

69.

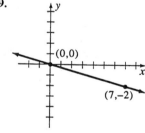

59. 105.6 feet   **61.** 8.1%   **63.** 19 centimeters

69. **(a)** $(3, 5)$ **(c)** $(2, 5)$ **(e)** $\left(\dfrac{17}{8}, -7\right)$

Problem Set 7.4 (page 360)

1. $x - 2y = -7$ **3.** $3x - y = -10$ **5.** $3x + 4y = -15$

7. $5x - 4y = 28$ **9.** $5x - 2y = -23$ **11.** $2x + y = 18$

13. $x + 3y = 5$ **15.** $x - y = 1$ **17.** $5x - 2y = -4$

19. $x + 7y = 11$ **21.** $x + 2y = -9$ **23.** $7x - 5y = 0$

25. $y = \dfrac{3}{7}x + 4$ **27.** $y = 2x - 3$ **29.** $y = -\dfrac{2}{5}x + 1$

31. $y = 0(x) - 4$ **33.** $2x - y = 4$ **35.** $5x + 8y = -15$

37. $x + 0(y) = 2$ **39.** $0(x) + y = 6$ **41.** $x + 5y = 16$

71.

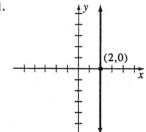

73. $y = 30x - 60$

75. $y = \dfrac{1}{1000}x + 2$ **77.** $y = \dfrac{9}{5}x + 32$

85. **(a)** $2x - y = 1$ **(b)** $5x - 6y = 29$ **(c)** $x + y = 2$
(d) $3x - 2y = 18$

Problem Set 7.5 (page 369)

1. $(-3, -1)$; $(3, 1)$; $(3, -1)$ **3.** $(7, 2)$; $(-7, -2)$; $(-7, 2)$
5. $(5, 0)$; $(-5, 0)$; $(-5, 0)$ **7.** x axis   **9.** y axis
11. x axis, y axis, and origin   **13.** x axis   **15.** None
17. Origin   **19.** y axis   **21.** All three   **23.** x axis   **25.** y axis

27.
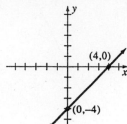

29.
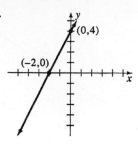

31.
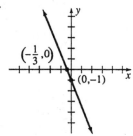

33.
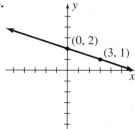

35.
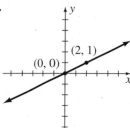

37.
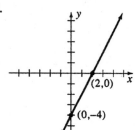

39.
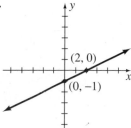

41.
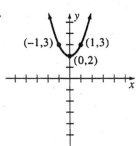

43.
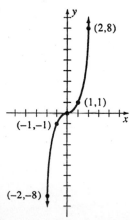

45.
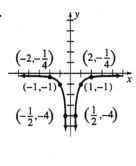

47.
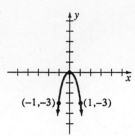

49.
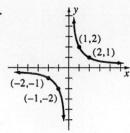

51.
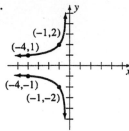

53.
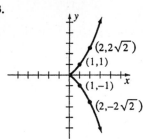

55.
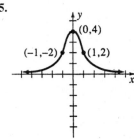

57.
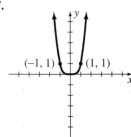

59.
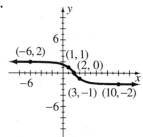

Chapter 7 Review Problem Set (page 376)

1. $(1, 2)$, $(-1, 10)$ **2.** $(0, 2)$
3. $(2, 3)$, $(-2, 9)$ **4.** $(-3, 0)$

5.

x	-1	0	1	4
y	-7	-5	-3	3

6.

x	-3	-1	0	2
y	5	1	-1	-5

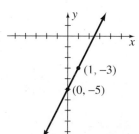

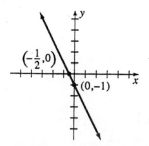

7.

x	-2	0	2	4
y	-5	-2	1	4

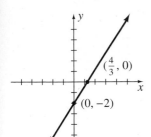

8.

x	-3	0	3
y	-3	-1	1

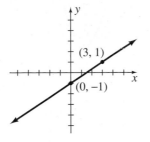

17.

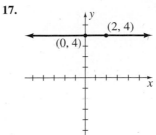

18.

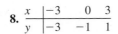

9.

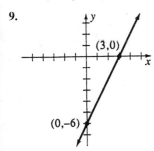

10.

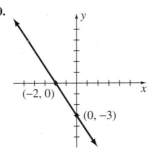

19. (a)

h	1	2	3	4
C	225	300	375	450

20. (a)

v	100	200	350	400
t	15	30	52.50	60

19. (b)

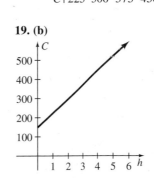

20. (b)

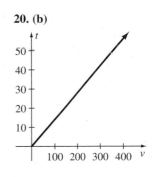

19. (d) 262.50, 412.50   **20. (d)** 37.50, 45

11.

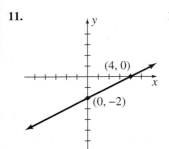

12.

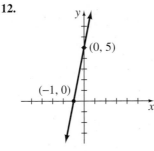

21.

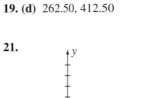

22.

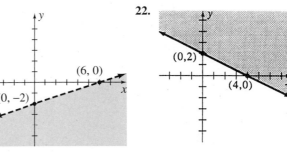

13.

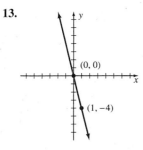

14.

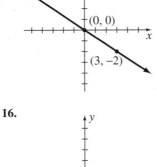

23.

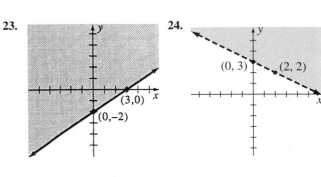

24.

15.

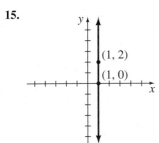

16.

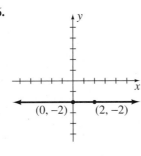

25.

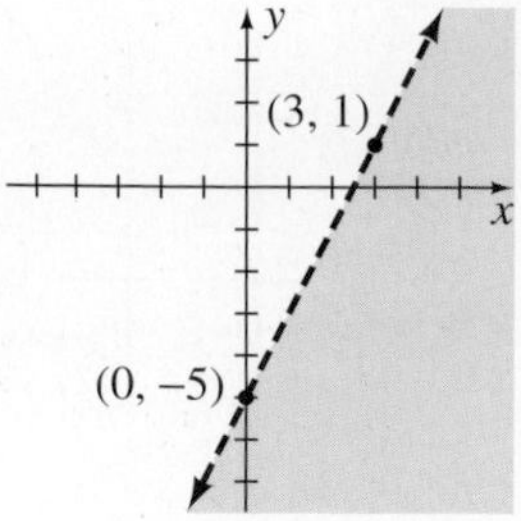

26.

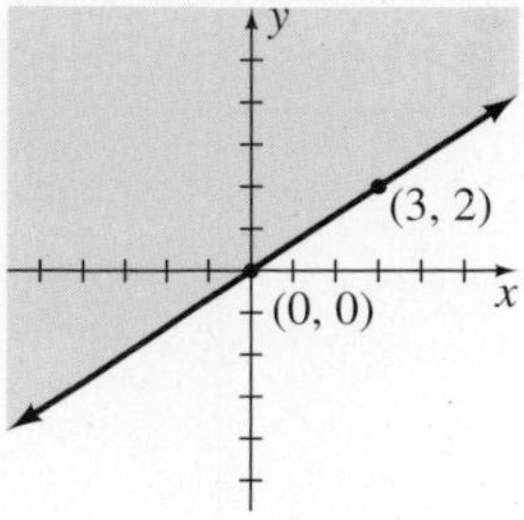

27. **(a)** $\sqrt{53}$ **(b)** $\sqrt{58}$ **28.** 5, 10, and $\sqrt{97}$

29. The distances between $(-3, -1)$ and $(1, 2)$ and between $(1, 2)$ and $(5, 5)$ are 5.

30. **(a)** $\frac{6}{5}$ **(b)** $-\frac{2}{3}$ **31.** 5 **32.** -1

33.

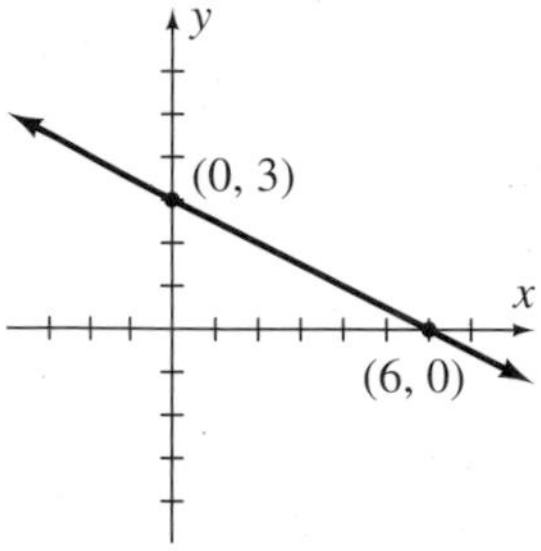

34.

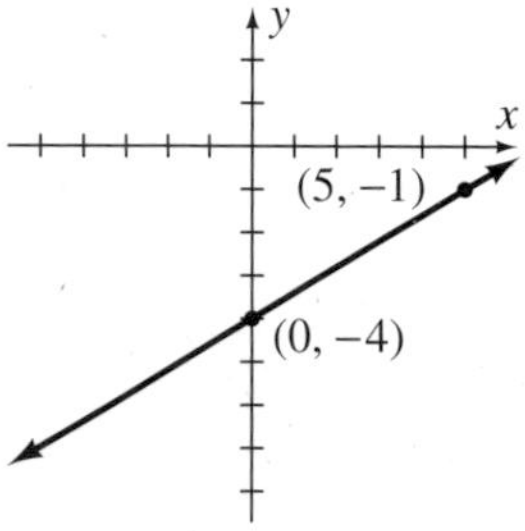

35.

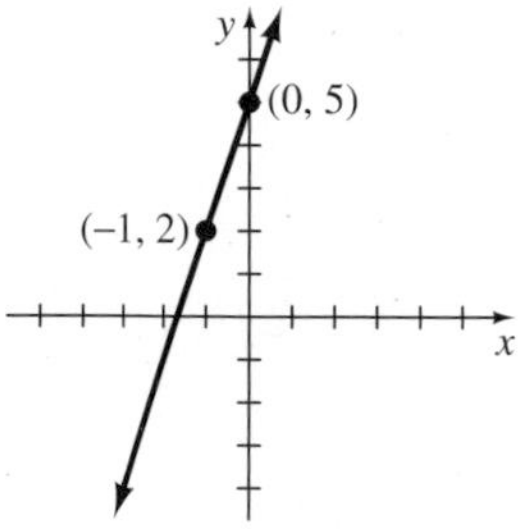

36.

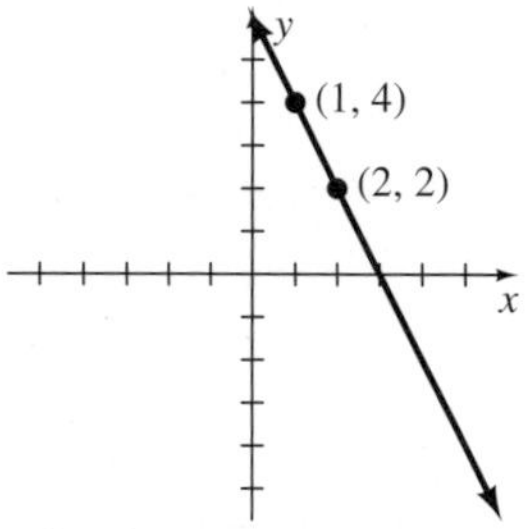

37. 316.8 ft **38.** 8 in. **39.** **(a)** $m = -4$ **(b)** $m = \frac{2}{7}$

40. $m = -\frac{5}{3}$ **41.** $m = -\frac{4}{5}$ **42.** $3x + 7y = 28$

43. $2x - 3y = 16$ **44.** $x + y = -2$ **45.** $7x + 4y = 1$

46. $x - y = -4$ **47.** $x - 2y = -8$ **48.** $2x - 3y = 14$

49. $4x + y = -29$ **50.** $y = \frac{3}{200}x - 600$ **51.** $y = \frac{1}{5}x - 20$

52. $y = 8x$ **53.** $y = 300x - 150$

54. **(a)** y axis **(b)** origin **(c)** origin **(d)** x axis

55.

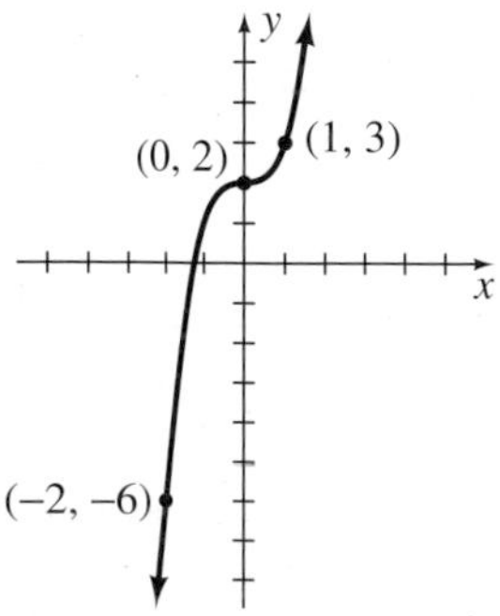

56.

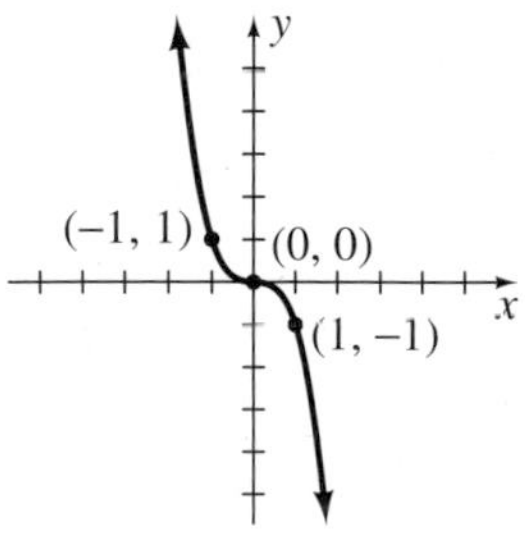

57.

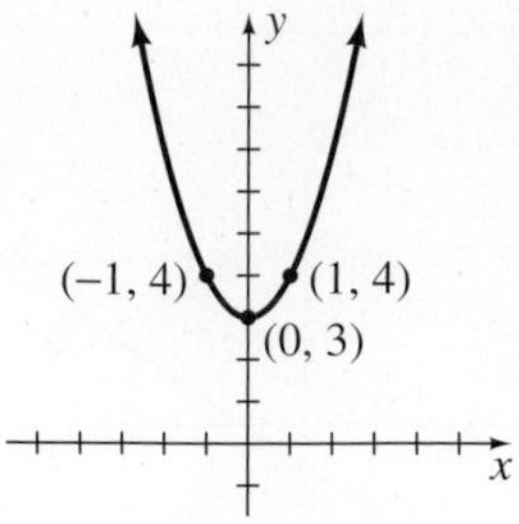

58.

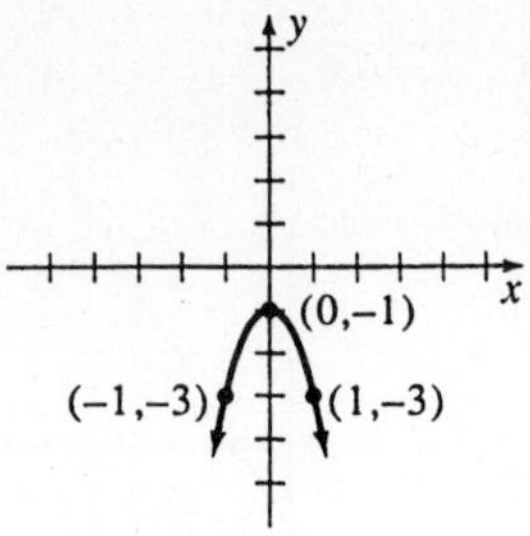

Chapter 7 Test (page 379)

1. $-\frac{6}{5}$ **2.** $\frac{3}{7}$ **3.** $\sqrt{58}$ **4.** $3x + 2y = 2$ **5.** $y = -\frac{1}{6}x + \frac{4}{3}$

6. $5x + 2y = -18$ **7.** $6x + y = 31$ **8.** Origin symmetry

9. x axis, y axis, and origin symmetry

10. x axis symmetry **11.** $\frac{7}{2}$ **12.** $\frac{9}{4}$ **13.** $\frac{10}{9}$

14. $-\frac{5}{8}$ **15.** 480 feet **16.** 6.7% **17.** 43 centimeters

18.

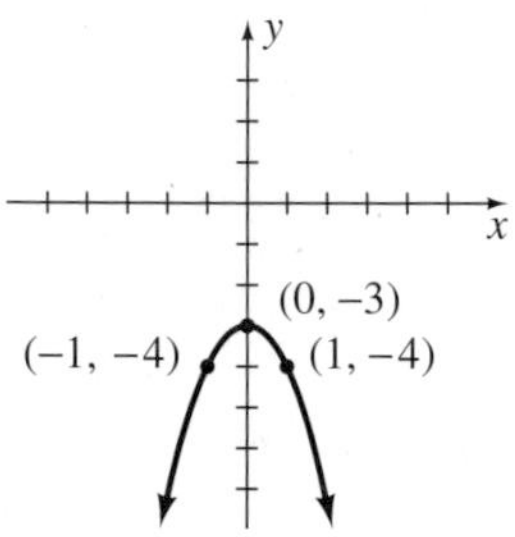

19.

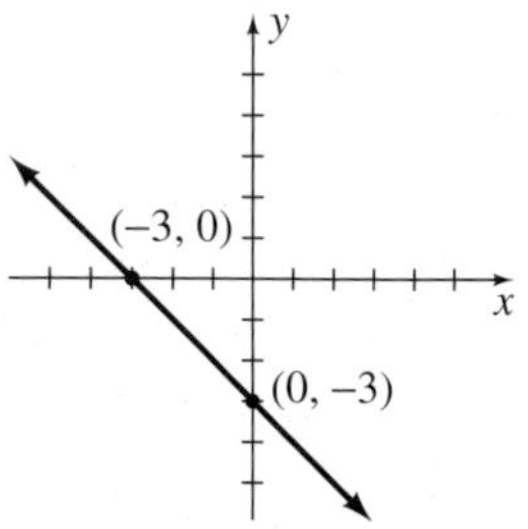

20.

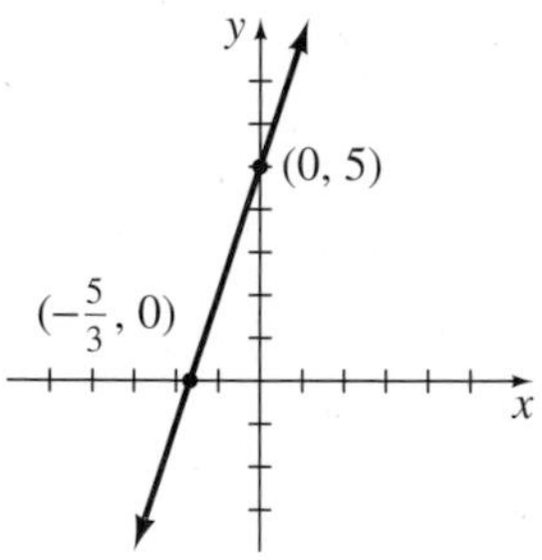

21.

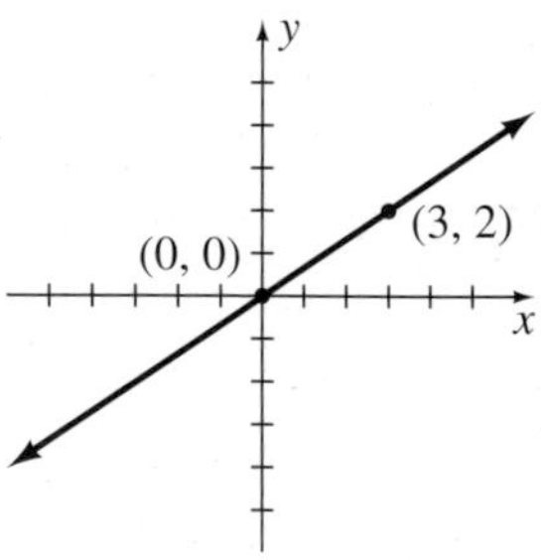

22.

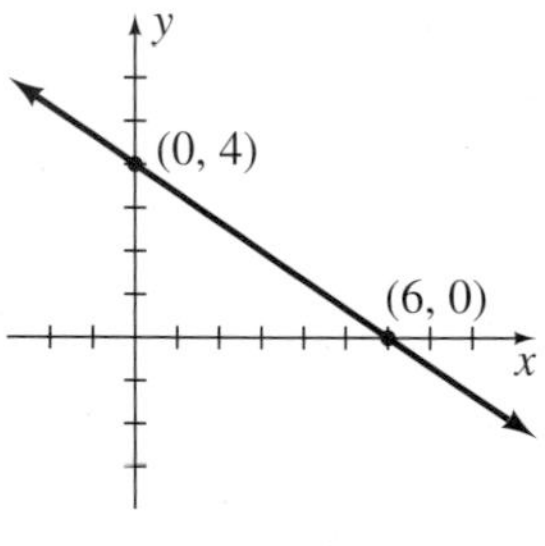

23.

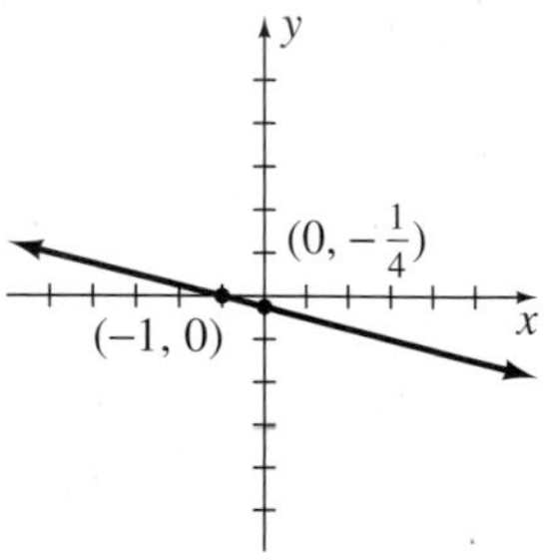

24.

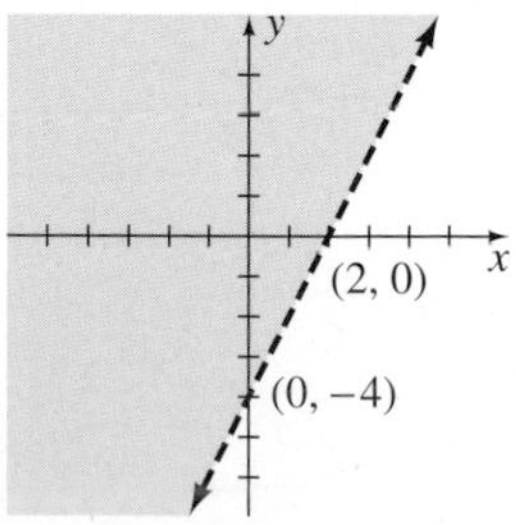

25.

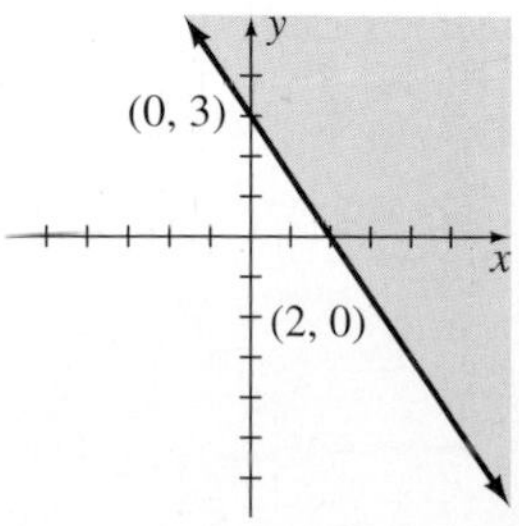

Chapter 8

Problem Set 8.1 (page 389)

1. Yes   **3.** No   **5.** Yes   **7.** Yes   **9.** No   **11.** Yes   **13.** Yes
15. $f(3) = -1; f(5) = -5; f(-2) = 9$
17. $g(3) = -20; g(-1) = -8; g(2a) = -8a^2 + 2a - 5$
19. $h(3) = \dfrac{5}{4}; h(4) = \dfrac{23}{12}; h\left(-\dfrac{1}{2}\right) = -\dfrac{13}{12}$
21. $f(5) = 3; f\left(\dfrac{1}{2}\right) = 0; f(23) = 3\sqrt{5}$
23. $-2a + 7, -2a + 3, -2a - 2h + 7$
25. $a^2 + 4a + 10, a^2 - 12a + 42,$
   $a^2 + 2ah + h^2 - 4a - 4h + 10$
27. $a^2 - 3a + 5, -a^2 - 9a - 13, -a^2 - a + 7$
29. $f(4) = 4; f(10) = 10; f(-3) = 9; f(-5) = 25$
31. $f(3) = 6; f(5) = 10; f(-3) = 6; f(-5) = 10$
33. $f(2) = 1; f(0) = 0; f\left(-\dfrac{1}{2}\right) = 0; f(-4) = -1$
35. 3   **37.** -7 **39.** $-2a - h + 4$ **41.** $6a + 3h - 1$
43. $3a^2 + 3ah + h^2 - 2a - h + 2$
45. $-\dfrac{2}{(a - 1)(a + h - 1)}$ **47.** $-\dfrac{2a + h}{a^2(a + h)^2}$
49. $D = \left\{x \mid x \geq \dfrac{4}{3}\right\}; R = \{f(x) \mid f(x) \geq 0\}$
51. $D = \{x \mid x \text{ is any real number}\}; R = \{f(x) \mid f(x) \geq -2\}$
53. $D = \{x \mid x \text{ is any real number}\};$
   $R = \{f(x) \mid f(x) \text{ is any nonnegative real number}\}$
55. $D = \{x \mid x \text{ is any nonnegative real number}\};$
   $R = \{f(x) \mid f(x) \text{ is any nonpositive real number}\}$
57. $D = \left\{x \mid x \geq \dfrac{5}{2}\right\}, R = \{f(x) \mid f(x) \geq 0\}$
59. $D = \{x \mid x \geq -4\}, R = \{f(x) \mid f(x) \geq -2\}$
61. $D = \{x \mid x \text{ is any real number}\}, R = \{f(x) \mid f(x) \leq -6\}$
63. $D = \{x \mid x \neq -2\}$
65. $D = \left\{x \mid x \neq \dfrac{1}{2} \text{ and } x \neq -4\right\}$
67. $D = \{x \mid x \neq 2 \text{ and } x \neq -2\}$
69. $D = \{x \mid x \neq -3 \text{ and } x \neq 4\}$
71. $D = \left\{x \mid x \neq -\dfrac{5}{2} \text{ and } x \neq \dfrac{1}{3}\right\}$
73. $D = \{x \mid x \text{ is any real number}\}$ **75.** $D = \left\{x \mid x \leq \dfrac{3}{4}\right\}$
77. $(-\infty, -4] \cup [4, \infty)$ **79.** $(-\infty, \infty)$
81. $(-\infty, -5] \cup [8, \infty)$ **83.** $\left(-\infty, -\dfrac{5}{2}\right] \cup \left[\dfrac{7}{4}, \infty\right)$
85. $[-1, 1]$ **87.** 30.40 **89.** $12.57; 28.27; 452.39; 907.92$
91. $48; 64; 48; 0$
93. $55; 60; 67.50; 75$ **95.** $125.66; 301.59; 804.25$

Problem Set 8.2 (page 396)

1.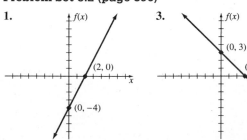

3.

5.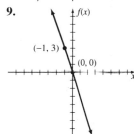

7.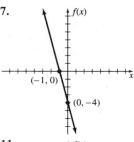

9.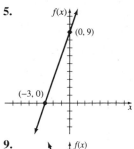

11.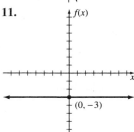

13.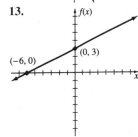

15.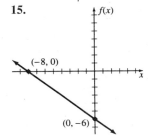

17. $f(x) = \dfrac{2}{3}x + \dfrac{11}{3}$ **19.** $f(x) = -x - 4$

21. $f(x) = -\dfrac{1}{5}x + \dfrac{21}{5}$

23. **(a)** 0.42

(b)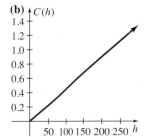

(c) Answers may vary.   **(d)** 1.01
25. $f(x) = 0.25x + 30$
27. $26; 30.50; 50; 60.50$
29. $f(p) = 0.8p; 7.60; 12; 60;$
   $10; 600$

33.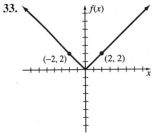

35.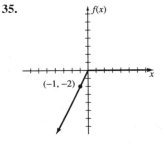

37.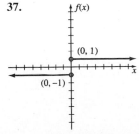

Problem Set 8.3 (page 405)

1.

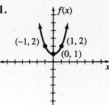

3.

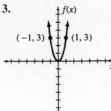

5.

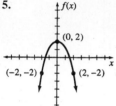

7.

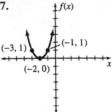

9.

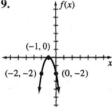

11.

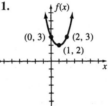

13.

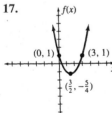

15.

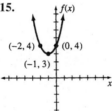

17.

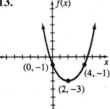

19.

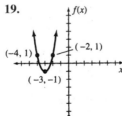

21.

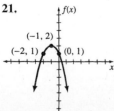

23.

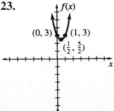

25.

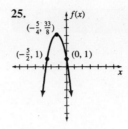

27.

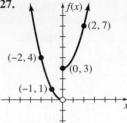

29.

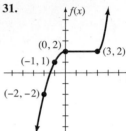

31.

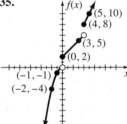

33.

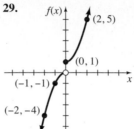

35.

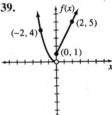

37.

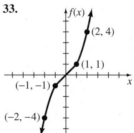

39.

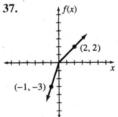

41.

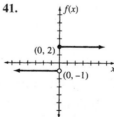

43.

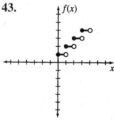

45.

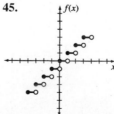

Problem Set 8.4 (page 414)

1.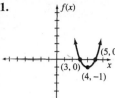

3.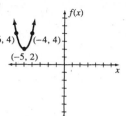

5.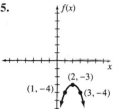

7.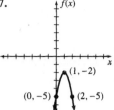

9.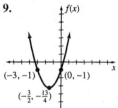

11.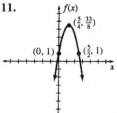

13.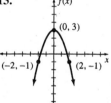

15.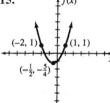

17.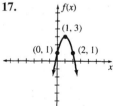

19.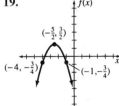

21. -2 and 2; $(0, -12)$ **23.** 0 and 2; $(1, -5)$
25. 3 and 5; $(4, -1)$ **27.** 6 and 8; $(7, -2)$
29. 4 and 6; $(5, 1)$ **31.** $7 + \sqrt{5}$ and $7 - \sqrt{5}$; $(7, 5)$

33. No x intercepts; $\left(\dfrac{9}{2}, -\dfrac{3}{4}\right)$

35. $\dfrac{1 + \sqrt{5}}{2}$ and $\dfrac{1 - \sqrt{5}}{2}$; $\left(\dfrac{1}{2}, 5\right)$ **37.** -11 and 8

39. 3 and 9 **41.** $2 - i\sqrt{7}$ and $2 + i\sqrt{7}$
43. 70 **45.** 144 feet   **47.** 25 and 25
49. 60 meters by 60 meters
51. 1100 subscribers at $\$13.75$ per month

Problem Set 8.5 (page 424)

1.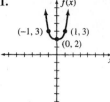

3.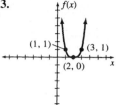

5.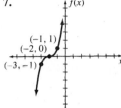

7.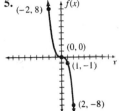

9.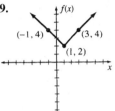

11.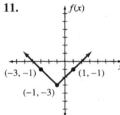

13.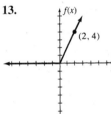

15.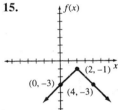

17.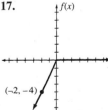

19.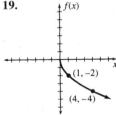

21.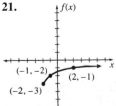

23.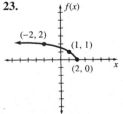

25.

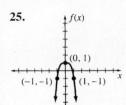

27.

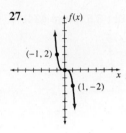

29.

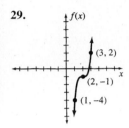

31. (a)

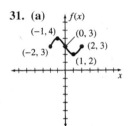

(c)

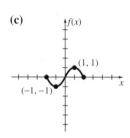

Problem Set 8.6 (page 431)

1. $(f + g)(x) = 8x - 2, D = \{\text{All reals}\}$;
$(f - g)(x) = -2x - 6, D = \{\text{All reals}\}$;
$(f \cdot g)(x) = 15x^2 - 14x - 8, D = \{\text{All reals}\}$;
$(f/g)(x) = \dfrac{3x - 4}{5x + 2}, D = \left\{\text{All reals except } -\dfrac{2}{5}\right\}$

3. $(f + g)(x) = x^2 - 7x + 3, D = \{\text{All reals}\}$;
$(f - g)(x) = x^2 - 5x + 5, D = \{\text{All reals}\}$;
$(f \cdot g)(x) = -x^3 + 5x^2 + 2x - 4, D = \{\text{All reals}\}$;
$(f/g)(x) = \dfrac{x^2 - 6x + 4}{-x - 1}, D = \{\text{All reals except } -1\}$

5. $(f + g)(x) = 2x^2 + 3x - 6, D = \{\text{All reals}\}$;
$(f - g)(x) = -5x + 4, D = \{\text{All reals}\}$;
$(f \cdot g)(x) = x^4 + 3x^3 - 10x^2 + x + 5, D = \{\text{All reals}\}$;
$(f/g)(x) = \dfrac{x^2 - x - 1}{x^2 + 4x - 5}, D = \{\text{All reals except } -5 \text{ and } 1\}$

7. $(f + g)(x) = \sqrt{x - 1} + \sqrt{x}, D = \{x|x \geq 1\}$;
$(f - g)(x) = \sqrt{x - 1} - \sqrt{x}, D = \{x|x \geq 1\}$;
$(f \cdot g)(x) = \sqrt{x^2 - x}, D = \{x|x \geq 1\}$;
$(f/g)(x) = \dfrac{\sqrt{x - 1}}{\sqrt{x}}, D = \{x|x \geq 1\}$

9. $(f \circ g)(x) = 6x - 2, D = \{\text{All reals}\}$;
$(g \circ f)(x) = 6x - 1, D = \{\text{All reals}\}$

11. $(f \circ g)(x) = 10x + 2, D = \{\text{All reals}\}$;
$(g \circ f)(x) = 10x - 5, D = \{\text{All reals}\}$

13. $(f \circ g)(x) = 3x^2 + 7, D = \{\text{All reals}\}$;
$(g \circ f)(x) = 9x^2 + 24x + 17, D = \{\text{All reals}\}$

15. $(f \circ g)(x) = 3x^2 + 9x - 16, D = \{\text{All reals}\}$;
$(g \circ f)(x) = 9x^2 - 15x, D = \{\text{All reals}\}$

17. $(f \circ g)(x) = \dfrac{1}{2x + 7}, D = \left\{x\Big|x \neq -\dfrac{7}{2}\right\}$;
$(g \circ f)(x) = \dfrac{7x + 2}{x}, D = \{x|x \neq 0\}$

19. $(f \circ g)(x) = \sqrt{3x - 3}, D = \{x|x \geq 1\}$;
$(g \circ f)(x) = 3\sqrt{x - 2} - 1, D = \{x|x \geq 2\}$

21. $(f \circ g)(x) = \dfrac{x}{2 - x}, D = \{x|x \neq 0 \text{ and } x \neq 2\}$;
$(g \circ f)(x) = 2x - 2, D = \{x|x \neq 1\}$

23. $(f \circ g)(x) = 2\sqrt{x - 1} + 1, D = \{x|x \geq 1\}$;
$(g \circ f)(x) = \sqrt{2x}, D = \{x|x \geq 0\}$

25. $(f \circ g)(x) = x, D = \{x|x \neq 0\}$;
$(g \circ f)(x) = x, D = \{x|x \neq 1\}$

27. 4; 50   **29.** 9; 0   **31.** $\sqrt{11}$; 5

Problem Set 8.7 (page 438)

1. $y = kx^3$ **3.** $A = klw$ **5.** $V = \dfrac{k}{P}$ **7.** $V = khr^2$

9. 24   **11.** $\dfrac{22}{7}$ **13.** $\dfrac{1}{2}$ **15.** 7   **17.** 6   **19.** 8   **21.** 96

23. 5 hours   **25.** 2 seconds   **27.** 24 days   **29.** 28

31. \$2400   **37.** 2.8 seconds   **39.** 1.4

Chapter 8 Review Problem Set (page 447)

1. 7; 4; 32   **2. (a)** -5 **(b)** $4a + 2h - 1$
(c) $-6a - 3h + 2$

3. $D = \{x| x \text{ is any real number}\}; R = \{f(x)| f(x) \geq 5\}$

4. $D = \left\{x\Big| x \neq \dfrac{1}{2}, x \neq -4\right\}$

5. $(-\infty, 2] \cup [5, \infty)$

6.

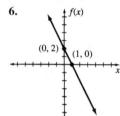

7.

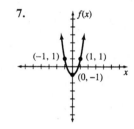

8.

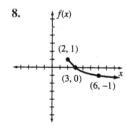

9.

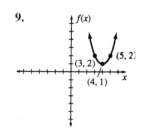

10.

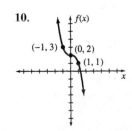

11.

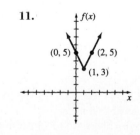

12.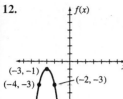

13.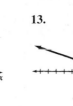

14.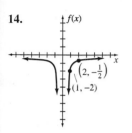

15.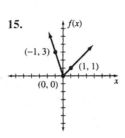

16.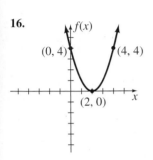

17.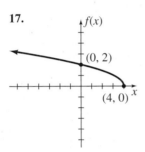

18.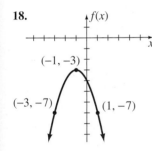

19.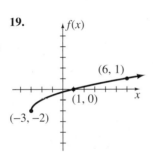

20.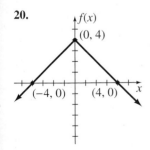

21.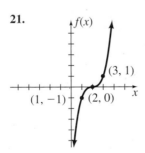

22.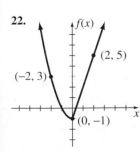

23.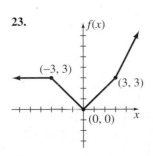

24. $x^2 - 2x$; $-x^2 + 6x + 6$; $2x^3 - 5x^2 - 18x - 9$;
$$\frac{2x + 3}{x^2 - 4x - 3}$$

25. $(f \circ g)(x) = -6x + 12$, $D = \{\text{All reals}\}$;
$(g \circ f)(x) = -6x + 25$, $D = \{\text{All reals}\}$

26. $(f \circ g)(x) = 25x^2 - 40x + 11$, $D = \{\text{All reals}\}$;
$(g \circ f)(x) = 5x^2 - 29$, $D = \{\text{All reals}\}$

27. $(f \circ g)(x) = \sqrt{x - 3}$, $D = \{x | x \geq 3\}$;
$(g \circ f)(x) = \sqrt{x - 5} + 2$, $D = \{x | x \geq 5\}$

28. $(f \circ g)(x) = \dfrac{1}{x^2 - x - 6}$, $D = \{x | x \neq 3 \text{ and } x \neq -2\}$;

$(g \circ f)(x) = \dfrac{1 - x - 6x^2}{x^2}$, $D = \{x | x \neq 0\}$

29. $(f \circ g)(x) = x - 1$, $D = \{x | x \geq 1\}$;
$(g \circ f)(x) = \sqrt{x^2 - 1}$, $D = \{x | x \leq -1 \text{ or } x \geq 1\}$

30. $(f \circ g)(x) = \dfrac{x + 2}{-3x - 5}$, $D = \left\{x | x \neq -2 \text{ and } x \neq -\dfrac{5}{3}\right\}$;

$(g \circ f)(x) = \dfrac{x - 3}{2x - 5}$, $D = \left\{x | x \neq 3 \text{ and } x \neq \dfrac{5}{2}\right\}$

31. $f(5) = 23$; $f(0) = -2$; $f(-3) = 13$
32. $f(g(6)) = -2$; $g(f(-2)) = 0$

33. $f(g(1)) = 1$; $g(f(-3)) = 5$ **34.** $f(x) = \dfrac{2}{3}x - \dfrac{16}{3}$

35. $f(x) = 2x + 15$ **36.** \$0.72
37. $f(x) = 0.7x$; \$45.50; \$33.60; \$10.85
38. -4 and 2; $(-1, -27)$ **39.** $3 \pm \sqrt{14}$; $(3, -14)$
40. No x intercepts; $(7, 3)$ **41.** 2 and 8
42. 112 students **43.** 9 **44.** 441 **45.** 128 pounds
46. 15 hours

Chapter 8 Test (page 449)

1. $\dfrac{11}{6}$ **2.** 11 **3.** $6a + 3h + 2$

4. $\left\{x | x \neq -4 \text{ and } x \neq \dfrac{1}{2}\right\}$ **5.** $\left\{x | x \leq \dfrac{5}{3}\right\}$

6. $(f + g)(x) = 2x^2 + 2x - 6$; $(f - g)(x) = -2x^2 + 4x + 4$;
$(f \cdot g)(x) = 6x^3 - 5x^2 - 14x + 5$

7. $(f \circ g)(x) = -21x - 2$ **8.** $(g \circ f)(x) = 8x^2 + 38x + 48$

9. $(f \circ g)(x) = \dfrac{3x}{2 - 2x}$ **10.** 12; 7 **11.** $f(x) = -\dfrac{5}{6}x - \dfrac{14}{3}$

12. $\{x | x \neq 0 \text{ and } x \neq 1\}$ **13.** 18; 10; 0

14. $(f \cdot g)(x) = x^3 + 4x^2 - 11x + 6$; $\left(\dfrac{f}{g}\right)(x) = x + 6$

15. 6 and 54 **16.** 15 **17.** -4 **18.** \$96
19. $s(c) = 1.35c$; \$17.55 **20.** -2 and 6; $(2, -64)$
21.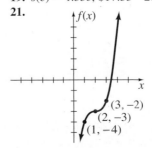

22.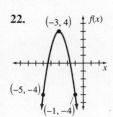

23.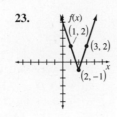

24.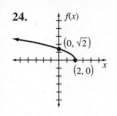

25.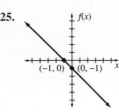

59. $\left(-\infty, -\dfrac{11}{5}\right) \cup (3, \infty)$ **60.** $[-4, 2]$ **61.** $\left[-\dfrac{5}{3}, 1\right]$

62. $(-8, 3)$ **63.** $(-\infty, 3)$ **64.** $\left[-\dfrac{9}{11}, \infty\right)$

65. $\left(-5, -\dfrac{1}{2}\right) \cup (2, \infty)$ **66.** $(-\infty, 3] \cup (7, \infty)$

67. $(-6, -3)$ **68.** $(-\infty, -3) \cup \left(0, \dfrac{1}{2}\right)$ **69.** 6

70. $(5, 8)$ **71.** $\dfrac{2}{5}$ **72.** $3x + 5y = -11$ **73.** 43; 24

74. $2\sqrt{x + 2} - 1; \sqrt{2x + 1}$

75. $(-\infty, -10] \cup [3, \infty)$ **76.** $-2a + 6 - h$

Chapters 1–8 Cumulative Review Problem Set (page 450)

1. 9   **2.** $\dfrac{9}{7}$ **3.** $\dfrac{1}{8}$ **4.** $\dfrac{1}{4}$ **5.** $\dfrac{72}{17}$ **6.** -0.4 **7.** $\dfrac{3}{2}$ **8.** 27

9. 4   **10.** 81   **11.** -8 **12.** -1 **13.** 2   **14.** 75   **15.** -31

16. $\dfrac{4x^2 y}{9}$ **17.** $\dfrac{3x + 7}{4x - 9}$ **18.** $\dfrac{2(x^2 - 2x + 4)}{x - 2}$

19. $\dfrac{y - 2}{x}$ **20.** $\dfrac{27}{8a^2}$ **21.** $\dfrac{x + 4}{x(x + 5)}$ **22.** $\dfrac{16x + 43}{90}$

23. $\dfrac{35a - 44b}{60a^2 b}$ **24.** $\dfrac{2}{x - 4}$ **25.** $\dfrac{2y - 3xy}{3x + 4xy}$

26. $\dfrac{5y^2 - 3xy^2}{x^2 y + 2x^2}$ **27.** $\dfrac{3a^2 - 2a + 1}{2a - 1}$ **28.** $-\dfrac{12}{x^3 y}$ **29.** $\dfrac{8y}{x^5}$

30. $-\dfrac{a^3}{9b}$ **31.** $\dfrac{2\sqrt{2}}{5}$ **32.** $\dfrac{2\sqrt{2}}{7}$ **33.** $4xy^3\sqrt{3xy}$

34. $2(\sqrt{5} + \sqrt{3})$ **35.** $2xy\sqrt[3]{6xy^2}$ **36.** $\sqrt[3]{2}$

37. $40 + 13i$ **38.** $2 + 14i$ **39.** $0 - \dfrac{5}{4}i$ **40.** $\dfrac{2}{5} + \dfrac{6}{5}i$

41. $\left\{-\dfrac{21}{16}\right\}$ **42.** $\left\{\dfrac{40}{3}\right\}$ **43.** $\{6\}$ **44.** $\left\{-\dfrac{5}{2}, 3\right\}$

45. $\left\{-3, \dfrac{5}{3}\right\}$ **46.** $\{-6, 0, 6\}$ **47.** $\left\{\dfrac{1 \pm 3\sqrt{5}}{3}\right\}$

48. $\left\{\dfrac{-5 \pm 4i\sqrt{2}}{2}\right\}$ **49.** $\left\{\dfrac{3 \pm i\sqrt{23}}{4}\right\}$ **50.** $\{-5, 7\}$

51. $\left\{-6, \dfrac{1}{2}\right\}$ **52.** $\{-5, 8\}$ **53.** $\{-17\}$

54. $\left\{\dfrac{-7 \pm \sqrt{41}}{2}\right\}$ **55.** $\{12\}$ **56.** $\{-3\}$

57. $\left\{\pm\dfrac{\sqrt{5}}{2}, \pm\dfrac{\sqrt{3}}{3}\right\}$ **58.** $\{\pm\sqrt{3}, 4\}$

77.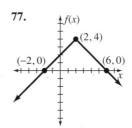

78.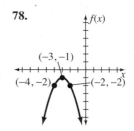

79.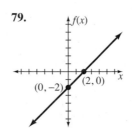

80.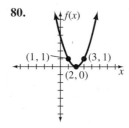

81.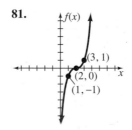

82.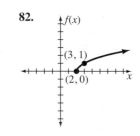

83. 17, 19, and 21   **84.** 14 nickels, 20 dimes, and 29 quarters
85. 48° and 132°   **86.** $600   **87.** $1700 at 8% and $2000 at 9%
88. 66 mph and 76 mph   **89.** 4 quarts   **90.** 69 or less
91. -3, 0, or 3   **92.** 1 inch
93. $1050 and $1400   **94.** 3 hours
95. Meat 420 calories; vegetable 210 calories; fruit 140 calories
96. $40   **97.** 10°, 60°, and 110°

Chapter 9

Problem Set 9.1 (page 457)

1. $Q: 4x + 3; R: 0$ **3.** $Q: 2x - 7; R: 0$ **5.** $Q: 3x - 4; R: 1$
7. $Q: 4x - 5; R: -2$ **9.** $Q: x^2 + 3x - 4; R: 0$
11. $Q: 3x^2 + 2x - 4; R: 0$ **13.** $Q: 5x^2 + x - 1; R: -4$
15. $Q: x^2 - x - 1; R: 8$ **17.** $Q: -x^2 + 4x - 2; R: 0$

19. $Q: -3x^2 + 4x - 2; R: 4$ **21.** $Q: 3x^2 + 6x + 10; R: 15$
23. $Q: 2x^3 - x^2 + 4x - 2; R: 0$
25. $Q: x^3 + 7x^2 + 21x + 56; R: 167$
27. $Q: x^3 - x + 5; R: 0$ **29.** $Q: x^3 + 2x^2 + 4x + 8; R: 0$
31. $Q: x^4 - x^3 + x^2 - x + 1; R: -2$

33. $Q: x^4 - x^3 + x^2 - x + 1; R: 0$
35. $Q: x^4 - x^3 - x^2 + x - 1; R: 0$
37. $Q: 4x^4 - 2x^3 + 2x - 3; R: -1$
39. $Q: 9x^2 - 3x + 2; R: -\dfrac{10}{3}$
41. $Q: 3x^3 - 3x^2 + 6x - 3; R: 0$

Problem Set 9.2 (page 462)

1. $f(3) = 9$ **3.** $f(-1) = -7$ **5.** $f(2) = 19$ **7.** $f(6) = 74$
9. $f(-2) = -65$ **11.** $f(-1) = -1$ **13.** $f(8) = -83$
15. $f(3) = 8751$ **17.** $f(-6) = 31$ **19.** $f(4) = -1113$
21. Yes **23.** No **25.** Yes **27.** Yes **29.** No **31.** Yes
33. Yes **35.** $f(x) = (x - 2)(x + 3)(x - 7)$
37. $f(x) = (x + 2)(4x - 1)(3x + 2)$
39. $f(x) = (x + 1)^2(x - 4)$
41. $f(x) = (x - 6)(x + 2)(x - 2)(x^2 + 4)$
43. $f(x) = (x + 5)(3x - 4)^2$ **45.** $k = 1$ or $k = -4$
47. $k = 6$ **49.** $f(c) > 0$ for all values of c
51. Let $f(x) = x^n - 1$. Because $(-1)^n = 1$ for all even positive
integral values of n, $f(-1) = 0$ and $x - (-1) = x + 1$ is a
factor.
53. (a) Let $f(x) = x^n - y^n$. Therefore $f(y) = y^n - y^n = 0$ and
$x - y$ is a factor of $f(x)$. (c) Let $f(x) = x^n + y^n$. Therefore
$f(-y) = (-y)^n + y^n = -y^n + y^n = 0$ when n is odd, and
$x - (-y) = x + y$ is a factor of $f(x)$.
57. $f(1 + i) = 2 + 6i$
61. (a) $f(4) = 137; f(-5) = 11; f(7) = 575$
  (c) $f(4) = -79; f(5) = -162; f(-3) = 110$

Problem Set 9.3 (page 471)

1. $\{-3, 1, 4\}$ **3.** $\left\{-1, -\dfrac{1}{3}, \dfrac{2}{5}\right\}$ **5.** $\left\{-2, -\dfrac{1}{4}, \dfrac{5}{2}\right\}$

7. $\{-3, 2\}$ **9.** $\{2, 1 \pm \sqrt{5}\}$ **11.** $\{-3, -2, -1, 2\}$

13. $\{-2, 3, -1 \pm 2i\}$ **15.** $\{1, \pm i\}$ **17.** $\left\{-\dfrac{5}{2}, 1, \pm\sqrt{3}\right\}$

19. $\left\{-2, \dfrac{1}{2}\right\}$ **27.** $\{-3, -1, 2\}$ **29.** $\left\{-\dfrac{5}{2}, \dfrac{1}{3}, 3\right\}$

31. 1 positive and 1 negative solution
33. 1 positive and 2 nonreal complex solutions
35. 1 negative and 2 positive solutions *or* 1 negative and 2 nonreal complex solutions
37. 5 positive solutions *or* 3 positive and 2 nonreal complex
solutions *or* 1 positive solution and 4 nonreal complex
solutions
39. 1 negative and 4 nonreal complex solutions
47. (a) $\{4, -3 \pm i\}$ (c) $\{-2, 6, 1 \pm \sqrt{3}\}$ (e) $\{12, 1 \pm i\}$

Problem Set 9.4 (page 481)

1. 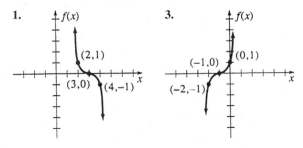   **3.**

5.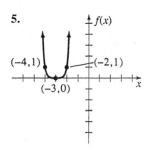

7.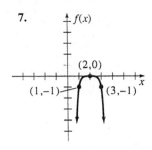

9.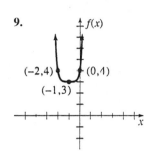

11.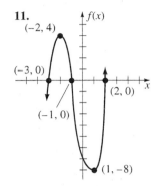

13. 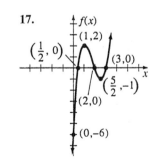   **15.**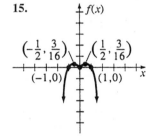

17. 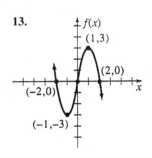   **19.**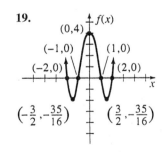

21. 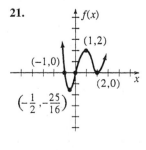   **23.**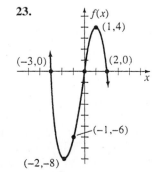

25.

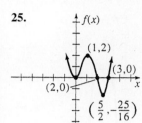

27.

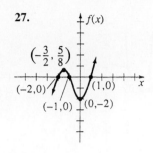

11.

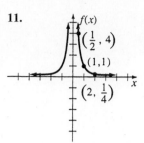

13.

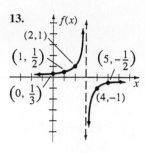

29.

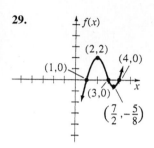

31.

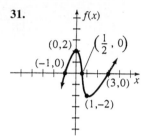

15.

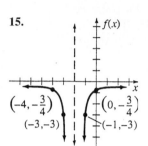

17.

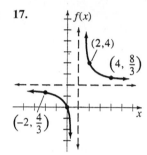

33.

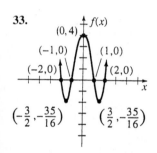

19.

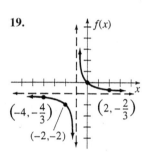

21.

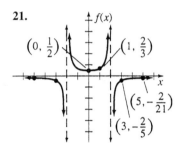

23.

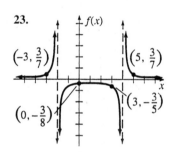

35. (a) −144   **(b)** −3, 6, and 8
    (c) $f(x) > 0$ for $\{x | x < -3$ or $6 < x < 8\}$; $f(x) < 0$ for
    $\{x | -3 < x < 6$ or $x > 8\}$
37. (a) −81   **(b)** −3 and 1   **(c)** $f(x) > 0$ for
    $\{x | x > 1\}$; $f(x) < 0$ for $\{x | x < -3$ or $-3 < x < 1\}$
39. (a) 0   **(b)** −4, 0, and 6
    (c) $f(x) > 0$ for $\{x | x < -4$ or $0 < x < 6$ or $x > 6\}$;
    $f(x) < 0$ for $\{x | -4 < x < 0\}$
41. (a) 0   **(b)** −3, 0, and 2
    (c) $f(x) > 0$ for $\{x | -3 < x < 0$ or $0 < x < 2\}$;
    $f(x) < 0$ for $\{x | x < -3$ or $x > 2\}$
43. 1.7 inches
47. (a) 1.6   **(c)** 6.1   **(e)** 2.5
53. (a) −2, 1, and 4; $f(x) > 0$ for $(-2, 1) \cup (4, \infty)$; $f(x) < 0$
    for $(-\infty, -2) \cup (1, 4)$
    (c) 2 and 3; $f(x) > 0$ for $(3, \infty)$; $f(x) < 0$ for $(2, 3) \cup$
    $(-\infty, -2)$ **(e)** −3, −1, and 2; $f(x) > 0$ for
    $(-\infty, -3) \cup (2, \infty)$; $f(x) < 0$ for $(-3, -1) \cup (-1, 2)$
55. (a) −3.3; (0.5, 3.1), (−1.9, 10.1)
    (c) −2.2, 2.2; (−1.4, −8.0), (0, −4.0), (1.4, −8.0)

Problem Set 9.5 (page 490)

1. V.A. $x = -3$; H.A. $y = 0$
3. V.A. $x = 1$; H.A. $y = 4$
5. V.A. $x = -3, x = -4$; H.A. $y = 0$
7. V.A. $x = -3, x = 3$; H.A. $y = 0$
9. V.A. none; H.A. $y = 5$

25.

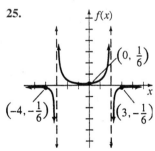

27.

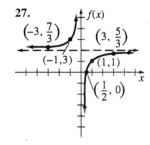

29.

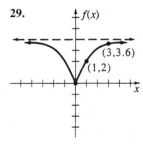

31.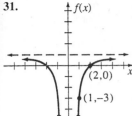

35. (a)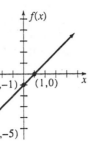

(b) 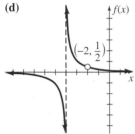 **(c)**

(d)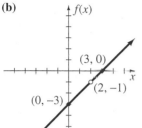

Problem Set 9.6 (page 498)

1. $y = x - 1$ **3.** $y = x + 2$ **5.** $y = 3x - 5$

7. 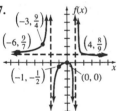 **9.**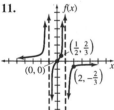

11. 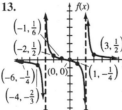 **13.**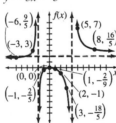

15. 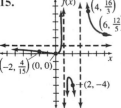 **17.**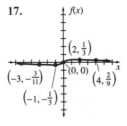

19. 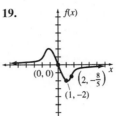 **21.**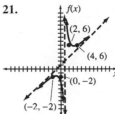

23. 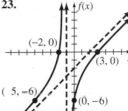 **25.**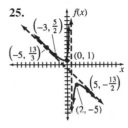

Chapter 9 Review Problem Set (page 503)

1. $Q: 3x^2 - x + 5$; $R: 3$ **2.** $Q: 5x^2 - 3x - 3$; $R: 16$
3. $Q: -2x^3 + 9x^2 - 38x + 151$; $R: -605$
4. $Q: -3x^3 - 9x^2 - 32x - 96$; $R: -279$ **5.** $f(1) = 1$
6. $f(-3) = -197$ **7.** $f(-2) = 20$ **8.** $f(8) = 0$
9. Yes **10.** No **11.** Yes **12.** Yes **13.** $\{-3, 1, 5\}$

14. $\left\{-\dfrac{7}{2}, -1, \dfrac{5}{4}\right\}$ **15.** $\{1, 2, 1 \pm 5i\}$ **16.** $\{-2, 3 \pm \sqrt{7}\}$

17. 2 positive and 2 negative solutions *or* 2 positive and 2 non-real complex solutions *or* 2 negative and 2 nonreal complex solutions *or* 4 nonreal complex solutions
18. 1 negative and 4 nonreal complex solutions

19. 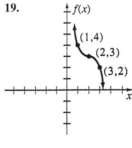 **20.**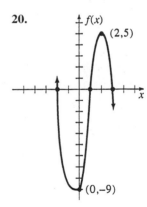

21. 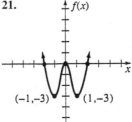 **22.**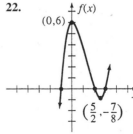

23.
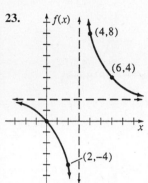

24.
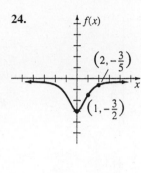

25.
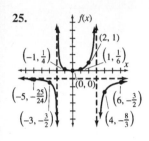

26.
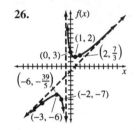

16. $-7, 0,$ and $\frac{2}{3}$ **17.** $x = -3$ **18.** $f(x) = 5$ or $y = 5$

19. y-axis symmetry **20.** Origin symmetry

21.
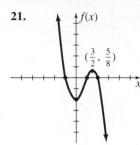

22.
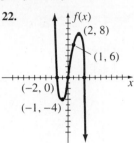

23.
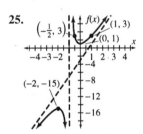

24.
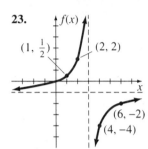

25.
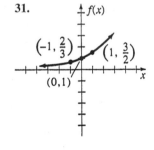

Chapter 9 Test (page 504)

1. Q: $3x^2 - 4x - 2$; R: 0
2. Q: $4x^3 + 8x^2 + 9x + 17$; R: 38 **3.** -24 **4.** 5
5. 39 **6.** No **7.** No **8.** Yes **9.** No **10.** $\{-4, 1, 3\}$

11. $\left\{-4, \dfrac{3 \pm \sqrt{17}}{4}\right\}$ **12.** $\{-3, 1, 3 \pm i\}$

13. $\left\{-4, 1, \dfrac{3}{2}\right\}$ **14.** $\left\{-\dfrac{5}{3}, 2\right\}$

15. 1 positive, 1 negative, and 2 nonreal complex solutions

Chapter 10

Problem Set 10.1 (page 512)

1. $\{6\}$ **3.** $\left\{\dfrac{3}{2}\right\}$ **5.** $\{7\}$ **7.** $\{5\}$ **9.** $\{1\}$ **11.** $\{-3\}$

13. $\left\{\dfrac{3}{2}\right\}$ **15.** $\left\{\dfrac{1}{5}\right\}$ **17.** $\{0\}$ **19.** $\{-1\}$ **21.** $\left\{\dfrac{5}{2}\right\}$

23. $\{3\}$ **25.** $\left\{\dfrac{1}{2}\right\}$

27.
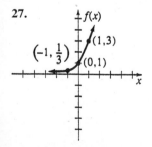

29.
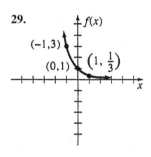

31.
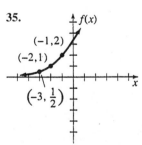

33.
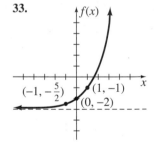

35.
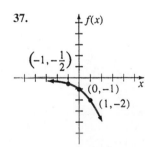

37.
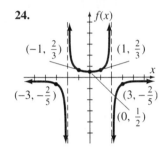

39.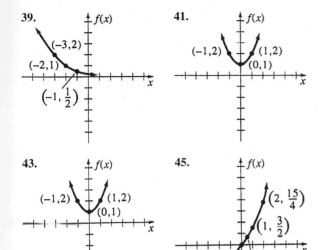

41.

43.

45.

51.

	4%	5%	6%	7%
Compounded annually	1480	1629	1791	1967
Compounded semiannually	1486	1639	1806	1990
Compounded quarterly	1489	1644	1814	2002
Compounded monthly	1490	1647	1819	2010
Compounded continuously	1492	1649	1822	2014

53.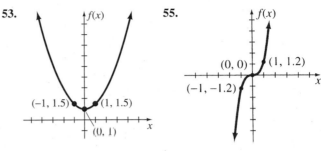

55.

Problem Set 10.2 (page 521)

1. (a) $1.55 (b) $4.17 (c) $2.33 (d) $2.28 (e) $21,900
(f) $246,342 (g) $658
3. $283.70 **5.** $659.74 **7.** $1251.16 **9.** $2234.77
11. $9676.41 **13.** $13,814.17 **15.** $567.63
17. $1422.36 **19.** $5715.30 **21.** $14,366.56
23. $26,656.96 **25.** 5.9% **27.** 8.06%
29. 8.25% compounded quarterly
31. 50 grams; 37 grams **33.** 2226; 3320; 7389
35. 2000 **37.** (a) 6.5 pounds per square inch
(c) 13.6 pounds per square inch

39.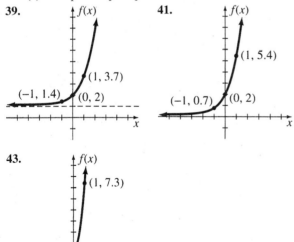

41.

43.

49.

	4%	5%	6%	7%
5 years	1221	1284	1350	1419
10 years	1492	1649	1822	2014
15 years	1822	2117	2460	2858
20 years	2226	2718	3320	4055
25 years	2718	3490	4482	5755

Problem Set 10.3 (page 531)

1. Yes **3.** No **5.** Yes **7.** Yes **9.** Yes
11. No **13.** No
15. (a) Domain of f: $\{1, 2, 5\}$; Range of f: $\{5, 9, 21\}$
(b) $f^{-1} = \{(5, 1), (9, 2), (21, 5)\}$
(c) Domain of f^{-1}: $\{5, 9, 21\}$; Range of f^{-1}: $\{1, 2, 5\}$
17. (a) Domain of f: $\{0, 2, -1, -2\}$;
Range of f: $\{0, 8, -1, -8\}$
(b) f^{-1}: $\{(0, 0), (8, 2), (-1, -1), (-8, -2)\}$
(c) Domain of f^{-1}: $\{0, 8, -1, -8\}$;
Range of f^{-1}: $\{0, 2, -1, -2\}$
27. No **29.** Yes **31.** No **33.** Yes **35.** Yes
37. $f^{-1}(x) = x + 4$ **39.** $f^{-1}(x) = \dfrac{-x - 4}{3}$
41. $f^{-1}(x) = \dfrac{12x + 10}{9}$ **43.** $f^{-1}(x) = -\dfrac{3}{2}x$
45. $f^{-1}(x) = x^2$ for $x \geq 0$ **47.** $f^{-1}(x) = \sqrt{x - 4}$ for $x \geq 4$
49. $f^{-1}(x) = \dfrac{1}{x - 1}$ for $x > 1$
51. $f^{-1}(x) = \dfrac{1}{3}x$ **53.** $f^{-1}(x) = \dfrac{x - 1}{2}$

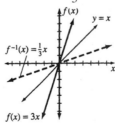

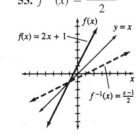

55. $f^{-1}(x) = \dfrac{x + 2}{x}$ for $x > 0$

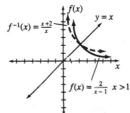

57. $f^{-1}(x) = \sqrt{x + 4}$ for $x \geq -4$

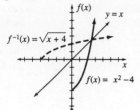

59. Increasing on $[0, \infty)$ and decreasing on $(-\infty, 0]$
61. Decreasing on $(-\infty, \infty)$
63. Increasing on $(-\infty, -2]$ and decreasing on $[-2, \infty)$
65. Increasing on $(-\infty, -4]$ and decreasing on $[-4, \infty)$

71. (a) $f^{-1}(x) = \dfrac{x + 9}{3}$ (c) $f^{-1}(x) = -x + 1$

(e) $f^{-1}(x) = -\dfrac{1}{5}x$

Problem Set 10.4 (page 540)

1. $\log_2 128 = 7$ **3.** $\log_5 125 = 3$ **5.** $\log_{10} 1000 = 3$

7. $\log_2 \left(\dfrac{1}{4}\right) = -2$ **9.** $\log_{10} 0.1 = -1$ **11.** $3^4 = 81$

13. $4^3 = 64$ **15.** $10^4 = 10,000$ **17.** $2^{-4} = \dfrac{1}{16}$

19. $10^{-3} = 0.001$ **21.** 4   **23.** 4   **25.** 3   **27.** $\dfrac{1}{2}$ **29.** 0

31. -1 **33.** 5   **35.** -5 **37.** 1   **39.** 0   **41.** $\{49\}$

43. $\{16\}$ **45.** $\{27\}$ **47.** $\left\{\dfrac{1}{8}\right\}$ **49.** $\{4\}$ **51.** 5.1293

53. 6.9657   **55.** 1.4037   **57.** 7.4512   **59.** 6.3219
61. -0.3791 **63.** 0.5766   **65.** 2.1531   **67.** 0.3949
69. $\log_b x + \log_b y + \log_b z$ **71.** $\log_b y - \log_b z$

73. $3 \log_b y + 4 \log_b z$ **75.** $\dfrac{1}{2} \log_b x + \dfrac{1}{3} \log_b y - 4 \log_b z$

77. $\dfrac{2}{3} \log_b x + \dfrac{1}{3} \log_b z$ **79.** $\dfrac{3}{2} \log_b x - \dfrac{1}{2} \log_b y$

81. $\log_b \left(\dfrac{x^2}{y^4}\right)$ **83.** $\log_b \left(\dfrac{xz}{y}\right)$ **85.** $\log_b \left(\dfrac{x^2 z^4}{z^3}\right)$

87. $\log_b \left(\dfrac{y^4 \sqrt{x}}{x}\right)$ **89.** $\left\{\dfrac{9}{4}\right\}$ **91.** $\{25\}$ **93.** $\{4\}$ **95.** $\{-2\}$

97. $\left\{-\dfrac{4}{3}\right\}$ **99.** $\left\{\dfrac{19}{8}\right\}$ **101.** $\{9\}$ **103.** $\varnothing$ **105.** $\{1\}$

Problem Set 10.5 (page 548)

1. 0.8597   **3.** 1.7179   **5.** 3.5071   **7.** -0.1373 **9.** -3.4685
11. 411.43   **13.** 90,095   **15.** 79.543   **17.** 0.048440
19. 0.0064150   **21.** 1.6094   **23.** 3.4843   **25.** 6.0638
27. -0.7765 **29.** -3.4609 **31.** 1.6034   **33.** 3.1346
35. 108.56   **37.** 0.48268   **39.** 0.035994
41.

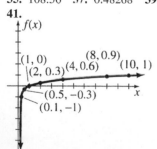

43.

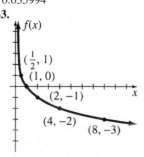

45.

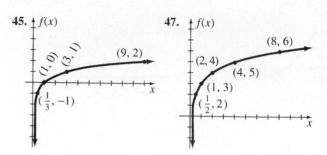

47.

49.

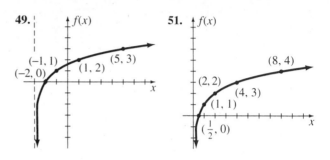

51.

53.

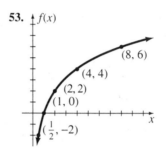

55. 0.36   **57.** 0.73   **59.** 23.10   **61.** 7.93

Problem Set 10.6 (page 556)

1. $\{2.33\}$ **3.** $\{2.56\}$ **5.** $\{5.43\}$ **7.** $\{4.18\}$ **9.** $\{0.12\}$
11. $\{3.30\}$ **13.** $\{4.57\}$ **15.** $\{1.79\}$ **17.** $\{3.32\}$ **19.** $\{2.44\}$

21. $\{4\}$ **23.** $\left\{\dfrac{19}{47}\right\}$ **25.** $\left\{\dfrac{-1 + \sqrt{33}}{4}\right\}$ **27.** $\{1\}$

29. $\{8\}$ **31.** $\{1, 10,000\}$ **33.** 5.322   **35.** 2.524   **37.** 0.339
39. -0.837 **41.** 3.194   **43.** 4.8 years   **45.** 17.3 years
47. 5.9%   **49.** 6.8 hours   **51.** 6100 feet   **53.** 3.5 hours
55. 6.7   **57.** Approximately 8 times   **65.** $\{1.13\}$
67. $x = \ln(y + \sqrt{y^2 + 1})$

Chapter 10 Review Problem (page 565)

1. 32   **2.** -125 **3.** 81   **4.** 3   **5.** -2 **6.** $\dfrac{1}{3}$ **7.** $\dfrac{1}{4}$

8. -5 **9.** 1   **10.** 12   **11.** $\{5\}$ **12.** $\left\{\dfrac{1}{9}\right\}$ **13.** $\left\{\dfrac{7}{2}\right\}$

14. $\{3.40\}$ **15.** $\{8\}$ **16.** $\left\{\dfrac{1}{11}\right\}$ **17.** $\{1.95\}$ **18.** $\{1.41\}$

19. $\{1.56\}$ **20.** $\{20\}$ **21.** $\{10^{100}\}$ **22.** $\{2\}$ **23.** $\left\{\dfrac{11}{2}\right\}$

24. $\{0\}$ **25.** 0.3680   **26.** 1.3222   **27.** 1.4313   **28.** 0.5634

29. (a) $\log_b x - 2 \log_b y$ (b) $\dfrac{1}{4} \log_b x + \dfrac{1}{2} \log_b y$

(c) $\frac{1}{2}\log_b x - 3\log_b y$ **30.** (a) $\log_b x^3 y^2$ (b) $\log_b\left(\dfrac{\sqrt{y}}{x^4}\right)$

(c) $\log_b\left(\dfrac{\sqrt{xy}}{z^2}\right)$ **31.** 1.585   **32.** 0.631

33. 3.789   **34.** −2.120

35. (a)

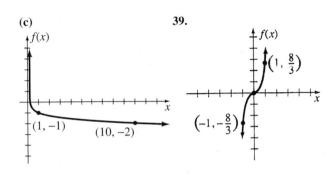

(b)

(c)

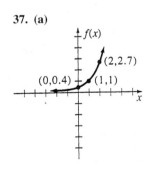

36. (a)

(b)

(c)

37. (a)

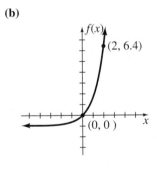

(b)

(c)

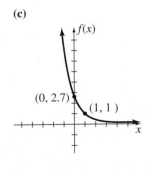

38. (a)

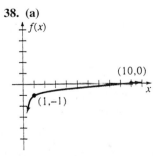

(b)

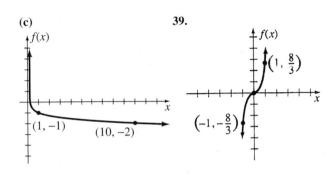

(c)

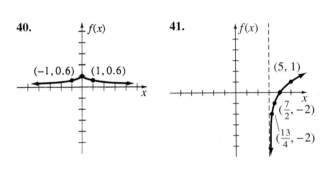

39.

40.

41.

42.

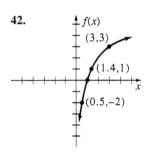

43. $11,166.48   **44.** $2642.13   **45.** $8985.50   **46.** Yes

47. No   **48.** Yes   **49.** Yes   **50.** $f^{-1}(x) = \dfrac{x-5}{4}$

51. $f^{-1}(x) = \dfrac{-x-7}{3}$ **52.** $f^{-1}(x) = \dfrac{6x+2}{5}$

53. $f^{-1}(x) = \sqrt{-2-x}$

54. Increasing on $(-\infty, 4]$ and decreasing on $[4, \infty)$

55. Increasing on $[3, \infty)$ **56.** Approximately 10.2 years

57. Approximately 28 years   **58.** Approximately 8.7%

59. 61,070; 67,493; 74,591   **60.** Approximately 4.8 hours

61. 133 grams   **62.** 8.1

Chapter 10 Test (page 567)

1. $\dfrac{1}{2}$ **2.** 1 **3.** 1 **4.** -1 **5.** $\{-3\}$ **6.** $\left\{-\dfrac{3}{2}\right\}$ **7.** $\left\{\dfrac{8}{3}\right\}$

8. $\{243\}$ **9.** $\{2\}$ **10.** $\left\{\dfrac{2}{5}\right\}$ **11.** 4.1919 **12.** 0.2031

13. 0.7325 **14.** $f^{-1}(x) = \dfrac{-6 - x}{3}$ **15.** $\{5.17\}$

16. $\{10.29\}$ **17.** 4.0069 **18.** $f^{-1}(x) = \dfrac{3}{2}x + \dfrac{9}{10}$

19. \$6342.08 **20.** 13.5 years **21.** 7.8 hours
22. 4813 grams

23.

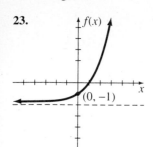

24.

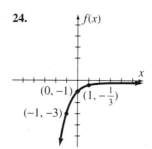

25.

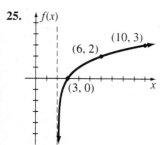

45. $8xy\sqrt{13x}$ **46.** $\dfrac{\sqrt{6xy}}{3y}$ **47.** $11\sqrt{6}$ **48.** $-\dfrac{169\sqrt{2}}{12}$

49. $-16\sqrt[3]{3}$ **50.** $\dfrac{-3\sqrt{2} - 2\sqrt{6}}{2}$

51. $\dfrac{6\sqrt{15} - 3\sqrt{35} - 6 + \sqrt{21}}{5}$ **52.** 0.021 **53.** 300

54. 0.0003 **55.** $32 + 22i$ **56.** $-17 + i$ **57.** $0 - \dfrac{5}{4}i$

58. $-\dfrac{19}{53} + \dfrac{40}{53}i$ **59.** $-\dfrac{10}{3}$ **60.** $\dfrac{4}{7}$ **61.** $2\sqrt{13}$

62. $5x - 4y = 19$ **63.** $4x + 3y = -18$

64. $2x + 3y = 29$ **65.** $y = -\dfrac{3}{4}x - 3$ **66.** $x = -2$

67.

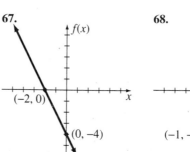

68.

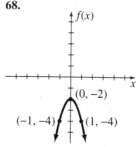

69.

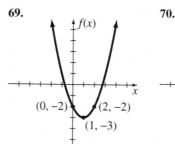

70.

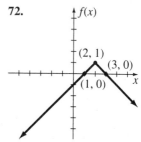

71.

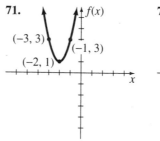

72.

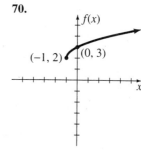

Chapters 1–10 Cumulative Review Problem Set (page 568)

1. -6 **2.** -8 **3.** $\dfrac{13}{24}$ **4.** 56 **5.** $\dfrac{13}{6}$ **6.** $-90\sqrt{2}$

7. $2x + 5\sqrt{x} - 12$ **8.** $-18 + 22\sqrt{3}$

9. $2x^3 + 11x^2 - 14x + 4$ **10.** $\dfrac{x + 4}{x(x + 5)}$ **11.** $\dfrac{16x^2}{27y}$

12. $\dfrac{16x + 43}{90}$ **13.** $\dfrac{35a - 44b}{60a^2b}$ **14.** $\dfrac{2}{x - 4}$

15. $2x^2 - x - 4$ **16.** $\dfrac{5y^2 - 3xy^2}{x^2y + 2x^2}$ **17.** $\dfrac{2y - 3xy}{3x + 4xy}$

18. $\dfrac{(2n - 5)(n + 3)}{(n - 2)(3n + 13)}$ **19.** $\dfrac{3a^2 - 2a + 1}{2a - 1}$

20. $(5x - 2)(4x + 3)$ **21.** $2(2x + 3)(4x^2 - 6x + 9)$
22. $(2x + 3)(2x - 3)(x + 2)(x - 2)$
23. $4x(3x + 2)(x - 5)$ **24.** $(y - 6)(x + 3)$

25. $(5 - 3x)(2 + 3x)$ **26.** $\dfrac{81}{16}$ **27.** 4 **28.** $-\dfrac{3}{4}$

29. -0.3 **30.** $\dfrac{1}{81}$ **31.** $\dfrac{21}{16}$ **32.** $\dfrac{9}{64}$ **33.** 72 **34.** 6

35. -2 **36.** $\dfrac{-12}{x^3y}$ **37.** $\dfrac{8y}{x^5}$ **38.** $-\dfrac{a^3}{9b}$ **39.** $4\sqrt{5}$

40. $-6\sqrt{6}$ **41.** $\dfrac{5\sqrt{3}}{9}$ **42.** $\dfrac{2\sqrt{3}}{3}$ **43.** $2\sqrt[3]{7}$ **44.** $\dfrac{\sqrt[3]{6}}{2}$

73.

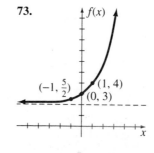

74.

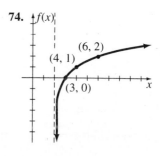

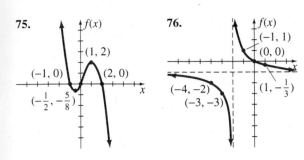

75. (graph)

76. (graph)

77. $(g \circ f)(x) = 2x^2 - 13x + 20$; $(f \circ g)(x) = 2x^2 - x - 4$

78. $f^{-1}(x) = \dfrac{x + 7}{3}$ **79.** $f^{-1}(x) = -2x + \dfrac{4}{3}$

80. $k = -3$ **81.** $y = 1$ **82.** 12 cubic centimeters

83. $\left\{-\dfrac{21}{16}\right\}$ **84.** $\left\{\dfrac{40}{3}\right\}$ **85.** $\{6\}$ **86.** $\left\{-\dfrac{5}{2}, 3\right\}$

87. $\left\{0, \dfrac{7}{3}\right\}$ **88.** $\{-6, 0, 6\}$ **89.** $\left\{-\dfrac{5}{6}, \dfrac{2}{5}\right\}$

90. $\left\{-3, 0, \dfrac{3}{2}\right\}$ **91.** $\{\pm 1, \pm 3i\}$ **92.** $\{-5, 7\}$ **93.** $\{-29, 0\}$

94. $\left\{\dfrac{7}{2}\right\}$ **95.** $\{12\}$ **96.** $\{-3\}$ **97.** $\left\{\dfrac{1 \pm 3\sqrt{5}}{3}\right\}$

98. $\left\{\dfrac{-5 \pm 4i\sqrt{2}}{2}\right\}$ **99.** $\left\{\dfrac{3 \pm i\sqrt{23}}{4}\right\}$

100. $\left\{\dfrac{3 \pm \sqrt{3}}{3}\right\}$ **101.** $\{1 \pm \sqrt{34}\}$

102. $\left\{\pm\dfrac{\sqrt{5}}{2}, \pm\dfrac{\sqrt{3}}{3}\right\}$ **103.** $\left\{\dfrac{-5 \pm i\sqrt{15}}{4}\right\}$

104. $\{-4, 1, 7\}$ **105.** $\left\{-\dfrac{1}{2}, \dfrac{5}{3}, 2\right\}$ **106.** $\left\{\dfrac{3}{2}\right\}$

107. $\{81\}$ **108.** $\{4\}$ **109.** $\{6\}$ **110.** $\left\{\dfrac{1}{5}\right\}$

111. $(-\infty, 3)$ **112.** $(-\infty, 50]$

113. $\left(-\infty, -\dfrac{11}{5}\right) \cup (3, \infty)$ **114.** $\left(-\dfrac{5}{3}, 1\right)$

115. $\left[-\dfrac{9}{11}, \infty\right)$ **116.** $[-4, 2]$

117. $\left(-\infty, \dfrac{1}{3}\right) \cup (4, \infty)$ **118.** $(-8, 3)$

119. $(-\infty, 3] \cup (7, \infty)$ **120.** $(-6, -3)$
121. 17, 19, and 21   **122.** 14 nickels, 20 dimes, and 29 quarters
123. 48° and 132°   **124.** $600
125. $1700 at 8% and $2000 at 9%
126. 66 miles per hour and 76 miles per hour
127. 4 quarts   **128.** 69 or less   **129.** -3, 0, or 3
130. 1-inch strip   **131.** $1050 and $1400   **132.** 3 hours

Chapter 11

Problem Set 11.1 (page 578)

1. $\{(3, 2)\}$ **3.** $\{(-2, 1)\}$ **5.** Dependent   **7.** $\{(4, -3)\}$
9. Inconsistent   **11.** $\{(7, 9)\}$ **13.** $\{(-4, 7)\}$ **15.** $\{(6, 3)\}$
17. $a = -3$ and $b = -4$

19. $\left\{\left(k, \dfrac{2}{3}k - \dfrac{4}{3}\right)\right\}$, a dependent system

21. $u = 5$ and $t = 7$ **23.** $\{(2, -5)\}$

25. $\varnothing$, an inconsistent system   **27.** $\left\{\left(-\dfrac{3}{4}, -\dfrac{6}{5}\right)\right\}$

29. $\{(3, -4)\}$ **31.** $\{(2, 8)\}$ **33.** $\{(-1, -5)\}$

35. $\varnothing$, an inconsistent system   **37.** $a = 2$ and $b = -\dfrac{1}{3}$

39. $s = -6$ and $t = 12$ **41.** $\left\{\left(-\dfrac{1}{2}, \dfrac{1}{3}\right)\right\}$

43. $\left\{\left(\dfrac{3}{4}, -\dfrac{2}{3}\right)\right\}$ **45.** $\{(-4, 2)\}$ **47.** $\{(5, 5)\}$

49. $\varnothing$, an inconsistent system   **51.** $\{(12, -24)\}$
53. $t = 8$ and $u = 3$ **55.** $\{(200, 800)\}$ **57.** $\{(400, 800)\}$
59. $\{(3.5, 7)\}$ **61.** 17 and 36   **63.** 15°, 75°   **65.** 72
67. 12   **69.** 8 single rooms and 15 double rooms
71. 2500 student tickets and 500 nonstudent tickets
73. $500 at 4% and $1500 at 6%
75. 3 miles per hour   **77.** $22.00
79. 30 five-dollar bills and 18 ten-dollar bills

85. $\{(4, 6)\}$ **87.** $\{(2, -3)\}$ **89.** $\left\{\left(\dfrac{1}{4}, -\dfrac{2}{3}\right)\right\}$

Problem Set 11.2 (page 587)

1. $\{(-4, -2, 3)\}$ **3.** $\{(-2, 5, 2)\}$ **5.** $\{(4, -1, -2)\}$
7. $\{(3, 1, 2)\}$ **9.** $\{(-1, 3, 5)\}$ **11.** $\{(-2, -1, 3)\}$
13. $\{(0, 2, 4)\}$ **15.** $\{(4, -1, -2)\}$ **17.** $\{(-4, 0, -1)\}$
19. $\{(2, 2, -3)\}$
21. 4 pounds of pecans, 4 pounds of almonds, and 12 pounds of peanuts
23. 7 nickels, 13 dimes, and 22 quarters
25. 40°, 60°, and 80°
27. $500 at 4%, $1000 at 5%, and $1500 at 6%
29. 50 of type A, 75 of type B, and 150 of type C

Problem Set 11.3 (page 596)

1. Yes   **3.** Yes   **5.** No   **7.** No   **9.** Yes   **11.** $\{(-1, -5)\}$
13. $\{(3, -6)\}$ **15.** $\varnothing$ **17.** $\{(-2, -9)\}$ **19.** $\{(-1, -2, 3)\}$
21. $\{(3, -1, 4)\}$ **23.** $\{(0, -2, 4)\}$
25. $\{(-7k + 8, -5k + 7, k)\}$ **27.** $\{(-4, -3, -2)\}$
29. $\{(4, -1, -2)\}$ **31.** $\{(1, -1, 2, -3)\}$
33. $\{(2, 1, 3, -2)\}$ **35.** $\{(-2, 4, -3, 0)\}$
37. $\varnothing$ **39.** $\{(-3k + 5, -1, -4k + 2, k)\}$
41. $\{(-3k + 9, k, 2, -3)\}$ **45.** $\{(17k - 6, 10k - 5, k)\}$

47. $\left\{\left(-\dfrac{1}{2}k + \dfrac{34}{11}, \dfrac{1}{2}k - \dfrac{5}{11}, k\right)\right\}$ **49.** $\varnothing$

Problem Set 11.4 (page 605)

1. 22   **3.** -29 **5.** 20   **7.** 5   **9.** -2 **11.** $-\dfrac{2}{3}$ **13.** -25
15. 58   **17.** 39   **19.** -12 **21.** -41 **23.** -8 **25.** 1088

27. -140 **29.** 81 **31.** 146 **33.** Property 11.3
35. Property 11.2 **37.** Property 11.4 **39.** Property 11.3
41. Property 11.5

Problem Set 11.5 (page 611)

1. $\{(1, 4)\}$ **3.** $\{(3, -5)\}$ **5.** $\{(2, -1)\}$ **7.** $\varnothing$

9. $\left\{\left(-\dfrac{1}{4}, \dfrac{2}{3}\right)\right\}$ **11.** $\left\{\left(\dfrac{2}{17}, \dfrac{52}{17}\right)\right\}$ **13.** $\{(9, -2)\}$

15. $\left\{\left(2, -\dfrac{5}{7}\right)\right\}$ **17.** $\{(0, 2, -3)\}$ **19.** $\{(2, 6, 7)\}$

21. $\{(4, -4, 5)\}$ **23.** $\{(-1, 3, -4)\}$

25. Infinitely many solutions **27.** $\left\{\left(-2, \dfrac{1}{2}, -\dfrac{2}{3}\right)\right\}$

29. $\left\{\left(3, \dfrac{1}{2}, -\dfrac{1}{3}\right)\right\}$ **31.** $(-4, 6, 0)$ **37.** $(0, 0, 0)$

39. Infinitely many solutions

Problem Set 11.6 (page 618)

1. $\dfrac{4}{x - 2} + \dfrac{7}{x + 1}$ **3.** $\dfrac{3}{x + 1} - \dfrac{5}{x - 1}$

5. $\dfrac{1}{3x - 1} + \dfrac{6}{2x + 3}$ **7.** $\dfrac{2}{x - 1} + \dfrac{3}{x + 2} - \dfrac{4}{x - 3}$

9. $\dfrac{-1}{x} + \dfrac{2}{2x - 1} - \dfrac{3}{4x + 1}$ **11.** $\dfrac{2}{x - 2} + \dfrac{5}{(x - 2)^2}$

13. $\dfrac{4}{x} + \dfrac{7}{x^2} - \dfrac{10}{x + 3}$ **15.** $\dfrac{-3}{x^2 + 1} - \dfrac{2}{x - 4}$

17. $\dfrac{3}{x + 2} - \dfrac{2}{(x + 2)^2} + \dfrac{1}{(x + 2)^3}$

19. $\dfrac{2}{x} + \dfrac{3x + 5}{x^2 - x + 3}$ **21.** $\dfrac{2x}{x^2 + 1} + \dfrac{3 - x}{(x^2 + 1)^2}$

Chapter 11 Review Problem Set (page 623)

1. $\{(3, -7)\}$ **2.** $\{(-1, -3)\}$ **3.** $\{(0, -4)\}$

4. $\left\{\left(\dfrac{23}{3}, -\dfrac{14}{3}\right)\right\}$ **5.** $\{(4, -6)\}$ **6.** $\left\{\left(-\dfrac{6}{7}, -\dfrac{15}{7}\right)\right\}$

7. $\{(-1, 2, -5)\}$ **8.** $\{(2, -3, -1)\}$ **9.** $\{(5, -4)\}$
10. $\{(2, 7)\}$ **11.** $\{(-2, 2, -1)\}$ **12.** $\{(0, -1, 2)\}$
13. $\{(-3, -1)\}$ **14.** $\{(4, 6)\}$ **15.** $\{(2, -3, -4)\}$
16. $\{(-1, 2, -5)\}$ **17.** $\{(5, -5)\}$ **18.** $\{(-12, 12)\}$

19. $\left\{\left(\dfrac{5}{7}, \dfrac{4}{7}\right)\right\}$ **20.** $\{(-10, -7)\}$ **21.** $\{(1, 1, -4)\}$

22. $\{(-4, 0, 1)\}$ **23.** $\varnothing$ **24.** $\{(-2, -4, 6)\}$ **25.** -34
26. 13 **27.** -40 **28.** 16 **29.** 51 **30.** 125

31. $6\dfrac{2}{3}$ quarts of the 1% milk and $3\dfrac{1}{3}$ quarts of the 4% milk

32. 7 centimeters by 21 centimeters
33. \$1200 at 1% and \$3000 at 1.5%
34. 5 five-dollar bills and 25 one-dollar bills
35. 30 review problems and 80 new material problems
36. \$900 at 4% and \$1600 at 6%
37. 20 nickels, 32 dimes, and 54 quarters
38. 24 five-dollar bills, 30 ten-dollar bills, 10 twenty-dollar bills
39. $40°, 60°, 80°$ **40.** $25°, 45°,$ and $110°$
41. \$2100 on Bank of US; \$1600 on Community Bank; and \$2700 on First National
42. 6 inches, 12 inches, 15 inches

Chapter 11 Test (page 625)

1. III **2.** I **3.** III **4.** II **5.** 8 **6.** $-\dfrac{7}{12}$ **7.** -18

8. 112 **9.** Infinitely many **10.** $\{(-2, 4)\}$ **11.** $\{(3, -1)\}$

12. $x = -12$ **13.** $y = -\dfrac{13}{11}$ **14.** $x = 14$ **15.** $y = 13$

16. Infinitely many **17.** None **18.** $\left\{\left(\dfrac{11}{5}, 6, -3\right)\right\}$

19. $\{(-2, -1, 0)\}$ **20.** $x = 1$ **21.** $y = 4$ **22.** 2 liters
23. 30 express washes **24.** 5 batches of cream puffs, 4 batches of eclairs, and 10 batches of Danish rolls
25. $100°, 45°,$ and $35°$

Chapter 12

Problem Set 12.1 (page 632)

1. $\begin{bmatrix} 3 & -5 \\ 8 & 3 \end{bmatrix}$ **3.** $\begin{bmatrix} -2 & 21 \\ -7 & 2 \end{bmatrix}$ **5.** $\begin{bmatrix} -2 & 1 \\ -3 & 19 \end{bmatrix}$

7. $\begin{bmatrix} -1 & -5 \\ 2 & 3 \end{bmatrix}$ **9.** $\begin{bmatrix} -12 & -14 \\ -18 & -20 \end{bmatrix}$ **11.** $\begin{bmatrix} 2 & -11 \\ -7 & 0 \end{bmatrix}$

13. $AB = \begin{bmatrix} 4 & -6 \\ 8 & -12 \end{bmatrix}, BA = \begin{bmatrix} -5 & 5 \\ 3 & -3 \end{bmatrix}$

15. $AB = \begin{bmatrix} -5 & -18 \\ -4 & 42 \end{bmatrix}, BA = \begin{bmatrix} 19 & -39 \\ -16 & 18 \end{bmatrix}$

17. $AB = \begin{bmatrix} 14 & -28 \\ 7 & -14 \end{bmatrix}, BA = \begin{bmatrix} 0 & 0 \\ 0 & 0 \end{bmatrix}$

19. $AB = \begin{bmatrix} -14 & -7 \\ -12 & -1 \end{bmatrix}, BA = \begin{bmatrix} -2 & -3 \\ -32 & -13 \end{bmatrix}$

21. $AB = \begin{bmatrix} 1 & 0 \\ 0 & 1 \end{bmatrix}, BA = \begin{bmatrix} 1 & 0 \\ 0 & 1 \end{bmatrix}$

23. $AB = \begin{bmatrix} 0 & -\dfrac{5}{3} \\ \dfrac{17}{6} & -3 \end{bmatrix}, BA = \begin{bmatrix} 0 & -\dfrac{17}{6} \\ \dfrac{5}{3} & -3 \end{bmatrix}$

25. $AB = \begin{bmatrix} 1 & 0 \\ 0 & 1 \end{bmatrix}, BA = \begin{bmatrix} 1 & 0 \\ 0 & 1 \end{bmatrix}$

27. $AB = \begin{bmatrix} 3 & -2 \\ 4 & 5 \end{bmatrix}, BA = \begin{bmatrix} 5 & 4 \\ -2 & 3 \end{bmatrix}$

29. $AD = \begin{bmatrix} 1 & 1 \\ 9 & 9 \end{bmatrix}, DA = \begin{bmatrix} 3 & 7 \\ 3 & 7 \end{bmatrix}$

49. $A^2 = \begin{bmatrix} -1 & -4 \\ 8 & 7 \end{bmatrix}, A^3 = \begin{bmatrix} -9 & -11 \\ 22 & 13 \end{bmatrix}$

Problem Set 12.2 (page 639)

1. $\begin{bmatrix} 3 & -7 \\ -2 & 5 \end{bmatrix}$ **3.** $\begin{bmatrix} -5 & 8 \\ 2 & -3 \end{bmatrix}$ **5.** $\begin{bmatrix} \dfrac{2}{5} & \dfrac{1}{5} \\ \dfrac{3}{10} & \dfrac{1}{10} \end{bmatrix}$

7. Does not exist **9.** $\begin{bmatrix} -\dfrac{5}{7} & \dfrac{2}{7} \\ -\dfrac{4}{7} & \dfrac{3}{7} \end{bmatrix}$ **11.** $\begin{bmatrix} -\dfrac{3}{5} & \dfrac{1}{5} \\ 1 & 0 \end{bmatrix}$

13. $\begin{bmatrix} -\dfrac{4}{5} & \dfrac{3}{5} \\ \dfrac{1}{5} & -\dfrac{2}{5} \end{bmatrix}$ **15.** $\begin{bmatrix} 2 & -\dfrac{5}{3} \\ 1 & -\dfrac{2}{3} \end{bmatrix}$ **17.** $\begin{bmatrix} \dfrac{1}{2} & \dfrac{1}{2} \\ \dfrac{1}{2} & -\dfrac{1}{2} \end{bmatrix}$

19. $\begin{bmatrix} 30 \\ 36 \end{bmatrix}$ **21.** $\begin{bmatrix} 0 \\ 5 \end{bmatrix}$ **23.** $\begin{bmatrix} -4 \\ 13 \end{bmatrix}$ **25.** $\begin{bmatrix} -4 \\ -13 \end{bmatrix}$ **27.** $\{(2, 3)\}$

29. $\{(-2, 5)\}$ **31.** $\{(0, -1)\}$ **33.** $\{(-1, -1)\}$ **35.** $\{(4, 7)\}$

37. $\left\{\left(-\dfrac{1}{3}, \dfrac{1}{2}\right)\right\}$ **39.** $\{(-9, 20)\}$

Problem Set 12.3 (page 645)

1. $\begin{bmatrix} 1 & 3 & -3 \\ 3 & -6 & 7 \end{bmatrix}$; $\begin{bmatrix} 3 & -5 & 11 \\ -7 & 6 & 3 \end{bmatrix}$; $\begin{bmatrix} 1 & 10 & -13 \\ 11 & -18 & 16 \end{bmatrix}$;

$\begin{bmatrix} 10 & -12 & 30 \\ -18 & 12 & 16 \end{bmatrix}$

3. $[-1 \quad -7 \quad 13 \quad 7]$; $[5 \quad 5 \quad -5 \quad 17]$;
$[-5 \quad -20 \quad 35 \quad 9]$; $[14 \quad 8 \quad -2 \quad 58]$

5. $\begin{bmatrix} 8 & -3 & -2 \\ 9 & 2 & -3 \\ 7 & 5 & 21 \end{bmatrix}$; $\begin{bmatrix} -2 & -1 & 4 \\ -11 & 6 & -11 \\ -7 & 5 & -3 \end{bmatrix}$; $\begin{bmatrix} 21 & -7 & -7 \\ 28 & 2 & -2 \\ 21 & 10 & 54 \end{bmatrix}$;

$\begin{bmatrix} 2 & -6 & 10 \\ -24 & 20 & -36 \\ -14 & 20 & 12 \end{bmatrix}$

7. $\begin{bmatrix} 0 & 2 \\ -1 & 10 \\ 1 & -9 \\ 2 & 9 \end{bmatrix}$; $\begin{bmatrix} -2 & -2 \\ 5 & -4 \\ -11 & 1 \\ -16 & 13 \end{bmatrix}$; $\begin{bmatrix} 1 & 6 \\ -5 & 27 \\ 8 & -23 \\ 13 & 16 \end{bmatrix}$; $\begin{bmatrix} -6 & -4 \\ 14 & -2 \\ -32 & -6 \\ -46 & 48 \end{bmatrix}$

9. $AB = \begin{bmatrix} 11 & -8 & 14 \\ 4 & -16 & 8 \\ -28 & 22 & -36 \end{bmatrix}$; $BA = \begin{bmatrix} -20 & 21 \\ 8 & -21 \end{bmatrix}$

11. $AB = \begin{bmatrix} 22 & -8 & 1 & 3 \\ -42 & 36 & -26 & -20 \end{bmatrix}$; BA does not exist.

13. $AB = \begin{bmatrix} -12 & 5 & -5 \\ 14 & -2 & 4 \\ -10 & 13 & -5 \end{bmatrix}$; $BA = \begin{bmatrix} -1 & 0 & -6 \\ 10 & -2 & 16 \\ -8 & 5 & -16 \end{bmatrix}$

15. $AB = [-9]$; $BA = \begin{bmatrix} -2 & 1 & -3 & -4 \\ -6 & 3 & -9 & -12 \\ 4 & -2 & 6 & 8 \\ -8 & 4 & -12 & -16 \end{bmatrix}$

17. AB does not exist; $BA = \begin{bmatrix} 20 \\ 2 \\ -30 \end{bmatrix}$

19. $AB = \begin{bmatrix} 9 & -12 \\ -12 & 16 \\ 6 & -8 \end{bmatrix}$; BA does not exist.

21. $\begin{bmatrix} -\dfrac{1}{5} & \dfrac{3}{10} \\ \dfrac{2}{5} & -\dfrac{1}{10} \end{bmatrix}$ **23.** $\begin{bmatrix} 4 & -1 \\ -7 & 2 \end{bmatrix}$ **25.** $\begin{bmatrix} -\dfrac{4}{5} & -\dfrac{1}{5} \\ \dfrac{3}{5} & -\dfrac{2}{5} \end{bmatrix}$

27. $\begin{bmatrix} \dfrac{7}{2} & -3 & \dfrac{1}{2} \\ -\dfrac{1}{2} & 0 & \dfrac{1}{2} \\ -\dfrac{1}{2} & 1 & -\dfrac{1}{2} \end{bmatrix}$ **29.** $\begin{bmatrix} -50 & -9 & 11 \\ -23 & -4 & 5 \\ 5 & 1 & -1 \end{bmatrix}$

31. Docs not exist **33.** $\begin{bmatrix} \dfrac{4}{7} & -1 & -\dfrac{9}{7} \\ -\dfrac{3}{14} & \dfrac{1}{2} & \dfrac{6}{7} \\ \dfrac{2}{7} & 0 & -\dfrac{1}{7} \end{bmatrix}$

35. $\begin{bmatrix} \dfrac{1}{2} & 0 & 0 \\ 0 & \dfrac{1}{4} & 0 \\ 0 & 0 & \dfrac{1}{10} \end{bmatrix}$ **37.** $\{(-3, 2)\}$ **39.** $\{(2, 5)\}$

41. $\{(-1, -2, 1)\}$ **43.** $\{(-2, 3, 5)\}$ **45.** $\{(-4, 3, 0)\}$
47. (a) $\{(-1, 2, 3)\}$ (c) $\{(-5, 0, -2)\}$ (e) $\{(1, -1, -1)\}$

Problem Set 12.4 (page 654)

1.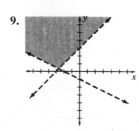

3.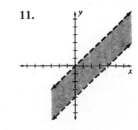

5.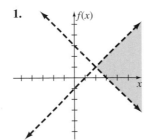

7.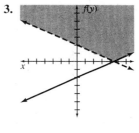

9.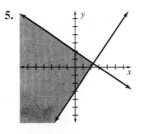

11.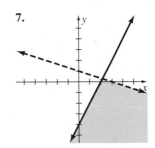

13.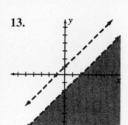

15.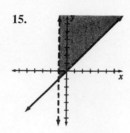

17. $\varnothing$

19.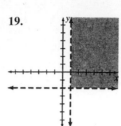

21.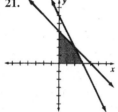

23.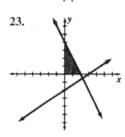

25. Minimum of 8 and maximum of 52
27. Minimum of 0 and maximum of 28
29. 63   **31.** 340   **33.** 2   **35.** 98
37. $5000 at 9% and $5000 at 12%
39. 300 of type A and 200 of type B
41. 12 units of A and 16 units of B

Chapter 12 Review Problem Set (page 662)

1. $\begin{bmatrix} 7 & -5 \\ -3 & 10 \end{bmatrix}$ **2.** $\begin{bmatrix} 3 & 3 \\ 3 & -6 \end{bmatrix}$ **3.** $\begin{bmatrix} 2 & 1 \\ -6 & 8 \\ -2 & 2 \end{bmatrix}$

4. $\begin{bmatrix} 19 & -11 \\ -6 & 22 \end{bmatrix}$ **5.** $\begin{bmatrix} 7 & 1 \\ -14 & 20 \\ 1 & -2 \end{bmatrix}$ **6.** $\begin{bmatrix} -11 & -3 & 15 \\ 24 & 2 & -20 \\ -40 & -5 & 38 \end{bmatrix}$

7. $\begin{bmatrix} 16 & -26 \\ 0 & 13 \end{bmatrix}$ **8.** $\begin{bmatrix} 26 & -36 \\ -15 & 32 \end{bmatrix}$ **9.** $\begin{bmatrix} -27 \\ 26 \end{bmatrix}$

10. Does not exist.   **14.** $\begin{bmatrix} 4 & -5 \\ -7 & 9 \end{bmatrix}$ **15.** $\begin{bmatrix} -3 & 4 \\ 7 & -9 \end{bmatrix}$

16. $\begin{bmatrix} -\dfrac{3}{8} & \dfrac{1}{8} \\ \dfrac{1}{4} & \dfrac{1}{4} \end{bmatrix}$ **17.** Does not exist.   **18.** $\begin{bmatrix} \dfrac{5}{7} & -\dfrac{3}{7} \\ \dfrac{4}{7} & \dfrac{1}{7} \end{bmatrix}$

19. $\begin{bmatrix} \dfrac{2}{7} & \dfrac{1}{7} \\ -\dfrac{1}{3} & 0 \end{bmatrix}$ **20.** $\begin{bmatrix} \dfrac{39}{8} & -\dfrac{17}{8} & -\dfrac{1}{8} \\ 2 & -1 & 0 \\ \dfrac{1}{8} & \dfrac{1}{8} & \dfrac{1}{8} \end{bmatrix}$

21. $\begin{bmatrix} 8 & -8 & 5 \\ -3 & 2 & -1 \\ -1 & -1 & 1 \end{bmatrix}$ **22.** Does not exist.

23. $\begin{bmatrix} -\dfrac{20}{3} & -\dfrac{7}{3} & \dfrac{1}{3} \\ -\dfrac{1}{3} & -\dfrac{2}{3} & -\dfrac{1}{3} \\ -\dfrac{5}{3} & -\dfrac{1}{3} & \dfrac{1}{3} \end{bmatrix}$ **24.** $\{(-2, 6)\}$ **25.** $\{(4, -1)\}$

26. $\{(2, -3, -1)\}$ **27.** $\{(-3, 2, 5)\}$ **28.** $\{(-4, 3, 4)\}$

29.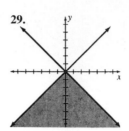

30.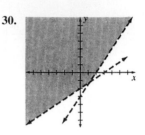

31.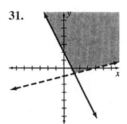

32.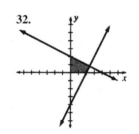

33. 37   **34.** 56   **35.** 57   **36.** 1700
37. 75 one-gallon and 175 two-gallon freezers

Chapter 12 Test (page 664)

1. $\begin{bmatrix} 9 & -1 \\ 4 & -6 \end{bmatrix}$ **2.** $\begin{bmatrix} -11 & 13 \\ -8 & 14 \end{bmatrix}$ **3.** $\begin{bmatrix} -1 & -3 & 11 \\ -4 & -5 & 18 \\ 37 & -1 & 9 \end{bmatrix}$

4. Does not exist   **5.** $\begin{bmatrix} -35 \\ 8 \end{bmatrix}$ **6.** $\begin{bmatrix} -5 & 8 \\ 4 & -3 \end{bmatrix}$

7. $\begin{bmatrix} 4 & 9 \\ 13 & -16 \\ 24 & 23 \end{bmatrix}$ **8.** $\begin{bmatrix} -3 & -5 \\ -20 & 8 \end{bmatrix}$ **9.** $\begin{bmatrix} 8 & 33 \\ -12 & 13 \end{bmatrix}$

10. $\begin{bmatrix} 1 & -34 \\ 16 & -19 \end{bmatrix}$ **11.** $\begin{bmatrix} -3 & 2 \\ -5 & 3 \end{bmatrix}$ **12.** $\begin{bmatrix} 7 & 5 \\ 3 & 2 \end{bmatrix}$

13. $\begin{bmatrix} 4 & \dfrac{3}{2} \\ 1 & \dfrac{1}{2} \end{bmatrix}$ **14.** $\begin{bmatrix} \dfrac{4}{7} & -\dfrac{5}{7} \\ -\dfrac{1}{7} & \dfrac{3}{7} \end{bmatrix}$

15. $\begin{bmatrix} -\dfrac{4}{3} & -\dfrac{5}{3} & 1 \\ -\dfrac{4}{3} & -\dfrac{8}{3} & 1 \\ \dfrac{1}{3} & \dfrac{2}{3} & 0 \end{bmatrix}$ **16.** $\begin{bmatrix} 1 & 2 & -10 \\ 0 & 1 & -3 \\ 0 & 0 & 1 \end{bmatrix}$

17. $\{(8, -12)\}$ **18.** $\{(-6, -14)\}$ **19.** $\{(9, 13)\}$
20. $\left\{\left(\dfrac{7}{3}, -\dfrac{1}{3}, \dfrac{13}{3}\right)\right\}$ **21.** $\{(-1, 2, 1)\}$

22.
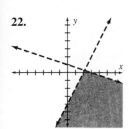

23.
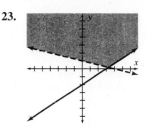

24.
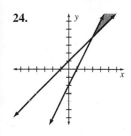

25. 4050

Chapters 1–12 Cumulative Review Problem Set (page 665)

1. Multiplicative Inverse Property
2. Associative Property of Multiplication
3. Commutative Property of Addition
4. Identity Property of Addition

5. 35   **6.** $-\dfrac{16}{3}$ **7.** -1 **8.** $-\dfrac{43}{72}$ **9.** $-\dfrac{3}{2}$ **10.** -11

11. 1   **12.** $\dfrac{3}{2}$ **13.** $\begin{bmatrix} -4 & -4 \\ 5 & -2 \end{bmatrix}$ **14.** $\begin{bmatrix} -8 & 13 \\ -8 & -7 \end{bmatrix}$

15. $\begin{bmatrix} 18 & 31 \\ -18 & 4 \end{bmatrix}$ **16.** $\begin{bmatrix} 7 & 21 \\ -25 & 15 \end{bmatrix}$ **17.** -23

18. -139 **19.** $9x + 7y = -3$ **20.** $2x + 3y = 2$
21. $5x + 2y = 17$ **22.** $x - y = -3$

23. $\dfrac{9}{64a}$ **24.** $\dfrac{4n^6}{9m^{10}}$ **25.** $2\sqrt{17}$ **26.** $3\sqrt[3]{3}$

27. $\dfrac{4\sqrt{5}}{5}$ **28.** $\dfrac{\sqrt{14a}}{6a^2}$ **29.** $\dfrac{3x}{2}\sqrt{3y}$ **30.** $2a\sqrt{2b}$

31. $\dfrac{\sqrt[3]{6}}{2}$ **32.** $4cd^2\sqrt[3]{2c^2d}$ **33.** $\dfrac{3(\sqrt{5} + 1)}{2}$

34. $\dfrac{12\sqrt{6} - 16\sqrt{2}}{11}$ **35.** $x = 2 + 3y$ **36.** $x = \dfrac{4y - 13}{9}$

37. $x = \dfrac{by}{c - d - ay}$ **38.** $x = \dfrac{6c - 3a}{8}$ **39.** $\dfrac{c^2 + 2c - 2}{c - 1}$

40. $-\dfrac{(4a + 3)(a - 2)}{(3a - 2)(a + 1)}$ **41.** $f(-1) = -14$

42. $f(-2) = 7$

43. $f(0) = -9, f(-1) = -12, f(a) = -2a^2 + a - 9$

44. $f(0) = 0, f(3) = 6, f(-1) = -1, f(-3) = -9$ **45.** -2

46. $6a + 3h - 1$ **47.** D: $\left\{x \mid x \neq -1 \text{ and } x \neq \dfrac{2}{3}\right\}$

48. D: $\{x \mid x \neq 1 \text{ and } x \neq -1\}$

49. D: $\left\{x \mid x \geq -\dfrac{2}{3}\right\}$; R: $\{f(x) \mid f(x) \geq 0\}$

50. D: $\{x \mid x \text{ is real}\}$; R: $\{f(x) \mid f(x) \geq 0\}$

51. D: $\{x \mid x \text{ is real}\}$; R: $\{f(x) \mid f(x) \leq -1\}$

52. D: $(-\infty, -5] \cup [5, \infty)$ **53.** D: $(-\infty, \infty)$

54. D: $\left(-\infty, -\dfrac{1}{4}\right] \cup [3, \infty)$

55. $(f \circ g)(x) = 3x^2 + 9x - 13$, D: $\{x \mid x \text{ is real}\}$;
$(g \circ f)(x) = 9x^2 + 3x - 6$, D: $\{x \mid x \text{ is real}\}$

56. $(f \circ g)(x) = 2x - 2$, D: $\{x \mid x \neq 1\}$;
$(g \circ f)(x) = \dfrac{x}{2 - x}$, D: $\{x \mid x \neq 0 \text{ and } x \neq 2\}$

57. $\left\{-\dfrac{5}{12}\right\}$ **58.** $\left\{-\dfrac{21}{13}\right\}$ **59.** $\left\{-4, \dfrac{20}{3}\right\}$ **60.** $\left\{-\dfrac{1}{2}\right\}$

61. $\left\{-\dfrac{7}{2}, 1\right\}$ **62.** $\left\{-\dfrac{3}{2}, 0, \dfrac{3}{2}\right\}$ **63.** $\left\{-\dfrac{9}{4}, \dfrac{7}{3}\right\}$

64. $\left\{-\dfrac{4}{3}, 5\right\}$ **65.** $\left\{\dfrac{7}{3}, 3\right\}$ **66.** $\{25\}$ **67.** $\varnothing$

68. $\{-4, 4\}$ **69.** $\{8\}$ **70.** $\{25\}$ **71.** $\left\{0, \dfrac{7}{3}\right\}$

72. $\left\{-\dfrac{\sqrt{5}}{2}, \dfrac{\sqrt{5}}{2}\right\}$ **73.** $\left\{\dfrac{-11 - 5\sqrt{5}}{2}, \dfrac{-11 + 5\sqrt{5}}{2}\right\}$

74. $\left\{\dfrac{-1 - i\sqrt{55}}{4}, \dfrac{-1 + i\sqrt{55}}{4}\right\}$

75. $\left\{-\sqrt{3}, \sqrt{3}, -3i\sqrt{2}, 3i\sqrt{2}\right\}$

76. $\left\{\dfrac{6 - \sqrt{30}}{2}, \dfrac{6 + \sqrt{30}}{2}\right\}$ **77.** $\{-5, 2, 3\}$

78. $\{-1, 3, 2 - i, 2 + i\}$ **79.** $\left\{\dfrac{3}{2}\right\}$ **80.** $\left\{\dfrac{1}{3}\right\}$ **81.** $\left\{\dfrac{1}{20}\right\}$

82. $\{7\}$ **83.** $\{-2\}$ **84.** $\left\{-\dfrac{3}{2}\right\}$ **85.** $\{1.37\}$ **86.** $\{4.61\}$

87. $\{-1.75\}$ **88.** $\{1.75\}$ **89.** $\left(-\infty, -\dfrac{1}{2}\right)$ **90.** $[6, 12]$

91. $\left(-6, \dfrac{22}{3}\right)$ **92.** $\left(-\infty, \dfrac{8}{3}\right) \cup \left(\dfrac{8}{3}, \infty\right)$

93. $\left(-\infty, -\dfrac{7}{2}\right] \cup [0, \infty)$ **94.** $(-1, 3)$ **95.** $\{(2, 5)\}$

96. $\{(-27, -5)\}$ **97.** $\{(-1, 0, 3)\}$

98.   **99.**
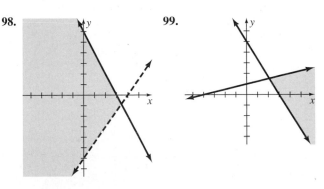

100.

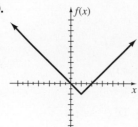

101.

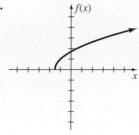

102.

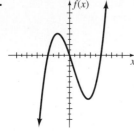

103. 45 miles   **104.** $5 + \sqrt{17}, 5 - \sqrt{17}$

105. Side: $\dfrac{4}{9\pi}$ units   Radius: $\dfrac{4}{3\pi}$ units   **106.** 65 miles per hour

107. 12.63 years   **108.** 2 cups of orange juice

109. (a) $1216.65   **(b)** $1218.99   **(c)** $1220.19   **(d)** $1221.00
(e) $1221.40

110. 50°, 55°, 75°   **111.** 5 cups

112. 6 servings of dry; 5 servings of wet; 2 servings of vitamins

113. 8 singles; 3 fives; 7 twenties

114. Sophie's rate: 4 mph; Finn's rate: 2 mph; Current: 1 mph

115. 32 "cricket" figures; 18 "beetle" figures

Chapter 13

Problem Set 13.1 (page 675)

1. $x^2 + y^2 - 4x - 6y - 12 = 0$
3. $x^2 + y^2 + 2x + 10y + 17 = 0$
5. $x^2 + y^2 - 6x = 0$ **7.** $x^2 + y^2 = 49$
9. $x^2 + y^2 + 6x - 8y + 9 = 0$ and
$x^2 + y^2 + 6x + 8y + 9 = 0$
11. $x^2 + y^2 + 12x + 12y + 36 = 0$
13. $x^2 + y^2 - 8x + 4\sqrt{3}y + 12 = 0$ and
$x^2 + y^2 - 8x - 4\sqrt{3}y + 12 = 0$
15. $(5, 7); r = 5$ **17.** $(-1, -8); r = 2\sqrt{3}$
19. $(10, -5); r = \sqrt{3}$
21. $(3, 5), r = 2$ **23.** $(-5, -7), r = 1$ **25.** $(5, 0), r = 5$
27. $\left(0, \dfrac{5}{2}\right); r = \dfrac{\sqrt{29}}{2}$ **29.** $(0, 0), r = 2\sqrt{2}$
31. $\left(\dfrac{1}{2}, 1\right), r = 2$ **33.** $6x + 5y = 29$
35. $x^2 + y^2 + 6x + 8y = 0$
37. $x^2 + y^2 - 4x - 4y + 4 = 0$ and
$x^2 + y^2 + 20x - 20y + 100 = 0$
39. $x + 2y = 7$ **41.** $x^2 + y^2 + 12x + 2y - 21 = 0$

Problem Set 13.2 (page 683)

1. $V(0, 0), F(2, 0),$
$x = -2$

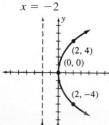

3. $V(0, 0), F(0, -3),$
$y = 3$

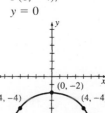

5. $V(0, 0), F\left(-\dfrac{1}{2}, 0\right),$
$x = \dfrac{1}{2}$

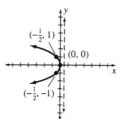

7. $V(0, 0), F\left(0, \dfrac{3}{2}\right),$
$y = -\dfrac{3}{2}$

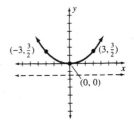

9. $V(0, -1), F(0, 2),$
$y = -4$

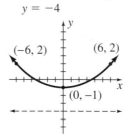

11. $V(3, 0), F(1, 0),$
$x = 5$

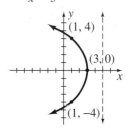

13. $V(0, 2), F(0, 3),$
$y = 1$

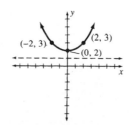

15. $V(0, -2),$
$F(0, -4),$
$y = 0$

17. $V(2, 0)$, $F(5, 0)$,
$x = -1$

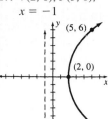

19. $V(2, -2)$, $F(2, -3)$,
$y = -1$

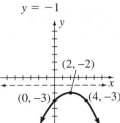

21. $V(-2, -4)$, $F(-4, -4)$,
$x = 0$

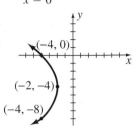

23. $V(1, 2)$, $F(1, 3)$,
$y = 1$

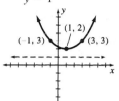

25. $V(-3, 1)$,
$F(-3, -1)$,
$y = 3$

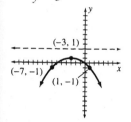

27. $V(3, 1)$, $F(0, 1)$,
$x = 6$

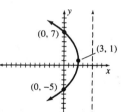

29. $V(-2, -3)$,
$F(-1, -3)$,
$x = -3$

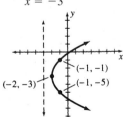

31. $x^2 = 12y$ **33.** $y^2 = -4x$ **35.** $x^2 + 12y - 48 = 0$
37. $x^2 - 6x - 12y + 21 = 0$ **39.** $y^2 - 10y + 8x + 41 = 0$
41. $y^2 = \dfrac{-25}{3}x$ **43.** $y^2 = 10x$
45. $x^2 - 14x - 8y + 73 = 0$ **47.** $y^2 + 6y - 12x + 105 = 0$
49. $x^2 + 18x + y + 80 = 0$ **51.** $x^2 = 750(y - 10)$
53. $10\sqrt{2}$ feet **55.** 62.5 feet

Problem Set 13.3 (page 691)

For Problems 1–21, the foci are indicated above the graph, and the vertices and endpoints of the minor axes are indicated on the graph.

1. $F(\sqrt{3}, 0)$,
$F'(-\sqrt{3}, 0)$

3. $F(0, \sqrt{5})$,
$F'(0, -\sqrt{5})$

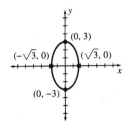

5. $F(0, \sqrt{6})$
$F'(0, -\sqrt{6})$

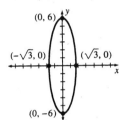

7. $F(\sqrt{15}, 0)$
$F'(-\sqrt{15}, 0)$

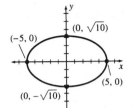

9. $F(0, \sqrt{33})$
$F'(0, -\sqrt{33})$

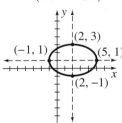

11. $F(2, 0)$
$F'(-2, 0)$

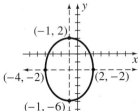

13. $F(2 + \sqrt{5}, 1)$
$F'(2 - \sqrt{5}, 1)$

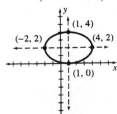

15. $F(-1, -2 + \sqrt{7})$
$F'(-1, -2 - \sqrt{7})$

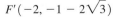
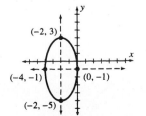

17. $F(1 + \sqrt{5}, 2)$
$F'(1 - \sqrt{5}, 2)$

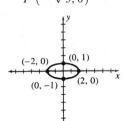

19. $F(-2, -1 + 2\sqrt{3})$
$F'(-2, -1 - 2\sqrt{3})$

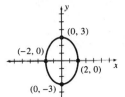

21. $F(3 + \sqrt{3}, 0)$
$F'(3 - \sqrt{3}, 0)$

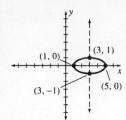

23. $F(4, -1 + \sqrt{7})$
$F'(4, -1 - \sqrt{7})$

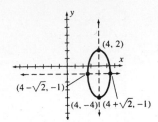

9. $F(0, \sqrt{30})$,
$F(0, -\sqrt{30})$
$y = \pm\dfrac{\sqrt{5}}{5}x$

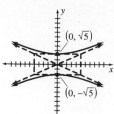

11. $F(\sqrt{10}, 0)$,
$F'(-\sqrt{10}, 0)$
$y = \pm 3x$

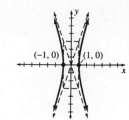
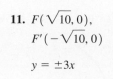

25. $F(0, 4)$, $F'(-6, 4)$

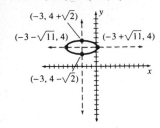

27. $16x^2 + 25y^2 = 400$ **29.** $36x^2 + 11y^2 = 396$
31. $x^2 + 9y^2 = 9$ **33.** $100x^2 + 36y^2 = 225$
35. $7x^2 + 3y^2 = 75$ **37.** $3x^2 - 6x + 4y^2 - 8y - 41 = 0$
39. $9x^2 + 25y^2 - 50y - 200 = 0$ **41.** $3x^2 + 4y^2 = 48$
43. $\dfrac{10\sqrt{5}}{3}$ feet

13. $F(1 + \sqrt{13}, -1)$,
$F'(1 - \sqrt{13}, -1)$
$2x - 3y = 5$ and
$2x + 3y = -1$

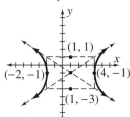

15. $F(1, 7)$,
$F'(1, -3)$
$3x - 4y = -5$ and
$3x + 4y = 11$

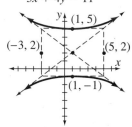

Problem Set 13.4 (page 700)

For Problems 1–25, the foci and equations of the asymptotes are indicated above the graphs. The vertices are given on the graphs.

1. $F(\sqrt{13}, 0)$,
$F'(-\sqrt{13}, 0)$
$y = \pm\dfrac{2}{3}x$

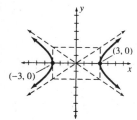

3. $F(0, \sqrt{13})$,
$F'(0, -\sqrt{13})$
$y = \pm\dfrac{2}{3}x$

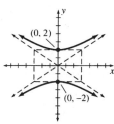

17. $F(13 + \sqrt{13}, -1)$,
$F'(3 - \sqrt{13}, -1)$
$2x - 3y = 9$ and
$2x + 3y = 3$

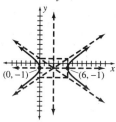

19. $F(-3, 2 + \sqrt{5})$,
$F'(-3, 2 - \sqrt{5})$
$2x - y = -8$ and
$2x + y = -4$

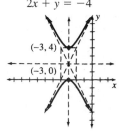

5. $F(0, 5)$,
$F(0, -5)$
$y = \pm\dfrac{4}{3}x$

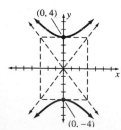

7. $F(3\sqrt{2}, 0)$
$F(-3\sqrt{2}, 0)$
$y = \pm x$

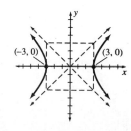

21. $F(2 + \sqrt{6}, 0)$,
$F'(2 - \sqrt{6}, 0)$
$\sqrt{2}x - y = 2\sqrt{2}$ and
$\sqrt{2}x + y = 2\sqrt{2}$

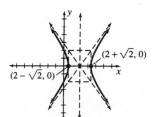

23. $F(0, -5 + \sqrt{10})$,
$F'(0, -5 - \sqrt{10})$
$3x - y = 5$ and
$3x + y = -5$

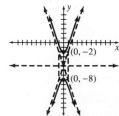

25. $F(-2 + \sqrt{2}, -2), F'(-2 - \sqrt{2}, -2)$
$x - y = 0$ and $x + y = -4$

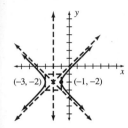

27. $5x^2 - 4y^2 = 20$ **29.** $16y^2 - 9x^2 = 144$
31. $3x^2 - y^2 = 3$ **33.** $4y^2 - 3x^2 = 12$
35. $7x^2 - 16y^2 = 112$
37. $5x^2 - 40x - 4y^2 - 24y + 24 = 0$
39. $3y^2 - 30y - x^2 - 6x + 54 = 0$
41. $5x^2 - 20x - 4y^2 = 0$ **43.** Circle
45. Straight line   **47.** Ellipse   **49.** Hyperbola
51. Parabola

Problem Set 13.5 (page 707)

1. $\{(1, 2)\}$ **3.** $\{(1, -5), (-5, 1)\}$
5. $\{(2 + i\sqrt{3}, -2 + i\sqrt{3}), (2 - i\sqrt{3}, -2 - i\sqrt{3})\}$
7. $\{(-6, 7), (-2, -1)\}$
9. $\{(-3, 4)\}$

11. $\left\{\left(\dfrac{-1 + i\sqrt{3}}{2}, \dfrac{-7 - i\sqrt{3}}{2}\right),\right.$
$\left.\left(\dfrac{-1 - i\sqrt{3}}{2}, \dfrac{-7 + i\sqrt{3}}{2}\right)\right\}$

13. $\{(-1, 2)\}$ **15.** $\{(-6, 3), (-2, -1)\}$
17. $\{(5, 3)\}$ **19.** $\{(1, 2,), (-1, 2)\}$
21. $\{(-3, 2)\}$ **23.** $\{(2, 0), (-2, 0)\}$

25. $\left\{(\sqrt{2}, \sqrt{3}), (\sqrt{2}, -\sqrt{3}), (-\sqrt{2}, \sqrt{3}), (-\sqrt{2}, -\sqrt{3})\right\}$

27. $\{(1, 1), (1, -1), (-1, 1), (-1, -1)\}$

29. $\left\{\left(2, \dfrac{3}{2}\right), \left(\dfrac{3}{2}, 2\right)\right\}$ **31.** $\{(9, -2)\}$ **33.** $\{(\ln 2, 1)\}$

35. $\left\{\left(\dfrac{1}{2}, \dfrac{1}{8}\right), (-3, -27)\right\}$ **43.** $\{(-2.3, 7.4)\}$

45. $\{(6.7, 1.7), (9.5, 2.1)\}$ **47.** None

Chapter 13 Review Problem Set (page 714)

1. $F(4, 0), F'(-4, 0)$ **2.** $F(-3, 0)$

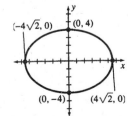

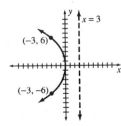

3. $F(0, 2\sqrt{3}),$
$F'(0, -2\sqrt{3})$
$y = \pm\dfrac{\sqrt{3}}{3}x$

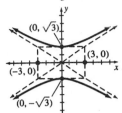

4. $F(\sqrt{15}, 0),$
$F'(-\sqrt{15}, 0)$
$y = \pm\dfrac{\sqrt{6}}{3}x$

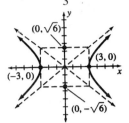

5. $F(0, \sqrt{6}),$
$F'(0, -\sqrt{6})$

6. $F\left(0, \dfrac{1}{2}\right)$

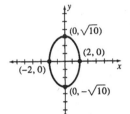

7.

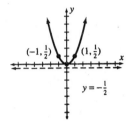

8. $F(4 + \sqrt{6}, 1), F'(4 - \sqrt{6}, 1)$
$\sqrt{2}x - 2y = 4\sqrt{2} - 2$ and $\sqrt{2}x + 2y = 4\sqrt{2} + 2$

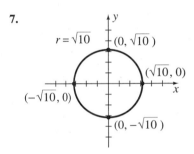

9. $F(3, -2 + \sqrt{7}), F'(3, -2 - \sqrt{7})$

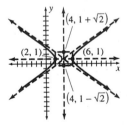

10. $F(-3, 1)$, $x = -1$ **11.** $F(-1, -5)$, $y = -1$

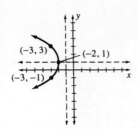 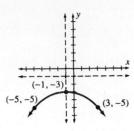

12. $F\left(-5 + 2\sqrt{3}, 2\right)$, $F'\left(-5 - 2\sqrt{3}, 2\right)$

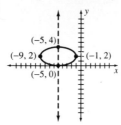

13. $F\left(-2, -2 + \sqrt{10}\right)$, $F'\left(-2, -2 - \sqrt{10}\right)$

$\sqrt{6}x - 3y = 6 - 2\sqrt{6}$ and $\sqrt{6}x + 3y = -6 - 2\sqrt{6}$

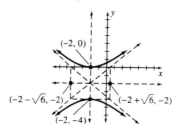

14. Center at $(3, -2)$ and $r = 4$

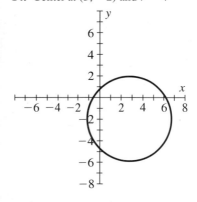

15. $x^2 + 16x + y^2 - 6y + 68 = 0$
16. $y^2 = -20x$ **17.** $16x^2 + y^2 = 16$ **18.** $25x^2 - 2y^2 = 50$
19. $x^2 - 10x + y^2 + 24y = 0$ **20.** $4x^2 + 3y^2 = 16$

21. $x^2 = \dfrac{2}{3}y$ **22.** $9y^2 - x^2 = 9$

23. $9x^2 - 108x + y^2 - 8y + 331 = 0$
24. $y^2 + 4y - 8x + 36 = 0$
25. $3y^2 + 24y - x^2 - 10x + 20 = 0$
26. $x^2 + 12x - y + 33 = 0$ **27.** $4x^2 + 40x + 25y^2 = 0$
28. $4x^2 - 32x - y^2 + 48 = 0$ **29.** $\{(-1, 4)\}$ **30.** $\{(3, 1)\}$
31. $\{(-1, -2), (-2, -3)\}$

32. $\left\{\left(\dfrac{4\sqrt{2}}{3}, \dfrac{4}{3}i\right), \left(\dfrac{4\sqrt{2}}{3}, -\dfrac{4}{3}i\right), \left(-\dfrac{4\sqrt{2}}{3}, \dfrac{4}{3}i\right),\right.$

$\left. \left(-\dfrac{4\sqrt{2}}{3}, -\dfrac{4}{3}i\right)\right\}$ **33.** $\{(0, 2), (0, -2)\}$

34. $\left\{\left(\dfrac{\sqrt{15}}{5}, \dfrac{2\sqrt{10}}{5}\right), \left(\dfrac{\sqrt{15}}{5}, -\dfrac{2\sqrt{10}}{5}\right),\right.$

$\left. \left(-\dfrac{\sqrt{15}}{5}, \dfrac{2\sqrt{10}}{5}\right), \left(-\dfrac{\sqrt{15}}{5}, -\dfrac{2\sqrt{10}}{5}\right)\right\}$

Chapter 13 Test (page 715)

1. $(0, -5)$ **2.** $(-3, 2)$ **3.** $x = -3$ **4.** $(6, 0)$ **5.** $(-2, -1)$
6. $(-3, -9)$ **7.** $y^2 + 8x = 0$ **8.** $x^2 - 6x + 12y - 39 = 0$
9. $x^2 + 2x + y^2 - 12y + 12 = 0$ **10.** 6 units
11. $(-7, 1)$ and $(-3, 1)$ **12.** $(-2\sqrt{3}, 0)$ and $(2\sqrt{3}, 0)$
13. $(-5, 8)$ **14.** $25x^2 + 9y^2 = 900$
15. $x^2 - 12x + 4y^2 + 16y + 36 = 0$ **16.** $y = \pm\dfrac{3}{2}x$
17. $(-1, 6)$ and $(-1, 0)$ **18.** $(\pm 3, 0)$ **19.** $x^2 - 3y^2 = 36$
20. $8x^2 + 16x - y^2 + 8y - 16 = 0$ **21.** 2

22. $\left\{(3, 2), (-3, -2), \left(4, \dfrac{3}{2}\right), \left(-4, -\dfrac{3}{2}\right)\right\}$

23. 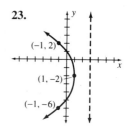   **24.**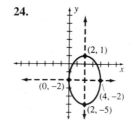

25.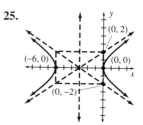

Chapter 14

Problem Set 14.1 (page 723)

1. $-4, -1, 2, 5, 8$ **3.** $2, 0, -2, -4, -6$ **5.** $2, 11, 26, 47, 74$
7. $0, 2, 6, 12, 20$ **9.** $4, 8, 16, 32, 64$
11. $a_{15} = -79$; $a_{30} = -154$ **13.** $a_{25} = 1$; $a_{50} = -1$
15. $2n + 9$ **17.** $-3n + 5$ **19.** $\dfrac{n + 2}{2}$ **21.** $4n - 2$

23. $-3n$ **25.** 73   **27.** 334   **29.** 35   **31.** 7   **33.** 86
35. 2700   **37.** 3200   **39.** -7950 **41.** 637.5   **43.** 4950
45. 1850   **47.** -2030 **49.** 3591   **51.** 40,000   **53.** 58,250
55. 2205   **57.** -1325 **59.** 5265   **61.** -810 **63.** 1276
65. 660   **67.** 55   **69.** 431   **75.** 3, 3, 7, 7, 11, 11
77. 4, 7, 10, 13, 17, 21   **79.** 4, 12, 36, 108, 324, 972
81. 1, 1, 2, 3, 5, 8   **83.** 3, 1, 4, 9, 25, 256

Problem Set 14.2 (page 732)

1. $3(2)^{n-1}$ **3.** 3^n **5.** $\left(\dfrac{1}{2}\right)^{n+1}$ **7.** 4^n **9.** $(0.3)^{n-1}$

11. $(-2)^{n-1}$ **13.** 64 **15.** $\dfrac{1}{9}$ **17.** -512 **19.** $\dfrac{1}{4374}$

21. $\dfrac{2}{3}$ **23.** 2 **25.** 1023 **27.** $19{,}682$ **29.** $394\dfrac{1}{16}$

31. 1364 **33.** 1089 **35.** $7\dfrac{511}{512}$ **37.** -547 **39.** $127\dfrac{3}{4}$

41. 540 **43.** $2\dfrac{61}{64}$ **45.** 4 **47.** 3 **49.** No sum **51.** $\dfrac{27}{4}$

53. 2 **55.** $\dfrac{16}{3}$ **57.** $\dfrac{1}{3}$ **59.** $\dfrac{26}{99}$ **61.** $\dfrac{41}{333}$ **63.** $\dfrac{4}{15}$

65. $\dfrac{106}{495}$ **67.** $\dfrac{7}{3}$

Problem Set 14.3 (page 736)

1. $\$53{,}500$ **3.** $31{,}550$ students **5.** 7320 **7.** 125 liters
9. 512 gallons
11. $\$116.25$ **13.** $\$163.84$; $\$327.67$ **15.** $\$19{,}950$

17. 1936 feet **19.** $\dfrac{15}{16}$ gram **21.** 2910 feet

23. 325 logs **25.** 5.9% **27.** $\dfrac{5}{64}$ gallon

Problem Set 14.4 (page 742)

These problems call for proof by mathematical induction and require class discussion.

Chapter 14 Review Problem Set (page 746)

1. $6n - 3$ **2.** 3^{n-2} **3.** $5(2^n)$ **4.** $-3n + 8$ **5.** $2n - 7$

6. 3^{3-n} **7.** $-(-2)^{n-1}$ **8.** $3n + 9$ **9.** $\dfrac{n+1}{3}$ **10.** 4^{n-1}

11. 73 **12.** 106 **13.** $\dfrac{1}{32}$ **14.** $\dfrac{4}{9}$ **15.** -92 **16.** $\dfrac{1}{16}$

17. -5 **18.** 85 **19.** $\dfrac{5}{9}$ **20.** 2 or -2 **21.** $121\dfrac{40}{81}$

22. 7035 **23.** $-10{,}725$ **24.** $31\dfrac{31}{32}$ **25.** $32{,}015$ **26.** 4757

27. $85\dfrac{21}{64}$ **28.** $37{,}044$ **29.** $12{,}726$ **30.** -1845

31. 225 **32.** 255 **33.** 8244 **34.** $85\dfrac{1}{3}$ **35.** $\dfrac{4}{11}$ **36.** $\dfrac{41}{90}$

37. $\$750$ **38.** $\$46.50$ **39.** $\$3276.70$ **40.** $10{,}935$ gallons

Chapter 14 Test (page 748)

1. -226 **2.** 48 **3.** $-5n + 2$ **4.** $5(2)^{1-n}$ **5.** $6n + 4$

6. $\dfrac{729}{8}$ or $91\dfrac{1}{8}$ **7.** 223 **8.** 60 terms **9.** 2380 **10.** 765

11. 7155 **12.** 6138 **13.** $22{,}650$ **14.** 9384 **15.** 4075

16. -341 **17.** 6 **18.** $\dfrac{1}{3}$ **19.** $\dfrac{2}{11}$ **20.** $\dfrac{4}{15}$ **21.** 3 liters

22. $\$1638.30$ **23.** $\$4655$
24. and **25.** Instructor supplies proof.

Appendix A

Practice Exercises (page 755)

1. $2 \cdot 13$ **2.** $2 \cdot 2 \cdot 2 \cdot 2$ **3.** $2 \cdot 2 \cdot 3 \cdot 3$
4. $2 \cdot 2 \cdot 2 \cdot 5$ **5.** $7 \cdot 7$ **6.** $2 \cdot 2 \cdot 23$
7. $2 \cdot 2 \cdot 2 \cdot 7$ **8.** $2 \cdot 2 \cdot 2 \cdot 2 \cdot 3 \cdot 3$
9. $2 \cdot 2 \cdot 2 \cdot 3 \cdot 5$ **10.** $2 \cdot 2 \cdot 3 \cdot 7$ **11.** $3 \cdot 3 \cdot 3 \cdot 5$
12. $2 \cdot 7 \cdot 7$ **13.** 24 **14.** 24 **15.** 48 **16.** 36 **17.** 140
18. 462 **19.** 392 **20.** 72 **21.** 168 **22.** 60 **23.** 90
24. 168 **25.** $\dfrac{2}{3}$ **26.** $\dfrac{3}{4}$ **27.** $\dfrac{2}{3}$ **28.** $\dfrac{9}{16}$ **29.** $\dfrac{5}{3}$ **30.** $\dfrac{4}{3}$
31. $\dfrac{15}{28}$ **32.** $\dfrac{12}{55}$ **33.** $\dfrac{10}{21}$ **34.** $\dfrac{65}{66}$ **35.** $\dfrac{3}{10}$ **36.** $\dfrac{2}{3}$

37. $\dfrac{3}{8}$ cup **38.** $\dfrac{1}{6}$ of the bottle **39.** $\dfrac{2}{9}$ of the disk space

40. $\dfrac{1}{3}$ **41.** $\dfrac{5}{7}$ **42.** $\dfrac{8}{11}$ **43.** $\dfrac{5}{9}$ **44.** $\dfrac{5}{13}$ **45.** 3 **46.** 2

47. $\dfrac{2}{3}$ **48.** $\dfrac{3}{8}$ **49.** $\dfrac{2}{3}$ **50.** $\dfrac{5}{9}$ **51.** $\dfrac{8}{15}$ **52.** $\dfrac{7}{24}$ **53.** $\dfrac{9}{16}$

54. $\dfrac{11}{12}$ **55.** $\dfrac{37}{30}$ **56.** $\dfrac{29}{24}$ **57.** $\dfrac{59}{96}$ **58.** $\dfrac{19}{24}$ **59.** $\dfrac{13}{12}$ pounds

60. $\dfrac{5}{16}$ **61.** $\dfrac{1}{4}$ **62.** $\dfrac{5}{3}$ **63.** $\dfrac{37}{30}$ **64.** $\dfrac{4}{5}$ **65.** $\dfrac{1}{3}$ **66.** $\dfrac{27}{35}$

67. $\dfrac{7}{26}$ **68.** 30 **69.** $\dfrac{7}{20}$ **70.** $\dfrac{11}{32}$ ounce

Appendix B

Practice Exercises (page 760)

1. $x^8 + 8x^7y + 28x^6y^2 + 56x^5y^3 + 70x^4y^4 + 56x^3y^5 + 28x^2y^6 + 8xy^7 + y^8$
3. $x^6 - 6x^5y + 15x^4y^2 - 20x^3y^3 + 15x^2y^4 - 6xy^5 + y^6$
5. $a^4 + 8a^3b + 24a^2b^2 + 32ab^3 + 16b^4$
7. $x^5 - 15x^4y + 90x^3y^2 - 270x^2y^3 + 405xy^4 - 243y^5$
9. $16a^4 - 96a^3b + 216a^2b^2 - 216ab^3 + 81b^4$
11. $x^{10} + 5x^8y + 10x^6y^2 + 10x^4y^3 + 5x^2y^4 + y^5$
13. $16x^8 - 32x^6y^2 + 24x^4y^4 - 8x^2y^6 + y^8$
15. $x^6 + 18x^5 + 135x^4 + 540x^3 + 1215x^2 + 1458x + 729$
17. $x^9 - 9x^8 + 36x^7 - 84x^6 + 126x^5 - 126x^4 + 84x^3 - 36x^2 + 9x - 1$

19. $1 + \dfrac{4}{n} + \dfrac{6}{n^2} + \dfrac{4}{n^3} + \dfrac{1}{n^4}$

21. $a^6 - \dfrac{6a^5}{n} + \dfrac{15a^4}{n^2} - \dfrac{20a^3}{n^3} + \dfrac{15a^2}{n^4} - \dfrac{6a}{n^5} + \dfrac{1}{n^6}$
23. $17 + 12\sqrt{2}$ **25.** $843 - 589\sqrt{2}$
27. $x^{12} + 12x^{11}y + 66x^{10}y^2 + 220x^9y^3$
29. $x^{20} - 20x^{19}y + 190x^{18}y^2 - 1140x^{17}y^3$
31. $x^{28} - 28x^{26}y^3 + 364x^{24}y^6 - 2912x^{22}y^9$

33. $a^9 + \dfrac{9a^8}{n} + \dfrac{36a^7}{n^2} + \dfrac{84a^6}{n^3}$

35. $x^{10} - 20x^9y + 180x^8y^2 - 960x^7y^3$ **37.** $56x^5y^3$

39. $126x^5y^4$ **41.** $189a^2b^5$ **43.** $120x^6y^{21}$ **45.** $\dfrac{5005}{n^6}$

Index

Abscissa, 326
Absolute value:
    definition of, 12, 90
    equations involving, 90
    inequalities involving, 92
    properties of, 12
Addition:
    of complex numbers, 275
    of functions, 425
    of matrices, 628, 640
    of polynomials, 109
    of radical expressions, 239
    of rational expressions, 175
    of real numbers, 12–13
Addition property of equality, 42
Addition property of inequality, 76
Additive inverse property, 22
Algebraic equation, 42
Algebraic expression, 27
Algebraic inequality, 74
Analytic geometry, 326
Arithmetic sequence, 718
Associative property:
    of addition, 21
    of multiplication, 21
Asymptotes, 485, 494
Augmented matrix, 589
Axes of a coordinate system, 326
Axis of symmetry, 399, 677

Base of a logarithm, 534
Base of a power, 24
Binary operations, 21
Binomial, 108
Binomial expansion, 757
Binomial theorem, 757

Cartesian coordinate system, 326
Change-of-base formula, 555
Checking:
    solutions of equations, 43
    solutions of inequalities, 78
    solutions of word problems, 46
Circle, 670
Circle, equation of, 670
Circumference, 72
Closure property:
    for addition, 20
    for multiplication, 20
Coefficient, numerical, 108
Cofactor, 600
Common difference of an arithmetic
    sequence, 719
Common logarithm, 544
Common logarithmic function, 545
Common ratio of a geometric sequence, 725

Commutative property:
    of addition, 21
    of multiplication, 21
Complementary angles, 53
Completely factored form:
    of a composite number, 127
    of a polynomial, 128
Completing the square, 289
Complex fraction, 184
Complex number, 274
Composite function, 426
Composite number, 127, 749
Composition of functions, 426
Compound interest, 514
Compound statement, 83
Conic sections:
    circle, 670
    ellipse, 684
    hyperbola, 693
    parabola, 676
Conjugate, 245, 278
Conjugate axis, 695
Conjunction, 83
Consecutive integers, 45
Consistent system of equations, 572
Constant function, 393
Constant of variation, 432
Coordinate geometry, 326
Coordinate of a point, 11, 326
Counting numbers, 3
Cramer's rule, 607, 609
Critical numbers, 309
Cross-multiplication property, 198
Cube root, 230
Cylinder, right circular, 72

Decimals:
    nonrepeating, 4
    repeating, 4, 730
    terminating, 4
Decreasing function, 510, 529
Degree:
    of a monomial, 108
    of a polynomial, 108
Denominator:
    least common, 49
    rationalizing a, 234
Dependent equations, 573
Descartes, René, 323
Descartes' rule of signs, 469
Determinant, 598
Difference of squares, 135
Difference of two cubes, 137
Difference quotient, 385
Dimension of a matrix, 589
Directrix, 677

Direct variation, 432
Discriminant, 297
Disjunction, 83
Distance formula, 343
Distributive property, 23
Division:
　of complex numbers, 278
　of functions, 425
　of polynomials, 190
　of radical expressions, 246
　of rational expressions, 171
　of real numbers, 16
Division algorithm for polynomials, 454
Domain of a function, 382

e, 517
Effective annual rate of interest, 518
Elementary row operations, 589–590
Elements:
　of a matrix, 589
　of a set, 2
Elimination-by-addition method, 574
Ellipse, 684
Empty set, 3
English system of measure, 33
Equal complex numbers, 274
Equality:
　addition property of, 42
　multiplication property of, 43
　reflexive property of, 6
　substitution property of, 6
　symmetric property of, 6
　transitive property of, 6
Equation(s):
　consistent, 572
　definition of, 42
　dependent, 573
　equivalent, 42
　exponential, 507, 549
　first-degree in one variable, 42
　first-degree in two variables, 328
　first-degree in three variables, 582
　inconsistent, 572
　linear, 328
　logarithmic, 539, 549
　polynomial, 463
　quadratic, 281
　radical, 249
Equivalent equations, 42
Equivalent fractions, 754
Equivalent inequalities, 76
Equivalent systems of equations, 575
Evaluating algebraic expressions, 29
Expansion of a binomial, 757
Expansion of a determinant by minors, 599
Exponent(s):
　integers as, 222
　natural numbers as, 24
　negative, 223
　properties of, 222, 223, 507
　rational numbers as, 254
　zero as an, 222

Exponential decay, 515
Exponential equation, 507, 549
Exponential function, 508
Extraneous solution or root, 250

Factor, 128
Factoring:
　complete, 128
　difference of cubes, 137
　difference of squares, 135
　by grouping, 130
　sum of cubes, 137
　trinomials, 141, 143
Factor theorem, 460
First-degree equations:
　in one variable, 42
　in two variables, 328
　in three variables, 582
Formulas, 64
Function(s):
　composite, 426
　constant, 393
　definition of, 382
　domain of a, 382
　exponential, 508
　graph of a, 383
　identity, 393
　inverse of a, 525
　linear, 392
　logarithmic, 542
　one-to-one, 524
　piecewise-defined, 384
　polynomial, 474
　quadratic, 398
　range of a, 382
　rational, 484
Functional notation, 383
Fundamental principle of fractions, 164, 751

General term of a sequence, 718, 726
Geometric sequence, 725
Graph:
　of an equation, 326
　of a function, 383
　of an inequality, 75
Graphing suggestions, 416
Graphing utilities, 333, 336

Half-life of a substance, 515
Heron's formula, 236
Horizontal asymptote, 485
Horizontal line test, 530
Horizontal translation, 401, 419
Hyperbola, 693

i, 274
Identity element:
　for addition, 21
　for multiplication, 22
Identity function, 393
Imaginary number, 275
Inconsistent equations, 572

Increasing function, 510, 529
Index:
    of a radical, 231
    of summation, 722
Inequalities:
    equivalent, 76
    graphs of, 75
    involving absolute value, 92
    linear in one variable, 337
    linear in two variables, 337
    quadratic, 308
    sense of, 76
    solutions of, 76
Infinite geometric sequence, 729
Infinite sequence, 718
Integers, 3
Intercepts, 328
Intersection of sets, 84
Interval notation, 75, 86
Inverse of a function, 525
Inverse variation, 434
Irrational numbers, 4
Isosceles right triangle, 285
Isosceles triangle, 344

Joint variation, 435

Law:
    of decay, 519
    of exponential growth, 518
Least common denominator, 49
Least common multiple, 49, 176, 749
Like terms, 27
Linear equation(s):
    graph of a, 326
    slope-intercept form for, 356
    standard form for, 328
Linear function:
    definition of, 392
    graph of a, 392
Linear inequality, 337
Linear programming, 651
Linear systems of equations, 572, 582
Literal equations, 68
Literal factor, 27, 108
Logarithm(s):
    base of a, 534
    common, 544
    definition of, 534
    natural, 546
    properties of, 536–538
Logarithmic equations, 539, 549
Logarithmic function, 542
Lower bound, 473

Major axis of an ellipse, 686
Mathematical induction, 738
Matrix, 589
Maximum value, 398, 411
Metric system of measure, 33
Minimum value, 398, 411
Minor axis of an ellipse, 686

Minors, expansion of a determinant by, 599
Monomial(s):
    definition of, 108
    degree of, 108
    division of, 116
    multiplication of, 114
Multiple, least common, 49, 176, 749
Multiple roots, 464–465
Multiplication:
    of complex numbers, 277
    of functions, 425
    of matrices, 630, 641
    of polynomials, 119
    of radical expressions, 243
    of rational expressions, 170
    of real numbers, 15
Multiplication property of equality, 43
Multiplication property of inequality, 77
Multiplication property of negative
    one, 22
Multiplication property of zero, 22
Multiplicative inverse of a matrix, 634
Multiplicative inverse property, 22
Multiplicity of roots, 464–465

nth root, 230
Natural exponential function, 517
Natural logarithm, 546
Natural logarithmic function, 546
Natural numbers, 3
Normal distribution curve, 520
Notation:
    functional, 383
    interval, 75, 86
    scientific, 259
    set, 2–3
    set-builder, 3
    summation, 722
Null set, 3
Number(s):
    absolute value of, 11
    complex, 274
    composite, 127, 749
    counting, 3
    imaginary, 275
    integers, 3
    irrational, 4
    natural, 3
    prime, 127, 749
    rational, 3
    real, 3
    whole, 3
Numerical coefficient, 108
Numerical expression, 2

Oblique asymptote, 494
One, multiplication property of, 22
One-to-one function, 524
Open sentence, 42
Operations, order of, 6
Ordered pair, 324
Ordered triple, 582

Ordinate, 326
Origin, 325
Origin symmetry, 366

Parabola, 398, 676
Parallel lines, 357
Perfect-square trinomial, 289
Perpendicular lines, 357
Piecewise-defined functions, 384
Point-slope form, 355
Polynomial(s):
    addition of, 109
    completely factored form of, 128
    definition of, 108
    degree of a, 108
    division of, 190
    multiplication of, 119
    subtraction of, 109
Polynomial equations, 463
Polynomial functions, 474
Primary focal chord, 677
Prime factor, 128
Prime number, 127, 749
Principal root, 229
Principle of mathematical induction, 738
Problem-solving suggestions, 51–52, 206, 207,
    302–303, 734
Properties of absolute value, 12
Properties of determinants, 601–603
Properties of equality, 42–43
Properties of inequality, 76–77
Properties of real numbers, 20–23
Proportion, 198
Pure imaginary number, 275
Pythagorean theorem, 152, 285

Quadrant, 325
Quadratic equation(s):
    definition of, 281
    discriminant of a, 297
    formula, 294
    nature of solutions of, 297
    standard form of, 282
Quadratic formula, 294
Quadratic function:
    definition of a, 398
    graph of a, 398
Quadratic inequality, 308

Radical(s):
    addition of, 239
    changing form of, 232
    definition of, 229
    division of, 246
    index of a, 231
    multiplication of, 243
    simplest form of, 232, 233, 240
    subtraction of, 239
Radical equation, 249
Radicand, 229
Radius of a circle, 670
Ratio, 198

Ratio of a geometric sequence, 725
Rational exponents, 255
Rational expression, 165
Rational functions, 484
Rationalizing a denominator, 234
Rational number, 3
Rational root theorem, 465
Real number, 4
Real number line, 10
Reciprocal, 171
Rectangle, 72
Rectangular coordinate system, 325
Reduced echelon form, 591
Reducing fractions, 164
Reflection, 419, 420
Reflexive property of equality, 6
Relation, 383
Remainder theorem, 459
Richter number, 553
Roots of an equation, 42

Scalar multiplication, 629, 641
Scientific notation, 259
Sense of an inequality, 76
Sequence:
    arithmetic, 718
    definition of, 718
    general term of, 718
    geometric, 725
    infinite, 718
Set(s):
    element of a, 2
    empty, 3
    equal, 3
    intersection of, 84
    notation, 2–3
    null, 3
    solution, 42
    union of, 85
Shrinking, vertical, 421
Similar terms, 27
Simplest radical form, 232, 233, 240
Simplifying numerical expressions, 6, 755
Simplifying rational expressions, 164
Slope, 344
Slope-intercept form, 356
Solution(s):
    of equations, 42
    extraneous, 250
    of inequalities, 74
    of a system, 572
Solution set:
    of an equation, 42
    of an inequality, 75
    of a system, 572
Square matrix, 598, 642
Square root, 229
Standard form:
    of complex numbers, 274
    of equation of a circle, 670
    of equation of a straight line, 357
    of a quadratic equation, 282

Stretching, vertical, 421
Subscripts, 67
Subset, 5
Substitution method, 573
Substitution property of equality, 6
Subtraction:
    of complex numbers, 275
    of functions, 425
    of matrices, 629
    of polynomials, 109
    of radical expressions, 239
    of rational expressions, 175
    of real numbers, 13
Suggestions for solving word problems, 51–52,
        206, 207, 302–303, 734
Sum:
    of an arithmetic sequence, 720
    of a geometric sequence, 726
    of an infinite geometric sequence, 729
Summation notation, 722
Sum of two cubes, 137
Supplementary angles, 53
Symmetric property of equality, 6
Symmetry, 364
Synthetic division, 454
System(s):
    of linear equations in two variables, 572
    of linear equations in three variables, 582
    of linear inequalities, 649
    of nonlinear equations, 702

Term(s):
    addition of like, 28, 108
    of an algebraic expression, 27, 108
    like, 27, 108
    similar, 27, 108
Test numbers, 309
Transformations, 418
Transitive property of equality, 6
Translating from English to
        algebra, 31

Translation:
    horizontal, 401, 419
    vertical, 400, 418
Transverse axis, 694
Trapezoid, 66
Triangle, 66
Triangular form, 594
Trinomial, 108
Turning points, 476

Union of sets, 85
Upper bound, 472

Variable, 2
Variation:
    constant of, 432
    direct, 432
    inverse, 434
    joint, 435
Variation in sign, 469
Vertex of a parabola, 399, 677
Vertical asymptote, 485
Vertical line test, 384
Vertical shrinking, 421
Vertical stretching, 421
Vertical translation, 400, 418

Whole numbers, 3

x-axis reflection, 419
x-axis symmetry, 365
x intercept, 328

y-axis reflection, 420
y-axis symmetry, 364
y intercept, 328

Zero:
    addition property of, 21
    as exponent, 222
    multiplication property of, 22
Zeros of a polynomial function, 410, 474

Properties of Absolute Value

$|a| \geq 0$

$|a| = |-a|$

$|a - b| = |b - a|$

$|a^2| = |a|^2 = a^2$

Properties of Exponents

$b^n \cdot b^m = b^{n+m}$

$\dfrac{b^n}{b^m} = b^{n-m}$

$(b^n)^m = b^{mn}$

$(ab)^n = a^n b^n$

$\left(\dfrac{a}{b}\right)^n = \dfrac{a^n}{b^n}$

Multiplication Patterns

$(a + b)^2 = a^2 + 2ab + b^2$

$(a - b)^2 = a^2 - 2ab + b^2$

$(a + b)(a - b) = a^2 - b^2$

$(a + b)^3 = a^3 + 3a^2b + 3ab^2 + b^3$

$(a - b)^3 = a^3 - 3a^2b + 3ab^2 - b^3$

Factoring Patterns

$a^2 - b^2 = (a + b)(a - b)$

$a^3 - b^3 = (a - b)(a^2 + ab + b^2)$

$a^3 + b^3 = (a + b)(a^2 - ab + b^2)$

Properties of Logarithms

$\log_b b = 1$

$\log_b 1 = 0$

$\log_b rs = \log_b r + \log_b s$

$\log_b\left(\dfrac{r}{s}\right) = \log_b r - \log_b s$

$\log_b r^p = p(\log_b r)$

Interval Notation	Set Notation
(a, ∞)	$\{x \mid x > a\}$
$(-\infty, b)$	$\{x \mid x < b\}$
(a, b)	$\{x \mid a < x < b\}$
$[a, \infty)$	$\{x \mid x \geq a\}$
$(-\infty, b]$	$\{x \mid x \leq b\}$
$(a, b]$	$\{x \mid a < x \leq b\}$
$[a, b)$	$\{x \mid a \leq x < b\}$
$[a, b]$	$\{x \mid a \leq x \leq b\}$